COMBAT FLEETS OF THE WORLD
1976/77

BOOKS BY HENRI LE MASSON
of the Académie de Marine

- *La Victoire sur Mer* (translation of the memoirs of Admiral Sims). Payot, 1925.
- *La Marine Française se Bat.* Hachette, 1944.
- *Forces sur la Mer.* Éditions Maritimes et d'Outre-Mer, 1945.
- *Le Deuxième Conflit Mondial* (with others). Éditions G. P., 1946–1947.
- *De la "Gloire" au "Richelieu."* Horizons de France, 1946.
- *Les Lévriers de la Mer.* Horizons de France, 1948.
- *La Marine de Guerre Moderne:* Porte-avions, Sous-marins, Escorteurs. Horizons de France, 1951.
- *La Locomotion Moderne* (with others). Éditions S.N.E.P., 1951.
- *Navires d'Aujourd'hui.* Hachette, 1951.
- *La Dixième Flotte* (translation of a historical work by Ladislas Farago (USA), with F. Dominique Barbier). Presses de la Cité, 1965.
- *Duel en Deux Heures* (translation of a novel by Nicolas Monsarrat). Presses de la Cité, 1965.
- *Batiments de Guerre d'Aujourd'hui.* Éditions Maritimes et d'Outre-Mer, 1965.
- *Histoire du Torpilleur en France: 1872-1940*, published by the Académie de Marine, 1966. Sold by Éditions Maritimes et d'Outre-Mer.
- *Du "Nautilus"* (*1800*) *au "Redoubtable."* (Analytical history of the submarine in the French Navy). Presses de la Cité, 1969.
- *The French Navy* in "Navies of the Second World War" series, MacDonald & Co. Ltd, London, 1969. Sold by Éditions Maritimes et d'Outre-Mer.
- *Propos Maritimes.* Éditions Maritimes et d'Outre-Mer, 1970.
- *Le Navire de Combat a Travers les Ages* (translation of the book by D. Macintyre and Basil W. Bathe), with Francine Le Masson. Stock, 1971.
- *Guérilla sur Mer* (Éditions France-Empire, 1973).

BOOKS BY JEAN LABAYLE COUHAT

- FRENCH WARSHIPS OF WORLD WAR I ⎫ published by Ian Allan, London, sold by Éditions Maritimes
- FRENCH WARSHIPS OF WORLD WAR II ⎭ et d'Outre-Mer in France.
- Articles for *Revue Maritime, Marine, Revue de Défense Nationale*, and *Armées d'Aujourd'hui.*

Flottes de Combat is published every other year by Éditions Maritimes et d'Outre-Mer.

COMBAT FLEETS OF THE WORLD 1976/77:
Their Ships, Aircraft, and Armament

Edited by
JEAN LABAYLE COUHAT

Translated by
Commander James J. McDonald, U.S. NAVY (Retired)

This work was founded in 1897 by Captain de Balincourt, French Navy; continued from 1928 to 1943 by Captain Vincent-Brechignac, French Navy, and from 1943 to 1974 by Henri Le Masson. This, the first English edition, was prepared under the direction of the staff of the United States Naval Institute.

Naval Institute Press

Published in 1976 by
The United States Naval Institute
Annapolis, Maryland

Second printing with some corrections and new photographs 1976.

© Editions Maritimes et D'Outre-Mer, Paris 1976.
Copyright © 1976 United States Naval Institute.
This English-language edition is published by
arrangement with Editions Maritimes et D'Outre-Mer, Paris.

Library of Congress Catalog Card Number: 76-2958.
ISBN 0-87021-183-8

All photographs are official, unless otherwise credited, and have
been issued by the national authorities concerned; new drawings
in this issue are by Henri Simoni, unless otherwise credited.

Printed in the United States of America

CONTENTS

ACKNOWLEDGMENTS

The 1976/77 issue of *Les Flottes de Combat* is the first for which I have been responsible. Also, *Combat Fleets of the World,* published under the auspices of the United States Naval Institute, Annapolis, Maryland, is the first English-language edition of this work. In preparing this material, I have come to appreciate the amount of credit that is due my predecessor and friend, H. Le Masson of the Académie de Marine. In fact, it is thanks to him and to the many years he devoted to this work, that it has earned a considerable international reputation.

In contrast to the 1974 issue, this latest *Combat Fleets of the World* contains the excellent line drawings of the talented Henri Simoni. Its sections on weapons and systems have been completely revised, and many new photographs have been included.

I wish to thank all those who in any way helped in the preparation of this issue, especially the officers of the French Navy General Staff who, with the courtesy that one has come to associate with naval personnel, very kindly furnished me with much important information. I should also like to thank those French and other naval attachés and foreign navy departments who replied so graciously to my inquiries.

As were previous issues, this one is greatly indebted to those who contributed editorial details and photographs. My gratitude is due especially to Messrs. G. Arra, J. C. Bellonne, Aldo Fraccaroli, Colonel Guiglini, Captain Allan Kull, Dr. Giorgio Giorgirini — contributors to the *Almanacco Navale,* to Captain J. N. Moore, editor of *Jane's Fighting Ships,* and to Norman Polmar for the numerous and interesting pieces of information that he has sent to me; to Messrs. Jurg Meister, Martinelli, Pellegrini, J. I. Taibo, and Stephen Terzibaschitsch. I wish also to thank Siegfried Breyer, whose ship silhouettes appear in the U.S.S.R. section, and Commander James J. McDonald, U.S. Navy (Ret.), Captain K. Estes, USMC, Department of History, U.S. Naval Academy and Katherine McInnis, former assistant editor of the U.S. Naval Institute *Proceedings,* for their help in producing this English-language edition.

J.L.C.

INTRODUCTION

The reader of *Combat Fleets of the World 1976/77* will note that countries that have no naval tradition are now building naval forces either to assert their sovereignty or to protect their coastal waters and their maritime claims. These nations have called upon the Soviet Union, the People's Republic of China, or the nations of the Western World for help. Many of them already have small, ultra-modern combatant ships in service, a number of which are fitted with highly destructive guided missiles, notably the Gabriel and Styx systems. In some cases, these missiles are in the hands of small nations which are strategically situated in relation to important waterways.

Since the last issue of *Flottes de Combat,* gas-turbine propulsion, used alone or linked to another system, has come into increasing use. Only the U.S. Navy, and the French Navy with its PA 75, have shown any real interest in nuclear propulsion for surface vessels.

Those nuclear attack submarines which have short- or medium-range anti-surface missiles are especially powerful adversaries for surface ships. If the efforts being expended to make them nearly impervious to passive detection were to succeed, they would undoubtedly be—at least for large navies—the prime offensive weapons of the future. However, since this kind of submarine is extremely costly, we should not be surprised to note a renewed interest in conventional submarines which, when fitted with the same weapons and systems, can provide valuable service.

The latest trend in shipborne strategic missiles is to increase their range and fit them with MIRVed warheads as a protection against countermeasures. Tactical missiles launched on or below the surface can now be inexpensively mounted on even the smallest ships. Fast and hard to detect until close to the target, these missiles can escape most countermeasures. Furthermore, their massive destructive power enables the smallest units to inflict bitter humiliation on much bigger and stronger units. Tactical anti-ship missiles—which will give rise to completely new concepts and doctrines of surface warfare—will certainly benefit from foreseeable increases in range, velocity, and warhead destructive power.

Microelectronics and the ever-widening use of digital computers have improved the performance of surface-to-air missile systems in two areas. Possible targets may now be evaluated continuously, making it possible to assign available fire-control directors to the most immediate threats. Also, reaction times have been shortened which reduces the danger of saturation raids by attackers.

Finally, the latest development in the field of submarine detection is the use of passive sensors towed by both surface ships and submarines.

U.S.A.

Since the last issue of *Flottes de Combat,* the nuclear-powered aircraft carrier *Nimitz* has entered service, as have the nuclear cruisers *California* and *South Carolina* and the last of forty-six *Knox*-class frigates.

Two *Nimitz*-class, 90,000-ton (full load) aircraft carriers and five 10,000-ton nuclear-powered *Virginia*-class cruisers are being built, have been ordered, or are planned. A plan to build fifty-six 3,500-ton, gas-turbine-powered patrol frigates to augment the 4,100-ton *Knox*-class has been approved, and the prototype is being built. The *Spruance,* prototype of thirty 7,800-ton super-destroyers, has been commissioned and will soon be joined by a number of sister ships.

The first of ten 15,000-ton SSBN submarines has been laid down, and she will be commissioned by 1978 or 1979. Each of these submarines will carry twenty-four Trident-1 missiles, which have a 4,000-mile range.

The commissioning of the *Los Angeles*-class attack submarines has been delayed and the first ship of this class will not enter service until mid-1976. The U.S. Navy is giving priority to these fast submarines and expects that twenty-six of them will be operational by the early 1980s.

For the near future, the U.S. Navy, complying with the wishes of the Congress, has established a new five-year construction program. Before 1980, two nuclear-powered aircraft carriers, CVN-69 and CVN-70 from the old programs, will replace two *Midway*-class carriers. Under consideration are aircraft carriers of about 50,000 tons, which would carry twin-engined Viking ASW fixed-wing aircraft and all-weather YF-18 fighters. Also under consideration are the so-called strike cruiser (CSGN), which would be nuclear-powered equivalents of the latest Soviet ships of this type. Additionally, a less expensive ship, based on the *Spruance* design, has been requested under the Fiscal Year 1977 Program and is to carry the Aegis guidance system. It will be called the DDG 47.

Disappointed that Congress canceled construction of the Sea Control Ship aircraft carriers, the Navy has begun studies of a new V/STOL support ship in hopes that it will eventually receive congressional approval.

The delivery of five 40,000-ton, *Tarawa*-class, amphibious assault ships, which have docking wells and flight decks, has fallen behind schedule. The first two ships of this class will not enter service until 1976. If these ships are equipped with V/STOL aircraft, they could substitute for aircraft carriers on some missions.

A wide-ranging modernization program for logistic support ships has been proposed.

Finally, on 1 July 1975 a new classification system for U.S. Navy ships was introduced. Destroyer Leaders (DLG and DLGN), once called frigates, of more than 5,000 standard displacement tons, have been reclassified as cruisers (CG and CGN), while those of lesser displacements have been classified as missile-destroyers (DDG). Destroyer escorts (DE and DEG) are now called frigates and are classified as FF and FFG.

U.S.S.R.

Under the energetic direction of Admiral Sergei Gorshkov, who has been its Commander-in-Chief since 1956, the Soviet Navy has improved in every area. The Okean 1975 Fleet Exercises, in which more than 200 ships and dozens of aircraft participated in the Mediterranean and on three oceans, showed the versatility of the Soviet Navy.

Having long compensated for technological inferiority with superiority in numbers of units, the Soviet Navy is now concentrating on quality production. During the past two years, several D-class SSBN submarines have joined the Soviet fleet to reinforce the thirty-four Y-class SSBN ships built between 1967 and 1974. With a 9,500-ton displacement and carrying twelve missiles with a 4,200-mile range, the D-class is the world's largest submarine. At least one super D-class boat with sixteen missiles is under construction.

In the SSN-class, improved versions of both the Charlie- and Victor-class submarines have come into service. Charlie-class boats, which are armed with missiles that can be fired when submerged, pose a considerable threat to any surface force. Victor-class boats are equipped with an ASW weapon system similar to the U.S. Navy's Subroc.

The 35,000-ton aircraft carrier *Kiev* was commissioned in 1975 and her sister ship, the *Minsk*, will enter service in some eighteen months.

The fact that the most sophisticated Soviet ships have radar-directed Gatling-type guns indicates that the Soviet Navy has given careful consideration to defense against the Sea Skimmer missile systems of Western navies.

GREAT BRITAIN

Economic difficulties have compelled the British government to make drastic cuts in defense spending. Although the Royal Navy has been less affected by these cuts than have the other services, it will probably have to place a number of ships in reserve and to postpone the delivery dates of some now under construction. The latter include the antisubmarine cruiser *Invincible*, five 3,600-ton *Sheffield*-class guided-missile destroyers, two 3,900-ton *Weapon*-class frigates, five *Amazon*-class frigates, four *Swiftsure*-class SSN submarines, and two replenishment ships. Since 1974, the guided-missile destroyer *Sheffield* and three *Amazon*-class frigates have been commissioned. In May 1975, the Minister of Defense announced that approval had been given for the Royal Navy to begin construction of two additional *Invincible*-class cruisers and to purchase twenty-five Harrier jet aircraft. The first of these cruisers may be ordered during FY 1975-76 and, during this same year, contracts will be signed for additional Weapon-class frigates and for the twelfth Royal Navy SSN.

This construction, whether underway or planned, ensures that in the early 1980s the Royal Navy will have what it has today, a modern and well-balanced fleet. A modern and mobile logistic force, eight times greater in tonnage than that of the French Navy, will support that fleet. The Royal Navy has ordered five large trawler-class patrol craft to guard offshore oil-drilling rigs.

FRANCE AND OTHER EUROPEAN COUNTRIES

Although France is building a sixth nuclear, ballistic-missile submarine on schedule, the maintenance of her fleet is far from satisfactory. Lack of funds, inflation, emphasis on habitability at the expense of materiel will all cause delay in some projects. For example, the construction of antiaircraft corvettes will have to await better days.

The steady growth of the French Navy is being slowed by the difficulty the nation has in recognizing that the essential element in the defense of France is now the navy. Surrounded as she is by friendly nations, France is just beginning to realize that her economic development depends, as does that of most West European countries, on free use of the sea. Not only is that use now threatened by the spectacular growth of Soviet naval power but also, and perhaps even more important, it depends on the manner in which the new maritime nations act.

The French Navy has the following ships in different stages of construction: Three *Georges Leygues*-class corvettes, four *Agosta*, 1,200-ton submarines, thirteen light frigates, four light patrol boats, a replenishment oiler, *La Durance*, and a repair ship, *Jules Verne*. In 1976 a second *La Durance*-class oiler will be laid down, as will the prototype of a minehunter which France, Belgium, and The Netherlands have decided to build to a common design. Appropriations that have been authorized will permit the ships now on the way to be completed, and allow construction to begin on the PA-75 and the first French nuclear attack submarine.

The West German Navy has now completed the construction of eighteen 450-ton, 206-class submarines. Twenty (Exocet) fast missile boats (type S 148) ordered from French and German shipyards are nearing completion. On order are ten large S 143 patrol boats armed with the MM 38 Exocet system, the first of which is to be commissioned in January 1976 and the last in late 1977.

In the meantime, ships in service are being modernized and all commissioned ships are being rearmed. The SM 1 surface-to-air missile system is being installed in the three *Lütjens*-class ships, which are also having their equipment computerized, and Exocet systems are being installed in the *Hamburg*-class destroyers. Additionally, ten minesweepers are to be converted to minehunters before the end of 1977. Conversion of the first, the *Lindau*, has been completed. Development studies for 3,600-ton ASW frigates have been completed, and the Bundesmarine anticipates ordering eight of them in the near future. These ships are quite similar in design to the Dutch *Kortenaer*-class frigates.

The Dutch parliament has authorized the replacement of conventional *Holland*- and *Friesland*-class destroyers by the new "standard" frigates. Eight of these superb 3,600-ton ASW *Kortenaer*-class ships have been ordered and the prototype should be commissioned in 1978. Four more units have been requested. The 4,300-ton *Tromp* and *De Ruyter* destroyers (ASW and AA types) are entering service. The first trials of the *Tromp* were very satisfactory, and she was commissioned in September 1975.

Sweden and Norway are giving priority to the construction of gun and missile patrol boats to meet the requirements of missions and patrols that are peculiar to their areas of operation. The Swedish Navy is building twelve *Spica II*-class patrol boats, and has on order sixteen missile patrol boats whose design is based on the 150-ton *Jägaren* class.

The Norwegian Navy has ordered fourteen units similar to those described above and is continuing to modernize its escort ships by installing Penguin and Sea Sparrow missile systems. The Norwegian Navy is also collaborating with West Germany in designing a 750-ton submarine (type 210) to replace the type-207 boats, and has ordered two new small minelayers.

The Spanish Navy, which continues to update its fleet, has just commissioned four submarines identical to the French Navy's *Daphne*-class. It has also signed an agreement with the French to build two 1,200-ton *Agosta*-class submarines in Spain. Five 4,100-ton *Baleares*-class guided-missile destroyers are soon to be commissioned. Eight 1,500-ton escort ships and twelve 150–400-ton, *Lazaga*-class and *Barcelo*-class patrol boats have been laid down.

The Spanish Navy is thinking of building a helicopter carrier to replace the *Dedalo*, and is considering a ship similar in design to the French PA-75.

The Italian Navy has at last received parliamentary approval for a 10-year naval program. It has received authorization for the *Lupo*, first of a pair of 2,500-ton escort vessels, whose primary mission will be anti-surface warfare. Two *Nazario Sauro*-class 200-ton submarines are being built, and the commissioning of the fleet support ship *Stromboli* will add strength to the logistic force of the Italian Navy.

Greece is adding to her naval forces by ordering from France four heavy *Combattante III*-class missile patrol boats and is studying the possibility of adding two 1,000–1,500-ton frigates, the French type A 69 is being favored as of now. In addition, the Greek Navy has, with Italian assistance, begun to modernize its ex-American destroyers by installing 76-mm Oto Melara guns and Albatros SAM systems. The West German Navy is about to give Greece nine *Jaguar*-class torpedo boats and a mine transport.

MIDDLE EAST

Israel's Navy now plays a major defense role, as its performance during the 1973 war showed. Her large, *Reshef*-class missile patrol boats and her flotilla of twelve (Saar II and III) PGM boats proved highly efficient during that conflict. More of the latter are now under construction or have been ordered, three of them for the South African Navy. Israel now exports naval weapons and systems, among them the Gabriel system, which Singapore's Navy has adopted. This system's 20,000-meter range was not considered great enough during the Yom Kippur war, and it is therefore going to be doubled under the Gabriel II development project.

The Turkish Navy is taking steps to keep from falling behind Greece. The two escort ships, *Berk* and *Peyk*, of all-Turkish construction have been commissioned, and

two large patrol boats and two 1,000-ton submarines have been laid down in West Germany. In addition, the Bundesmarine is planning to turn over to Turkey ten *Jaguar*-type torpedo boats, five minesweepers, and two replenishment ships.

Already second to none in the Persian Gulf, the Iranian Navy hopes to become — under the direction of the Shah — first in the Indian Ocean. Orders have been placed in the United States for four *Spruance*-class super-destroyers, and in France for twelve missile patrol boats. The possibility of acquiring an aircraft carrier is now being considered. For a while the Iranian Navy was interested in the U.S. Sea Control Ship, but is now considering buying a Royal Navy *Invincible*-class throughdeck cruiser.

As the result of an agreement with the United States, the Iranian Navy plans to acquire three old *Tang*-type submarines, to form the nucleus of the modern submarine force it hopes to build. These three submarines will be used for training purposes. Manning all the sophisticated ships it has ordered will probably be the most serious problem the Iranian Navy will have to solve in the near future.

ASIA

The Japanese Navy, which is composed mostly of new ships, may be considered second only to the Soviet Pacific Fleet in Asia. The important shipbuilding program that the Japanese have undertaken should furnish them by the end of this decade with a modern, light, conventional fleet (helicopter-cruisers, guided-missile and ASW destroyers, frigates and submarines) and a strong naval air arm of about 200 first-line aircraft. With its 45,000 officers and men and its extensive ship-building capacity, the Japanese Navy could — if the international situation made it necessary — rapidly double its potential.

Up to now, the navy of the People's Republic of China has concentrated its efforts on light forces — patrol boats, guided-missile boats, hydrofoils and submarines — and has shared with its shore-based air arm the responsibility of protecting the coastal areas. Now it is thinking in terms of ocean-going forces. It is continuing to build destroyers and escort ships, some armed with guided missiles based on Soviet developments. But, more important, there are now reports that the People's Republic of China has two nuclear-powered attack submarines, one of which is experimental.

With the assistance of the Soviet Union, India is developing her navy in the Indian Ocean, now one of the world's most sensitive maritime zones. She has already acquired eight Foxtrot submarines and ten Petya-class, 1,300-ton frigates. At the same time, India has developed her shipbuilding industry and is now capable of building ships of 3,000 tons or more (*Nilgiri*-class frigates).

LATIN AMERICA

The Argentine Navy will soon commission its first DDG, the *Sheffield*-class, 3,600-ton *Hercules*, now being completed in the Vickers shipyard. Her sister ship, the *Santissima Trinidad*, being built at Rio Santiago, recently suffered severe damage at the hands of saboteurs. Two more destroyers of the same class and three *Amazon*-class frigates may be authorized in the near future.

The Exocet missile system will be mounted on two of the six *Niteroi* general-purpose frigates being built for Brazil in shipyards in Great Britain and at Rio de Janeiro. In addition, the Brazilian Navy is endeavoring to incorporate into its active fleet the numerous, but in many cases over-age, ships provided by the U.S. Navy.

J.L.C.

ABBREVIATIONS AND TERMS

Ships' names are in bold-face capitals. Hull dimensions are in meters, calibers in millimeters, speeds in knots, ranges in nautical miles; speeds and ranges of aircraft are in kilometers/hr and kilometers, unless otherwise indicated.

D: Displacement: in most cases, the standard displacement as defined by the Treaty of Washington (1922). Where possible, full load (fl) is given; otherwise, normal (avg) displacement, or trial displacement is given. In the case of submarines, two displacements are usually given; the first figure is surface displacement; the second figure is submerged displacement. The figure for standard displacement, when available, precedes those for surface/submerged displacements.

Dim: Hull dimensions: length overall × beam × draft (full load unless otherwise stated): 1 for light, m for mean. Length may be length overall, length between perpendiculars (pp), or length at the waterline (wl).

S: Speed in knots — in some cases, trial speed may be given. If two speeds are given for a surface ship, the top speed is given first, followed by the cruising speed. Submarine speeds are given in the following order: surfaced/submerged.

Man: Ship's company (manning): officers, petty officers, men.

Range: Cited in nautical miles at a given speed.

A: Armament: number of guns/caliber — TT/torpedo tubes or launchers with caliber. Figures given in parentheses show the number of mounts and whether they are single, double, or triple, etc. e.g., (III × 2) indicates two triple mounts.

Armor: Armor protection, thickness given in millimeters.

M: Machinery — GT: geared turbine (in some cases type of turbine — Parsons, etc., is given). Designations such as COSAG, CODAG/CODOG, COGAG/COGOG are given when such combinations of various machinery sets should be shown. Props indicate propellers. Electric refers to electric generating power.

Boilers: In most cases, number and type are given. Steam pressure is expressed in kilos/sq cm (cm²); steam superheat in degrees Centigrade.

Dates: All dates are given in the following sequence: day/month/year.

Example

Ship's name	Bldr	Laid down	L	In serv.
SUFFREN	Lorient	12-62	15-5-65	1967

D: 5,100 tons (6,000 fl) **Dim:** 157.60 (148 pp) × 15.54 × 6.10
S: 34/18 kts **Range:** 5,000/18
A: 2/100-mm AA (I × 2) — 2/30-mm AA (I × 2) — 1 AA Masurca MM (II × 1) — 1 Malafon ASW ML (I × 1) — 4 ASW TT (I × 4)
Man: 38 officers, 118 petty officers, 270 men
M: Rateau geared turbine; 2 props; 72,500 hp
Boilers: 4 rated at 45 kg/cm²; superheat: 450°C.

A	Armament
AA	Anti-aircraft
A & C, At & Ch	Shipbuilding yard
ARM	Anti-radiation missile
Ast Nav	Naval shipyard
ASW	Antisubmarine warfare
Author.	Authorized
avg	Average, normal (D)
Bldr	Builder
BPDMS	Base point defense missile system
Ch, Ch Nav	Builder, naval shipyard
C N, Cant Nav	Naval shipyard
COGAG/CODAG/COSAG/ COGOG/CODOG	Combined propulsive machinery systems, diesel, gas turbine, steam. CO means *combined*, a means *and*, o means *on;* for example, CODOG means combined diesel on gas.
CSGN	Nuclear-powered, guided-missile, strike cruiser
D	Displacement
DD, DDM	Dry dock, dry dock company
Dim	Dimensions
Electric	Electric power-generating capacity
Electron equipt	Electronic equipment
ELINT	Electronic intelligence
Eng	Engineering
FF, FFG,	Frigate, guided-missile frigate
fl	Full load
fwd	Forward
H	Helicopter
HF, MF, LF	High, medium, low, frequency
grt	Gross register tons
GT	Geared turbine
hp	Horsepower
kg	Kilogram
Kon. Mij.	Royal company
kts	Knots
kw	Kilowatt
L	Launched
MAP	Mutual Assistance Pact (U.S. and allies)
Man	Manpower on board ship, crew, ship's company
MBU	ASW rocket designator
ML	Missile launcher
mm	Millimeters
MM 38/MM 40	Exocet System (France)

N.B.	New Brunswick	SAM	Surface-to-air missile
N.S.	Nova Scotia	SB	Shipbuilding
NSY	Naval shipyard	S.F.C.N.	Société Francaise de Construction Navale
pp	Between perpendiculars	SSBN	Fleet ballistic submarine
NDY/HMDY	Naval dockyard, Her Majesty's dockyard	SSM	Surface-to-surface missile
NTDS	Naval tactical data system	SY	Shipyard
RDY	Royal dockyard	TT	Torpedo tubes/launchers
RL	Rocket launcher	VDS	Variable-depth sonar
rpm	Revolutions per minute	Wks	Works
S	Speed	wl	Waterline

CONVERSION TABLES

♦ METERS (m.) to FEET (ft.)
based on 1 inch = 25.4 millimeters

m	0	1	2	3	4	5	6	7	8	9
	ft.	ft.	ft.	ft.	ft.	ft.	ft.	ft.	ft.	ft.
—	—	3.28084	6.5617	9.8425	13.1234	16.4042	19.6850	22.9659	26.2467	29.5276
10	32.8084	36.0892	39.3701	42.6509	45.9317	49.2126	52.493	55.774	59.005	62.336
20	65.617	68.898	72.178	75.459	78.740	82.021	85.302	88.583	91.863	95.144
30	98.425	101.706	104.987	108.268	111.549	114.829	118.110	121.391	124.672	127.953
40	131.234	134.514	137.795	141.076	144.357	147.638	150.919	154.199	157.480	160.761
50	164.042	167.323	170.604	173.884	177.165	180.446	183.727	187.008	190.289	193.570
60	196.850	200.131	203.412	206.693	209.974	213.255	216.535	219.816	223.097	226.378
70	229.659	232.940	236.220	239.501	242.782	246.063	249.344	252.625	255.905	259.186
80	262.467	265.748	269.029	272.310	275.590	278.871	282.152	285.433	288.714	291.995
90	295.276	298.556	301.837	305.118	308.399	311.680	314.961	318.241	321.522	324.803
100	328.084	331.365	334.646	337.926	341.207	344.488	347.769	351.050	354.331	357.611
10	360.892	364.173	367.454	370.735	374.016	377.296	380.577	383.858	387.139	390.420
20	393.701	396.982	400.262	403.543	406.824	410.105	413.386	416.667	419.947	423.228
30	426.509	429.790	433.071	436.352	439.632	442.913	446.194	449.475	452.756	456.037
40	459.317	462.598	465.879	469.160	472.441	475.722	479.002	482.283	485.564	488.845
50	492.126	495.407	498.688	501.97	505.25	508.53	511.81	515.09	518.37	521.65
60	524.93	528.22	531.50	534.78	538.06	541.34	544.62	547.90	551.18	554.46
70	557.74	561.02	564.30	567.59	570.87	574.15	577.43	580.71	583.99	587.27
80	590.55	593.83	597.11	600.39	603.67	606.96	610.24	613.52	616.80	620.08
90	623.36	626.64	629.92	633.20	636.48	639.76	643.04	646.33	649.61	652.89
200	656.17	659.45	662.73	666.01	669.29	672.57	675.85	679.13	682.41	685.70
10	688.98	692.26	695.54	698.82	702.10	705.38	708.66	711.94	715.22	718.50
20	721.78	725.07	728.35	731.63	734.91	738.19	741.47	744.75	748.03	751.31
30	754.59	757.87	761.15	764.44	767.72	771.00	774.28	777.56	780.84	784.12
40	747.40	790.68	793.96	797.24	800.52	803.81	807.09	810.37	813.65	816.93
50	820.21	823.49	826.77	830.05	833.33	836.61	839.89	843.18	846.46	849.74
60	853.02	856.30	859.58	862.86	866.14	869.42	872.70	875.98	879.26	882.55
70	885.83	889.11	892.39	895.67	898.95	902.23	905.51	908.79	912.07	915.35
80	918.63	921.92	925.20	928.48	931.76	935.04	938.32	941.60	944.88	948.16
90	951.44	954.72	958.00	961.29	964.57	967.85	971.13	974.41	977.69	980.97
300	984.25	987.53	990.81	994.09	997.38	1000.66	1003.94	1007.22	1010.50	1013.78
10	1017.06	1020.34	1023.62	1026.90	1030.18	1033.46	1036.75	1040.03	1043.31	1046.59
20	1049.87	1053.15	1056.43	1059.71	1062.99	1066.27	1069.55	1072.83	1076.12	1079.40
30	1082.68	1085.96	1089.24	1092.52	1095.80	1099.08	1102.36	1105.64	1108.92	1112.20
40	1115.49	1118.77	1122.05	1125.33	1128.61	1131.89	1135.17	1138.45	1141.73	1145.01
50	1118.29	1151.57	1154.86	1158.14	1161.42	1164.70	1167.98	1171.26	1174.54	1177.82

♦ MILLIMETERS (mm.) to INCHES (in.)
based on 1 inch = 25.4 millimeters

mm	0	1	2	3	4	5	6	7	8	9
	in.	in.	in.	in.	in.	in.	in.	in.	in.	in.
—	—	0.03937	0.07874	0.11811	0.15748	0.19685	0.23622	0.27559	0.31496	0.35433
10	0.39370	0.43307	0.47244	0.51181	0.55118	0.59055	0.62992	0.66929	0.70866	0.74803
20	0.78740	0.82677	0.86614	0.90551	0.94488	0.98425	1.02362	1.06299	1.10236	1.14173
30	1.18110	1.22047	1.25984	1.29921	1.33858	1.37795	1.41732	1.45669	1.49606	1.53543
40	1.57480	1.61417	1.65354	1.69291	1.73228	1.77165	1.81102	1.85039	1.88976	1.92913
50	1.96850	2.00787	2.04724	2.08661	2.12598	2.16535	2.20472	2.24409	2.28346	2.32283
60	2.36220	2.40157	2.44094	2.48031	2.51969	2.55906	2.59843	2.63780	2.67717	2.71654
70	2.75591	2.79528	2.83465	2.87402	2.91339	2.95276	2.99213	3.03150	3.07087	3.11024
80	3.14961	3.18898	3.22835	3.26772	3.30709	3.34646	3.38583	3.42520	3.46457	3.50394
90	3.54331	3.58268	3.62205	3.66142	3.70079	3.74016	3.77953	3.81890	3.85827	3.89764
100	3.93701									

CONVERSION FACTORS

Meter	Yard	Foot	Inch	Centimeter	Millimeter
1	1.093 61	3.280 84	39.370 1	100	1 000
0.914 4	1	3	36	91.44	914.4
0.304 8	0.333 333	1	12	30.48	304.8
0.254	0.027 777 8	0.083 333	1	2.54	25.4 j
0.01	0.010 936 1	0.032 808 4	0.393 701	1	10
0.001	0.001 093 61	0.003 280 84	0.039 370 4	0.1	1

Nautical mile	Statute mile	Meters
1	= 1.151 52	= 1 853.18

♦ Boiler working pressure

Kilogram per square centimeter (atmosphere) — *Pounds per square inch*

| 1 | equivalent → | 14.223 3 |
| 0.070 307 | ← equivalent | 1 |

♦ Conversion for Fahrenheit and Centigrade scales

1 degree Centigrade = 1.8 degrees Fahrenheit
1 degree Fahrenheit = 5/9 degree Centigrade
$t\,°F = 5/9(t - 32)°C.$
$t\,°C = (1.8\,t + 32)°F.$

♦ Weights

1 kilogram = 2.204 62 *pounds* (av)
1 *pound* = 0.453 592
1 ton (metric) = 0.984 21 *ton*
1 *ton* = 1.016 05 *metric ton*

♦ Power

1 (CV) = 0.986 32 *horsepower* (HP) 0.735 88 kilowatt (Greenwich) (75 kgm/s)
1 *horsepower* (HP) = 1.013 87 (CV) 0.746 08 kilowatt (Greenwich)

Naval branch of the national defense force (*Defense Force Sea Wing*)

◆ *3 Kawkab class patrol boats*
KAWKAB (1-69), **THOABAN** (1-69), **BANIYAS** (7-69).
Bldr: Keith Nelson (G. B.)

ABU DHABI

Kawkab (patrol boat)

D: 25 tons (32 fl)   **Dim:** 17.52 (15.84 pp) × 4.72 × 1.37
A: 2/20-mm AA (I × 2)   **Man:** 2 officers, 9 men
M: 2 Caterpillar diesels; 2 props; 750 hp
Endurance: 1 week   **Range:** 300 miles

REMARKS: Fiberglass hull, 2/12-kw generators, used in coastal patrol, hydrographic studies, surveillance of petroleum leases. Keith Nelson design. Decca radar. Freshwater evaporator provides 900 liters daily.

◆ *6 Dhafeer class patrol boats*

DHAFEER (2-68)	**DURGHAM** (9-68)	**GHADUNFAR** (5-68)
HAZZA (5-68)	**TIMSAH** (9-68)	**MURAYJIB** (2-70)

Bldr: Keith Nelson, Isle of Wight. Fiberglass hull

D: 10 tons   **S:** 19 kts   **Dim:** 12.50 × 3.65 × 1.10
A: 1/12.7-mm machine gun   **Man:** 1 officer, 5 men
M: 2 Cummins diesels; 2 props; 370 hp   **Range:** 150

◆ *4 police patrol boats placed in service 8, 9, and 11, 1974*

D: . . .   **S:** 26 kts   **Dim:** 9.10 × 2.75 × 0.84
M: 2 T 6-354 Perkins diesels

ALBANIA

ALGERIA

PERSONNEL: 3,000 men

MERCHANT MARINE (1-7-74): 20 ships — 57,368 grt

The following are of either Soviet or Chinese origin.

— 4 *W* class (1,100/1,600 tons, 17/13 kts) submarines, two operational,

— 4 *Kronstadt* class patrol boats (300 tons, 25 kts),

— 4 *Shanghai* class patrol boats (120 tons, 30 kts) transferred in 1974,

— 2 *T 43* class minesweepers (410 tons, 17 kts),

— 6 *T 301* class minesweepers (130 tons, 10 kts),

— 12 torpedo boats, *P 4* class, (40 tons, 40 kts),

— 30 hydrofoil torpedo boats, *Huchwan* class, (Chinese transfer),

— 3 *Toplevo* class water barges,

— 1 *Khobi* class small tanker,

— 2 small transports,

— 1 *Nyriat* class submarine rescue ship,

— 1 *Sekstan* class degaussing ship,

— 4 tugs,

— 2 *Poluchat* class torpedo recovery ships,

— 1 barracks ship.

PERSONNEL (1975): 3,000 men with about 300 to 350 officers, not necessarily on full time active duty with the navy.

MERCHANT MARINE (1-7-74): 75 ships — 239,815 grt
(tankers: 4 — 87,051 grt)

The Algerian navy is made up of ships from the U.S.S.R. See that section for characteristics.

MISSILE AND TORPEDO-LAUNCHING SMALL CRAFT

♦ 6 *Komar* class guided missile boats transferred in 1966: **671** to **676.**

♦ 3 *Osa I* class guided missile boats transferred in 1967: **R 167, R 267, R 367.**

♦ 10 *P-6* class torpedo boats transferred in 1963-68, of which 4 are armed, the others, without torpedo tubes, were transferred to the Coast Guard Service.

PATROL BOATS

♦ 6 *SO 1* class transferred from 10-65 to 10-67: **P 651** to **P 656.**
They carry 2 torpedo tubes.

MINESWEEPERS

♦ 2 *T 43* class transferred in 1968: **M 221, M 222.**

VARIOUS

A 640 VASOUYA, *Sekstan* class hydrographic trawler, procured in 1964.
A 641, *Poluchat* class torpedo recovery ship, 60 tons.
VP 650 YAVDEZAN, harbor tug, procured in 1965.
DJEBEL ANTAR, DJEBEL HONDA, fishery protection and customs vessels.

Huchwan (hydrofoil)

ARGENTINA

WARSHIPS IN SERVICE OR UNDER CONSTRUCTION AS OF 1 OCTOBER 1975

	L	Tonnage	Main armament
♦ *4 submarines*			
2 SALTA	1972–73	900	8 TT
2 SANTA FE (obsolete)	1945–46	1,517	10 TT
♦ *1 aircraft carrier*			
25 DE MAYO	1943	15,892	10/40-mm AA — 14 A
♦ *2 cruisers*			
2 NUEVE DE JULIO (obsolete)	1936–38	10,800	15/152-mm
♦ *13 guided-missile destroyers and conventional destroyers*			
2 HERCULES	1972–73	3,150	1/114-mm AA, 1 Sea Dart system, 1 ASW helicopter
2 SEGUI (obsolete)	1944	2,200	6/127-mm AA, 6 ASW torpedo tubes
1 COMODORO PY (obsolete)	1944	2,400	6/127-mm AA, 6 ASW torpedo tubes
5 BROWN (obsolete)	1942–43	2,050	4/127-mm AA, 5 torpedo tubes
♦ *4 frigates*			
2 MURATURE	1943–45	1,000	4/105-mm

♦ *11 patrol boats, 2 fast patrol boats, 6 minesweepers*

NAVAL PROGRAM

4 British *Amazon* class frigates

NAVAL AVIATION

The air squadron on board the *25 de Mayo* is made up of 16 *A* 4-B Skyhawk aircraft and 4 S-61 helicopters.
Land-based naval aircraft are obtained from several sources; they include the following types: Macchi, Albatros, Neptune, Alouette III, SNJ.

PERSONNEL: 21,000 men including 2,300 officers and 3,000 Marines.

MERCHANT MARINE (1-7-74): 366 ships — 1,408,129 grt (tankers: 63 — 520,047 grt)

AIRCRAFT CARRIER

♦ *1 British Colossus class*

	Bldr	Laid down	L	In serv.	Modernized
25 DE MAYO	Cammell Laird	12–42	30-12-43	5–45	III-1969

(ex-*Venerable,* ex-*Karel Doorman*)

D: 15,892 tons (19,896 fl)
Dim: 212.67 (192.04 pp) × 24.49 (40.66) × 7.50
S: 24.5 kts **Man:** 1,509 men **Range:** 12,000/14
A: 10/40-mm AA — 14 aircraft: 8 planes, 6 helicopters.
Electron Equipt: Radars: 2/LW 02, 1/SRG 109 (height-finding), 1/SRG 105, 1/SRG 103, CT HSA
M: Parsons GT; 2 props. **Electric:** 2,500 kw.
Boilers: 4 Admiralty 3-drum type; steam pressure 30.23 kg/cm² since refit. 40,000 hp. **Fuel:** 3,200 tons

REMARKS: Purchased by The Netherlands from the British Navy in 1948. Rebuilt from 1955 to 1958 by Wilton-Fijenoord, angled flight deck of 165.80 meters, steam catapult, mirror optical landing equipment, new anti-aircraft guns, and new radar equipment of Dutch conception and construction. Modified for service in the tropics. Partially air-conditioned. In 1967 new boilers were installed from the British aircraft carrier *Leviathan* which was never completed. Purchased in 1968 by Argentina. She is equipped with the British C.A.A.I.S. data display system.

25 De Mayo

SUBMARINES

♦ *2 Salta (German 209 class)*

	Bldr	L	In serv.
S 31 SALTA	Howaldtswerke	22-11-72	5-74
S 32 SAN LUIS	Howaldtswerke	7-73	5-74

Salta (S 31)   Photo 1972

D: 980 tons surfaced/1,230 submerged   **Dim:** 55 × 6.60 × 5.90
S: 21 kts submerged; 12 with snorkel.   **Man:** 5 officers, 26 men
A: 8/533-mm torpedoes forward — 6 reserve torpedoes
M: diesel-electric propulsion with 4 Maybach diesels, each linked to an AEG generator of 420 kw; single Siemens electric propulsion motor, 5,000 kw; 1 prop.   **Fuel:** 50 tons diesel

REMARKS: Built in four sections at Howaldtswerke in Kiel and assembled at the navy yard in Rio Santiago. Part of the electronic equipment is French. An extension of the German *205/206* class (IKL plans of Professor Ulrich Gabler); submarine is of single hull construction, said to be 1,000 tons. Ordered by the following countries: 4 by Greece, 2 by Ecuador, 2 by Peru, 2 by Colombia, 4 by Turkey, and 2 by Venezuela. The Vickers company is interested in producing this class of submarine with Howaldtswerke.

♦ *2 ex-U.S. Guppy class transferred in 7-71*

	Bldr	L
S 21 SANTA FE (ex-*Catfish*, SS-339)	Electric Boat Co.	19-11-44
S 22 SANTIAGO DEL ESTERO	Electric Boat Co.	14-1-45

(ex-*Chivo*, SS-341)
(For photograph: *see photo under Turkey of the Murat Reis*).
D: 1,517 tons surfaced; 1,870 normal/2,340 submerged
S: 18/14 kts   **Range:** 10,000/10   **Dim:** 93.60 × 8.40 × 5.25
A: 10/533-mm torpedoes (6 forward, 4 aft)   **Man:** 9 officers, 76 men

M: 3 Gen. Elec. diesels, each of 1,625 hp, with 2 electric motors of 2,700 hp each; 2 props.   **Fuel:** 300 tons diesel

REMARKS: Replaced the *S 11* (ex-*Lamprey*, SS-372) and *S 12* (ex-*Macabi*, SS-375) transferred in 1960, returned to the U.S.A., 9-71, and scrapped.

CRUISERS

♦ *2 ex-U.S. Brooklyn class (over age)*

	Bldr	Laid down	L	In serv.
C 4 GENERAL BELGRANO	New York SB Co.	4-35	12-3-38	10-38
(ex-*Diecisiete de Octubre*, ex-*Phoenix*, CL-46)				
C 5 NUEVE DE JULIO	Newport News	4-35	3-12-36	8-38
(ex-*Boise*, CL-47)				

General Belgrano

D: 10,800 tons (13,500 fl)   **Dim:** 185.33 × 20.70 × 7.40
S: 25/24 kts   **Man:** 980 men   **Range:** 7,600/15
A: 15/125-mm   (III × 5) — 8/127-mm AA   (I × 8) — 28/40-mm   AA (IV × 4) — 16/20-mm AA
Armor: Belt: 76 to 127   Decks: 76 to 52   Turret: 127   Conning tower: 203
M: Westinghouse GT; 4 props; 100,000 hp; 8 Babcock Express boilers, 31 kg. pressure   **Fuel:** 2,100 tons

REMARKS: Purchased in the U.S.A. 12-1-51. Ships have "bulges" and two helicopters. Similar to Brazilian and Chilean cruisers which are former American ships. "Sea Cat" system installed in *General Belgrano*. (The cruiser *Argentina* was stricken in 1974.)

GUIDED MISSILE DESTROYERS

♦ *2 guided missile Vickers class 42 ordered 18-5-70*

	Bldr	Laid down	L
D 01 HERCULES	Vickers, Barrow	1971	24-10-72
D 02 SANTISIMA TRINIDAD	Ast. Nav. Rio Santiago	2-72	9-11-74

See *Sheffield* design in the Great Britain section.
D: 3,150 tons (3,600 fl)   **Dim:** 125 (119.60 pp) × 14.34 × 6.7
S: 28 kts (18 cruising)   **Range:** 4,000/18   **Man:** 270 men
A: 1/114-mm AA Mk 8 — 2/20-mm AA — 1 Sea Dart (II × 1) 1 WG 13 Lynx ASW helicopter.

GUIDED MISSILE DESTROYERS (*continued*)

Electron Equipt: Radars: 1/965 M, 1/992, 2/909, ADA SW4, 2 Knebworth
Corvus. Sonar: 1/177, 1/174, 1/170 B, 1/162
M: COGOG propulsion; 2 Olympus gas turbine TM 3 B — 27,200 hp high speed —
2 Tyne RM 1A gas turbines — 4,100 hp each for cruising — reversible pitch
props. with 5 blades.
Electric: 4,000 kw

REMARKS: Same as the British *Sheffield*. Two more ships of the same class will
probably be ordered.

DESTROYERS

♦ *1 ex-U.S. Gearing class, transferred 1-73*

		Bldr	L	In serv.
D 27 COMORODO PY (ex-*Perkins, DD-877*)		Consolidated Steel	7-12-44	4-54

D: 2,400 tons (3,600 fl) **Dim:** 119.17 × 12.45 × 5.80
Man: 15 officers, 260 men. **S:** 360 kts **Range:** 2,400/25, 4,800/15.
A: 6/127-mm AA 38-cal. (II × 3) — 2 ASW hedgehogs — 6/324-mm ASW TT
(III × 2) Mk 32 for Mk 44 torpedoes
Electron Equipt: Radars: 1/SPS 40, 1/SPS 10 — Sonar: 1/SQS 29.
M: Westinghouse GT, 4 Babcock boilers; 2 props; 60,000 hp. **Fuel:** 650 tons.

REMARKS: Had undergone Fram II modernization, will be armed with MM38 Exocet.

♦ *2 ex-U.S. Allen M. Sumner class, transferred 7-72*

	Bldr	L	In serv.
D 25 SEGUI (ex-*Borie, DD-704*)	Federal SB & DD	21-5-44	8-44
D 26 HIPOLITO BOUCHARD (ex *Hank, DD-702*)	Federal SB & DD	4-7-44	9-44

D: 2,200 tons (3,300 fl) **Dim:** 114.75 × 12.45 × 5.80
Man: 14 officers, 260 men **S:** 30 kts **Range:** 1,260/30 — 4,600/15
A: (*704*): (has had Fram II modernization) 6/127-mm AA 38-cal (II × 3),
6/324-mm ASW TT (III × 2), Mk 32 — 2 tubes for Mk 25 wire-guided
torpedoes, 2 hedgehogs forward — (*702*): 6/127-mm AA
(III × 2) — 4/76-mm AA (II × 2) — 6/324-mm ASW T (III × 2), Mk
32 — 2 hedgehogs forward ASW depth charge racks.
Electron Equipt: Radars: 1/SPS 40, 1/SPS 10 — Sonar: 1/SQS 29.
M: GT; 4 Babcock boilers; 2 props; 60,000 hp. **Fuel:** 650 tons

REMARKS: Will be armed with MM 38 Exocet.

♦ *5 ex-U.S. Fletcher class, transferred in 1961-62, 1971-72*

	Bldr	L	In serv.
D 20 BROWN (ex-*Heerman, DD-532*)	Bethlehem, San Fran.	5-12-42	7-43
D 21 ESPORA (ex-*Dortch, DD-670*)	Federal SB & DD	20-6-42	8-43
D 22 ROSALES (ex-*Stembel, DD-644*)	Bath Iron Works	8-5-43	7-43
D 23 Almirante DOMECQ GARCIA (ex-*Braine, DD-630*)	Bath Iron Works	7-3-43	5-43
D 24 Almirante STORNI (ex-*Cowell, DD-547*)	Bethlehem, San Pedro	18-4-43	8-43

D: 2,050 tons (2,850 fl) **Dim:** 114.85 (wl) × 12.03 × 5.50
Man: 15 officers, 247 men **S:** 30 kts **Range:** 1,260/30, 4,400/15
A: 4/127-mm AA (I × 4) — 6/76-mm AA (II × 3) — 5/533-mm torpedo tubes
(V × 1) — 2 ASW fixed TT — 2 hedgehogs — 1 depth charge rack.

Brown

Electron Equipt: Radars: 1/SP 6 and 1/SPS 10. Sonar: 1/SQS 4
M: Gen. Elec. GT; 2 props, 60,000 hp.
Boilers: 4 Babcock and Wilcox **Fuel:** 650 tons

REMARKS: Same class as the *Knapp* (*DD-653*), purchased for spare parts.

FRIGATES

♦ *4 British Amazon class are to be purchased.*

	Bldr	Laid down	L	In serv.
P 20 MURATURE	Ast. Nav. Rio Santiago	6-38	7-45	11-46
P 21 KING	Ast. Nav. Rio Santiago	1939	43	7-46

King

D: 913 tons, 1,000 normal, 1,032 fl **Dim:** 76.80 × 8.85 × 2.50
S: 16 kts **Range:** 6,000/12 **Man:** 140 men
A: 3/105-mm — 4/40-mm AA — 4 mortars
M: Werkspoor 4-stroke diesels; 2 props; 2,500 hp. **Fuel:** 90 tons diesel

PATROL BOATS (former U.S. tugs, except for the GC class)

	Bldr	L
A 1 COMMANDANTE GENERAL IRIGOYEN (ex-*ATF 152*)	Charleston SB & DD	2-11-44

PATROL BOATS (*continued*)

A 2 COMMANDANTE GENERAL ZAPIOLA   Charleston SB & DD   22-6-42
(ex-*ATF 68*)

- **D:** 1,235 tons (1,675 fl)   **Dim:** 62.50 (59.45 pp) × 11.65 × 4.70
- **S:** 16 kts   **Man:** 85 men
- **A:** 1/76-mm — 4/40-mm (may be reduced)
- **M:** diesel-electric propulsion; 1 prop; 3,000 hp.

A 4 THOMPSON (ex-*Sombrero Key*)   Pendleton (New Orleans)   1943

- **D:** 1,825 tons (fl)   **Dim:** 58.32 × 11.30 × 5.50
- **S:** 11 kts   **Man:** 60 men
- **M:** Enterprise diesels; 2 props; 2,250 hp   **Fuel:** 532 tons

A 5 DIAGUITA (ex-*ATA 124*), **A 6 YAMANA** (ex-*ATA 126*), **A 7 CHIRIGUANO** (ex-*ATA 227*), **A 8 SANAVIRON** (ex-*ATA 228*), **A 9 ALFEREZ SOBRAL** (ex-*ATA 210*), **A 10 COMORODO SOMELLERA** (ex-*ATA 187*).

Bldr: Levingstone Shbldg., Texas 1944-45.

- **D:** 689 tons (800 fl)   **Dim:** 43.60 (40.75 pp) × 10.37 × 3.65
- **S:** 12 kts   **Man:** 49 men.   **Range:** 16,500   **A:** 2/20-mm AA
- **M:** Diesel-electric propulsion; 1 prop; 1,850 hp.   **Fuel:** 154 tons diesel

GC 21 LYNCH, GC 22 TOLL, GC 23 EREZCANO.

Bldr: Ast. Nav. Rio Santiago (1944-65).

- **D:** 100 tons (117 fl)   **Dim:** 27.44 × 5.80 × 1.85
- **S:** 22 kts   **Man:** 16 men   **A:** 1/20-mm
- **M:** 2 Maybach diesels, 2,700 hp.

GC XL 31 — Small craft of the same characteristics used for security operations; no other information.

FAST PATROL BOATS

	Bldr	L	In serv.
ELPR 1 INTREPIDA	Lürssen (Bremen-Vegesack)	12-12-74	20-7-74
ELPR 2 INDOMITA	Lürssen (Bremen-Vegesack)	5-74	Spring 1975

Intrepida   Photo Terzibaschitsch 4-74

- **D:** 240 tons   **Dim:** 44.90 × (42.30 pp) × 7.10 × 2.50 (prop.)
- **S:** 40 kts   **Range:** 1,450/20   **Man:** 34 men
- **A:** 1/76-mm AA — 2/40-mm AA — 2/533-mm wire-guided torpedoes.
- **M:** 4 MTU diesels; 4 props; 12,000 hp   **Electric:** 330 kw

REMARKS: Anti-rolling stabilizers.

MINESWEEPERS

♦ *6 British "-ton" class* (bought in 1967)

	L		L
M 1 NEUQUEN (ex-*Hickleton*)	26-1-55	**M 4 TIERRA DEL FUEGO** (ex-*Bevington*)	17-3-53
M 2 RIO NEGRO (ex-*Tarlton*)	1954	**M 5 CHACO** (ex-*Rennington*)	27-11-58
M 3 CHUBUT (ex-*Santon*)	18-8-55	**M 6 FORMOSA** (ex-*Ilmington*)	1954

Transferred in 1968.

- **D:** 370 tons (425 fl)   **Dim:** 46.33 (42.68 pp) × 8.76 × 2.50
- **S:** 15 kts   **Man:** 27 men   **Range:** 3,000/8
- **A:** 1/40-mm   **M:** Diesels; 2 props; 2,500/3,000 hp   **Fuel:** 45 tons diesel

M5 and *M6* are fitted out as minehunters.

HYDROGRAPHIC VESSELS

Q . . . N. . . — Laid down in 3-72 in Argentina.

- **D:** 2,100 tons   **S:** 12 kts   **Dim:** 76 × 13.20 × 4.50
- **M:** Diesel; 1 prop; 1,300 hp.

Q . . . COMODORO RIVADAVIA. Bldr: Mestrina, Argentina. L: 2-12-72.

- **D:** 655 tons   **S:** 12 kts   **Dim:** 50.90 × 8.80 × 2.60.

A 3 GOYENAS (ex-*Dry Tortugas*) sister ship to the A 4 *Thompson*, classified hydrographic ship in 1970.

Q . . . ISLAS ORCADAS (ex-*Eltanin*, *T-AGOR-8*). Transferred 12-73.

Bldr: Avondale (U.S.A.) 16-1-57.

- **D:** 2,040 tons (4,942 fl)   **Dim:** 80 × 15.70 × 5.70
- **S:** 13 kts   **Man:** 8, plus 38 oceanographers
- **M:** Diesel-electric; 2 props; 3,200 hp.

REMARKS: Former small transport.

ICEBREAKER

Q 4 GENERAL SAN MARTIN. Bldr: A. G. Weser, Bremen. L: 24-6-54.

ICEBREAKER (*continued*)

D: 4,850 tons (5,300 fl)   **Dim:** 84.70 × 18.60 × 6.40
S: 16 kts   **Man:** 160 men.   **Range:** 35,000/10
A: 1/105-mm — 2/40-mm AA   **Cargo Load:** 1,600 tons
M: diesel-electric propulsion; 2 props; 6,500 hp.   **Fuel:** 1,100 tons diesel.

REMARKS: Oceanographic research vessel. Has a fixed-wing aircraft and helicopter.

AMPHIBIOUS SHIPS

♦ *1 ex-U.S. LSD*

B 10 CANDIDO DE LASALA (ex-*Gunston Hall, LSD-5*) — Bldr: Moore D.D. —
L: 1-5-43.

D: 4,032 tons (8,700 fl)   **Dim:** 139 × 21.90 × 4.90
S: 15 kts   **Man:** 17 officers, 309 men   **Range:** 8,000/15
A: 12/140-mm AA   **M:** 2 triple expansion, 7,000 hp

REMARKS: Transferred 24-4-70 Docking well 103 × 13.30. 2 cranes: 35 tons

♦ *1 LST (De Soto County class)*

Q 42 CABO SAN ANTONIO — Bldr: Ast. Nav. Rio Santiago 1966-70

D: 4,300 tons (8,000 fl)   **Dim:** 135 × 18.80 × 5.50
S: 17 kts   **Man:** 124 men
A: 6/76-mm AA (II × 3) — 2 helicopters   **M:** diesels; 14,000 hp.

♦ *3 ex-U.S. LST (1944)* (ex-*875, 998, 872, 1108*)

Q 46 CABO SAN ISIDORO   **Q 50 CABO SAN PIO** (BDT 10)
Q 44 CABO SAN GONZALO

D: 2,370 tons (4,080 fl)   **Dim:** 99.98 × 15.24 × 4.25
S: 11 kts   **Man:** 80 men   **Range:** 9,500/9
M: 2 diesels; 1,800 hp.   **Fuel:** 700 tons diesel

♦ *1 ex-U.S. LCIL*

Q 56 BDI 1 (ex-*LCIL 583*)

D: 230 tons (387 fl)   **Dim:** 48 × 7.20 × 1.50   **S:** 13 kts

♦ *Some LCM and LCVP landing craft*

EDVP 1, 2, 3, 7, 8, 10, 12, 13, 17, 19, 21, 24, 28, 29, 30 (ex-U.S. LCVPs).
LCM 1 — 4 (1971) built in Argentina

LOGISTIC SUPPORT

♦ *2 Bahia Aguirre class transports*

	Bldr	L	In serv.
Q 2 BAHIA AGUIRRE	Halifax (Canada)	15-5-49	1951
Q 6 BAHIA BUEN SUCESO	Halifax (Canada)	15-6-49	1951

D: 3,100 tons (5,255 fl)
Dim: 95.10 × 14.33 × 7.92 (light cruising) × 5.63
A: 2/105-mm — 2/40-mm AA (B 8)   **S:** 15 kts
M: 2 Nordberg diesels; 3,750 hp.   **Fuel:** 400 tons diesel

♦ *1 San Julian class transport*

Bahia Aguirre

Q 7 SAN JULIAN (ex-*FS-281*) (1-45). Bldr: Wheeler SB Co.

D: 930 tons   **Dim:** 55 × 9.95 × 3.40   **S:** 10 kts
M: Diesels; 2 props; 1,000 hp. Former U.S. transport.

TANKERS

	Bldr	L	In serv.
B 18 PUNTA MEDANOS	Swan Hunter	20-2-50	10-50

D: 16,300 tons (fl)   **S:** 18 kts   **Dim:** 143 × 18.90 × 10.67 (light)
Cargo load: 8,250 tons   **Range:** 13,700   **Man:** 99 men
M: Parsons GT; 2 props; 9,500 hp.   **Fuel:** 1,500 tons
Boilers: 2 Babcock and Wilcox (28 kg/cm² pressure)

Libertad [see following page]   J. C. Bellonne

TANKERS (*continued*)

B 16 PUNTA DELGADA (ex-U.S. *AOG-66*) — (4-45) — 6,000 tons, 1,400 hp
B 12 PUNTA ALDA (1937) — 1,900 tons, 1,800 hp, 8 kts.

♦ *7 tugs*

R 33 GUAYACURU and **R 32 QUILMES** (368 tons, 650 hp)
R 29 PEHUENCHE and **R 30 TONOCOTE** (330 tons, 600 hp)
R 4 TOBA (600 tons, 1,200 hp)
R 10 HUARPE (370 tons, 800 hp)
R 1 ONA (560 tons)

FRANCISCO DE GURRUCHAGA (ex U.S. *ATF-156 Luiseno*)

REMARKS: Purchased and transferred (1-7-75)

♦ *1 sailing training vessel*

Q 2 LIBERTAD   Bldr: Ast. Nav. Rio Santiago.   L: 30-5-56.   In serv.: 1962.
  D: 3,025 tons (3,625 fl)   **Dim:** 94.25 × 13.75 × 6.75
  S: 12 kts   **Man:** 222 men and 140 cadets   **Range:** 12,000
  A: 1/76-mm — 4/40-mm — 4/47-mm.
  M: Diesels; 2 props; 2,400 hp.

PERSONNEL: 17,000 (approx.) 2,000 officers

MERCHANT MARINE (1-7-74): 394 ships — 1,168,367 grt
(tankers: 13 — 255,408 grt)

WARSHIPS IN SERVICE OR UNDER CONSTRUCTION AS OF 1 OCTOBER 1975

	L	Tons	Main armament
♦ *6 submarines*			
6 OXLEY	1965-75	1,610	8/533-mm TT
♦ *1 aircraft carrier*			
MELBOURNE	1945	16,000	15 aircraft
♦ *7 destroyers*			
3 PERTH	1963-66	3,370	1 Tartar system, 2/127-mm Ikara
3 VENDETTA/DUCHESS	1951-56	2,800	6/114-mm
♦ *8 frigates*			
6 YARRA	1958-67	2,100	2/114-mm, Ikara
2 PATROL FRIGATES authorized			
♦ *6 minesweepers*			

NAVAL AVIATION:

Only ship-based aircraft belong to the Navy. This group is made up of an attack squadron using A4-G Skyhawks, another of twin-engine ASW S2E Trackers and a third of Wessex ASW helicopters, being replaced by Sea Kings. Three training and transport squadrons augment the combat aircraft squadrons, a total of about 70 aircraft.

Shore-based aviation is under the direction of the RAAF; it includes a squadron of eight SP2H Neptunes and another of P3 Orions. Eight P3C will be purchased to replace the Neptunes.

WEAPONS AND SYSTEMS:

The Australian Navy uses U.S. equipment and systems on its 3 *Perth* class guided missile destroyers and British weapons and systems on its other ships, but some of its air-search and fire control radars have been purchased in the Netherlands (radars LW02, HSA, etc.).

Except for the *Perth* class ships, the sonars are all of British origin. The Australian Navy has perfected an unusual ASW weapon, the Ikara. Similar to the French Malafon, it is a combination of a Mk 44 or Mk 46 torpedo coupled with a guided missile and guidance equipment; it has a maximum range of about 20,000 yards.

AIRCRAFT CARRIER

	Bldr	Laid down	L	In serv.
R 21 MELBOURNE	Vickers-Armstrong	4-43	28-2-45	11-55
(ex-*Majestic*)	Identification letter (flight deck) — M.			

Converted for ASW in 1968.

D: 16,000 tons (20,000 fl)
Dim: 211.25 (198 wl) × 24.38 (39.01 max.) × 7.15.
S: 23 kts **Man:** 109 officers and 1,100 to 1,120 men.
A: 1/40-mm AA. About 15 aircraft.
Electron Equipt: Radars: 1/LW 02, 1/293, 1/992.
M: Parsons GT; 2 props; 42,000 hp.
Boilers: 4 Admiralty, 28 kg pressure.   **Fuel:** 3,200 tons.

REMARKS: Steam catapults, 6° angled flight deck, optical mirror landing equipment. Modernized in 1968.

AUSTRALIA

Melbourne (R 21)   1972

SUBMARINES

♦ *6 British Oberon class*

:	Bldr	Laid down	L	In serv.
S 57 OXLEY	Scott's	7-64	24-9-65	3-67
S 59 OTWAY	Scott's	6-65	29-11-66	12-67
S 70 OVENS	Scott's	6-66	5-12-67	1969
S 60 ONSLOW	Scott's	5-67	29-8-68	1970
S ... ORION	Scott's	1973	16-9-74	6-77
S ... OTAMA	Scott's	5-73	. . .	12-77

Oxley (S 57)

SUBMARINES (continued)

D: 1,610 tons surfaced (2,410 submerged)
Dim: 93.62 (73.45 pp) × 8.07 × 5.48
S: 17.5/15 kts   **Man:**   6 officers, 62 men.
A: 8/533-mm TT (6 fwd, 2 aft — all contained within pressure hull — 14 torpedoes in reserve)
M: Standard Admiralty diesel engines; diesel-electric propulsion surfaced. 3,700/6,000 hp.

REMARKS: Completion of *Orion* and *Otama* delayed because of deficiencies in the electrical equipment.

NOTE: The British submarine *Odin* on loan while awaiting the delivery of the *Orion* and the *Otama*.

DESTROYERS

♦ *3 guided missile (Charles F. Adams class, U.S.)*

	Bldr	Laid down	L	In serv.
D 38 PERTH	Defoe S.B. Co. (U.S.)	9-62	26-9-63	7-65
(ex-U.S. *DDG 25*)				
D 39 HOBART	Defoe S.B. Co. (U.S.)	4-63	9-1-64	8-66
(ex-U.S. *DDG 26*)				
D 41 BRISBANE	Defoe S.B. Co. (U.S.)	2-63	5-3-66	1-68
(ex-U.S. *DDG 27*)				

Perth (D 38)

D: 3,370 tons (4,500 fl)   **Dim:**   134.18 (128 pp) × 14.32 × 6
S: 35 kts   **Man:**   21 officers, 312 men   **Range:**   1,600/30 — 6,000/14
A: 1 Mk 13 Tartar missile (I × 1 aft) — 2/127-mm AA (I × 2) Mk 42 — 6 ASW Mk 32 torpedo tubes (III × 2) — 2 ASW Ikara launching systems, one to each side.
Electron Equipt: Radars: 1/SPS 40, 1/SPS 10, 1/SPS 52, 2/SPG 51
      Sonar: 1/SQS 23 — NTDS.
M: GT; 2 props; 70,000 hp.   **Fuel:** 900 tons.

Boilers: 4 Babcock and Wilcox (84 kg/cm² — superheat 520°).
Electric: 2,000 kw

REMARKS: Being refitted in the U.S.: NTDS — new missiles — Mk 68 fire control system

♦ *2 U.S. Navy "Patrol Frigate" class*

N . . .   N . . .
   Ordered from the U.S.A. in 1974. American prototype must have passed all tests prior to contract becoming definitive. See U.S. section for characteristics.

♦ *3 Vendetta/Duchess class*

	Bldr	Laid down	L	In serv.
D 08 . VENDETTA	Cockatoo D. & Eng. Co.	7-52	3-5-54	11-58
D 11 VAMPIRE	Williamstown Nav. DY	7-49	27-10-56	6-59
D 154 DUCHESS	J. Thornycroft	7-48	9-4-51	10-52

D: 2,800 tons (3,600 fl)   **Dim:**   118.87 (111.55 pp) × 13.10 × 5.10
S: 30 kts   **Man:**   327 men   **Range:**   3,700/20
A: 6/114-mm AA Mk 6 (II × 3) — 6/40-mm Bofors AA (II × 2, I × 2) — 1 Limbo Mk 10 ASW mortar
M: Parsons GT; 2 props; 54,000 hp.
Boilers: 2 Foster Wheeler.   **Fuel:**   584 tons.   **Electric:**   . . . kw.

Vampire (D 11)   1972

REMARKS: D 08 and D 11 given refit from 6-70 to 5-73. *Duchess*, loaned by Great Britain until 1971, was then purchased by the Royal Australian Navy and modified in 1973 as a school ship. The 114-mm aft and the ASW Squid mortar were removed and replaced by a large deckhouse.

FRIGATES

♦ *6 similar to the British Leander class*

	Bldr	Laid down	L	In serv.
F 45 YARRA	Williamstown Nav. DY	1957	30-9-58	7-61
F 46 PARRAMATTA	Cockatoo D & Eng. Co.	1957	31-1-59	7-61
F 48 STUART	Cockatoo D. & Eng. Co.	3-59	8-4-61	6-63
F 49 DERWENT	Williamstown Nav. DY	6-59	17-4-61	4-64
F 50 SWAN	Williamstown Nav. DY	2-65	16-12-67	6-70
F 53 TORRENS	Cockatoo D. & Eng. Co.	5-65	28-9-68	1971

FRIGATES (*continued*)

D: 2,100 tons (2,700 fl)   **Dim:** 112.75 (109.75 pp) × 12.50 × 3.90 (avg)
S: 27 kts   **Man:** 13 officers, 238 men   **Range:** 4,500/12
A: 2/114-mm AA Mk 6 (II × 1 fwd.) — 1 Seacat missile launcher — 1 Limbo Mk 10 mortar — 1 ASW Ikara missile launcher (30 missiles).

Yarra (F 45)   1974

Electron Equipt: Radars: 1/293, 1/LW02, CT HSA on *F 50* and *F 53*, 1/275 on the others
Sonars: 1/177, 1/170, 1/199 (except for *F 48* and *F 49*).
M: GT; 2 props; 34,000 hp.   **Boilers:** 2 Babcock

Swan (F 50)   Photo 1972
Compare this profile with that of the *F 45 Yarra*.

REMARKS: *F 50* and *F 53* have different profiles than the four others. The first four will be given a refit between May of 1976 and June of 1980. *F 50* has been used in Turana missile experiments.

Ikara ASW Missile Launcher

MINESWEEPERS

♦ *6 coastal minesweepers, British "-ton" class*

M 1102 SNIPE	(5-1-53)	**M 1152 TEAL**	(28-2-55)
(ex-*Alcaston*)		(ex-*Jackton*)	
N 1121 CURLEW	(6-10-53)	**M 1183 IBIS**	(18-11-55)
(ex-*Chediston*)		(ex-*Singleton*)	
M 1139 HAWK	(17-9-55)	**M 1185 GULL**	(1-7-54)
(ex-*Somerleyton*)		(ex-*Swanston*)	

D: 370 tons (425 fl)   **Dim:** 46.33 (42.68 pp) × 8.76 × 2.50
S: 15 kts   **Man:** 3 officers, 25 men
A: 1/40-mm AA — 2/20-mm AA
M: Napier-Deltic diesels; 2 props; 2,000 hp.   **Fuel:** 45 tons diesel.

REMARKS: Bought in 1962 after refitting. Air-conditioned and stabilized. *1102, 1121* and *1139* equipped as minehunters.

MINESWEEPERS (*continued*)

Hawk (M 1139)   Shbldg. & Sh. Record

♦ *3 British "-ham" type inshore minesweepers*

Y 299 OTTER (ex-*Popham* 10-1-55), **Y 298 SEAL** (ex-*Wintringham* 24-5-55),
Y 280 TORTOISE (ex-*Neasham* 1955).

D: 120 tons (159 fl)	**Dim:** 32.43 (30.48 pp) × 6.45 × 1.70	
S: 14 kts (9 sweeping)	**Man:** 15 men	**Range:** 1,500/12
M: Davey-Paxman diesels; 2 props; 1,000 hp	**Fuel:** 15 tons diesel	

NOTE: Transferred in 1966; assigned to the school of diving and underwater demolition.

PATROL CRAFT

♦ *12 for patrol in the coastal waters of Borneo and Australia*

**P 81 ACUTE, P 82 ADROIT, P 83 ADVANCE, P 87 ARDENT, P 89 ASSAIL,
P 90 ATTACK, P 91 AWARE, P 97 BARBETTE, P 98 BARRICADE,
P 99 BOMBARD, P 100 BUCCANEER, P 101 BAYONET.**

Bldr: Australia; ordered in 1965, delivered 1967.

P 86 Archer and *P 95 Bandolier*, sold in 1973 to Indonesia and transferred in 1973 and 1974 respectively. *P 88 Arrow* sunk 25-12-74 in the Typhoon "Tracey."

Buccaneer (P 100)   1972

D: 146 tons (fl)	**Dim:** 32.76 (30.48 pp) × 6.20 × 1.90	
S: 24/21 kts	**Man:** 3 officers, 19 men	
A: 1/40-mm 2 machine guns	**Radar:** Kelvin Hughes Mk 975	
M: 2 Davey-Paxman Ventura, 16-cylinder diesels.	**Fuel:** 20 tons diesel	

REMARKS: Steel hull; light alloy superstructure; air-conditioned. The same type ship as the *P 84 Aitape*, *P 82 Lavada*, *P 93 Lae*, *P 94 Madang*, *P 85 Samarai* transferred to Papua, New Guinea, in 1974.

HYDROGRAPHIC SHIPS

	Bldr	Laid down	L	In serv.
A 573 MORESBY	State DY, Newcastle, NSW	1961	7-9-63	3-64

D: 1,714 tons (2,350 fl)	**Dim:** 95.70 (wl) × (86.70 pp) × 12.80 × 4.60	
S: 19 kts	**Man:** 13 officers, 133 men	
M: Diesel-electric propulsion; 3 CSVM generators, each 1,330 kw/800 rpm; 2 electric motors, each 2,500 hp/250 rpm; 2 props.		

NOTE: 2/40-mm AA and a helicopter carried on board. Ship is air-conditioned.

♦ *1 improved Moresby class*

	Bldr	Laid down	L	In serv.
A 291 COOK	Australia	1971	. . .	. . .

D: 2,300 tons (fl)	**Dim:** 96 × 13.41 × . . .	
S: 20 kts	**Range:** 10,600/10	**Man:** 130, with 13 scientists
M: Diesels; 2 props; 4,000 hp.	**Fuel:** 400 tons	

REMARKS: Adapted for oceanographic research; one helicopter with hangar.

HYDROGRAPHIC SHIPS *(continued)*

♦ *1 Flinders class*

	Bldr	Laid down	L	In serv.
A 312 FLINDERS	Williamstown Nav. DY	1971	27-4-73	6-73

D: 800 tons   **Dim:** 45.78 × 10.05 × . . .
M: diesels   **S:** 14 kts   **Man:** 47 men

REMARKS: Similar to the Philippine ship *Atyimba*. Replaces the *Paluma*, stricken in 1972.

♦ *1 British River class*

A 266 DIAMANTINA (ex-*F 377*) (6-4-44)

D:	1,489 tons (2,200 fl)	**Dim:**	91.84 × 11.18 × 4.39
S:	19.5 kts	**Man:**	140 men
A:	1/40-mm — 1 helicopter.	**Range:**	7,700/12 — 5,000/16.5
M:	reciprocating; 2 props; 5,500 hp; 2 boilers.	**Fuel:**	645 tons

LOGISTIC SUPPORT

♦ *1 tanker*

AO 195 SUPPLY (ex-*Tide Austral*)

Bldr: Harland and Wolf — L 1-9-54. — In serv. 9-62

Supply (AO 195)

See chapter on Great Britain for characteristics.

♦ *1 supply ship*

	Bldr	Laid down	L	In serv.
A 215 STALWART	Cockatoo D&E, Sydney	3-64	9-65	10-66

Stalwart (AO 215)

D:	15,500 tons	**Dim:**	157.12 (143.25 pp) × 20.57 × 7.80
S:	18 kts	**Man:**	478 men. **A:** 4/40-mm AA
M:	Scott-Sulzer diesels, (6 cyl) Mk RD 68; 2 props; 14,400 hp.		
Electric:	5,000 kw		

REMARKS: Air-conditioned quarters and workshops for maintenance of destroyers and missiles. Helicopter platform.

VARIOUS

BASS — BANKS (1960). Used for naval reserve training.

D:	260 tons (fl)	**Dim:**	28 × 6.70 × 2.50
S:	10 kts	**Man:**	12 **M:** diesels

A 314 KIMBLA — Bldr: Walkers (Australia) — L: (23-3-55) — net layer

D:	733 tons (970 fl)	**Dim:**	54.55 × 9.75 × 4.30
S:	11 kts	**Man:**	32 men
A:	1/40-mm AA — 1/20-mm	**M:**	Triple expansion; 1 prop.

SDB 1321, 1324, 1325. Thornycroft patrol boats (1940-41)

    D: 64 tons (fl)   **S:**   10 kts

♦ *6 LCU ex-army landing craft transferred in 1973*

L 134 BALIKPAPAN, L 127 BRUNEI, L 128 LABUAN, L 129 TARAKAN, L 130 WEVAK, L 133 BETANG (Bldr: Australia, 1972-73).

D:	180 tons (360 fl)	**Dim:**	44.50 × 12.20 × 1.90
S:	8 kts	**Man:**	2 officers, 11 men
M:	diesels; 2 props; 675 hp.		

REMARKS: Same characteristics as the *L 131 Salamaua* and *L 132 Buna* transferred to Papua, New Guinea, in 1974.

♦ *12 munition barges.*

AUSTRIA

♦ *2 patrol boats for the Danube*

NIEDERÖSTERREICH

Niederösterreich

D:	71 tons	**Dim:**	29 × 5.4 × 1.1
S:	22 kts	**Man:**	9 men
A:	1/20-mm AA — 2 machine guns	**M:**	2 diesels; 1,600 hp

OBERST BRECHT smaller than the above.

♦ *7 river patrol boats*

A: 1 machine gun

BAHAMAS

Merchant Marine (1-7-74): 129 ships — 153,202 grt
(tankers: 6 — 48,735 grt)

♦ *4 patrol boats*

ACKLINS, ANDROS, ELEUTHERA, SAN SALVADOR
Bldr: Keith Nelson (G.B.) 1971-72 — Hull in fiberglass.

D:	30 tons	**Dim:**	18.68 × 4.77 × 1.40
S:	19.5 kts	**Man:**	11 men
M:	2 Caterpillar diesels	**A:**	2/20-mm

See patrol craft of Abu Dhabi section.

Andros   Photo 1972

BANGLADESH | BARBADOS

MERCHANT MARINE (1-7-74): 98 ships — 115,612 grt
(tankers: 14 — 9,935 grt)

PERSONNEL: about 700 men

♦ *3 river patrol boats* (**P 101, P 102, P 103**)

 D: 100 tons **A:** 1/25-mm

♦ *1 Poluchat class patrol boat:* **P 104**

 Dim: 100 tons **A:** 2/25-mm

REMARKS: These 4 units were delivered by the U.S.S.R. at the beginning of 1972.

♦ *1 Ajay class surveillance patrol boat given by India*

PADMA (ex-*P 3136 Akshay*) — Bldr: Hooghly D&E, Calcutta (1-62)

 D: 120 tons (160 fl) **Dim:** 35.75 (33.52 pp) × 6.10 × 1.90
 S: 18 kts **A:** 1/40-mm AA **M:** 2 diesels

♦ *1 British "-ham" class minesweeper transferred by India in 1973*

 D: 120 tons (159 fl) **Dim:** 32.43 × 6.45 × 1.70
 A: 1/20-mm AA **S:** 14 kts **Man:** 25 men
 M: Davey-Paxman diesels; 2 props; 1,000 hp. **Fuel:** 25 tons diesel.

PERSONNEL:

MERCHANT MARINE (1-7-74): 30 ships — 3,897 grt

♦ *4 police patrol boats*

 Bldr: Aquarius Boat, Great Britain, 1973-75.

GC 601 GEORGE FERGUSON
GC 602 . . .
GC 603 . . .
GC 604 . . .

 D: 30 tons   **Dim:** 20 × 5.25 × 1.50
 S: 21 kts **A:** 1/20-mm **Man:** 11 men
 Range: 650/12   **M:** diesels; 2 props

♦ *3 police patrol boats, 12-meter Lewis class*

 Bldr: Aquarius Boat

GC 402 COMMANDER MARSHALL
GC 403 T. T. LEWIS

 D: 11.5 tons **Dim:** 12.10 × 3.60 × 1
 S: 21 kts **Man:** 4 men
 M: Caterpillar Mk 334 TA diesels; 2 props; 290 hp

♦ *1 LST (ex-USS Kemper County LST-854) transferred 24-6-75*

PERSONNEL: 4,350 including 300 officers

NAVAL AVIATION: About 10 helicopters (Sikorsky HSS and 3 Alouette III B) used for minehunting. 1 Alouette may be taken on board the *Zinnia* or the *Godetia*.

MERCHANT MARINE: (1-7-74): 251 ships — 1,214,707 grt
(tankers: 20 — 333,522 grt)

BELGIUM

FRIGATES

♦ *4 Westhinder E 71 class*

	Bldr	Laid down	L	In serv.
F 910 WIELINGEN	Cockerill (Hoboken)	3-74	Mid-76	5-78
F 911 WESTDIEP	Cockerill (Hoboken)	9-74	8-12-75	11-78
F 912 WANDELAAR	Boëlwerf (Temse)	5-3-75	Early 76	5-79
F 913 WESTHINDER	Boëlwerf (Temse)	8-12-75	Early 75	11-77

Westhinder class

D: 1,860 (2,340 fl)   **Dim:** 106.38 (103) × 12.30 × 5.30 (sonar)
S: 28 kts on gas turbine   **Range:** 4,500/18 — 5,000/14
A: 1/100-mm AA, model 68 — 4/38-mm AA — 1 Sea Sparrow BPDMS launcher (8 missiles) — 6 ASW TT (III × 2) — 1/375-mm Bofors sextuple rocket launcher — 2 launching racks for L 5 torpedoes, 2 Knebworth corvus.
Man: 14 officers, 146 men
Electron Equipt: Radar: 1 air-search, 1 navigation, 1 multi-purpose.
        Sonar: 1 hull-mounted dome.
M: CODOG propulsion, 2 shafts with variable pitch propellers; 2 Cockerill-Ougrée diesels, each 3,000 hp (1,000 rpm); 1 Rolls-Royce Olympus gas turbine TM 3 B, of 27,500 hp, 5,600 rpm.   **Fuel:** 190 tons diesel.
Electric: 2,000 kw.

REMARKS: Welded hull, 2 self-activating Vosper-Thornycroft stabilizers; 15 knots on 1 diesel, 20 knots on 2; for more than 20 kts the gas turbine is brought on the line. Canadian hull sonar. French 100-mm Model 1968. Belgian-Dutch automatic surface and air search radar system, including fire control and an automatic tactical data system.

MINESWEEPERS AND MINEHUNTERS

♦ *7 AM/MSO ocean-going class*

		L
M 902 VAN HAVERBEKE	(ex-*MSO 522*)	29-10-59
M 903 A. F. DUFOUR	(ex-*MSO 498*)	13-8-54
M 904 DE BROWH		. . .
M 906 BREYDEL	(ex-*AM 504*)	25-3-55
M 907 ARTEVELDE	(ex-*AM 503*)	19-6-54

M 908 GEORGES TRUFFAUT	(ex-*AM 515*)	1-11-55
M 909 FRANCOIS BOVESSE	(ex-*AM 516*)	28-2-56

All, except the *M-903*, are fitted out as minehunters.
Bldr: U.S. from 1954-55. *M-903* is the former Norwegian *Lagen* transferred 5-66.

Artevelde (M 907)   Photo 1973 J. C. Bellonne

D: 720 tons (780 fl)   **Dim:** 52.67 (50.30 pp) × 10.67 × 3.20
S: 15/14 kts   **Man:** 5 officers, 67 men   **A:** 1/40-mm AA Mk 3
Range: 3,000/10 — 2,400/12
M: General Motors diesels; 2 variable pitch props; 1,600 hp
Fuel: 53 tons diesel

♦ *9 U.S. AMS/MSC coastal minesweepers*

2 of U.S. construction converted to minehunters (1953)

M 934 (ex-*AMS-259*) VERVIERS		M 935 (ex-*AMS-260*) VEURNE	

7 Belgian construction

	L		L
M 927 SPA	31-6-54	M 931 KNOKKE	12-8-54
M 928 STAVELOT	26-3-55	M 932 NIEUWPOORT	12-3-55
M 929 HEIST	9-7-55	M 933 KOKSIJDE	4-6-55
M 930 ROCHEFORT	5-6-54		

Bldr: Boëlwerf (*927/929*) Béliard, Ostend (*930/933*)

D: 330 tons (390 fl)   **Dim:** 44 (42.10 pp) × 8.30 × 2.60
S: 13.5/12 kts   **A:** 1/40-mm AA   **Range:** 2700/10.5
Man: 4 officers, 17 petty officers, 19 men.   **Fuel:** 30m³ diesel
M: General Motors diesels, 2 props, 80 hp

♦ *12 AMI inshore minesweepers (wooden hull)*

MINESWEEPERS AND MINEHUNTERS (*continued*)

Rochefort (M 930)

Veurne (M 935)   *Note the differences in bridge structures*

	L		L
M 471 HASSELT	5-68	**M 479 HUY** (ex-*MSI 91*)	17-11-56
M 473 LOKEREN	18-5-57	**M 480 SERAING** (ex-*MSI 92*)	16-3-57
M 474 TURNHOUT	7-9-57	**M 482 VISE** (ex-*MSI 94*)	7-9-57
M 475 TONGEREN	16-11-57	**M 483 OUGRÉE** (ex-*MSI 95*)	16-11-57
M 476 MERKSEM	5-4-58	**M 484 DINANT** (ex-*MSI 96*)	5-4-58
M 477 OUDENAERDE	3-5-58	**M 485 ANDENNE** (ex-*MSI 97*)	3-5-58
M 478 HERSTAL	6-8-56		

Bldr: Kruibeke

D: 160 tons (190 fl). **Dim:** 34.50 (32.50 pp) × 6.70 × 2.10
Man: 1 officer, 7 petty officers, 9 men **S:** 15 kts **Range:** 2,300/10
A: 2/12.7-mm machine guns (II × 1)

M: 2/630-hp diesels, 2 props **Fuel:** 18 m³ diesel

REMARKS: Designed to sweep the Schelde River; fitted for magnetic, acoustic and mechanical sweeping to a depth of 4.50 to 10 m.

Dinant (M 484)

LOGISTIC SUPPORT

	Bldr	Laid down	L	In serv.
A 961 ZINNIA	Cockerill (Hoboken)	11-66	6-5-67	11-67

Zinnia (A 962)   *Photo 1973 Martinelli*

D: 1,705 tons (2,435 fl) **Dim:** 99.50 (94.20 wl) × 14 × 3.60
S: 18 kts (20 on trials) **Range:** 4,000/14
Man: 13 officers, 46 petty officers, 64 men
A: 3/40-mm AA (I × 3) — 1 Alouette II helicopter with folding hangar
M: Cockerill-Ougrée diesels, V 12 TR 240 CO; 2 props; 5,000 hp
Fuel: 150 m³ diesel, 300 m³ for supply to minesweepers. Anti-rolling devices.

	Bldr	Laid down	L	In serv.
A 960 GODETIA	Boëlwerf (Temse)	1-64	7-12-65	2-66

LOGISTIC SUPPORT (*continued*)

Godetia (A 960)   Photo 1973 J. C. Bellonne

Godetia (A 960)   Photo 1970 Terzibaschitsch

D:	1,700 tons (2,300 fl)	**Dim:**	91.83 (87.85 pp) × 14 × 3.50

Man: 10 officers, 37 petty officers, 48 men
A: 2/40-mm AA (II × 1)   **Range:** 2,250/15   **S:** 18 kts
M: 4 ACEC-M.A.N. diesels linked to 2 variable pitch props; 5,400 hp.

REMARKS: Used as fishery protection ships. 15 knots on one diesel engine. Stabilized by liquid anti-rolling devices. Ship can be protected against radioactive fallout by closed circuit ventilation. Can accommodate oceanographic research personnel on board and has space for laboratory. Cargo hold with crane to unload supplies or small boats.

PATROL BOATS (former river gunboats) — 1953-54.

P 901 LEIE	P 903 MEUSE	P 905 SCHELDE
P 902 LIBERATION	P 904 SAMBRE	P 906 SEMOIS

Libération   Photo 1970

Bldr: Theodor (Regensburg)

D:	30 tons (fl)	**Dim:**	23.25 × 3.80 × 0.90
S:	19 kts	**Man:**	1 officer, 6 men
M:	2 MWM diesels, 440 hp	**A:**	2/12.7-mm machine guns

REMARKS: *Liberation* is 26 meters in length, 4 meters in beam.

VARIOUS

A 958 ZENOBE GRAMME — School sailing ship (1961). Fitted out as Bermudian Ketch (240 m³ sail area)

D:	149 tons	**Dim:**	28.15 × 6.85 × . . .
S:	10 kts	**M:**	1 MWM diesel, 220 hp.

A 950 VALCKE — 110 tons, 600 hp. **A 951 HOMMEL, A 952 WESP, A 959 MIER** — 22 tons, 600 hp. Tugs.

A 962 MECHELEN (ex-MSC class minesweeper). Used as an oceanographic research ship.

PERSONNEL: 3,400 officers, 28,000 men, plus 500 officers and 13,000 men in the "Fuzileiros Navais" (Marine Corps equivalent).

NAVAL AVIATION: Established in 1963. Uses Westland Whirlwind helicopters (being replaced by U.S. SH3-D Sea King and Westland Wasp). The Air Force makes available to the Navy S-2-F Trackers and P-2-V Neptunes.

MERCHANT MARINE (1-7-74): 471 ships — 2,428,972 grt (tankers: 52 — 885,567 grt)

MAIN WARSHIPS IN SERVICE OR UNDER CONSTRUCTION AS OF 1 OCTOBER 1975.

	L	Tons	Main armament
♦ *1 small aircraft carrier (ASW)*			
MINAS GERAIS (obsolete)	1944	15,890	10/40-mm AA, 12 aircraft
♦ *10 submarines*			
3 HUMAITÁ	1972-74	1,610	8 TT
5 RIO GRANDE DO SUL (obsolete)	1942	1,525	10 TT
2 GOIAS	1945	1,650	10 TT
♦ *1 cruiser*			
1 ALMIR. TAMANDARE (obsolete)	1936-38	10,000	15/152-mm, 8/127-mm AA
♦ *20 destroyers and fast frigates*			
4 NITEROI (ASW)	1973-75	3,200	1/120-mm AA, 1/40-mm AA, 1 Ikara missile launcher 1 Sea Cat missile launcher 1 ASW Bofors, 6 ASW TT 1 helicopter
2 CONSTITUÇÃO (general purpose)	1974-75	3,150	2/120-mm AA, 2/40-mm AA 4 Exocet missile launchers 1 Sea Cat missile launcher 1 ASW Bofors, 6 ASW TT 1 helicopter
7 PARA (obsolete)	1942-44	2,050	5/127-mm AA, 5/533-mm TT
5 MATO GROSSO (obsolete)	1944	2,200	6/127-mm AA, 6 ASW TT
2 MARCILIO DIAZ (obsolete)	1944-45	2,400	2/127-mm AA, 6 ASW TT, ASROC
♦ *10 escort vessels*			
10 IMPERIAL MARINHEIRO	1954	911	1/76-mm AA
♦ *6 coastal patrol boats*			
♦ *15 river patrol and small craft*			
♦ *10 minesweepers*			

LIGHT AIRCRAFT CARRIER (ASW)

♦ *1 British Colossus class*

BRAZIL

	Bldr	Laid down	L	In serv.
A 11 MINAS GERAIS (ex-*Vengeance*)	Swan Hunter	11-42	23-3-44	1-45

Minas Gerais (A 11) 1973

D: 15,890 tons (19,890 fl)   **Dim:** 211.25 × 36.44 (24.50 hull) × 7.15
S: 24 kts   **Man:** 1,000 ship's company plus 300 aviation personnel
A: 10/40-mm AA (IV × 2) — 12 aircraft — 6 helicopters.
Range: 12,000/14 — 6,200/23
M: Parsons GT; 2 props; 42,000 hp   **Electric:** 2,500 kw.
Boilers: 4/28 kg/cm² pressure   **Fuel:** 2,200 tons

REMARKS: Purchased from Great Britain in 12-56; refitted in Rotterdam in 1960 with new weapons, steam catapult, angled flight deck (8.5°), mirror optical landing equipment, new radars and new elevators.

SUBMARINES

♦ *3 British Oberon class, ordered 8-69*

	Bldr	Laid down	L	In serv.
S 20 HUMAITÁ	Vickers-Barrow	11-70	5-10-71	18-6-73
S 21 TONELEROS	Vickers-Barrow	1-71	22-11-72	mid-77
S 22 RIACHUELO	Vickers-Barrow	1973	6-9-75	mid-76

D: 1,610 tons standard, 2,030 surfaced, 2,400 submerged
Dim: 90 × 8.02 × 5.50   **A:** 8/533-mm torpedoes — 6 TT forward — 2 TT aft
S: 17.5/15 kts   **Man:** 68 men
M: diesel-electric propulsion surfaced. Standard Admiralty 16-cyl. diesels; 2 electric generators, each 1,280 kw; 2 electric motors; 2 props; 3,700 to 6,000 hp.

SUBMARINES (continued)

♦ Humaitá class (cont.)

REMARKS: *Toneleros* will be a year late entering active service due to a fire on board during construction. See British *Oberon*. Batteries made up of 224 elements in 2 sections with a 7,240-ampere capacity for 5 hours. Underway cruising with snorkel may be maintained for six weeks at a maximum speed of 11 knots. "One-man control" system for emersion and diving. Digital tactical data system.

♦ *5 ex-U.S. Guppy II class, transferred in 5-72, 7-72 and 1973.*

	Bldr	L
S 10 GUANABARA (ex-*Dogfish*, SS-350)	Electric Boat Co.	27-10-45
S 11 RIO GRANDE DO SUL (ex-*Grampus*, SS-523)	Boston NSY	15-12-44
S 12 BAHIA (ex-*Sea Leopard*, SS-483)	Portsmouth NSY	2-3-45
S 13 RIO DE JANEIRO (ex-*Odax*, SS-484)	Portsmouth NSY	10-4-45
S 14 CEARA (ex-*Amberjack*, SS-522)	Boston NSY	15-12-44

Rio de Janeiro (S 13)   1972

D: 1,517 tons standard, 1,950 surfaced, 2,540 submerged
Dim: 93.80 × 8.20 × 5.20   **S:** 18/13-15 kts   **Range:** 10,000/10
A: 10/533-mm TT, 6 fwd and 4 aft   **Man:**   86 men
M: diesel-electric propulsion; 3 generator groups; 2 electric motors; 2 props; 4,800/5,200 hp.   **Fuel:** 300 tons diesel.

REMARKS: Similar to the *Balao* class, but the 4th group of generators has been removed to make room for a larger sonar. Two batteries of 126 elements. Refitted in 1952-54.

♦ *2 ex-U.S. Guppy III class, transferred in 1973-74.*

	Bldr	L
S 15 GOIAS (ex-*Trumpetfish*, SS-425)	Wm. Cramp	13-4-45
S 16 AMAZONAS (ex-*Greenfish*, SS-351)	Electric Boat Co.	21-12-45

D: 1,650 tons standard, 1,975 surfaced, 2,540 submerged
Dim: 99.40 × 8.20 × 5.20   **S:**   20/13-15 kts
Man: 86 men   **Range:**   10,000/10
Electron Equipt: BQG 4 sonar. **A:**   10/533-mm torpedo tubes, 6 fwd, 4 aft.
M: diesel-electric propulsion; 4 groups of generators (6,400 hp); 2 electric motors (5,400 hp).

Goiaz (S 15)   Photo 1975

CRUISERS

	Bldr	Laid down	L	In serv.
C 12 TAMANDARE	Newport News S.B. Co.	12-36	15-4-38	5-39

Tamandare (C 12)   circa 1970

(ex-*Saint Louis*, CL-49)

D: 10,000 tons (13,500 fl)   **Dim:**   185.33 × 20.10 (with bulges) × 7.00
S: 20 kts (cruising)   **Range:**   14,500/15
A: 15/152-mm (III × 5) — 8/127-mm AA (II × 4) — 28/40-mm AA (IV × 7) — 20/20-mm AA (I × 20) — 1 helicopter
Electron Equipt: 1/SPS 12, 1/SPS 10.
Man: 980 men (peacetime), 1,280 (war)
Armor: **Belt:** 38 to 101   **Decks:** 76 to 52.   **Turrets:** 127
Conning Tower: 203
M: Westinghouse GT; 4 props; 100,000 hp.
Boilers: 8 Babcock Express, 43 kg pressure.   **Fuel:** 2,100 tons

REMARKS: Purchased from the U.S.A. in 1950.

FRIGATES

♦ *6 Vosper-Thornycroft Mk 10 class, ordered 20-9-70*

(a) ASW class	Bldr	Laid down	L	In serv.
F 40 NITEROI	Thornycroft, Woolston	5-1972	8-2-74	mid-76
F 41 DEFENSORA	Thornycroft, Woolston	12-1972	11-3-75	. . .
F 44 INDEPENDÊNCIA	Ast. Ilha das Cobras (Rio)	6-1972	. . .	1976
F 45 UNIÃO	Ast. Ilha das Cobras (Rio)	14-6-72	14-3-75	1977
(b) anti-surface class				
F 42 CONSTITUCÃO	Thornycroft, Woolston	3-1972	. . .	8-79
F 43 LIBERAL	Thornycroft, Woolston	1-5-75	. . .	8-79

D: 3,800 tons (fl)
S: 30.5 kts (28 cruising on gas turbines, 22 on diesels)
Dim: 129.24 (121.92 pp) × 13.49 × 5.94 (depth includes sonar)
Range: 1,300/28 — 4,200/19 (4 diesels); 5,300/17.5 (2 diesels)
A: ASW class — 1/114-mm Mk 8 Vickers automatic — 2/40-mm Bofors, 70-cal (I × 2) — ASW Ikara system — 1 ASW Bofors system 375-mm, twin barrel — 2 triple Seacat AA systems — 6/ASW Mk 32 TT (III × 2) — 1 Lynx WG 13 helicopter — 1 depth charge mortar (5 charges). Surface warfare class: similar but without the Ikara system and with a second 114-mm Mk 8 aft and 4 launchers (II × 2) for the MM 38 Exocet system.
Electron Equipt: Radars: 1/Plessey AWS 2 with Mk 10 IFF (air search), 1/Hollandse Signaalapparaten ZWO-6 with RRA, 2/Selenia RTN-10 X (guidance system)
Sonars: fitted on board all ships: 1/EDO 610 E, the 4 ASW ships, 1 EDO 700 E (towed).
M: CODAG propulsion, 2 Rolls-Royce Olympus TM3B gas turbines, each 28,000 hp; 4 MTU diesels, 16 cylinders in a V, each 3,940 hp coupled to one drive shaft in pairs; 2 variable pitch Escher-Wyss props. **Fuel:** 450 tons diesel. 50 tons fresh water. 26 tons helicopter fuel. **Endurance:** 60 days.
Electric: . . . kw **Man:** 21 officers, 180 men

REMARKS: Fitted with retractable stabilizers.

♦ *5 ex-U.S. Gearing class destroyers*

	Bldr	L
D 21 INHAÚMA (ex-. . .)		

D 22 JACEGUAI (ex-. . .)
D 23 FRONTIN (ex-. . .)
D 24 GREENHALGH (ex-. . .)

D 25 MARCILIO DIAZ (ex-*Henry W. Tucker, DDR-875*)	Consolidated Steel Corp.	8-11-44
D 26 MARIZ E BARROS (ex-*Brinkley Bass, DD-887*)	Consolidated Steel Corp.	26-5-45

Marcilio Diaz (D 25) 1974

D: 2,400 tons (3,500 average, 3,600 fl)
Dim: 119.17 × 12.45 × 3.80 (light) **S:** 30 kts
Man: 14 officers, 260 men **Range:** 2,400/25 — 4,800/15.
A: 2/127-mm 38 (II × 1) — 1 Asroc ASW system — 6/324-mm ASW TT (III × 2) Mk 32 for Mk 43 or Mk 44 torpedoes. Platform and hangar for helicopter.
Electron Equipt: Radars: 1/SPS 10, 1/SPS 40
Sonar: 1/SQS 23
M: GT; 4 Babcock boilers; 2 props; 60,000 hp **Fuel:** 650 tons

REMARKS: Modernized with FRAM I. *D 25* and *26* transferred in 12-1973. The transfer of number *D 21* to *D 24* has not as yet been decided although new names have already been assigned. The American ships involved are not as yet known. *D 25* and *D 26* reached Brazil 6-74.

♦ *5 ex-U.S. Allen Sumner class*

	Bldr	L
D 34 MATO GROSSO (ex-*Compton, DD-705*)	Federal SB (Kearney)	17-9-44
D 35 SERGIPE (ex-*Buck, DD-761*)	Bethlehem (San Fran.)	11-2-44
D 36 ALAGOAS (ex-*James C. Owens, DD-776*)	Bethlehem (San Pedro)	1-10-44
D 37 RIO GRANDE DO NORTE (ex-*Strong, DD-758*)	Bethlehem (San Fran.)	23-4-44

FRIGATES (*continued*)

D 38 ESPIRITO SANTO   Bethlehem (San Pedro) 6-2-44
(ex-*Lowry, DD-770*)

Mato Grosso (D 34)   1973

D: 2,200 tons (3,320 fl)   **Dim:** 114.75 × 12.45 × 5.80
S: 30 kts   **Man:** 15 officers, 260 men   **Range:** 1,260/30 — 4,600/15
A: 6/127-mm (II × 3) — 4/76-mm AA (II × 2) — 2 hedgehogs — 6/324-mm
ASW TT Mk 32 (III × 2)
Electron Equipt: Radars: 1/SPS 10, 1/SPS 6
                      Sonar: 1/SQS 32
M: GT; 2 props; 60,000 hp; 4 Babcock boilers   **Fuel:** 650 tons
REMARKS: *D 34* transferred 27-9-72, the others in 1973.

Maranhão (D 33)   1972

♦ *7 ex-U.S. Fletcher class*

	Bldr	L
D 27 PARA (ex-*Guest, DD-472*)	Boston Naval SY	20-2-42

D 28 PARAIBA (ex-*Bennett, DD-473*)   Boston Naval SY   16-4-42
D 29 PARANA (ex-*Cushing, DD-797*)   Bethlehem Steel   30-9-43
D 30 PERNAMBUCO (ex-*Hailey, DD-556*)   Todd SY (Seattle)   9-3-43
D 31 PIAUI (ex-*Lewis Hancock, DD-675*)   Federal SB (Kearney)   1-8-43
D 32 SANTA CATARINA   Bethlehem (San Pedro) 31-10-43
(ex-*Irwin, DD-794*)
D 33 MARANHÃO (ex-*Shields, DD-596*)   Puget Sound B&DD   25-9-44

D: 2,050 tons (2,850 tons fl)   **Dim:** 114.85 × 12.03 × 5.50
S: 30 kts   **Man:** 15 officers, 247 men   **Range:** 1,260/30 — 4,400/15
A: *27/28/29:* 5/127-mm (I × 5) — 6 or 10 (*29*) 40-mm AA — the others: 4/127-mm
AA — 6/76-mm AA (II × 3); on all ships: 5/533-mm TT (V × 1) — 2 ASW
fixed TT — 2 hedgehogs — 1 depth charge rack
Electron Equipt: Radars: 1/SPS 10, 1/SPS 6
                      Sonar: 1/SQS 4, 29 or 32
M: General Electric GT; 2 props; 60,000 hp; 4 Babcock and Wilcox boilers
Fuel: 650 tons

REMARKS: Transferred under the Mutual Aid Agreement in 1959 (*D27/28*), 1961
(*D29/30*), 1967-68 all others except *D 33*, 8-72. ASW torpedo tubes (Mk 44 torpedoes) on *D 31/33*.

ESCORT VESSELS ("Corvettes")

♦ *10 Imperial Marinheiro class*

Imperial Marinheiro (V 15)   1971

V 15 IMPERIAL MARINHEIRO (24-11-54)   **V 20 ANGOSTURA**
V 16 IGUATEMI   **V 21 BAHIANA** (11-54)
V 17 IPIRANGA (29-6-54)   **V 22 MEARIM** (8-54)
V 18 FORTE DE COIMBRA (11-6-54)   **V 23 PURUS** (6-11-54)
V 19 CABOCLO (28-8-54)   **V 24 SOLIMÕES** (24-11-54)

D: 911 tons   **Dim:** 55.72 × 9.55 × 4.60
A: 1/76-mm — 4/20-mm AA   **Man:** 60 men   **S:** 15 kts
M: Sulzer diesels; 2 props; 2,160 hp.   **Fuel:** 135 tons diesel.

REMARKS: Heavy tugs built in Holland. Used in customs and coast guard service. Can
be converted for minesweeping or minelaying. The *V-15* is used as a submarine
tender. Officially designed "corvettes."

PATROL BOATS

♦ *6 coastal patrol, Piratini class*

PATROL CRAFT (*continued*)

	In serv.		In serv.
P 10 PIRATINI	30-11-70	**P 13 PARATI**	7-71
P 11 PIRAJÁ	1-71	**P 14 PENEDO**	9-71
P 12 PAMPEIRO	3-71	**P 15 POTI**	10-71

Parati (P 13)   1972

D: 105 tons (fl)   **Dim:** 30.50 (29 pp) × 6.05 × 1.90
S: 15.5 kts   **Man:** 2 officers, 14 men   **Range:** 1,000/15 — 1,700/12
A: 1 ASW weapon, 3 machine guns   **M:** 4 diesels; 2 props; 1,100 hp

REMARKS: These patrol craft are based on the WPB-95 class of the U.S. Coast Guard.

Raposo Tavares (P 21)   1974

RIVER PATROL CRAFT

♦ *2 river patrol craft ordered in 1970 from Ilha das Cobras Naval Dockyard, Rio*

P 20 PEDRO TEIXEIRA L: 11-6-72   **P 21 RAPOSO TAVARES** L: 11-6-72
   D: 700 tons (fl)   **Dim:** 62 × 9.35 × 1.65

S: 13 kts   **Range:** 5,500/10
A: 1/40-mm — 6 machine guns — 2/81-mm mortars
M: 4 MEP-MAN diesels, V6V type; 4,000 hp; 2 props

Platform for helicopters

♦ *3 river patrol craft, Roraima class. In service 1975-76*

	Bldr	L
P 30 RORAIMA	MacLaren, Niteroi	9-11-72
P 31 RONDÔNIA	MacLaren, Niteroi	10-1-73
P 32 AMAPÁ	MacLaren, Niteroi	9-3-73

D: 340 tons   **Dim:** 45 × 8.45 × 1.37
S: 14.5 kts   **Man:** 9 officers, 54 men   **Range:** 6,000/11
A: 1/40 mm — 6 machine guns — 2 mortars
M: 2 M.A.N. diesels; 912 hp; 2 props

♦ *1 river monitor*

	Bldr	Laid down	L	In serv.
U 17 PARNAIBA	Rio de Janeiro	6-36	2-9-37	11-37

(*Mato Grosso flotilla*)

D: 620 tons   **Dim:** 54.50 × 10.20 × 1.50
S: 12 kts   **Range:** 1,350/10   **Man:** 90 men
A: 1/76-mm — 2/47-mm — 2/40-mm AA — 6/20-mm
Armor Belt: 76   **Main deck:** 38
M: Triple expansion; 2 props; 1,300 hp; 2 or 3 boilers   **Fuel:** 70 tons

♦ *4 river patrol boats*

Ordered in 1974 from Inconav Niteroi Shipbuilders, delivered in 1975-76.

U 40 RIO PARDO   **U 42 RIO CHUI**
U 41 RIO NEGRO   **U 43 RIO OIAPOQUE**
   D: 150 tons   **Dim:** 35.38 × 6.50 × 1.90
   M: 2 diesels; 548 hp   **S:** 14 kts

Will carry 600 passengers

♦ *6 river patrol boats built in The Netherlands in 1956.*

U20 RIO DOCE   **U 23 RIO REAL**
U 21 RIO DAS CONTAS   **U 24 RIO TURVO**
U 22 RIO FORMOSO   **U 25 RIO VERDE**
   D: 150 tons   **Dim:** 35 × 6 × 2.10   **M:** 450 hp

Can carry 600 passengers.

♦ *1 command transport ship*

G 15 PARAGUASSU (Former river transport ship *Guarapuava*, bought in 1971)
refitted for the Mato Grosso flotilla and used as a river buoy tender.
   D: 285 tons   **Dim:** 40 × 7 × 1.20
   S: 12 kts   **Range:** 2,500/10   **M:** diesel, 1 prop

MINESWEEPERS

♦ *6 German Schutze (R55) class, two ordered in 1973*

	L		L
M 15 ARATU	27-5-70	**M 17 ATALAIA**	14-4-71
M 16 ANHATOMIRIM	4-11-70	**M 18 ARACATUBA**	1971

MINESWEEPERS (*continued*)

M 19 ABROLHOS   7-5-74   **M 20 ALBARDÃO**   5-9-74

Bldr: Abeking and Rasmussen (German Fed. Repub.)

Anhatomirim (M 16)   1972

Aratu (M 15)   1971

D:	230 tons	**Dim:**	47.20 × 7.16 × 2.10	**A:** 1/40-mm AA
S:	24 kts	**Range:**	710/20	

M: 4 Maybach diesels; 2 Escher-Wyss props; 4,500 hp
Fuel: 22 tons diesel   **Man:** 39 men

Juruena (M 14)

REMARKS: Fitted for magnetic, mechanical, and acoustic minesweeping. M 19 commissioned 16-4-75, M 20 commissioned 21-7-75

♦ *2 ex-U.S. YMS (1942) reclassified as auxiliary ships 26-8-74*

M 11 JAVARI (ex-*Cardinal, MSC-4*)   **M 13 JURUÁ** (ex-*Jackdaw, MSC-21*)

D:	270 tons (350 fl)	**Dim:**	41.45 × 7.45 × 2.45 (stern)
S:	12 kts (10 cruising)	**Range:**	2,300/8.5
A:	4/20-mm AA (II × 2)	**Fuel:**	19 tons diesel
M:	2 General Motors diesels; 2 props; 1,000 hp		

HYDROGRAPHIC SHIPS

	Bldr	Laid down	L	In serv.
H 21 SIRIUS	Ishikawajima (Tokyo)	12-56	30-7-57	12-57
H 22 CANOPUS	Ishikawajima (Tokyo)	12-56	20-11-57	3-58

Canopus (H 22)

D:	1,800 tons (fl)	**Dim:**	77.90 × 12.03 × 3.70
S:	15 kts	**A:**	1/76-mm AA — 4/20-mm AA
Man:	102 men	**M:**	Sulzer diesels, 2 props; 2,700 hp

REMARKS: 1 helicopter, 1 LCVP, 3 small craft. Fully equipped. Variable pitch props.

♦ *6 hydrographic boats (wooden hull). (Amazon River)*

	In serv.		In serv.
H 11 PARAIBANO	10-68	**H 15 ITACURUSSÁ**	3-71
H 12 RIO BRANCO	10-68	**H 16 CAMOCIM**	1971
H 14 NOGUEIRA DA GAMA	3-71	**H 17 CARAVELAS**	1971
(ex-*Jaceguai*)			

Bldr: Bormann (Rio de Janeiro)

Nogueira de Gama (H 14)   1971

HYDROGRAPHIC SHIPS (continued)

D: 32 tons (50 fl) **Dim:** 16 × 4.60 × 1.30
S: 11 kts **Man:** 2 officers, 9 men
M: 1 General Motors diesel, 165 hp **Range:** 600/11

H 31 ARGUS (6-12-57) — **H 32 ORION** (5-2-58) — **H 33 TAURUS** (7-1-58)
Bldr: Rio de Janeiro SY

Orion (H 32)

D: 250 tons (300 fl) **Dim:** 44.80 (42.06 pp) × 6.10 × 2.45
S: 17 kts (15 cruising) **Range:** 1,200/15
A: 2/20-mm AA; ASW depth charges
M: Caterpillar diesels; 2 props; 1,200 hp **Fuel:** 35 tons diesel

REMARKS: Based on the Portuguese *Azevia* class. Orion modernized in 1973/74.

U 10 ALMIRANTE SALDANHA	Bldr	L	In serv.
	Vickers	19-12-33	6-34

Al Saldanha (U 10)

D: 3,225 tons (3,825 fl) **Dim:** 92 × 15.70 × 5.50
S: 11 kts **Man:** 356 men **Range:** 12,000/10

REMARKS: Former 4-masted schooner with auxiliary motor (6-cylinder diesel, 1,400 hp), refitted in 7-1961.

♦ *1 oceanographic ship (planned)*

ALVARO ALBERTO

D: ... **Dim:** 60 × 12 × 4.30
S: 13 kts **Man:** 26 men, 17 scientists

♦ *1 ex-U.S. oceanographic ship transferred in 1974*

ALMIRANTE CAMARA (ex-*Sands, T-AGOR-6*)
D: 1,020 tons (1,370 fl) **Dim:** 70 (63.70 pp) × 11.28 × 6.30 (fl)
S: 12.5 kts **Range:** 12,000/12
Man: 8 officers, 18 men, 15 oceanographers
M: diesel-electric; 2 props (1 forward); 1,000 hp

REMARKS: An auxiliary motor powers a small maneuvering propeller for station-keeping purposes at extremely low rpm.

BUOY AND LIGHT TENDERS

	Bldr	Laid down	L	In serv.
H 34 GRACA ARANHA	Elbin, Niteroi	End 1970	23-6-74	12-74

D: 1,253 tons **Dim:** 75.57 × 13 × 3.71
S: 13 kts **Man:** 101 men
M: diesel; 1 variable pitch prop; 2,000 hp; 1 bow thruster.

♦ *5 130-ton buoy maintenance ships*

H 13 M JOÃO DOS SANTOS, H 24 CASTELHANOS, H 28 FAROLEIRO SANTANA, H 27 FAROLEIRO AREAS, H 30 FAROLEIRO NASCIMENTO.

AMPHIBIOUS SHIPS

♦ *2 Ex-U.S. LSTs*

G 26 DUQUE DE CAXIAS (ex-*Grant County, LST-1174*) transfered 11-72.

Duque de Caxias (G 26) Photo 1975

D: 3,860 tons (7,100 fl) **Dim:** 134.70 × 16.90 × 5.50
S: 16 kts **A:** 6/76-mm AA (II × 3)
M: 4 Nordberg diesels; 2 variable pitch props; 14,000 hp.

REMARKS: Can carry 700 men. Air-conditioned. 4 LCVP in davits; 1 LCV and 2 motorized causeways which can be dropped where needed. Platform for helicopters.

G 28 GARCIA DAVILA (ex-*Outagamie County, LST-1073*) 1944
D: 1,490 tons (4,100 fl) **Dim:** 100 × 15.25 × 3.36
M: General Motors diesels, 2 props **A:** 8/40-mm AA

REMARKS: G 28 transferred 25-5-71.

AMPHIBIOUS SHIPS (*continued*)

Garcia Davila (G 28) 1972

♦ *28 LCVP built in Japan in 1959-60*

♦ *7 EDVO* (landing craft for vehicles and personnel). Built in Brazil in 1971. Hulls built of synthetic materials.

   Dim: 11 × 3.20 × 0.60 (fwd), 1 (aft)   **M:** Brazilian Scania diesel

Can carry 36 men with full-pack or 1 jeep with trailer and 17 men or 1/105-mm howitzer or an anti-tank gun and 18 men.

♦ *4 EDCG* — Bldr: Rio SY 1974-75. U.S. LCU class.

LOGISTIC SUPPORT

Custodio de Mello (U 26) 1971

♦ *4 transports*

	Bldr	Laid down	L	In serv.
U 26 CUSTÓDIO DE MELLO	Ishikawajima (Tokyo)	12-53	10-6-54	9-54
G 16 BARROSO PEREIRA	Ishikawajima (Tokyo)	12-53	7-8-54	12-54
G 21 ARI PARREIRAS	Ishikawajima (Tokyo)	12-55	24-8-56	12-56
G 22 SOARES DUTRA	Ishikawajima (Tokyo)	12-55	13-12-56	3-57

   D: 4,800 tons (8,600 fl)   **Dim:** 119.20 × 16 × 6.10
   S: 16 kts   **Man:** 118 men. Can carry 1,972 troops (497 average).
   A: 4/76-mm (*U-26*) — 2/76-mm and 2/20-mm on the others.
   Cargo capacity: 4,200 tons   **M:** GT; 2 props; 2 boilers; 4,800 hp.

REMARKS: Platform for helicopter on stern. Refrigerated storeroom. Living spaces mechanically ventilated and partially air-conditioned. *Custodio de Mello* is used as an underway training ship.

♦ *1 repair ship ex-U.S. LST transferred in 1963.*

G 24 BELMONTE (ex-U.S. *Helios, ARB-12*)

Belmonte (G 24)

   D: 2,030 tons   **Dim:** 100 × 15.25 × 3.36
   S: 9 kts   **A:** 8/40-mm AA
   M: General Motors diesels, 2 props

REMARKS: 1/60-ton winch crane. 2/10-ton booms.

♦ *2 oilers*

G 27 MARAJO (31-1-68) — Oiler — Bldr: Ishikawajima Rio Do Brasil
   D: 7,200 tons   **Dim:** 137.10 (127.69 pp) × 19.22 × 7.35
   S: 13.6 kts   **Range:** 9,200/14.5   **Man:** 80 men
   M: 1 Sulzer diesel, 8,000 hp   **Cargo capacity:** 10,500 tons

G 17 POTENGI (16-3-38) — Oiler — Bldr: Papendrecht (Holland)
   D: 600 tons   **Dim:** 54 × 7.20 × 1.80
   S: 10 kts   **Cargo capacity:** 450 tons
   M: diesel, 550 hp. *Mato Grosso River flotilla.*

♦ *7 small service transports.*

TENENTE FABIO, TENENTE RAUL
   D: 55 tons   **Dim:** 20.28 × 5.10 × 1.20   **Cargo capacity:** 22 tons
   M: diesel, 135 hp. 1/10-ton derrick   **Range:** 350   **S:** 10 kts

Munitions barges: **SÃO FRANCISCO DOS SANTOS** (1964), **UBIRAJARA DOS SANTOS** (1968), **OPERARIO LUIS LEAL** (1968), **MIGUEL DOS SANTOS** (1968), **APRENDIZ LÉDIO CONCEIÇÃO** (1968)

♦ *12 tugs*

BRAZIL (*continued*)

LOGISTIC SUPPORT (*continued*)

K 10 GASTÃO MOUTINHO (ex-U.S. *Skylark, ASR-20;* ex-*Yustaga, ATF-165*)

D: 1,780 tons (2,140 fl). **Dim:** 75.50 × 12.70 × 4.30.
S: 14.5 kts **A:** 2/76-mm, 2/40-mm AA
M: diesel-electric; 1 prop; 3,000 hp

REMARKS: Purchased in 6-1973.

R 11 MARTIN DE OLIVEIRA (ex-*Gastão Moutinho*)

D: 588 tons **Dim:** 49.42 × 7 × 2.44 **S:** 10.5 kts

R 21 TRITÃO (ex-U.S. *ATA-234*), **R 22 TRIDENTE** (ex-U.S. *ATA-235*), **R 23 TRIUNFO** (ex-U.S. *ATA-236*), launched in 1944 in U.S.A.; in service in 1947.

D: 534 tons (835 fl) **Dim:** 43.61 × 10.34 × 4.03
S: 13 kts **A:** 2/20-mm AA **M:** diesel-electric, 1,500 hp.

R 14 LAURINDO PITTA (Vickers 1910, rebuilt 1969).

D: 514 tons **Dim:** 39.04 × 7.77 × 3.35 (aft)

R 20 VAN DEN KOLK (Great Britain, 1910) **D:** 350 tons

R 26 ANTONIO JÕAO (80 tons), **R 31 AUDAZ, R 32 CENTAURO, R 33 GUARANI, R 34 LAMEGO, R 35 PASSO DE PATRIA, R 36 VOLUNTÁRIO.**

VARIOUS

♦ *1 station vessel* (ex-U.S. destroyer)

U 28 BAURU (ex-U.S. *Reybold, DE-177*)

REMARKS: Last of 6 DEs transferred in 1944.

♦ *6 small craft of 11 tons*

R 54 ANCHOVA	**R 55 ARENQUE**	**R 56 ATUM**
R 57 ACARA	**R 58 AGULHA**	**R 59 ARUANA**

♦ *3 floating docks*

G 25 ALFONSO PENA (ex-U.S. *ARD-14*) — **D:** 5,200 fl **Dim:** 150 × 24.7

ALTE J. GONCALVES (ex.-U.S. *AFLD-4*) can lift 1,000 tons. **Length:** 60 m.
CIDADE DE NATAL (ex-U.S. *AFLD-39*) can life 2,800 tons. **Length:** 119 m.

BRUNEI

♦ *1 fast patrol boat*

PAHLAWAN — Bldr: Vosper Ltd, Portsmouth (5-12-66)

D: 75 tons (89 fl) **Dim:** 30.26 (27.44 pp) × 7.30 × 2.15
S: 50 kts **Man:** 3 officers, 16 men
A: 2/20-mm — 21 12.7-mm machine guns — SS-12 missiles.
M: Bristol Marine gas turbines Proteus type; 3 props; 10,500 hp; 2 diesels are used in cruising (10 kts).

REMARKS: Refitted in 1972 by Vosper-Thornycroft at Singapore.

♦ *2 patrol boats*

PERWIRA (5-1974). **PEMBURU** (30-1-75)

Bldr: Vosper-Thornycroft, Singapore

D: 38.5 tons **Dim:** 21.40 (pp) × 6.10 × 1.20
S: 32 kts **Range:** 600/20
A: 2/20-mm (II × 1) — 2 machine guns
M: 2 MTU diesels; 2,700 hp

♦ *3 Masna class patrol boats*

AMOB 112 MASNA (19-9-70), **AMOB 113 SALEHA** (18-9-70)
AMOB 114 NORAIN comm. 11-71

Bldr: Vosper-Thornycroft Private Ltd., Singapore. In service: 1971-73.

D: 23.5 tons **Dim:** 18.90 × 4.80 × 1.40
S: 25/23 kts **Man:** 8 men
A: 2/20-mm Hispano and machine guns **Range:** 600/23
M: 2 GM diesels 16-cyl. Mk V 71 N; 1,240 hp

REMARKS: Wooden hull, superstructure in light metal, Decca radar. Manned by the Brunei Malayan Regiment.

♦ *3 small boats*

BENDAHARA — KEMAINDERA — MAHARAJALELA

D: 10 tons **Dim:** 14.10 × 3.60 × 0.90 **Man:** 6 men
A: 2 machine guns. **Radar:** Decca 202 **S:** 20 kts
M: 2 General Motors diesels, 334 hp.

♦ *1 SRN 6 class hydrofoil*

♦ *25 armed river barges*

PERSONNEL: approximately 4,000 men

NAVAL AVIATION: 6 Soviet "Hound" helicopters

MERCHANT MARINE (1-7-74): 166 ships — 864,939 grt
                          (tankers: 19 — 288,567 grt)
NOTE: All Bulgarian ships are of Soviet origin.

SUBMARINES

♦ *2 W class*

SLAVA, POBIEDA

D:	1,100 tons (1,600 fl)	**Dim:**	74 × 6.60 × 4.80
S:	17/13 kts	**A:**	6/533-mm TT (4 forward, 2 aft)

♦ *2 R class*

N . . .   N . . .

D:	1,400 tons (1,800 fl)	**Dim:**	75 × 7 × 5.40
S:	17/15 kts	**A:**	8/533-mm TT (4 forward, 4 aft)

PATROL SHIPS

♦ *2 Riga class*

DERSKY, SMELY

D: 950 tons   **S:** 28 kts
A: 3/100-mm — 3/533-mm TT — 2 ASW MBU 2500 rocket launchers

♦ *7 SO1 class (1960-64)*

D: 250 tons (fl)   **S:** 25 kts
A: 4/25-mm AA — 4 ASW MBU 1800 rocket launchers — depth charges

♦ *2 Kronstadt class (1955).*

D: 300 tons   **S:** 23 kts
A: 1/85-mm AA — 2/37-mm AA — 2 hedgehogs — mines

♦ *10 MO V class*

GUIDED MISSILE AND TORPEDO BOATS

♦ *3 OSA I class*

D: 150 tons (210 fl)   **Dim:** 40.10 × 7 × 2
S: 35 kts   **A:** 4 Styx systems — 4/30-mm (II × 2)
Electron Equipt: 1/Square Tie, 1/Drum Tilt
M: diesel; 15,000 hp; 3 props

♦ *6 Shershen class*

D: 190 tons   **Dim:** 34 × 8 × 1.50   **S:** 45 kts
A: 4/533-mm TT, 4/30-mm AA   **M:** diesels; 3 props; 10,000 hp

♦ *8 P 4 class*

D: 40 tons   **S:** 40 kts   **A:** 2/533-mm TT or 4/25-mm AA (II × 2)

MINESWEEPERS

♦ *4 Vanya class*

D: 280 tons   **Dim:** 40 × 6 × 2   **S:** 18 kts   **A:** 2/30-mm AA

♦ *2 T 43 class*

D:	600 tons (fl)	**Dim:**	61 × 8.40 × 2.70
S:	17 kts	**A:**	4/37-mm AA

♦ *4 T 301 class*

D:	150 tons (fl)	**Dim:**	31 × 4.90 × 1.50
S:	10 kts	**A:**	2/20-mm AA

♦ *A dozen small inshore minesweepers: PO 2 class*

AMPHIBIOUS SHIPS

♦ *10 Vydra class LCT*

D:	500 tons (fl)	**Dim:**	50 × 8 × 2.20
M:	diesels; 400 hp	**S:**	10 kts

♦ *10 MFP class LCU*

VARIOUS

♦ *3 coastal oilers*

♦ *7 tugs*

♦ *2 salvage ships*

♦ *2 diving vessels*

♦ *6 barracks ships*

BURMA

PERSONNEL: about 6,200 including reserves.

MERCHANT MARINE (1-7-74): 40 ships — 54,877 grt (tankers: 2 — 1,478 grt)

FRIGATES

♦ *1 British River class purchased in 1947*

MAYU (ex-*Fal*) — Bldr: Smith's Dock, Middlesborough, Eng. (9-11-42)

  D: 1,460 tons (2,170 fl)   **S:** 19 kts   **Dim:** 93.50 × 11.16 × 4.40
  A: 2/102-mm — 4/40-mm AA   **Range:** 4,200/12   **Man:** 140 men
  M: Triple expansion; 2 props; 5,500 hp.   **Boilers:** 2   **Fuel:** 440 tons

♦ *1 British Algerine class purchased in 1957-58*

YAN MYO AUNG (ex-*Mariner*) — Bldr: Canada (9-5-44)

  D: 990 tons (1,237 fl)   **S:** 16 kts   **Dim:** 68.58 × 10.82 × 3.50
  A: 1/102-mm — 4/40-mm AA — fitted to plant 16 mines.   **Man:** 140 men
  M: Triple expansion; 2 props; 2,000 hp.   **Boilers:** 2   **Range:** 3,000/15

♦ *2 ex-U.S. escort vessels purchased in 1965-66*

YAN GYI AUNG (ex-U.S. *Creddock, MSF-356*) — Bldr: Willamette (U.S.A.) (22-7-44)

YAN TAING AUNG (ex-U.S. *Farmington, PCE-894*) — Bldr: (U.S.A.) (1943)

  D: 600 tons (903 fl)   **Dim:** 56.24 × 10.06 × 2.80
  S: 17 kts   **A:** 1/76-mm — 6/40-mm AA   **Man:** 80/95 men
  M: General Motors diesels; 2 props; 2,400 hp

PATROL BOATS

♦ *T 201 to T 205 — British "Dark" class — 1956-57*

T 201   Shbldg. and Sh. Record

  D: 50 tons (64 fl)   **S:** 42 kts (trials)   **Dim:** 22 × 5.80 × 1.90
  A: 1/114-mm — 1/40-mm AA   **M:** Napier Deltic diesels; 2 props; 5,000 hp
  Man: 13 men

INDAW, INLAY, INMA, INYA (1943) ex-British *LCG*

  D: 381 tons   **S:** 13 kts   **Dim:** 47 × 6.70 × 1.30
  A: 2/94-mm — 2/20-mm   **Man:** 39 men   **M:** 2 Paxman diesels; 1,000 hp

♦ **NAWARAT — NAGAKVAY** — Bldr: Dawbon DY, Rangoon (1961)

  D: 400 tons (450 fl)   **S:** 12 kts   **Dim:** 49.70 × 8.23
  A: 2/25-pound guns (Army ordnance) — 2/40-mm AA   **Man:** 43 men
  M: 2 Paxman-Ricardo overhead diesels of 1,160 hp

GUNBOATS AND VARIOUS

♦ **PGM 401 to 406** (ex-U.S. *43/46* and *51/52*) — Bldr: U.S.A. (1959)

  D: 100 tons   **S:** 16 kts   **Dim:** 29 × 5.80 × 1.60
  A: 1/40-mm AA — 2 machine guns   **Man:** 17 men
  M: 4 General Motors diesels; 2 props; 1,000 hp

♦ **MGB 101, 102, 103, 105, 106, 108, 110.** Former U.S. CGS boats with new hulls built in 1960-61 in Burma.

  D: 49 tons (66 fl)   **S:** 11 kts   **Dim:** 25 × 4.85 × 1.60
  Man: 16 men   **A:** 1/40-mm AA — 1/20-mm AA
  M: 4 General Motors diesels; 2 props; 800 hp

♦ **Y 301 to 312** — Bldr: Uljanik, Pula (1957-60).

  D: 120 tons   **S:** 13 kts   **Dim:** 32 × 7.25 × 0.80
  A: 1/40-mm AA — 1/37-mm   **Man:** 29 men
  M: 2 Mercedes-Benz diesels; 4-cyl., 1,100 hp

♦ *8 river transports fitted with gun mounts*

SABAN, SAGU, SEINDA, SETKAYA, SETYAHAT, SHWETHIDA, SHWEPAZUN, SINMIN.

♦ *10 30-to-40-ton river boats built in Burma in 1951-52*

♦ *25 30-to-40-ton river boats built in Yugoslavia in 1965*

♦ *1 transport* **PYIDAWATE** *(2,217 tons) built in 1962*

♦ *2 hydrographic ships,* **THU TAY THI** *(1,100 tons) built in Yugoslavia in 1965, and* **YAY BO** *(108 tons) built in The Netherlands. The first has a helicopter platform.*

♦ *8 LCM* (**701** *to* **708**) *built in 1963.*

♦ *1 service craft (ex-U.S. LCU-1620) used as a transport.*

♦ *1 torpedo transport* **YAN LONG AUNG** *(520 tons) built in Japan in 1967.*

CAMBODIA

Before the country was taken over by the Communist Party, the Cambodian Navy had several ships given to it by the French Navy or the U.S.A. Their whereabouts is unknown (1-6-75) except for the *E 311* which took refuge in Thailand.

PERSONNEL: 6,000 men as well as 4,500 "Marines" for coastal riverine defense.

MERCHANT MARINE: (1-7-74): 3 ships — 2,090 grt

ESCORT SHIPS

♦ **E 311** (ex-*Flamberge*, ex-*PC-1086*) ⎫ Former U.S. patrol craft,
E 312 (ex-*Inconstant*, ex-*PC-1171*) ⎭ transferred in 1955-56.

D:	325 tons (400 fl)	**Dim:**	52.95 × 7.05 × 3.25
S:	18 kts	**Range:**	6,000/10 — 2,300/18
A:	1/76-mm — 1/40-mm AA — 5/20-mm AA	**Man:**	4 officers, 59 men
M:	General Motors diesels; 2 props; 3,600 hp.	**Fuel:**	62 tons diesel

♦ **P 111** (ex-U.S. *LSIL-9039*, ex-*LSIL-875*) former landing craft
P 112 (ex-*Médecin Capitaine Le Gall*, ex-U.S. *LSI*) former landing craft

D:	230 tons (380 fl)	**Dim:**	48.80 × 7.10 × 1.90
S:	15 kts	**Range:**	8,000/12
A:	1/76-mm — 1/40-mm — 2/20-mm — 4 machine guns	**Man:**	58 men
M:	2 General Motors diesels; 1,000 hp.	**Fuel:**	110 tons diesel

PATROL BOATS

♦ *20 U.S. PCF Swift class*
Bldr: U.S.A. See South Vietnam

D:	16 tons (18 fl)	**Dim:**	15.60 × 4.12 × 1.50
S:	25 kts	**Man:**	1 officer, 5 men
A:	2/12.7-mm machine guns — 11 81-mm mortar		
M:	Gray marine diesels 12 V 71; 2 props; 960 hp.		

REMARKS: 24 to 36-hour endurance. Hull is of aluminum.

AMPHIBIOUS

♦ **T 916** (French *EDIC*) — Bldr: Franco-Belge (1968)

D:	292 tons (670 fl)	**Dim:**	59 × 12 × 1.60 fl
A:	2/20-mm	**Man:**	18 men
S:	8 kts	**M:**	2 MGO diesels; 1,000 hp.

T 916 1973

♦ *3 ex-U.S. LCU* **T 917, T 918, T 919**

D:	180 tons (360 fl)	**Dim:**	36.28, 10.36 × 1.80
S:	8 kts	**Man:**	14 men
A:	2/20-mm	**Range:**	700/7

M:	3 diesels; 675 hp.

REMARKS: Can carry 150 to 400 troops.

RIVER FLOTILLA

♦ *4 small supply ships, ASPB class* — Bldr: Gunderson, U.S.A.

D:	28.7 tons	**Dim:**	15.27 × 6.64 × 1.14
S:	20 kts	**Man:**	1 officer, 4 men
A:	1/20-mm AA — 1/81-mm mortar aft — 2 machine guns		
M:	fast diesels Mk 12 V 71; 2 props; 850 hp	**Range:**	200/10

♦ *20 ex-U.S. LCM 6 class, AC series* — Bldr: U.S.A.

AC 8 1973

D:	75 tons (fl)	**Dim:**	18.44 × 5.34 × 1.05
S:	8 kts	**Man:**	1 officer, 10 men
A:	1/40-mm — 1/81-mm mortar — 1/20-mm — 12.7-mm machine guns. A few have a 105-mm mount forward.	**M:**	2 diesels

♦ *23 ATC (ex-U.S. LCM 6 or 8)(armored troop transports)* — Bldr: U.S.A. — Hull number and letter.

D:	66 tons (fl)	**Dim:**	17.07 × 5.34 × 1.02
S:	8 kts	**Man:**	1 officer, 6 men
A:	1/20-mm — 2/12.7-mm machine guns — 4 grenade launchers		
M:	diesels. Can take a 2.5-ton truck on board, have a platform for a light helicopter.		

♦ *4 MSM type river minesweepers (converted LCMs)*
Same characteristics as the ATC class above.

♦ *1 CCB (Communication Command Boat)*

A:	1/40-mm — 1/20-mm — radio transmitters and receivers.

♦ *About 50 U.S. PBR type with a hull number*

RIVER FLOTILLA (*continued*)

River patrol boat US/PBR type   1973

Bldr: United Boat Builders
  D: 18 tons   **Dim:** 9.45 × 3.20 × 0.36/0.45 (depending on speed)
  S: 22 kts   **Man:** 1 officer, 4 men
  A: 2/50-cal. machine guns (fwd) (II × 1) — 2/50-cal. machine guns (aft) —
         1/81-mm mortar aft.
REMARKS: Water jet propulsion, no prop or rudder. 2 diesels, 440 hp

LOGISTIC SUPPORT AND SUPPLY SHIPS

— 1 floating dock, 350 tons, transferred by France 1955
— 1 floating dock, 1,000 tons, transferred by U.S.A. 1972
— 1 60-ton floating crane, 2 floating bases MSB class, transferred by U.S.A. 1972
— 3 LCM-6 fitted out for logistic support. Docking ships for the PBR. 1/5-ton crane.
  1 electric generator 150 kw.
— 1 floating dock, ex-U.S. *AFDL-25*, transferred (loan) 30-6-47.

CAMEROON

PERSONNEL: 200 men

MERCHANT MARINE: (1-7-74): 18 ships — 3,199 grt

♦ *3 small coastal surveillance craft.*

LE VALEUREUX — Bldr: Estérel Naval SY (1970)
  D: 45 tons   **Dim:**   26.80 × 4.97 × 1.55
  S: 25 kts   **Range:** . . ./15
  A: 2/20-mm AA   **Man:**   1 officer, 8 men
  M: 2 diesels; 2 props; 960 hp.

BRIGADIER M'BONGA TOUNDA — Bldr: Estérel Naval SY (1967)
Customs ship, manned by the Navy.
  D: 20 tons (fl)   **Dim:** 18.15 (17.03 pp) × 4.03 × 1.10
  S: 22.5 kts   **Man:** 8 men
  A: 1 12.7-mm machine gun
  M: Caterpillar diesels D 333 TA; 2 props; 540 hp
REMARKS: Same characteristics as the 2 Mauritanian *Imrag'Ni* class.

QUARTIER MAITRE ALFRED MOTTO — Bldr: A.C.R.E., Libreville, Gabon
  D: 96 tons (fl)   **Dim:** 29.10 × 6.20 × 1.85 (aft)
  S: 15.5 kts   **Man:** 2 officers, 15 men
  A: 2/20-mm AA — 2 machine guns   **M:** 2 Baudoin diesels; 1,290 hp.

♦ *3 LCVP type landing craft*

SOUELLABA, INDEPENDANCE, REUNIFICATION, MANOKA, MACHTIGAL
The *Souellaba* built at the A.C.R.E., Libreville, Gabon.
  D: 11 tons   **S:** 10 kts

♦ *1 LCM*

BAKASI — Bldr: Carena, Abidjan, Ivory Coast. (1973)
  D: 57 tons (fl)   **Dim:** 17.50 × 4.28 × 1.30
  S: 9 kts   **M:** 2 Baudoin diesels; 490 hp

♦ *2 10-ton harbor small craft*

SANAGA, BIMBIA

The Canadian Armed Forces have been completely unified. Six operational commands have been set up: Mobile Command, Maritime Command, Air Transport Command, Air Defense Command, Training Command, and Material Command. The Maritime Command is in charge of the Navy ships, the ship-based aircraft, and all of the units of the former Maritime Air Command (RCAF). Its principal role is ASW, but it can also be called upon to transport men and equipment for the Mobile Command.

PERSONNEL (1975): about 14,000 men

MERCHANT MARINE (1-7-74): 1,231 ships — 2,409,998
(tankers: 66 — 264,110 grt)

NAVAL AVIATION: Made up of ship-based helicopters on ASW helicopter destroyers (DDH), maritime patrol aircraft, and ASW aircraft, formerly carrier-based but now maintained at land bases.

Identifying letters are as follows: HS (ASW helicopter), HU (supply helicopter), VS (ASW planes), MP (maritime patrol planes), VU (supply planes), VS (experimental planes).

Primary strength as follows:
— About 20 ASW CHSS 2 Sea King helicopters (see U.S.A. section). These helicopters are armed with Mk 44 or Mk 46 torpedoes and sensors (AQS 13 sonar, for example) and are used to search for hostile submarines. Upon landing, they are automatically secured and parked in the hangar, thanks to the ingenious "Bear Trap" recovery system.
— About 20 CS 2 F ASW 2-engine Tracker aircraft (see U.S.A. section).
— About 30/4-engine Argus aircraft.
The CL 28 Argus is an ASW plane with an extended flight radius. **Wingspan:** 43.50. **Length:** 39.20. **Weight:** 67 tons. **Engines:** 4 Wright, each of 3,700 hp. **Speed:** 250 knots. **Search S:** 163 knots. **Endurance:** 20 hours. **Range:** 3,900 miles. **Height:** 25,000 feet. Radar dome. Can carry mines, torpedoes, depth charges including an atomic depth charge, and air-to-surface rockets. It will be replaced by the P3C Orion 18 of which will be purchased and designated CP-3C.

ASW Tracker

CANADA

WARSHIPS IN SERVICE OR UNDER CONSTRUCTION AS OF 1 OCTOBER 1975

	L	Tons	Main armament
♦ *3 submarines*			
3 OJIBWA	1962-65	1,610	8/533-mm TT
♦ *20 destroyers*			
4 IROQUOIS	1970-71	3,551	1/127-mm AA, 1/BPMDS Sea Sparrow, ASW
(helicopter carriers)			weapons, 2 Sea King helicopters.
16 ST. LAURENT	1951-63	2,400	2 or 4/76-mm AA, ASW weapons; 9 carry
(several variations in weapons)			a Sea King helicopter.

♦ *6 minesweepers, 1 hydrofoil ship*

WEAPONS AND SYSTEMS

A. MISSILES

♦ **Surface-to-air missiles.** The Canadian Navy has adopted the short range surface-air NATO Sea Sparrow for its four DDH *Iroquois*-class destroyers. The missile is designed to attack aircraft or missiles flying at a low altitude, at a trans-sonic or slightly supersonic speed.

The characteristics are:
— Length: 3.660 m — Diameter: 0.200 m — Wingspan: 1.020 m — Weight: 204 kg.
— Speed: Mach 3.5 — Practical anti-aircraft range: 8 to 10,000 m.

The GMLS launching system, designed by Raytheon Canada, is made up of two loaders and two launchers. The launchers are fixed one to port and one to starboard, perpendicular to the axis of the ship. These launchers are retractable and are housed in the structure forward of the bridge. Each launcher has four missiles ready to be fired. The launchers can be trained and elevated.

B. GUNS

The following guns are presently used:
— **76-mm Mk 22.** Twin AA (U.S. model) mounted behind a plastic spray shield.
— Length: 50 calibers. — Muzzle velocity: 822 m/s
— Maximum firing rate: 50 rounds per minute per barrel — Arc of elevation: −15° to +85°
— Maximum effective anti-aircraft range: 4 to 5,000 m.
Fitted on the *Saint Laurent, Restigouche, Mackenzie,* and *Annapolis*-class destroyers.
— **76-mm Mk 6.** Twin barrel, automatic (Canadian model).
— Length: 70 calibers. Muzzle velocity: . . . m/s
— Maximum firing rate: 60 rounds per minute per barrel
— Maximum effective anti-aircraft range: 5,000 m.
Installed forward on the *Restigouche* and *Mackenzie*-class destroyers.
— **127-mm Oto-Melara-Compact**
Type (see Italy) installed on the *Iroquois*-class DDH.

C. ASW WEAPONS

In service:

♦ *Depth Charge and Torpedo Launchers:*

C. ASW WEAPONS (*continued*)
— British Mk 10 Limbo mortar on all destroyers,
— U.S. ASROC on 4 *Restigouche*-class destroyers.

♦ *Torpedoes.*

— SPS 501 long range air-search, improvement of the former, installed in the DDH *Iroquois* class.

D. ELECTRONICS
Radars: in service:
— SPS 12 long range air-search.
— SPS 501 long range air-search, improvement of the earlier classes, installed in the DDH *Iroquois* class.
— SPS 10 and Sperry Mk 2 navigation.
— SPQ 2 D combination search (Italian radar) installed in the DDH *Iroquois* class.
Sonars: in service:
— SQS 503 hull MF.
— SQS 504 towed MF, Type 503 transducer.
— SQS 505 hull LF installed in the DDH *Iroquois* class.
— SQS 505 towed LF installed in the DDH *Iroquois* class.
— SQS 501 for detection of submarines lying on the sea bottom.
Dissemination of tactical information: Litton CSS 280 system, installed in the DDH *Iroquois* class.

Okanagan (SS 74)   1970

SUBMARINES

♦ *3 British Oberon class submarines, Canadian Ojibwa class*

		Bldr	Laid down	L	In serv.
SS 72	OJIBWA	H.M. Dockyard, Chatham	9-62	29-2-64	9-65
SS 73	ONANDAGA	H.M. DY, Chatham	6-64	25-9-65	6-67
SS 74	OKANAGAN	H.M. DY, Chatham	3-65	17-9-66	6-68

D: 1,610 tons standard, 2,030 surfaced, 2,400 submersed
Dim: 89.92 (87.45 bp) × 8.07 × 5.48   **S:** 17.5/15
A: 8/533-mm TT (6 fwd, 2 aft) — 22 torpedoes   **Man:** 6 officers, 59 men
M: diesel-electric surface propulsion, Standard Admiralty, 16-cyl.; 3,700/6,000 hp.

REMARKS: Same characteristics as the British *Oberon* class. The *Ojibawa* was begun under the name of *Onyx* for the Royal Navy and transferred while still under construction. The living spaces have been modified for Canadian weather conditions.

Ojibwa (SS 72)   Shbldg. and Sh. Record

Ojibwa (S 72)   Official photo

DESTROYERS

♦ *4 helicopter destroyers, Iroquois class*

DDH

	Bldr	Laid down	L	In serv.
280 IROQUOIS	Marine Industries, Sorel	1-69	28-11-70	8-72
281 HURON	Marine Industries, Sorel	1-69	3-4-71	6-73
282 ATHABASCAN	Davie S.B., Lauzon	6-69	27-11-70	9-73
283 ALGONQUIN	Davie S.B., Lauzon	9-69	23-4-71	6-73

Iroquois (DDH 280)   1972

Iroquois (DDH 280)   1972

Annapolis (DDH 265)

D: 3,551 tons (4,200 fl)   **Dim:** 128.92 (121.31 pp) × 15.24 × 4.42
S: 30/29 kts   **Man:** 22 officers, 258 men   **Range:** 4,500/20
A: 1 BPDMS Sea Sparrow system — 1/127-mm AA — 1 Mk 10 Limbo mortar — 6 Mk 32 TT (III × 2) — 2 ASW Sea King helicopters
Electron Equipt: Radars: 1/SPS 502, 1/SPQ 2 D, M 22 director built by Signaal Apparaten, CCS-280
    Sonars: 1/SQS 505 (hull), 1 SQS 505 (towed)
M: COGOG propulsion; 2 five-bladed reversible pitch props; 50,000 hp (see Remarks).   **Electric:** 2,750 kw

REMARKS: 2 Mk FT4A2 Pratt and Whitney gas turbines, 25,000 hp each, and for a cruising speed of 18 knots, 2 Mk FT 12 H 3, 3,700 hp each. Two paired stacks, angled to avoid corrosion of the antennas by stack gasses.

♦ *2 helicopter frigates Annapolis class*

	Bldr	Laid down	L	In serv.
DDH 265 ANNAPOLIS	Halifax Shipyards Ltd	9-61	27-4-63	8-64
DDH 266 NIPIGON	Marine Industries, Sorel	7-60	10-12-61	5-64

D: 2,400 tons (3,000 fl)   **Dim:** 113.10 × 12.80 × 4.40 (normal)
S: 28 kts   **Man:** 12 officers, 234 men
A: 2/76-mm AA Mk 22 (II × 1) fwd — 1 Mk 10 Limbo mortar — 6 ASW 324-mm TT Mk 32 (III × 2) — Sea King helicopter
Electron Equipt: Radars: 1/SPS 12, 1/SPS 10
    Sonar: 1/SQS 503, 1 SQS 504, 1/SQS 501
M: English-Electric GT; 2 props; 30,000 hp
Boilers: 2 Babcock Wilcox   **Electric:** 1,400 kw

♦ *4 Mackenzie class (DDE — E for escort)*

	Bldr	Laid down	L	In serv.
DDE 261 MACKENZIE	Canadian-Vickers	10-58	25-5-61	10-62

DESTROYERS (*continued*)

DDE 262 SASKATCHEWAN	Victoria Machinery	8-59	1-2-61	2-63
DDE 263 YUKON	Burrard DD, Vancouver	10-59	27-7-61	5-63
DDE 264 QU'APPELLE	Davie S.B., Lauzon	1-60	2-5-62	9-63

Qu'appelle (DDE 264)   1972

D: 2,380 tons (2,890 fl)   **Dim:** 111.50 × 12.80 × 4.10 (av)
S: 28 kts   **Man:** 12 officers, 233 men
A: 4/76-mm (II × 1 Mk 22, II × 1 Mk 6) — 2 Mk 10 Limbo mortars — 2 ASW 324-mm Mk 32 TT
Electron Equipt: Radars: 1/SPS 12, 1/SPS 10
                 Sonars: 1/SQS 503, 1/SQS 501
M: English-Electric GT; 2 props; 30,000 hp
Boilers: 2 Babcock Wilcox   **Electric:** 1,400 kw

♦ *4 modified Restigouche class*

	Bldr	Laid down	L	In serv.
DDE 236 GATINEAU	Davie S.B., Lauzon	4-53	3-6-57	2-59
DDE 257 RESTIGOUCHE	Canadian-Vickers	7-53	22-11-54	6-58
DDE 258 KOOTENAY	Burrard DD, Vancouver	8-52	15-6-54	3-59
DDE 259 TERRA NOVA	Victoria Machinery	6-53	21-6-55	6-59

Terra Nova (DDE 259)   1970

D: 2,390 tons (2,900 fl)   **Dim:** 113.10 × 12.80 × 4.30 (normal)
S: 28 kts   **Man:** 13 officers, 237 men
A: 2/76-mm AA Mk 6 (II × 1) fwd — 1 Asroc system — 1 Mk 10 Limbo mortar
Electron Equipt: Radars: 1/SPS 10, 1/SPS 12
                 Sonar: 1/SQS 501, 1/SQS 503
M: English-Electric GT; 2 props; 30,000 hp
Boilers: 2 Babcock Wilcox   **Electric:** 1,400 kw

Mackenzie (DDE 261)

Gatineau (DDE 236)

♦ *6 helicopter frigates St. Laurent class*

	Bldr	Laid down	L	In serv.
DDH 206 SAGUENAY	Halifax Shipyards	4-51	30-7-53	12-56
DDH 207 SKEENA	Burrard DD, Vancouver	4-51	19-8-52	3-57
DDH 229 OTTAWA	Canadian-Vickers	6-51	29-4-53	11-56
DDH 230 MARGAREE	Halifax Shipyards	9-51	29-3-56	10-57
DDH 233 FRASER	Burrard DD, Vancouver	12-51	19-2-53	6-57
DDH 234 ASSINIBOINE	Marine Industries, Sorel	5-52	12-2-54	8-56

Photo on following page.

D: 2,260 tons (2,800 fl)   **Dim:** 119.5 × 12.8 × 4 (normal)
S: 28 kts   **Man:** 13 officers, 237 men

DESTROYERS (*continued*)

A: 2/76-mm AA Mk 22 — 1 Mk 10 Limbo mortar — 6 ASW 324-mm Mk 32 TT (III × 2) — 1 Sea King helicopter

Electron Equipt: Radars: 1/SPS 12, 1/SPS 10
                      Sonar: 1/SQS 503, 1/SQS 504, 1/SQS 501

M: English-Electric GT; 2 props; 30,000 hp

Boilers: 2 Babcock Wilcox   **Electric:** 1,400 kw

REMARKS: *DDH 205 Saint Laurent* taken out of service in 1974.

Saguenay (DDH 206)   1972

Ottawa (DDH 229)   1970

♦ *1 experimental hydrofoil ship*

	Bldr	L	Trials
FHE 400 BRAS D'OR	Marine Industries, Sorel	7-68	1969

(FHE for "Fast hydrofoil escort")

D: 237.5 tons   **Dim:** (hull) 46 × 6.55 × 5.08 (cruising)
S: 50/60 kts in calm seas   **Man:** 17 men
A: 12 ASW TT (III × 4: two groups each side)
M: Pratt and Whitney Mk FT 4 A gas turbine; 22,000 hp

REMARKS: Outboard length of lifting foils: 27.43 m. Draft hullborne: 7.21; draft foilborne: 1.32. At 15 knots cruising speed, a Davey-Paxman diesel (2,000 hp) drives 2 variable pitch props. After experiments, this ship was placed in reserve.

MINESWEEPERS

♦ *6 Western Europe class*

MCB	Bldr	Laid down	L	In serv.
159 FUNDY	Davie S.B., Lauzon	3-55	14-6-56	11-56
160 CHIGNECTO	Geo T. Davie Levis	10-55	26-2-57	8-57
161 THUNDER	Port Arthur S.B., Ont.	9-55	27-10-56	10-57
162 COWICHAN	Yarrows Ltd., Victoria	7-56	26-2-57	12-57
163 MIRAMICHI	Victoria Machinery	2-56	22-2-57	10-57
164 CHALEUR	Marine Industries, Sorel	2-56	17-11-56	9-57

Miramichi (163)

D: 370 tons (415 fl)   **Dim:** 50 (46.05 pp) × 9.21 × 2.80
S: 15 kts   **Man:** 3 officers, 35 men
A: 1/40-mm AA   **Range:** 4,500/11
M: General Motors diesels; 2 props; 2,500 hp.   **Fuel:** 52 tons diesel

REMARKS: 159 to 164 have taken the names of minesweepers transferred to France in 1954. Four, the *143 Gaspé*, the *146 Comox*, the *148 Ungava*, and the *157 Trinity*, were transferred to Turkey in 1958. Hull of composite construction. Used for school ships. Five have already been stricken.

OCEANOGRAPHIC AND HYDROGRAPHIC SHIPS

	Bldr	Laid down	L	In serv.
AGOR 172 QUEST	Burrard DD, Vancouver	1967	9-7-68	8-69

Quest (Agor 172) 1970

D: 2,130 tons **Dim:** 77.20 (71.62 pp) × 12.80 × 4.60
S: 15 kts **Man:** 56 men **Range:** 8,000/12.
M: Fairbanks-Morse diesel-electric propulsion; 2 props; 3,000 hp.

REMARKS: Modification of the *Endeavour* with the same engine. Carries a helicopter. See *Endeavour* remarks.

	Bldr	L	In serv.
Agor 171 ENDEAVOUR	Yarrows Ltd, Victoria	17-8-61	2-65

Endeavour (Agor 171)

D: 1,560 tons **Dim:** 71.85 (65.53 wl) × 11.73 × 4
S: 16 kts **Range:** 10,000/12 **Man:** 54 men including 14 scientists
M: Fairbanks-Morse diesel-electric propulsion, 9 cylinders; General Electric generator; 2 props; 3,400 hp.

REMARKS: (for both ships). Reinforced hulls for navigation in ice fields. Excellent loading equipment, cranes of 5 and 9 tons. Bulb-shaped stems. Anti-rolling and pitching devices. Civilian crews.

AGOR 516 LAYMORE, former small coastal supply ship AKS class, modified and reclassified in 1966. Built in U.S.A.

D: 560 grt **Dim:** 53.60 × 9.75 × 2.50
S: 10.5 kts **M:** General Motors diesels; 1,000 hp

AGOR 114 BLUETHROAT (1955)
D: 785 tons (870 fl) **Dim:** 47 × 9.90 × 3
S: 13 kts **M:** Diesel; 12,000 hp.; 2 props

AGOR 113 SACKVILLE (1941)
D: 1,085 tons (1,350 fl) **Dim:** 61.5 × 9.90 × 4.30
S: 16 kts **M:** Triple expansion; 2,750 hp; 1 prop.

REMARKS: Former Flower class corvette.

AGOR 170 FORT FRANCES (1943)
D: 1,040 tons (1,335 fl) **Dim:** 67.50 × 10.50 × 3.30
S: 16.5 kts **M:** 2 triple expansion; 2,000 hp

REMARKS: Former *Algerine* class minesweeper. Out of commission.

♦ *2 multi-purpose supply ships Protector class*

AOR	Bldr	Laid down	L	In serv.
509 PROTECTEUR	St. John SB & DD (NB)	10-67	18-7-68	6-69
510 PRESERVER	St. John SB & DD (NB)	8-67	29-5-69	9-70

Protecteur (AOR 509) J. C. Bellonne 1972 Photo

D: 9,000 tons (24,000 fl) **Dim:** 172 (166.42 pp) × 23.16 × 9.15
S: 20 kts **Range:** 7,500/11.5
A: 1/76-mm AA — 1 Sea Sparrow missile launcher
Man: 15 officers, 212 men, 57 passengers
M: Canadian General Electric GT; 1 prop; 21,000 hp.
Boilers: 2 **Electric:** 3,500 kw

REMARKS: Flight deck and hangar space for 3 Sea King helicopters. Four replenishment-at-sea stations, 1 elevator aft of the navigation bridge, 2/15-ton cranes on the afterdeck. Cargo capacity: 13,250 tons, with 12,000 tons of distillate fuel, 600 tons of diesel oil, 400 tons of jet fuel, frozen and dry foods, spare parts, munitions, etc. 1 bow prop. Daily fresh water distillation capacity: 80 tons.

OCEANOGRAPHIC AND HYDROGRAPHIC SHIPS (*continued*)

♦ *1 multi-purpose supply ship Provider class*

	Bldr	Laid down	L	In serv.
AOR				
508 PROVIDER	Davie SB, Lauzon	6-61	5-7-62	9-63

Provider (AOR 508)

D: 7,300 tons (22,000 fl) **Dim:** 168 (159.40 pp) × 23.17 × 9.15
Cargo capacity: 14,700 tons **S:** 20 kts **Man:** 11 officers, 147 men
Range: 5,000/20 **M:** GT; 1 prop; 21,000 hp.
Boilers: 2 **Fuel:** 1,200 tons **Electric:** 2,140 kw.

REMARKS: Platform and hangar for 2 helicopters. Can carry 12,000 tons of distillate fuel, 1,200 tons of diesel, 1,000 tons of aviation gas, 250 tons of provisions, munitions, and various spare parts.

LOGISTIC SUPPORT

♦ *2 repair ships*

ARE 100 CAPE BRETON (ex-*Flamborough*) (7-10-44)
ARE 101 CAPE SCOTT (ex-*Beachy Head*) (27-9-44)
   Bldr: Burrard D.D., Vancouver — In reserve (see Remarks).

Cape Scott (ARE 101)

D: 8,450 tons (11,270 fl) **Dim:** 133.80 × 18.88 × 8.84
M: GT; 2,500 hp; 2 Foster-Wheeler boilers **S:** 11 kts

REMARKS: Purchased from the British Navy in 1951. Refitted (1958-59). Helicopter platform. Equipped as repair ships for pierside service.

♦ *4 netlayers*

	L		L
YMG 180	21-11-50	**YMG 184**	28-12-51
PORTE SAINT-JEAN		PORTE DE LA REINE	
YMG 183	21-7-52	**YMG 185**	28-8-51
PORTE SAINT-LOUIS		PORTE QUEBEC	

D: 300 tons (429 fl) **Dim:** 38 × 8.50 × 3.90
S: 11 kts **A:** 1/40-mm AA **Man:** 3 officers, 20 men
M: diesel-electric propulsion; 1 prop; 600 hp.

REMARKS: Trawler-like profile; can be used as auxiliary minesweepers and netlayers. YMG 106 *Porte Dauphine* transferred to the Transportation Ministry.

VARIOUS

XMT 11 and **XMT 12** — Bldr: Ferguson Industries, Pictou (N.S.), 1962-63
   D: 110 tons (fl) **Dim:** 26.50 × 6.10 × 1.50
   S: 10.54 kts; diesel power

Mobile base for divers working in depths of up to 75 m; decompression chamber.

AOC 501 DUNDALK, AOC 502 DUNDURN, small tankers
   D: 950 tons **Dim:** 54 × 10 × 4 **S:** 10 kts; one diesel, 700 hp.

QW3 ORIOLE — Sailing yacht for training

♦ *25 tugs of various classes with 2 of 840 tons and 1,800 hp* (**ATA 531 ST ANTHONY, ATA 533 ST CHARLES**) *and 3 of 462 tons and 1,000 hp.* (**ATA 527 HEATHERTON, ATA 528 RIVERTON, ATA 529 CLIFTON**).

CANADIAN COAST GUARD

The Canadian Coast Guard is a civilian organization in the Federal Transportation Ministry. It mans some 150 ships including two weather station cutters, 20 icebreakers, and about 30 helicopters.

♦ *Weather cutters*

QUADRA (4-7-66), **VANCOUVER** (29-6-65)
   Bldr: Burrard DD, Vancouver

   D: 5,600 tons (fl) **Dim:** 121 × 15.50 × 5.30
   S: 18 kts **Man:** 96 men **Range:** 8,400/14. Stabilizers
   M: turbo-electric propulsion; 2 props; 7,500 hp; 2 Babcock boilers

♦ *20 icebreakers*, the most powerful of which are the following:

NORMAN MC LEOD ROGERS (1969)
   Bldr: Vickers, Montreal

   D: 6,320 tons (fl) **Dim:** 90 × 19.50 × 6.10 **S:** 15 kts
   M: CODAG-electric propulsion; 12,000 hp; 1 helicopter; the first icebreaker with gas turbines used for surge power.

VARIOUS (*continued*)

LOUIS S. ST LAURENT (3-12-66)
  Bldr: Vickers, Montreal
  D: 13,000 tons (fl)   **Dim:** 111.80 × 24.39 × 9.45   **S:** 17.5 kts
  M: turbo-electric propulsion; 3 props; 24,000 hp.
  Range: 16,000/13. Quarters for 216 men. 2 helicopters.

JOHN A. MACDONALD (1959)
  Bldr: Davie SB, Lauzon
  D: 9,160 tons (fl)   **Dim:** 96 × 21.30 × 8.55   **S:** 15.5 kts
  M: diesel electric propulsion; 15,000 hp.

JOHN CABOT (1965)
  Bldr: Vickers, Montreal
  D: 6,375 tons (fl)   **Dim:** 94 × 18 × 6.45   **S:** 15 kts
  M: diesel-electric propulsion; 9,000 hp.
  Range: 10,000/12   **Man:** 85 men

CANADIAN MOUNTED POLICE

About 30 small patrol craft.

PERSONNEL (1968): 2,000 men including 160 officers.

MERCHANT MARINE (1-7-74): 34 ships — 54,099 grt
(tankers: 4 ships — 1,454 grt)

CEYLON

Sri Lanka

FRIGATE

♦ *1 ex-Canadian River class frigate*

F 232 GAJABAHU (ex-Israeli *Misnak*, ex-Canadian *Hallowell*) — 8-8-44.
D: 1,445 tons (2,360 fl) **Dim:** 91.90 × 11.07 × 3.65
S: 19.5 kts **Man:** 106 men. **A:** 1/102-mm — 3/40-mm
Range: 6,000/12. **M:** Triple expansion; 2 props.
Boilers: 2 **Fuel:** 645 tons

REMARKS: Bought from Israel in 1959.

PATROL BOATS

♦ *6 Chinese Shanghai II class delivered in 2-72 and 75.*

SURAYA WEERAYA — N . . . — N . . . — N . . . — N . . . — N . . .
D: 120 tons (fl) **S:** 30 kts **Dim:** 39.60 × 5.70 × 1.70.
A: 4/37-mm AA (II × 2) — 4/25-mm AA (II × 2)
M: 4 diesels — 5,000 hp. **Man:** 28 men

HANSAYA, LIHINIYA — Bldr: Korody Marine, Venice.
D: 36 tons **Dim:** 20 × 4.25 × 1.25
M: 3 General Motors diesels 450 hp **S:** 13 kts

MINESWEEPER

♦ *1 ex-Soviet class, no information.*

PATROL BOATS

♦ *1 ex-Soviet guided missile OSA 1 class*

♦ *1 ex-Soviet modified Stenka class patrol boat*
DIYAKAWA, KORAWAKKA, SERUWA, TARAWA — Bldr: Italy.
D: 13 tons **Dim:** 15 × 3.70 × 0.95.
M: 2 Foden diesels. — 240 hp **S:** 15 kts
Seruwa and *Tarawa* are hydrographic vessels.

♦ *1 hydrofoil (1964)*
Dim: 7 × 3.12 × 0.40 (at high speed) **S:** 40 kts
M: 2 Volvo motors, each of 100 hp.

♦ *12 patrol boats (1966-68)* — Bldr: Thornycroft, Singapore.
No. **101** and **102** — **201** and **210**.
D: 15 tons **Dim:** 13.86 × 3.65 × 0.92
A: 1 machine gun. **Man:** 6 men. **S:** 25 kts
M: 2 General Motors or Thornycroft engines.

TUG
ALIYA
D: 503 (fl) **S:** 10 kts **Electric:** 850 hp.

CHILE

PERSONNEL: 15,300 men (of which about 2,000 are Marines and 1,400 are officers). Civil service personnel with a more or less military status number about 6,600 men.

PROGRAM: A third submarine of the *O'Brien* class may be ordered, as well as two new Condell class frigates, a guided missile destroyer flotilla leader, and a supply-tanker.

NAVAL AVIATION: Established in 1923, in 1930 it was merged with the aviation arm of the military (Fuerza Aera de Chile) but re-established in 1953. However, its growth has been restrained by the Air Force which retains responsibility for the airspace over the ocean. The naval air arm has about 20 aircraft (Beechcraft, T 34, C 45 and 47) and about 15 helicopters (Bell and HSS 2 ASW class).

MERCHANT MARINE (1-7-74): 135 ships — 364,364 grt
(6 tankers — 72,555 grt)

WARSHIPS IN SERVICE OR UNDER CONSTRUCTION AS OF 1 OCTOBER 1975

	L	Tons	Main armament
♦ *4 submarines*			
2 O'BRIEN class	1973	1,610	8/533-mm TT
2 THOMPSON class (obsolete)	1944	1,526	10/533-mm TT
♦ *3 cruisers*			
1 ALMIRANTE LATORRE	1944	8,200	7/152-mm AA, 4/57-mm AA, 6/533-mm TT
2 O'HIGGINS (obsolete)	1936-37	9,700	15/152-mm, 8/127-mm
♦ *4 destroyers*			
2 WILLIAMS	1958	2,730	4/102-mm AA
2 BLANCO ENCALADA (obsolete)	1943-44	2,050	4/127-mm, 5/533-mm TT
♦ *6 frigates*			
2 CONDELL	1972-73	2,350	2/114-mm AA 4/MM 38
4 SERRANO (obsolete)	1943-44	1,400	1/127-mm, 3/40-mm AA
2 PORTALES (obsolete)			
♦ *4 torpedo boats*	1965-66	134	2/40-mm AA, 4/533-mm TT

♦ *8 patrol boats of various types*

WEAPONS AND SYSTEMS

The greatest part of the materiel and equipment of the Chilean Navy is of U.S. or British origin and is already outmoded. Among the most modern weapons are the guns on board the *Almirante Latorre* and the *Almirante Williams*-class destroyers.

♦ 152-mm Bofors:

This gun is mounted in a twin and triple barreled-turret; dates from 1942 and is on board the *Almirante Latorre*.
— Muzzle velocity 900 m/sec
— Arc: +70°
— Maximum firing rate: 10 rounds/minute/barrel
— Projectile: 46 kg
— Maximum range surface target: 26,000 m
— Maximum range surface target (effective): 15,000 m
— Maximum range air target (effective): 10,000 m

♦ 102 Vickers AA

Single barrel automatic mount on the *Almirante Williams* and the *Almirante Riveros*. Dates from 1955.

— Turret weight: about 26 tons
— Muzzle velocity: 900 meters/second
— Arc: +75°
— Maximum firing rate: 40 rounds/minute
— Projectile: 16 kg
— Maximum range surface target: 18,500 m
— Maximum range surface target (effective): 12,000 m
— Maximum range air target: 12,000 m
— Maximum range air target (effective): 8000 m

♦ Missiles

The Chilean Navy has adopted the French MM38 Exocet system.

SUBMARINES

♦ *2 British Oberon class*

	Bldr	Laid down	L	In serv.
S 22 O'BRIEN	Scott Lithgow	1970	22-12-72	1975
S 23 HYATT	Scott Lithgow	1971	26-9-73	. . .

O'Brien (S 22)   1974 Scotts Photo

D: 1,610 tons standard/2,030 surfaced/2,400 submerged
Dim: 89.92 (87.45 pp) × 8.07 × 5.48   **S:** 17.5/15 kts   **Man:** . . .
A: 8/533-mm TT (6 fwd, 2 aft) — 22 torpedoes.
M: diesel-electric propulsion surfaced; Admiralty 16-cylinder standard diesels. 3,700/6,000 hp

REMARKS: Delivery of these submarines was a year late because of a number of discrepancies found in the electrical equipment.

♦ *2 ex-U.S. Balao class transferred in 1961 and 1962 under the Mutual Assistance Pact.*

	Bldr	Laid down	In serv.
S 20 THOMSON (ex-*Springer, SS-414*)	Mare Island NSY	3-8-44	10-44
S 21 SIMPSON (ex-*Spot, SS-413*)	Mare Island NSY	20-5-44	8-44

SUBMARINES (continued)

Thomson (S 20)   1969

D: 1,526 tons standard/1,816 surfaced/2,425 submerged
Dim: 95 × 8.20 × 5.20   **S:** 20/10 kts   **Man:** 80 men
A: 10/533-mm TT (6 fwd, 4 aft)   **Range:** 12,500/9.5.
M: diesel-electric propulsion and electric; 2 props; 6,500/2,750 hp.
Fuel: 300 tons diesel.

REMARKS: Refitted in U.S.A., the **S 20** in 1966, the **S 21** in 1968.

CRUISERS

◆ *1 ex-Swedish Göta Lejon purchased in 7-1971*

	Bldr	Laid down	L	In serv.
04 ALMIRANTE LATORRE	Eriksbergs	9-43	17-11-45	15-12-47

Almirante Latorre (04)   1972

D: 8,200 tons (10,000 fl)   **Dim:** 182 (174 wl) × 16.50 × 6.50
S: 33 kts   **Man:** 26 officers, 429 men (peace), 30 officers, 618 men (war).
A: 7/152-mm AA (III × 1, II × 2) — 4/57-mm AA — 11/40-mm AA —
         6/533-mm TT (III × 2), ASW mortars — depth charge racks — 120 mines.
Electron Equipt: Radars: 1/LW 03 (Dutch), 1/227 and 1/293 (British),
                    Band X firecontrol
A: **Belt:** 80-100   **Main deck:** 40 to 60   **Turrets:** 135 (fwd), 30
         (sides), 50 (top)
M: De Laval GT; 2 props; 100,000 hp.
Boilers: 4 Penhoët, 32 kg pressure, superheat to 375°.

◆ *2 ex-U.S. Brooklyn class*

	Bldr	Laid down	L	In serv.
02 O'HIGGINS	New York Naval SY	3-35	30-11-36	9-37
(ex-*Brooklyn*, CL-40)				
03 CAPITAN PRAT	New York SB Corp.	5-34	2-10-37	11-38
(ex-*Nashville*, CL-43)				

D: 9,700 tons (13,500 fl)   **Dim:** 185.33 × 18.80 × 7
S: 30/25 kts   **Man:** 890/970 men
A: 15/132-mm (III × 5) — 8/127-mm (I × 8) — 28/40-mm AA (IV × 4) —
         24/20-mm AA (I × 24)
Armor: Belt: 76 to 127 — Main deck: 76 — Upper deck: 52 — Turrets: 127 —
         Navig. Bridge: 203
M: Westinghouse GT; 4 props; 100,000 hp.   **Range:** 14,500/15
Boilers: 8 Babcock and Wilcox, 31 kg pressure.   **Fuel:** 2,100 tons

REMARKS: Bought at the end of 1950. *O'Higgins* has "bulges" and a superstructure
which is slightly smaller than that of the *Prat*. The latter refitted in U.S.A.
(1957-58).

DESTROYERS

◆ *2 ex-U.S. Sumner class delivered 1-74*

	Bldr	L	In serv.
D 16 PORTALES (ex-*Douglas H. Fox, DD-779*)	Federal SB	13-3-44	17-5-44
D 17 ZENTENO (ex-*Charles S. Sperry, DD-697*)	Todd-Pacific	30-9-44	26-12-44

D: 2,200 tons (3,300 fl)   **Dim:** 114.75 × 12.45 × 3.80 (light)
S: 30 kts   **Range:** 1,260/30 — 4,600/15.
A: 6/127-mm 38-cal. (II × 3) — 6/324-mm ASW TT (III × 2) Mk 32 + 2 Mk 25
         fixed TT   **Man:** 14 officers, 260 men
M: GT; 2 props; 60,000 hp   **Boilers:** 4 Babcock   **Fuel:** 650 tons

REMARKS: FRAM II modernization.

◆ *2 ex-U.S. Fletcher class transferred in 1962.*

	Bldr	L	In serv.
D 14 BLANCO ENCALADA	Bath Iron Wks.	7-8-43	10-43
(ex-*Wadleigh, DD-689*)			
D 15 ALMIRANTE COCHRANE	Todd-Pacific	6-6-44	9-44
(ex-*Rooks, DD-804*)			

D: 2,050 tons (2,850 fl)   **Dim:** 114.85 × 12.03 × 5.50
S: 30 kts   **Man:** 15 officers, 247 men   **Range:** 1,260/30; 4,400/15

Cochrane (D 15)   1970

DESTROYERS (*continued*)

A: 4/127-mm AA 38-cal (I × 4) — 6/76-mm AA (II × 3) — 5/533-mm TT
(V × 1) — 2 ASW TT (fixed) — 2 hedgehogs — 2 depth charge projectors
Electron Equipt: U.S. Radars: 1/SPS 6, 1/SPS 10 — Sonar: 1/SQS 29
M: General Electric GT; 2 props
Boilers: 4 Babcock and Wilcox; 60,000 hp.

♦ *2 Almirante Williams class*

	Bldr	Laid down	L	In serv.
D 18 ALMIRANTE RIVEROS	Vickers-Armstrongs	1957	12-12-58	31-12-60
D 19 ALMIRANTE WILLIAMS	Vickers-Armstrongs	20-6-56	5-5-58	26-3-60

Almirante Riveros (D 18)

D: 2,730 tons (3,300 fl)   **Dim:** 122.50 (113.99 pp) × 13.10 × 3.90
S: 34.5 kts   **Man:** 17 officers, 249 men   **Range:** 6,000/16
A: 4/102-mm AA (I × 4) — 6/40-mm AA — 4 MM 38 Exocet — 1 Sea Cat
BPDMS system — 5/533-mm TT (I × 5) — 2 ASW squids
Electron Equipt: Plessey AWS I equipment.
M: Parsons-Pamatreda GT; 2 props; 2 Babcock and Wilcox boilers; 50,000 hp.

REMARKS: Refitted in Great Britain (1971-72).

FRIGATES

♦ *2 British Leander class ordered 14-1-70*

	Bldr	Laid down	L	In serv.
PF 06 CONDELL	Yarrow & Co	6-71	6-12-72	21-12-73
PF 07 LYNCH	Yarrow & Co	12-72	12-6-73	1975

D: 2,450 tons (2,900 fl)   **Dim:** 113.38 (109.73 pp) × 12.50 × 5.49 (fl)
S: 27 kts   **Range:** 4,500/12   **Man:** 263 men
A: 4/MM 38 Exocet, 2/114-mm Mk VI (II × 1) — 1 Sea Cat (IV × 1) —
2/20-mm — 6 324-mm ASW TT Mk 32 (IV × 2) — 1 helicopter.
Electron Equipt: Radars: 1/965, 1/992 Q, 1/GWS 22
Sonars: 1/177, 1/170 B, 1/162
M: General Electric GT; 2 props; 2 Babcock boilers   **Fuel:** 460 tons

Condell (PF 06)   1974 J. C. Bellonne

♦ *4 ex-U.S. APDs*

	L
26 SERRANO (ex-*Odum*, APD-71)	19-1-44
27 ORELLA (ex-*Jack C. Robinson*, APD-72)	8-1-44
28 RIQUELME (ex-*Jos. E. Campbell*, APD-49)	26-6-43
29 URIBE (ex-*Daniel T. Griffin*, APD-38)	25-2-43

Orella (27)   1972

D: 1,400 tons (2,049 fl)   **Dim:** 93.26 × 11.28 × 4.70
S: 23 (fl) kts   **Man:** 212 men
A: 1/127-mm — 3/40-mm AA   **Range:** 5,000/15, 2,000/23
M: turbo-electric propulsion; 2 props; 12,000 hp   **Boilers:** 2
Fuel: 350 tons

REMARKS: 3 transferred in 11-66, 1 in 1-67. Two armed as ASW frigates (26, 27), two
as transports (28, 29).

TORPEDO BOATS

♦ *4 German Lürssen class*

81 FRESIA — 82 GUACOLDA — 83 QUIDORA — 84 TEHUALDA
Bldr: Bazan (Cadiz) (1965-66)
D: 134 tons (fl)   **Dim:** 36 × 5.60 × 2.20

TORPEDO BOATS (*continued*)

Fresia (81)   1970

A: 2/40-mm AA — 4/533-mm TT   **Man:** 20 men   **S:** 33/32 kts
M: 2 Mercedes-Benz diesels; 2 props; 4,800 hp   **Range:** 1,500/15

PATROL BOATS

♦ **AGS 64 YELCHO** (ex-U.S. tug *Tekesta ATF-93*, 1943), transferred 1960

Yelcho   1970

D: 1,235 tons (1,675 fl)   **Dim:** 62.50 × 11.65 × 4.70
A: 1/76-mm — 4/40-mm AA   **Man:** 5 officers, 59 men
S: 16.5 kts   **M:** diesel-electric propulsion; 3,000 hp.

REMARKS: Used for oceanographic research in the Antarctic.

♦ **60 LIENTUR — 62 LAUTARO —** Bldr: Levingstone SB Orange, Texas (1944)

D: 534 tons (835 fl)   **Dim:** 43.90 × 10.15 × 5.20
A: 1/76-mm — 2/20-mm AA   **S:** 12.5 kts   **Man:** 46 men
M: General Motors diesels, 2 props, 1,500 hp.   **Fuel:** 187 tons diesel

Lautaro (62)   1970

ATF 65 SERGENTE ALDEA (ex-U.S. Tug *Arikara, ATF-98*)
   D: 1,235 tons (1,675 fl)   **Dim:** 61.70 × 11.60 × 4.70
   A: 1/76-mm AA   **S:** 15 kts   **Man:** 85 men
   M: Diesel-electric; 3,000 hp; 1 prop

REMARKS: Transferred 7-6-71. Used as a patrol boat.

♦ **P 37 PAPUDO —** Bldr: U.S.A. (ex-U.S. *PC-1616*)
   D: 340 tons   U.S. PC model. See *Sultan Hisar* in Turkey section.

♦ *Small trawlers purchased in 1966*

PC 76 CABO ODGER — PC 75 MARINERO FUENTALBAS
   Bldr: A.S.M.A.R., Chile (1966-67). Profile of U.S. type trawler.
   D: 215 tons   **Dim:** 24.40 × 6.40 × 2.75   **S:** 9 kts
   A: 1/20-mm   **M:** 1 Cummins diesel; 340 hp.   **Range:** 2,600/9

♦ *1 Antarctic patrol ship, transport, and research*

	Bldr	Laid down	L	In serv.
AP 45 PILOTO PARDO	Haarlemsche Scheepsbouw	1957	1958	8-58

Piloto Pardo (AP 45)

PATROL BOATS (continued)

D: 1,250 tons (2,545 fl)   **Dim:** 83 × 11.90 × 7.40 (fl)
S: 14 kts   **Man:** 44 men, 24 passengers   **Range:** 6,000
A: 1/102-mm — 1/76-mm — 2/40-mm AA — 1 helicopter
M: diesel-electric propulsion; 1 prop; 2,000 hp

LOGISTIC SUPPORT

♦ *3 tankers*

AO 53 ARAUCANO — Bldr: Burmeister and Wain (21-6-66)

Araucana (AO 53)   1969

D: 18,030 tons (fl)   **Dim:** 160.93 × 21.95 × 8.80
A: 4/40-mm AA (I × 4)   **S:** 17 kts
M: Babcock and Wilcox diesel, type 62 VT 2 BF 140 9-cyl. 1 prop.; 10,800 hp.

REMARKS: Can replenish two ships at sea simultaneously.

	Bldr	Laid down	L	In serv.
AO 52 ALMIRANTE JORGE MONTT	Seine Maritime	1954	14-1-56	3-56

J. Montt (AO 52)   1968

D: 17,500 tons (fl)   **Dim:** 167.09 (158.40 pp) × 20.57 × 9.21
S: 14 kts   **Range:** 16,500/14
M: Rateau-Bretagne GT; 1 prop; 6,300 hp; boilers: 2 Babcock and Wilcox

REMARKS: Cargo capacity: 17,750 tons; 24 bunkers (25,530 m³); cargo holds: 2,290 m³. Gun platforms for 2/120-mm and 6/20-mm AA.

AOG 54 BEAGLE (ex-U.S. *Genesee, AOG-8*) transferred in 7-72.

Beagle (AOG 54)   1972

D: 1,850 tons (light) (4,570 fl)   **Dim:** 93.50 × 13.60 × 4.75
S: 14 kts   **Range:** 6670/10
A: 1/76-mm   **M:** diesel electric; 3,100 hp

♦ *8 transports*

47 AQUILES (ex-Danish *Tjaldur*) — Bldr: Aalborg Vaerft (1953)

Aquiles (AP 47)

D: 1,395 tons   **Dim:** 82 × 13.42 × 5.20
S: 16 kts   **Man:** 32 men, 406 passengers
M: B and W diesel; 1 prop; 3,600 hp.   **Range:** 5,500/16

REMARKS: Former mixed cargo purchased in 1967.

91 AGUILA (ex-U.S. *Aventinus, ARVE-3*, ex-*LST-1092*) — Bldr: U.S.A. (25-3-45)
D: 1,600 tons (fl)   **Dim:** 100.04 × 15.24 × 4.35   **S:** 11 kts
M: General Motors diesels; 2 props; 1,800 hp.   **Range:** 6,000/11.

REMARKS: Transferred in 1964. Repair ship fittings dismantled; used as transport.

88 COMMANDANTE HEMMERDINGER (ex-U.S. *New London County, LST-1066*)
89 COMMANDANTE ARAYA (ex-U.S. *Nye County, LST-1067*)   ⎬ Bldr: U.S.A. 1943-44.
97 COMMANDANTE TORO (ex-U.S. *LST-277*)
D: 4,080 tons (fl)   **Dim:** 100.04 × 15.24 × 4.35.   **S:** 11 kts
M: General Motors diesels; 2 props; 1,700 hp.   **Range:** 6,000/11.

REMARKS: Transferred February (1) and August 1973 (2).

LOGISTIC SUPPORT (*continued*)

LSM 94 OROMPELLO — U.S.A. (1963-64). **LSM 95 ELICURA** (A.S.M.A.R., 1968).

    D: 290 tons (750 fl)   **Dim:** 43.90 (42.05 pp) × 100.37 × 6.90
    S: 10.5 kts   **Range:** 2,900/9   **Man:** 20 men
    M: diesel; 2 props; 900 hp   **Fuel:** 77 tons diesel

1 LSM 92 ASPIRANTE MOREL (ex-*414*) (transferred in 1960).

TRAINING SHIP

	Bldr	L	In serv.
BE 43 ESMERALDA (ex-*Don Juan de Austria*)	Bazan, Cadiz	12-5-53	9-54

    D: 3,673 tons   **Dim:** 94.10 × 13.10 × 8.70   **S:** 11 kts
    A: 4/47-mm   **Man:** 271 men, 80 midshipmen   **Range:** 8,000/8.
    M: Fiat diesel; 1,400 hp.

REMARKS: Four-masted schooner, ordered by Spain, sold to Chile in 1953. Similar to the Spanish *Juan Sebastian de Elcano*.

VARIOUS

♦ *Tugs*

ATA 73 COLO COLO — Bldr: England (1929)

    D: 790 tons   **Dim:** 41.38 × 8.72 × 4.07   **S:** 13 kts (11 cruising)
    M: Reciprocating 1 prop; 1,500 hp. Used as buoy tender and beacon repair ship.

YT 104 ANCUD, YT 105 MONREAL, YT 120 REYES, YT 127 CAUPOLICAN, YT 128 CORTEZ.

♦ 1 floating dock ex-*U.S. ARD 25*, bought 20-8-73.

PERSONNEL: 116,000 men in the following categories:
Navy: 36,000
Naval air arm: 20,000
Land-based personnel: 60,000 (including 20,000 Marines).

NAVAL AVIATION:

The naval air arm which is actually under the control of the Navy is unlikely to consist of more than 400 aircraft, including 200 MIG 17, 19 or 21 interceptors, 150 light bombers such as the IL 28 and TU 2, and about 50 transport planes and seaplanes. Its principal mission is the defense of the coast and the protection of naval surface forces near the coast. A few of the aircraft are equipped, it is believed, for minelaying. Control of naval aircraft is integrated with the continental air defense system.

MERCHANT MARINE: (1-7-74): 360 ships — 1,870,567 grt)
(tankers: 40 — 276,218 grt)

SUBMARINES

Nuclear submarines:

♦ *2 Attack*

	Bldr	In serv.
HAN	Luta	1974
N . . .	Luta	. . .

Conventional submarines:

♦ *1 ballistic missile submarine of the Soviet G class*

    D: 2,300 tons surfaced/2,750 submerged   **Dim:** 98.80 × 8.50 × 6.50
    S: 14 kts submerged
    A: 3 ballistic missiles — 10/533-mm TT (6 fwd, 4 aft)

REMARKS: Plans furnished by the Soviet Union during that period when relations between the two countries were good. The medium range missiles are possibly of Chinese origin.

♦ *33 Soviet R class built in China*

R type submarine

    D: 1,400 tons surfaced/1,800 submerged   **Dim:** 75 × 7 × 5.40
    S: 15.5 kts submerged
    A: 8/533-mm TT (6 fwd, 4 aft) — 18 torpedoes or 36 mines

CHINA

People's Republic of China

♦ *20/21 Soviet W class*

    D: 1,050 tons surfaced/1,350 submerged   **Dim:** 75 × 6 × 5
    S: 16 kts submerged
    A: 6/533-mm TT (4 fwd, 2 aft) — 14 torpedoes, or missiles

REMARKS: A few were delivered by the U.S.S.R., the others built in China, probably at the Chiang Nan shipyard at Kao Chang Miao, near Shanghai.

♦ *3 very old M V class transferred by the U.S.S.R.*

    D: 350 tons surfaced/420 submerged   **Dim:** 53 × 6.70 × 4.20
    A: 2/533-mm TT   **S:** 13/10 kts

REMARKS: Used for training.

DESTROYERS

♦ *6 Guided missile Luta class*

	Bldr	L	In serv.
LUTA	Dairen SY	1970	1972
N . . .	Dairen SY	. . .	1973
N . . .	Dairen SY	. . .	1973
N . . .	Dairen SY	. . .	1974
N . . .	Dairen SY	. . .	. . .
N . . .	Dairen SY	. . .	. . .

Luta   1974

    D: ca. 3,500 tons   **Dim:** 130 × 13.70 × 4.60   **S:** 32 kts
    A: 4/130-mm (II × 2) — 4/57-mm AA — 4/25-mm AA (II × 2) — 6 systems similar to Styx (III × 2)
    M: GT; 45,000 hp; 2 props   **Range:** 4,000/15   **Man:** 200 men

REMARKS: Chinese copy of the Soviet Kotlin class.

♦ *4 Gordyi class transferred by the U.S.S.R. (1931-41)*

ANSHAN, CHANG CHUN, CHI LIN, FU CHUN
    D: 1,660 tons (2,150 fl)   **Dim:** 112.86 × 10.20 × 3.80   **Man:** 197 men
    S: 35 kts when built, certainly much less today.

DESTROYERS (*continued*)

A: 4/130-mm (I × 4) — 2/76-mm AA — 4/37-mm AA — 4 Styx system (II × 2)
M: GT; 2 props; 48,000 hp   **Boilers:** 3   **Fuel:** 540 tons

FRIGATES

♦ *4 Soviet Riga Class (1951-1957)*
CHIENG TU, KUEI LIN, KUEI YANG, K'UN MING
D: 1,450 tons   **S:** 28 kts   **Dim:** 88 × 10 × 3.90
A: 3/100-mm (I × 3) — 4/37-mm AA (II × 2) — 2 Styx systems (II × 1)
M: GT; 2 props; 20,000 hp

♦ *5 Kiangnan class*

(233)

D: 1,500 tons   **S:** 28 kts   **Dim:** 92 × 10 × 3.90
A: 3/100-mm (I × 3) 1 fwd, 2 aft — 4/37-mm AA (II × 2) 1 fwd, 1 aft —
4/25-mm AA (II × 2)

REMARKS: Chinese version of the Riga class. Built in Canton after 1968.

♦ *1 to 3 of the Kian-Tung class*
Bldr: Huntung, Shanghai
D: 1,600 tons   **S:** ...   **Dim:** ...   **A:** ...   **M:** ...

REMARKS: Will be fitted with AA missiles.

GUIDED MISSILE AND TORPEDO PATROL BOATS

♦ *50 of the Soviet OSA I class (ca. 1960)*
D: 190 tons (fl)   **Dim:** 37 × 9 × 1.80   **S:** 40 kts (36 cruising)
Man: 25 men   **M:** 3 diesels; 9,000 hp.
A: 4/30-mm AA (II × 2) — 4 systems similar to Styx

REMARKS: The electronic equipment of these ships may be slightly different from that of the Soviet OSA I ships.

♦ *1 Hola class*
An improved version of the OSA I class armed with 6 surface to surface missiles. The mast is streamlined.

♦ *7/8 Soviet Komar class (ca. 1960)*
D: 73 tons (fl)   **Dim:** 25.3 × 6.10 × 1.70   **S:** 34/32 kts
A: 2/25-mm AA (II × 2) — 2 Styx systems   **M:** Diesel, 4 props; 4,800 hp.

♦ *40 Oku class*
Chinese version of the Komar class

♦ *100 Huchwan class hydrofoils (since 1966)*
D: 45 tons   **Dim:** 29 × 4.90 × 1 or 31 × 7.50   **S:** over 40 kts
A: 2 torpedoes, 450-mm — 2/14.5-mm machine guns (II × 1)

REMARKS: Identical to the hydrofoils delivered to Albania, Pakistan, and Rumania.

♦ *4/5 Moma class hydrofoils*
D: 50 tons   **Dim:** ...   **S:** over 40 kts   **A:** 2 Styx missile systems

♦ *70 Soviet P 4 torpedo patrol boats (since 1966)*
D: 30 tons   **Dim:** 16.80 × 3.75 × 1
S: 32 kts   **A:** 2/14.5-mm machine guns (II × 1) — 2/450-mm TT

♦ *80 Soviet P 6 class torpedo boats (since 1966)*
D: 73 tons (fl)   **Dim:** 25.30 × 6.10 × ...   **S:** 33/32 kts
A: 4/25-mm AA (II × 2) — 2/533-mm TT   **M:** Diesel; 4 props; 4,800 hp

PATROL CRAFT AND GUNBOATS

♦ *20 Soviet Kronstadt class (since 1957)*
D: 380 tons   **Dim:** 51.80 × 6.70 × 2.50   **S:** 18 kts
A: 1/85-mm — 2/37-mm AA — 2 depth charge projectors
M: diesel; 2,200 hp; 2 props

REMARKS: Six could have been delivered by the U.S.S.R., the others built in Shanghai and Canton. Other information indicates that only two were built in China, the balance in the Soviet Union.

♦ *7 Hainan class*
D: 200 tons   **Dim:** 40.50 × 6 × 2   **S:** 20 kts
A: 4/37-mm AA (II × 2) — 4/25-mm AA (II × 2)

REMARKS: Chinese version of the Soviet S 01 class but has a lower profile in the water.

♦ *280 Shanghai I, II and III class*
D: 100 to 120 tons   **Dim:** 39.50 × 5.30 × 1.70
S: 30 kts   **Man:** 25 men   **M:** 4 diesels; 5,000 hp.
A: 4/37-mm AA (II × 2) — 4/25-mm AA (II × 2) — 2 TT except on the Shanghai II class — 1 ASW weapon of hedgehog type with a very short range.

REMARKS: See photo in Tanzania section. The Shanghai III class has a 57-mm AA in place of the 37-mm guns.

♦ *Shantung class*
Improved version of earlier models. An unknown number of possibly the Chinese designation of the Shanghai III class.

♦ *80 Swatow class*
D: 67 tons (fl)   **S:** 40 kts   **Dim:** 25.10 × 6 × 1.80
A: 4/37-mm AA (II × 2) — 2 heavy machine gun mounts — 8 depth charges
M: 4 diesels; 4,000 hp.

REMARKS: Derived from the Soviet P 6 class.

PATROL CRAFT AND GUNBOATS (*continued*)

♦ *40 Whampoa class*
A modified Swatow class.

MINESWEEPERS

♦ *1 Woosung class*
Characteristics unknown.

♦ *23 Soviet T 43 class*

D: 700 tons (fl)   **Dim:** 60 × 9 × 2.15   **S:** 14 kts   **M:** diesels
A: 4/37-mm AA (II × 2) — 4/25-mm AA (II × 2) — 4 hedgehogs

REMARKS: The majority have been transferred from the U.S.S.R.; the others were built in China.

♦ About 100 small coastal minesweeper-minelayers of various types, the majority converted motorized junks.

AMPHIBIOUS SHIPS

♦ 15 or 16 U.S. *LSTs* of 1,600 tons, 11 knots, transferred before the civil war to the Nationalist China Navy and later captured by the communist forces. Possible names: **CHANG PAI SHAN, TA PIEH SHAN, CHUNG, CHING KANG SHAN, MENG SHAN.** Those which remain in service — and there are not likely to be many — are used as transports or station vessels.

♦ 14 ex-U.S. *LSMs* dating from 1944-45. Some may be used as minelayers.

♦ 10 or 11 *LCUs* (ex-*LCT*), all of U.S. origin.

♦ 500 *LCMs* (300 of the *Yunnan* class) built in China.

LOGISTIC SUPPORT

There is no reliable information on the logistic support available to the Chinese fleet, but it may be expected that certain old ships of U.S. or Japanese origin (such as certain *LSTs*) without any military value today, or a few cargo ships, have been modified as depot ships, repair ships, etc.

VARIOUS

♦ Several dozen river patrol craft.

River patrol boat   1966

♦ Several hundred armed junks, certain of them modified for mine laying.

PERSONNEL: 8,000 men, 1,200 of whom are Marines.

MERCHANT MARINE (1-7-74): 54 ships — 211,083 grt
(tankers: 2 — 4,050 grt)

COLOMBIA

SHIPS IN SERVICE OR UNDER CONSTRUCTION AS OF 1 OCTOBER 1975

	Tonnage	L	Main armament
♦ *4 submarines*			
2 PIJAO	1,000	1974	8/533-mm TT
2 INTREPIDO	100	. . .	. . .
♦ *4 destroyers*			
2 VEINTE DE JULIO	2,650	1956	6/120-mm AA, 4/533-mm TT
2 CALDAS	2,200	1944	6/127-mm AA, 6 ASW TT
1 ANTIOQUIA	2,050	1943	4/127-mm AA
♦ *5 frigates*			
2 CAPITAN PADILLA	1,450	1943-44	1/127-mm AA
1 BOYACA	1,450	1956	2/76-mm AA, ASW weapons
♦ *3 river gunboats*			
♦ *22 patrol boats*			

SUBMARINES

♦ *2 German type 209*

	Bldr	L	In serv.
PIJAO	Howaldtswerke, Kiel	19-6-74	17-4-75
N . . .	Howaldtswerke, Kiel		. . .

D: 980 tons standard/1,105 surfaced/1,230 submerged
Dim: 55 × 6.60 × 5.90
A: 8/533-mm TT fwd — 6/reserve torpedoes **Man:** 5 officers, 26 men
M: diesel-electric propulsion with 4 Maybach diesels linked to an AEG generator of 420 kw (max.); a single Siemens propulsion electric motor of 5,000 kw; 1 prop. **Fuel:** 50 tons diesel
S: 22 kts for a few minutes. **Endurance:** 30 days.

♦ *2 midget submarines*

INTREPIDO, INDOMABLE — Bldr: Cosmos, Livorno, Italy

D: 70 tons **Dim:** 23 × . . . × . . .
Can transport: 2,050 kg of explosives; 8 frogmen fully equipped; 2 submarine vehicles (for the frogmen) supported by a fixed system on lower part of the hull, one on each side.
Man: 5 men **S:** 8.5 kts

REMARKS: Similar submarines have been bought by the Pakistani and Chinese (Taiwan) navies.

DESTROYERS

♦ *2 Swedish Halland class*

	Bldr	Laid down	L	In serv.
05 VEINTE DE JULIO	Kockums (Malmö)	10-55	26-6-55	15-6-58
06 SIETE DE AGOSTO	Götaverken	11-55	19-6-56	31-10-58
(ex-*13 de Junio*)				

D: 2,650 (3,300 fl) **Dim:** 121.05 × 12.40 × 4.70 (fl)
S: 25 kts (cruising) **Range:** 450/30 **Man:** 21 officers, 227 men

Siete de Agosto (06)   Shipbldg. and Sh. Record

A: 6/120-mm AA automatic (II × 3) — 4/40-mm AA (I × 4) — 4/533-mm TT (IV × 1) — 1 ASW Bofors quadruple barrel 375-mm.
M: De Laval double reduction GT; 2 props; 55,000 hp
Boilers: 2 Penhoët-Motala-Verkstad **Fuel:** 524 tons

REMARKS: Based on the Swedish Halland class

♦ *2 ex-U.S. Allen M. Sumner class, transferred 1-7-72 and 16-12-73*

	Bldr	Laid down	L	In serv.
02 CALDAS	Bethlehem (San Pedro)	1944	29-8-44	12-44
(ex-*Willard Keith, DD-775*)				
03 SANTANDER	Federal S.B. & D.D.	1943	26-3-44	8-6-44
(ex-*Waldron, DD-699*)				

D: 2,200 tons (3,300 fl) **Dim:** 114.75 × 12.45 (wl) × 5.80
S: 30 kts **Electron Equipt:** SPS 12/U.S. (air search).
A: 6/127-mm semi-automatic, 38-cal. (II × 3) — 4/76-mm AA (II × 2) 6/324-mm ASW TT (III × 2) Mk 32 — 2 hedgehogs (fwd), depth charges.
M: GT; 4 Babcock boilers; 2 props; 60,000 hp. **Fuel:** 650 tons

REMARKS: *Santander* has had FRAM II modernization.

♦ *1 ex-U.S. Fletcher class, transferred in 1961*

	Bldr	Laid down	L	In serv.
01 ANTIOQUIA (ex-*Hale, DD-642*)	Bath Iron Wks	11-42	4-4-43	6-43

D: 2,050 tons (2,850 fl) **Dim:** 114.85 (fl) × 12.03 × 5.50
S: 30 kts **Man:** 14 officers, 235 men
A: 4/127-mm semi-automatic, 38-cal. (I × 4) 6/76-mm AA 5/533-mm TT (V × 1), 2 launchers for ASW torpedoes, 2 hedgehogs (fwd), 1 depth charge rack.
Range: 1,260/35, 4,400/15
Electron Equipt: Radars: SPS 6 (air search) and 10/U.S.

DESTROYERS (continued)

M: General Electric GT; 4 Babcock boilers; 2 props; 60,000 hp.
Fuel: 650 tons

FRIGATES

♦ *1 ex-U.S. destroyer escort, transferred 8-7-72*

	Bldr	Laid down	L	In serv.
07 BOYACA	New York S.B. Corp.	10-55	24-11-56	6-57

(ex-*Hartley, DE-1029*)

D: 1,450 tons (1,914 fl)   **Dim:** 95.70 × 11.26 × 4.30
S: 25 kts   **Man:** 11 officers, 150 men.   **Range:** 4,500/15
A: 2/76-mm automatic (II × 1) — 1 ASW rocket launcher Mk 108 Weapon Able, 2 ASW Mk 32 TT (III × 2)
Electron Equipt: Radars: SPS/6 and 10/U.S.
M: De Laval GT; 2 Foster Wheeler boilers; 1 prop; 20,000 hp.
Fuel: 400 tons

REMARKS: Twin rudder. Superstructure built of light metal alloy.

♦ *2 ex-U.S. LPR type, transferred in 1965-69*

DT 04 ALMIRANTE TONO (ex-*Bassett, LPR-73*) — L: 15-1-44
DT 15 CORDOBA (ex-*Ruchamkin, LPR-89*) — L: 15-6-44

Cordoba   A and J Pavia

D: 1,450 tons (2,050 fl)   **Dim:** 93.26 × 11.28 × 4.70
A: 1/127-mm — 3 or 6/40-mm AA   **S:** 23 kts
Man: 204 men   **Range:** 5,000/15, 2,000/23.   **Fuel:** 350 tons
M: turbo-electric propulsion; 2 props; 12,000 hp; 2 boilers

REMARKS: Used as fast transports (100 men).

RIVER GUNBOATS

CF 33 CARTAGENA — Bldr: Yarrow & Co. (Glasgow) 1930.

D: 142 tons   **Dim:** 41.90 × 7.16 × 0.80
S: 15.5 kts   **Range:** 2,100/15   **Man:** 39 men
A: 2/76-mm — 1/20-mm AA — 4/7.7-mm machine guns
Armor: Principal parts of the ship against small arms.
M: Gardner diesels; 2 props (in tunnels); 600 hp.
Fuel: 24 tons diesel

Cartagena

CF 35 RIOHACHA — CF 37 ARAUCA — Bldr: Unial, Barranquilla (1955)

D: 170 tons (184 fl)   **Dim:** 47.25 × 8.23 × 1
S: 13 kts   **Range:** 1,000/12
A: 2/76-mm AA — 4/20-mm AA   **Man:** 27 to 43 men
M: Caterpillar diesels; 2 props; 800 hp.

Arauca

PATROL BOATS

AN 203 OLAYA HERRERA — Bldr: Magdalena SY, Barranquilla (1960)

D: 40 tons   **S:** 17 kts   **Dim:** 21 × 4.20 × 1
A: 1/12.7-mm machine gun   **M:** diesels; 2 props; 570 hp.

AN 204 PEDRO GUAL   **AN 205 ESTEBAN JARAMILLO**
AN 206 CARLOS E. RESTREPO

PATROL BOATS (*continued*)

Bldr: K. G. Bardenfleth, Schurenstedt (1964-65)

D: 123.5 tons   **Dim:** 32.77 (pp) × 5.49 × 1.85.
S: 25/26 kts   **A:** 1/20-mm AA   **M:** 2 Maybach diesels; 2,500 hp.

		Bldr	L
AN 01 GENERAL RAFAEL REYES		Lürssen (Bremen-Vegesack)	10-11-55
AN 02 GENERAL VASQUEZ COBO		Lürssen (Bremen-Vegesack)	27-9-55

General Rafael Reyes

D: 145 tons   **Dim:** 37.97 (34.75 pp) × 7.01 × 1.53
S: 18 kts (20 trials)   **Man:** 20 men   **Range:** 1,000
A: 1/40-mm AA — depth charges
M: Maybach diesels; 2 props; 2,400 hp.

CARLOS ALBAN — JORGE SOTO DEL CORVAL — NITO RESTREDO. In
service since 1971.

D: 100 tons   **S:** 19 kts
A: 2/20-mm

SMALL BOATS

GC 101 CAPITAN BINNEY — Bldr: Cartagena Naval DY (1947) — Buoy and
Lighthouse Service

D: 23 tons   **Dim:** 19.20 × 3.35 × 1.05
S: 13 kts   **M:** diesels, 115 hp.   **Fuel:** 3 tons diesel

GC 100 ESPARTANA — Bldr: Cartagena Naval DY — L: 22-6-50

Alfonso Vargas (river gunboat)

D: 50 tons   **Dim:** 29.26 × 3.96 × 1.22
S: 13.5 kts   **Man:** 11 men
M: 2 diesels; 300 hp   **Fuel:** 6 tons diesel
A: 1/20-mm AA, 4 machine guns

River patrol boats

LR 122 JUAN LUCIO (2-5-53)
LR 123 ALFONSO VARGAS (3-7-52)
LR 124 FRITZ HAGALE (19-7-52)
LR 125 ALBERTO RESTREPO (1-10-52)
LR 126 HUMBERTO CORTES (26-11-52)
LR 127 CALIBIO
LR 128 CARLOS GALINDO (1954)

Bldr: Cartagena Naval DY

D: 33 tons   **Dim:** 25 × 3.66 × 0.85
S: 13 kts   **Man:** 13 men
A: 1/20-mm AA — 4 mortars.   **Fuel:** 3.5 tons diesel
M: 2 General Motors diesels; 260/290 hp.

LR 130 PALACE	**LR 133 TRIUNFANTE**
LR 131 VENGADORA	**LR 134 INDEPENDIENTE**
LR 132 DILIGENTE	**LR 135 VOLADORA**
	LR 136 TORMENTOSA

Bldr: Cartagena Naval DY — 1952-54.

No other information; these are small patrol craft.

SURVEY SHIPS

BO 151 SAN ANDRES (ex-*Rockville*, *PCER-851*) — Bldr: U.S.A. (22-2-44)
— Bought 5-6-69.

D: 674 tons (858 fl)   **Dim:** 56.20 × 10.05 × 3
S: 15 kts   **Man:** 60 men
M: General Motors diesels; 2 props; 1,800 hp.

BO 153 QUINDIO (ex-U.S. *Y-443*)

D: 300 tons   **Dim:** 40 × 9.10 × 2.50
S: 10 kts   **M:** 1 diesel, 700 hp.

FB 16 GORGONA — Bldr: Lidingo Verken — L: 28-5-54.

D: 560 tons   **Dim:** 41.15 × 9 × 2.83
S: 13 kts   **M:** 2 Nohab diesels; 2 props; 900 hp.

LOGISTIC SUPPORT

♦ *4 oilers*

BT 62 MAMONAL (ex-*Tonti, AOG-76*) — Bldr: Todd SB (Houston) — Transferred in
1965

D: 5,984 tons   **Dim:** 99 × 14.75 × 6.60
S: 10 kts   **Man:** 33 men
M: 1 diesel; 1,400 hp   **Cargo capacity:** 3,925 tons

BT 63 SANCHO JIMENO (ex-*Kiamichi, AOG-73*) — Bought in 1952

D: 11,385 tons   **Dim:** 168 × 20.70 × 9.15
S: 12.5 kts   **M:** 1 MAN diesel; 6,650 hp
Cargo capacity: 16,800 tons

LOGISTIC SUPPORT (*continued*)

Gorgona

BT 65 COVENAS (ex-*Randfonn*, Nor.) — Bldr: Götaverken, 1950 — Bought in 1966.

D: 5,996 tons   **Dim:** 157.07 × 19.50 × 9.30
S: 14 kts   **Man:** 7 officers, 42 men
M: 1 diesel; 6,000 hp.   **Cargo capacity:** 16,270 tons

BT 67 TUMACO (ex-U.S. *Chewaucan AOG-50*)

REMARKS: Was transferred to Colombia in 7-71.

♦ *5 small transports*

TM 41 BELL SALTER (ex-*Souris*)

D: 60 tons   **Dim:** 25 × 4.25 × 1.80
S: 8 kts   **M:** 2 GM diesels; 1,500 hp

TM 43 CIUDAD DE QUIBO — Bldr: Sander, Delfzijl, Neth.

D: 633 tons   **Dim:** 50.30 × 7.20 × 2.80
S: 11 kts   **Man:** 11 men
M: diesel; 1 prop; 390 hp   **Fuel:** 32 tons

TF 51 MARIO SERPA (1953) — **TF 52 HERNANDO GUTIERREZ** (1953) — **BD 33 SOCORRO** — Bldr: Cartagena Naval DY

D: 70 tons   **Dim:** 25 × 5.50 × 0.75   **Man:** 10 men
S: 9 kts   **M:** 2 General Motors diesels; 270 hp

Fitted to carry 56 troops on the rivers.

♦ *15 tugs*

RM 72 PEDRO DE HEREDIA (ex-*Choctaw*, ATF-*70*) (10-*42*)

D: 1,235 tons (1,765 fl)   **S:** 16.5 kts   **Dim:** 62.50 × 11.70 × 4.80
M: diesel-electric propulsion; 3,000 hp, added in 1961.

RM 74 BAHIA HONDA (ex-*Kalmia*, *ATA-184*), **RM 75 BAHIA UTRIA** (ex-*Koka*, *ATA-185*) — transferred 1-7-71.

D: 534 tons (835 fl)   **S:** 13 kts   **Dim:** 43 × 10 × 4.
M: diesel-electric propulsion; 1 prop; 1,500 hp.

RR 81 CAPITAN CASTRO, RR 82 CANDIDO LEGUIZAMO,
RR 84 CAPITAN ALVARO RUIS,
RR 86 CAPITAN RIGOBERTO GIRALDO,
RR 87 CAPITAN VLADIMIR VALEK, RR 88 TENIENTE LUIS BERNAL

D: 50 tons   **Dim:** 20 × 4.25 × 0.75 ⎫
S: 10 kts   **M:** 2 diesels 260 hp ⎬ for river patrol
⎭

RM 71 ANDAGOYA (1928)

D: 100 tons   **S:** 12 kts   **M:** Diesel, 300 hp

RM 73 TENIENTE SORZANO (ex-*U.S.*)

D: 54 tons   **S:** ...   **M:** Diesel, 240 hp

RR 90 ABADIA MENDEZ (1924)

D: 40 tons   **S:** 10 kts   **M:** Diesel, 100 hp

RM 89 TENIENTE MIGUEL SILVA ⎫
RM 90 JOVES FIALLO   ⎬ for river patrol

S: 9 kts   **M:** Diesel, 260 hp

VARIOUS

♦ *1 school sailing ship*

GLORIA — delivered 7-9-68. Bldr: Celaya (Bilbao) — Three-masted schooner; fore and main masts are square-rigged.

Gloria   1969 Marius Bar

COLOMBIA (*continued*)

VARIOUS (*continued*)

    Dim: 64.50 × 10.60 × 6.60.   Hull welded steel.
    M: 1 diesel; 500 hp.   **S:** 10 kts

♦ *1 small hospital ship*

LETITIA, former river gunboat *Rio Hacha* class.

CONGO

Peoples' Republic of the

PERSONNEL: 180 men

MERCHANT MARINE (1-7-74): 6 ships — 1,534 grt

The naval forces are divided in 2 groups:
    — Coastal navy
    — River navy.
♦ The first group has 3 *Shanghai*-class coastal patrol boats (ex-Chinese), delivered in 3-75.
♦ The second group has:
    4 river patrol boats of 10 tons
    2 locally constructed small craft
    10/40-to-75 hp Johnson outboards (probably in poor condition).

PERSONNEL: about 6,000 men

MERCHANT MARINE (1-7-74): 259 ships — 409,064 grt
(tankers: 9 ships — 51,908 grt)

CUBA

PATROL BOATS

♦ *6 Soviet Kronstadt class transferred 2-62.*

D:	300 tons (350 fl)	**S:**	22 kts	**Dim:**	51 × 6 × 2.80
A:	1/85-mm — 2/37-mm AA			**Man:**	40 men
M:	diesels; 2 props			**Fuel:**	20 tons diesel

♦ *12 Soviet SO 1 class transferred: six in 1964 and six in 1967*

D: 215 (250 fl)   **S:** 25 kts   **Dim:** 44.80 × 6.10 × 3.10
A: 4/25-mm AA (II × 2) — 4 ASW MBU 1500 rocket launchers — depth charge racks.
M: diesels; 3 props; 3,500 hp   **Man:** 30 men

♦ *1 U.S. PCE class*

PE 202 SIBONEY (ex-*PCE 893*, 5-5-43)

D:	640 tons (795 fl)	**Dim:**	56.24 × 10.06 × 2.80
S:	15 kts	**Man:**	99 men
A:	1/76-mm AA — 1/40-mm AA — 6/20-mm AA		
M:	2 GM diesels; 2 props; 2,000 hp.	**Fuel:**	diesel

REMARKS: Former coastal convoy vessel, bought in U.S.A. in 1947. Refitted in 1956-57 in U.S.A.

GC 104 ORIENTE (ex-*SC-1000*)
GC 106 LAS VILLAS (ex-*SC-1290*)
GC 107 HABANA (ex-*SC-1291*)
GC 108 PINAR DEL RIO (ex-*SC-1391*)

Bldr: U.S.A. 1942-43.

D:	110 tons (125/130 fl)	**Dim:**	33.70 × 5.70 × 2
A:	2/20-mm AA — depth charges	**Range:**	2,000/10 — 1,150/15
S:	15 kts	**Man:**	25 men
M:	2 General Motors diesels; 2 props; 800 hp.	**Fuel:**	15 tons diesel.

REMARKS: Former submarine chasers.

GC 101 LEONCIO PRADO — Bldr: Havana 1946

D:	80 tons			**Dim:**	33.53 × 4.47 × 1.90
A:	1/20-mm AA	**S:**	15 kts	**Range:**	14,000/10
M:	2/8-cyl. diesels; 2 props; 1,000 hp.				

REMARKS: Resembles earlier models closely. Wooden hull. One stack.

GC 11, 13, 14, 32, 33, 34 (1943).

D:	44.5 tons	**Dim:**	25.30 × 4.90 × 1.40
S:	17 kts (**11** to **14**), 12 kts (**32** to **34**)	**A:**	1/37-mm — depth charges
M:	2 motors; 1,200 hp or 460 hp	**Man:**	10 men.

REMARKS: Former small boats of the U.S. Coast Guard. The first three have Sterling gasoline engines, the other three have Superior diesels and are not as fast.

♦ *1 ex-Soviet Zhuk class*

D: 50 tons   **S:** 34 kts   **Dim:** 23 × . . . × . . .
A: 2/14.5-mm machine guns (II × 1)

GUIDED MISSILE AND TORPEDO BOATS

All Soviet classes, transferred by the U.S.S.R. since 1962

♦ *6 OSA 1 class, delivered in 1972 (2), 1973 (2), and 1974 (2)*

D: 190 tons (fl)   **S:** 36 kts   **Dim:** 37 × 7 × 1.80
A: 4 Styx systems — 4/30-mm AA (II × 2)
Electron Equipt: Radars: 1/Square Tie, 1/Drum Tilt
M: 3 diesels; 3 props; 9,000 hp

GUIDED MISSILE AND TORPEDO BOATS (continued)

♦ *20 Komar class (1961-63), 12 delivered in 1962, 8 in 1966*

    D: 80 tons (110 fl)   **S:** 40 kts   **Dim:** 26 × 6 × 1.80
    A: 2 Styx systems, 2/25-mm AA (II × 1)
    Electron Equipt: Radar: 1/Square Tie
    M: 2 diesels; 2 props; 5,000 hp

♦ *12 P6-class torpedo boats (before 1955) delivered in 1962*

    D: 50 tons (75 fl)   **S:** 40 kts   **Dim:** 26 × 6 × 1.80
    A: 4/25-mm AA (II × 2) — 2/533-mm TT
    M: 2 diesels; 2 props; 5,000 hp

♦ *12 P4 class (before 1955) delivered in 1962 and 1964*

    D: 40 tons (. . . fl)   **S:** 40/38 kts   **Dim:** 22 × 4.70 × 1.50
    A: 2/14.5-mm Mg. (Aft) — 2/450-mm TT

SURVEILLANCE CRAFT

R 41, 42 (ex-U.S. *PT-715, 716*)

    Bldr: U.S.A. (1944)

    D: 35 tons   **Dim:** 21.64 × 5.87 × 1.53
    S: 40 (trials) kts   **A:** 2 machine guns — N/torpedoes
    M: 3 Packard motors; 3 props; 3,600 hp   **Fuel:** gasoline

REMARKS: Bought in the U.S.A. in 1948.

♦ *7 coast guard boats*

GF 528, GF 725, GF 825, GF 720 — Similar to 40-foot U.S. Coastal Guard small craft **GF 101, GF 102, GF 701** — similar to 70-foot U.S. Coast Guard small craft
    Assigned to the Department of the Interior. Hull numbers painted in red to distinguish these small boats from navy ships.

♦ *1 fast patrol boat*

GUANABACOA — Bldr: Cadiz

    S: 22 kts   **A:** 1 ASW depth charge projector

♦ *6 fast Camilo Cienfuegos*

MARTI — CAMILO CIENFUEGOS — MACEO — FINLAY — CUARTEL MONCADA — ESCAMBRAY — Bldr: Spain (1971-72)
No other information.

♦ *14 harbor patrol boats*

SV 1-6 (1953)

    D: 6.5 tons   **Dim:** 9.70 × 3.05 × 0.85
    S: 18 kts   **M:** 2 Chrysler motors; 230 hp

SV 7-14 (1958)

    D: . . .   **Dim:** 12.50 × . . . × . . .
    S: 25 kts   **M:** 2 General Motors diesels.

LOGISTIC SUPPORT AND VARIOUS

♦ *1 landing craft*

    Bldr: Spain (1972)
No other information.

A 21 GRANMA — Yacht

A 1, 2, 3 — Bldr: U.S.A., 1949

    D: 58 tons   **Dim:** 22.50 × 4.60 × 1.60   **M:** 2 Gray diesels; 225 hp.
Used as auxiliary vessels.

ENRIQUE COLLAZO — Bldr: Great Britain (1906) — Buoy tender

    D: 815 tons   **Dim:** 64 × 10.50 × 2.80
    M: Triple expansion; 2 props; 680 hp

SF 10 BERTHA (1944) — Buoy tender

    D: 100 tons   **S:** 10 kts   **Dim:** 31.50 × 5.75 × 3.40
    M: 2 Gray diesels

DIEZ DE OCTUBRE (ex-*ATR 4*) — Bldr: U.S.A. (1943) — Tug

    D: 852 tons   **Dim:** 50.35 (47.25 bp) × 10.15 × 4.90
    S: 12 kts   **A:** 1/76-mm AA — 2/20-mm AA
    M: Triple expansion; 1 prop; 1,600 hp.
    Boilers: 1 Babcock (D), 1 Foster Wheeler (V).

REMARKS: Bought in the U.S.A. in 1948. One of 90 similar ships with wooden hulls built as salvage tugs for convoys.

♦ *1 training ship*

VIETNAM HEROICO — Former supply ship

    D: 10,170 tons (fl)   **Dim:** 132 × 17
    S: 15.5 kts   **Man:** 62 men and 15 instructors

REMARKS: Serves as a school ship for the Merchant Marine.

CYPRUS

PERSONNEL: 330 men

MERCHANT MARINE (1-7-74): 722 ships — 3,394,880 grt
(tankers, 51 — 601,362 grt)

♦ *2 ex-German R-class minesweepers (1943):*

1971 G. Arra

D: 130 tons   **S:** 18 kts   **A:** 1/40-mm — 1/20-mm

♦ *6 Soviet P 4 class torpedo boats, 4 transferred 10-64 and 2 in 2-65.*

D: 30 tons   **S:** 32 kts   **Dim:** 16.80 × 3.75 × 1.05
A: 2/14.5-mm Mg. (II × 1) machine guns — 2/450-mm TT
Radar: 1/Skin Head.
Man: 12 men   **M:** diesels; 2 props; 2,400 hp.

♦ *10 small former fishing boats, 50 tons displ.*

A: 1 or 2/20-mm

REMARKS: Several probably were lost during the July 1974 crisis.

♦ A contract for the delivery of 2 small craft (32 m.) built in the Esterel shipyard was signed 13 January 1975 with Greece. It is possible that these ships will remain Greek property. Delivery planned for 9 and 11-75.

DENMARK

PERSONNEL: 6,000 men including 900 officers.

NAVAL AVIATION: About 15 helicopters including 8 Alouette III class.

NAVAL PROGRAM: The naval program anticipates the construction between now and 1980 of the following:
— 3 corvettes to replace the 4 *Triton* class.
— 10 *Willimoes*-class guided missile patrol boats to replace the 6 *Flyveskiten*-class torpedo boats which have been condemned, and are now being scrapped, and the 4 *Falken* class.
— 2 minelayers which will replace the 2 *Lougen* class.
— 1 modified *Hvidbjörnen*-class fishery protection ship.
— the installation of the Harpoon system on the 2 *Peder Skram* class ships.

MERCHANT MARINE (1-7-74): 1,349 ships — 4,460,219 grt
(tankers: 70 ships — 2,197,994 grt)

WARSHIPS IN SERVICE OR UNDER CONSTRUCTION AS OF 1 OCTOBER 1975

	L	D	Main armament
♦ *6 submarines*			
2 NARHVALEN	1968-70	370	8 TT
4 DELFINEN	1956-63	550	4 TT
♦ *11 frigates*			
2 PEDER SKRAM	1965	2,030	4/127-mm, 4/40-mm AA
4 BELLONA	1954-55	760	2/76-mm AA, 1/40-mm AA
4 HVIDBJÖRNEN	1961-62	1,345	1/76-mm, 1 helicopter
1 HVIDBJÖRNEN mod	1975		1/76-mm, 1 helicopter
♦ *20 guided missile and torpedo boats*			
10 based on the Swedish *Spica* class		250	1/76-mm TT or surface-to-surface missiles
	Constr.		
6 SOLOVEN	1965-67	95	4/533-mm TT
4 FALKEN	1961-62	119	1/40-mm AA, 4/533-mm TT
♦ *22 patrol boats*			
9 BARSÖ	1969	155	
2 MAAGEN	1960	175	1/40-mm AA
9 DAPHNE	1960-63	150	1/40-mm AA
2 divers			
♦ *7 minelayers*			
4 FALSTER	1962-63	1,880	4/76-mm AA — 400 mines
3 LOUGEN	1941-50	260	
♦ *12 minesweepers (8 coastal and 4 inshore)*			

SUBMARINES

♦ *2 German type*

	Bldr	Laid down	L	In serv.
S 320 NARHVALEN	RDY Copenhagen	2-65	10-9-68	2-70
S 321 NORDKAPEREN	RDY Copenhagen	1-66	18-12-69	12-70

SUBMARINES (*continued*)

Narhvalen (S 320)   1970 photo

D:	370 tons surfaced/480 submerged	**Dim:**	45.41 × 4.60 × 4.58
S:	17/10 kts	**A:**	8/533-mm TT, fwd.
M:	diesel electric; 1 prop; 1,200/1,700 hp.		

REMARKS: Modeled on the German *U-4* and Norwegian *Ula* classes.

♦ *4 Delfinen class*

	Bldr	Laid down	L	In serv.
S 326 DELFINEN	RDY Copenhagen	7-54	5-5-56	9-58
S 327 SPÆKHUGGEREN	RDY Copenhagen	12-54	20-2-57	6-59
S 328 TUMLEREN	RDY Copenhagen	5-56	22-5-58	1-60
S 329 SPRINGEREN	RDY Copenhagen	1-61	26-4-63	10-64

Delfinen (S 326)

D:	550 tons surfaced/643 submerged	**Dim:**	54 × 4.70 × 3.80
S:	13/12 kts	**Man:**	33 men
A:	4/533-mm TT, fwd	**Range:**	4,000/8.5
M:	Burmeister & Wain diesels and motors; 2 props; 1,200 hp		

FRIGATES

♦ *2 Peder Skram (Danish design)*

	Bldr	Laid down	L	In serv.
F 352 PEDER SKRAM	Helsingör Vaerft	9-64	20-5-65	6-66
F 353 HERLUF TROLLE	Helsingör Vaerft	12-64	8-9-65	4-67

D:	2,030 tons (2,720 fl)	**Dim:**	112.50 (108 pp) × 12 × 3.60
S:	28 kts	**Man:**	200 men

Peder Skram (F 352)   1970 Photo St. Steensen

Herluf Trolle (F 353)   1974 Photo J. C. Bellonne

A:	4/127-mm (II × 2) — 4/40-mm AA (I × 4) — 2 ASW TT (one port, one stbd) — 1 BPDMS Sea Sparrow system
M:	CODOG propulsion; 2 diesels (4,800 hp); 2 gas turbines (37,000 hp); 2 Ka-Me-Wa props

REMARKS: The gas turbines are GG4A-3 Pratt and Whitney-Stal-Laval models and the diesels General Motors 567 D 16-cylinder in a V (800 rpm). Speed with diesels: 16 kts The 127-mm guns are U.S. semi-automatic of 38 caliber.

♦ *4 Italian Airone class*

		L			L
F 344 BELLONA		9-1-55	**F 346 FLORA**		25-6-55
F 345 DIANA		19-12-54	**F 347 TRITON**		19-9-54

Orders for "offshore" ships given to the Italian shipyards Naval Meccanica, Tirreno, and Naval Meccanica, Taranto.

D:	760 tons (870 fl)	**Dim:**	75 (69.49 pp) × 9.50 × 3.00
S:	20 kts (16 cruising)	**Man:**	109 men
A:	2/76-mm AA — 1/40-mm — ASW weapons including two hedgehogs		

REMARKS: *Triton* is used as a training ship. Officially classified as "corvettes."

FRIGATES (*continued*)

The 3 frigates which will replace the *Triton* class will have the following characteristics:

D: 1,320 tons **S:** 28 kts **Dim:** 84 (80 pp) × 10.30 × 3.10
A: 8 Harpoon — 1 BPDM Sea Sparrow — 1/76-mm Oto Melara compact
M: CODOG system with 1 Olympus gas turbine; 1 diesel

◆ *1 modified Hvidbjörnen class*

	Bldr	Laid down	L	In serv.
BESKYTERREN	1970	...	...	1975

D: ... **Dim:** 74.4 × 11.8 × 4.5
S: 18 kts **Range:** 6,000/13
A: 1/76-mm AA — 1 helicopter **Man:** 60 men
M: 4 B & W Alpha diesels; 1 variable pitch prop; 7,440 hp.

REMARKS: Will serve as a fisheries protection ship. The helicopter is an Alouette III.

◆ *4 Hvidbjörnen class*

		Bldr	Laid down	L	In serv.
F 348	HVIDBJÖRNEN	Aarhus Flydedok	6-61	23-11-61	12-62
F 349	VÆDDEREN	Aalborg Naval SY	10-61	6-4-62	3-63
F 350	INGOLF	Svendborg Skibsvaerft	12-61	27-7-62	6-63
F 351	FYLLA	Aalborg Naval SY	6-62	18-12-62	7-63

Hvidbjörnen (F 348) photo

D: 1,345 tons (1,650 fl) **Dim:** 72.60 × 11.60 × 4.90
S: 18 kts **Range:** 6,000/13
A: 1/76-mm AA — 1 helicopter **Man:** 10 officers, 60 men
M: 4 G.M. diesels linked to a variable pitch prop; 6,400 hp.

REMARKS: Used for fisheries protection. Can also be used as hydrographic ships and will serve as frigates in wartime. Alouette III helicopter. Reinforced bow.

PATROL BOATS

◆ *9 Barsö class*

Y 300 BARSÖ	Y 301 DREJÖ	Y 302 ROMSÖ	Y 303 SAMSÖ
Y 304 THURÖ	Y 305 VEJRÖ	Y 306 FARÖ	Y 307 LAESÖ
Y 308 ROMÖ			

Bldr: Denmark, the first six in 1969, the last three from 1972-73.

D: 155 tons **S:** 11 kts **Dim:** 25.50 × 6 × 2.80

Thurö (Y 304) 1970 photo

	Bldr	In serv.
Y 384 MAAGEN	Helsingör Vaerft	5-60
Y 385 MALLEMUKKEN	Helsingör Vaerft	5-60

Mallemukken (Y 385) 1966 photo

D: 175 tons (190 fl) **Dim:** 27 × 7.20 × 2.75
S: 10 kts **A:** 1/40-mm AA **M:** diesel; 1 prop; 350 hp.

REMARKS: Steel hull; profile of a whale hunter ship; based in Greenland.
Two patrol boats fitted for fisheries protection duty and as hydrographic ships have been placed in service — **Y 386 AGDLEK** (in service 8-3-74) and **Y 387 AGPA** (in service 14-5-74).

D: 300 tons **S:** 12 kts **Dim:** 31.20 × 7.7 × 2.92
M: 1,800-hp B&W diesel

PATROL BOATS (continued)

◆ *9 Daphne class*

	Bldr	Laid down	L	In serv.
P 530 DAPHNE*	RDY Copenhagen	4-60	10-11-60	12-61
P 531 DRYADEN	RDY Copenhagen	7-60	1-3-61	4-62
P 532 HAVMANDEN*	RDY Copenhagen	11-60	16-5-61	8-62
P 533 HAVFRUEN	RDY Copenhagen	3-61	4-10-61	12-62
P 534 NAJADEN*	RDY Copenhagen	9-61	20-6-62	4-63
P 535 NYMFEN	RDY Copenhagen	4-62	1-11-62	10-63
P 536 NEPTUN*	RDY Copenhagen	9-62	29-5-63	12-63
P 537 RAN	RDY Copenhagen	12-62	10-7-63	5-64
F 538 ROTA	RDY Copenhagen	6-63	26-11-63	1-65

Havmanden (Daphne class)   1970 photo

D: 150 tons   **Dim:** 38 × 6.75 × 2
S: 20 kts   **A:** 1/40-mm AA — ASW weapons   **Man:** 23 men
M: 2 diesels of 1,300-hp and 1 diesel of 100-hp; 3 props

REMARKS: Danish version of the wartime German *Raumboote*, whose qualities were highly valued. The 100-hp engine is used in cruising.
* Offshore commands.

Y 383 TEISTEN (1951). Motorized auxiliary ketch — based in the Faroe islands.
   D: 130 tons   **Dim:** 25 × 6.10 × 2.90
   S: 9 kts   **M:** diesel; 1 prop; 180 hp.   **A:** 1/20-mm

Y 371 ERTHOLM (1951).
   D: 70 tons   **Dim:** 24.60 × 6.20 × 2.80
   S: 10 kts   **M:** diesel; 120 hp

GUIDED MISSILE AND TORPEDO PATROL BOATS

◆ *10 Willemoes class based on the Swedish Spica class (Lürssen design)*
Bldr: Royal Dock Yard Copenhagen (Ordered in 1972).

	L	In serv.		L	In serv.
P 540 BILLE	15-4-74		P 545 NORBY		
P 541 BREDAL			P 546 RODSTEEN		
P 542 HAMMER			P 547 SEHESTED		
P 543 HUITFELDE			P 548 SUENSON		
P 544 KRIEGER			P 549 WILLEMOES		

   D: 250 tons   **Dim:** 46 (42.40 pp) × 7.40 × . . .
   S: 35 kts   **Man:** 30 men
   A: 1/76-mm Oto Melara compact — 4 surface-to-surface Harpoon missiles or 4/533-mm TT
   M: 2 GM diesels; 3 Rolls-Royce Proteus gas turbines; 3 Ka-Me-Wa props; 12,750 hp/800 hp.

REMARKS: Draft is 2 meters. In addition to the 76-mm Oto Melara compact, armament will include 2 Harpoon and 2/533-mm TT.

◆ *4 Falken class*

	Bldr	Laid down	L	In serv.
P 506 FALKEN	RDY Copenhagen	11-60	19-12-61	4-10-62
P 507 GLENTEN	RDY Copenhagen	1-61	15-5-62	15-12-62
P 508 GRIBBEN	RDY Copenhagen	5-61	18-7-62	26-4-63
P 509 HÖGEN	RDY Copenhagen	9-61	4-10-62	6-6-63

Falken (P 506)   1970 Terzibaschitsch

   D: 119 tons   **Dim:** 35.90 × 5.40 × 2
   S: 40   **A:** 1/40-mm AA (aft) — 1/20-mm AA (fwd) — 4/533-mm TT
   M: Mercedes-Benz diesels; 3 props; 9,000 hp.   **Man:** 23 men

REMARKS: Derived from the German *Schnellboote* designs.

◆ *6 British Brave class*

	Bldr	Laid down	L	In serv.
P 510 SÖLÖVEN	Vosper (Portsmouth)	8-62	19-4-63	2-65
P 511 SÖRIDDEREN	Vosper (Portsmouth)	10-62	22-8-63	2-65
P 512 SÖBJÖRNEN	RDY Copenhagen	7-63	19-8-64	9-65
P 513 SÖHESTEN	RDY Copenhagen	8-63	31-3-65	1966
P 514 SÖHUNDEN	RDY Copenhagen	2-64	12-1-66	1-67
P 515 SÖULVEN	RDY Copenhagen	6-64	27-4-66	3-67

   D: 95 tons (114 fl)   **Dim:** 30.26 (27.44 pp) × 7.30 × 2.15
   S: 50 kts   **A:** 2/40-mm AA — 4/533-mm TT   **Man:** 4 officers, 22 men
   M: Bristol Siddeley Marine Proteus gas turbines; 3 props; 10,500 hp (12,750 max). Cruising, 2 General Motors GV 71 diesels (**S:** 10 kts)

GUIDED MISSILE AND TORPEDO PATROL BOATS (*continued*)

Sölöven (P 510)

MINELAYERS

♦ *4 Falster class*

	Bldr	Laid down	L	In serv.
N 80 FALSTER	Nakskov Skibsvaerft	4-62	19-9-62	11-63
N 81 FYEN	Frederikshavn Vaerft	4-62	3-10-62	9-63
N 82 MÖEN	Frederikshavn Vaerft	10-62	6-6-63	4-64
N 83 SJÆLLAND	Nakskov Skibsvaerft	1-63	14-6-63	7-64

Falster (N 80)

D: 1,880 tons **Dim:** 77 (72.50 pp) × 12.50 × 3.
S: 16.5 kts **Man:** 10 officers, 108 men
A: 4/76-mm AA (II × 2) — 300 mines (4 minelaying tracks)
M: General Motors diesels; 2 variable pitch props; 4,800 hp.

REMARKS: NATO design. The Turkish ship *Nusret* is identical.
The *Falster*-class minelayers will be fitted with a BPDM Sea Sparrow. The characteristics of the two new minelayers will be:

D: 570 tons **S:** 14 kts **Dim:** 44.70 × 9 × 2.70
M: diesels **A:** 2/20-mm or 1/20-mm AA — 50/60 mines

♦ *2 Lougen/Langeland class*

	Bldr	Laid down	L	In serv.
N 40 LAALAND	RDY Copenhagen	1940	1941	1946
N 41 LOUGEN	RDY Copenhagen	1940	1941	1946
N 42 LANGELAND	RDY Copenhagen	17-5-50	1950	1951

Langeland (N 42) 1970 Terzibaschitsch

D: 260 tons (40 and 41) **Dim:** 34.20 × 6.60 × 2.00 (40 and 41)
   310 tons (42)   40.70 × 7.20 × 2.20 (42)
S: 10 kts **Man:** 32 men (40 on 42)
A: 2/20-mm AA (40 and 41) — 2/40-mm AA (42) — 2/20-mm AA.
M: 2 B & W diesels; 2 props

REMARKS: *Langeland* has a small mast attached to her stack and her 2/40-mm AA are on two gun platforms, will soon be scrapped.

MINESWEEPERS

♦ *8 U.S. MSC (AMS) type.*

M 571 AARÖSUND	**M 574 GRÖNSUND**	**M 577 ULVSUND**
M 572 ALSSUND	**M 575 GULDBORGSUND**	**M 578 VILSUND**
M 573 EGERNSUND	**M 576 OMÖSUND**	

Bldr: U.S.A. (1953-56); transferred in 1955-56

D: 350 tons (376 fl) **Dim:** 43.00 (41.50 pp) × 7.95 × 2.55
S: 13 kts (8 sweeping) **Range:** 2,500/10
A: 2/20-mm AA (II × 1) **Man:** 38 men
M: 2 General Motors diesels; 2 props; 1,200 hp. **Fuel:** 40 tons diesel

REMARKS: Hull entirely of wood. The first three are the ex-*MSC 127-129*; the others the ex-*256, 257, 221, 263, 264*. Same profile as the French *Acacia* class.

♦ *4 inshore Vig class*

M 579 ASVIG (11-5-60)	**M 581 SANDVIG** (1-3-61).
M 580 MOSVIG (14-9-60)	**M 582 SÆLVIG** (14-7-61).

Bldr: RDY Copenhagen

MINESWEEPERS (*continued*)

Asvig (M 579)   photo

D: 180 tons   **S:** 14 kts   **Dim:** 32.45 × 6.45 × 1.70
A: 2/20-mm AA (II × 2)   **Man:** 2 officers, 16 men
M: Werkspoor diesels; 2 props; 1,100 hp.   **Fuel:** 15 tons diesel
Endurance: 4 days

REMARKS: Based on the Dutch *Van Straelen* class.

LOGISTIC SUPPORT

♦ *1 submarine support ship*

A 542 HENRIK GERNER (1936)

(A 542)

D: 2,200 tons   **S:** 14 kts   **Dim:** 81 × 12 × 2.50
Man: 230 men   **A:** 6/40-mm AA   **M:** B & W diesel.

REMARKS: Former steamer *Hammershus*, refitted in 1964.

♦ *2 coastal oilers*

A 568 RIMFAXE and **569 SKINFAKE** (ex-U.S. *Y-226* and *Y-229*)
   D: 1,390 tons (fl)   **S:** 10 kts   **Dim:** . . .
   M: 1 General Motors diesel; 1 prop; 560 hp.   **Man:** 23 men

VARIOUS

♦ *1 royal yacht:* **A 540 DANNEBROG** (1931)
   D: 1,130 tons   **S:** 14 kts   **M:** 2 diesels

♦ *7 Faeno class (naval militia)*

Type Faenö

MHV 69 FAENÖ, MHV 81 ASKÖ, MHV 82 ENÖ, MHV 83 MANÖ, MHV 84 BAAGÖ, MHV 85 HJORTÖ, MHV 86 LYÖ. — Bldr: Denmark — 1940-41.
   D: 74 tons   **Dim:** 24.40 × 4.90 × 1.60
   S: 11 kts   **A:** 1/20-mm AA — 2 machine guns
   Man: 11 men   **M:** diesel; 1 prop; 350 hp.

♦ *3 MHV 70 class (naval militia)*

MHV 70, 71, 72 — Bldr: RDY Copenhagen 1957
   D: 76 tons   **S:** 10 kts   **Dim:** 20.05 × 5.05 × 2.50
   A: 1/20-mm AA   **Man:** 12 men   **M:** diesel; 1 prop; 200 hp.

♦ *4 icebreakers (manned by the Ministry of Commerce)*

DANBJÖRN (1965)   **ISBJÖRN** (1965)
   D: 3,685 tons   **S:** 14 kts   **Dim:** 75.60 × 16.80 × 6
   M: diesel-electric; 11,880 hp   **Man:** 34 men

ELBJÖRN (1953)
   D: 898 tons (1,400 fl)   **S:** 12 kts   **Dim:** 47 × 12.10 × 4.35
   M: diesel-electric; 3,600 hp.

STOREBJÖRN (1931)
   D: 2,580 tons   **Dim:** 59.10 × 14.75 × 5.70

PERSONNEL: 370 officers and 3,630 men

MERCHANT MARINE (1-7-74): 20 ships — 11,963 grt
(tankers: 1 ship — 674 grt)

FRIGATES

♦ *1 Canadian River class transferred in 1947*

	Bldr	L
451 (ex-*F 101*) **MELLA** (ex-*Presidente Trujillo*, ex-*Carlplace*)	Davie S.B. (Lauzon)	6-7-44

(F 101)

D:	1,445 tons (2,300 fl)	**S:** 19 kts **Dim:** 92.35 × 11.45 × 4.30
A:	1/40-mm AA — 4/20-mm AA — 2/47-mm saluting guns	
Man:	15 officers, 135 men **Range:** 7,700/12 **Fuel:** 645 tons	
M:	Triple expansion; 2 props; 5,500 hp. **Boilers:** 2 (3-drum)	

REMARKS: Bought in 1947. Serves as a training ship.

♦ *2 U.S. PF type transferred in 1949*

	Bldr	L
453 (ex-*F 103*) **CAP. GENERAL PEDRO SANTANA** (ex-*Presidente Troncoso*, ex-*Pueblo*, *PF-13*)	Kaiser SY (Richmond, Cal.)	20-1-44
452 (ex-*F 104*) **GREGORIO LUPERON** (ex-*Presidente Peynado*, ex-*Knoxville*, *PF-74*)	Leatham Smith SB (Superior, Wis.)	10-7-43

D:	1,400 tons (2,400 fl)	**Dim:** 92.6 × 11.43 × 4.40
S:	18-16 kts	**Range:** 7,500/12
A:	3/76-mm — 4/40 mm AA (II × 2) — 6/20-mm AA	
M:	Triple expansion; 2 props; 5,500 hp	**Boilers:** 2 small-tube
Fuel:	290 tons **Man:** 140 men	

REMARKS: In reserve.

DOMINICAN REPUBLIC

Gregorio Luperon (old p. number)

♦ *2 ex-Canadian corvettes, British Flower class, 1940*

401 (ex-*C 101*) **CRISTOBAL COLON** (ex-*Lachute*)	9-6-44	}	Bought in 1947
402 (ex-*C 103*) **JUAN ALEJANDRO ACOSTA** (ex-*Louisburg*)	13-7-43		

Juan Alejandro Acosta (old p. number)

D:	980 tons (1,350 fl)	**Dim:** 63.52 (58.91 pp) × 9.75 × 4.87
S:	16 kts	**Range:** 5,500/9 — 2,900/15
A:	1/102-mm — 1/40-mm AA — 2/20-mm AA	
M:	Triple expansion; 1 prop; 2,750 hp.	**Boilers:** 2 drums
Fuel:	280 tons	**Man:** 53 men

FRIGATES (continued)

REMARKS: Worn out. The *401* has 1/76-mm AA — 2/40-mm AA (II × 1) — 6/20-mm AA — 4 machine guns.

♦ *ex-U.S. Admirable class minesweeper-escorts, transferred in 1-66*

		Bldr	L
BM 454 SEPARACION (ex-*Skirmish, MSF-303*)	Assoc. Shbldg.	16-8-43
BM 455 TORTUGERO (ex-*Signet, MSF-302*)	Assoc. Shbldg.	16-8-43

D:	600 tons (903 fl)	**Dim:**	56.24 × 10.06 × 2.76 (light)
S:	15 kts	**A:**	1/76-mm AA — 4/40-mm AA
Man:	100 men	**Range:**	5,600/9
M:	General Motors diesels; 2 props; 1,800 hp	**Fuel:**	260 tons diesel

PATROL BOATS

♦ *3 patrol boats from the U.S. Coast Guard*

203 (ex-*P-104*) **RESTAURACION** (ex-*Galathea, PC-108*)	Purchased	1932
204 (ex-*P-105*) **INDEPENDENCIA** (ex-*Icarus, PC-110*)	from the	1931
205 (ex-*P-106*) **LIBERTAD** (ex-*Rafael Atoa,*	U.S. Coast Guard	1931
ex-*Thetis, PC-115*)		

D:	335 tons	**Dim:**	49.58 × 7.60 × 2.50
S:	14 kts	**Man:**	40 men
A:	1/76-mm AA — 1/40-mm AA — 1/20-mm AA
M:	Winton diesels; 2 props; 1,280 hp.

REMARKS: *203* and *205* in reserve.

GC 102 BETELGEUSE (ex-*PGM-77*) — Bldr: U.S.A. (1965) Transferred 1-66.

D:	130 tons (147 fl)	**Dim:**	30.80 (30.20 pp) × 6.40 × 1.85
S:	18.5 kts	**Man:**	20 men
A:	1/40-mm AA — 2/20-mm AA — 2/12.7-mm machine guns
M:	diesels; 2 props; 2,200 hp.

One of many gunboats of this class transferred to smaller navies by the United States in 1966-67.

♦ *4 small coastal surveillance boats*

GC 101 RIGEL	**GC 106 BELLATRIX**
GC 103 PROCION	**GC 107 CAPELLA**

Added in 1969. Bldr: Sewart Seacraft (Berwick, La.)

D:	60 tons	**Dim:**	26 × 5.50 × 1.50	**Man:**	9 men
S:	19/18 kts	**A:**	1 to 3 small caliber machine guns
M:	General Motors diesels; 2 props; 1,100 hp.	**Range:**	400/12

REMARKS: Bow rather sharply slanted.

AMPHIBIOUS CRAFT

♦ *1 U.S. LSM*

301 SIRIO (ex-*LSM-483*) — Bldr: U.S.A. (10-3-45). Transferred in 1960.

D:	734 tons (1,100 fl)	**Dim:**	62.80 × 10.40 × 2.10
S:	12 kts	**Man:**	30 men	**Fuel:**	164 tons diesel
M:	2 General Motors diesels, 1,800 hp.

♦ *2 U.S. LCUs*

302 (ex-*LA 2*) **SAMANA** — **303 ENRIQUILLO** (ex-*17 de Julio*, ex-*LA 3*). Bldr: Dominican Naval SY (1957-58).

D:	128 tons (310 fl)	**Dim:**	36.40 × 11 × 1.15
S:	8-7 kts	**A:**	1/12.7-mm machine gun	**Man:**	17 men
M:	3 G.M. diesels; 3 props; 450 hp	**Fuel:**	80 tons diesel.

VARIOUS

♦ *1 salvage vessel*

CG 105 CAPITAN ALSINA

D:	100 tons	**Dim:**	31.50 × 5.80 × 1.75 — Wooden hull
A:	2/20-mm AA	**S:**	17 knots
M:	2 G.M. diesels; 2 props; 1,000 hp

♦ *1 buoy tender bought in 1949*

1 CAPOTILLO (ex-*FB 101*) (ex-*Camillia*) — Bldr: U.S.A. (1911)

D:	327 tons	**S:**	10 kts

♦ *2 oilers*

BT 4 CAPITAN W. ARVELO (ex-U.S. *YO-215*) 1944-45.
BT 5 CAPITAN BEOTEGUI (ex-U.S. *YO-213*). Loaned by U.S. in 1964.

♦ *Small survey ships*

1 hydrographic small craft **LA 5 MAIMON** bought in 1960.

D:	21 tons	**Dim:**	16 × 2.80 × 1.20	**S:**	14 kts
Man:	4 men	**M:**	Two diesels; 500 hp.

♦ *2 small craft*

LA 7 PUERTO HERMOSO — LA 8 ATLANTIDA

♦ *Several tugs*

RM 21 MACORIS (ex-U.S. *Kiowa, ATF-73*) transferred in 1973.

D:	1,280 tons (1,700 fl)		**Dim:**	61.70 × 11.60 × 4.70
A:	1/76-mm AA — 4/40-mm AA	**S:**	13 kts
M:	4 diesel-electric groups; 1 prop; 1,500 hp

DOMINICAN REPUBLIC (*continued*)

VARIOUS (*continued*)

RM 18 CAOMABO (ex-U.S. *Sagamore*, *ATA*-208).
  D: 534 tons (835 fl)   **S:** 13 kts   **Dim:** 44 × 10.3 × 4
  A: 1/76-mm — 2/20-mm AA   **M:** diesel-electric; 1,500 hp.

RP 12 HERCULES, RP 13 GUACANAGARIX (500 hp) — **RP 20 ISABELA** (300 hp) — **PR 14 MAGUANA, RP 15 SANTANA, RP 16 BOHECHIO, RP 17 RIO HAINA, RP 18 CONSUELO, RP 19 CALDERAS** — small coastal tugs.

DUBAI

♦ *2 police small boats*
  Bldr: Fairey Marine (Gt.Br.)
  D: ...   **S:** 26 kts   **Dim:** 9.10 × 2.75 × 0.84
  M: 2 Perkins diesels T-6 354

ECUADOR

PERSONNEL: 4,500 men

MERCHANT MARINE (1-7-74): 38 ships — 128,413 grt
                    (tankers: 15 ships — 72,534 grt)

SUBMARINES

♦ *2 German 209 mod* (*IK 79*) *ordered in 1974.* — Bldr: Howaldtswerke (Hamburg)
        L   L
N ...   N ...

REMARKS: For characteristics see Argentine section, *Salta* class submarines. However, they are a little longer (59.50 m).

FRIGATES

♦ The purchase of two frigates is being studied.

♦ *2 ex-British Hunt class bought in 1955*

	Bldr	L
D 01 PRESIDENTE ALFARO (ex-*Quantock*)	Scotts SB & E (Greenock)	22-4-40
D 02 PRESIDENTE VELASCO IBARRA (ex-*Meynell*)	Swan Hunter & Wigham Richardson	9-4-40

  D: 904 tons (1,450 fl)   **Dim:** 82.90 × 8.60 × 2.40
  S: 22/21 kts   **Man:** 146 men   **Range:** 2,000/12 — 800/20
  A: 4/102-mm (II × 2) — 4/37-mm AA — 2/20-mm AA — depth charge projectors — depth charge racks

Pr. v. Ibarra (D 02)   1970

  M: Parsons GT; 2 props; 19,000 hp; 2 boilers
  Fuel: 280 tons

♦ *1 U.S. fast transport transferred in 1967*

E 12 Veintecinco de JULIO (ex-*Enright*, *APD-66*) — Bldr: U.S.A. (29-3-43)
  D: 1,400 tons (2,049 fl)   **Dim:** 93.25 × 11.25 × 4.70
  S: 23 kts   **Man:** 212 men   **A:** 1/127-mm — 3/40-mm AA
  M: turbo-electric propulsion; 2 props; 12,000 hp; 2 boilers
  Fuel: 350 tons   **Range:** 5,000/15 — 2,000/23

♦ *2 ex-U.S. PCE transferred in 1960*

E 21 ESMERALDAS (ex-*PCE 846*, 20-12-43) — **E 22 MANABI** (ex-*PCE 874*, 11-5-43)
  D: 640 tons (903 fl)   **Dim:** 56 × 10 × 2.90
  S: 15 kts   **A:** 1/76-mm AA — 6/40-mm AA
  Man: 100 men   **M:** 2 diesels; 1,800 hp.

PATROL BOATS

♦ *2 ex-U.S. PGM transferred in 1965*

LC 61 QUITO (ex-*PGM 75*), **LC 62 GUAYAQUIL** (ex-*PGM 76*).

Guayaquil   1970

PATROL BOATS (continued)

Bldr: Petersen (U.S.A.) — 1964–65.

D:	130 tons (147 fl)	**Dim:**	30.80 (30.20 pp) × 6.40 × 1.85
S:	20 kts	**A:**	1/40-mm — 2/20-mm
Man:	15 men	**M:**	4 diesels; 2 props; 2,200 hp.

GUIDED MISSILE PATROL BOATS

♦ *3 ordered at the Lürssen shipyards (F.R.G.)*

L   L   L

N . . .   N . . .   N . . .

D: . . .   **S:** 40 kts   **Dim:** 49.90 (42.50 pp) × 7 × 2.40 (prop.)
A: 4/MM 38 Exocet systems — 1 76/mm AA Oto Melara compact — 2/35-mm
AA (II × 1).   **Electron Equipt:** Thomson CSF fire control.
Range: 700/40, 1,850/16   **M:** 4 MTU diesels; 4 props; 14,000 hp.
Electric: 330 kw.   **Man:** 34 men

TORPEDO PATROL BOATS

♦ *3 Manta class*

L 91 MANTA (1–71), **L 92 TULCAN** (12–70), **L 93 TENA** (1971).

Manta (L 91)   1971

Bldr: Lürssen, Vegesack (F.R.G.).

D:	119 tons (134 fl)	**Dim:**	36.20 × 5.80 × . . .
S:	35 kts	**Range:**	1,500/15 — 700/30 **Man:** 19 men
A:	1/40-mm AA — 2/533-mm TT — 2/51-mm rocket launchers		
M:	3 Mercedes Benz diesels; 3 props; 9,000 hp.		
Fuel:	21 tons		

AMPHIBIOUS CRAFT

♦ *2 small landing boats*

T 31 JAMBELLI (ex-*LSM-539*), **T 32 TARQUI** (ex-*LSM-55*). Bldr: U.S.A. 1945.

D:	513 tons (1,090 fl)	**S:**	13 kts	**Dim:**	61.87 × 10.30 × 2.40
A:	2/40-mm AA	**Man:**	60 men	**M:**	2 diesels; 1,400 hp.

Used as transports.

VARIOUS

♦ *6 surveillance small boats.* Hull numbers: *LP 81* to *86.*

LSP 1 to **LSP 6** — Bldr: Herrman Havighorst (Bremen-Blumenthal) 1954–55.

D:	45 tons (64 fl)			**Dim:**	23.40 × 4.60 × 1.80
S:	22/20 kts	**Man:**	8/9 men	**Range:**	550/16
A:	machine gun and depth charges				
M:	B and K diesel; 1,000/1,200 hp.				

Flush deck hull; sharply angled bow; cone-shaped stack.

T 33 ATAHUALPA (ex-U.S. *YW-131*) fresh water barge, bought in 5–63.

D:	415 tons (1,235 fl)	**M:**	1 diesel	**S:**	11.5 kts

T 34 CALICUCHIMA (ex-U.S. *FS-525*) small transport loaned by the U.S.A. (1963).

D:	650 tons (950 fl)	**M:**	2 diesels; 500 hp.	**S:**	11.5 kts

Used in the Galapagos islands.

R 102 SANGAY (ex-*Loja*) (1952) small supply ship bought in 1964.

D:	295 tons (390 fl)	**Dim:**	31 × 7.90 × 4.25
S:	12 kts	**M:**	diesel

O 111 ORION (ex-*Mulberry, AN-27*) (1945) transferred in 1965.

D:	560 tons (805 fl)	**S:**	12 kts	**Man:**	20 men
M:	diesel-electric; 800 hp	**A:**	1/76-mm		

SMALL SURVEY SHIPS

R 103 COTOPAXI tug (ex-*R. T. Ellis*) bought in U.S.A. in 1947.

D:	150 tons	**Dim:**	25 × 6.62 × 2.90
S:	9 kts	**M:**	diesel; 1 prop; 650 hp.

R 101 CAYAMBE (ex-*Los Rios*, ex-*Cusabo, ATF-155*) Seagoing tug, bought in 1961.
Apache class.

D:	1,280 tons	**S:**	16 kts	**M:**	3,000 hp.

PERSONNEL: 14,500 men (approx.) with more than 1,500 officers

MERCHANT MARINE (1-7-74): 134 ships — 247,591 grt
(tankers: 18 ships — 68,596 grt)

NAVAL AVIATION: A branch of the Air Force which includes a few IL 28 torpedo attack planes, a few Badger class, and about 24 Mi 4 ASW helicopters, all of these aircraft from the U.S.S.R.

WARSHIPS IN SERVICE OR UNDER CONSTRUCTION AS OF 1 OCTOBER 1975

	L	D	Main armament
◆ *12 submarines*			
6 Soviet R class	1957	1,400	8/533-mm TT
6 Soviet W class	1955	1,050	6/533-mm TT
◆ *5 destroyers*			
4 EL NASSER	1950-54	2,600	4/130-mm — 2/85-mm AA — 10/533-mm TT
1 EL FATEH	1944	2,575	4/114-mm AA — 6/40-mm AA — ASW weapons
◆ *4 frigates*			
◆ *16 guided missile boats*			
7 Osa-class guided missile boats	post-1966	190	4 Styx systems
3 Komar-class guided missile boats	1961-63	80	2 Styx systems
6 Egyptian Komar class boats			2 Otomat (?)
◆ *28 small torpedo boats*			
◆ *15 patrol boats*			
◆ *13 minesweepers*			

SUBMARINES

◆ *6 Soviet R class (transferred since 5-66)*

D: 1,400 tons surfaced/1,800 submerged **Dim:** 75 × 7 × 5.40
S: 17/15 kts **Range:** 7,000/5 snorkel
A: 8/533-mm TT (6 fwd, 2 aft) — 18 torpedoes or 36 mines
M: Diesel propulsion and electric

◆ *6 Soviet W class (transferred from 6-57 to 8-62)*
D: 1,050 tons surfaced/1,350 submerged **Dim:** 75 × 6 × 5

EGYPT

United Arab Republic

S: 16-17/13 kts **Range:** 6,000/5
A: 533-mm TT (4 fwd, 2 aft) — 14 torpedoes or 28 mines
M: diesels and electric motors; 2 props

DESTROYERS

◆ *1 British Z class*

	Bldr	Laid down	L	In serv.
EL FATEH (ex-*Zenith*)	Fairfield	5-42	6-6-44	22-12-44

D: 1,470 tons (1,925 fl) **Dim:** 91.30 × 11.73 × 3.45
S: 14 kts **Range:** 4,500/12 **Man:** 180 men
A: 6/102-mm AA (II × 3) — 4/40-mm AA — 2/20-mm — 4 depth charge projectors
M: GT; 2 props; 2 boilers; 4,500 hp. **Fuel:** 370 tons

◆ *4 Soviet Skory class*

6 OCTOBER (ex-*El Zaffer*)	U.S.S.R.	Built between
EL NASSER	U.S.S.R.	1950 and 1954
DAMIET	U.S.S.R.	Transferred in the spring of
SUEZ	U.S.S.R.	1956 (2) and in 1964 (2)

D: 2,600 tons (3,200 fl) **Dim:** 121.50 × 12.50 × 4.60
S: 35 kts **Man:** 250 men

DESTROYERS (*continued*)

M: GT; 2 props; 62,000 hp   **Range:** 4,700/18
A: 4/130-mm (II × 2) — 2/85-mm AA — 7/37-mm AA (I × 7) — 10/533-mm TT (V × 2) — 2 depth charge projectors — 2 depth charge racks — 80 mines eventually.

REMARKS: The ex-*El Zaffer* and the *Damiet* were replaced in 1968 by two ships of the same class and with the same names, but with AA guns and new fire control radar.

FRIGATES

♦ *1 British Hunt class*

	Bldr	L
PORT SAID (ex-*Mohamed Ali El Kebit*, ex-*Cottesmore*)	Yarrow & Co.	5-9-40

D: 904 tons (1,450 fl)   **Dim:** 82.90 × 8.60 × 2.40
S: 25 kts   **Man:** 146 men   **Range:** 2,000/12 — 800/25
A: 4/102-mm (II × 2) — 2/40-mm AA — 2/20-mm AA
M: Parsons GT; 2 props; 19,000 hp; 2 boilers   **Fuel:** 280 tons

REMARKS: Transferred in 11-49.

♦ *1 British River class*

	Bldr	Laid down	L	In serv.
RACHID (ex-*HMS Spey*)	Smith's Dock Co., Ltd.	7-41	18-12-41	3-42

D: 1,460 tons (2,175 fl)   **Dim:** 91.85 × 11.17 × 4.34 (fl)
S: 19 kts   **Range:** 7,700/12 — 5,000/16
A: 1/102-mm — 2/40-mm AA — 7/20-mm AA — 4 depth charge projectors
M: Triple expansion; 2 props; 5,500 hp; 2 boilers   **Fuel:** 440 tons

♦ *1 British Black Swan class bought in 12-49*

	Bldr	Laid down	L	In serv.
EL TARIK (ex-*El Malek Farouk*, ex-*HMS Whimbrel*)	Yarrow & Co.	10-41	25-8-42	1-43

D: 1,730 tons (2,575 fl)   **Dim:** 110.55 × 10.88 × 4.80
S: 31 kts   **Man:** 250 men   **Range:** 2,800/20 — 1,000/30
A: 4/114-mm AA (I × 4) — 6/40-mm AA — 4 depth charge projectors
M: Parsons GT; 2 props; 40,000 hp.   **Boilers:** 2 Admiralty
Fuel: 580 tons

REMARKS: Bought in England in 1955; delivered the summer of 1956. A refit in England (1963-64) was primarily the installation of new electronic equipment.

♦ *1 ex-British, ex-Yugoslav escort ship*

	Bldr	L
EL SUDAN (ex-*Partizanka*, ex-*Nada*, ex-*Mallow*)	Harland and Wolff	22-5-40

D: 1,060 tons (1,340 fl)   **Dim:** 62.50 × 10.06 × 4.50
S: 15 kts   **Man:** 85 men
A: 1/102-mm — 2/20-mm AA   **Range:** 7,000/10   **Fuel:** 230 tons
M: Triple expansion; 1 prop; 2,800 hp   **Boilers:** 2 drum

PATROL BOATS

♦ *12 Soviet SO 1 class transferred since 1962-63*

D: 200 tons (fl)   **S:** 27 kts   **Dim:** 34 × 4 × 1.80
A: 4/25-mm AA (II × 2) — 4/MBU 1800 rocket-launchers — Some are armed with 2 TT
M: 3 diesels; 3 props; 3,500 hp   **Man:** 30 men

REMARKS: Some are equipped with 2 TT.

♦ **NISR 1, 2, 3,** (16-5-63) — Bldr: Castro, Port Said
    D: 110 tons   **A:** 1/20-mm. Used for coastal patrol.

MINESWEEPERS

♦ *6 ex-Soviet T 43 class*

BAHAIRA	**CHARKIEH**	**GHARBIA**
ASSIUT	**DAQHALA**	**SINAI**

Bldr: U.S.S.R. (1953). Transferred since 1956, 1 in 1970.
D: 410 tons (530 fl)   **Dim:** 61 × 8.40 × 2.70
S: 17 kts   **M:** diesels   **A:** 4/37-mm AA (II × 2)

♦ *ex-British Bangor class minesweeper escort vessel*

NASR (ex-*HMS Bude*) — 4-9-40
    D: 672 tons (900 fl)   **Dim:** 55 × 8.55 × 2.90
    A: 1/102-mm — 1/76-mm — 2/40-mm AA   **Man:** 60 men
    M: Triple expansion; 2 props; 2,400 hp.   **Boilers:** 2 to 3 drums

♦ *4 ex-Soviet Yurka class delivered in 1969*

ASSUAN, GUIZEN, QENA, SUHAG
    D: 550 tons (fl)   **Dim:** 55 × 9.70 × 2
    S: 18 kts   **A:** 4/30-mm AA (II × 2)
    M: Diesels; 2 props; 4,000 hp.   **Electron Equipt:** 1/Don, 1/Drum Tilt

♦ *2 Soviet T 301 class delivered in 1962-63*

EL FAYOUD, EL MANUFIEH
    D: 150 tons (fl)   **S:** 10 kts   **Dim:** 31 × 4.90 × 1.50
    A: 2/37-mm AA   **M:** Diesels; 480 hp

GUIDED MISSILE AND TORPEDO BOATS

Equipped with multitube rocket-launchers for land targets: 2 OSA 1, 3 Shershen, 2 P 6, 4 P 4, and 5 Vydra.

♦ *7 ex-Soviet Osa 1 guided missile boats transferred since 1966*

D: 190 tons   **S:** 32 kts (cruising)   **Dim:** 37 × 9 × 1.80
A: 4/30-mm AA (II × 2) — 4 Styx systems (I × 4)
Electron Equipt: 1/Square Tie, 1/Drum Tilt
M: 3 diesels; 3 props; 9,000 hp.

♦ *3 ex-Soviet Komar-class guided missile boats, transferred since 1966*

D: 80/110 tons (fl)   **S:** 40 kts   **Dim:** 26.80 × 6.40 × 1.80
A: 2/25-mm AA — 2 Styx system (I × 2)
M: diesels; 4 props; 4,800 hp.

♦ *6 built in Egypt, based on the Komar class*
REMARKS: Could be fitted with 2 Otomat surface-to-surface missiles.

♦ *Soviet Shershen class torpedo boats*

D: 190 tons   **S:** 33/32 kts (cruising)   **Dim:** 34 × 8 × 1.50
A: 4/30-mm AA (II × 2) — 4/533-mm TT (I × 4)
Electron Equipt: 1/Square Tie, 1/Drum Tilt.
M: 3 diesels; 9,000 hp; 3 props

REMARKS: A few are armed with multiple rocket launchers for shore fire support.

♦ *20 ex-Soviet P 6 class torpedo boats, transferred since 1960*

D: 73 tons (fl)   **S:** 33/32 kts (cruising)   **Dim:** 26.80 × 6.40 × 1.80
A: 4/25-mm AA (II × 2) — 2/533-mm TT   **M:** 2 props; 4,800 hp.

REMARKS: A few are armed with multiple rocket-launchers for shore fire support.

P 4 with octuple rocket-launcher mounted on the bow.

♦ *2 ex-Soviet P 4 class torpedo boats*

D: 30 tons   **S:** 32 kts   **Dim:** 16.80 × 3.75 × 1.05
A: 2/14.5-mm AA (II × 1) — 2/450-mm TT (I × 2)
M: diesels; 2 props; 2,400 hp.

♦ *2 Yugoslavian 108 class bought in 1956*

D: 56 tons (fl)   **Dim:** 23.80 × 6.30
S: 35 kts   **A:** 1/40-mm — 4 torpedoes
Man: 17 men   **M:** 3 Packard motors; 3 props; 4,500 hp.

REMARKS: Used as targets.

AMPHIBIOUS SHIPS

♦ *3 Soviet Polnocnyi class transferred in 1974*
See Soviet section for characteristics.

♦ *1 Soviet MP 4 class built in Egypt in 1970*

D: 780 tons (fl)   **S:** 12 kts   **Dim:** 56 × 9 × 2.70
M: diesel; 1 prop; 1,100 hp

♦ *5 ex-Soviet SMB 1 class LCUs*

D: 420 tons (fl)   **S:** 15 kts

♦ *9 ex-Soviet Vydra-class LCUs*

D: 500 tons (fl)   **S:** 11 kts
A: 8/15-barrel rocket-launchers for firing at land targets — 4/14.5-mm AA (II × 2)

♦ *10 to 12 LCM from different sources*

VARIOUS

♦ *4 Soviet Okhtensky class tugs transferred in 1966*
AL ISKANDARAN, EL AGAMI, EL MEY, N . . .

♦ *2 Soviet Nyriat-class salvage ships transferred in 1964*

♦ *2 Soviet Poluchat-class torpedo recovery boats*

♦ *2 PO 2-class net layers*

♦ *1 Soviet Sekstan class degaussing ship*

♦ *2 Fairmile-class small boats*

♦ *9 Bertram assault boats (U.S.A.)*

EQUATORIAL GUINEA

PERSONNEL: 100 men

Soviet equipment delivered in 1974.

♦ *1 P 6 class torpedo boat*

♦ *1 Poluchat class patrol boat*

♦ *2 surveillance small boats*

PC 14   1974 Photo

D:	80 tons (101 fl)	**S:**	20 kts	**Dim:**	28.80 × 5.80 × 1.55
A:	3/20-mm AA	**Man:**	15 men	**Range:**	1,500/10
M:	4 diesels; 2 props; 2,200 hp.				

REMARKS: ex-U.S. CG; transferred by the U.S.A. in 1958 (3), 1961 (1) and 1962 (1).

♦ *4 patrol boats*

GB 21, 22, 23, 24 (ex-*John, Caroline, Patrick, Jacqueline*)
  Bldr: Seward Seacraft (Berwick, La.) 1966-67.

| **D:** | 15 tons | **S:** | 20 kts | **Length:** | 13 m. |
| **A:** | 2/12-mm — 7-mm or 20-mm. | | | **Man:** | 7 men |

ETHIOPIA

PERSONNEL: 1,200 men including 230 officers.

MERCHANT MARINE (1-7-74): 23 ships — 29,034 grt
(tankers: 1 ship — 2,051 grt.)

PATROL BOATS

♦ *1 ex-Dutch minesweeper bought in 1970.*

MS 41 (ex-*M 829 Elst*) — Bldr: Netherlands (21-3-56).

D:	373 tons (417 fl)	**S:**	14 kts	**Dim:**	46.62 × 8.78 × 2.30
A:	2/40-mm AA			**Man:**	40 men
M:	2 Werkspoor diesels; 2 props; 2,500 hp.				

Profile: see *Dokkum*, Netherlands section.

♦ *5 ex-U.S.A.*

PC 11 (ex-CG-*WVP 95309*)	**PC 14** (ex-U.S. *PGM-54*)
PC 12 (ex-CG-*WPV 95310*)	**PC 15** (ex-U.S. *PGM-58*)
PC 13 (ex-U.S. *PGM-53*)	Bldr: Petersen (U.S.A.) — 1955-62.

GB 23   1974 Photo

ETHIOPIA (*continued*)

TRAINING SHIP

	Bldr	L
A 01 ETHIOPIA (ex-*Orca*, AVP-19)	Lake Washington SY	4-10-42

D: 1,766 tons (2,800 fl)   **Dim:** 94.70 (91.50 pp) × 12.52 × 3.65
S: 18 kts   **Man:** 215 men
A: 1/127-mm, 38-caliber — 5/40-mm AA
M: diesel; 2 props; 6,000 hp.
Transferred in 1-62. Similar to the *Pietro Cavezzale* (Italy).

VARIOUS

2 ex-U.S. *LCVP* and U.S. *LCM* bought, 2 in 1962, 2 in 1971.

FINLAND

The naval force, limited to 10,000 tons and 4,500 men by the Treaty of Paris, is a separate establishment under the orders of the chief of the armed forces. Submarines and torpedo boats are excluded from the fleet and there is no naval aviation.

PERSONNEL (1975): about 2,000 including 150 officers.

MERCHANT MARINE (1-7-74): 362 ships — 1,507,582 grt
(tankers: 52 ships — 731,782 grt)

NAVAL PROGRAM

Present plans are to bring the Finnish navy to the following strength by 1988, having passed 8,000 tons in 1983 and reaching 8,600 at the later date, the warships being divided as follows:

♦ 6 frigates (4 now)

♦ 24 fast small boats (19 now)

♦ 2 minelayers (1 now)

♦ 14 minesweepers

♦ 8 patrol boats (5 now) with minesweeping capability.

This goal will require considerable effort because by 1980 nearly all of the ships found in today's Finnish forces will be out of commission.

WARSHIPS IN SERVICE OR UNDER CONSTRUCTION AS OF 1 OCTOBER 1975

	D	L	Main armament
♦ *4 frigates*			
2 RIGA class (Soviet)	1,450	1955	3/100-mm — 4/37-mm AA — 3/533-mm TT —
2 TURUNMAA class (Finnish)	650	1967	1/120-mm AA — 3/40-mm AA

♦ *3 minelayers*

♦ *4 guided missile patrol boats Osa 1 class*

♦ *25 gunboats including 13 Nuoli and 2 Vasama*

WEAPONS AND SYSTEMS

Made up especially of Bofors 40-mm AA and a few Soviet Styx missile systems. The *Turunmaa*-class frigates have a single barrel automatic Bofors 120-mm gun with the following characteristics:

— weight without munitions: 28.5 tons
— length: 46 calibers
— muzzle velocity: 800 m/sec
— training speed: 40°/sec
— elevation speed: 30°/sec
— arc of elevation: −10° to +80°
— maximum rate of fire: 80 rounds/min
— projectile weight: 35 kg
— maximum effective range, surface fire: 12,000 m

FRIGATES

♦ *2 Soviet Riga class, transferred in the spring of 1964*

HAMEENMAA, USIMAA — Bldr: U.S.S.R. (post-1955)

Hameenmaa

FRIGATES (*continued*)

D: 1,450 (fl) **S:** 28/27 kts **Dim:** 88 × 10 × 3.90
A: 3/100-mm AA — 4/37-mm AA — 3/533-mm TT (III × 1) — 1 hedgehog, 4 depth charge projectors, 2 depth charge racks **Man:** 175 men
Electron Equipt: Radars: 1/Neptune, 1/Slim Net, 1/Sun Visor B.
M: GT; 2 props; 2 boilers; 20,000 hp.

♦ *2 Finnish Turunmaa class*

	Bldr	Laid down	L	In serv.
TURUNMAA	Wärtsilä, Helsinki	3-67	11-7-67	8-68
KARJALA	Wärtsilä, Helsinki	3-67	16-8-67	10-68

Karjala

D: 650 tons (770 fl) **S:** 35 kts **Dim:** 74.10 × 7.80 × 2.60 (light)
A: 1/120-mm Bofors automatic, 3/40-mm AA, depth charges
M: CODOG propulsion: 1 Bristol-Siddeley Olympus gas turbine; 3 Mercedes-Benz diesels; 22,000 hp; Vosper stabilizers; 3 props
Man: 70 men
REMARKS: Flush deck hull; closed bridge, sharp profile. Cruises on the diesel engines (3 × 1,100 hp) at 17 knots. Ka-Me-Wa variable pitch propellers.

MISSILE AND GUNBOATS

♦ *4 Soviet guided missile Osa class boats, transferred in 1975* (For characteristics, see U.S.S.R. section.) **Tuima, Tuisku, Tuula, Tyrsky**

♦ **ISKU** *guided missile boat* — Bldr: Finland — 1970

D: 115 tons **S:** 25 kts **Dim:** 26.35 × 8.70 × 2
A: 2/30-mm AA — 4 Styx missiles (U.S.S.R.)
M: 4 diesels; 4 props; 4,800 hp.

♦ *2 British Dark Hunter class*

VASAMA I, VASAMA II — Bldr: Saunders Roe Anglesey Ltd — 1955-57

D: 70 tons (fl) **Dim:** 21.75 (20.42 pp) × 5.85 × 1.85
S: 42 kts **Man:** 13 men **A:** 2/40-mm AA — mines
M: Napier-Deltic diesels; 2 props; 5,000 hp.

♦ *Suomen Turku class* (**Nuoli 1 to 13**)

N 1 to N 11 (1961-63)

D: 64 tons (fl) **Dim:** 22 × 6.50 × 1.50
S: 40 kts **A:** 1/40-mm — 1/20-mm
M: 3 diesels; 2,700 hp. **Electron Equipt:** Band X radars

♦ **KAAKKURI** **KOSKELO** **KUOVI** **TAVI**
   KIISLA **KUIKKA** **KURKI** **TELKKÄ**

Bldr: Finland — 1956-59

D: 75 tons (97 fl) **S:** 16 kts **Dim:** 29.42 × 5.02 × 1.05
A: 2/20-mm AA **Man:** 8 men
M: Mercedes-Benz diesels; 2 props; 1,000 hp.

REMARKS: Steel hull, ice-strengthened.

VIIMA — Bldr: Finland — 1964

D: 130 tons **S:** 25 kts **Dim:** 35.81 × 6.60 × 2.30
A: 1/20-mm **M:** diesels; 3 props; 4,050 hp.

MINESWEEPERS

R 1 RIHTNIEMI	**R 3 RIILATI**	**R 5 ROYTTA**
R 2 RYMÄTTYLÄ	**R 4 RUISSALO** (6-59)	Bldr: Rauma SY — 1956-59.

Riilathi   1972

D: 110 tons (130 fl) **Dim:** 33.12 × 5.60 × 1.55
S: 15 kts **Man:** 20 men **A:** 1/40-mm — 1/20-mm AA Madsen
M: Mercedes-Benz diesels; 2,500 hp; 2 variable pitch props

♦ *6 Kuha class inshore minesweepers*

	In serv.		In serv.
KUHA	28-6-74	N...	
N...		N...	
N...		N...	

D: 90 tons (fl) **S:** ... **Dim:** 26.60 × 6.90 × ... **Man:** 15 men
M: 2 diesels 300-hp; 1 trainable prop for precision maneuvering

MINESWEEPERS (*continued*)

Kuha type inshore minesweeper   1975

MINELAYERS

	Bldr	L
KEIHÄSSALMI	Valmet Oy, Helsinki	16-3-57

D: 290 tons (360 fl)   **S:** 15 kts   **Dim:** 51.20 × 7.00 × 1.90
A: 2/40-mm AA — 2/20-mm AA — 100 mines   **Man:** 60 men
M: MAN diesels; 2 props; 2,000 hp.

	Bldr	Laid down	L	In serv.
RUOTSINSALMI	Hietalahden, Helsinki	1937	5-40	2-41

D: 270 tons (310 fl)   **Dim:** 45.72 × 7.00 × 1.60
S: 15 kts   **M:** diesels; 2 props; 1,200 hp.
A: 2/40-mm AA — 2/20-mm AA — 100 mines

PATROL BOATS (manned by the maritime police)

VALPAS — Bldr: Finland — 1972.
SILMÄ — Bldr: Laivateollisnus, Turku — 1963.
   D: 490 tons   **S:** 13 kts   **Dim:** 49.10 × 7.93 × 3.70
   A: 1/20-mm   **M:** diesel; 1 prop; 1,300 hp.

UISKO — Bldr: Valmet Oy, Helsinki — 1959.

Uisko

   D: 350 tons   **S:** 14 kts   **Dim:** 43.30 × 6.60 × 3.90
   A: 1/20-mm AA   **M:** diesel; 1 prop; 1,800 hp.

TURSAS — Bldr: Crichton-Vulcan, Turku — 1938-41
   D: 360 tons   **S:** 12 kts   **Dim:** 40 × 7 × 4.40
   A: 1/20-mm AA   **M:** diesel; 1 prop

VMV 11, 13, 15, 16 — Bldr: Finland — 1935
   D: 35 tons   **S:** 18 kts   **Dim:** 26 × 4.30 × 1.40
   A: 1/20-mm AA   **Man:** 9 men
   M: 2 semi-diesels; 2 props; 1,200 hp.

   The maritime police also man 7 small craft, 4 tons, 8.40m long, with two 55-hp motors.

TRAINING SHIP

		Bldr	L	Accepted
MATTI KURKI (ex-*HMS Porlock Bay*)		Chas. Hill & Sons	14-6-45	3-62

TRAINING SHIP (*continued*)

D: 1,600 tons (2,530 fl) **Dim:** 93.57 × 11.83 × 5.40
S: 19 kts **Man:** 180 men
A: 4/102-mm (II × 2) — 6/40-mm AA (II × 2, I × 2) — 1 squid.
M: Triple expansion; 2 props; 6,000 hp; 2 boilers **Fuel:** 690 tons

Former British *Bay*-class frigate, transferred in 1962.

ICEBREAKERS

		D	Dim	HP	S
OTSO	1936	900	44 × 11.40 × 5	1,800 (altern.)	13
SISU	24-9-38	2,010	65 × 14.40 × 5.30	4,800/6,000 (D)	16
VOIMA	27-11-52	4.415	83.51 × 19.40 × 6.20	14,000	16.5
KARHU	20-10-57	3,370	74.15 × 17.40 × 6.10	7,500	16
MURTAJA	30-9-58	3,370	74.15 × 17.40 × 6.10	7,500	16
SAMPO	9-2-60	3,370	74.15 × 17.40 × 6.10	7,500	16
TARMO	1-63	4,890	84.50 × 21.20 × 6.20	12,000	16
VARMA	27-3-68	4,890	84.50 × 21.20 × 6.20	12,000	16
APU	1970	4,890	84.50 × 21.20 × 6.20	12,000	17
URHU	1975	7,800	85.70 × 21.70 × 6.40	12,000	17
LOUHI	1939	2,075		4,000	
(ex-Sisu)					

Tarmo

The last 9 have diesel-electric propulsion. The Louhi, which had been as Sisu under the direction of the Department of Civil Navigation, was transferred to the navy in 1975. Louhi equipped as a tender for the guided missile Osa class boats.

VARIOUS

		D	Dim	S	A
1 — PANSIO, PORKKALA	1940–47	162	28 × 6.50 × 2.70	10	1/40-mm, 1/20-mm
PUKKIO	1939	162	27 × 6.70 × 2.50	10	1/40-mm, 1/20-mm
2 — K 1 to K 6	1956–59	60	23 × 7.90 × 1.80	9 ⎫ transports
3 — SEILI	1942	190	43.6 × 6.10 × 1.30	10 ⎭
4 — KORSHOLM	1968	570	39 × 8.50 × 3.20	10	
5 — PUTSAARI	1965	460	45 × 8.70 × 2.90	10	cable layer

(1) Tug type; can carry 20 mines. (2) LCU type. (3) Ex-German landing craft, MFP type. (4) Command ship.

FRANCE

"For the first time in its history, the Navy is among the most important components in the military might of France and its contribution will become more significant every day."

General Charles DE GAULLE (1965)

"This strategic nuclear strength . . . the completion of this force and of certain of its components, especially the submarine, is without question a great scientific and technical exploit."

Valéry GISCARD D'ESTAING (1974)

The two important elements of the French Navy:

The aircraft carrier, keystone of general purpose forces.

The SSBN, nucleus of the strategic deterrent forces.

PERSONNEL (1975): 68,315 on active duty including 4,371 officers, 26,692 warrant officers and chief petty officers, and 37,352 petty officers and other enlisted personnel. These budgetary figures include female (458) regulars, 26 female reservists and among the drafted personnel 26 ensigns, 814 midshipmen and petty officers and 15,603 petty officers and other enlisted personnel.

MERCHANT MARINE (1-7-74): 1,341 ships — 8,834,569 grt
(tankers: 125 ships — 5,508,682 grt)

WARSHIPS IN SERVICE, UNDER CONSTRUCTION OR PLANNED AS OF 1 OCTOBER 1975

		L	D	A
♦ *aircraft carriers*				
2	CLEMENCEAU (fixed-wing)	1958–59	22,000	8/100-mm AA, 40 aircraft
1	PH 75	constr.	18,000	
1	JEANNE D'ARC (helo)	1961	10,000	4/100-mm AA, 6 MM 38 Exocet 8 heavy helicopters
♦ *31 submarines*				
1	SSN 72	1976	2,500	4 TT
4	AGOSTA	1974–76	1,200	4 TT
6	REDOUTABLE (nucl)	1967–77	7,500	16 missiles, 4 TT
1	GYMNOTE	1964	3,800	4 missiles
9	DAPHNÉ	1959–69	870	6 TT
4	ARÉTHUSE	1957–68	543	4 TT
6	NARVAL	1954–56	1,320	8 TT
♦ *1 anti-aircraft cruiser*				
1	COLBERT	1956	8,500	1 Masurca, 2/100-mm AA, 12/57-mm AA
♦ *5 destroyers*				
3	TOURVILLE (ASW)	1972–74	4,580	1 Malafon, 6/MM 38, 3/100-mm AA, 2 TT, 2 H WG 13 Lynx
2	SUFFREN (AA)	1965–66	5,090	1 Masurca, 2/100-mm AA, 1 Malafon
♦ *4 corvettes (ASW)*				
3	GEORGES LEYGUES	constr.	3,800	2/100-mm, 4 MM 38, 2 H WG 13 Lynx
1	ACONIT	1970	3,000	2/100-mm AA, 1 Malafon, ASW weapons
♦ *15 destroyers*				
5	D'ESTRÉES (ASW)	1953–54	2,750	2/100-mm AA, 1 Malafon, ASW weapons
1	LA GALLISSONNIÈRE	1960	2,750	2/100-mm AA, 1 Malafon, 1 H
1	DUPERRÉ	1956	2,750	1/100-mm AA, 4 MM 38, 1 H WG 13 Lynx
4	LA BOURDONNAIS	1955	2,750	6/127-mm AA, 6/57-mm AA, 6 TT, 1 RL
4	KERSAINT (AA)	1953–54	2,750	1 Tartar, 6/57-mm AA, 1 RL, 6 TT
♦ *15 fast frigates*				
15	LE CORSE	1952–56	1,290	4 or 6/57-mm AA, 1 RL, 12 T
♦ *9 dual purpose frigates*				
1	BALNY	1962	1,650	2/100-mm AA, ASW mortar
8	CDT. RIVIÈRE	1958–63	1,750	4 MM 38, 2/100-mm AA, 1 ASW mortar
♦ *50 escorts, patrol craft or station vessels*				
14	D'ÉSTIENNE D'ORVES	1973–78	1,260	1/100-mm AA, 1 RL, ASW weapons
11	FOUGUEUX	1954–57	325	2/40-mm AA ASW weapons
1	LA COMBATTANTE	1963	182	1/30-mm AA, 1/SS 11 SSM
9	ARCTURUS	1954–57	400	1/40-mm AA, 1/20-mm AA
6	LA MALOUINE	1952–54	370	1/40-mm AA
5	JASMIN	1954–55	140	1/20-mm AA
4	TRIDENT	constr.	115	1/40-mm, 6/SS 12 SSM
♦ *53 minesweepers (A: ocean-going, B: coastal)*				
5	CIRCÉ (minehunters)	1970–72	495	1/20-mm AA, 2 remotely controlled sleds.
12	ALENÇON (A)	1953–54	700	1/40-mm AA
1	MERCURE (B)	1957	365	1/20-mm AA
9	ANTARÈS (B)	1952–55	400	1/40-mm AA
19	ACACIA (B)	1953–54	300	2/20-mm AA

WEAPONS AND SYSTEMS OF THE FRENCH NAVY

(A) MISSILES

♦ *Strategic ballistic missiles*

(a) M 1:

Two-stage engine, not stabilized aerodynamically, solid propulsion
— total height: 10.40 m
— first stage height: 5.20 m
— second stage height: 2.60 m
— diameter: 1.50 m
— total weight: 18,000 kg
— weight first stage: 12,000 kg
— weight second stage: 5,700 kg
— thrust 1st stage: 45 tons
— thrust 2nd stage: 18 tons
— length of thrust: 1st stage, 60 sec
           2nd stage, 60 sec
— warhead: 400 kilotons
— range: about 2,500 km
Le Terrible and *Le Redoutable* carry the M 1

(b) M 2:

Similar characteristics to those of the M 1 but 19 tons (total weight) and a longer range. Warhead: 500 kilotons. Introduced into service in *Le Foudroyant.*

(c) M 20:

This missile is designed to replace the M 1 and M 2 on board *Le Terrible, Le Foudroyant,* and *Le Redoutable.* It will carry a thermonuclear warhead and new equipment which are more refined than those in the M 1 and M 2 missiles. In the upper part of the missile will be found the chief elements controlling re-entry and the terminal flight. These may include a thermonuclear warhead in the megaton range, new systems to protect against anti-missile efforts, and a greater penetration capability. Its range, about 3,000 km, will be almost the same as the M 2. *L'Indomptable* will carry the M 2.

(d) M 4:

The M 2 will be replaced beginning in 1980 by a new missile of greater range, the M 4, which will carry multiple warheads of about 150 kilotons. It is possible that this missile will be on board the 6th SSBN, *L'Inflexible.* The launching tubes will have to be enlarged before she enters service.

WEAPONS AND SYSTEMS OF THE FRENCH NAVY *(continued)*

♦ *Missiles surface-to-air*

Masurca

Medium range system (30 nautical miles, can intercept between 100–75,000 ft) launched by means of a solid propellant booster which in a few seconds brings it to a speed close to Mach 3; a slower burning solid propellant maintains this speed for the duration of the flight.
Characteristics:

	Missile only	*Booster*
— Length	5.380 m	3.320 m
— Diameter	0.406 m	0.570 m
— Span of fins		1.500 m
— Weight	950 kg	1,148 kg
— Warhead	100 kg	—

— Missile and booster: length 8.600 m — weight 2,098 kg
The MOD 2 beam-riding missile is no longer used and the MOD 3, a homing missile is the only system still in service, (semi-active homing).

The missile follows a trajectory determined by proportional navigation, keeping its antenna pointed at the target which is illuminated by the launching ship's radar transmitter.
The Masurca system is made up of:
* A target designator and weapon assignment console, including a computer. This system employs the shipboard search radar and the Senit automatic tactical data system.
* two guidance systems, each with:
— a DRBR 51 tracking radar
— a director carrying the rear reference beam and illumination beam for the control system
— an illumination beam
— a twin launcher
— storage and maintenance facilities including 2 horizontal ready service drums containing 18 missiles in addition to missiles in the magazines
— IFF and control equipment.
The system is installed in the *Suffren*-class guided missile destroyers and in the *Colbert.*

Tartar

An American system of short range (15 nautical miles), with interception altitudes between 100 and 75,000 ft in the ITR and SM 1A version, and of medium range (25 nautical miles) with air interception from 100 to 75,000 feet in the SM 1 version. These 3 types can be used in surface warfare (range 25,000 m max.).
In its complete form the system has:
— the missile (1 stage solid propulsion)
   length: 4.600 m
   diameter: .410 m
   weight: 590 kg
   semi-active homing guidance proximity fuze
— 1 single MK 13 GMLS
— 1 vertical stowage-loading system containing 40 missiles
— various computers
— height-finding SPS 39 A or B radar
— 2 tracking radars SPG 51

The system is mounted on T 47 class destroyers modified for Tartar.
A more sophisticated system, the SM 2 version with a longer range, will be installed in the planned *C 70* class AA corvettes. Check U.S. section for characteristics.

Crotale

Air Force missile adapted for naval use
— Length: 2.930 m
— Diameter: 0.156 m
— Span: cruciform (0.540 m with wings extended), anti-pitching ailerons mounted forward.
— Weight: 85.1 kg
— Range: 8,000 m
— Interception ranges: 150 to 12,000 feet
— Guidance system: Beam riding, then detonation by infrared fuze incorporated in the missile.
— Octuple missile launcher: The system to be installed on the *F 67,* the *Jeanne d'Arc* and the *C 70* class corvettes will be used with the DRBV 51 C radar and will have a special extractor and a Thomson tracking radar in the KU band. Additional missiles will be carried in the magazine.

♦ *Surface-to-surface missiles*

MM 38 Exocet (built by SNIAS)

Homing missile (solid fuel propellant): **Weight:** about 700 kg (explosive charge more than 150 kg); **S:** Mach 1; **Range** more than 37 km.
Usual missile silhouette, cylindrical body with a pointed nose, cruciform wings with arrow shape.
Length: 5.20 m.; **diameter:** .35 m.; **wing span:** 1 m.
The fire control solution requires a fix on the target provided by the surface radar

MM 38 ramps on board the *Tourville*   1975 Photo

WEAPONS AND SYSTEMS OF THE FRENCH NAVY (*continued*)

of the firing ship and uses the necessary equipment for launching the missile and determining the correct range and height bearing of the target.

The missile is launched at a slight elevation (about 15°). After the boost phase, it reaches its flight altitude and is stabilized between 3 and 15 meters. Stabilization is maintained by a radio-electric sensor.

During the first part of the flight, the missile is automatically guided by an inertial device which has received the azimuth of the target. When within certain distance from the target, an automatic electromagnetic director begins to seek the target, picks it up and directs the missile. Great effort has been made to protect the missile from enemy countermeasures during this phase.

Detonation takes place upon impact or by proximity fuze, according to interception conditions, size of the target ship and the condition of the sea.

The MM 38 is mounted (1-7-76) on board the *Jeanne d'Arc*, the 3 *Tourville* type ships, the *Duperré*, the *d'Estienne d'Orves*, the frigates *Commandant Bory* and *Doudart de Lagrée*. It will also be mounted on the type *A 69* and *A 70* frigates. It will probably be mounted as well on board the *Duquesne*, the *Suffren* and 6 other frigates, as well as the cruiser *Colbert* in which the mounts for four ramps have been fitted for trials only.

MM 40 Exocet (Bldr: SNIAS)

An offshoot of the MM 38 and the AM 39, the MM 40 will be an over-the-horizon, surface-to-surface missile with the range adapted to the radar performance but able to use fire control data relayed by a third means. Maximum range will be at least 65 km. The missile introduces a new fiberglass cylindrical launcher to replace the conventional metal launcher which reduces the weight and fittings of the launcher and therefore yields an increase in fire power because of the greater number of missiles which can be carried on board.

The MM 40 is still being developed.

SS 11

Wire guided system with line-of-sight alignment on the target.

Length:	1.215 m
Diameter:	0.164 m
Wingspan:	0.500
Weight:	30.4 kg
Range:	3,000 m

SS 12 M

Similar system to SS 11

Length:	1.870 m
Diameter:	0.210 m
Wingspan:	0.650
Weight:	75 kg (upon firing)
Warhead:	30 kg (about)
Range:	5,500 m

Mounted on the fast missile patrol boat *La Combattante*.

◆ *Air-to-surface missiles*

AM 39 (Bldr: SNIAS)

Anti-ship missile fired by airplane or helicopter. This is the air-sea version of the MM 38; after detachment by gravity, and with a retro-firing booster motor, the missile acquires a trajectory similar to that of the MM 38. Thereupon it has the same flight characteristics as the MM 38.

Length:	4.633 m
Diameter:	0.348 m
Wingspan:	1.004 m
Weight:	65 kg (before launching)
Range:	50 to 70 km according to altitude and speed at launching.
Radar:	Active homing seeker head (EMD)*

This is known as a "fire and forget" missile which permits the aircraft to renew its attack after having fired, or to seek a new target. This system may be used with the Atlantic and the Super Étendard aircraft. It is equally appropriate for such heavy or medium weight helicopters as the Super Frelon.

AS 11

Bldr:	SNIAS
Length:	1.210 m
Diameter:	0.164 m
Wingspan:	0.50 m
Weight:	29.900 kg

Wire-guided system with optical alignment on the target.
Used for training for the CM 175 and the HSS 1.

AS 12

Bldr:	SNIAS
Length:	1.870 m
Diameter:	0.210 m
Wingspan:	0.650 m
Weight:	75 kg
Range:	Maximum 7,500 to 8,000 m; minimum 1,500 m

Wire-guided system with optical alignment on the target.
Used by the BR 1150 Atlantic and the BR 1050 Alizé.

AS 20

Used in firing training of the AS 30 on the Étendard IV M

Bldr:	SNIAS
Length:	2.60 m
Diameter:	0.25 m
Wingspan:	0.80 m
Weight:	140 kg
Radio command	
Range:	4,000 m to 8,000 m

AS 30

System developed for firing from a maneuvering aircraft at middle, low, or very low altitude. Used by the Étendard IV M.

Bldr:	SNIAS
Length:	3.785 m
Diameter:	0.342 m
Wingspan:	1.000 m
Total weight:	528 kg
Range:	maximum 9 to 12,000 m.; minimum 1,500 m.
Radio command	

*EMD = Electronique Marcel Dassault

1. Masurca.

2. Tartar.

3. Four-barrel 305 mortar automatically loaded.

4. Six barrel, trainable 375-mm ASW rocket launcher.

1

2

3

4

WEAPONS AND SYSTEMS OF THE FRENCH NAVY (*continued*)

AS 37 Martel

Bldr: Matra and Hawker Siddeley Dynamics
2 types, television and anti-radar. Only the latter is used in the French Navy.
Length: 4.122 m
Diameter: 0.40 m
Wingspan: 1.192 m
Total weight: 531 kg
Range: over 20,000 m
Passive homing head (EMD); the missile homes on the radar emissions of the enemy vessel. Immediately after firing, the missile is on its own, permitting the aircraft to return to base. To be used with BR 1150 Atlantic.

♦ *Air-to-air missile*

R 530

Bldr: Matra
2 types, infrared and radar homing
Length: IR type: 3.198 m; EM type: 3.284 m
Diameter: 0.263 m
Wingspan: 1.103 m
Weight: IR type: 193.5 kg, EM type: 192 kg
Range: maximum 10,000 m: minimum 5,000 m
Semi passive: homing EMD or infra-red homing

Sidewinder

The French Navy also uses this air-to-air American missile (see U.S. section).

Magic

Bldr: Matra
Length: 2.900 m
Diameter: 0.157
Wingspan: 0.660 m
Weight: 89 kg
Range: 300/8,000 m
Infrared homing

(B) GUNS

100 M 1953 and 1968 models.

Single barrel automatic, for use against aircraft, surface vessels, or land targets. The 1968 model is a lighter version of the '53 model. The ammunition is the same.
Characteristics of the '68 model:
Weight of the gun mount: 22 tons
Length of barrel: 55 calibre
Range at 40° elevation: 17,000 m
Maximum effective range for surface fire: 15,000 m
Maximum effective range for anti-aircraft fire: 8,000 m
Maximum rate of fire: 60 rounds/minute
Arc of elevation: −15° to +80°
Maximum Speed: training, 40°/sec., elevation, 25°/sec
The 100 M (1953) uses an analog fire control system with electro-mechanical and electronic equipment for the fire control solution. The director can be operated in optical and radar modes.

The 100 M (1968) uses a digital fire control system, central units, memory disks, mathematical input on records or magnetic tape. Light radar gun director. Optical equipment can be added.

The 57-mm (1951 model)

Twin barrel automatic mount:
Length of barrel: 60 calibers
Muzzle velocity: 865 m/sec
Maximum range: 13,000 m
Effective anti-aircraft range: 5,000 m
Maximum rate of fire: 60 rounds/min per barrel
Arc of elevation: −8° to 90°
Maximum rate of fire: 60 rounds per minute, per barrel.

127-mm (1948 model)

Twin-barrel semi-automatic for use against aircraft, surface vessels, or land targets. The French model can use American ammunition.
Length of barrel: 54 calibers
Muzzle velocity: 810 m/sec
Maximum anti-aircraft range: 14,000 m
Effective anti-aircraft range: 9,000 m
Maximum surface range: 22,400 m
Effective surface range: 18,000 m
Weight: 48 tons
Weight of turret: 14 tons
Maximum rate of fire: 18 rounds per minute

30-mm

Single automatic barrel:
Length: 2.440 m/m
Weight: 4 tons
Muzzle velocity: 1,000 m/sec
Maximum effective range: 2,800 m
Maximum rate of fire: 650 rounds per minute

(C) ANTISUBMARINE WEAPONS (surface vessels)

♦ *Malafon* (Bldr: Latécoère in partnership with St. Trôpez) L 4 torpedo-carrying glider launched with the assistance of a double booster, stabilization by automatic pilot, radio command guidance. *Glider:* speed 230 m/sec. *Range:* 12,000 m. *Missile:* length 6.15 m, diameter 0.65 m., span 3.30 m., total weight, including torpedo, 1,500 kg. The Malafon is installed in the 2 *Suffren*-class destroyers, the *La Galissionnière*, the ASW T 47, the *Aconit* and the *Tourville* class destroyers.

♦ *375-mm rocket launchers, 1964 or 1972* models: Sextuple mount. Automatic loading in vertical position. Firing rate, 1 rocket/second. Range: 1,600 m. Time or proximity fuze.

♦ *305 Mortar:* Quadruple mount. Automatic loading, ASW projectile weight, 230 kg; range: 400 to 3,000 m. Can also fire a 100 kg projectile against land targets; range 6,000 m.

(D) TORPEDOES

Surface Ships

Class	Weight in kg	Caliber in mm	Speed in kts
K 2	1,100	550	50
L 3	900	550	25

WEAPONS AND SYSTEMS OF THE FRENCH NAVY (*continued*)

L 4	500	533	30
L 5 mod 1 and mod 4	1,000	533	35

Submarines

Z 13	1,700	550	30
E 12	1,600	550	25
E 14	900	550	25
L 5 mod 3	1,300	533	35
F 17	1,300	533	35

Aircraft

In addition to the U.S. torpedoes Mk 44 and 46, French naval aircraft use the L 4 torpedo.

(E) SONARS

Surface ships	Class	Frequency	Av. depth when used with variable depth sonar (VDS)
DUBA 1 . . .	Hull	HF	2,500 m
DUBA 3 . . .	Hull	HF	3,000 m
DUBV 24 . . .	Hull	LF	6,000
DUBV 23 . . .	Bow	LF	see remarks
DUBV 43 . . .	Towed	LF	see remarks
DUBA 25 . . .	Hull	MF	see remarks
DUBM 20	Hull sonar		
DUBM 41	Towed sonar	Minehunters *Circe* class	

REMARKS: **DUBV 23** and **DUBV 43** are used simultaneously and under normal sound propagation conditions achieve ranges of 8,000 to 10,000 meters, and in certain bathymetric conditions, 20,000 m.
The **DUBA 25** is a new sonar designed for the A 69 class.

Submarines — Carry listening devices, active-passive sonars, and telemetric equipment.

Helicopters	AQS 13	MF	U.S. sonar
	DUAV 1	HF	
	HS 71	HF	equips the "Lynx" WG 13 helicopter

(F) COMBAT INFORMATION SYSTEMS

SENIT — This system has 4 principal roles:
— establishing the combat situation from manual collection of information coming from detection equipment on board and automatic or manual collection of information coming from external sources;
— dissemination of this combat situation to the ship and other vessels by automatic means (links 11 and 14);
— decision-making assistance;
— transmission of all required information to the target designation console.
Although their general concept is similar, there are several versions of the Senit System, which differ in construction, and, for each type, programming to assure fulfillment of the various missions assigned each type of ship.
— *Senit 1:* system with 1 or 2 computers found in the *Duquesne*, the *Suffren*, and the *Colbert*.
— *Senit 2:* single computer system found in the T 47 Tartar class as well as the *Duperré*.

— *Senit 3:* built around a central computer system consisting of 2 computers and 2 memory banks, the entire group designed for control of various weapons (guns, Malafon ASW system, torpedoes). Installed in the *Aconit* and the 3 F 67 class ships.
These three systems are based on equipment of American origin, some built in France under license.
— *Senit 4:* a system conceived by the French Navy programming center and designed around the French Iris 55 N computer. Will be fitted in the C 70 class.
— *Senit 5:* also designed by the French Navy programming center, it will be fitted on small ships. It uses the 15 M minicomputer which is of French origin.

(G) RADARS

♦ *Air search*

DRBV 20 A: Metric
DRBV 20 C: Metric, long-range. Mounted on aircraft carriers.
DRBV 22 A: Mounted in T 47 ASW version, T 53 class, fast frigates, patrol vessels.
DRBV 22 C: *Ile d'Oléron*
DRBV 22 D: *Jeanne d'Arc, Henri-Poincaré*
DRBV 23 B: Mounted in aircraft carriers.
DRBV 23 C: Mounted in the *Colbert;* transistorized model of the 23 B
DRBV 26: Mounted in the *Tourville*, the *Georges Leygues*, and the *Duperré*
DRBV 13: Doppler pulse radar. Has several uses, installed in the *Aconit*.

♦ *Three-dimensional*

DRBI 10: Mounted in aircraft carriers, T 53 destroyers, the *Colbert*, the *Jeanne d'Arc*, the *Ile d'Oléron*
DRBI 23: Mounted in the *Duquesne* and *Suffren*
SPS 39: American radar. Mounted on Tartar-equipped T 47 class destroyers
DRBJ 11: Pulse coded radar for the C 70 AA class guided missile destroyers

♦ *Surface and low-altitude air search*

DRBV 50: Mounted on aircraft carriers, *Jeanne d'Arc*, T 47 ASW class destroyers, the *Rhin*, the *Ile d'Oléron*, *Victor Schoelcher*, *Commandant Bourdais*, the *Colbert*, the *La Galissonnière*.
DRBV 51: Will be mounted on C 70 corvettes, F 67 frigates, small craft of the A 69 class, and the *Duperré*

♦ *Navigation*

DECCA RM-416
DRBN 31: Mounted on certain minesweepers and coastal patrol craft.
DRBV 31: Mounted on the Tartar-equipped T 47 class destroyers, as well as the T 53 class and a few fast frigates.

♦ *Fire control*

DRBC 31: 57-mm, 100-mm of the aircraft carriers, *Duperré*
DRBC 32 A: Mounted on ASW modified T 47 class destroyers. 100-mm guns of the *Suffren* class guided missile destroyers, and some fast frigates, and the *Jeanne d'Arc*.
DRBC 32 B: 100-mm guns of the *Aconit*
DRBC 32 C: Mounted on the *Colbert*, the *Duperré*, and the C 70 guided missile destroyers.
DRBC 32 D: Mounted on the *Tourville* class
DRBC 32 E: Mounted on the A 69 class patrol craft.
SPG 51: U.S. tracking radar used with the Tartar system on the type T 47 modified destroyers.
DRBR 51: Tracking radar for the Masurca.

WEAPONS AND SYSTEMS OF THE FRENCH NAVY (*continued*)

(H) COUNTER MEASURES

The French Navy uses the Syllex chaff launcher which will eventually be replaced by the Sagaie, an improved system.

AIRCRAFT CARRIERS

	Author	Bldr	Laid down	L	In serv.
R 98 CLEMENCEAU	*1953*	Brest	11-55	21-12-57	11-61
R 99 FOCH	*1955*	Ch. de l'Atlantique	2-57	28-7-60	7-63

D: 22,000 tons (27,307 mean) (32,780 fl)
Dim: 265 (238 pp) × 31.72 beam × 51.20 flight deck × 7.50 draft light × 8.60 fl
S: 32 kts (33 on trials)   **Range:** 7,500/18 — 4,800/24
A: 8/100-mm AA model 1953 (I × 8) — 40 aircraft
Armor: Reinforced flight deck, armored bulkheads in engine room and magazines, bridge superstructure in reinforced steel.
Man: Ship's company, 65 officers, 332 warrant and petty officers, 831 men
M: Two Parsons GT; two props; 126,000 hp
Boilers: 6 pressure 45 kg/cm² — superheat: 450°   **Fuel:** 3,720 tons
Electric: 14,000 kw
Electron Equipt: Radars: 1/DRBV 20 C,   1/DRBV 23 B,   2DRBI 10,
    1/DRBV 50,
    1/DRBC 31
    Sonars: 1/SQS 505

REMARKS: Flight deck 257 m. in length; deck angled at 8°, 165.50 × 29.50; deck forward of the angled deck: 93 × 28; width of the deck abeam the island: 35. Hangar dimensions, 180 × 22 to 24 × 7 (height). Two elevators 16 m long, 11 m in width one forward on the main flight deck, one slightly abaft the island, able to raise a 15-ton aircraft 8.50 m in 9 seconds. Two 50-meter Mitchell-Brown BS type steam catapults, able to launch 15/20-ton aircraft at 110 knots, one forward, another on the angled deck. Optical mirror landing equipment (optical equipment of French manufacture).

The propulsion machinery was built by the Chantiers de l'Atlantique. Living spaces are air-conditioned. Island medium-sized with 3 bridges: flag, navigation, aviation. Communication systems, especially with fighter aircraft, are a significant aspect of the ships' capabilities.

The *Foch*, built in a special drydock at St. Nazaire, was towed to Brest for the installation of its armament.

Aviation fuel: 1,800 m³ of jet fuel and 109 m³ of aviation gasoline carried by the *Foch*. 1,200 m³ of jet fuel and 400 m³ of aviation gasoline by the *Clemenceau*. Work is being carried on to adapt these ships for the Super-Étendard aircraft.

Clemenceau (R 98)   1974 Photo Guiglini

Clemenceau (R 98)   1974 Photo J. C. Bellonne

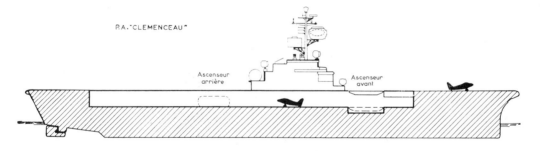

P.A. "CLEMENCEAU"

Ascenseur
arrière

Ascenseur
avant

Starboard and stern profiles Clemenceau (R 98)

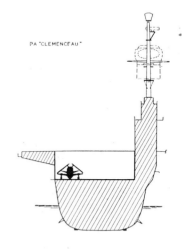

P.A. "CLEMENCEAU"

Foch (R 99)

HELICOPTER CARRIER "tentative diagram"

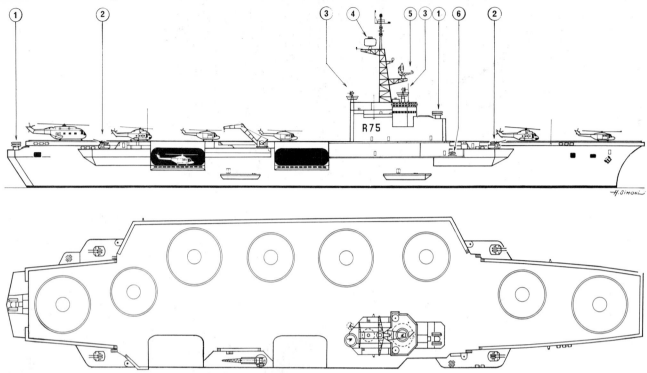

1: Crotale — 2: 40 Breda-Bofors — 3: Radar DRBC 32 — 4: Radar DRBV C 51 — 5: Radar DRBV 26 — 6: Sagaie System *NB: Contrary to this diagram, it has been decided to mount 2 Crotale systems in place of the after 40-mm and to put 2/100-mm turrets in place of the forward 40-mm.*

♦ *1 nuclear propulsion type PH 75 (ASW and amphibious assault)*

	Bldr	Laid down	In serv.
N . . .	Brest Navy Yard		1981

D: 16,400 tons 18,400 (fl)
Dim: 208 × 202 flight deck × 26.4 (wl.) × 46 flight deck
S: 28 kts   **Man:**   850 men, 50 staff
Range: Under nuclear power, unlimited — 3,000/18 diesel engines
A: 2 BPDM systems (Crotale VIII × 2) — 2/100-mm (I × 2), helicopters, (see Remarks)
Electron Equipt: Radars: 1/DRBV 26, 1/DRBV 51 C, 2/Decca, 2/DRBC 32
                   Sonars: 1/DUBA 25 — 2 Sagaie systems — SÉNIT
M: 1 CAS 230 reactor furnishes steam to a 2 turbo-reduction-condensers groups; 65,000 hp; 2 props; 2 AGO standby diesels
Electric: 9,400 kw

REMARKS: The installations for aircraft operation include the following: 1 hangar 84 × 21 × 6.50, 2 lateral elevators (15 tons in 11 seconds), 1 fixed crane, 1 mobile crane, munition-handling rooms, magazines, workshops, fuel tanks for 1,000 m³ of TR jet fuel.

The *PH 75* will be able to launch about 25 WG13 Lynx or about 10 Super-Frélon or fifteen Army type Puma helicopters, or a combination of these, space being available for all of them on the hangar deck. In addition to the CIC, Operation Center, and Communications Center, the *PH 75* can fulfill her intervention mission with 1 special landing force made up of units from the Special Intervention Forces (*Forces Terrestres d'Intervention*, FTI) and supporting air elements (*Composante Air des Forces d'Intervention*, CAFI), and 1 Helicopter Movement Command Center (PCMH). The *PH 75* can carry almost 1,000 troops or passengers in designated quarters and 500 additional personnel in supplementary spaces in the hangar area. Forty-five days' rations can be carried for ship's company (890 men) and thirty days' for 1,500 passengers.

Jeanne d'Arc (R 97)

1975 Jeanne d'Arc

On the superstructure, in addition to the navigation bridge, may be found:
— the helicopter control bridge
— a modular type information and operations center
— a combined control center for amphibious landing operations

The engine spaces are divided into two rooms, each with two boilers and a turbine, and are completely separated by a bulkhead.

A surface-to-air Crotale BPDMS will be installed in the future.

♦ *1 cruiser helicopter ship (author. 1957)*

	Bldr	Laid down	L	Trials	In serv.
R 97 JEANNE D'ARC	Brest	7-60	30-9-61	7-63	7-64

(ex-*La Résolue*)

D: 10,000 tons (12,365 fl)
Dim: 182 (172 wl) × 24 × 22 (wl) × 7.32 (fl)
A: 6/MM 38 Exocet — 4/100-mm 1953 (I × 4) — 8 helicopters (see Remarks)
Electron Equipt: Radars: 1/DRBV 22 D, 1/DRBV 50, 1/DRBN 32, 1/DRBI 10. Sonar: 1/SQS 503 — 2 Syllex installations.
Man: Regular ship's company. 30 officers, 183 warrant officers and rated men, + 404 other enlisted.
M: Two Rateau-Bretagne GT; two props; 40,000 hp.   **Electric:** 4,400 kw.
Boilers: 4 dissymmetric multitube type rated at 45 kg/cm² — superheat: 450°
Fuel: 1,360 tons.   **S:** 26.5 kts   **Range:** 6,000/15

REMARKS: Has replaced as a training vessel for officer cadets the former cruiser *Jeanne d'Arc*. When on this mission, the ship carries only 4 heavy helicopters. In wartime she would be used as an antisubmarine helicopter carrier, amphibious assault helicopter carrier, or as a troop transport. The number of heavy helicopters embarked can be quickly augmented by simple structural changes. The hull is welded throughout. Landing platform: 62 × 21 m.

The aircraft installations include:
— Aft of the island structure the flight deck permits simultaneous takeoff of 2 Super Frelon helicopters while 2 machines can be stationed forward of the takeoff area and 2 others astern, one on each side of the elevator.
— A 12-ton capacity elevator is located aft on the flight deck and the hangar deck.
— The hangar deck is below the flight deck and can accommodate 8 helicopters during wartime, taking some of the living quarters used by midshipmen. At the after end of the hangar is an inspection area for the helicopters as well as all necessary machine shops for maintenance and repair including helicopter electronic equipment. Here also are located the handling rooms for the weapons and ammunition for the helicopters (torpedoes, rockets, etc.).

There are three fire control directors for the 100-mm guns, each served by three automatically controlled radar directors.

Jeanne d'Arc (R 97)

1975 Jeanne d'Arc

NAVAL AVIATION

1. The Naval Air establishment which is part of the Navy, is made up of combatant flotillas, maintenance squadrons or sections, bases, schools, and special services necessary to insure the efficient operation of the flight components.

Naval air is manned by naval personnel.

Administrative naval air problems are handled by the Aeronautical Division of the Naval General Staff and the Central Service Branch of Naval Air, both headed by a flag officer.

Operational and training matters concerning Naval Air are directed by the Navy Staff, which includes in its various bureaus, aviation officers.

Primary training for fixed-wing pilots is provided by the Air Force; helicopter pilots are given initial training by the Army as well as the Air Force. Specialization of these pilots in multi-engine aircraft or in carrier-based fixed-wing and rotary aircraft is provided by Naval Air. The latter also trains navigators and maintenance crews (Naval Air School at Rochefort).

2. The combat flotillas are:

(a) those embarked which, flying from aircraft or helicopter carriers, carry out intercept, attack, reconnaissance or CAP missions and engage in antisubmarine warfare.

(b) maritime patrol flotillas and antisubmarine warfare flotillas which are land-based.

3. The service support squadrons and sections have various missions: schools, training exercises, transportation, logistical support for sea-going forces, experimental and salvage operations.

4. Authority over the embarked flotillas and squadrons is assigned to a rear admiral, the Commander Aircraft Carriers and seagoing aviation. (ALPA)

Maritime patrol squadrons are commanded by a rear admiral (ALPATMAR)

Shore-based flotillas, squadrons and sections are commanded by the Préfets Maritimes (Naval District Commandants) through the regional aviation commanders.

5. Bases: Nimes-Garon, Saint-Mandrier (helicopters), Saint-Raphael (experimental station), Hyères, Cuers (maintenance), Ajaccio-Aspretto (training), Lorient-Lann Bihoué, Lanvéoc-Poulmic (helicopters), Landivisiau.

Units	Shipboard or landbased	Missions	Aircraft
Combat Flotillas			
12-F, 14-F	Ship	All-weather interception	**Crusader (F-8-E FN)**
11-F, 17-F	Ship	Attack	**Étendard-IV-M**
16-F	Ship	Reconnaissance	**Étendard-IV-P**
4-F, 6-F	Ship	Surveillance	**Alizé**
31-F, 32-F	Ship	Antisubmarine warfare (helicopter)	**HSS-1, (31-F), Super Frelon (32-F)**
33-F	Ship	Troop transport	**HSS-1**
34-F	Ship	Antisubmarine warfare (helicopter)	**Alouette III**
25-F	Land	Maritime patrol and antisubmarine warfare	**Neptune (P2V-7)**
21-F, 22-F, 23-F, 24-F	Land	Maritime patrol and antisubmarine warfare	**Atlantic**
Support Squadrons			
2-S, 3-S	Land	All-weather Instruction	**Piper Navajo** **Nord 262**
9-S		Reconnaissance	**DC-3, DC-4, Neptune (P2H)**
12-S	Land	General service	**Neptune (P2V-7)**
55-S	Land	Multi-engine pilot training	**Nord 262**
56-S	Land	Navigation (non-pilot) personnel training	**C-47**
59-S	Ship	Carrier qualification training	**CM-175, Étendard IV-M, Alizé**
20-S	Land	Experimental aircraft (planes, helicopters)	**Alouette II and III, HSS 1, Super-Frelon**
22-S, 23-S	Land and ship	Liaison, salvage Search and Rescue	**Alouette II and III**
27-S	Land	General services	**Super-Frelon**
Sections			
	Land or ship	General services	**C-47 — Catalina — CM 175 — MS 760 C-54 — N-262 MS-733 Alouette III — HSS-1 Falcon X**

Super Étendard (Attack aircraft)

Étendard IV M (Attack aircraft)

Crusader (interception) taking off

Étendard IV P (reconnaissance aircraft)

Alizé (Early warning and ASW aircraft, carrier-based)

Lynx WG 13 (ASW close support, logistic support helo)

Super Frélon (ASW helo)

Super-Frélon (ASW, helo carrier-based)

Alouette III (Search and rescue, utility helo)

Atlantic (ASW)

Atlantic (ASW)

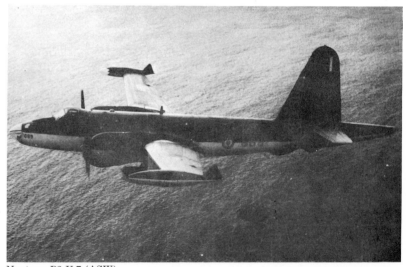

Neptune P2 V 7 (ASW)

Type	Mission	Wingspan	Length	Height	Weight (max.) kilos	Motor	Maximum speed in mach or in knots	Maximum ceiling	Range	Weapons	Remarks
♦ *Ship-based planes:* **CRUSADER F8 E (FN)** (Ling-Temco-Vought)	All-weather interceptor	10.72	16.61	4.80	13,000	1 *J 57 P20 A* Pratt and Whitney jet with after-burner	Mach 1.8	50,000 ft	1,500 miles 2 hr 30	20-mm guns, Air to air missiles	(1) May be outfitted with a small photo balloon for reconnaissance missions.
SUPER-ÉTENDARD	Fleet air defense, attack, reconnaissance photo	9.60	14.35	3.85	11,500	1 *8 K 50* SNECMA jet developing 5 tons of thrust	Mach 1 (11,000 kts) Mach 0.97 low altitude			2/30-mm guns, bombs, rockets, combination or *AM 39*	The *MK II Atlantic* which will enter service at the beginning of the 1980s will have the same airframe, engines, and
ETENDARD IV M (Dassault)	Attack aircraft	9.60	14.35	3.85	10,200	1 SNECMA jet *Atar 8*	Mach 1.3	35,000 ft	750 miles 1 hr 45 or 2 hr 15 with supplemental reserve tank	30-mm guns, air-surface missiles (or air-to-air), 68-mm rockets, various bombs of 50 to 400 kg	characteristics as the *Mk I* but its weapon system will be entirely new, built around a digital tactical
ÉTENDARD IV P	Reconnaissance photo	9.60	14.50	3.85	10,200	1 SNECMA jet *Atar 8*	Mach 1.3	35,000 ft	750 miles 1 hr 45 or 2 hr 15 with supplemental reserve tank	100-mm rockets, 68-mm rockets, photo-flash bombs	computer. It will be able to transport 3 tons of weapons, e.g.,
ALIZÉ (BR 1050) (Bréguet)	AEW, anti-submarine warfare	15.60	13.66	5	8,200	1 Rolls-Royce *Dart 21* turbo prop (1,925 hp + 230 kg of thrust)	240 kts	1,100 ft	685 miles 4 hr 45	Air-to-surface missiles, *Mk 44* torpedoes, 100-mm rockets, ASW depth charges, 50 to 250 kg bombs, acoustic buoys, mortar type projectiles	4 *Martel* under the wings or 2 *AM 39* inboard. (2) Localization, classification and attack of contacts picked up by an anti-submarine ship.
♦ *Land-based planes:* **NEPTUNE P2V-7** (Lockheed)	Patrol, anti-submarine warfare	31.50	31.70	10.80	34,280	2 *R 3350 32 Wa* Wright engines × 3,250 hp + 2 Westinghouse turbo-reactors type *J34* × 1,540 kg	240 kts	25,000 ft	3,200 miles 16 hr	*L 4* or *Mk 44* torpedoes, ASW depth charges, sono-buoys, mortar type projectiles (ASW), photo flash bombs	(3) Detection, identification and neutralization of small surface vessels with weak anti-aircraft defense.
ATLANTIC MK1 (BR 1150) (Bréguet)	Patrol, anti-submarine warfare (1)	36.30	31.75	11.33	43,500	2 Rolls-Royce *Tyne 20* turbo props × 6,000 hp	300 kts	30,000 ft	4,300 miles 17 hr	Air-to-surface missiles, *L 4* or *Mk 44* torpedoes, ASW depth charges, sono-buoys, mortar type projectiles (ASW), photo flash bombs	
♦ *Helicopters:* **HSS** (Sikorsky)	Antisubmarine warfare, troop carrier	17.07 (rotor diameter)	20.06	4.73	6,000	1 *R 1820.84* Wright, 1,525 hp	110 kts	9,000 ft	380 miles 4 hr 30	*Mk 44* torpedoes, air-to-surface missiles, ASW depth charges	
SUPER-FRELON (SNIAS)	Antisubmarine warfare	18.90 (rotor diameter)	23	6.35	13,000	3 *C3* Turboméca III turboshafts, each with 1,500 hp	145 kts	10,000 ft	420 miles 3 hr 30	*Mk 44* torpedoes, ASW torpedoes	
LYNX (WG 13) (Westland-SNIAS)	Antisubmarine warfare (2) Surface attack aircraft (3)	12.80 (rotor diameter)	15.2	3.20	4,150	2 *BS 360* Rolls-Royce turboshafts, each with 900 hp	150 kts	12,000 ft	1 hr 30, half hovering, half in flight 2 hr 30 with 3 men and 4 missiles	*Mk 44* and *Mk 46* torpedoes Air-to-surface missiles	

The French Navy uses as training aircraft the *Nord 262,* the *C 47,* the *CM 175,* and the *Falcon X.* In logistic units there are the *MS 760, Nord 262, MS 733, Piper Navajo, C 47* and *C 54,* the *CM 175,* and the helicopters *Alouette II* and *III, HSS1,* and the *Super-Frelon.* In the Pacific Experimental Area, air logistics are furnished by the *Neptune* bimotor and *Super-Frelon* helicopters.

STRATEGIC SUBMARINES (Nuclear-Powered Ballistic Missile)

◆ *6 nuclear-powered (SSBN)*

	Bldr	Laid down	L	Trials	In serv.
S 611 (Q 252)	Cherbourg	1964	29-3-67	1969	1-12-71
LE REDOUTABLE					
S 612 (Q 253)	Cherbourg	1967	12-12-69	1971	1-1-73
LE TERRIBLE					
S 610 (Q 257)	Cherbourg	1969	4-12-71	5-73	7-74
LE FOUDROYANT					
S 613 (Q 258)	Cherbourg	1971	17-9-74	12-75	12-76
L'INDOMPTABLE					
S 614 (Q 259)	Cherbourg	1973	. . .-75	12-76	4-79
LE TONNANT					
S . . . ( )	Cherbourg				1982
L'INFLEXIBLE					

Le Redoutable (S 611)   1970 E.C.P.A.

The sail of the Redoutable (S 611)   1970 E.C.P.A.

D: 7,500 tons surfaced/9,000 submerged   **S:**   20 kts maximum
Dim: 128 × 10.60 × 10
A: (a) strategic weapons: 16 ballistic missiles;
       (b) tactical weapons: 4 TT, 18 torpedoes
Man: twin crews of 15 officers and 120 men for each ship, manning in rotation.
M: 1 nuclear reactor producing pressurized steam for propulsion; 1 prop.

Le Redoutable (S 611)   1971 E.C.P.A.

REMARKS: The *Redoutable* (authorized in March 1963) and other submarines of this class are the principal elements of the French naval deterrent. The steel hull is of great strength and the ship can submerge more than 200 meters.

The propulsion system consists of a reactor with enriched uranium and distilled water under pressure giving the required heat energy for the production of steam to produce the power for two turbine installations and two turbo-alternators. An auxiliary main engine with electrical energy can substitute for the main engines in an emergency. The range of the auxiliary propulsion engine is about 5,000 nautical miles.

Le Terrible (S 612)   1971 E.C.P.A.

	Bldr	Laid down	L	In serv.
S 655 GYMNOTE	Cherbourg	3-63	17-3-64	10-66

D: 3,000/3,250 tons   **S:**   11/10 kts   **Dim:**   84 × 10.60 × 7.60
M: 4 diesel-electric motors × 620 kw and 2 electric engines; 2 props; 2,600 hp
Man: 8 officers, 35 petty officers, 35 other enlisted

REMARKS: An experimental submarine used for testing missiles designed for the SSBNs, 4 vertical missile launching tubes.

STRATEGIC SUBMARINES (*continued*)

Gymnote (S 655)   1972 E.C.P.A.

ATTACK SUBMARINES

♦ *1 nuclear-powered*

	Bldr	Laid down	L	In serv.
S . . . N . . .	Cherbourg	1976	. . .	1981

D:	2,265 tons (Geneva convention) **Dim:** 72.10 × 7.60 × 6.40
	2,385 tons (surfaced), 2,670 (submerged)
A:	4/533-mm TT, 14 torpedoes or mines **S:** 25 kts
Man:	9 officers, 35 warrant and chief petty officers, 22 rated and non-rated men
M:	A nuclear power system made up of an integrated reactor-exchanger able to deliver constant power of 48 MW thermal units for the necessary steam to two turbo-alternators. A single electric motor drives a single shaft and an emergency diesel generator group can be cut into the propulsion line in case of nuclear breakdown.

REMARKS: The prototype of a new class of nuclear attack submarines. Fire control, torpedo-launching, and submarine detection systems are the same as the *Agosta* class.

♦ *4 high-speed, Agosta class.* (Authorized in the 1970-75 program)

	Bldr	Laid down	L	In serv.
S 620 AGOSTA	Cherbourg	1972	19-10-74	1977
S 621 BÉVÉZIERS	Cherbourg	17-5-73	14-6-75	1977
S 622 LA PRAYA	Cherbourg	1974	10-75	1978
S 623 OUESSANT	Cherbourg	1974	1-76	1978

Agosta (S 620)   19-10-74 M.N.

D:	1,200 tons (Geneva convention) **Dim:** 67.57 × 6.80 × 5.40
	1,450 (surfaced), 1,725 (submerged)
A:	4/550-mm TT forward — 20 torpedoes (rapid-loading)
Man:	7 officers, 43 men **S:** 20 kts (submerged)
M:	1 drive shaft; a 3,500-kw main engine; a cruising engine of 23 kw; 2 generating plants (SEMT-Pielstick A 16 PA 4 185,850 kw)
Range:	8,500 nautical miles with snorkel at 19 knots.
Endurance:	45 days

REMARKS: Ocean-going submarines. Weapons and equipment similar to the refitted *Daphne*-class submarine. Fire control, centralized in one computer bank. Air-conditioned. Retractable deck fittings on hull exterior. Advanced silencing techniques for quiet operations both inboard and outboard. Spain and the Union of South Africa have each purchased two of these submarines. Because of construction delays, the *Agosta* and the *Bévéziers* will not enter active service until 1977. *La Praya* and the *Ouessant* will not join the fleet until 1978.

♦ *Ocean-going Narval class*

	Author	Bldr	Laid down	L	In serv.
S 631 NARVAL	1949	Cherbourg	6-51	11-12-54	12-57
S 632 MARSOUIN	1949	Cherbourg	9-51	21-5-55	10-57
S 633 DAUPHIN	1950	Cherbourg	5-62	17-9-55	8-58
S 634 REQUIN	1950	Cherbourg	6-52	3-12-55	8-58
S 637 ESPADON	1954	A. Normand	12-55	15-9-58	4-60
S 638 MORSE	1954	Seine Maritime	2-56	10-12-58	5-60

Narval (S 631)

D:	1,320 tons, 1,635 (surfaced), 1,910 (submerged)
Dim:	77.63 × 7.82 × 5.40 **A:** 6/550-mm TT forward
Man:	7 officers, 56 men **S:** 15 kts (surface), 18 (submerged)
Range:	15,000 with snorkel at 8 knots **M:** 2 props. See remarks.

REMARKS: Exceptionally strong hull welded throughout, streamlined sail. Endurance at sea 45 days. Rebuilt from 1966 to 1970 with special attention to the machinery spaces. They now have diesel-electric propulsion (two main engines of 1,500 hp, two electric cruising motors of 40 hp, three diesel-electric generators (SEMT-Pielstick 12 PA 4). Complete modernization of detection devices, weapons (6 TT forward, 14 in reserve, and mines), and sail (streamlined). Considered to be very good diesel submarines.

ATTACK SUBMARINES (*continued*)

Doris (S 643)   1975

Flore (S 645)   1975 J. C. Bellonne

♦ *9 Daphné class*

		Author	Bldr	Laid down	L	In serv.
S 641	DAPHNÉ	1955	Dubigeon	3–58	20-6-59	6–64
S 642	DIANE	1955	Dubigeon	7–58	4-10-60	6–64
S 643	DORIS	1955	Cherbourg	19–58	14-5-60	8–64
S 645	FLORE	1956	Cherbourg	19–58	21-12-60	5–64
S 646	GALATÉE	1956	Cherbourg	19–58	22-9-61	7–64
S 648	JUNON	1960	Cherbourg	7–61	11-5-64	2–66
S 649	VÉNUS	1960	Cherbourg	8–61	24-9-64	1–66
S 650	PSYCHÉ	1964	Brest	5–65	28-6-67	7–69
S 651	SIRÈNE	1964	Brest	5–65	28-6-67	3–70

D: 700 tons (Geneva convention)   **Dim:** 57.75 × 6.76 × 4.62
          869 surfaced, 1,043 submerged
A: 12/550-mm, 8 forward, 4 aft   **Man:** 6 officers, 39 men
S: 13.5 kts (surface), 16 kts (submerged)
M: Diesel-electric propulsion (SEMT-Pielstick), 2 props; 1600 hp
Range: 4,500 nautical miles, 5 knots with snorkel

REMARKS: Development of the *Aréthuse*-class submarine. Superquiet when submerged. Modernized, beginning in 1971, with special attention given to detection equipment and weapons. Can submerge to more than 300 meters. This type of submarine has been purchased by the following countries: Portugal, four in 1964; Pakistan, three in 1966; the Union of South Africa, three in 1967; and Spain has built 4 submarines of this type with French technical assistance.

Vénus (S 649)   1972 J. C. Bellonne

♦ *4 Aréthuse class*

		Author	Bldr	Laid down	L	In serv.
S 635	ARÉTHUSE	1953	Cherbourg	3–55	9-11-57	10–58
S 636	ARGONAUTE	1953	Cherbourg	3–55	29-6-57	2–59
S 639	AMAZONE	1954	Cherbourg	End of 1955	3-4-58	7–59
S 640	ARIANE	1954	Cherbourg	End of 1955	12-9-58	3–60

D: 400 tons (Geneva convention)
          543 (surfaced), 669 (submerged)
A: 4/550-mm TT forward, 4 T in reserve
Man: 6 officers, 34 men   **S:** 12.5 kts (surfaced), 16 kts (submerged)
M: Diesel-electric propulsion; 12-cylinder SEMT-Pielstick motors; 1 prop;
          1,060/1,300 hp.

REMARKS: Ballast tanks reduced to a minimum, can submerge to more than 200 meters. Quiet and maneuverable, handy submarines.

Aréthuse (S 635)   1972 G. Arra.

Doris (S 643)   1972 J. C. Bellonne

GUIDED MISSILE CRUISER

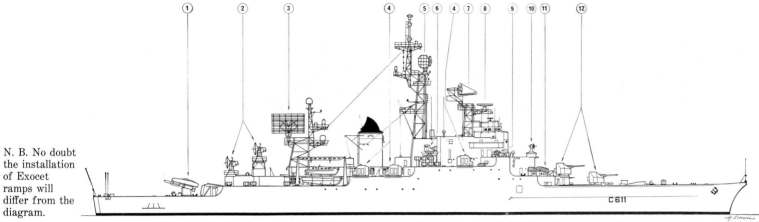

N. B. No doubt the installation of Exocet ramps will differ from the diagram.

1: *Masurca* launcher — 2: *DRBR 51* radars — 3: *DRBV 20* radar — 4: 57-mm mounts — 5: *DRBI 10 D* radar — 6: 57-mm firing director — 7: *DRBV 23 C* radar — 8: *DRBV 50* radar — 9: *Syllex* systems — 10: *DRBC 32 C* radar — 11: *Exocet* launchers — 12: 100-mm (1968) gun mounts.

1953 program

	Bldr	Laid down	L	In serv.
C 611 COLBERT	Brest	12-53	24-3-56	5-59

D: 8,500 tons (11,300 fl)
Dim: 180 (175 pp) × 19.7 (20.2 max) × 7.66
S: 31.5 kts   **Range:** 4,000/25
A: 1 Masurca system — 2/100-mm AA mod 1968 (I × 2) — 12/57-mm AA (II × 6)
Electron Equipt: Radars: 1 navigation Decca, 1/DRBV 50, 1/DRBV 23 C, 1/DRBV 20, 2/DRBR 51, 1/DRBR 32 C, 1/DRBC 31, 1/DRBI 10 D, SENIT — counter-measures consist of 2 Syllex systems
Armor: Deck: 50 mm;   Belt: 50 to 80 mm
M: C.E.M. Parsons GT; 2 props; 86,000 hp   **Electric:** 4,920 kw
Boilers: 4 dissymmetric multi-tubular, 45 kg/cm², superheat 450°
Man: (after refitting) 24 officers, 188 petty officers, 348 men

REMARKS: Converted into a surface-to-air guided missile cruiser between 4-70 and 10-72. Together with the guided missile destroyers *Duquesne* and *Suffren*, this ship, thanks to the power and precision of the Masurca system, provides a high degree of anti-aircraft protection to ships at sea at a medium range. The capability of the SENIT tactical data system enables the ship to maintain real time control of the surface and air situation at the center of a widely dispersed formation, which makes this an excellent command ship, able as well to coordinate the air defense of the formation. If necessary the ship can be used as a command post for an inter-service operation overseas. During the refit the bridge superstructure was rebuilt, the electronic equipment for command and control was modernized, the electric power increased, and living spaces were improved, including air-conditioning. The ship will eventually be armed with the MM 38 Exocet system; only the bedplates have been installed at the present time.

Colbert (C 611)   1972 E.C.P.A.

Machinery and boilers are installed in two separate compartments, each with two boilers and a turbine, separated by an 18-meter-long watertight bulkhead.

Colbert (C 611)   J. C. Bellonne 1974

Colbert (C 611)   1973 E.C.P.A.

GUIDED MISSILE DESTROYERS

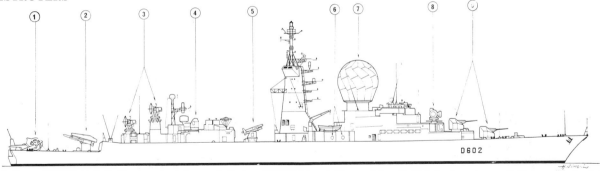

1: Sonar *DUBV 43* — 2: *Masurca* launcher — 3: Radars *DRBR 51* — 4: 30-mm AA — 5: *Malafon* launcher — 6: Catapaults for L 5 Ts — 7: Radar *DRBI 23* — 8: 100-mm director with *DRBC 32 A* radar — 9: 100-mm mounts.

2 Suffren class (Authorized 1960-65)

	Bldr	Author	Laid down	L	Trials	In serv.
D 602 SUFFREN	Lorient	1960	12-62	15-5-65	12-65	1967
D 603 DUQUESNE	Brest	1960	11-64	11-2-66	7-68	4-70

- **D:** 5,090 tons (6,090 fl)   **Dim:** 157.60 (148 pp) × 15.54 × 6.10
- **S:** 34 kts   **Range:** 5,000/18
- **Man:** 23 officers, 143 petty officers, 189 men
- **A:** 1 Masurca system, model 3 missiles — 2/100-mm (I × 2) model 1953 — 2/30-mm AA (I × 2) — 1 Malafon system, — 2 launchers for L 5 TT
- **Electron Equipt:** Radars: 1/DRBI 23, 1/DRBV 50, 2/DRBR 51, 1/DRBC 32 A, 1/DRBN 32 — SENIT
  Sonars: 1/DUBV 23, 1/DUBV 43 — 2 Syllex systems
- **M:** 1 double reduction Rateau turbine; 2 props
- **Boilers:** 4 multitubular automatically controlled; steam pressure 45 kg/cm^2 superheat 450°; 72,500 hp   **Electric:** 4,000 kw

REMARKS: The French Navy has returned to the term "frigate" to designate guided missile ships of medium tonnage. Three pairs of non-retractable, anti-rolling stabilizers are installed, energized by 2 central gyroscopes, only one of which is normally in use. Living and operational spaces are air-conditioned.

These ships are extremely seaworthy; they roll very little and pitch only slightly; there is little vibration.

They will have 4/MM 38 Exocet missile launchers.

Duquesne (D 603)   1973 E.C.P.A.

Suffren (D 602) 1972 J. C. Bellonne

Duquesne (D 603) 1971 J. C. Bellonne

Suffren (D 602) 1974 E.C.P.A.

Duquesne (D 603) 1974 E.C.P.A.

ANTISUBMARINE FRIGATES   ◆ *3 F 67 type (ex-C 67 A). (Authorized 1965-70)*

	Author	Bldr	Laid down	L	In serv.
D 610 TOURVILLE	1967	Lorient	3-70	13-5-72	21-6-74
D 611 DUGUAY TROUIN	1967	Lorient	1-71	1-6-73	9-75
D 612 DE GRASSE	1970	Lorient	1972	30-11-74	11-76

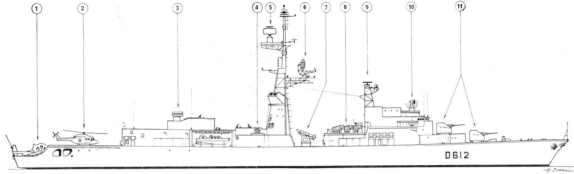

Profile of the **De Grasse**

1: Sonar *DUBV 43* — 2: *Lynx* helicopters — 3: *Crotale* — 4: *Syllex* system — 5: *DRBV 51* radar — 6: *DRBV 26* radar — 7: *Malafon* launcher — 8: *Exocet* launchers — 9: Navigation radar — 10: *DRBC 32 D* radar — 11: 100-mm mounts (1968 model).

D: 4,580 tons (5,745 fl)   **Dim:** 152.75 (142 pp) × 15.30 × 5.70
S: 31 kts   **Range:** 5,000/18
A: 3/100-mm AA (1968 model) — 6/MM 38 Exocet — 1 Malafon missile launcher (13 missiles) — 2 fixed tubes for antisubmarine torpedoes (L 5 model) — 2 WG 13 Lynx helicopters
Man: 25 officers, 90 petty officers, 188 men
M: 2 double reduction GT; 2 props   **Electric:** 4,400 kw
Boilers: 4 dissymmetrical multitubular boilers; steam pressure 45 kg/cm² superheat 450°; 54,400 hp
Electron Equipt: Radars: 1/DRBV 26, 1/DRBV 51, 1/DRBC 32 D, 2 DECCA 1226 — SENIT — 2 Syllex systems.
     Sonars: 1/DUBV 23, 1/DUBV 43.

REMARKS: These ships are designed for antisubmarine warfare and can operate in a formation in a high air threat environment. Trials on the *Tourville* indicated that these ships will have good sea-keeping qualities, similar to those of the *Suffren* class. The *De Grasse* has a Crotale BPDMS in place of the after 100-mm gun mount.

Tourville (D 610)   1973 E.C.P.A.

Tourville (D 610)   1974 D.C.A.N.

ANTISUBMARINE CORVETTES

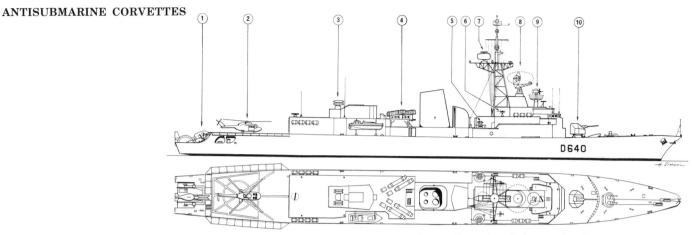

1: *DUBV 43* Sonar — 2: *Lynx* Helicopter — 3: *Crotale* — 4: *Exocet* launchers — 5: *Sagaie* system — 6: 20-mm
AA — 7: *DRBV 51* radar — 8: *DRBV 26* radar — 9: *DRBC 32 E* radar — 10: 100-mm mount (1968 model).

♦ *3 C 70 type (Authorized 1970-75)*

	Bldr	Laid down	L	Trials	Antici- pated In serv.
D 640 GEORGES LEYGUES	Brest	6-74	6-9-75	1977	1978
D 641 DUPLEIX	Brest	9-75	. . .	1978	1979
D 642 MONTCALM	Brest	9-75	. . .	1978	1979

D: 3,800 tons (4,100 fl) **Dim:** 139 (129 pp) × 14 × 5.73 (fwd)
S: 29.75 kts (planned) **Man:** 19 officers, 109 petty officers, 114 men
A: 4 MM 38 Exocet — 1/100-mm anti-aircraft single turret (model 1968) with
Vega firecontrol system — 1/BPDM, Crotale 2/20-mm mounts — 2 torpedo
tubes, L 5 torpedoes, 10 total — 2 WG 13 Lynx helicopters with sonar and
torpedoes. By replacing these, the helicopters can be used in an anti-surface
role using 4 AS 12.
M: CODOG propulsion system, 2 gas turbines; 2 SEMT-Pielstick diesels (16 PA 6
model); 2 variable pitch props; 42,000 hp (gas turbine); 10,000 hp (diesel)
Electric: 3,400 kw
Electron Equipt: Radars: 1/DRBV 26, 1/DRBV 51, 1/DRBC 32 E —
2/DECCA 1226 — SENIT — 2 Sagaie systems
Sonars: 1/DUBV 23, 1/DUBV 43

REMARKS: The *Georges Leygues* is the first of a series of corvettes which should
number at least 24 ships by 1985, divided in two principal categories, one antisubmarine (the first three laid down will be so designed), the other primarily
anti-aircraft. They will have the same hull and propulsion system and also the same
surface-to-surface armament. The design of the ships will be modified, using the
best characteristics that develop between now and 1985. Living spaces in the
Georges Leygues are designed for 250 men including 21 officers. Special efforts have
been made to improve living conditions by giving rooms to petty officers, improving
watch conditions, cutting the number of men living in division compartments, and
improving the sanitary facilities. This should result in an acceptable resolution of
the problems of habitability.

Launching of an MM 38 Exocet   1972 Photo E.C.P.A.

ANTISUBMARINE CORVETTES (continued)

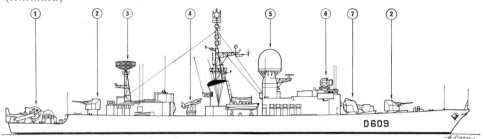

1: *DUBV 43* sonar — 2: 100-mm mounts (1968 model) — 3: *DRBV 22 A* — 4: *Malafon* launcher — 5: *DRBV 13* radar — 6: 100-mm director — 7: 305-mm mortar

Aconit (D 609)   1974 Martinelli

Aconit (D 609)   1974 Martinelli

♦ *1 C 65 class (1965-1970 program)*

	Bldr	Laid down	L	In serv.
D 609 ACONIT	Lorient	1967	7-3-70	30-3-73

D: 3,500 tons (3,900 fl)   **Dim:** 127 × 13.40 × 4.05 (5.80 fl)
S: 27 kts   **Range:** 5,000/18
A: 2/100-mm AA (model 1968) — 1/305-mm ASW mortar — 1 Malafon system — 2 L 5 ASW torpedo tubes   **Man:** 15 officers, 88 petty officers, 125 men
M: Double reduction Rateau GT; 1 prop

Boilers: 2 multitubular, automatic and dissymmetric boilers; steam pressure 45 kg/cm², superheat 450°; 28,650 hp (31,500 hp max)
Electric: 2,960 kw
Electron Equipt: Radars: 1/DRBV 13, 1/DRBN 32, 1/DRBV 22 A, 1/DRBC 32 B — SENIT
    Sonars: 1/DUBV 23, 1/DUBV 43 — 2 Syllex systems
REMARKS: The *Aconit* is a predecessor of the *F 67* type frigate, but does not carry a helicopter. One console controls the SENIT functions and the weapons. Propulsion machinery is very compact, ship is equipped with stabilizers.

ASW DESTROYERS

D'Estrées (D 629)   1972 J. C. Bellonne

D'Estrées (D 629)   1972 J. C. Bellonne

Duperré (D 633)   1974 Guiglini

Duperré (D 633)   1974 Guiglini

♦ *1 antisubmarine modified T 53 class (1972)*

	Bldr	Laid down	L	In serv.
D 633 DUPERRÉ	Lorient	11-54	23-6-56	10-57

D: 3,900 tons (fl)

Dim, S, Range, M, and **Boilers** are the same as the *La Galissonnière* class

A: 1/100-mm AA (1968 model) — 4 MM 38 launcher for ASW TT (L 5 model, 8 in number) — 1 WG 13 Lynx helicopter, 2 Syllex systems

M: 15 officers, 257 men   **Electric:** 1,640 kw

Electron Equipt: Radars: 1/DRBV 22 A, 1/DRBV 51, 1/DRBC 32 E — 2 Decca (1 navigation, 1 surface search) — SENIT
Sonars: 1/DUBV 23, 1/DUBV 43

REMARKS: From 1967 to 1971, ship was used for experimentation. Conversion in Brest from 1972 to 1974 into a command vessel. Returned to active service 21-5-74 in the most final evolution of the ASW version of the *T 47* type destroyer. Hangar has maintenance facilities. Flight deck has a helicopter recovery system similar to that found on the *F 67* frigates and *C 70* corvettes, but simpler.

♦ *5 antisubmarine (T 47 type converted destroyer)*

	Bldr	Laid down	L	In serv.
D 627 MAILLE BRÉZÉ	Lorient	10-53	26-9-54	5-57
D 628 VAUQUELIN	Lorient	3-54	26-9-54	11-56
D 629 D'ESTRÉES	Brest	5-53	27-11-54	3-57
D 631 CASABIANCA	F.C. de la Gironde	10-53	13-11-54	5-57
D 632 GUÉPRATTE	A.C. de Bretagne	8-53	8-11-54	6-57

Returned to service after conversion between 1-1968 and 1-1971

D: 3,900 fl   **Dim:** 132.50 × 12.72 × 4.35   **S:** 32 kts
Range: 5,000/18   **Man:** 15 officers, 92 petty officers, 153 men
A: 2/100-mm AA model 53 (I × 2) — 2/20-mm AA — 1 Malafon ASW — 1/375-mm ASW rocket launcher — 6 TT (III × 2) for K 2 or L 3 ASW torpedoes
Electron Equipt: Radars: 1/DRBV 22 A, 1/DRBV 50, 1/DRBN 32, 2/DRBC 32 A
Sonars: 1/DUBV 23, 1/DUBV 43
M: GT; 2 props; 63,000 hp   **Electric:** 1,440 kw   **Fuel:** 800 tons
Boilers: 4 boilers; steam pressure 35 kg/cm^2; superheat 385°

ASW DESTROYERS (*continued*)

REMARKS: Successful conversion; weapon system renewed, air-conditioned living spaces. Electrical system and safety installations completely redesigned. The T 47 class ships which have been refitted do not have the SENIT system.

♦ *1 T 56 class*

	Bldr	Laid down	L	In serv.
D 638 LA GALISSONNIÈRE	Lorient	11-58	12-3-60	7-62

La Galissonnière (D 638)   1973 J. C. Bellonne

D: 2,750 tons (3,740 fl)   **Dim:** 132.80 × 12.70 × 5.40 (aft)
S: 34 kts (32 fl)   **Range:** 5,000/18
A: 2/100-mm AA Model 54 — 6/550-mm TT (III × 2) K 2 and L 3 T — 1 Malafon system — 1 ASW Helicopter (The hangar overhead is used as the helicopter platform.)
Electron Equipt: Radars: 1/DRBV 22 A, 1/DRBV 50, 1/DRBN 32, 1/DRBC 32 A
           Sonars: 1/DUBV 23, 1/DUBV 43
M: GT; 2 props; 63,000 hp   **Fuel:** 800 tons
Boilers: 4 boilers, steam pressure 35 kg/cm²; superheat 385°
Electric: 1,740 kw   **Man:** 15 officers, 93 petty officers, 162 men

La Galissonnière (D 638)

GUIDED MISSILE DESTROYERS

♦ *4 T 47 type with Tartar*

	Bldr	Laid down	L	In serv.
D 622 KERSAINT	Lorient	6-51	3-10-53	3-56
D 624 BOUVET	Lorient	11-51	3-10-53	5-56
D 625 DUPETIT THOUARS	Brest	3-52	4-3-54	9-56
D 630 DU CHAYLA	Brest	7-53	27-11-54	6-57

Bouvet (D 624)   1972 G. Arra.

Dupetit Thouars (D 625)   1974 J. C. Bellonne

Dupetit Thouars (D 625)   1974 J. C. Bellonne

GUIDED MISSILE DESTROYERS (*continued*)

Kersaint (D 622)   1974 J. C. Bellonne

Same hull and machinery as the *La Bourdonnais class*

A: Single Mk 13 launcher (40 SM 1 or SM 1 A missiles) — 6/57-mm AA (II × 3) — 1/375-mm RL (model 1954) mounted forward — 6/550-mm TT (III × 2) for K 2 or L 3 ASW torpedoes

Electron Equipt: Radars: 1/DRBV 20, 1/SPS 39 A or B, 1/DRBV 31, 2/SPG 51 B, 1/DRBC 31 — SENIT

         Sonars: 1/DUBA 1 1/DUBV 24

Man: 17 officers, 83 petty officers, 177 men   **Electric:** 1,600 kw

DESTROYERS

♦ *4 T 53 type*

	Bldr	Laid down	L	In serv.
D 634 LA BOURDONNAIS	Brest	8-54	15-10-55	3-58
D 635 FORBIN	Brest	8-54	15-10-55	2-58
D 636 TARTU	A.C. de Bretagne	11-54	2-12-55	2-58
D 637 JAURÉGUIBERRY	F. C. de la Gironde	9-45	5-11-55	7-58

La Bourdonnais (D 634)   1974 Martinelli

D: 2,750 tons (3,740 fl)   **Dim:** 128.60 × 12.70 × 5.40 aft
S: 34 kts (32 fl)   **Range:** 5,000/18

Man: 15 officers, 261 men
A: 6/127-mm AA (II × 3) — 6/57-mm AA (II × 3) — 6/550-mm TT for ASW K 2 and L 3 torpedoes — 1/365-mm RL model 54
Electron Equipt: Radars: 1/DRBV 22 A, 1/DRBI 10 A, 1/DRBI 31
         Sonars: 1/DUBA, 1/DUBV 24
M: GT; 2 props; 63,000 hp   **Electric:** 1,160 kw   **Fuel:** 800 tons
Boilers: 4 boilers, steam pressure 35 kg/cm²; superheat 385°

REMARKS: Fitted for aircraft direction and detection. ASW rocket-launcher aft of the second stack. *Forbin* attached as school ship (1973). Forward 57-mm mount removed. Aftermost 127-mm mount removed. Helicopter platform substituted. *D 634* placed in reserve 1976.

Forbin (D 635)   E.C.P.A.

FRIGATES

♦ *E 50 type*

	Bldr	Laid down	L	In serv.
F 763 LE BOULONNAIS	Loire	3-52	12-5-53	8-56

Le Corse, Le Bordelais and *Le Brestois* have been stricken.

♦ *E 52 type*

	Bldr	Laid down	L	In serv.
A. F 765 LE NORMAND	F.C. de la Mediterranée	7-53	13-2-54	11-56
F 766 LE PICARD	A.C. Loire	11-53	31-5-54	9-56
F 767 LE GASCON	A.C. Loire	2-54	23-10-54	3-57
F 768 LE LORRAIN	F.C. de la Mediterranée	2-54	19-6-54	1-57
F 769 LE BOURGUIGNON	Penhoët	1-54	28-1-56	7-57
F 770 LE CHAMPENOIS	A.C. Loire	5-54	12-3-55	6-57
F 771 LE SAVOYARD	F.C. de la Mediterranée	11-53	7-5-55	8-57
F 772 LE BRETON	Lorient	6-54	23-4-55	8-57
F 733 LE BASQUE	Lorient	12-54	25-2-56	10-57
F 774 L'AGENAIS	Lorient	8-55	23-6-56	5-58
F 775 LE BÉARNAIS	Lorient	12-55	23-6-56	10-58

FRIGATES (continued)

Le Béarnais (F 775)   1975 J. C. Bellonne

L'Alsacien (F 776)   1975 J. C. Bellonne

B. F 776 **L'ALSACIEN**	Lorient	7-56	26-1-57	8-60
F 777 **LE PROVENÇAL**	Lorient	2-57	5-10-57	11-59
F 778 **LE VENDÉEN**	F.C. de la	3-57	27-7-57	10-60
	Mediterranée			

Le Brestois (F 762) Scrapped 1-7-75   1972 G. Arra

Le Vendéen (F 778)   1972 J. C. Bellonne

D: 1,250 tons, 1,528 trials, 1,702 (fl)
Dim: 99.80 (95 pp) × 10.30 × 4.10 (fl)
S: 27 kts (29 on trials)   **Range:** 4,500/15
A: 6/57-mm AA (II × 3) — 2/20-mm AA — 12 TT for K 2 and L 3 ASW torpedoes — 1/375-mm ASW rocket launcher (1954 model); *L'Alsacien, Le Provençal* and *Le Vendéen* have only 4/57-mm AA and a 305-mm mortar. See Remarks.
Man: 10 officers, 51 petty officers, 110 men
Electron Equipt: *E 52:* Radars: 1/DRBV 22 A, 1/DRBV 31, 1/DRBC 31 or 32
                Sonars: 1/DUBV 24, 1/DUBA 1 except for *771, 772, 773* which have 1/DUBV 1, 1/DUBA 1.
        E 50: Radars: 1/DRBV 20, 1/DRBN 32, 1/DRBC 31
                Sonars: 1/DUBV 1, 1/DUBA 1
M: GT; 2 props; 20,000 hp   **Electric:** 720 kw except B: 790 kw.
Boilers: 2 boilers, steam pressure 35 kg/cm²; superheat 385°

FRIGATES (*continued*)

Le Breton (F 772)   1974 J. C. Bellonne

REMARKS: Weapons suit different on the *E 50* Class and the *E 52* Class (see photos). The Strombos-Valensi stack can be seen on *Le Bordelais* and the three *E 52-B* ships. Bridges differ on *L'Agenais, Le Breton, Le Basque, Le Béarnais, L'Alsacien, Le Provençal* and *Le Vendéen, Le Basque, Le Breton,* and *Le Savoyard* have been assigned to the Naval Group of Trials and Measurements and have been outfitted with various navigational and communications equipment; they now carry 4/57-mm AA (II × 2). The *F 768* has been put out of commission as of 31-12-75, the *F 770* on 4-8-75. The *F 769* and *F 772* will be placed in the reserve fleet in 1976.

Le Basque (F 773)   1969 M.N.

♦ *9 Commandant Rivière Class*

	Author	Bldr	Laid down	L	In serv.
F 733 COMMANDANT RIVIÈRE	1955	Lorient	4-57	11-10-58	12-62
F 725 VICTOR SCHOELCHER	1956	Lorient	10-57	11-10-58	10-62
F 726 COMMANDANT BORY	1956	Lorient	3-58	11-10-58	3-64
F 727 AMIRAL CHARNER	1956	Lorient	11-58	12-3-60	12-62
F 728 DOUDART DE LAGRÉE	1956	Lorient	3-60	15-4-61	3-63
F 729 BALNY	1956	Lorient	3-60	17-3-62	2-70
F 740 COMMANDANT BOURDAIS	1956	Lorient	4-59	15-4-61	3-63
F 748 PROTET	1957	Lorient	9-61	7-12-62	5-64
F 749 ENSEIGNE DE VAISSEAU HENRY	1957	Lorient	1962	14-12-63	1-65

Enseigne de Vaisseau Henry (F 749)   1973 D.C.A.N.

D: 1,750 tons (2,250 fl)   **S:** 25 kts (26.6 on trials)
  except *Balny*: 1,650 tons (1,950 fl)
Dim: 103 (98 pp) × 11.50 × 3.80 (average) 4.30 fl
Man: 10 officers, 61 petty officers, 96 men   **Fuel:** 210 tons
Range: 4,500/15 — 6,000/10-12
  Balny: 8,000/12
A: 4 MM 38 Exocet — 2/100-mm AA (I × 2) 1953 model — 2/30- or 40-mm AA — 1/305-mm mortar — 6 TT for K 2 and L 3 torpedoes (III × 2)
Electron Equipt: Radars: 1/DRBV 22 A,   1/DRBV 50,   1/DRBN 32, 1/DRBC 32 A
  Sonars: 1/DUBA 3, 1/SQS 17
Electric: 1,280 kw
M: 4 SEMT-Pielstick diesels, 12 cylinders in V (except *Balny*) — 16,000 hp; 2 props
  Balny: Experimental CODAG propulsion; 2 AGO 16-cylinder diesels in V (3,600 hp) with a Turbomeca M 38 gas turbine (11,800/16,700 hp); 1 prop with variable pitch and reversible blades. *Bory* (see Remarks).

REMARKS: Designed for escort duty in different climates; air-conditioned; 45 days' storage space for fresh food. Can embark a flag officer and staff or an 80-man commando unit on board. Two 9-meter LCPs in davits, each can carry 25 men,

FRIGATES (continued)

making 11 knots at full load. These ships have excellent maneuvering qualities: turning circle at 20 knots, 160 meters. Trial speeds of 26.3 to 26.6 knots were attained at rated power and with an 1,800 to 1,850-ton displacement.

Bory: The original free piston and gas turbine generators have been replaced (1974–75) by SEMT-Pielstick diesels. The after 100-mm gun mounts of the *740* and the *749* were removed in 1973 and the after deck converted for a helicopter. This installation is no longer being made and all the ships (except the *Balny*) will have 4/MM 38 mounted in place of the number 2 (100-mm) mount. Mount number 3 will be re-installed. The *Bory* and the *Doudart de Lagrée* will be the first to receive this refitting; they will also have installed 1/DRBC 32 C. MM 38 Exocet launchers are being installed in the *Commandant Bory*.

Amiral Charner (F 727)   1974 E.C.P.A.

Enseigne de Vaisseau Henry (F 749)   1973 D.C.A.N.

DESTROYER ESCORTS

♦ *14 A 69 type.* All built at Lorient.

	Laid down	L	In serv.
F 781 D'ESTIENNE D'ORVES	8-72	1-6-73	11-75
F 782 AMYOT D'INVILLE	9-73	9-74	5-76
F 783 DROGOU	10-73	9-74	7-76
F 784 DÉTROYAT	1974	1975	2-77
F 785 JEAN MOULIN	15-1-75	1-2-76	3-77
F 786 QUARTIER MAITRE ANQUETIL	1-8-75	15-8-76	9-77
F 787 COMMANDANT DE PIMODAN	1-9-75	15-8-76	10-77
F 788 SECOND MAITRE LE BIHAN	15-2-76	1-3-77	2-78
F 789 LIEUT. DE VAISS. LE HENAFF	15-3-76	1-3-77	3-78
F 790 LIEUT. DE VAISS. LAVALLÉE	1-9-76	15-9-77	10-78
F 791 COMMANDANT L'HERMINIER	1-10-76	15-9-77	11-78
F 792 PREMIER MAITRE L'HER	15-3-77	1-4-78	3-79
F 793 COMMANDANT BLAISON	15-4-77	1-4-78	4-79
F 794 ENSEIG. DE VAISS. JACOUBET			

Enseigne de Vaisseau Henry (F 749)   1973 D.C.A.N.

D'Estienne d'Orves (F 781)   1975 M.N.

DESTROYER ESCORTS (*continued*)

D'Estienne d'Orves (F 781)

1975 M.N.

D: 1,170 tons   **S:** 24 kts   **Dim:** 80 (76 pp) × 10.30 × 3

A: 2 MM 38 Exocet — 1/100-mm (1968 model) — 2/20-mm — 1/375-mm RL — 4 non-rotating TT for L 3 and L 5 torpedoes.

Man: 5 officers, 29 petty officers, 41 men   **Endurance:** 15 days

M: 2 SEMT-Pielstick diesels 12 PC 2; 2 reversible props with variable pitch   **Electric:** 840 kw

Electron Equipt: Radars: 1/DRBV 51, 1/DRBC 32 E, 1/DRBN 32
               Sonar: 1/DUBA 25

REMARKS: Designed for coastal antisubmarine warfare. They are also available for scouting missions, instruction, and to show the flag overseas. Can carry a troop detachment of 1 officer and 17 men. The 100-mm gun fire control consists of a monopulse band X radar and semi-analogue, semi-digital computer, and has an optical sight. Only ships fitted for overseas duty will carry 2/MM 38 missiles. Funds have been voted for continuation of work on the frigate *F 74 Enseigne de Vaisseau Jacoubet.*

COASTAL ESCORTS

♦ *11 Le Fougueux class*

	Bldr	L
P 630 L'INTREPIDE	Const. Méc. de Normandie	12-12-58
P 635 L'ARDENT	Augustin Normand	17-7-58
P 637 L'ETOURDI	F.C. de la Mediterranée	5-2-58
P 638 L'EFFRONTE	Augustin Normand	27-11-59
P 639 LE FRONDEUR	Const. Méc. de Normandie	26-2-59
P 640 LE FRINGANT	F.C. de la Mediterranée	6-2-59
P 644 L'ADROIT	Lorient	5-10-57
P 645 L'ALERTE	Lorient	5-10-57
P 646 L'ATTENTIF	Lorient	5-10-57
P 647 L'ENJOUE	Lorient	5-10-57
P 648 LE HARDI	Const. Méc. de Normandie	17-9-58

L'Ardent (P 635)

1975 M.N.

D: 325 tons (400 fl)   **Dim:** 53.03 × 7.26 × 3.10 fl

A: *641, 642, 643:* 2/40-mm AA — 2/20-mm AA — 1 fwd hedgehog — 4 depth charge projectors — 2 depth charge racks. All others: 2/40-mm AA — 1/120-mm mortar fwd — 2 depth charge projectors — 2 depth charge racks.

Man: 4 officers, 42 men

S: 18.7 kts (22 under trials)   **Range:** 3,000/12, 2,000/15

M: 4 SEMT-Pielstick diesels built by S.G.C.M.; 2 props; 3,240 hp

Electron Equipt: 1 Decca radar and 1 QCU 2 sonar.

REMARKS: 6 others have been built in France and allocated as follows: 3 to Portugal, 1 to Yugoslavia, 1 to Germany, 1 to Ethiopia, later given to Italy. The *Intrepid* has been modified for use in torpedo trials. *P 641 Le Fougueux, P 642 L'Opiniatre* and *P 643 L'Agile* stricken in 1975. *P 633, P 637, P 646,* and *P 647* put in reserve in 1976.

PATROL BOATS

♦ *6 ex-coastal minesweepers built in Canada*

PATROL BOATS (*continued*)

P 651 LA MALOUINE (ex-*Cowichan*)
P 652 LA LORIENTAISE
   (ex-*Miramichi*)
P 653 LA DUNKERQUOISE
   (ex-*Fundy*)

P 654 LA BAYONNAISE
   (ex-*Chignecto*)
P 655 LA DIEPPOISE (ex-*Chaleur*)
P 657 LA PAIMPOLAISE
   (ex-*Thunder*)

La Dieppoise (P 655)   J. C. Bellonne

Bldrs: Port Arthur SB, St. John Drydock, Marine Industries, Davie SB, Canadian Vickers. Launched from 11-51 to 1953

D:	370 tons (470 fl)	**Dim:**	50 (46.05 pp) × 9.21 × 2.80
S:	15 kts	**Range:**	4,500/11
A:	1/40-mm AA	**Man:**	4 officers, 31 men
M:	General Motors Diesels; 2 props; 2,500 hp	**Fuel:**	52 tons

REMARKS: Transferred in 1954 under the Mutual Assistance Pact (MAP). Wooden hull and duralumin used throughout. Used as station vessels overseas. Air-conditioned. Numbers *651* and *654* placed in reserve in 1976.

♦ *9 ex-coastal minesweepers, Sirius class*

	Bldr	L
P 650 ARCTURUS	C.N. Caen	12-3-54
P 656 ALTAIR	C.M.N., Cherbourg	27-3-56
P 658 CROIX DU SUD	Seine Maritime	13-6-56
P 659 CANOPUS	Augustin Normand	31-12-55
P 660 ÉTOILE POLAIRE	Seine Maritime	5-3-57
P 707 VEGA	Normans	14-1-53
P 703 ANTARÈS	Cherbourg	21-1-56
P 741 ERIDAN	Penhoet	18-5-54
P 743 SAGITTAIRE	Seine Maritime	12-1-55

D:	400 tons (440 fl)	**Dim:**	46.40 (42.70 pp) × 8.55 × 2.50
S:	15 kts	**Man:**	3 officers, 35 men
A:	1/40-mm AA and 1/20-mm or 2/20-mm	**Range:**	3,000/10
M:	SEMT-Pielstick diesels, 16 cylinders constructed by S.G.C.M.		

REMARKS: Minesweeping equipment removed.

Arcturus   1970 Photo M.N.

♦ *5 ex-minesweepers English "-ham" class* — Built in Great Britain 1954-55

P 661 JASMIN (ex-*Stedham*)
P 662 PETUNIA (ex-*Pineham*)
P 784 GÉRANIUM (ex-*Tibenham*)
P 787 JONQUILLE (ex-*Sulham*)
P 788 VIOLETTE (ex-*Mersham*)

Petunia (P 662)   1975 M.N.

D:	140 tons (170 fl)	**Dim:**	33.43 × 6.45 × 1.70
A:	1/20-mm AA	**Man:**	2 officers, 10 men
S:	14 kts	**Endurance:**	4 days
M:	Paxman diesel; 2 props; 550 hp	**Fuel:**	15 tons

REMARKS: *P 784, 787,* and *788* are manned by the gendarmerie. The *788* will be replaced by the *A 742 Paqnerette* in 1976.

♦ *4 Tecimar small craft*

P 770	**P 771**	**P 772**	**P 774**

PATROL BOATS (*continued*)

P 472 and P 474

1974 Tecimar

D: 30 tons **S:** 25 kts **Dim:** 13.30 × 4.10 × 1.10
A: 1/12.7-mm and 1/7.5-mm machine gun
M: 2 General Motors diesels, Model V-71, 6 cylinders; 240 hp

REMARKS: Molded hull of stratified polyester. Manned by the gendarmerie.

♦ *1 Combattante I class*

	Laid down	L	In serv.
P 730 LA COMBATTANTE	4-62	20-6-63	3-64

Bldr: Const. Méc. de Normandie

La Combattante (P 730)

1974 M.N.

D: 180 tons (202 fl) **Dim:** 45 × 7.35 × 2.45 fl
S: 23 kts **Man:** 3 officers, 22 men
A: 4 SS 11 (IV × 1) — 2/40-mm AA
Range: 2,000/12 **Electric:** 120 kw
M: SEMT-Pielstick diesels; 2 variable pitch props; 3,200 hp

REMARKS: Antimagnetic hull of laminated wood and plastic. Can carry a commando group of 80 men and equipment for a short passage.

♦ *4 Trident class for overseas service*

		Bldr	In serv.
P 670	TRIDENT	Auroux, Arcachon	6-76
P 671	GLAIVE	Auroux, Arcachon	11-76
P 672	EPÉE	C.N.M. Cherbourg	7-76
P 673	PERTUISANE	C.N.M. Cherbourg	9-76

D: 115/130 tons **S:** 26 kts **Dim:** 37 × 5.50 × 1.60
A: 1/40-mm AA, 6 SS 12 missiles **Man:** 1 officer, 17 men
M: 2 AGO V 12 CZSHR diesels; 2 props; 4,000 hp **Range:** 1,500/15

The French Navy has purchased the trawlers *Cayolle* and *Iscran* for training purposes.

D: 156 tons **S:** 10 kts **Dim:** 36 × 6.72 × 2.60
M: 1 Dentz diesel; 560 hp **Endurance:** 4 days

MINEHUNTERS

♦ *5 Circé class*

		Laid down	L	In serv.
M 712	**CYBELE**	15-9-70	2-3-72	28-9-72
M 713	**CALLIOPE**	4-4-70	20-10-71	28-9-72
M 714	**CLIO**	4-9-69	10-6-71	18-5-72
M 715	**CIRCÉ**	30-1-69	15-12-70	18-5-72
M 716	**CÉRÈS**	2-2-71	10-8-72	8-3-73

Bldr: Const. Méc. de Normandie (Cherbourg)

Calliope (M 713)

1974 J. C. Bellonne

Clio

1972

MINEHUNTERS (continued)

D: 465 tons (av)   **Dim:** 50.90 (46.50 pp) × 8.90 × 3.40
S: 15 kts   **Man:** 4 officers, 13 petty officers, 31 men
A: 1/20-mm — 2 remotely controlled sleds with charges
M: diesel; 1 prop; 1,800 hp.   **Range:** 3,000/12

REMARKS: Designed for the detection and destruction of mines laid as deep as 60 meters. Hull made of laminated wood; anti-magnetic and silent aspects stressed. Two independent propulsion systems, one for navigation at sea, the other for minesweeping, both with remote control. Special rudders with small screw-propellers mounted at the base of the after end of the rudder and energized by a 260-hp electric motor giving a speed of 7 knots and permitting exceptional ma-neuverability. Detection and identification of mines by DUBM 20 sonar. The destruction of the mines is accomplished either by divers (six in each crew), or by the P.A.P. (*poisson auto-propulsé*) wireguided sled device. It is 2.70 m long, 1.10 m in diameter, weighs 700 kg, and is moved by two lateral electric batteries linked to electric motors which drive it at 6 knots for a distance of 500 m. It has a television camera and projector and sends an image of the mine to the ship; it can deposit its explosive charge of 100 kg near the mine. After the sled has been recovered, the charge is detonated by ultra-sonic waves. These ships do not have minesweeping gear. An agreement has been signed by the Royal Netherlands Navy, the Belgian Navy, and the French Navy for the joint construction of a new type of minehunter based on the *Circé* class. Fifteen ships will be built for each country and will carry the remotely controlled underwater minehunting sled and a new type of sonar. France will build the prototype.

OCEAN-GOING MINESWEEPERS

♦ *12 ex-U.S. MSO class* (ex-AM). [Numbers between parentheses indicate American designation.]
L: 1953-54.

M 610 OUISTREHAM (ex-*AM 513*)	**M 618 MYTHO** (ex-*AM 475*)
M 612 ALENÇON (ex-*AM 453*)	**M 619 VINH-LONG** (ex-*AM 477*)
M 613 BERNEVAL (ex-*AM 450*)	**M 620 BERLAIMONT** (ex-*AM 500*)
M 615 CANTHO (ex-*AM 476*)	**M 622 AUTUN** (ex-*AM 502*)
M 616 DOMPAIRE (ex-*AM 454*)	**M 623 BACCARAT** (ex-*AM 505*)
M 617 GARIGLIANO (ex-*AM 452*)	**M 624 COLMAR** (ex-*AM 514*)

Eight are fitted out as minehunters.

Berneval

Garigliano (M 617)   1974 M.N.

D: 700 tons (780 fl)   **Dim:** 50.29 × 10.67 × 3.15
S: 13.5 kts (14 trials)   **Range:** 3,000/10   **Man:** 5 officers, 53 men
A: 1/40-mm AA   **Fuel:** 47 tons diesel
M: 2 General Motors diesels; 2 variable pitch props; 1,600 hp

REMARKS: Authorized in 3 groups, transferred by the United States since 1953 under the Mutual Assistance Pact. Wooden hull similar to the U.S. *MSO-421* class (*Agile*): numbers *620/623* and *609, 610, 624* have slight variations. The *Origny* modified in 1960 for oceanographic studies.

Numbers *609, 610, 620, 622, 623,* and *624* have an exhaust stack which is obviously higher in silhouette. The *Bir Hacheim* (ex-*AM 451*) was returned to the United States (4-70) and allocated to Uruguay. The *Garigliano, Mytho, Cantho, Vinh-Long* and *Dompaire* will be modified into minehunters between 1975 and 1977.

COASTAL MINESWEEPERS

♦ *9 French-built*

	Bldr	L
M 704 ALGOL	2	15-4-53
M 737 CAPRICORNE*	5	8-8-56
M 740 CASSIOPÉE	3	16-11-53
M 747 BÉTELGEUSE*	6	12-7-54
M 749 PHÉNIX*	5	23-5-55
M 755 CAPELLA*	5	6-10-55
M 756 CÉPHÉE*	5	3-1-56
M 757 VERSEAU*	5	26-4-56
M 759 LYRE*	3	3-5-56

Bldrs: (1) C.N.M., Cherbourg; (2) Augustin Normand, Le Havre; (3) Penhoët, St. Nazaire; (4) Seine Maritime; (5) Ch. de Normandie, Cherbourg; (6) C.N. Caen.
In service since 6-54: 10 in 1954, 7 in 1955, 9 in 1956; the others since 1957.

D: 400 tons (440 fl)   **Dim:** 46.40 (42.70 pp) × 8.55 × 2.50
S: 15 kts (11.5 sweep.)   **Man:** 3 officers, 35 men
A: 1/40-mm AA, 1 or 2/20-mm AA.   **Range:** 3,000/10

COASTAL MINESWEEPERS (*continued*)

M: Free piston generators (SIGMA) and gas turbines (Alsthom or GT), except for those marked with an asterisk which have 16-cylinder SEMT-Pielstick diesels, built by SGCM; 2 props; 2,000 hp. **Fuel:** 48 tons

REMARKS: Based on the American AMS and British "-ton" minesweepers. Hull in laminated wood and light aluminum which produces a strong, rigid, and light body. Keel and stern in heavy wood. Has mechanical, magnetic, and acoustic minesweeping gear. The *Capricorne* has been given greater degaussing treatment than the other ships. All have one diesel-electric engine (500 hp). The *Algol*, *Antares*, and *Cassiopée* are assigned to Naval Test and Measurements Group. Three identical ships have been allocated to Yugoslavia (*D 25**, *D 26**, and *D 27**). Since 1-6-73, five have been re-classified patrol craft (P) and armed as such. The *Aries* was loaned to Morocco in 1975. *M 704* and *M 740* will be put out of active service in 1976.

Capricorne (M 737)   1973 E.C.P.A.

♦ *21 MSC class* (*ex-U.S. AMS*) [American numbers shown between parentheses.]

M 632 PERVENCHE (*141*)	**M 675 ÉGLANTINE** (*117*)
M 633 PIVOINE (*125*)	**M 677 GIROFLÉE** (*85*)
M 635 RÉSÉDA (*126*)	**M 679 GLYCINE** (*118*)
M 638 ACACIA (*69*)	**M 680 JACINTHE** (*115*)
M 639 ACANTHE (*70*)	**M 681 LAURIER** (*86*)
M 668 AZALÉE (*67*)	**M 682 LILAS** (*93*)
M 670 BLEUET (*116*)	**M 684 LOBELIA** (*96*)
M 671 CAMÉLIA (*68*)	**M 687 MIMOSA** (*99*)
M 672 CHRYSANTHÈME	**M 688 MUGUET** (*97*)
M 674 CYCLAMEN (*119*)	

Bldr: U.S.A. (1951–54) Transferred between 1953 and 1955.

D: 300 tons (372 fl) **Dim:** 43.00 (41.50 pp) × 7.95 × 2.55
S: 13 kts (8 sweep.) **Man:** 3 officers, 35 men
A: 2/20-mm AA (II × 1) **Range:** 2,500/10
M: 2 General Motors diesels; 2 props; 1,200 hp (cruising)
Fuel: 40 tons

Lilas   1972 Photo J. C. Bellonne

REMARKS: These minesweepers are part of a series of 27 ships transferred under the Mutual Assistance Pact beginning in 1953. In contrast with the *Sirius* type, the hulls of these ships are made entirely of wood. [M 667] *AJONC* is used as a base ship for the diving school and has been designated *A 701*. [M 676] *Gardenia* and [M 683] *Liseron* are used as base ships for underwater mine demolition teams and have been named *A 711* and *A 623*. *M 680 Jacinthe* was modified in 1968 as a minelayer. Minesweeping gear and winches have been removed, and an additional deck is extended from the bridge aft. Two additional cathead drums and two wire leads have been fitted from this deck to the stern of the ship. *M 631, 634, 686*

Magnolia (M 685)   C. Martinelli

COASTAL MINESWEEPERS (continued)

returned to the U.S.A. and transferred, 2 to Turkey (1969), one to Uruguay (1968). *M 669 Bégonia* and *678 Glaïeul* returned in 1974. *M 673 Coquelicot* loaned to the Tunisian navy in 1973. *Magnolia* will be fitted out for mine demolition divers in 1976. *M 638, 639, 640,* and *663* will be decommissioned in 1976.

Camélia (M 671)

1974 M.N.

♦ *1 Special type DB 1*

	Bldr	Laid down	L	In serv.
M 765 MERCURE	Const. Méc. de Normandie	1-55	21-2-57	12-58

D: 365 tons (400 fl) **Dim:** 44.35 (42 pp) × 8.27 × 4.04
S: 15 kts **A:** 2/20-mm AA (II × 1)
M: 2 Mercedes-Benz diesels MB 820 EB; 2 Ka-Me-Wa variable pitch props; 4,000 hp

REMARKS: Anti-magnetic qualities. Wooden hull with longitudinal metal banding, also anti-magnetic. Hull itself done in wooden forms with laminated wood which is straight or curved, assembled or glued under heavy pressure following C.M.N.

Mercure (M 765)

procedures. The navigation bridge is light alloy. The propulsion machinery and the electric generators have special bases and are mounted on anti-shock equipment.

A small cabin for the engineman on watch is provided near the stack, slightly below the main deck. This permits operation of the ship with no necessity for personnel to be stationed in the engineroom during minesweeping operations.

The minesweeping equipment includes mechanical cutters for moored mines, magnetic tail with floating gear, acoustic sweep with electric hammer, low frequency acoustic sweeper, explosive sweeper, and ten buoys. The *Mercure* is a prototype for the six sweepers ordered from the C.M.N. by the German Federal Republic. The *Mercure* will be fitted out as a salvage vessel for fishing fleets.

AMPHIBIOUS SHIPS

♦ *2 Assault Transports*

	Author	Bldr	Laid down	L	In serv.
L 9021 OURAGAN	1960	Brest	6-62	9-11-63	6-65
L 9022 ORAGE	(22-7-65)	Brest	6-66	22-4-67	3-68

D: 5,800 tons (8,500 fl) **S:** 17.3 kts **Range:** 4,000/15
Dim: 149 (144.50 pp) × 21.50 × 4.90 (8.70 max load)
A: 6/40-mm AA — 2/120-mm mortars — landing areas for 4 helicopters
Electron Equipt: Radars: . . . — Sonars: 1/SQS 17 on 9021
M: SEMT-Pielstick diesels; 2 props with variable pitch, reversible; 8,640 hp **Electric:** 2,650 kw
Man: *Orage:* 10 officers, 46 petty officers, 145 men
Ouragan: 9 officers, 54 petty officers, 144 men

REMARKS: The *Orage*, assigned to the Pacific Experimental Center has the same characteristics as the *Ouragan*, but some of the equipment was not installed at the first fitting-out: gun batteries, the submarine detection gear, the surgical compartments, the inboard movable decks, etc. Decontamination areas have been stressed and are of the latest model.

Assault transports whose mission it is to carry and place in operation far from home bases:

AMPHIBIOUS SHIPS (continued)

Orage (L 9022) — 1973 J. C. Bellonne

Ouragan (L 9021) — 1975 J. C. Bellonne

(a) helicopters which can land a full commando, sustain troops already ashore, and provide fire support and communication liaison.

(b) landing craft carrying personnel or material (tanks, vehicles, supplies, etc). 349 troops including 14 officers can be carried on board, or 470 for a short distance.

A submergible well 120 meters long can be sunk under 3 meters of water and has a stern gate 14 × 5.5 meters. When ballasted down, displacement reaches 14,400 tons. Movement of the water control sluices and valves is automatic using pumps (3,000 m³/h) controlled from a central post. A removable deck in six sections covers the after part of the well for 36 meters and allows the landing and takeoff of heavy helicopters. Another temporary deck 90 meters in length (15 sections) increases if necessary the stowage space for cargo or vehicles, but reduces the number of landing craft which can be carried inasmuch as the original well is then diminished by half.

If used as a transport, she can carry either two landing craft for infantry and tanks (LCU) carrying 11 light tanks or trucks, or 18 LCM type VI boats with tanks; or, vehicles, and, in addition, heavy helicopters on a landing platform. If employed as a cargo carrier, she can carry 1,500 tons of material. Power lifting equipment includes two 35-ton cranes. Combined command center permits the direction of helicopter and amphibious operations simultaneously.

Ouragan (L 9021) — 1975 J. C. Bellonne

♦ *Type BDC ships (Tank Landing Ships)*

	Bldr	Laid down	L	In serv.
L 9003 ARGENS (*BDC 2*)	A.C. de Bretagne	10-58	7-4-59	6-60
L 9004 BIDASSOA (*BDC 5*)	Seine Maritime	1-60	30-12-60	7-61
L 9007 TRIEUX (*BDC 1*)	A.C. de Bretagne	12-58	6-12-58	3-60
L 9008 DIVES (*BDC 4*)	Seine Maritime	5-59	29-6-60	4-61
L 9009 BLAVET (*BDC 3*)	A.C. de Bretagne	4-59	15-1-60	1-61

Argens (L 9003) — 1972 G. Arra

AMPHIBIOUS SHIPS (continued)

Trieux (L 9007) and Blavet (L 9009)   1970 M.N.

BDC   E.C.P.A.

D:	1,400 tons, 1,750 (av), 4,225 (fl)
Dim:	102.12 (96.60 pp) × 15.54 × 3.20
A:	3/40-mm — 1/20-mm AA — 1/120-mm mortar mounted fwd — 3/40-mm AA (the others)
Man:	6 officers, 69 men **Range:** 18,500/10 **S:** 11 kts
M:	SEMT-Pielstick diesels; 2 props

REMARKS: Design derived from U.S. LST. Can carry 1,800 tons of cargo, 4 LCVP landing craft, and a maximum of 807 passengers. MacGregor type loading hatches. *Trieux* and *Blavet* have been modified as helicopter carriers with a hangar for two Alouette III helicopters.

♦ *2 small cargo carriers* (Batral)

	Bldr	Laid down	L	In serv.
L 9030 CHAMPLAIN	Brest	1973	17-11-73	5-10-74
L 9031 FRANCIS GARNIER	Brest	1973	17-11-73	21-6-74

Francis Garnier (L 9031)   1975 M.N.

D:	750 tons (1,330 fl)	**Dim:**	80 (68 pp) × 13 × . . .
S:	16 kts (13 cruising)	**Man:**	4 officers, 35 men
M:	2 diesels; 1,800 hp; 2 props	**Range:**	4,500/13

REMARKS: Bow-door design, embarkation ramp, helicopter platform. Living quarters for a leopard landing team (5 officers, 15 non-commissioned officers, 118 men) and its 12 vehicles including the "Leopard" armored personnel carriers. Is scheduled to receive: 2/40-mm AA, 2/81-mm mortars.

♦ *12 French LCT class ships:* EDIC (Ships for landing troops and tanks)

Modeled on the LCT 4

9091 (7-1-58)	**L 9094** (24-7-58)	**L 9071** (4-11-67)	**L 9074** (22-7-69)
9092 (2-12-58)	**L 9096** (11-10-58)	**L 9072** (1968)	**L 9082** (1964)
9093 (17-4-58)	**L 9070** (30-3-67)	**L 9073** (1968)	**L 9083** (1964)

Bldrs: 7 Ch. Franco-Belges; 2 Toulon Naval DY; 2 Ch. de La Perrière; 1 Lorient

L 9096   1974 D.C.A.N.

D:	250 tons (670 fl)	**Dim:**	59 × 11.95 × 1.30 (1.62 fl)
S:	8 kts	**M:**	MGO diesels; 2 props; 1,000 hp
A:	2/20-mm AA	**Man:**	1 officer, 15 men

Can carry 11 trucks or 5 LVTs

AMPHIBIOUS SHIPS (*continued*)

REMARKS: The *L 9095* was transferred to Senegal on 1-7-74. The *L 9081* has been modified as a floating workship and the *L 9084* as an electronic store ship (B.A.M.E.) They are listed later.

L 9092   1972 J. C. Bellonne

♦ *C.T.M. 1 to 16 (1966-67) (Motorized barge for cargo transport)*

D:	56 tons (150 fl)	**Dim:**	23.80 × 6.35 × 1.17
Man:	6 men	**S:** 9.5 kts	**Cargo capacity:** 90 tons. Bow door.
M:	Hispano diesels HS 103 S; 2 props; 225 hp		**Fuel:** 3.4 tons diesel

REMARKS: Able to carry various cargoes.

LCM (model **3** or **6**) about 20

D: 26/52 tons   **Dim:** 15.25 × 4.30 × 1.20   **S:** 8 kts
Load 1 30-ton tank

REMARKS: *LCT 9061* has been transferred to the Comoro Islands.

SPECIAL DUTY SHIPS

♦ *1 trials and measurement ship*

	Bldr	L	In serv.
A 603 HENRI POINCARÉ (ex-*Maina Morasso*)	Adriatico	10-60	3-68

Henri Poincaré (A 603)   1974 D.C.A.N.

D:	24,000 (fl)	**Dim:** 180 (160 pp) × 22.20 × 9.40	**A:** 2/20-mm AA
Man:	11 officers, 58 petty officers, 145 men, and 4 civil service technicians.		
Electron Equipt:	Radar: 1/DRBV 22 D	**S:** 15 kts	
M:	Parsons GT; 10,000 hp; 1 prop; 1 bow prop.		
Boilers:	2 Foster-Wheeler (48 kg/cm²; superheat 445°)	**Range:**	11,800/13.5

REMARKS: Flagship of the Naval Test and Measurement Group (Group "M"), for making at-sea tests, measurements, and conducting various experiments as may be requested by the Navy or any other organization, civil as well as military.

The chief mission of the *Henri Poincaré* is to measure as closely as possible the trajectory of ballistic missiles (MSBS and SSBS) fired from the experimental station at Landes or by missile-carrying nuclear submarines and to compute their flight characteristics, especially from re-entry until impact.

The secondary mission of the ship is to help the flag officer to control the naval and air elements in the test area especially in recovery and security functions.

A former Italian tanker, the ship was entirely rebuilt by DCAN at Brest from 1964 and 1967 and received specific equipment: 3 radars (tracking and trajectory measuring for ballistic tests) and a sonar dome. Automatic tracking station. Astro-observatory. Camera-equipped theodolite. Infrared equipment. Transit navigational system. Aerology, meteorologic, and oceanographic equipment. Excellent communication equipment. Programming and transcribing center for all experiments and installations. Heavy helicopter platform. Hangar deck for 2 heavy and 5 light helicopters. Radars: 1 Savoy and 2 Bearn.

♦ *1 experimental guided missile ship*

A 610 ILE D'OLÉRON (ex-*München*) — Bldr: Germany (1939)

Ile d'Oléron (A 610)   1974 C. Martinelli

D:	5,500 tons (6,500 fl)	**Dim:** 115.05 × 15.24 × 6.50	
S:	14.5 kts	**Range:** 7,200/12, 5,900/14	**Electric:** 1,400 kw
M:	MAN 6-cylinder diesels; 1 prop; 3,500 hp		**Fuel:** 340 tons diesel
Electron Equipt:	1/DRBV 22 C, 1/DRBV 50, 1/DRBI 10		

REMARKS: Taken from the Germans as a war prize. Converted in 1957-58 to an experimental ship for missiles.

SPECIAL DUTY SHIPS (*continued*)

♦ *1 deep-diving submarine*

A 648 ARCHIMÈDE — Bldr: Toulon

D: 200 tons   **Weight:** 60 tons
Dim: 21 × 5 × 5.20 — Can reach 11,000 meters in depth

Archimède   1972 J. C. Bellonne

REMARKS: Painted bright yellow

♦ *1 ship for experiments and underwater research*

	Author	Bldr	Laid down	L	In serv.
A 646 TRITON	1967	Lorient	1967	7-3-70	1972

Triton (A 646)   1971 J. C. Bellonne

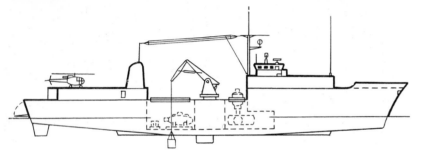

D: 1,410 tons (1,510 fl)   **Dim:** 74 (68 pp) × 11.85 × 3.65 (aver)
S: 13 kts   **Range:** 4,000/13
Man: 4 officers, 41 men. Divers: 5 commissioned and 12 enlisted
M: 2 MGO V 12 ASHR diesels generating 660 kw which are linked by reduction gear to a Voith-Schneider 30 G cycloidal propeller at the stern; forward a Voith-Schneider 26 G cycloidal propeller is powered by two electric motors, generating 400 kw with a reduction gear.

REMARKS: Assigned to the GISMER (*Groupe d'Intervention Sous la Mer*), for deep sea diving and observation. Decompression chamber, laboratories; underwater television, etc., have all been provided. Extremely maneuverable at very slow speeds; can stay positioned above a point 300 meters deep. Helicopter platform; can be used in submarine rescue operations. **Electric:** 960 kw (propulsion plant), 640 kw (auxiliary). Navigational radar, sonar for deep water area search.

Using a 15-ton crane, can lift (a) a 13.5-ton submersible chamber which can be sunk to 250 meters and which can carry two 4-man diving teams (this bell does not float but is wire-tethered); (b) the two-man submarine *Griffon* for underwater exploration to 600 meters. Can be hand-controlled. **D:** 14.2 to 16.7 tons. **Dim:** 7.80 × 2.30 × 3.10 (height), 1 electric motor. **Range:** 24 hours/4 knots. (c) diving devices, sleds (troika, automatically guided). Painted white.

A 643 AUNIS (ex-*Regina Pacis*) — Bldr: Roland Werft — 1956

Aunis (A 643)   1974 M.N.

D: 2,900 tons   **S:** 12 kts   **Dim:** 94.43 × . . . × 11.60
M: 2 MAN diesels; 1 prop; 2,400 hp
Man: 3 officers, 47 men   **Range:** 4,500/12

REMARKS: Former munitions carrier purchased as a transport ship in 1966. Modified in Toulon (1972–74). Used for deep sea diving and sonar experiments in the "Cormoran" project.

SURVEY SHIPS

	Bldr	Laid down	L	In serv.
A 757 D'ENTRECASTEAUX	Brest	7-69	30-5-70	1971

D: 2,400 tons (fl)   **S:** 15 kts   **Dim:** 89 × 13 × 3.90
Man: 6 officers, 73 men, 38 hydrographic specialists
Electron Equipt: 1/DRBV 50
Range: 10,000/12   **M:** 2 diesel-electric main engines × 1,000 kw; 2 variable pitch props. For extremely slow maneuvering, 2 retractable Schottel propellers, also variable pitch, one fwd, one aft.

SURVEY SHIPS (continued)

D'Entrecasteaux (A 757)   1974 J. C. Bellonne

REMARKS: Can take soundings and surveys to a depth of 6,000 meters. 2 radars, 1 sonar; helicopter platform and hangar (Alouette type). Booms, one LCPS, three hydrographic small craft. Painted white.

A 640 ORIGNY

Origny (A 640)   1974 M.N.

D: 780 (fl)   **S:** 13.5 kts   **Dim:** 50.29 × 10.67 × 3.15
M: 2 General Motors diesels; 2 variable pitch props; 1,600 hp

REMARKS: Ex-MSO class minesweeper. Painted white.

HYDROGRAPHIC AND SURVEY SHIPS

♦ *2 modified trawlers*

	Bldr	L	In serv.(1)
A 756 L'ESPÉRANCE (ex-*Jacques Coeur*)	Gdynia, Poland	1962	1969
A 766 L'ESTAFETTE (ex-*Jacques Cartier*)	Gdynia, Poland	1962	1972

(1) for the French Navy

L'Estafette (A 766)   1973 M.N.

D: 956 tons (1,360 fl)   **Dim:** 63.45 (59.75 pp) × 9.82 × 5.85 fl
S: 13.5 kts   **Man:** 3 officers, 29 men; 14 hydrographic service personnel
M: MAN diesels; 1 prop; 1,870 hp.   **Range:** 7,500/13

REMARKS: Former ocean-going fishing trawlers, purchased in 1968-69. Painted white.

	Bldr	L	In serv.
A 758 LA RECHERCHE (ex-*Guyane*)	Ziegler, Dunkerque	4-51	3-62

La Recherche (A 758)   1972 J. C. Bellonne

HYDROGRAPHIC AND SURVEY SHIPS (*continued*)

D: 810 tons (910 fl)   **Dim:** 67.50 (62 pp) × 10.40 × 4.50
S: 13.5 kts   **Range:** 3,100/10
Man: 2 officers, 21 men; 48 hydrographic personnel
M: 1 MABS 398 Werkspoor diesel, 8 cylinders 4 t.; 1,535 hp

REMARKS: Authorized by the French Overseas Ministry. Bought in 1960. Painted white.

♦ *2 specially constructed ships*

	Bldr	Laid down	L	In serv.
A 780 ASTROLABE	Seine Maritime	1962	27-5-63	7-64
A 781 BOUSSOLE	Seine Maritime	6-62	11-4-63	7-64

Astrolabe (A 780)   1968 M.N.

D: 330 tons (440 fl)   **Dim:** 42.70 (36.65 pp) × 8.45 × 2.90
S: 12.5 kts   **Man:** 1 officer, 32 men   **Range:** 4,000/12
A: (*780*): 1/40-mm — 2/12.7-mm machine guns
M: 2 Beaudoin DV 8; 1 variable pitch prop; 800 hp

REMARKS: Authorized in 1961. Air conditioned. Carries two radio-controlled small boats, 4.5 tons each. Painted white.

♦ *Survey vessels*

(Trawlers modified in 1962-63)

A 682 ALIDADE (ex-*Evelyne Marie*, 1952)
A 683 OCTANT (ex-*Michel Marie*, 1955)

D: 128 tons (133 fl)   **S:** 9 kts   **Dim:** 24 × 6.10 × 3.23
M: 2 diesels; 1 variable pitch prop; 200 hp   **Range:** 2,000
Man: 1 officer, 12 men

REMARKS: Endurance 12 days. Painted white.

A 794 CORAIL — Bldr: Thuin, Belgium (1967)

D: 54.78 tons (light)   **Dim:** 17.80 × 4.92 × 1.83
M: Caterpillar diesel; 250 hp   **S:** 10.3 kts

REMARKS: Painted white.

Alidade (A 682)   1972 G. Arra

Corail (A 794)   1975

LOGISTIC SUPPORT

♦ *5 BSL: Medium tonnage ships, each specializing in a particular area for the maintenance of different ships of the fleet.*

	Author	Purpose	Bldr	Laid down	L	In serv.
A 621 RHIN	1959	electronics	Lorient	5-61	17-3-62	3-64
A 622 RHONE	1960	submarines	Lorient	2-62	8-12-62	10-64

D: 2,075 tons (2,445 fl)   **Dim:** 101.05 (92.05 pp) × 13.10 × 3.65
S: 16.5 kts   **Man:** (*621, 622*): 6 officers, 142 men
A: 3/40-mm AA   **Range:** 13,000/13
Electron Equipt: 1/DRBV 50   **Electric:** 920 kw
M: 2 SEMT-Pielstick diesels; 1 prop; 3,200 hp.

REMARKS: Equipped with a 5-ton crane and 12-meter radius; carry 2 LCP(S); Helicop-

LOGISTIC SUPPORT (*continued*)

Rhin (A 621)

Rhin (A 621)   1974 J. C. Bellonne

ter platform; hangar for 2 helicopters. (Alouette type on the *621*). The *Rhin* carries stores and equipment to maintain 2 or 3 large ships for 2 months, plus 12 destroyers, minesweepers, and amphibious ships (maintenance and exchange); 1,700 m³ of storerooms, 700 m³ of workshops, many air-conditioned.

Rhône (A 622)   1972 G. Arra

The *Rhône* is fitted out for the surveillance and assistance of fishing vessels in the North Atlantic.

	Author	Purpose	Bldr	Laid down	L	In serv.
A 618 RANCE	1964	experimental	Lorient	8-64	5-5-65	2-66

Rance (A 618)

Different profile from the other BSL-class ships. An additional deck has been fitted between the navigating bridge and the stack; laboratory ship; radioactive decontamination chambers. Carries three helicopters. **Man:** 10 officers, 140 men, 118 passengers. Assigned to the Pacific Test Center.

	Author	Purpose	Bldr	Laid down	L	In serv.
A 615 LOIRE	1962	minesweepers	Lorient	7-65	1966	6-67
A 617 GARONNE	1964	repair ship	Lorient	11-63	8-8-64	9-65

Loire (A 615)

Garonne (A 617)   1974 J. C. Bellonne

D: 2,320 tons   **S:** 15 kts   **Dim:** 101.50 (92.05 pp) × 13.80 × 3.70
A: (615) 3/40-mm AA   **Range:** 13,000/13
Man: (*615*) 9 officers, 44 petty officers, 87 men
       (*617*) 10 officers, 211 men
M: 2 SEMT-Pielstick diesels 12 PA 4, 1 prop, 3,600 hp.

LOGISTIC SUPPORT (*continued*)

REMARKS: (*615*) helicopter platform; 5-ton crane and 12-meter radius. (*617*) designed for overseas service; metal-working and carpenter shops; no armament; extra deck with lower overhead; no helicopter facilities; fantail has a crane mounted in the center.

The *Loire* is fitted out for the protection and assistance of fishing vessels in the North Atlantic.

♦ *Fresh stores transport*

A 733 SAINTONGE (ex-*Santa Maria*) — Bldr: Duchèsne et Bossière (1956)

Saintonge (A 733)   M.N.

D:	300 tons (990 fl)	**Dim:**	54 × 8.50 × 3.22	**S:** 10 kts
Man:	2 officers, 13 men	**M:**	1 MAK diesel; 760 hp	
Fuel:	51 tons	**Cargo capacity:**	500 tons	

♦ *1 C.E.P. base ship*

A 608 MOSELLE (ex-*Foucauld*)	Bldr	L	In serv.
	Swan Hunter	17-7-47	1967

Moselle (A 608)   1972 J. C. Bellonne

D:	8,200 to 8,700 tons	**Dim:**	146.25 (136.55 pp) × 18.85 × 6.95
S:	15 kts	**Man:**	7 officers, 70 men **Cargo capacity:** 5,380 tons
M:	Doxford diesels; 2 props; 8,800 hp		

REMARKS: Former steamer for the Chargeurs Réunis Company in service after refitting in 1967. Living spaces air-conditioned for 120 officers, 125 non-commissioned officers, 255 passengers.

♦ *1 squadron oiler and supply ship, La Durance class*

A 629 LA DURANCE	Bldr	Laid down	L	In serv.
	Brest	1973	6-9-75	7-76

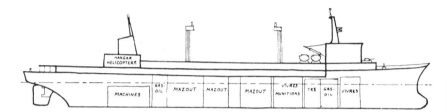

D:	17,450 (fl)	**Dim:**	157.30 (149 pp) × 21.20 × . . .
S:	19 kts (fl)	**Man:**	149 men, 45 passengers
A:	2/40-mm AA (I × 2)	**Cargo capacity:**	9,950 tons
M:	2 SEMT-Pielstick diesels 16 PC 3; 1 variable pitch and reversible prop; 20,000 hp **Electric:** 5,400 kw **Fuel:** 750 tons		

REMARKS: 2 underway replenishment stations, can supply 2 ships alongside and one astern. Capacity: 7,500 tons black oil, 1,500 tons diesel fuel, 500 tons of JP 5, 130 tons distilled water, 170 tons fresh provisions, 150 tons of munitions, 50 tons of spare parts.

♦ *2 fleet oilers La Seine class*

A 627 LA SEINE (7-8-48) — **A 628 LA SAONE** (27-2-48) — Bldr: A.C. de France

La Seine (A 627)   1975 M.N.

LOGISTIC SUPPORT (continued)

D: 8,550 tons (24,200 fl)   **Dim:** 160 × 22.14 × 10
S: 18 kts (14 cruising) **A:** 3/40-mm AA **Man:** 9 officers, 168 men
M: Parsons GT; 2 props; 15,800 hp **Boilers:** 3/27 kg/cm^2, superheat 350°

REMARKS: Carry 9,000 tons of black oil, 1,800 tons of jet fuel, 750 tons diesel fuel, 275 tons of fresh provisions including 82,000 liters of wine. Fast system on *La Saone* for transferring at sea.

♦ *5 oilers*

A 675 ISÈRE (ex-*Caltex Strasbourg*) — Bldr: A.C. Seine Maritime (22-6-59)

Isère (A 675)   M.N.

D: 7,440 tons (26,700 fl)   **Dim:** 170.38 (167 pp) × 21.72 × 9.25
S: 16 kts **Man:** 6 officers, 86 men **Cargo capacity:** 18,200 tons
M: Parsons GT; 1 prop; 2 boilers; 8,260 hp

REMARKS: French tanker purchased in 1965 and refitted with 2 underway fueling stations as well as an astern fueling station.

A 626 LA CHARENTE (ex-*Beaufort*) — Bldr: Haldnes, Tönsberg (1957) C.E.P.

La Charente (A 626)   1974 M.N.

D: 7,440 tons (26,000 fl)   **Dim:** 179 × 21.90 × 9.25
S: 17.5 kts **Man:** 6 officers, 94 men **Cargo capacity:** 19,000 tons
A: 4/40-mm AA (I × 4).
M: General Electric GT; 1 prop; 2 boilers; 12,000 hp

REMARKS: Norwegian tanker purchased in 5-64. Modified to serve as flagship in the Indian Ocean. Helicopter platform and hangar on stern.

A 625 PAPENOO (ex-*Bow Queen*)   **A 632 PUNARUU** (ex-*Bow Cecil*)
Bldr: Built in Norway in 1969

Punaruu (A 632)   1975 M.N.

D: 1,195 tons (2,928 fl) **S:** 12 kts **Dim:** 83 × 13.85 × 5.50
M: 2 diesels; 1 variable pitch prop; 1 bow prop; 2,050 hp

REMARKS: Former Norwegian tankers purchased at the end of 1969, highly automated ships. 2,500 m^3 capacity in 10 tanks.

A 630 LAC TONLÉ SAP

Lac Tonlé Sap (A 630)   1972 J. C. Bellonne

LOGISTIC SUPPORT (*continued*)

D: 800 tons (2,700 fl)   **S:** 11 kts   **Dim:** 71.65 × 11.30 × 4.80
A: 3/20-mm AA   **Range:** 6,300/11   **Man:** 2 officers, 35 men
M: 2/5-cyl. Fairbanks-Morse diesels; 2 props; 1,150 hp

REMARKS: Self-propelled gasoline barge, U.S. class. 1,700 tons cargo capacity; purchased in 1945. *Lac Chambon* scrapped in 1975.

♦ *1 petroleum supply ship*

	Bldr	Laid down	L	In serv.
A 619 ABER WRACH	C.N.M., Cherbourg	11-62	11-63	1966

Aber Wrach (A 619)   1972 E.C.P.A.

D: 1,220 tons (3,500 fl)   **Dim:** 86.55 (80 pp) × 12.20 × 4.80
S: 12 kts   **Man:** 3 officers, 45 men
A: 1/40-mm AA   **Range:** 5,000/12
M: 1 SEMT-Pielstick diesel; 1 variable pitch prop; 200 hp
Cargo capacity: 2,200 tons

REMARKS: Carries diesel oil, jet fuel, gasoline for ports and underway fueling (astern) or anchored alongside.

♦ *1 repair ship*

	Author	Bldr	Laid down	L	In serv.
A 620 JULES VERNE (ex-*Achéron*)	1961	Brest	1969	30-5-70	3-76

     D: 6,485 tons (10,250 fl)   **S:** 18 kts   **Dim:** 147 × 21.50 × 6.50
     M: 2 SEMT-Pielstick diesels; 1 prop; 21,500 hp

REMARKS: Designed 10 years ago as a munitions carrier but not completed. To be converted to a general repair and electronic maintenance ship.

♦ *1 auxiliary repair ship (B.A.A.)*

L 9081 — C.N. Franco-Belges (1964)

     D: 310 tons (685 fl)   **Dim:** 59 (52.9 pp) × 11.9 × 1.65
     S: 8 kts   **Range:** 1,800/8   **Man:** 15 men
     M: 2 MGO diesels; × 500 hp each (1,300 rpm)

REMARKS: Hull size and machinery same as EDIC.

♦ *1 auxiliary electronics maintenance ship (B.A.M.E.)*

L 9084 — C.N. Franco-Belges (7-5-62)
     Same characteristics as *L 9081*.

AUXILIARY VESSELS

♦ *1 coastal transport*

A 644 BERRY (ex-*Médoc*) — Bldr: Roland Werft, Bremen — L: 10-9-58

Berry (A 644)   1974 Guiglini

D: 1,148 tons (2,700 fl)   **Dim:** 86.70 (78.50 pp) × 11.60 × 4.60
S: 15 kts   **Cargo capacity:** 1,550 tons
M: 2 MWM diesels (M.A.N. in *643*) geared to 1 prop; 2,400 hp

REMARKS: Former cargo ship *Worm* purchased and modified in 1964-66.

A 638 SAHEL (1951) — fuel carrier — Bldr: C.N. de Caen

Sahel (A 638)   1974 Guiglini

D: 630 tons (1,450 fl) **Dim:** 53.70 × 9 × 4.40
S: 12 kts **Cargo capacity:** 750 m³
A: 2/20-mm AA **M:** diesels, 2 prop, 1,400 hp

A 614 FALLERON (ex-*Welle*) — German war capture

D: 200 tons (429 fl) **Dim:** 39 × 6.70 **Man:** 11 men
M: 1 Sulzer diesel; 280 hp **Range:** 1,600/8 **S:** 8 kts

REMARKS: Will soon be stricken.

A 734 ISSOLE

D: 610 tons (fl) **S:** 10 kts **Dim:** 48.72 × 7 × 2.95
M: 2 diesels × 500 hp

♦ *3 coastal support ships* (B.S.R.)

Bldr: Ch. de la Perrière, Lorient

	In serv.
A . . . CHAMOIS	1975
A . . . N . . .	1976
A . . . N . . .	1976

D: 400 tons **S:** 14.5 kts **Dim:** 41.50 (36.96 pp) × 7.50 × 3.18
M: 2 SACM MGO V 16 diesels; 1,100 hp; 2 variable pitch props **Man:** 10

REMARKS: Similar to the 14 civilian-manned F.I.S.H. class designed for the supply of petroleum platforms. Hydraulic crane mounted for the recovery of torpedoes. Can be used for coastal towing and oil spill cleanup. Bow prop and 2 rudders. After winch with 28-ton power traction.

♦ *8 inshore minesweepers*

A 735 HIBISCUS (ex-*Sparham*)	A 739 ŒILLET (ex-*Isham*)
A 736 DAHLIA (ex-*Whippingham*)	A 740 HORTENSIA (ex-*Mileham*)
A 737 TULIPE (ex-*Frettenham*)	A 741 ARMOISE (ex-*Vexham*)
A 738 CAPUCINE (ex-*Petersham*)	A 742 PAQUERETTE (ex-*Kingham*)

D: 140 tons (170 fl) **Dim:** 32.43 × 6.45 × 1.70
S: 14 kts (9 sweeping) **Man:** 2 officers, 10 men
A: 1/20-mm AA **Endurance:** 4 days
M: Paxman diesels; 2 props; 550 hp **Fuel:** 15 tons

Armoise (A 741) 1972 J. C. Bellonne

REMARKS: The *A 742* will be modified as a patrol craft for the gendarmerie to replace the *P 788 Violette* which will be reassigned as an auxiliary craft.

♦ *11 netlayers*

	Bldr	Laid down	L	In serv.
A 731 TIANÉE	Brest	1-4-73	1-11-73	1975

Tianée (A 731) 1974 M.N.

D: 842 tons (905 fl) **S:** 12 kts **Dim:** 54.30 × 10.60 × . . .
Man: 1 officer, 12 petty officers, 24 men **Range:** 5,200/12
M: 2 diesels of 480 kw; 1,200 hp; 1 prop

REMARKS: Living quarters air-conditioned, transverse thruster.

		Bldr	L
A 760	CIGALE	A.C. de la Rochelle-Pallice	23-9-54
A 761	CRIQUET	A.C. Seine Maritime	3-6-54
A 762	FOURMI	A.C. Seine Maritime	6-7-54
A 763	GRILLON	Penhoët	18-2-54
A 764	SCARABÉE	Penhoët	21-11-53

D: 770 tons (850 fl) **Dim:** 46.28 (44.50 pp) × 10.20 × 3.20
A: 1/40-mm AA — 4/20-mm AA **Range:** 5,200/12

LOGISTIC SUPPORT (*continued*)

Criquet (A 761) 1972 G. Arra

Man: 1 officer, 36 men   **Fuel:** 125 m³ diesel oil
M: Diesel-electric propulsion; 2 SEMT diesels; 1 prop; 1,600 hp

REMARKS: Offshore command.

◆ *3 U.S. AN class*

	Bldr	L
A 727 ARAIGNÉE (ex-*Hackberry*, AN-*25*)	American SB, Toledo	6-3-41
A 730 LIBELLULE (ex-*Rosewood*, AN-*31*)	American SB, Toledo	1-4-41
A 777 LUCIOLE	American SB, Toledo	16-3-41
(ex-*Sandalwood*, AN-*32*) (C.E.L.)		

Libellule (A 730) 1972 G. Arra

D: 560 tons (850 fl)   **Dim:** 50 × 9.30 × 4.80
S: 13 kts   **Range:** 7,200/12   **Man:** 2 officers, 37 men
A: 3/20-mm AA — 1/76-mm AA — 2 depth charge projectors
M: Diesel-electric propulsion; 2 General Motors V 6 type diesels; 1 electric motor; 1 prop; 1,300 hp

REMARKS: *A 730* in reserve in 1976.

◆ *2 ex-German ships*

	Bldr	L	In serv.
A 755 COMMANDANT ROBERT GIRAUD (ex-*Immelman*)	Norderwerft, Hamburg	12-41	9-47

Commandant Robert Giraud (A 755) 1971 A. Fraccaroli

D: 1,220 (fl)   **S:** 12 kts   **Dim:** 78 × 11 × 3.60
Man: 1 officer, 53 men   **Range:** 9,000/10   **Fuel:** 236 tons
M: 4 M.A.N. diesels; 2 props; 5,720 hp

REMARKS: Former German hydroplane maintenance ship, classified as net layer in 1963. 18-ton crane. 18-meter radius. Will be put in reserve in 1976.

	Bldr	In serv.	In serv. In France
A 759 MARCEL LE BIHAN (ex-*Greif*)	Lübecker Flender-werke	1937	8-48

Marcel Le Bihan (A 759) 1973 J. C. Bellonne

D: 800 tons (1,250 fl)   **S:** 13 kts   **Dim:** 72 × 10.60 × 3.20 (fl)
A: 4/20-mm AA (II × 2)   **Range:** 2,500/13
Man: 3 officers, 47 men, + 22 spaces for additional men
M: 2/16-cylinder GMC diesels; 2 Voith-Schneider props; 2,800 hp

REMARKS: Transferred from the U.S.A., Feb. 1948; 13-ton crane. Tender for Bathyscape Research Group in 1961.

AUXILIARY VESSELS (*continued*)

♦ *5 port netlayers*

	Bldr	L
Y 749 LA PRUDENTE	A.C. de la Manche	13-5-68
Y 750 LA PERSÉVÉRANTE	A.C. de la Rochelle-Pallice	14-5-68
Y 751 LA FIDÈLE	A.C. de la Manche	26-8-68

La Persévérante (Y 750)   1969 Marius Bar

D:	446 tons (626 fl)	**Dim:**	43.50 (42 pp) × 10 × 2.80
S:	10 kts	**Range:**	4,000/10
Man:	1 officer, 8 petty officers, 21 men	**Electric:**	440 kw
M:	diesel-electric propulsion; 2 Baudoin diesels; 1 prop; 620 hp		

REMARKS: Lifting power: 25 tons

Y 667 TUPA — 292 tons, 210-hp motor

Y 688 CALMAR — Converted into an anchorage maintenance barge.

♦ *5 diving tenders*

A 701 AJONC   **A 711 GARDENIA**   **A 723 LISERON**

Liseron (A 723)   1974 M.N.

D:	225 tons (270 fl)	**S:** 9.5 kts	**Dim:** 26 × 6.90 × 3
M:	1 Baudoin diesel DV 8; 400 hp		**Man:** 1 officer, 10 men

REMARKS: Former coastal minesweepers. *Magnolia* (ex-*M-685*) to be modified in 1976 for the same operation.

A 710 MYOSOTIS

Myosotis (with her old number)   1974 M.N.

REMARKS: Former British coastal minesweeper, "-ham" class

♦ *1 base ship assigned to the Commandos Training*

A 722 POSEIDON — SICNAV Saint Malo (completed 6-8-75)

D:	220 tons (fl)	**Dim:**	40.50 (38.50 pp) × 7.20 × . . .
S:	13 kts	**Man:**	42 men
M:	1 diesel 600 hp	**Endurance:**	8 days

REMARKS: To replace the *A 715* which has been scrapped. Was completed 6-8-75.

♦ *2 torpedo recovery ships*

A 698 PÉTREL (ex-*Cap Lopez*, ex-*Yvon Loic II*) — Bldr: Dubigeon — 1960

Yves Grangeon

AUXILIARY VESSELS (*continued*)

D: 277 tons (318 fl)   **Dim:** 30 × 7.80 × 3.50
S: 10 kts   **Man:** 5 petty officers, 14 men
M: 2 Baudoin diesels DV 6; 1 variable pitch prop; 600 hp

A 699 PÉLICAN (ex-*Kerfany*) — Bldr: Avondale (U.S.A.) — 1951

Pélican   1972 J. C. Bellonne

D: 362 tons (425 fl)   **Dim:** 37 × 8.55 × 4
S: 11 kts   **Man:** 5 petty officers, 14 men
M: Burmeister and Wain diesel; 1 prop; 650 hp

♦ *13 small personnel transports, port-based*

Y 710 SYLPHE — Bldr: C.N. Franco-Belges — (1959-60)

D: 171 tons (189 fl)   **Dim:** 38.50 (36.75 pp) × 6.90 × 2.50
S: 12 kts   **Man:** 9 men   **M:** MGO diesel; 1 prop; 425 hp

Y 604 ARIEL (1963)	**Y 698 ALPHÉE** (10-6-69)	**Y 613 FAUNE** (8-9-71)
Y 661 KORRIGAN (1064)	**Y 741 ELFE** (14-4-70)	**Y 622 DRYADE** (1973)
	Y . . . N	Y . . . N

Bldr: Soc. Française de Constr. Navale (formerly Franco-Belges)

Ariel   1972 J. C. Bellonne

D: 195 tons (225 fl)   **S:** 15 kts   **Dim:** 40.50 × 7.45 × 3.30
M: MGO diesels (1,640 hp) or Poyaud diesel; (1,730 hp); 2 props
Man: 9 men, 400 passengers (250 seated).

REMARKS: *Ariel* assigned to C.E.R.E.S., near Toulon.

Y 735 MERLIN — Y 736 MÉLUSINE — Y 671 MORGANE — Bldr: C.N. Franco-Belges (1967-68) — **Y 671** — Bldr: A. du Mourillon

Mélusine   1968 Photo

D: 170 tons   **S:** 11 kts   **Dim:** 31.50 × 7.06 × 2.40
M: MGO diesels; 2 props; 960 hp   **Man:** 400 passengers

Y 664 LUTIN (ex-small craft *Georges Clemenceau*, purchased in 1965)

D: 68 tons   **S:** 10 kts   **M:** 400 hp

REMARKS: Assigned to the Detection School, Toulon.

♦ *3 small craft*

1 former British Fairmile class

A 716 OISEAU DES ILES (1942) seized by customs for smuggling, recovered by the Navy.

D: 140 tons (fl)   **Dim:** 34 × 5.60 × 1.30   **S:** 11.5 kts   **M:** 450 hp

Oiseau des Iles   1972 G. Arra

AUXILIARY VESSELS (*continued*)

1 24-meter boat (formerly on the Rhine flotilla)

Y 760 (ex-*P 9786*) — Bldr: Bodanwerft-Kressbronn — In serv. 1954

> **D:** 45 tons **S:** 18 kts **Dim:** 24.18 × 4.50 × 1.25
> **A:** 8/12.7-mm machine guns (IV × 2) **Fuel:** diesel oil, 4,000 liters
> **M:** 2 Daimler-Benz diesels (model Mb 836 Bb); 2 props; 1,000 hp

A 714 TOURMALINE — 37/45 tons

Tourmaline (A 714) 1974

♦ *2 small craft used for seamanship instruction*

Y 706 CHIMÈRE — **Y 711 FARFADET** — Bldr: Bayonne (1971)

> **D:** 100 tons **S:** 11 kts **M:** 1,200-hp diesel.

♦ *1 self-propelled port fuel barge*

Y 641 FORMÈNE

> **D:** 280 tons light (1,400 fl) **S:** 5 kts **Capacity:** 1,000 m³ of fuel

♦ *6 firefighting boats*

Y 745 AIGUIÈRE — **Y 618 CASCADE** — **Y 746 EMBRUN** — **Y 645 GAVE** —
Y 646 GEYSER — **Y 684 OUED.**

VARIOUS

♦ *1 archeological underwater research ship*

A 789 ARCHÉONAUTE — Bldr: Auroux, Arcachron (25-8-67)

Archéonaute 1972 J. C. Bellonne

> **D:** 120 tons (fl) **S:** 12 kts **Dim:** 29.30 × 6 × 1.70
> **M:** Baudoin diesels; 600 hp; 2 variable pitch props
> **Man:** 2 officers, 4 men, 3 scientific research personnel, 6 divers

REMARKS: Ordered by the Office of Cultural Affairs, manned by navy personnel. Laboratory and workshops, decompression chamber, underwater television.

♦ *1 radiological surveillance ship*

Y 743 PALANGRIN — Commissioned in 1969

> **D:** 44 tons **M:** 1/220-hp diesel

Y 743

TRAINING SHIPS

A 649 L'ÉTOILE
A 650 LA BELLE POULE (1932)

> Bldr: C.N.M. Assigned to Naval Academy Reserve Officers School.
> **D:** 227 tons (275 fl) **Dim:** 32.25
> **M:** Sulzer diesel **S:** 6 kts — 125 hp

A 653 LA GRANDE HERMINE (ex-*La Route Est Belle*, ex-*Menestrel*)

14-meter yawl (1932) purchased in 1964 for the Reserve Officers School

A 652 MUTIN Dundee annex — assigned to the seamanship school

> Bldr: Chauffeteau, les Sables (1927)
> **D:** 57 tons **Dim:** 22 × 6.30 × 3.40 (1.50 fwd)
> **M:** 1 Deutz diesel; 120 hp **Sails:** 240 meters

TUGS

♦ *Oceangoing tugs*

A . . . MALABAR — Bldr: Oelkers, Hamburg (L. 16-4-75)
A 669 TENACE — Bldr: Oelkers, Hamburg, 1971-73
A 674 CENTAURE — Bldr: de la Rochelle-Pallice, 1972-74

TUGS (continued)

(A 669)   1975 M.N.

Tenace (A 669)   1973 Télég. de Brest

D:	1,080 tons (trials) — 1,454 (fl)	**Dim:**	51 × 11.50 × 5.70
S:	15 kts for 1,080 tons	**Man:** 42 men	**Range:** 9,500/15
M:	diesel; 1 prop.	**Fuel:** 500 tons	

REMARKS: Living quarters air-conditioned. Power on after winch: 60 tons.

A 666 ELEPHANT
D: 880 tons   **S:** 11 kts   **M:** 2,000 hp

A 668 RHINOCEROS — A 660 HIPPOPOTAME
D: 640/940 tons   **S:** 12 kts
M: 1,850 hp; power on after winch: 20 tons

REMARKS: Slightly different ships

♦ *Coastal tugs*

A 665 GOLIATH — 380 tons — 900 hp (ex-*Goeland*)
A 684 COOLIE — 300 tons — 1,000 hp (ex-*US*)

Goliath (A 665)   1974 D.C.A.N.

♦ *12 of 230 tons, 11 knots and 1,000 hp — Power on after winch: 17 tons*

A 693 ACHARNÉ	A 667 HERCULE	A 685 ROBUSTE
A 686 ACTIF	A 687 LABORIEUX	A 692 TRAVAILLEUR
A 706 COURAGEUX	A 671 LE FORT	A 672 UTILE
A 694 EFFICACE	A 673 LUTTEUR	A 688 VALEUREUX

Lutteur (A 673)   1974 D.C.A.N.

♦ *Port tugs*
200 tons and 11 knots

Y 608 BAMBOU — Y 652 HAUT BARR

♦ *30 of 105 tons, 11 knots and 700 hp — Power on after winch: 10 tons*

Y 601 ACAJOU, Y 607 BALSA, Y 612 BOULEAU, Y 623 CHARME, Y 620 CHATAIGNER, Y 624 CHÊNE, Y 629 CORMIER, Y 717 ÉBÈNE, Y 618 ÉRABLE, Y 635 EQUEURDREVILLE, Y 644 FRÊNE, Y 654 HÊTRE, Y 655 HEVEA, Y 663 LATANIER, Y 666 MANGUIER, Y 638 MARRONIER, Y 668 MÉLÈZE, Y 669 MERISIER, Y 739 NOYER, Y 682 OKOUMÉ, Y 719

FRANCE (continued)
TUGS (continued)

OLIVIER, Y 686 PALÉTUVIER, Y 740 PAPAYER, Y 688 PEUPLIER, Y 689 PIN, Y 695 PLATANE, Y 720 SANTAL, Y 708 SAULE, Y 704 SYCOMORE.

Meleze (Y 668) 1975

♦ *32 of 56 tons, 9 knots and 250 hp — Towing power on after winch: 3.5 tons*

Y 602 AIGRETTE, Y 721 ALOUETTE, Y 730 ARA, Y 611 BENGALI, Y 625 CIGOGNE, Y 628 COLIBRI, Y 632 CYGNE, Y 729 EIDER, Y 723 ENGOULE-VENT, Y 687 FAUVETTE, Y 748 GELINOTTE, Y 648 GOELAND, Y 728 GRAND DUC, Y 653 HÉRON, Y 658 IBIS, Y 747 LORIOT, Y 727 MACREUSE, Y 725 MARABOUT, Y 675 MARTIN PÊCHEUR, Y 636 MARTINET, Y 670 MERLE, Y 621 MÉSANGE, Y 673 MOINEAU, Y 617 MOUETTE, Y 687 PASSEREAU, Y 690 PINGOUIN, Y 691 PINSON, Y 694 VERT, Y 724 SAR-CELLE, Y 726 TOUCAN, Y 643 TOURTERELLE, Y 722 VANNEAU.

Bengali (Y 611) 1975 D.C.A.N.

Y 680 MURENE — Y 634 ROUGET (1974)
D: 93 tons **S:** 10 kts
M: 380 hp. Towing power on after winch: 7 tons

GABON
Republic of

PERSONNEL: 50 men.

MERCHANT MARINE (1-7-74): 13 ships — 32,159 grt
(tankers: 1 ship — 347 grt)

♦ *3 coastal patrol vessels*

	Bldr	Laid down	L	In serv.
GC 01 PRESIDENT LÉON M'BA	Gabon	1967	6-1-68	1968

D: 85 tons **S:** 12.5 kts **Dim:** 28 × 6.20 × 1.54
M: diesel; 1 prop **A:** 1/75-mm — 12.7-mm machine gun
Range: 1,000/12 **Man:** 1 officer, 3 petty officers, 12 men

GC 02 PRESIDENT ALBERT BONGO — Bldr: de l'Esterel
D: 80 tons **S:** 30 kts **Dim:** 32 × 5.80 × 1.50
A: 2/20-mm **Man:** 17 men. **M:** 2 MTU diesels; 2,700 hp

REMARKS: Wooden hull treated with résorcine (anti-boring worm product).

GC 03 N'GUENE — Bldr: Swiftships U.S.A. Delivered: 4-75
D: 118 tons **S:** 27 kts **Dim:** 32.17 × 29.18 (pp) × . . . × 2.30 (prop)
A: 2/40-mm (I × 2) — 2/20-mm (I × 2) — 2/50-cal machine guns
Range: 825/25
M: 2 General Motors diesels; 3 props **Electric:** 80 kw. **Man:** 21 men

PERSONNEL: 15,500 men with about 5,000 on board ship.

MERCHANT MARINE (1-7-74): 431 ships — 1,223,859 grt
(tankers: 16 — 172,078 grt)

WARSHIPS IN SERVICE OR UNDER CONSTRUCTION AS OF 1 OCTOBER 1975

	L	D	Main battery
♦ *16 frigates*			
2 RIGA (Soviet)	1953-58	950	3/100-mm — 2/533-mm TT
16 HAI	1962-70	300	4/25-mm AA — 4/ASW RL
12 SO 1 (Soviet)	1960-63	215	4/25-mm AA — 4/ASW RL
♦ *About 60 to 70 missile or torpedo boats*			
12 OSA 1 (Soviet)	1964	150	4/Styx systems, 4/30-mm AA
15 SHERSHEN (Soviet)	1966	150	4/30-mm AA, 4/533-mm TT
35/40 ILTIS	1968	30	2/533-mm TT
♦ *Minesweepers*			
10 KRAKE	1956-58	650	1/85-mm AA — 10/25-mm AA
50 KONDOR	1968-71	225	6/25-mm AA
2 HABICHT	1952-54	550	1/85-mm AA — 8/25-mm AA

NAVAL AVIATION

Made up of about 15 Soviet Mi 4 "Hound" helicopters used for ASW and assault operations.

WEAPONS AND SYSTEMS

The majority of these are of the Soviet type. See chapter on U.S.S.R. for further details.

FRIGATES (KSS)

♦ *2 Soviet Riga class*

121 ERNST THAELMANN — 122 KARL MARX
Bldr: U.S.S.R. (1953-58)

D: 950 tons (1,600 fl) **Dim:** 88 × 10 × 3.90
S: 28 kts **Man:** 15 officers, 160 men
A: 3/100-mm (I × 3) — 4/37-mm AA (II × 2) — 2/533-mm TT (II × 1) — 2 depth charge projectors, 50 mines

GERMANY
Democratic Republic

M: GT; 2 props; 2 boilers; 20,000 hp.
Fuel: 300 tons **Range:** 2,400/15
Electron Equipt: Radars: 1/Don, 1/Slim net, 1/Sun Visor B

♦ *12 Hai III class (hull numbers, 400 series)*

Possible names: **BAD DOBERAN, BÜTZOW, GADEBUSCH, LUDWIGS LUST, LÜBZ, PARCHIM, PERLEBERG, STERNBERG,** etc.
Bldr: Peenewerft, Wolgast (1962-70).

1970

D: 300 tons (370 fl) **S:** 25 kts **Dim:** 56 × 5.80 × 3.10
A: 4/30-mm (II × 2) — 4/ASW MBU 1800 rocket launchers, and depth charge projectors.
Electron Equipt: Radars: 1/Pot Head, 1/Drum Tilt
  Sonar: 1/Tamir
M: CODOG propulsion system; 1 gas turbine × 10,000 hp; 2 diesels, total of 4,800 hp.

♦ *4 SO 1 Soviet class*

Possible names: **WOLF, PANTHER, TIGER, LUCHS**
Bldr: Peenewerft, Wolgast (1960-63)

FRIGATES (*continued*)

D: 215 tons (250 fl)   **S:** 28/26 kts   **Dim:** 45 × 5.50 × 2.20
A: 4/25-mm (II × 2) — 4/MBU 1800 rocket launchers
Electron Equipt: 1/Pot Head.   **Man:** 30 men
M: DMR diesels; 2 props; 3,500 hp.   **Fuel:** 20 tons

GUIDED MISSILE AND TORPEDO PATROL BOATS

◆ *12 Soviet OSA 1 class missile boats*

Possible names: **ALBERT GAST, ALAIN KÖBIS, FRITZ GAST, KARL MESEBERG, MAX REICHPIETSCH, PAUL WIEKZOREK, RICHARD SORGE, RUDOLF EGLHOFER, AUGUST LUTTGENS, PAUL EISENSCHNEIDER, PAUL SCHULZ, WALTER KRAMER.**

Bldr: U.S.S.R. — 1964

1968

1970

D: 150 tons (200 fl)   **Dim:** 40.10 × 7 × 2
A: 4/Styx (SS-N-2) systems — 4/37-mm AA (II × 2)   **S:** 35 kts
M: Diesels, 3 props; 10,000 hp.
Electron Equipt: 1 Square Tie, 1/Drum Tilt

◆ *15 Soviet Shershen class patrol torpedo boats*

Hull numbers possibly in the 800 series. Bldr: U.S.S.R. (since 1966)
D: 190 tons (fl)   **S:** 38 kts   **Dim:** 34 × 8 × 1.50
A: 4/533-mm torpedoes (2 on each side) — 4/30-mm AA (II × 2) — 2 depth
    charge racks
M: diesels; 3 props; 10,000 hp.
Electron Equipt: Radars: 1/Pot Drum, 1/Drum Tilt

◆ *5/40 Iltis patrol torpedo boats*

Hull numbers possibly in the 900 series.
    Bldr: VEB Rosslaner Schiffswerft (after 1962).

Type Iltis   1970

D: 25/30 tons   **S:** 50/45 kts   **Dim:** 18 × 5 × 1.20
A: 2 torpedoes   **M:** Probably diesels, 3,000 hp.   **Man:** 3 men

The torpedoes are fired from the stern as was done by British CMB torpedo craft in 1917–18.

GUIDED MISSILE AND TORPEDO PATROL BOATS (*continued*)

♦ *Libelle class torpedo-launching patrol boats*

D: 30 tons   **S:** 50 kts
A: 2 stern-launched TT — 2/14.5-mm MG (II × 1) — two chaff launchers

REMARKS: Probably designed to replace the MTB P6 class which have been scrapped.

MINESWEEPERS

♦ *10 Krake class*

BERLIN	**HALLE**	**ROSTOCK**
BRANDENBURG	**MAGDEBURG**	**SCHWERIN**
ERFURT	**POTSDAM**	**WEIMAR**
GERA		

Possible hull numbers: *221/225* and *241/245*,
   Bldr: Peenewerft, Wolgast (1956-58)

D: 650 tons   **S:** 18 kts   **Dim:** 70 (65 pp) × 8.10 × 3.60
A: 1/85-mm AA — 10/25-mm AA (II × 5) — 4 depth charge projectors — 30 mines
M: DMR diesels; 2 props; 3,400 hp.   **Man:** 82 men

♦ *2 Habicht class*

GREIFSWALD — WOLGAST — Bldr: R.D.A. (1955-56)

D: 550 tons (700 full load)   **Dim:** 65 × 8 × 2.50
S: 18 kts   **Man:** 78 men   **M:** 2 DMR diesels; 2,800 hp.
A: 2/57-mm AA (II × 2) or 1/85-mm AA — 8/25-mm AA (II × 4) — Can carry 20 mines.
Range: 4,000/13

REMARKS: Used as training ships.

♦ *50 Kondor class*

Including **EILENBURG, KAMENZ, STRALSUND, WITTSTOCH,** etc.
   Bldr: R.D.A. since 1968. — Hull numbers 300 series.

D: 225 tons (250 fl)   **S:** 24 kts   **Dim:** 52 × 7.20 × 2
A: 6/25-mm AA (II × 3)   **M:** Diesel; 2 props; 4,000 hp.

AMPHIBIOUS CRAFT

♦ *6 Robbe class*

EBERSWALDE	**GRIMMEN**	**LUBBEN**
EISENHUTTENSTADT	**HOYESWERDA**	**SCHWEDT**

   Bldr: R.D.A. — 1962-64.
D: 500 tons (1,100 fl)   **Dim:** 64 × 12 × 1.50 × 2.20 (aft)
S: 13/12 kts   **M:** Diesels; 2 props; 20,000 hp.

AMPHIBIOUS CRAFT (*continued*)

A: 2/57-mm AA (II × 1) — 2/25-mm AA (II × 1)
Range: 750 (econ.) REMARKS: Utility load 500 tons

♦ *12 Labo 100 class*
Bldr: Peenewerft, Wolgast — 1961-63
Including: **GERHARD PRENZLER, HEINZ WILKOWSKI, ROLF PETERS**

Type Labo

D: 150 tons (285 fl) **Dim:** 40 × 7.50 × 1.50
S: 13 kts **Man:** 15 men
A: 4/25-mm AA (II × 2) **M:** 4 diesels; 480 hp

REMARKS: Can carry 100 tons of freight or 4/5 tanks, trucks, etc.

♦ *5/6 Iltis class*
Modification of the *Iltis* class by removal of the torpedo tubes. Designed to carry underwater demolition teams.

PATROL BOATS

♦ *18/20 Bremse class*
  D: **S:** **Dim:**
  A:
  M:

INTELLIGENCE GATHERING VESSELS
HYDROGRAPH (1958)

Hydrograph

D: 700 tons **Dim:** 50.80 × 8.80 × 3.40
S: 10 kts **Man:** 32 men
M: diesel; 700 hp

REMARKS: — Soviet Okean class. Advanced countermeasure equipment.

♦ *2 based on the Kondor class*
KOMET, METEOR

HYDROGRAPHIC VESSELS

♦ *2 Karl F. Gauss class*
KARL F. GAUSS (1952) — **ALFRED MERZ** (1955).
  D: 200 tons **S:** 9.5 kts

♦ *1 Jordan class*
JORDAN — 1954.
  D: 135 tons **S:** 10 kts **M:** diesel

♦ *3 Arkona class*
ARKONA **DARSSER ORT** **STUBBENKAMMER**
  D: 55 tons **S:** 10 kts **M:** diesel

LOGISTIC SUPPORT

♦ *6 small oilers*

LOGISTIC SUPPORT (*continued*)

♦ *1 Baskunchak class*

LISEDOM

D: 2,500 tons　　**S:** 13 kts　　**Dim:** 70 × 8.9 × 3.8

♦ *3 Hildensee class*

C 37 (ex-*Hildensee*), **C 76** (ex-*Riems*), **C** . . . (ex-*Poel*)

Bldr: Peenewerft, Wolgast — 1960–61

D: 1,000 tons　　**Dim:** 58.50 × 8.90 × 3.75
S: 14 kts　　**Man:** 26 men
M: 2 diesels; 2,800 hp

VARIOUS

♦ *2 cable layers*
♦ *4 torpedo recovery boats Schwalbe class*
♦ *3 small transports*

RUDEN, VILM, RUGEN — Bldr: Mathias-Thesen-Werft, Wismar — 1955–57

D: 585 tons　　**M:** diesel
S: 9 kts

♦ *22 buoy tenders including:*

BREITLING, ESPER ORT, GOLWITZ, GRASS ORT, LANDTIEFF, PALMER ORT, RAMSAU, ROSEN ORT

♦ *4 diving ships*
♦ *6 salvage ships*
♦ *11 barracks ships*
♦ *4 ex-P6 MTB used as radar targets*

GERMANY

Federal Republic

PERSONNEL: approx. 35,000 men

MERCHANT MARINE (1-7-74): 2,088 ships — 7,980,453 grt.
(tankers: 33 ships — 2,140,639 grt.).

SHIPS IN SERVICE UNDER CONSTRUCTION OR ORDERED AS OF 1 OCTOBER 1975

	L	D	Main armament
♦ *24 submarines*			
18 206 class	1971-74	450	8/533-mm TT
6 205 class	1961-68	370	8/533-mm TT
♦ *destroyers*			
3 LÜTJENS class	1967-69	3,370	1 Tartar system 2/127-mm AA, 1 Asroc
4 HAMBURG class	1960-62	3,400	4/MM 38, 3/100-mm AA 8/40-mm AA, 5/533-mm TT
5 z class	1942-43	2,050	4/127-mm AA, 6/76-mm AA 5/533-mm TT
♦ *17 frigates*			
6 KÖLN class	1961-62	1,750	2/100-mm AA, 6/40-mm AA 2 ASW RL, 4 ASW TT
5 THETIS class	1960-62	604	2/40-mm AA, 1 ASW RL 2 ASW TT
1 H. BURKNER class	1961	982	2/40-mm AA, 1 ASW RL
♦ *30 guided missile boats*			
20 S 148 class	1972-76	234	4/MM 38, 1/76-mm AA 1/40-mm AA
10 S 143 class	1975-76	370	4/MM 38, 2/76-mm AA, 2/533-mm TT
♦ *22 torpedo boats*			
12 S 141 class	1957-60	160	2/40-mm AA, 4 to 6/533-mm TT
10 S 142 class	1961-63	160	2/40-mm AA, 2/533-mm TT
♦ *61 minesweepers*			

Breguet-Atlantic   1973

NAVAL AVIATION

Directly under the Navy are the following units:
— 2 groups of all-weather interceptor attack and reconnaissance aircraft Starfighter F 104 G (110 to 120 airplanes);
Starfighter features are as follows:
- length: 16.61 meters
- span: 6.68 meters
- takeoff weight: 9,900 kg
- motor: 1 GE S79 GE 11A turbo reactor, 7,170 kg thrust
- max. speed: Mach 2
- altitude: 50,000 feet
- range: 250 to 600 nautical miles according to equipment
- weapons: 4,000 kg maximum (bombs, rockets, Bull Pup, etc.)
— 1 BR 1150 Atlantic squadron, 20 of which 5 have been modified for electronic warfare.
— 1 Mk 41 Sea King squadron of 22 helicopters for search and rescue operations.

PROJECTS (1973)

— Combat hydrofoil study for NATO (S 161 type)
— ASW 3,000-ton corvette study. Construction of 12 ships is planned.
— studies for a 1,000-ton and another 1,800-ton submarine, planned for 1985.
— replacement of F 104 G Starfighters by the MRCA, although the high price of the latter aircraft may preclude realization of the project.

WEAPONS AND EQUIPMENT OF THE GERMAN FEDERAL REPUBLIC NAVY

With few exceptions, West German ships have weapons and systems of foreign navies.

A. *Missiles*

Surfact-to-air: Standard Tartar SM 1 A or SM 1 on board the 3 *Lütjens*-class destroyers
Surface-to-surface: MM 38 Exocet on board *Hamburg*-class destroyers and *S 148* and *S 143* missile-launching small craft.

B. *Heavy guns*

— Automatic 100-mm 1953 French Model on board the *Hamburg* and *Köln*-class, and a few supply ships
— OTO Melara compact 76-mm guns on board missile boats of the *S 148* and *S 143* classes
— 40-mm (70-caliber) Bofors, in single or twin mounts
— 40-mm Breda

C. *Antisubmarine warfare*

— Quadruple 375-mm Bofors rocket launchers, similar to French models, loaded in a vertical position.
— Torpedoes:

WEAPONS AND EQUIPMENT (continued)

— U.S. Mk 37 on destroyers and on *205*-class submarines as well as on *Jaguar*-class torpedo boats;
— U.S. Mk 44 on *Lütjens*-class guided missile destroyers and the BR 1150 Atlantic ASW patrol aircraft;
— Wire-guided Seal type (20,000 m. range) on torpedo boat *Zobel* (*S 142*), and *S 143* missile boats and the *206*-class submarines.

D. *Electronics*

In addition to the U.S. radars mounted in the guided missile *Lütjens*-class DDGs and the *Z*-class destroyers, the Federal Republic of Germany uses the following Dutch radars (Signaal Apparaten):

LW 02 long range air search (Band D)
SRG 105 multi-purpose search (Band E-F)
SRG 103 surface search (Band I)

Band X for 100-mm and 40-mm fire control.

The *S 148*-type missile patrol boats will have a Triton radar target designation (TH/CSF) and Vega fire control with Pollux radar (TH/CSF). The *S 143* missile patrol boats carry the AGIS fire control system combined with the Dutch HSA Mk 27 M tracking radar.

SUBMARINES

♦ *18/206 class*

S 192 U 13 28-9-71	**S 198 U 19** 15-12-72	**S 174 U 25** 23-5-73
S 193 U 14 1-12-72	**S 199 U 20** 17-1-73	**S 175 U 26** 14-6-74
S 194 U 15	**S 170 U 21** 8-3-73	**S 176 U 27** 21-8-73
S 195 U 16 22-8-72	**S 171 U 22** 23-3-73	**S 177 U 28** 22-1-74
S 196 U 17	**S 172 U 23** 9-3-73	**S 178 U 29** 3-11-73
S 197 U 18	**S 173 U 24** 26-6-73	**S 179 U 30** 26-3-74

Bldrs: Howaldtswerke-Deutsche Werft, Kiel; Rheinstahl Nordseewerke, Bremen

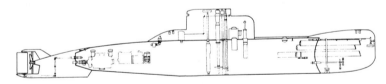

D: 450 tons surfaced/600 submerged   **S:** 17 kts (5 cruising)
Man: 22 men   **Range:** 4,500/5   **Dim:** 48 × 4.50 × 4
A: 8/533-mm TT — 16 wire-guided Seal, or Mk 37 torpedoes, or 12 to 18 mines
M: 1 1,500-hp electric motor; 2 diesels; 750 hp each, 500-kw generator

REMARKS: *U 13* to *U 24* authorized in 1969, *U 25* to *U 30* in 2-70.

♦ *6/205 class*

L	L	L
S 180 U 1 (21-10-64)	**S 188 U 9** (20-10-66)	**S 190 U 11** (2-9-68)
S 181 U 2 (25-1-62)	**S 189 U 10** (20-7-67)	**S 191 U 12** ( )

Bldrs: Howaldtswerke-Deutsche Werft, Kiel; Rheinstahl Nordseewerke, Bremen

D: 370 tons surfaced/450 submerged   **Dim:** 43.50 × 4.60 × 3.80

Submarine type 206 (S 192)   1974 Marineamt

Submarine type 205

A: 8/533-mm TT   **S:** 17/10 kts
M: 2 M.B. diesels; 2 electric motors; 1 prop; 1,200 — 1,500 hp.   **Man:** 21 men

REMARKS: The poor quality of the anti-magnetic steel used in the first six of this class (serious pitting) made it necessary to rebuild *U 1* and *U 2* with regular steel. Beginning with the *U 9* laid down in 1964, these submarines have been built with a new anti-magnetic steel. The *U 1* and *U 2* are now training ships, the *U 3* was stricken in 1968, the *U 4* and *U 8* in 1974.

♦ *Memorial ship: 1 XXI class submarine*

Y 880 WILHELM BAUER (ex-*U 2540*) — Bldr: Blohm and Voss — L: 13-1-45

D: 1,620 tons surfaced/1,820 submerged   **Dim:** 77 × 6.60 × 6.20
S: 17.5/15.5 kts   **Man:** 57 men
A: 4/533-mm TT forward
M: M.A.N. diesels and electric motor; 2 props; 4,000/5,000 hp
Range: 11,000/12

REMARKS: Sank in shallow water in 1945; raised and returned to service as an experimental ship in 9-60. Officially removed from service for scrapping 26-4-68, but eventually she was rebuilt again and put back in service 15-5-70 as an experimental ship.

DESTROYERS

♦ *3 U.S. guided missile destroyers, Charles F. Adams class (author. 1964)*

	Bldr	Laid down	L	In serv.
D 185 LÜTJENS	Bath Iron Works	3-66	11-8-67	3-69
D 186 MOLDERS	Bath Iron Works	4-66	13-4-68	9-69
D 187 ROMMEL	Bath Iron Works	8-67	1-2-69	5-70

Lütjens (D 185)   1974

D: 3,370 tons (4,500 fl)   **S:** 35 kts
Dim: 134.11 (131.56 pp) × 14.32 × 6 (fl)
Man: 21 officers, 319 men   **Range:** 1,600/30 — 6,000/14
A: 1 Tartar Mk 13 missile launcher — 40 SM 1 A or SM 1 missiles — 2/127-
            mm Mk 42 (I × 2) — 6 ASW Mk 32 TT (III × 2) — 1 ASW Asroc
Electron Equipt: Radars: 1/SPS 40, 1/SPS 10, 1/SPS 52, 2/SPG 51
            Sonar: 1/SQS 23
M: geared turbines; 2 props.
Boilers: 4 with steam pressure 84 kg/cm²; 70,000 hp.
Fuel: 900 tons

REMARKS: American numbers *DDG 28, 29, 30;* have several differences, especially in
the profile, from the *Charles F. Adams* design on which they are based. The
installation of the SM1 system and the computerization of various equipment has
been completed on the *D 187 Rommel* and is being completed on the two others.

♦ *4 Hamburg class*

	Bldr	L	In serv.
D 181 HAMBURG	H. C. Stülcken, Hamburg	26-3-60	3-64
D 182 SCHLESWIG-HOLSTEIN	H. C. Stülcken, Hamburg	20-8-60	10-64
D 183 BAYERN	H. C. Stülcken, Hamburg	14-8-62	10-65
D 184 HESSEN	H. C. Stülcken, Hamburg	4-5-63	4-65

D: 3,400 tons (4,400 fl)   **S:** 35 kts   **Man:** 280 men
Dim: 133.80 (128 pp) × 13.40 × 5.20 (fl)
A: 4/100-mm automatic (IV × 1) — 8/40-mm AA (II × 4) — 5/533-mm TT (3
            forward, 2 aft) — 2/305-mm ASW TT-2 four-barrel Bofors ASW rocket
            launchers (forward); can carry 60/80 mines.

Electron Equipt: Radars: 1/LW 02, 1/SRG 105, 1/SRG 103
            Sonar (German): 1 middle frequency hull
M: M.A.N. GT; 2 props   **Electric:** 5,400 kw.
Boilers: 4 with steam pressure 64 kg/cm², 460° superheat; 68,000 hp.

REMARKS: Will be equipped with 4/38 MM to replace mount C, the 533-mm torpedo
tubes will be replaced by two 305-mm tubes for the Mk 44 torpedo. Modernization
will take place between the beginning of 1975 and the end of 1977 in the following
order: *D 184, 181, 182,* and *183.* Chaff launchers will also be installed.

Hamburg (D 181)   1974

FRIGATES

♦ *6 Köln class*

Bldr: H. C. Stülcken, Hamburg

	L	In serv.
F 220 KÖLN	6-12-58	4-61
F 221 EMDEN	21-3-59	10-61
F 222 AUGSBURG	15-8-59	4-62
F 223 KARLSRUHE	24-10-59	12-62
F 224 LUBECK	23-7-60	7-63
F 225 BRAUNSCHWEIG	3-2-62	6-64

D: 1,750 tons (2,100 normal, 2,500 fl)   **Dim:** 109 (105 pp) × 10.56 × 3.70
                                                               (light)
S: 29.5 kts (20 on diesels)   **Man:** 212 men
Electron Equipt: Radar: 1/SRG 105, 1/SRG 103
            German sonar: 1 middle frequency, hull-mounted
A: 2/100-mm automatic AA (I × 2) — 6/40-mm AA (II × 2, I × 2) — 2 ASW
            four-barrelled Bofors rocket-launchers — 4 single ASW TT port and
            starboard.
M: 4 M.A.N. V-16-cylinder diesels, each with 3,000 hp and 2 Brown-Boveri gas
            turbines each 13,000 hp, a total of 38,000 hp; 2 props
Electric: 2,700 kw   **Fuel:** 333 tons

REMARKS: The rocket-launchers carry 72 projectiles. Mine-laying capability. 2 diesels
and 1 gas turbine on each of the 2 shafts.

FRIGATES (continued)

Karlsruhe (F 223)   1974

Z 4 (D 178)   1974

CORVETTES

♦ *5 former torpedo recovery boats, converted and designated "corvettes"*

P 6052 THETIS (21-3-60)	**P 6055 TRITON** (5-8-61)
P 6053 HERMES (9-8-60)	**P 6056 THESEUS** (20-3-62)
P 6054 NAJADE (6-12-60)	

Bldr: Roland Werft (Bremen-Hemelingen)

♦ *8 class 122*

The Federal German Navy intends to lay down as soon as possible eight 3,400-to-3,600-ton ships. These Class 122 ships will be based on The Netherlands *Kortenaer* standard frigate. They will have Harpoon and Sea Sparrow missiles.

♦ *4 ex-U.S. Fletcher class destroyers*

	Bldr	L
D 171 Z 2 (ex-*DD-500 Ringgold*)	Federal SB&DD	11-11-42
D 172 Z 3 (ex-*DD-516 Wadsworth*)	Bath Iron Works	10-1-43
D 178 Z 4 (ex-*DD-571 Claxton*)	Consolidated Steel	1-4-42
D 179 Z 5 (ex-*DD-572 Dyson*)	Consolidated Steel	15-4-42

D: 2,050 tons (2,750 fl).   **Dim:** 114.85 × 12.03 × 5.50
S: 30/32 kts   **Man:** 350 men
Range: 1,260/35 4,400/15
Electron Equipt: U.S.
A: 4/127-mm AA semi-automatic 38-cal (I × 4) — 6/76-mm (II × 3) — 5/533-mm TT (V × 1) — 2 hedgehogs — Z 1 is armed with 2 fixed 305-mm Mk 44 torpedoes.
M: General Electric GT; 2 props; 4 Babcock boilers, 60,000 hp.   **Fuel:** 650 tons

REMARKS: Loaned by the U.S.A., later transferred: the *Z 1* in 1958, the *Z 2* in 1959, the others in 1960. *Z 6* removed from service in 1968, *Z 1* in 1972.

Najade (P 6054)   1974

D: 604 tons   **S:** 23.5 kts   **Dim:** 69.70 × 8.50 × 2.30
A: 2/40-mm AA (II × 1 aft) — 1 ASW Bofors rocket launcher (fwd) — 2 ASW TT   **Man:** 5 officers, 43 men
M: 2 M.A.N. diesels; 2 props; 6,800 hp.

REMARKS: Well-designed ships for operations in the Belts and the Baltic.

CORVETTES (continued)

P 6141   1973

◆ **A 1459 HANS BURKNER** (16-6-61) — Bldr: Atlas Werke, Bremen

D: 982 tons   **Dim:** 80.70 × 9.40 × 2.80
S: 24 kts   **Man:** 49 men
M: 4 M.A.N. diesels; 2 props; 13,600 hp.
A: 2/40-mm AA (II × 1) — 1 four-barrel Bofors rocket launcher — 2 ASW
        torpedoes.

REMARKS: Named for the designer of the famous dreadnoughts of the Imperial Navy
from 1909 to 1918.

◆ *20 guided missile boats, type S 148*

L	L	L	L
P 6141 27-9-72	**P 6146** 21-5-73	**P 6151** 25-4-74	**P 6156** 30-10-74
P 6142 12-12-72	**P 6147** 20-9-72	**P 6152** 25-3-74	**P 6157** 13-2-75
P 6143 7-3-73	**P 6148** 10-9-73	**P 6153** 4-7-74	**P 6178** 26-2-75
P 6144 5-5-73	**P 6149** 11-1-74	**P 6154** 8-7-74	**P 6159** 15-5-75
P 6145 3-7-73	**P 6150** 10-12-73	**P 6155** 25-3-74	**P 6160** 26-5-75

Bldr: Construction Mécaniques de Normandie (Cherbourg) with Lürssen (Vegesack), who built the boats carrying even number designations from number *P 6146*.
All were armed at Lorient.

D: 234 tons (265 fl)   **Dim:** 47 (44 pp) × 7.10 × 2.50 full load
S: 35.5 kts
A: 4/MM 38 Exocet — 1/76-mm AA light OTO Melara compact 62-caliber
        (fwd) — 1/40-mm Bofors 70-caliber (aft); 8 mines will eventually be placed
        on board, four on each side at the stern, and the 40-mm will be removed.
Electron Equipt: Radars: 1 navigation, 1 Triton target designation radar, 1
                     Fire control director Vega with Pollux
M: 4 MTU diesels; MD 872 type with 3,600 hp (1,790 rpm); 4 props
        Fuel: 39 tons
Electric: 270 kw   **Range:** 900/30
Man: 4 officers, 17 petty officers, 9 men

P 6141   1973 M.N.

P 6141   1973

CORVETTES (*continued*)

REMARKS: Authorized 18-12-70. *La Combattante II A 4 L* class of the C.M.N. Steel hull; superstructure special lightweight metal; 2 rudders; trellis mast. The MM 38 are arranged in two pairs on the ship's axis abaft the bridge and with a 45° inclination, the forward set firing to starboard, the after set to port.

♦ *10 type S 143 missile-launching patrol boats*

	L		L
P 6111	(22-10-73)	P 6116	(12-12-74)
P 6112	(21-3-74)	P 6117	(6-3-75)
P 6113	(8-9-74)	P 6118	
P 6114	(74-4-75)	P 6119	(11-6-69)
P 6115	(18-8-74)	P 6120	

Authorized 29-4-71

Bldr: Lürssen, Vegesack (7), Kröger, Rendsburg (3).

Type 141   S. Terzibaschitsch

D: 160 tons (190 fl)   **Dim:** 42.80 × 7.14 × 2.20
S: 42 kts (trials 43.5)   **Man:** 39 men
A: 2/40-mm AA, 4 or 6/533-mm TT
M: Maybach diesels (16 cylinders) or Daimler-Benz (20 cylinders); 4 props; 4 × 3,000 hp

REMARKS: Wooden hull, frame, keel and superstructure of metal alloy. Can carry four mines in place of the torpedo tubes. *P 6062* and *P 6090* to be transferred to the Tunisian Navy. *P 6068, P 6070, P 6071, P 6072, P 6073, P 6075,* and *P 6077* to be transferred to the Greek Navy.

♦ *10 type S 142*

P 6092 ZOBEL (21-8-61)	P 6097 PUMA (26-10-61)
P 6093 WIESEL (16-3-61)	P 6098 GEPARD (14-4-62)
P 6094 DACHS (10-6-61)	P 6099 HYÄNE (31-3-62)

D: 425 tons   **Dim:** 57.45 (54.40 pp) × 7.62 × 2.82
S: 36 kts (32 fl)   **Man:** 40 men
A: 4/MM 38, 2/76-mm AA light OTO-Melara compact, one fwd, one aft, 1/533-mm Seal wire-guided torpedo on each side.
M: 4 MTU diesels 16 cylinders V; 4 non-variable props; 16,000 hp.
Fuel: 116 tons   **Range:** 2,600/16 — 1,600/30

REMARKS: Agis fire control coupled with HSA Mk 27 M search radar. Can make way for 2 hours at flank speed, 18,000 hp.

TORPEDO FAST PATROL BOATS (*Schnellboote*)

♦ *12 type S 141*

P 6062 WOLF (21-9-57)	P 6072 FALKE ( )
P 6064 PANTHER (18-10-58)	P 6073 GEIER (11-0-58)
P 6068 SEEADLER (1-2-58)	P 6074 BUSSARD (29-11-58)
P 6069 ALBATROS (20-3-58)	P 6075 HABICHT (21-2-59)
P 6070 KONDOR ( )	P 6077 KORMORAN (16-7-59)
P 6071 GREIF ( )	P 6090 PINGUIN (4-7-60)

Frettchen (P 6100)   1974

TORPEDO FAST PATROL BOATS (*Schnellboote*) (*continued*)

P 6095 HERMELIN (5-8-61)   **P 6100 FRETTCHEN** (20-11-62)
P 6096 NERZ (5-9-61)   **P 6101 OZELOT** (4-2-63)

Same characteristics as the *S 141* except: **D:** 225 tons **A:** 2/40-mm — 2 wire-guided Seal torpedoes. Fire control radar: HSA Mk 17. **Man:** 42 men

MINESWEEPERS

♦ *18 type 320*

M 1070 GÖTTINGEN (14-4-57)   **M 1079 DÜREN** (12-6-58)
M 1071 KOBLENZ (6-5-57)   **M 1080 MARBURG** (4-4-58)
M 1072 LINDAU (16-2-57)   **M 1081 KONSTANZ** (30-10-58)
M 1073 SCHLESWIG (1-10-57)   **M 1082 WOLFSBURG** (10-2-59)
M 1074 TÜBINGEN (12-8-57)   **M 1083 ULM** (10-2-59)
M 1075 WETZLAR (24-6-57)   **M 1084 FLENSBURG** (7-4-59)
M 1076 PADERBORN (5-12-57)   **M 1085 MINDEN** (9-6-59)
M 1077 WEILHEIM (4-2-58)   **M 1086 FULDA** (19-8-59)
M 1078 CUXHAVEN (10-4-58)   **M 1087 VÖLKLINGEN** (20-10-59)

Bldr: Burmester, Bremen-Burg

Marburg (1080)   1974

D:	365 tons (524 fl)	**Dim:**	44.70 × 8.30 × 2.50
S:	16 kts	**Man:**	46 men
A:	1/40-mm AA	**M:**	Maybach diesels, 2 props; 4,000 hp
Fuel:	40 tons diesel	**Range:**	850/16

REMARKS: *M 1084* and *1086* fitted out as minehunters. Ten others will be so fitted between 1975 and 1977 (Sonar: Plessey and the French PAP). Six others will be fitted with the Troika system between 1978 and 1980.

♦ *22 patrol minesweepers, types 340 and 341*

M 1051 CASTOR (12-7-62)   **M 1064 DENEB** (11-9-61)
M 1054 POLLUX (15-9-60)   **M 1065 JUPITER** (15-2-61)
M 1055 SIRIUS (15-3-61)   **M 1067 ALTAIR** (20-4-61)
M 1056 RIGEL (2-4-62)   **M 1069 WEGA** (10-10-62)
M 1057 REGULUS (18-12-61)   **M 1090 PERSEUS** (22-9-60)
M 1063 WAAGE (9-4-59)   **M 1092 PLUTO** (9-8-60)
M 1058 MARS (1-12-60)   **M 1093 NEPTUN** (9-6-60)

M 1059 SPICA (25-5-60)   **M 1094 WIDDER** (13-3-59)
M 1060 SKORPION (29-5-63)   **M 1095 HERKULES** (25-8-60)
Y 849 STIER (30-10-58)   **M 1096 FISCHE** (14-7-59)
M 1062 SCHUTZE (20-5-58)   **M 1097 GEMMA** (6-10-59)

Bldr: Schlichting, Travemünde; Schürenstedt, Bardenfleth; Abeking and Rasmussen, Lemwerde (1958-63)

REMARKS: The *Y 849* has no weapons.

♦ *22 patrol minesweepers, types 340 and 341*

Herkules (M 1095)   1974

Waage. Converted into a patrol boat; note the 40-mm AA on the stern.

D:	230 tons (280 fl)	**S:**	24.6 kts	**Dim:**	47.20 × 6.80 × 2.20
Man:	39 men	**A:**	1/40-mm AA (see Remarks)		
M:	Maybach or Mercedes-Benz diesels; 3,600 hp. 2 Escher-Wyss props				
Fuel:	22 tons				

REMARKS: Multi-purpose ships which can be employed as minesweepers, coastal patrol craft (Armam: 2/40-mm AA), and minelayers (two mine racks), the minesweeping gear having been removed in the latter two instances. *Stier* (former *M 1061*), a submarine rescue ship, has been given a new designation.

♦ *300 type*

	Bldr	Laid down	L	In serv.
Y 836 HOLNIS	Abeking	1964	20-5-66	1966

D:	180 tons	**Dim:**	35.60 × 7.40 × 2.10
S:	14.5 kts	**Man:**	21 men
A:	1/20-mm AA	**M:**	MB diesels; 2 props; 2,000 hp.	**Fuel:**	13 tons

MINESWEEPERS (*continued*)

Holnis (now carries number 836)

REMARKS: Assigned as a communications experimental ship.

♦ *20 types 343 (a) and 344 (b)*

(a) Y 1643 NIOBE (8-8-57)
   Y 806 HANSA (18-11-57)
   M 1650 ARIADNE (23-4-60)
   M 1651 FREYA (25-6-60)
   M 1652 VINETA (17-9-60)
   M 1653 HERTHA (18-2-61)
   M 1654 NYMPHE (20-9-62)
   M 1655 NIXE (3-12-62)
   M 1656 AMAZONE (27-2-63)
   M 1657 GAZELLE (14-8-63)

   Bldr: Kröger, Rendsburg

(b) Y 1652 FRAUENLOB (8-4-65)
   Y 1653 NAUTILUS (19-5-65)
   Y 1654 GEFION (16-9-65)
   Y 1655 MEDUSA (25-1-66)
   Y 1656 UNDINE (16-5-66)
   Y 1657 MINERVA (25-8-66)
   Y 1658 DIANA (15-12-66)
   Y 1659 LORELEY (14-3-67)
   Y 1660 ATLANTIS (20-6-67)
   Y 1661 ACHERON (11-10-67)

   Bldr: Kröger, Rendsburg

D: (a) 185 tons (210 fl)
      (b) 204 tons (230 fl)
Dim: 34.60 × 6.50 × 7.10   **S:** 14 kts
      37.90 × 7.20 × 2
Man: 4 officers, 24 men
Range: 740/14
A: 1/40-mm AA   **Fuel:** 30 tons

M: MB diesels; 2 props; 1,900 hp.
REMARKS: *Y 806* without weapons.

Minerva (Y 1657)

AMPHIBIOUS CRAFT

♦ *22 small landing craft, type 520*

L 700 FLUNDER	L 789 BRASSE
L 761 KARPFEN	L 790 BARBE
L 762 LACHS	L 791 DELPHIN
L 763 PLOTZE	L 792 DORSCH
L 764 ROCHEN	L 793 FELCHEN
L 765 SCHLEI	L 794 FORELLE
L 766 STOR	L 795 INGER
L 767 TUMMLER	L 796 MAKRELE
L 768 WELS	L 797 MURANE
L 769 ZANDER	L 798 RENKE
L 788 BUTT	L 799 SALM

   Bldr: Howaldtswerke, Hamburg, 1965-66.

Butt   1971 Photo Terzibaschitsch

AMPHIBIOUS CRAFT (*continued*)

D:	197 tons (397 fl)	**Dim:**	41.45 (39.93 pp) × 8.84 × 1.60
S:	12 kts	**M:**	2 GM diesels; 1,380 hp
A:	1/20-mm AA	**Man:**	17 men

REMARKS: Design based on the American LCU; carries 160/225 tons.

♦ *28 LCM 8 (U.S.) class landing craft*

LCM 1-28 (1965-67)

D:	116 tons (140 fl)	**Dim:**	23 × 6.10 × . . .
M:	2 diesels; 1,320 hp.	**S:**	11 kts
Cargo capacity:	60 tons (at 8 knots)		

LOGISTIC SUPPORT

♦ *11 flotilla supply ships 401 and 402 B class.*

(a) *For fast patrol boats*

A 58 RHEIN (10-12-59)	**A 64 RUHR** (18-8-60)
A 61 ELBE (5-5-60)	**A 66 NECKAR** (26-6-61)
A 62 WESER (11-6-60)	**A 68 WERRA** (26-3-63)
A 63 MAIN (23-7-60)	**A 69 DONAU** (26-12-60)

Elbe (A 61)   1974

(b) *For minesweepers*

A 54 ISAR (14-7-62)	**A 65 SAAR** (11-3-61)	**A 67 MOSEL** (15-12-60)

(c) *For submarines*

A 55 LAHN (21-11-61)	**A 56 LECH** (4-5-62)

Laid down: 1959/61 — In serv: 1961/64

D:	(a) 2,370 tons (2,540 fl)	
	(b) and (c) 2,460 tons (2,680 fl)	
Dim:	98.60 × 11.80 × 3.70 (light, 5.20 fl)	
S:	21/20 kts (trials, 22)	
Man:	98 men (space for 40 officers, 40 petty officers, 130 non-rated men)	
A:	2/100-mm AA (I × 2) — 4/40-mm AA (II × 2) — ASW weapons (except for 55, 56: 4/40-mm AA)	
Electron Equipt:	Radars: 1/SRG 105, 1/SRG 103, 2 band X fire control.	

Lahn (A 55)   1973

M:	6 Maybach diesels, each with 1,900 hp; Mercedes-Benz in the *55* and *56;* 2 variable pitch props

REMARKS: The small craft supply ships carry 200 tons of fuel oil, 40 reserve torpedoes, *55, 56* and *58* have an additional 200 tons of stores, *64, 66, 68,* and *69* are training ships. *65* and *67* have a helicopter platform and hospital spaces for rescued personnel, especially those from cold weather accidents. They are considered air-safety ships and are manned by civilian personnel. The *A 62 Weser* and *A 64 Rhur* will be transferred to the Greek and Turkish Navies respectively.

♦ *The German Federal Navy has built a number of supply ships with the same hull and machinery as given below, but the internal fitting-out and installed equipment will be determined by the ship function.*

Common characteristics:

D:	3,200/3,400 tons	**Dim:**	104 (98 pp) × 13.90 × 3.90
S:	17 kts	**Cargo:**	1,100 tons
M:	Maybach *MD 872* diesels; 2 Escher-Wyss props; 5,600 hp.		

(1) *8 multi-purpose supply ships, type 701*

A 1411 LÜNEBURG (5-3-65)	**A 1415 SAARBURG** (15-7-66)
A 1412 COBURG (15-12-65)	**A 1416 NIENBURG** (26-7-66)
A 1413 FREIBURG (15-4-66)	**A 1417 OFFENBURG** (10-9-66)
A 1414 GLÜCKSBURG (3-5-66)	**A 1418 MEERSBURG** (22-3-67)

Bldr: Flensburger Schiffbau; Vulkan, Vegesack; Blohm & Voss, Hamburg

Cargo capacity: 1,100 tons, with 640 tons black oil, 200 tons of munitions, 100 tons of spare parts, 130 tons of fresh water, 30 tons of provisions.

Man:	68 men
A:	4/40-mm AA (II × 2)

REMARKS: Four of them will be lengthened to accommodate missiles and torpedoes.

LOGISTIC SUPPORT (*continued*)

Saarburg (A 1415)

Coburg (A 1412)

(2) *2 ammunition ships, type 760*

A 1435 WESTERWALD (25-2-66)   **A 1436 ODENWALD** (5-5-66)

    Bldr: Lübecker Flenderwerke (*W*), Orenstein & Koppel, Lubec (*O.*).

    A: 4/40-mm AA (II × 2)   **Man:** 58 men

(3) *2 mine supply ships, type 762* — Bldr: Blohm & Voss, Hamburg

A 1437 SACHSENWALD (10-12-66)   **A 1438 STEIGERWALD** (10-3-67)

    D: 3,850 (full load)   **S:** 18 kts   **Range:** 3,500

    A: 4/40-mm   **Man:** 65 men

NOTE: The construction of additional *Sachsenwald* series of torpedo supply ships has been cancelled.

Westerwald (A 1435)   1974

Steigerwald (A 1438)   1974

♦ *1 munitions transport.*

A 1409 SCHWARZWALD (ex-*Almathée*). — Bldr: A.C. de Bretagne — L: 7-5-55

Schwarzwald (A 1400)   Photo Terzibaschitsch

LOGISTIC SUPPORT (*continued*)

D: 2,101 grt   **Dim:** 85 × 13 × 6.10
S: 14 kts   **M:** Pielstick diesel; 1 prop; 3,000 hp.
Armament removed.
REMARKS: Former cargo ship for the Soc. Navale Caennaise.

♦ *2 repair ships*

A 512 ODIN (ex-*Ulysses*, ARB-9)   **A 513 WOTAN** (ex-*Diomedes*, ARB-11)
Transferred by the U.S.A. in 6-61.

Odin (A 512)

D: 1,625 tons (3,455 fl)   **Dim:** 100 × 15.20 × 2.80
S: 11 kts   **A:** 8/40-mm (II × 4)
Man: 187 men (civil personnel)   **Range:** 2,000/11
M: General Motors diesels; 2 props; 1,800 hp.
Fuel: 438 tons

REMARKS: 2 modified former LSTs.

♦ *11 oilers*

4 type 703 — Bldr: Lindenau, Friedrichsort

A 1424 WALCHENSEE (10-7-66)   **A 1426 TEGERNSEE** (27-10-66)
A 1425 AMMERSEE (22-9-66)   **A 1427 WESTENSEE** (8-4-67)

Westensee (A 1427)   1974

D: 2,060 tons   **Dim:** 71 × 11.20 × 4.10
Cargo capacity: 1,130 tons   **S:** 12.5 kts
M: diesels; 2 props; 1,400 hp

A 1407 WITTENSEE (ex-*Sioux*) (23-9-58)
D: 1,200 tons   **Dim:** 63.55 × 9.90 × 4.57
Cargo capacity: 1,230 tons   **Man:** . . .
S: 12 kts   **M:** diesel; 1,250 hp

REMARKS: *Bodensee* has been stricken.

A 1428 HARZ (ex-*Clare Jung*) (1953) — 1,308/3,696 tons — **S:** 12 kts
A 1429 EIFEL (ex-*Friedrich Jung*) (1958) — 2,279/4,700 tons — **S:** 12 kts
A 1439 FRANKENLAND (ex-*Münsterland*, ex-*Powell*) (1950) — 16,060 tons (fl)
    S: 12 kts
A 1440 EMSLAND (ex-*Antonio Zotti*) — 9,211 tons (6,200 grt)
A 1441 MÜNSTERLAND (ex-*Angela Germana*) — 9,154 tons (6,131 grt)

♦ *10 ocean-going tugs* (can be used as icebreakers in port)

Bldr: Schichau, Bremerhaven (1965-68)

A 1451 WANGEROOGE   **A 1453 LANGEOOG**   **A 1455 NORDERNEY**
A 1452 SPIEKEROOG   **A 1454 BALTRUM**   **A 1456 JUIST**

Langeoog (A 1453)   1969

D: 854 tons (1,138 fl)   **S:** 13.5 kts   **Dim:** 51 × 11.50 × 4
A: 1/40-mm AA   **M:** 2 MWM diesel-electric motors; 1 prop; 2,400 hp

A 1457 HELGOLAND (8-4-65) — **A 1458 FEHMARN** (1965)
D: 1,643 tons   **Dim:** 68 × 12.70 × 4.40   **S:** 16.5 kts
A: 2/40-mm   **Man:** 36 men   **Range:** 6,000
M: 4 MWM diesels; 2 props; 3,600 hp

A 1401 EISVOGEL (5-5-60) — 650 tons — 2,400 hp
A 1402 EISBAR (9-6-60)
S: 13 kts   **Dim:** 38 × 10 × 4.60   **Man:** 14 men

LOGISTIC SUPPORT (*continued*)

Fehmarn (A 1458)   1974

♦ *15 port tugs*

4 of 265 tons built in 1963 — Bldr: Schichau, Bremerhaven

Y 820 SYLT   **Y 822 AMRUM**
Y 821 FOHR   **Y 823 NEUWERK**

   D: 266 tons   **S:** 12 kts   **Dim:** 30.60 × 7.50   **M:** 800 hp

♦ *1 of 500 tons*

Y 801 PELLWORM — **D:** 500 tons — **S:** 12 kts — **M:** 800 hp

10 from 36 to 100 tons

Y 812 LÜTJE HÖRN   **Y 817 NORDSTRAND**
Y 813 MELLUM   **Y 818 TRISCHEN**
Y 814 KNECHTSAND   **Y 819 LANGENESS**
Y 815 SCHARNHORN   **Y 802 PLON**
Y 816 VOGELSAND   **Y 803 BLAUORT**

♦ *14 torpedo recovery boats*

Y 851, Y 852, Y 853, Y 854, Y 855, Y 856, Y 872, Y 873, Y 874, Y 882, Y 883, Y 884, Y 885, Y 886.

   Sometimes these are ex-World War II *R-Boote* minesweepers; others are *TF 1-6, 106-108* (**L:** 24.50 m — **S:** 17 kts — **M:** 950 hp)

♦ *2 net-tenders*

Y 837 SP 1 (21-6-66)   **Y 838 WILHELM PULLWER** (16-8-66).

   Bldr: Werft Gebr. Schürenstedt K. G., Bardenfleth

   D: 132 tons   **S:** 12.5 kts   **Dim:** 31.75 × 6.35 × 2
   M: Daimler-Benz diesels; 2 Voith-Schneider props; 580 hp

TRAINING SHIPS

♦ *1 light cruiser*

	Bldr	Laid down	L	In serv.
A 59 DEUTSCHLAND	Nobiskrug, Rendsburg	1958	5-11-60	5-63

   D: 4,880 tons (5,400 fl)   **Dim:** 145.00 (137.90 pp) × 17.98 × 4.80 (fl)

Wilhelm Pullwer (Y 838)   1969

1974

S: 22 kts (18 cruising)   **Man:** 33 officers, 521 men (250 cadets)
A: 4/100-mm AA (I × 4) — 8/40-mm AA (II × 2, I × 4) — 4/305-mm ASW TT — 2 ASW rocket-launchers — 1 ASW helicopter. Can be used as a minelayer.
Electron Equipt: Radars: 1/LWO 3, 1/SRG 105, 1/SRG 103, 1 fire control.
   Sonar: 1 medium frequency
M: 4 diesels (2 Maybach and 2 Mercedes-Benz), each of 1,670 hp; 1 Wahodag GT 8,000 hp; 3 props, 2 reversible pitch.
Electric: 1,500 kw.

REMARKS: Quarters for 7 instructors and 250 cadets.

A 60 GORCH FOCK

   D: 1,760 tons (1,880 fl)   **Dim:** 81.26 × 12.02 × 4.85
   S: 10 kts   **M:** 1 M.A.N. diesel; 1 prop; 880 hp.

REMARKS: Sail training ship; 1,964 m² of sail area; living spaces for 200 cadets.

HYDROGRAPHIC VESSELS. — Certain ships in this activity are manned by personnel from the Communications Department.

Planet   Photo A. and J. Pavia

A 1450 PLANET — Bldr: Norderwerft, Hamburg — L: 23-9-65

    D: 1,950 tons   **Dim:** 80 × 12.60 × . . .
    S: 13.9   **Man:** 40 men and 22 civilian specialists
    M: Diesel-electric propulsion; 1 prop; 1,350 hp

A . . . PASSAU
    Former French *Mercure*-class minesweeper, placed in the reserve group in 1963, then refitted as an oceanographic research vessel in 1975.

VARIOUS

♦ *17 different auxiliary ships*

Y 805 MEMMERT — former U.S. *Y-106* (ex-*India*) 1941   **D:** 270 tons
    Lifting crane, torpedo workshop.

Y 841 WALTHER VON LEDEBUR — Bldr: Burmeister, Bremen (1966)

    D: 725 tons   **S:** 19 kts   **Dim:** 63.10 × 16.60 × 2.75
    M: Maybach diesels; 5,000 hp. Wooden hulls.

Used in minewarfare studies.

Y 877 H. C. OERSTED
Y 878 HERMANN VON HELMHOLTZ   former U.S. minesweepers
Y 881 ADOLF BESTELMEYER   YMS class (ex-*2213*, *247*, and *2279*) —
Y 889 RUDOLF DIESEL   270 tons; 1,000 hp — **S:** 11 kts
    877, 878 used in degaussing, *881* trials, *889*, mine experiments

Y 811 KNURRHAHN and **Y 809 ARCONA,** barracks ships

Y 1663 EIDER (480/750 tons), former Anglo-Canadian type trawler (*Isles* class) used in minesweeping exercises.

Y 882 OTTO MEYCKE (1944) 112 tons. Diving ship.

Y 888 FRIEDRICH VOGE — 500 hp — Test ship, will soon be scrapped.

Y 833, communications small craft.

Y 864, Y 867, Y 868, and **Y 869,** freshwater barges.

H. C. Oersted (Y 877)   Photo Terzibaschitsch

♦ *Air-rescue ships*

Y 857 (ex-*FL 5*), **Y 859** (*FL 7*), **Y 860** (*FL 8*)
Y 861 (*FL 9*), **Y 862** (*FL 10*), **Y 863** (*FL 11*)

    Y 857/860:   **D:** 60 tons (fl) — 2,000 hp   **S:** 25 kts
    Y 861/863:   **D:** 70 tons (fl) — 3,200 hp   **S:** 30 kts

REMARKS: Will soon be transferred to the army.

♦ *Radar experimental ships. Elint.*

A 50 ALSTER — former coastal patrol vessel with special equipment.
A 53 OKER (1960) — modified trawler — 1,187 tons
A 52 OSTE (ex-U.S.N.)

    S: 11 kts   **Dim:** 49 × 8.80 × 5.20   **D:** 567 tons

Oste   1969 Photo Terzibaschitsch

GHANA

PERSONNEL: 1,300 men

MERCHANT MARINE (1-7-74): 77 ships — 173,018 grt

◆ *2 Mk 1 Vosper corvettes*

	Bldr	L	In serv.
F 17 KROMANTSE	Vosper Ltd	5-9-63	9-64
F 18 KETA	Vickers-Armstrongs	18-1-65	8-65

D: 435 tons (590 fl) **Dim:** 53.95 (49.38 pp) × 8.70 × 3.05
S: 18 kts **Man:** 5 officers, 49 men
A: 1/102-mm — 1/40-mm AA — 1 Squid
M: 2/16-cyl. Bristol Siddeley-Maybach diesels; 2 props; 5,720 hp.
Fuel: 60 tons **Range:** 2,900/14 — 1,100/18

REMARKS: Stabilizers, quarters are air-conditioned.

◆ *3 Poluchat-class patrol boats bought in the U.S.S.R. in 1967*

P 20 — P 21 — P 23 — Bldr: U.S.S.R. (1962-63). (*P 22* stricken in 1970)

D: 86 tons (91 fl) **S:** 18 kts **Dim:** 30 × 4.50 × 1.40
A: 2/14.5-mm machine guns (II × 1) **Man:** 2 officers, 14 men
Range: 460/17
M: M 50 diesels; 2 props; **Fuel:** 9.25 tons
Probably not in service.

◆ *1 British "-ton" class coastal minesweeper*

M 16 EJURA (ex-*Aldington*) loaned in 1964

◆ *2 British "-ham" class inshore minesweepers*

M 12 AFADZATO (ex-*Ottringham*), **M 11 YOGADA** (ex-*Malham*), transferred in 1959
Characteristics: See section on Great Britain.

◆ *2 British SDB Ford class patrol boats*

P 13 ELMINA (18-10-62) — **P 14 KOMENDA** (17-5-62) — Bldr: Yarrow

D: 120 tons (160 fl) **Dim:** 35.70 × 6.20 × 2.10
S: 15 kts **Man:** 19 men
A: 1/40-mm — depth charges
M: 2 Davey-Paxman diesels; 1,100 hp. **Fuel:** 123 tons

The training ship *Achimota* has been sold.

◆ **ASUANTSI** (*ex-British MRC-1122*) *pontoon repair ship bought in 1965*

NOTE: The frigate ordered in 1956 at the Yarrow shipyard, which never entered service, was purchased by the Royal Navy and joined the fleet as HMS *Mermaid*.

◆ **SAHENE** — Bldr: West Germany

D: 160 tons **S:** ... **Dim:** 35.15 × 6.50 × 1.75
A: 2/40-mm AA **M:** ...

Kromantse (F 17)

The Navy's share of the Defense budget for 1975-76 is about 25%. The fiscal year begins on April 1st.

PERSONNEL: The total strength of the Royal Navy, including the Royal Marines, will be lowered progressively from 78,000 men (and women) on 1-4-75 to 77,400 on 31 March 1976, divided as follows:

Officers	10,100
Non-officers	63,900
Women	3,400
Total	77,400

PROGRAM: There is no "naval program" as such in the sense of the phrase as it is usually understood. During the year 1974-75 the following ships were placed in commission: the nuclear-powered attack submarines ("Fleet Submarines") *Sovereign* and *Swiftsure*, the guided missile destroyer *Sheffield*, the frigate *Amazon*, and the hydrographic ship *Hecla*. Under construction on 1-10-75 were the ASW cruiser *Invincible*; the nuclear-powered attack submarines *Superb, Sceptre*, and *Spartan*; the guided missile destroyers *Birmingham, Cardiff, Coventry, Newcastle*, and *Glasgow*; the frigates *Antelope, Active*, and *Ambuscade*, these three being built; the *Arrow, Alacrity, Ardent, Avenger* and *Broadsword* (type 22); the patrol boats *Kingfisher, 02, 03, 04*, and 2 logistic support ships. During the fiscal year 1975-76 which will end 31 March 1976, 2 additional guided missile destroyers of the *Sheffield* class will be ordered, a type 22 class frigate (*Battleaxe*), a nuclear-powered attack submarine, the twelfth in the Royal Navy, and a non-magnetic minesweeper-minehunter of fiberglass construction, the *Brecon*.

It must be remembered that the British supply ships (Royal Fleet Auxiliaries — R.F.A.) are manned by civil service personnel (4,600 men), that maritime patrol aircraft are part of the Royal Air Force and not the Royal Navy, and that this requires the services of at least 5,000 men, and that a number of services which are performed by naval personnel in other navies, are performed by civil service personnel in the Royal Navy.

MERCHANT MARINE (1-7-74): 3,603 ships — 31,566,298 grt
(tankers: 581 ships — 15,203,281 grt)

WARSHIPS IN SERVICE, UNDER CONSTRUCTION OR PROJECTED AS OF 1 OCTOBER 1975

	L	D	Main Battery
♦ *1 attack aircraft carrier*			
1 ARK ROYAL	1950	43,300	No AA batteries; 30/35 aircraft
♦ *4 amphibious warfare ships*			
1 HERMES	1952	23,000	2 Sea Cat systems
1 BULWARK	1948	22,300	8/40-mm AA, 20 helicopters
2 FEARLESS	1963-64	11,060	4 Sea Cat Systems, 2/40-mm AA
♦ *3 helicopter carrying cruisers*			
1 INVINCIBLE	Constr.	19,200	1 Sea Dart system, 16 helicopters
2 BLAKE	1944-45	9,550	2/152-mm AA, 2/76-mm AA, 3 or 4 helicopters.
♦ *15 anti-aircraft destroyers*			
6 SHEFFIELD	1971-75	3,150	1 Sea Dart system 1/114-mm AA

GREAT BRITAIN

	L	D	Main Battery
1 BRISTOL	1969	5,650	1 Sea Dart system, 1 Ikara, 1 Limbo, 1/114-mm AA
8 HAMPSHIRE	1960-67	5,200	3 Sea Slug/Sea Cat systems, 4/114-mm AA
♦ *66 Frigates*			
1 BROADSWORD	Constr.	3,850	1 Sea Cat systems, 1 helicopter WG 13 Lynx, 1/114-mm AA
8 AMAZON	1971-75	2,500	
7 TRIBAL	1959-61	2,300	2/114-mm AA, ASW weapons, 1 helicopter
4 SALISBURY	1953-57	2,170	2/114-mm AA, 2/40-mm AA, ASW weapons
3 LEOPARD	1954-57	2,300	4/114-mm AA, 1/40-mm AA, ASW weapons
1 MERMAID	1966	2,300	. . . ASW weapons
26 LEANDER	1961-68	2,350	2/114-mm AA, 1 Sea Cat system, 1 helicopt. with ASW weapons, MM 38 Exocet system may be installed
3 WHITBY	1954-55	2,150	2/114-mm AA, 2/40-mm AA, ASW weapons
9 ROTHESAY	1957-60	2,380	2/114-mm AA, 1 Sea Cat sys., 1 helicopt. with ASW weapons.
5 HARDY/EXMOUTH	1953-57	1,020	2/40-mm AA, ASW weapons
♦ *36 submarines*			
4 RESOLUTION (nuclear propulsion)	1966-68	7,500	16 Polaris A 3, 6/533-mm TT
6 SWIFTSURE (nuclear propulsion)	1971-75	3,500	5/533-mm TT
5 VALIANT (nuclear propulsion)	1963-70	3,500	6/533-mm TT
1 DREADNOUGHT (nuclear propulsion)	1960	3,000	6/533-mm TT
20 PORPOISE/OBERON	1956-66	1,610	6/533-mm TT

FORCE LEVEL BUDGET (1975-76): 150 operational ships; 21 in reserve, undergoing major overhaul, or modernization.

Type	Ships in service, about to enter service, or used for training	In reserve, major overhaul, or conversion
SSBN (Fleet Ballistic Sub.)	*Repulse, Renown, Revenge*	*Resolution*
Aircraft carriers	*Ark Royal*	
Helicopter cruisers	*Blake, Tiger*	
Guided missile destroyers	10	
Frigates	50	10
Fleet Submarines	*Walnut, Warspite, Sovereign, Courageous, Swiftsure*	*Dreadnought, Conqueror, Churchill*
Patrol Submarines	16	4
Minesweepers/minehunters	40	3
Patrol boats	6	
Amphibious: Commando carriers	*Hermes*	*Bulwark*
LPD	*Fearless, Intrepid*	
Hydrographic	13	

WEAPONS AND SYSTEMS OF THE ROYAL NAVY

A — MISSILES

♦ *Strategic Ballistic missiles*

The Royal Navy uses the U.S. Polaris A3, but the 3 non-maneuverable re-entry warheads, 200 kilo tons each, are of British design and construction.

♦ *Surface-to-air missiles*

Sea Dart (GWS 30): Builder: Hawker Siddeley Dynamics
Medium range system (25 miles, interception altitudes from 100 to 60,000 ft).
— Length: 4.400 m   Wingspan: 0.910 m
— Diameter: 0.420 m   Weight: 550 kgs
— Solid propellant then ramjet. Semi-active homing. Fitted on the *Bristol*, the *Sheffield*, and the *Invincible*. Mk 909 fire control radar.
— Mk 30 Mod 0 launcher on the *Bristol*, the lighter Mk *30* Mod 2 on the *Sheffield* class.

Sea Slug Mk 1 and Mk 2: Builder: Hawker Siddeley Dynamics
Short-range system (15 miles slant range, 500 to 50,000 feet).
— Length: 5.940 m   Weight: 900 kg (2,000 kg with boosters)
— Diameter: 0.410 m   Speed: Mach 1.8
— Wingspan: 1.420 m (1.600 with fins)
— Solid propulsion system with four solid boosters
— Mk 901, a beam-riding radar
— Fitted on the *County*-class DDG

Sea Wolf (GWS 25): Builder: BAC
Short-range missile system (5,000 m)
— Length: 1.900 m   Diameter: 0.300 m
— Wingspan: 0.450 m   Weight: 82 kg
— Radar guidance
— The launcher contains 6 missiles (total weight with missiles: 3,500 kg).
Will be fitted on type 22 class frigates and the *Amazon* class.

Sea Cat (GWS 20 and 22): Builder: Short and Harland
— Length: 1.470 m   Wingspan: 0.650 m
— Diameter: 0.200 m   Weight: 68 kg
— 2-stage solid propellant. Launcher contains 4 missiles.
— Guidance by GWS 22 radar or GWS 20 optical system.
♦ **Slam:** short-range missile fired by a submarine at periscope depth at helicopters.
♦ *Surface-to-surface missiles*
The Royal Navy has purchased the MM 38 Exocet (see section on France) and builds it under license.
♦ *Air-to-surface missiles*
AS 11 (see section on France)

Bull Pup: Builder: Martin (U.S.A.)
Solid propellant
— Length: 3.200 m   Weight: 260 kg (75 kg of explosive)
— Diameter: 0.300 m   Speed: Mach 2.0
— Wingspan: 0.940 m   Range: 12,000 m
— Radio command, guided by sight

Skua: Builder: BAC
Solid propellant
— Length: 2.830 m   Weight: 210 kg (20 kg of explosive)
— Diameter: 0.200 m   Speed: . . .
— Wingspan: 0.600 m   Range: 9,000 m
— Guidance: semi-active

Martel: Builder: Matra and Hawker Siddeley Dynamics
See section on France. The Royal Navy uses the television-guided version.

♦ *Air-to-air missiles*

Firestreak: Builder: Hawker Siddeley Dynamics.
— Length: 3.200 m   Weight: 136 kg
— Diameter: 0.930 m   Speed: Mach 2
— Wingspan: 0.750 m   Range: 6,000 m
— Infrared guidance.

Red Top: Builder: Hawker Siddeley Dynamics.
— Length: 3.500 m   Speed: Mach 3
— Wingspan: 0.910 m   Range: 10,000 m
— Infrared guidance
The Royal Navy uses U.S. Sparrow and Sidewinder missiles (see U.S.A. section).

B — GUNNERY

114 Mk 5
Single barrel, semi-automatic, deck-installed, hand-loaded.
— Maximum effective range in surface fire: 11,000 m
— Maximum effective range in anti-aircraft fire: 5,000 m

WEAPONS AND SYSTEMS
OF THE ROYAL NAVY (continued)

— Rate of fire: 8/10 rounds/minute.
Fitted on the *Tribal* class frigates.

114 Mk 6
Double barrelled, semi-automatic, triple purpose (air, surface and land targets)
- — Length of barrel: . . .
- — Muzzle velocity: 850 m/sec
- — Maximum effective range in surface fire: 13,000 m
- — Maximum effective range in anti-aircraft fire: 6,000 m
- — Rate of fire: 10/12 rounds/minute.

114 Mk 8
Single barrelled, automatic, triple purpose (air, surface and land targets); muzzle brake.
- — Length of barrel: 55 calibers
- — Maximum effective range in surface fire: 13,000 m.
- — Maximum effective range in anti-aircraft fire: 6,000 m.
- — Rate of fire: 25 rounds/minute.
- — Arc of elevation: $-10° + 53°$

Light gunmount in synthetic resin reinforced with fiberglass.
Installed on the *Bristol*, the *Sheffield* class, the *Amazon* classes.

152 Mk 26
Twin-barrelled automatic triple purpose (air, surface and land targets).
- — Length of tube: 50 calibers
- — Muzzle velocity: 800 m/sec
- — Maximum effective range in surface fire: 15,000 m
- — Maximum effective range in anti-aircraft fire: 8,000 m
- — Rate of fire: 25 rounds/min
- — Turret weight: 156 tons

Fitted in the helicopter cruisers *Blake* and *Tiger*. Fire control MRS 3.

76 Mk . . .
Twin-barrelled automatic anti-aircraft.
- — Length of tube: 70 calibers
- — Muzzle velocity: 1,400 m/sec
- — Maximum effective range in surface fire: 5,000 m
- — Rate of fire: 120 rounds/min/barrel.

Fitted in *Blake* and *Tiger*.

Bofors 40-mm
The Royal Navy uses 70-caliber equipment on single and dual gun mounts.

C — ASW WEAPONS

Mk 10 Mortar *Limbo*:
Triple-barrelled mortar based on the *Squid* of the last war. Range: 700 to 1,000 m

Ikara System
Mk 44 or Mk 46 torpedo launched by a solid fuel rocket motor. Maximum range: 18,000 m. Fitted on the *Bristol* and a few *Leander* class ships.

D — TORPEDOES

The Royal Navy uses the U.S. Mk 44 and Mk 46 ASW torpedoes.
Torpedoes of British origin are essentially:
- — the wire-guided ASW Mk 23 torpedo, submarine launched;
- — the wire-guided Mk 24 "Tigerfish" (ex "Ongar") which has experienced serious difficulties during development. This torpedo is designed for nuclear attack submarines.

E — SONARS

The Royal Navy uses the following sonars:

(*a*) *on surface craft.*

	Class	Frequency	Average range by isoceleric bathysphere
170 B	Hull	High	2,500 m
174	Hull	High	2,500 m
177	Hull, 360° scan	Middle	6,000 m
184	Hull, 360° scan	Middle	7,000 m
199	Towed	Middle	7,000 m
2016	Hull	Low	

REMARKS: The 199 is the British version of the Canadian SQS 504. The 2016 is a new multi-frequency sonar.

(*b*) *on submarines.*

186	Passive	Low
2001	Active-Passive	Low
2007	Passive	Low

F — DATA SYSTEMS

The data systems outlined below are either in service or will soon enter service:
(a) **ADA Systems** (Action Data Automation)
ADA WS1. Aerial defense system. Fitted on *County*-class DDG.
ADA WS2. Integrated AAW and ASW defense system. Fitted on the *Bristol*.
ADA WS 4. Integrated AAW and ASW defense system. Fitted on the *Sheffield* class.
ADA WS5. Aerial and ASW defense. *Invincible* class.
(b) **C.A.A.I.S. System** (Computer Assisted Action Information System). This is a simple system based on the *ADA* for small ships.

G — RADARS

The Royal Navy uses the following radars:

♦ *Air search*
965 Metric radar (long range).
965M The M is composed of 2/965 antennae, one placed on top of the other with the Mk 10 IFF built in.
STIR (Surveillance Target Indicator Radar) is a new radar designed for the *Invincible* and is able to operate in a strong electronic counter-measures environment.

♦ *Surface-to-air low altitude search (combination):*
992 and **992 Q   993** (E-F bands).
978 (3 cm) (band I).
967 Pulse doppler: (combination of radar bands H, G, and I
968   found in the Sea Wolf system (GWS 25).
1006 Band I (surface and submarine navigation).

WEAPONS AND SYSTEMS (*continued*)

Antrim (D 18)   1975

♦ *Height-finding*

277	**982** (bands E-F).
278	**983**

♦ *Gun Direction*

275 (band F)   **903** (Band I) built into the *MSR 3* fire control radar. Parts of the *114 Mk 6* equipment for the first and parts of the *152 Mk 26*, *114 Mk 6*, and *Mk 8* equipment for the second with the *MSR 3*.

♦ *Missile Guidance*

901   Sea Slug system (band I) *MSR 3* fire control for the Sea Cat.
909   Sea Dart system
910   Tracking radar used with the Sea Wolf (*GWS 25*) system.

H — COUNTER-MEASURE SYSTEM

The Royal Navy uses a launched decoy system ("chaff") called Corvus.

Ark Royal (R 09)

See following page   1970

The *Ark Royal*   1975

AIRCRAFT CARRIER

	Bldr	Laid down	L	In serv.
R 09 ARK ROYAL	Cammell Laird	5-43	3-5-50	2-55

D: 43,840 tons (53,840 fl)

Dim: 263.50 (flight deck) — 244.68 (wl) — 219.45 (pp) × 50.12 (flight deck), 34.40 (wl) × 11 (fl)

S: 31/30 kts

A: See Remarks

Armor: flight deck and belt 203-mm (max)

Electron Equipt: Radars: 2/965 M, 1/993, 1/978, 1/983, 1/982 — Corvus
The radar used for landing aircraft is covered by a radar dome.

Man: 1,745, with the flying squadrons embarked; quarters available for 2,750.

M: Parsons GT; 4 props; 152,000 hp.   **Boilers:** 8 Admiralty at 28 kg/cm²; superheat to 385°C   **Fuel:** 5,500 tons

Electric: 8,250 kw

REMARKS: Flight deck angle 8.5°. Hull 90% welded. Air-conditioned. Carries 30 to 35 aircraft. Had a thorough modernization between 1967 and 1970, but owing to rigorous budget cuts the Royal Navy was forced to limit this modernization to strict necessities although permitting the landing and take-off of F4 Phantom and Buccaneer aircraft:

— waist catapult able to launch the largest aircraft without wind across the deck;

— arresting gear capable of receiving the largest aircraft with just 25 knots of wind on deck.

Has no air defense weapons or modern radars, and with her present air group of Phantoms and Buccaneers, the *Ark Royal* is nevertheless the most powerful surface ship of the Western European navies. She will probably be withdrawn from service in 1980, possibly even earlier.

NOTE: The aircraft carrier *Eagle* (1946, 44,100 tons) was stricken in 1972.

AIR IDENTIFICATION

The British ships with flight decks are identified by a large capital letter painted on the after end of the flight deck:
Ark Royal   R   Bulwark   B   Hermes   H

NAVAL AVIATION

(FLEET AIR ARM)

Ship-based aviation, the Fleet Air Arm, is the only aviation component in the Royal Navy.

There does not exist, except at the level of formation commanders, any naval air command.

Land-based ASW aircraft belong to the R.A.F.

Since the reorganization of the latter, it constitutes the Eighteenth Group of Strike Command or "Maritime Group." While still part of the R.A.F. as regards personnel and equipment, the Royal Navy determines its employment.

The Fleet Air Arm is made up of:

(1) first-line squadrons (designation characterized by a group of three figures beginning with an 8), with about 150 aircraft. Missions: all-weather interception and attack, ASW, electronic warfare, helicopter assault.

(2) second-line squadrons: used in schools, tests and maintenance, characterized by a group of three figures beginning with a 7. Altogether some 150 aircraft.

"Phantom F-4 K" Interception   Photo British Crown Copyright

"Nimrod" (Maritime Group of the R.A.F.)   1970

COMBAT AIR CRAFT

Class	Mission	Wingspan	Length	Height	Weight	Engine	Max. speed in mach or in knots	Practical maximum ceiling in feet	Range	Weapons	Remarks
SHIP-BASED AIRCRAFT											
(A) AIRPLANES											
PHANTOM II (F4K) (McDonnel) 2-man	All weather attack, interception	11.70 8.36 wings folded	17.75	4.96	24,700	2 Rolls-Royce Spey 25 R engines with 5,670 kg of thrust each, 9,640 with after burners	Mach 2	70,000	780 miles (interception) 870 miles (troop support)	Sparrow, Martel	On board the *Ark Royal*.
BUCCANEER — Mk 1 and 2 (Blackburn)	Attack	13.41 6.10 wings folded	19.32	5.05 wings folded	28,000	Mk 1:2 Bristol-Siddeley Gyron jr 101 turbofans with 3,200 kg of thrust.	Mach 0.8	35,000	425 miles	4/1,000-lb bombs	Can carry a tactical nuclear bomb. On board the *Ark Royal*.
						Mk 2: 2 Rolls-Royce RB 168 turbofans with 5,105 kg of thrust each.	Mach 0.85	45,000	900 miles	Martel (4)	Bristol-Siddeley
HARRIER (Sea) (Hawker-Siddeley)	Attack	7.60	14.10	3.35	10,500	1 Rolls-Royce Pegasus turbo-jet with 9,750 kg of thrust.	Mach 0.96, Mach 1, (2 diving)	50,000	VTOL: 50 miles STOL: 250 miles	2,270 kg	For the *Invincible*. The Sea Harrier plane will have a Pegasus 104 motor in place of the 103 which is used by R.A.F. aircraft; the 104 is more resistant to corrosion. In defense missions the Sea Harrier will have air-to-air missiles and an Aden gun.
(B) HELICOPTERS											
WASP (Westland)	ASW	Rotor diam. 9.82	12.23	3.27	1,370	1 Blackburn Nimbus 102 turboshaft, 1,050 hp.	109 kts., 96 kts. cruising	12,000		1 Mk 44 torpedo	On board the frigate *Tribal*, *Whitby*, *Rothesay*, and *Leander* classes.
LYNX (Westland) (SNIAS)	ASW, anti-surface	12.80	15.20	3.20	4,150	2 Rolls-Royce BS 360 turboshafts, 900 hp each.	150 kts.	12,000	1 hr, 30 min., half hovering, half cruising.	2 Mk 44 or Mk 46 torpedoes Skua air-surface missiles	Franco-British helicopter. Will be on board the guided missile destroyers of the *Sheffield* class and the type 21 and 22 frigates. Anti-surface version has priority in the Royal Navy.
WESSEX Mk 3 (Westland) **Mk 5**	ASW assault transport	17.06	20.05	4.82	5,700	1 Napier Gazelle 161 NGA 13 turboshaft with 1,650 hp (Mk 3). 2 linked Bristol-Siddeley Gnome H 1400 turbo-shafts with 1,400 hp each (Mk 5).	120 kts.	6,000 hovering, 14,000 cruising	3 hours		On board the *County*-class destroyers and the assault helicopter carriers.
SEA KING (Westland)	ASW	19	22		9,300	2 Rolls-Royce Gnome H turboshafts, 1,500 hp each driving a 5-bladed rotor and a tail rotor.	124 kts.	10,000	3 hr. 15 min.	4 Mk 44 torpedoes or 4 depth charges. Sonar-radar	US SH3D Sikorsky built under license. On board the *Ark Royal* and the helicopter cruiser.
LAND-BASED AIRCRAFT (18th Group of the "Strike Command" of the R.A.F.											
NIMROD (Hawker Siddeley)	ASW detection and engagement	35.10	38.03	9	79,000	4 Rolls-Royce Spey (RB 168-20) Mk 250 jet engines, 5,200 hp thrust each.	450 kts.	40,000	11 hours	Bomb hold for 15 m weapons (6 torpedoes + 10 buoys). 2 Martel or 4 AS 12.	Can employ nuclear depth charges.
SHACKLETON Mk 3 (Avro)	AEW	36.75	28.20	5.30	45,000	4 Rolls-Royce Griffon 57 A engines 2,455 hp.	270 kts.	16,000	13 hours	Bombs, torpedoes	A few planes modified as radar and electronic warfare aircraft.

NAVAL AVIATION (*continued*)

BASES

The "Fleet Air Arm" bases are given ship names. The Royal Navy no longer mans any bases other than helicopter. They are:

R.N.A.S. Yeovilton (HMS *Heron*)
R.N.A.S. Culdrose (HMS *Sea Hawk*)
R.N.A.S. Prestwick (HMS *Gannet*)
R.N.A.S. Lee-on-Solent (HMS *Daedalus*)
R.N.A.S. Portland (HMS *Osprey*)

Fixed wing aircraft which are not ship-based are stationed at R.A.F. bases at Honington, Leuchars, and Lossiemouth.

Designation of aircraft — The classes of the aircraft are, in general designated by a conventional name (Phantom, etc.) followed by two designations of the version (Mk — for Mark — 1, 2, etc. and Mod. — for Modification). To specify the exact missions of an aircraft with special modifications or weapons suits, a special indication is inserted into the designation of the series.

"Buccaneer" (Assault)

Revue Maritime

Westland "Lynx" WG 13 Franco/British

1970

Westland "Wessex" Mk 3

1972

NAVAL AVIATION (continued)

Westland "Sea King" ASM   1972

Buccaneer Mk 2   1972

Phantom II F 4 K   1971

FLEET BALLISTIC MISSILE SUBMARINES

♦ *4 Resolution-class submarines*

	Bldr	Laid down	L	In serv.
S 22 RESOLUTION	Vickers-Armstrongs	26-2-64	15-9-66	10-67
S 23 REPULSE	Vickers-Armstrongs	12-3-65	4-11-67	7-69
S 26 RENOWN	Cammell Laird	25-6-64	25-2-67	2-69
S 27 REVENGE	Cammell Laird	19-5-65	15-3-68	7-69

Renown (S 22)   1968

D: 7,500 tons surfaced (8,100 submerged)
Dim: 129.54 × 10.05 × 9.15
S: 25/20 kts   **Man:** 13 officers, 134 men

Resolution (S 22)   Vickers

Repulse (S 23) 1970

Launching the submarine *Conqueror* (compare the forward hull fittings with those of the U.S. SSN submarines).

Dreadnought (S 101)

FLEET BALLISTIC MISSILE SUBMARINES (*continued*)

A: 16 Polaris A3 — 6/533-mm TT
M: 1 Rolls-Royce pressurized water reactor; 1 English-Electric turbine; 1 prop.
Electron Equipt: Sonars: 2001/2007

REMARKS: The characteristics are very similar to those of the U.S. *Lafayette* class including the propulsion machinery and the launching and guidance systems, and inertial navigation. The A 3 missiles with 3 MRV warheads of 200 kilo tons each were furnished by the U.S.A. but the re-entry vehicles are of British conception and construction.

The substitution of the Polaris A 3 by the Poseidon or the Trident I is no longer being considered.

FLEET SUBMARINES

(a) 1 Dreadnought class

	Bldr	Laid down	L	In serv.
S 101 DREADNOUGHT	Vickers, Barrow	12-6-59	21-10-60	4-63

D: 3,000 tons standard/3,500 surfaced/4,000 submerged
Dim: 81.08 × 9.75 × 7.80
S: 25/15 kts **A:** 6/533-mm TT fwd **Man:** 11 officers, 77 men
Electron Equipt: Sonars: 2001/2007
M: 1 U.S./S 5w reactor; GT; 1 prop.

REMARKS: Authorized in 1956. The first Admiralty studies for the ship had been entrusted to the nuclear branch of the Vickers Company, including Rolls-Royce for the reactor, Foster-Wheeler for the heat exchanger, and Vickers for the turbines. Finally, however, a Westinghouse S5W engine, furnished by the U.S.A. (1958), was adopted. The hull shape is similar to the U.S. nuclear submarine *Skipjack* except for the forward one-third. Endurance: 70 days. Major overhaul from 5-68 to 9-70; the core was renewed. The ship has since made a cruise under the North Pole.

Churchill (S 104) 1974

(b) 5 Valiant class

	Bldr	Laid down	L	In serv.
S 102 VALIANT	Vickers, Barrow	22-1-62	3-12-63	7-66
S 103 WARSPITE	Vickers, Barrow	12-63	25-9-65	4-67
S 104 CHURCHILL	Vickers, Barrow	6-67	20-12-68	7-70
S 105 CONQUEROR	Cammell Laird	12-67	29-8-69	11-71
S 106 COURAGEOUS (ex-*Superb*)	Vickers, Barrow	10-68	7-3-70	10-71

D: 3,500 tons standard/4,000 surfaced/4,500 submerged
Dim: 86.87 × 10.12 × 8.25 **Man:** 13 officers, 90 men
S: 25/20 kts **A:** 6/533-TT fwd
Electron Equipt: Sonars: 2001/2007
M: 1 pressurized water reactor; English Electric GT; 1 prop; 20,000 hp.

REMARKS: The propulsion plant of the *Valiant* and the *Warspite* (20,000 hp) is entirely British design and construction (Admiralty, Vickers, Rolls and English Electric Company). The hull of the *Valiant*-class submarines is a development of the *Dreadnought*. In 1967 the *Valiant* made a non-stop, submerged cruise from Singapore to Great Britain in 28 days (12,000 miles).

Churchill (S 104) 1970

Courageous (S 105) 1972

FLEET SUBMARINES (continued)

(c) 6 Swiftsure class

		Bldr	Laid down	L	In serv.
S 107	SWIFTSURE	Vickers, Barrow	6-6-69	7-9-71	17-4-73
S 108	SOVEREIGN	Vickers, Barrow	18-9-70	22-2-73	22-7-74
S 109	SUPERB	Vickers, Barrow	1-71	30-11-74	. . .
S 110	SCEPTRE	Vickers, Barrow	11-71	. . .	. . .
S 111	SPARTAN	Vickers, Barrow	2-73	. . .	. . .
S 112	N . . .	Vickers, Barrow	. . .	. . .	. . .

Swiftsure (S 107)   1972

D: 3,500 tons **Dim:** 82.90 × 10.12
S: 30/20 kts **A:** 5/533-mm TT
Man: 12 officers, 85 men
Electron Equipt: Sonars: 2001/2007

REMARKS: New high-performance class. Uses the Mk 23 Tigerfish wire-guided torpedo. Eventually will be fitted with an anti-surface missile which can be launched while submerged. The U.S. Harpoon missile has been chosen.

NOTE

It is noteworthy that the Royal Navy has given its most traditional names to nuclear submarines. These names have heretofore always been assigned to principal units of the fleet.

There is one exception to this, that of the submarine named *Churchill*, which can readily be understood, but this is one of the first times that the name of a man in politics has been given to a ship of the Royal Navy (in World War II there was an ex-U.S. destroyer named HMS *Churchill*).

PATROL SUBMARINES

♦ *7 Porpoise class*

		Bldr	Laid down	L	In serv.
S 01	PORPOISE	Vickers-Armstrongs	6-54	25-4-56	4-58
S 02	RORQUAL	Vickers-Armstrongs	1-55	5-12-56	10-58
S 03	NARWHAL	Vickers-Armstrongs	3-56	25-10-57	5-59
S 05	FINWHALE	Cammell Laird	9-56	21-7-59	8-60
S 06	CACHALOT	Scott's SB, Greenock	8-55	11-12-57	9-59
S 07	SEALION	Cammell Laird	6-58	31-12-59	7-61
S 08	WALRUS	Scott's SB, Greenock	2-53	22-9-59	2-61

♦ *13 Oberon class*

		Bldr	Laid down	L	In serv.
S 09	OBERON	HM Dockyard, Chatham	11-57	18-7-59	2-61
S 10	ODIN	Cammell Laird	3-59	4-11-60	5-62
S 11	ORPHEUS	Vickers-Armstrongs	4-59	17-11-59	11-60
S 12	OLYMPUS	Vickers-Armstrongs	3-60	14-6-61	7-62
S 13	OSIRIS	Vickers-Armstrongs	1-62	20-11-62	1-64
S 14	ONSLAUGHT	HM Dockyard, Chatham	4-59	24-9-60	8-62
S 15	OTTER	Scott's SB, Greenock	1-60	15-5-61	8-62
S 16	ORACLE	Cammell Laird	4-60	26-9-61	2-63
S 17	OCELOT	HM Dockyard, Chatham	11-60	5-5-62	8-63
S 18	OTUS	Scott's SB, Greenock	5-61	17-10-62	10-63
S 19	OPOSSUM	Cammell Laird	12-61	23-5-63	6-64
S 20	OPPORTUNE	Scott's SB, Greenock	10-62	14-2-64	12-64
S 21	ONYX	Cammell Laird	11-64	16-8-66	11-67

1968 A. and J. Pavia

D: 1,610 tons/2,030 surfaced/2,400 submerged
Dim: 89.92 (87.45 pp) × 8.07 × 5.48   **S:** 17.5/15 kts
Man: 6 officers, 65 men (62 beginning with the S 09, 57 in the S 19, S 20, S 21).
A: 6 TT fwd and 2 aft — 22/533-mm torpedoes, all internal.
Electron Equipt: Sonars: 186/187
M: diesel-electric propulsion surfaced; Standard Admiralty 16-cyl. diesel engines; 3,700/6,000 hp.

REMARKS: Conventional propulsion and hull form. Streamlined sail. Maximum depth: — 200 m. Snorkel. Air-conditioned. Excellent living spaces. Long endurance. Plastics used throughout in the design of the superstructure of the second series

PATROL SUBMARINES (continued)

ships (*Oberon, Odin, Onslaught,* for example) as well as light alloys (*Orpheus*). *Onyx* transferred to Canada (1-64) and renamed the *Ojibwa;* another ship has been built and given the same name. Three additional ships of this class have been ordered by Canada, 6 by Australia, 2 by Chile, and 3 by Brazil. The *Porpoise* is used as a submarine target. The *S 04 Grampus* of the same class has been placed on the disposal list to be removed in 1975-76 and the *S 02 Rorqual* has been placed in reserve.

Sea Lion (S 07)   Photo G. Arra

Sea Lion   Photo G. Arra

NOTE: In 1974 it was said that the Royal Navy would resume building conventional diesel engine submarines (B class), but this project does not seem to have been followed up, at least not for the present.

ANTISUBMARINE CRUISERS

♦ *1 Invincible class* (designated for the moment under the title "Through-deck cruiser")

	Bldr	Laid down	L	In serv.
CCH 1 INVINCIBLE	Vickers, Barrow	4-73	...	1980-81

D: 19,500 tons   **S:** 28 kts
Dim: 206.60 (loa) × 192.87 (wl) × 31.89 (max.) × 27.50 (wl) × 6.40 (avg)
A: 1 Sea Dart system, 16 aircraft
Electron Equipt: Radars: 1/965 M, 1/992 Q, 2/909 — ADA WS 5 — 2 Corvus
          Sonars: 1 hull-mounted dome.
M: 4 Rolls-Royce Olympus T3 B gas turbines, each 23,500 hp; 2 reversible pitch props
Electric: 9,000 kw.
Man: 850 men — living spaces for 1,000 men.

REMARKS: Flight deck of about 180/190 meters long with a 4 to 5° angle, 170 × 13 meters. Three hangar bays on the same level, hangars 1 and 3 practically as large as the hull, but the central hangar is narrower because of the gas turbine exhausts to starboard and a workshop to port. Two elevators, one forward of the middle hangar midships, the other on the port side forward of the after hangar. Aircraft capacity: 9 ASW Sea King helicopters, 7 Harriers. The 965 M air-search radar will eventually be replaced by a new type called STIR (Surveillance Target Indicator Radar) which will be able to continue functioning in a very strong electronic counter-measures environment. Construction of two ships of the same class or a development of this class has been announced by the British Defense Ministry on 15-5-75.

Blake class

	Bldr	Laid down	L	In serv.
C 99 BLAKE (ex-*Tiger*)	J. Brown, Clydebank	1-42	20-12-45	3-61
C 20 TIGER (ex-*Bellerophon*)	Fairfield SB, Govan	6-43	25-10-45	3-59

D: 9,550 tons (12,100 fl)   **Dim:** 172.80 (164 pp) × 19.50 × 7
S: 31.5 kts (29.5 cruising)   **Man:** 85 officers, 800 men
A: 2/152-mm AA (II × 1) — 2/76-mm AA (II × 1) — 2 Seacat missile launchers
          (IV × 2) — 4 ASW helicopters, Wessex Mk 3 or 3 Sea King
Electron Equipt: Radars: 1/965, 1/992 Q, 1/978, 2/903, 2/262.
Armor: Belt, 90; conning tower, 100; deck, 52; turrets, 26/52.
M: Parsons GT; 4 props; 72,500 hp
Boilers: 4 Admiralty 28.5 kg/cm² pressure; superheat to 355°
Range: 6,500/13 — 4,000/20 — 2,100/29.   **Fuel:** 1,850 tons

REMARKS: Survivors of a series of eight cruisers of the *Swiftsure* class laid down during the war. Converted into helicopter cruisers, the *Blake* from 1965 to 1968 and the *Tiger* from 1969 to 1972. The after 152-mm and 76-mm gun mounts were removed to be replaced by a hangar and a flight deck. The port and starboard 76-mm gun mounts have been replaced by two Sea Cat launchers. The conversion of the cruiser *Lion* was cancelled and the ship has been stricken.

ANTISUBMARINE CRUISERS (*continued*)

Invincible (CCH 1) artist's concept

Blake (C 99)   1975 G. Arra

Blake (C 99)   1975 G. Arra

Blake (C 99)   1974

Bristol (D 23)   1972 British Crown Copyright

Bristol (D 23)   1974 J. C. Bellonne

GUIDED MISSILE DESTROYERS (DDG)

◆ *1 type 82*

	Bldr	Laid down	L	In serv.
D 23 BRISTOL	Associated Shipbuilders (Wallsend on Tyne)	11-67	30-6-69	12-72

D: 5,650 tons (6,750 fl) **Dim:** 154.60 (149.90 wl) × 16.77 × 6.85
S: 28 kts (fl) **Man:** 29 officers, 378 men
A: 1 Sea Dart system (II × 1), 40 missiles — 1/114-mm AA Mk 8 — 1 Limbo Mk 10 mortar — 1 ASW Ikara system, (32 missiles) — 2 Corvus

Electron Equipt: Radars: 1/965 M, 1/992 Q, 1/978, 2/909 — ADA SW 2
Sonars: 1/177, 1/174, 1/170 B, 1/162
M: COSAG System; 2 props. On each shaft, 1 AEI GT of 15,000 hp and 1 Rolls-Royce Olympus gas turbine of 22,300 hp, a total of 74,600 hp.
Boilers: 2 **Electric:** 7,000 kw. **Range:** 5,000/18

REMARKS: Designed at first as an escort vessel for the 50,000-ton aircraft carrier *Furious* when construction of the latter was being considered. Eight destroyers of this class were to be built, but this ship, ordered in 10-66, is the only one of its kind that has been built. Stabilizers and air conditioning. The Sea Dart launcher is a Mk 30 Mod 0. The storage areas aft are two decks deep; the missiles are stowed here in a vertical position.

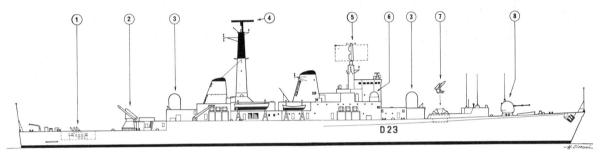

1: Limbo Mortar — 2: Sea Dart launcher — 3: 909 radar — 4: 992 Q radar — 5: 965 M radar — 6: Ikara fire control radar — 7: Ikara — 8: 114-mm AA Mk 8.

Bristol (D 23) 1974 J. C. Bellonne

GUIDED MISSILE DESTROYERS (DDG) (*continued*)

Bristol (D 23)

♦ *8 County class*
Auth. *55-56* (2), *56-57* (2), *61-62* (2), *64-65* (2), *65-66* (2).

	Bldr	Laid down	L	In serv.
A. D 02 DEVONSHIRE	Cammell Laird	3-59	10-6-60	11-62
D 08 HAMPSHIRE	John Brown (Clyde)	3-59	16-3-61	3-63
D 12 KENT	Harland & Wolff	3-60	27-9-61	8-63
D 16 LONDON	Swan Hunter	2-60	7-12-61	11-63
B. D 19 GLAMORGAN	Fairfield SB&E	5-62	9-7-64	10-66
D 18 ANTRIM	Fairfield SB&E	2-66	19-10-67	3-71
D 20 FIFE	Vickers-Armstrongs	9-62	9-7-64	6-66
D 21 NORFOLK	Swan Hunter	2-66	16-11-67	3-70

D: 5,200 tons (6,200 fl)   **Dim:** 158.55 (153.90 pp) × 16.46 × 6 (fl)
S: 32.5 kts (30 cruising)   **Range:** 3,500/28
A: (*a*) 4/114-mm AA Mk 6 (II × 2 fwd), 2/20-mm AA — 1 Sea Slug Mk 1 surface-to-air (30 missiles) — 2 Sea Cat systems (one on each side) (IV × 2) — 1 ASW Wessex Mk 3 helicopter. See Remarks.
(*b*) 4/MM 38 — 2/114-mm AA Mk 6 (II × 1), 2/20-mm AA — 1 Sea Slug Mk 2 system surface-to-air (30 missiles) — 2 Sea Cat systems (IV × 2) — 1 ASW Wessex Mk 3 helicopter.
Electron Equipt: Radars: 1/965 (965 M on the B group), 1/992 Q, 1/901, 1/278, 3 MSR 3 fire control — 2 Corvus — ADA SW 1
Sonars: 1/184 or 177, 1/170 B, 1/174, 1/162.
Man: 33 officers, 438 men
M: COSAG propulsion, 2 propellers. On each shaft, 1 A.E.I. GT (15,000 hp) and 2 linked G 6 gas turbines (7,500 hp each), 60,000 hp total.

Antrim (D 18)

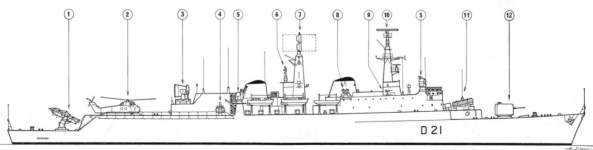

1: Sea Slug Launcher — 2: Wessex Mk 3 helicopter — 3: 901 radar — 4: Sea Cat — 5: MSR 3 fire control radar — 6: 278 radar — 7: 965 M radar — 8: Corvus — 9: 20-mm AA — 10: 992 Q radar — 11: Exocet launchers — 12: 114-mm AA Mk 6 mount.

Scale 1/1000

GUIDED MISSILE DESTROYERS (DDG) (*continued*)

Fife (D 20) before the installation of the MM 38 launchers.

Antrim (D 18)

Norfolk (D 21) with MM 38 launchers forward.

GUIDED MISSILE DESTROYERS (DDG) (*continued*)

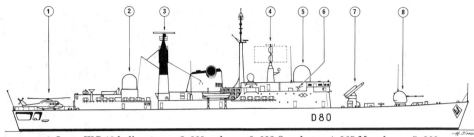

1: Lynx WG 13 helicopter — 2: 909 radar — 3: 992 Q radar — 4: 965 M radar — 5: 909 radar — 6: 20-mm AA — 7: Sea Dart launcher — 8: 114-mm AA mount Mk 8.

Boilers: 2 Babcock and Wilcox, 49.21 kg/cm² pressure; superheat to 510°.
Fuel: 600 tons
Electric: (*A*) 3,750 kw — (*B*) 4,750 kw.

REMARKS: Stabilizers. Twin rudders. Air conditioned. Remote control of the boilers and engines from a command post which is completely protected from radioactive contamination. The Sea Slug launcher is on the stern and its fire control radar is forward of the helicopter hangar. Missile stowage extends to the midships area and is over 100 meters in length; it is located inboard along the axis of the ship and contains 2 parallel rows of 15 missiles.

The *B* group has its mast slightly further aft than the *A*. D 06 is in special reserve. Photo of the *London*, page 152.

M: COGOG propulsion; 2 Olympus TM 3 B gas turbines × 27,200 hp for high speed; 2 Tyne RM 1 A gas turbines × 4,100 hp for cruising; 2 five-bladed reversible-pitch propellers
Range: 650/30, 4,500/18   **Electric:** 4,000 kw

REMARKS: Less sophisticated ships based on the *Bristol*. Ordered beginning 11-68. The cruising and high speed turbines are not linked to each other; each shaft must be driven by one or the other.

Mk 30 Mod 2 launcher for the Sea Dart systems. Installation of the MM-40 Exocet is being considered. The *Sheffield* does not have any ASW torpedo tubes.

♦ *6 type 42 Sheffield class*

		Bldr	Laid down	L	In serv.
D 80	**SHEFFIELD**	Vickers, Barrow	1-70	10-6-71	28-2-75
D 86	**BIRMINGHAM**	Cammell Laird	9-71	30-7-73	
D 118	**COVENTRY**	Cammell Laird	7-72	21-6-74	
D 108	**CARDIFF**	Vickers, Barrow	11-71	22-2-74	
D 87	**NEWCASTLE**	Swan Hunter	9-72	24-4-75	
D 88	**GLASGOW**	Swan Hunter	9-73		
D ...	N ...	...	...	...	...
D ...	N ...	...	...	...	...

D: 3,150 tons (3,600 fl)   **Dim:** 125 (119.50 pp) × 14.34 × 5
S: 28 kts (18 cruising)   **Man:** 312 men
A: 1/114-mm AA Mk 8 — 2/20-mm AA — 1 Sea Dart (II × 1) with 20 missiles stowed below — 1 ASW and anti-surface Lynx WG 13 helicopter — 6 Mk 32 ASW TT (II × 3)
Electron Equipt: Radars: 1/965 M, 1/992 Q, 2/909 — ADA SW 4 — 2 Corvus
  Sonars: 1/777, 1/174, 1/170 B, 1/162

Sheffield (D 80)   1975 Vickers

GUIDED MISSILE DESTROYERS (DDG) (*continued*)

Sheffield (D 80)   1975

Sheffield (D 80)   1975

FRIGATES

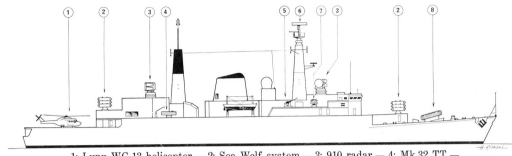

1: Lynx WG 13 helicopter — 2: Sea Wolf system — 3: 910 radar — 4: Mk 32 TT —
5: 40-mm AA — 6: 967/968 radar — 7: Corvus — 8: Exocet launchers.

Scale 1/1000

♦ *2 type 22, Weapon class*

		Bldr	Laid down	L	In serv.
F . . .	**BROADSWORD**	Yarrow, Scotstoun	7-2-75	. . .	1978
F . . .	**BATTLEAXE**	. . .	. . .	. . .	. . .

D: 3,860 tons   **Dim:** 131 × 14.75 × 4.30 (av)
S: 29 kts
A: 4 MM 38 — 2 Sea Wolf systems GWS 25 (VI × 2) — 2/40-mm AA — 6 Mk 32
ASW TT (III × 2) — 2 Lynx WG 13 helicopters
Electron Equipt: Radars: 1/967-968, 2/910 (GWS 25) — 1/1006
Sonar: 1/2016 — C.A.A.I.S. — 2 Corvus
M: COGOG propulsion; 2 Olympus TM 3 B gas turbines × 27,300 hp for high
speed; 2 Tyne RM 1 A × 4,100 hp for cruising.
Electric: . . .

REMARKS: The class is expected to number at least 12 ships. The 2016 is a new
multi-frequency sonar; it will also be fitted in the *Invincible*.

Frigate type 22   1973 Official sketch

FRIGATES (*continued*)

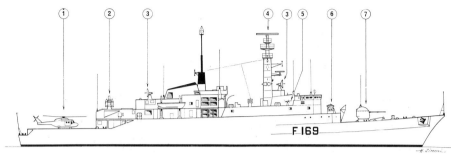

1: Lynx WG 13 helicopter — 2: Sea Cat system — 3: Sea Cat guidance radar (GSW 22) — 4: 992 Q radar — 5: 20-mm AA — 6: Corvus — 114-mm Mk 8 mount.

♦ *8 type 21, Amazon class*

	Bldr	Laid down	L	In serv.
F 169 AMAZON	Vosper-Thornycroft	11-69	26-4-71	11-5-74
F 172 AMBUSCADE	Yarrow, Scotstoun	5-70	6-71	21-8-75
F 170 ANTELOPE	Vosper-Thornycroft	3-71	16-3-72	30-6-75
F 171 ACTIVE	Vosper-Thornycroft	23-7-71	23-11-72	75
F 173 ARROW	Yarrow, Scotstoun	6-72	5-2-74	
F 174 ALACRITY	Yarrow, Scotstoun	10-72	18-9-74	
F 175 ARDENT	Yarrow, Scotstoun	9-73	9-5-75	
F 176 AVENGER	Yarrow, Scotstoun	1-74		

D: 2,500 tons (fl)   **Dim:** 117.04 × 12.80 × 3.70
S: 32 kts   **Man:** 11 officers, 159 men
Range: 4,500/18
A: 114-mm AA Mk 8 — 2/20-mm AA — 1 Sea Cat (IV × 1) — 1 Lynx WG 13 helicopter — 6 Mk 32 ASW TT (III × 2)
Electron Equipt: Radars: 1/992 Q, 1/978, 2 GSW 22 — C.A.A.I.S. — 2 Corvus
           Sonar: 1/177, 1/170 B, 1/174, 1/162
M: COGOG propulsion; 2 Olympus TM 3 gas turbines × 25,000 hp; 2 Tyne RB 209 gas turbines × 5,000 hp; 2 reversible-pitch props
Electric: . . .

Amazon (F 169)   1973

REMARKS: Frigate jointly conceived by Vosper-Thornycroft and Yarrow. Ordered 21-3-69 (1), 30-4-70 (2 and 3), 20-5-70 (4); remote control of engine room from the bridge; speed on cruising turbines: 18 knots. Supplies on board for 60 days. Ferranti digital system used in fire control. 4/MM 38 will be fitted on board the *F 173* and the following ships. These weapons will be installed later on the first four ships; the launchers will be paired and located forward of the bridge. The Sea Cat system will eventually be replaced by the Sea Wolf.

FRIGATES (*continued*)

Amazon (F 169)   1974 Vickers

Amazon (F 169)   1975

Amazon (F 169)   1975

FRIGATES (continued)

♦ *26 Fast frigates, Leander class*

Programs (starting with *F 10*): *1960-61* (3) — *1961-62* (3) — *1962-63* (3) — *1963-64* (3) — *1964-65* (3) — *1965-66* (3) — *1966-67* (2) — *1967-68* (2)

		Bldr	Laid down	L	In serv.
A.	F 109 LEANDER (ex-*Weymouth*)	Harland & Wolff	4-59	28-6-61	3-63
	F 104 DIDO (ex-*Hastings*)	Yarrow	12-59	21-12-61	1-64
	F 114 AJAX (ex-*Fowey*)	Cammell Laird	10-59	16-8-62	12-63
	F 127 PENELOPE (ex-*Coventry*)	Vickers-Armstrongs	3-61	17-8-62	4-64
	F 10 AURORA	John Brown	6-61	28-11-62	4-64
	F 15 EURYALUS	Scotts SB&E	10-61	6-6-63	9-64
	F 18 GALATEA	Swan Hunter	12-61	23-5-63	4-64
	F 38 ARETHUSA	J. Samuel White	9-62	5-11-63	5-65
	F 39 NAIAD	Yarrow	10-62	4-11-63	3-65
	F 28 CLEOPATRA	HMDY, Devonport	6-63	25-3-64	3-66
B.	F 45 MINERVA	Vickers-Armstrongs	7-63	19-12-64	5-66
	F 42 PHOEBE	Alex Stephen & Sons	6-63	8-7-64	4-66
	F 40 SIRIUS	HMDY, Portsmouth	8-63	22-9-64	6-66
	F 58 ARGONAUT	Hawthorn Leslie	11-64	8-2-66	9-67
	F 52 JUNO	Thornycroft	7-64	24-11-65	7-67
	F 47 DANAE	HMDY, Devonport	12-64	21-10-65	10-67
C.	F 58 HERMIONE	Stephen/Yarrow	12-65	26-4-67	7-69
	F 60 JUPITER	Yarrow	10-66	4-9-67	8-69
	F 57 ANDROMEDA	HMDY, Portsmouth	5-66	24-5-67	12-68
	F 69 BACCHANTE	Vickers-Armstrongs	10-66	29-2-68	2-70
	F 71 SCYLLA	HMDY, Devonport	5-67	8-8-68	1971
	F 75 CHARYBDIS	Harland & Wolff	1-67	28-2-68	6-69
	F 12 ACHILLES	Yarrow	12-67	21-11-68	7-70
	F 16 DIOMEDE	Yarrow	1-68	15-4-69	4-71
	F 70 APOLLO	Yarrow	5-69	15-10-70	5-72
	F 72 ARIADNE	Yarrow	1970	10-9-71	9-70

D: 2,350 tons (2,800 fl) **Dim:** 113.38 (109.73 pp) × 12.50 × 5.49 (fl)
S: 27 kts (trials: 30) **Man:** 17 officers, 245 men
A: 2/114 AA-mm Mk VI (II × 1) — 1 Sea Cat system (IV × 1) — 2/20-mm AA — 1 Mk 10 Limbo ASW mortar and 2 sextuple launchers for pyrotechnics and chaff — 1 Ikara ASW missile launcher replaces the 114-mm turret in the *109, 114, 10, 15, 18, 38, 39*, and the *127* which have 2 Sea Cat systems — 1 ASW Wasp helicopter — 4/MM 38s replace the 114-mm gun mount on the *28, 40, 42, 45, 47, 52, 56*, and *104*, which will have 2 Sea Cat systems.
Electron Equipt: Radars: 1/965, 1/993, 1/978, 1/903, 1/262 R — C.A.A.I.S. on those ships fitted with an Ikara system — 2 Corvus
Sonars: 1/171 or 1/184, 1/199 (towed) on a few ships, 1/170 B, 1/162.
M: double reduction White-English GT; 2 five-bladed props
Boilers: 2 Babcock and Wilcox; 30,000 hp.
Fuel: between 400 and 500 tons **Range:** 4,500/12
Electric: 1,600 kw (A) — 1,900 (B) — 2,500 kw (C)

Leander (F 109) launching an Ikara
(The 965 radar has been removed) 1973

Andromeda (F 57) 1972 G. Arra

Hermione (F 58) 1975 G. Arra

REMARKS: Improvement of the *Rothesay* class. Hull entirely welded; quarters air-conditioned; twin rudders; excellent sea-keeping qualities. Successive improvements to the propulsion and auxiliary machinery of the *Leander* class have necessitated classification in three groups; (1) Y 100 (the A group); (2) Y 131 (the B group); (3) U 160 (the C group).

The *Hermione* and following ships are 13.41 m in beam and have a standard displacement of 2,450 tons. *F 127* was fitted in 1970 with 3 Mk 32 ASW TT (III × 1). The *Penelope* has been modified for Sea Wolf system trials. Ships fitted with the Ikara system no longer have 965 radar.

FRIGATES (*continued*)

Ariadne (F 72)   1974

Achilles (F 12) (well for the 199 VDS)   1970 British Crown Copyright

Ariadne (F 72)   1974

Bacchante (F 69)   1975

FRIGATES (continued)

13 fast ASW frigates, type 12

A. ♦ 3 Whitby class

	Bldr	Laid down	L	In serv.
F 43 TORQUAY	Harland & Wolff	1953	1-7-54	5-56
F 73 EASTBOURNE	Vickers-Armstrongs	1954	29-12-55	1-58
F 77 BLACKPOOL	Harland & Wolff	1954	14-2-57	8-58

Torquay (F 43)　　　　　　1975

D: 2,150 tons (2,560 fl)　**Dim:** 112.77 (109.73 pp) × 12.50 × 5.26
S: 30 kts (26/25 usual)　**Man:** 18 officers, 231 men
A: 2/114-mm AA Mk VI (II × 1) — 2/40-mm AA (II × 1) — 1 Mk 10 Limbo
Electron Equipt: Radars: 1/978, 1/993, 1/293 Q, 1/275, 1/262.
　　　　　　Sonars: 1/174, 1/170, 1/162. C.A.A.I.S. on 43.
M: English Electric GT; 2 props.
Boilers: 2 Babcock 38.7 kg/cm² pressure; superheat 450°; 30,000 hp.
Fuel: 370 tons　　**Range:** 4,500/12　**Electric:** 1,140 kw

Yarmouth　　　　　　1968

REMARKS: Welded hull, air-conditioned, twin rudders. Cruising turbines for normal underway passage with automatic shift at a determined speed to high speed turbines. Bridge spacious and comfortable. Excellent sea-keeping qualities in heavy weather. In trials of the *Torquay*, 30 knots were attained with 75% of the anticipated power. *Torquay*, assigned to the school of navigators and electricians, has a C.A.A.I.S. (Computer Assisted Action Information System) fitted. *Eastbourne* is assigned to the machinists' school (weapons removed). *Scarborough* and *Tenby* of the same class purchased in 1974 by Pakistan. *Whitby* on the disposal list for 1975-76.

B. ♦ 9 Rothesay class

	Bldr	Laid down	L	In serv.
F 107 ROTHESAY	Yarrow, Scotstoun	1956	9-12-57	4-60
F 108 LONDONDERRY	Thornycroft	1956	20-5-58	7-60
F 115 BERWICK	Harland & Wolff	1958	15-12-59	6-61
F 106 BRIGHTON	Yarrow, Scotstoun	1958	30-10-59	9-61
F 113 FALMOUTH	Swan Hunter	1958	15-12-59	7-61
F 126 PLYMOUTH	HMDY, Devonport	1958	20-7-59	5-61
F 129 RHYL	HMDY, Portsmouth	1958	23-4-59	10-60
F 101 YARMOUTH	John Brown (Clyde)	1958	23-3-59	3-60
F 103 LOWESTOFT	Alex Stephen & Sons	1958	23-6-60	10-61

D: 2,380 tons (2,800 fl)　**Dim:** 112.77 (109.73 pp) × 12.50 × 5.20
S: 30 (26/25 actual)　**E:** 18 officers, 231 men

Rothesay (F 107)　　　　　　1972

FRIGATES (continued)

A: 2/114-mm Mk VI (II × 1) — Sea Cat — Mk 10 Limbo mortar — 2 sextuple RL for flares and chaffs — 1 ASW Wasp helicopter

Electron Equipt: Radars: 1/978, 1/993 or 1/293 Q, 1/275 1/262
Sonars: 1/174, 1/170, 1/162 — C.A.A.I.S. on *43*

M: same as *Whitby* class **Electric:** 1,460 kw.
Range: same as *Whitby* **Fuel:** 400 tons

REMARKS: Identical with the *Whitby* class when built with a few minor modifications; overhauls from 1966 to 1971.

♦ *7 frigates, type 81 Tribal (3 author. 55/56, 4 author. 56/57)*

		Bldr	Laid down	L	In serv.
F 117	**ASHANTI**	Yarrow, Scotstoun	2-58	9-3-59	11-61
F 119	**ESKIMO**	J. Samuel White	2-60	21-3-60	2-63
F 122	**GURKHA**	Thornycroft, Woolston	2-59	10-7-60	2-63
F 125	**MOHAWK**	Vickers-Armstrongs	11-60	5-4-62	12-63
F 131	**NUBIAN**	HMDY, Portsmouth	9-59	6-9-60	11-62
F 133	**TARTAR**	HMDY, Devonport	9-60	19-9-60	2-63
F 124	**ZULU**	Alex Stephen & Sons	12-60	3-7-62	4-64

Mohawk (F 125) (with a Wasp on the helo deck)   1968

Despite its heavy appearance the tripod mast is made of light metal and weighs only 2 tons. These ships will not be modernized. Their next overhaul will be a minor one and is likely to be the last.

Tartar (F 133)   1975 G. Arra

D: 2,300 tons (2,700 fl) **Dim:** 109.73 (106.68 pp) × 12.95 × 5.30 fl
S: 24/23 kts (actual) **Man:** 13 officers, 237-240 men **Range:** 4,500/12
A: 2/114-mm Mk V (I × 2, 1 fwd, 1 aft) — 1 Sea Cat (IV × 2) — 1 Mk 10 Limbo mortar — 1 ASW Wasp helicopter

Electron Equipt: Radars: 1/965, 1/978, 1/293 Q 1/903
Sonars: 1/177, 1/170 B, 1/162, 1/199 (towed) on *117* and *122*.

M: 1 Metrovik GT (15,000 hp) and 1 A.E.I. G6 (7,500 hp) gas turbine geared to a single propeller

Boiler: 1 Babcock and Wilcox; 22,500 hp. **Electric:** 960 kw.

REMARKS: Living quarters air-conditioned. COSAG propulsion machinery with remote control; the gas turbine permits almost instantaneous cold starts but is used only when high speeds are required. Denny-Brown stabilizers and twin rudders. Flush deck, welded hull which had to be reinforced after the trials of the 117.

Ashanti (F 117) (with the 199 VDS)   1972

FRIGATES (continued)

♦ *4 type 61, Salisbury class*

	Bldr	Laid down	L	In serv.
F 32 SALISBURY	HMDY, Devonport	23-1-52	25-6-53	2-57
F 59 CHICHESTER	Fairfield SB & E	1953	21-4-55	5-58
F 61 LLANDAFF	Hawthorn Leslie	1953	30-11-55	10-58
F 99 LINCOLN	Fairfield SB & E	1954	6-4-59	7-60

Lincoln (F 99) (Salisbury is identical)   1970

Llandaff (F 61) (Chichester is identical)   1968 Photo

D: 2,170 tons (2,400 fl)   **Dim:** 103.63 (100.58 pp) × 12.19 × 4.80 (fl)
S: 23 kts (operational)   **Man:** 9 officers, 198 men
A: 2/114-mm AA Mk VI (II × 1) — 2/40-mm AA (II × 1). *99* has Sea Cat missile launcher — 1 Squid (see Remarks)
Electron Equipt: Radars: 1/965 M, 1/982, 1/278, 1/293 Q, 1/275
            Sonars: 1/174, 1/170 B
M: 8 Admiralty Standard fast diesels with reduction gear, hydraulically linked 4 by 4 on two propeller shafts; 12,400 hp.
Fuel: 230 tons   **Range:** 4,500/15   **Electric:** 1,200 kw.

♦ *3 type 41, Leopard class*

	Bldr	Laid down	L	In serv.
F 14 LEOPARD	HMDY, Portsmouth	3-53	23-5-55	9-58
F 27 LYNX	J. Brown (Clydebank)	1953	12-1-55	3-57
F 37 JAGUAR	Wm. Denny (Dumbarton)	11-53	30-7-57	12-59

Jaguar (F 37)   1972 G. Arra

D: 2,300 tons (2,520 fl)   **Dim:** 103.63 (100.58 pp) × 12.19 × 4.80 (fl)
S: 23 kts   **Man:** 10 officers, 195 to 205 men
A: 4/114-mm AA Mk 6 (II × 2) — 1/40-mm AA — Squid.
Electron Equipt: Radars: 1/965, 1/978, 1/275, 2/262
            Sonars: 1/174, 1/170 B.
M: 8 Admiralty Standard fast diesels with reduction gear, hydraulically linked 4 by 4 on two propeller shafts; 12,400 hp.
Fuel: 230 tons diesel.   **Electric:** 1,200 kw.

REMARKS: These two series have the same welded hull and the same machinery. Anti-rolling stabilizers except on the *F 32*. 4/300-kw diesel generators as auxiliary machinery; on the *F 61* one is linked to a gas turbine. The original lattice masts have been replaced by mast-stacks called "macks" (contraction of mast and stack). *F 99* has reversible pitch propellers. In trials these ships reached 25 knots. The *Leopard* class is used as an overseas station vessel. *Panther* of this series has been transferred to India and renamed *Brahmaputra. Puma* scrapped in 1973.

FRIGATES (continued)

♦ *4 ASW "utility frigates" type 14*

	Bldr	Laid down	L	In serv.
F 48 DUNDAS	J. Samuel White	10-52	23-9-53	3-56
F 54 HARDY	Yarrow	2-53	25-11-53	12-55
F 80 DUNCAN*	Thornycroft	12-53	30-3-57	10-58
F 85 KEPPEL	Yarrow	3-53	31-8-54	7-56

*Modified as leader.

Dundas (F 48)

D: 1,180 tons (1,460 fl) **Dim:** 94.50 (91.44 pp) × 10.05 × 3.05
S: 25 kts (23 actual) **Man:** 8 officers, 132 men
A: 2/40-mm AA — 2 Mk 10 Limbo mortars mounted in echelon — a third 40-mm
gun has been removed as well as 4 ASW TT mounted on the four ships.
Electron Equipt: Radar: 1/978 — Sonars: 1/174, 1/170 B 1/162
M: GT; 1 prop; 15,000 hp.
Boilers: 2 Babcock **Range:** 4,500/12 **Electric:** . . . kw

Exmouth (F 84)   1975 G. Arra

REMARKS: Same turbine as the *Whitby* class. 1/40-mm installed on each side of the
mast. The hulls have had to be reinforced. *F 94 Palliser* and *F 97* have been placed
on the "For Disposal List" in the years 1975-1976. *F 85 Keppel* is in reserve.

♦ *1 "utility frigate" type 14 rebuilt with a gas turbine (1966-68)*

	Bldr	Laid down	L	In serv.
F 84 EXMOUTH	J. Samuel White (Cowes)	3-54	16-11-55	12-57

Same armament and equipment as the *Dundas* class. For speed and machinery, see
Remarks.

REMARKS: It was decided in February 1966 to remodel this ship in order to permit the
study of gas turbines as the propulsion machinery for Types *42* and *21*. The original
machinery was replaced by a COGOG assembly with a Ka-Me-Wa reversible pitch
propeller. Linked on the same shaft but able to be used at the same time are a
Bristol Olympus gas turbine (22,500 hp, but at reduced power) for high speed
cruising and for cruising speed, two Bristol Proteus gas turbines, each of 3,250 hp.
The latter, as well as the auxiliary machinery, are mounted in the former boiler
room. To shift from cruising to high speed and vice versa it is necessary to
disengage the propeller shaft and adjust the propeller pitch. This modification, a
joint effort by the technical staffs of the Admiralty, Yarrow ship builders, and the
Bristol-Siddeley organization, was completed by the Chatham Naval Dockyard. The
Exmouth was returned to service in 7-68. For 22,000 hp, the consumption rate is
about 0.24 g/hp/h.

♦ *1 based on the Leopard class*

	Bldr	Laid down	L	In serv.
F 76 MERMAID	Yarrow	1965	29-12-66	4-72

Mermaid   1973

D: 2,520 (fl) **Dim:** 103.40 × 12.20 × 4.80
S: 24/23 kts **Man:** 200/210 men
A: as designed for the country of Ghana: 2/102-mm AA (II × 1) — 4/40-mm AA
(I × 4) — 2/52-mm RL — 1 Squid
Electron Equipt: 1 Plessy ASW 1 air search

FRIGATES (*continued*)

M: 8 Admiralty Standard ASR 1 fast diesels (16 cylinders) with reduction gear linked hydraulically 4 by 4 on 2 drive shafts; 12,400 hp.
Fuel: 230 tons   **Range:** 4,800/15

REMARKS: Ordered in 1956 by the Royal Navy for Ghana and based on the Type 41. Because of the political situation the ship was not delivered and was repurchased by the British government at the end of 1971.

PATROL BOATS

♦ *4 Kingfisher class fisheries protection boats* — Bldr: Duston

	Laid down	L	In serv.
P 260 KINGFISHER	7-73	20-9-74	10-9-75
P 261 CYGNET	10-73	. . .	. . .
P 262 PETREL	11-73	. . .	. . .
P 263 SANDPIPER	12-73	. . .	. . .

Kingfisher (P260)

D: **Dim:** 36 × . . . × . . .
A: **S:**
M: **Man:**   **Range:**

REMARKS: Ships of the R.A.F. *Seal* class
 The Royal Navy has ordered 5 patrol boats of 1,250 tons from the Hall, Russell & Company shipyards in Aberdeen. They are designed to protect the North Sea oil installations and will enter service in 1977.

♦ *1 ex-trawler*

P 298 JURA
D: 1,200 tons   **S:** 14 kts   **Dim:** . . .
A: 1/40-mm

REMARKS: Designed to protect offshore oil installations

♦ *5 ex-"-ton" class minesweepers*

P 1007 BEACHAMPTON	P 1055 MONKTON	P 1089 WASPERTON
P 1093 WOLVERTON	P 1096 YARNTON	Refitted 1971-72.

A: 2/40-mm AA. For other characteristics, see "-ton" minesweepers.

♦ *2 "Seaward defense boats"* (SDB)

P 3104 DEE (ex-*Beckford*)   **P 3113 DROXFORD**
Bldr: Great Britain, Admiralty plans. Many have been transferred.
D: 12 tons (160 fl)   **Dim:** 35.70 × 6.10 × 2.10
S: 15 kts (trials: 18)

Yarnton (P 1096)   1972 British Crown Copyright

A: 1/40-mm — depth charges   **M:** Davey Paxman diesels, 1,100 hp
Man: 19 men   **Fuel:** 23 tons

♦ *1 guided missile ship*

P 276 TENACITY — Bldr: Vosper-Thornycroft — 18-2-69

1971

D: 220 tons (fl)   **S:** 39 kts   **Dim:** 44 × 8.10 × 2.40
A: being studied.   **M:** CODOG propulsion; 3 Rolls-Royce Proteus gas turbines; 2 Paxman diesels; 12,750 hp.
Range: 2,500/15   **Man:** 2 officers, 20 men

REMARKS: Built as an experimental venture; bought (1972) by the Royal Navy.

♦ *3 Scimitar class*

P 271 SCIMITAR (4-12-69), **P 274 CUTLASS** (19-2-70), **P 275 SABRE** (21-4-70)
Bldr: Vosper-Thornycroft, Portsmouth
D: 102 tons (fl)   **S:** 40 kts   **Dim:** 30.50 × 8.10 × 1.95
M: CODAG propulsion; 2 Proteus Rolls-Royce gas turbines and 2 Fodens diesels for cruising.
Man: 2 officers, 10 men   **Range:** 425/35 — 1,500/21.5

REMARKS: Designed for anti-missile boat training. Hull of laminated and glued wood. A third gas turbine allowed for in design. No weapons.

PATROL BOATS *(continued)*

Scimitar (P 271)

MINE WARFARE

♦ *2 minehunters with plastic and fiberglass hulls*

Bldr: Vosper-Thornycroft   L   In serv.

M . . . BRECON

D: 615 tons   **S:**   **Dim:** 59.10 × . . . × . . .
A:
M:

M 116 WILTON — Bldr: Vosper-Thornycroft — ordered 11-2-70 — L 18-2-72 — In serv.: 25-4-73.

REMARKS: Dimensions are those of the "-ton" class minesweepers. Machinery and fittings are those of the *Derriton* scrapped in 1970.

Wilton (M 1116)   1973

♦ *36 minehunters-minesweepers, Western European "-ton" class*

M 1110	BILDESTON*	6–52	M 1157	KIRKLISTON*	2–54
M 1133	BOSSINGTON*	12–55	M 1158	LALESTON†	. . .
M 1113	BRERETON*	3–55	M 1208	LEWISTON	11–54
M 1114	BRINTON*	8–52	M 1165	MAXTON*	5–56
M 1115	BRONINGTON*	3–53	M 1166	NURTON*	10–56
M 1125	CUXTON	. . .	M 1180	SHAVINGTON	. . .
M 1140	GAVINTON*	7–53	M 1181	SHERATON*	7–55
M 1141	GLASSERTON*†	12–53	M 1182	SHOULTON*†	9–54
M 1130	HIGHBURTON*	6–54	M 1200	SOBERTON	11–56
M 1147	HUBBERSTON*	9–54	M 1187	UPTON	3–56
M 1151	IVESTON*	6–54	M 1188	WALKERTON*†	11–56
M 1153	KEDLESTON*	12–53	M 1195	WOTTON*†	. . .
M 1154	KELLINGTON*	10–54			

The minesweepers marked with a † are used for the training of reserve personnel or as trial ships. Those marked with a * are fitted out as minehunters.

The following minesweepers have been assigned to the Royal-Naval Reserve and renamed:

CLYDE (ex-*Repton*), CURZON (ex-*Fittleton*), KILLIECRANKIE (ex-*Bickington*), KILMOREY (ex-*Alfriston*), MERSEY (ex-*Pollington*), MONTROSE (ex-*Stubbington*), NORTHUMBRIA (ex-*Wiston*), ST. DAVID (ex-*Crichton*), SOLENT (ex-*Crofton*), THAMES (ex-*Woolaston*), VENTURER (ex-*Hodgeston*).

Walkerton (M 1188)   1975 G. Arra

D: 370 tons (425 fl)   **Dim:** 46.33 (42.68 pp) × 8.76 × 2.50
S: 15 kts (cruising)   **Man:** 27 (peace), 39 (war)
A: 1/40-mm (often removed) — 2/20-mm AA
Range: 3,000/8 — 2,300/13
M: Mirrlees, Bickerton and Davey diesels (2,500 hp) On sweepers built since 1955, Napier-Deltic diesels of 3,000 hp; 2 props
Fuel: 45 tons

REMARKS: Several have been transferred to the navies of the Commonwealth countries. General characteristics are similar to those of French *Sirius* class or the U.S. MSC class; fast diesels with reduction gears. They are fitted with, or will have, anti-rolling stabilizers. About 20 have a tripod mast in place of a trellis mast. The *Shoulton* had two new fast Napier-Deltic diesels (1,700 rpm) installed in

PATROL BOATS (*continued*)

Kirkliston (M 1157)

1966-67 with a hydraulic transmission. The minechasers have a crew of 5 officers and 31 men, and 2/40-mm have been installed in the patrol craft. (See other page.) *Ashton* and *Chawton* have been placed on the "For Disposal List" in 1975.

INSHORE MINESWEEPERS

♦ *20 "-ham" class, (M 2603 and 2790)*

In 1975 the 4 with a number and the letter M were in service for the Royal Navy.

M 2603 ARLINGHAM (4-53) *TRV/PAS*
BIRDHAM (8-55) *RNXS*
BUCKLESHAM (8-53) *TRV*
M 2621 DITTISHAM (10-53) *TRV*
DOWNHAM (9-55) *TRV*
EVERINGHAM (3-54) *PAS*
M 2628 FLINTHAM (3-55) *TRV*
FRITHAM
FORDHAM (7-56) *DGV*
HAVERSHAM (6-54) *TRV*
LASHAM
ODIHAM (7-55) *RNXS*
PAGHAM (10-55) *RNXS*
PORTISHAM (11-55) *RNXS*
PUTTENHAM (6-56) *RNXS*
SHIPHAM (7-55) *RNXS*
THAKEHAM (9-57) *RNXS*
THATCHAM (1-57) . . .
M 2743 THORNHAM (1957)
TONGHAM (11-55) *DGV/PAS*
Used for training ships or other assignments.

♦ *2 Ley class (2002 and 2010)*

M 2002 AVELEY (2-53)   **M 2010 ISIS** (ex-*Cradley*)

D:	*Ham:* 120 tons (159 fl)	**Dim:**	32.43 (30.48 pp) × 6.45 × 1.70
	Ley: 128 tons (164 fl)	**S:**	14 kts (9 sweeping)
Range:	1,500/12		

"-ham" type

A:	1/40-mm AA fwd or 1/20-mm
Man:	2 officers, 13 men (22 wartime)
M:	Davey-Paxman diesels; 2 props; 1,000 hp.
Fuel:	15 tons

REMARKS: Used as port auxiliaries (PAS), degaussing ships (DVG), torpedo recovery ships or assigned to the Royal Naval Auxiliary Service. The two *Ley* class used as minehunters are of composite construction with wood and metal hulls; the others have wooden hulls. Fitted for the sweeping of all type mines from 4-5 meters to 55 meters; equipped with radar and fathometer. Four days endurance. Many have been scrapped, others transferred to foreign navies (France, Italy, etc.).

MINE SERVICE SHIPS

♦ *3 Miner class*

	L	In serv.
N 13 MINER III (RMAS)	16-11-39	3-40
N 15 BRITANNIC (ex-*Miner 5*) (PAS)	2-11-40	6-41
N 17 STEADY (ex-*Miner 7*) (PAS)	29-1-44	3-44

Britannic (N 15)   1972 G. Arra

MINE SERVICE SHIPS (*continued*)

D: 300 tons (355 fl)   **Dim:** 33.60 × 8.08 × 2.50
S: 10 kts   **M:** 2 Ruston diesels; 360 hp.

Britannic, cable layer. The others are assigned to various services, and are under the control of the Royal Maritime Auxiliary Service and the Port Auxiliary Service.

MINELAYER

♦ *1 experimental class*

	Bldr	Laid down	L	In serv.
N 21 ABDIEL	Thornycroft (Woolston)	5-66	22-1-67	10-67

Abdiel (N 21)   1967

D: 1,375 tons (1,460 fl)   **Dim:** 80.42 (74.67 pp) × 11.74 × 2.85
S: 16 kts   **Man:** 14 officers, 109 men
M: Paxman Ventura 16-cyl. diesels; 2 props; 2,690 hp.
Electric: 1,225 kw.
Has two radars, carries 44 mines.

COMMANDO SHIPS

	Bldr	Laid down	L	In serv.
R 12 HERMES	Vickers-Barrow	6-44	16-2-53	11-59

D: 27,800 (fl)   **S:** 28   **Dim:** 226.85 (198.12 pp) × 27.43 (wl) × 8.40
A: 2 Sea Cat Mk 2 (IV × 2) — 24 Wessex Mk 5 helicopters
Electron Equipt: 1/965, 1/978
M: Parsons GT   **Boilers:** 4 Admiralty; 2 props; 83,000 hp.
Fuel: 3,860 tons   **Electric:** 5,400 kw

REMARKS: Conversion contracted for in 1971-73 by the Devonport naval dockyard.

Hermes (R 12)   1974

Hermes (R 12)   1974

COMMANDO SHIPS (continued)

To be converted into an ASW aircraft carrier beginning in 1976. Will carry Harrier aircraft and will be used as a trial ship for the employment of these planes in 1978-79.

AMPHIBIOUS OPERATIONS

	Bldr	Laid down	L	In serv.
R 08 BULWARK	Harland & Wolff	5-45	22-6-48	10-54

Bulwark (R 08) 1972 J. C. Bellonne

D: 23,000 tons (27,300 fl)   **S:** 28 kts
Dim: 227.10 (198.12 pp) × 37.49 × 28.43 (wl) × 8.25
A: 8/40-mm AA (II × 4) — 20 Wessex Mk 5 helicopters
Electron Equipt: 1/982, 1/983
Man: 1,037 men + one Royal Marine commando (battalion) and one battery of howitzers
Armor: flight deck: 50-mm — 25-mm watertight bulkheads on each side below the waterline.
M: Parsons GT; 2 props; 83,000 hp.   **Boilers:** 4 Admiralty
Electric: 3,200 kw

REMARKS: Converted in 1959. Only one hangar; two center line elevators. The commmando (750 men) can be put ashore by helicopter or by 4 LCA landing craft which are hung in davits aft, two on each side. For short distances two commandos can be carried. Living quarters air-conditioned. Disposal of the *Bulwark* is being studied. *Albion* was scrapped in 1972.

ASSAULT SHIPS

	Author	Bldr	Laid down	L	In serv.
L 10 FEARLESS	1961-62	Harland & Wolff	7-62	19-12-63	11-65
L 11 INTREPID	1962-63	J. Brown (Clyde)	1-63	26-6-64	3-67

D: 11,060 tons (12,120 fl)
Dim: 158.50 (152.40 pp) × 24.38 × 6.20 — well deck flooded
D: 16,950 tons — draft 9.15
S: 21/20 kts   **Range:** 5,000/20
A: 4 Sea Cat rocket launchers (IV × 4) — 2/40-mm AA
Electron Equipt: Radars: 1/978, 2/262 R — C.A.A.I.S. — 2 Corvus

Man: 36 officers, 520 men, 380 to 700 troops
M: English Electric GT; 2 props
Boilers: 2 Babcock and Wilcox 38.66 kg/cm² pressure; superheat 454°; 22,000 hp.
Electric: 4,000 kw

REMARKS: The *Fearless* and the *Intrepid* are the equivalent ships to the U.S. LPD class and the French TCD class. These two ships have excellent command and communication means for an amphibious operation. They can launch 4 to 6 Wessex Mk 5 assault helicopters (landing platform but no hangar) and they have quarters for various size troop contingents, depending on the duration and distance of operations, but usually a single light infantry battalion and an artillery battery. On board are four LCA landing craft which can transport 35 men or a half-ton vehicle and 4 LCM 9 landing craft carrying either two Chieftain or Centurion tanks or four vehicles or 100 tons of supplies; four additional tanks can be carried on the tank deck. The various types of vehicles carried on board are divided among the tank deck, a lower deck, and a half-deck reserved for jeeps. The Skynet transmission system by satellites has had experiments carried out on board the *Intrepid*. The ship is assigned to the Naval School at Dartmouth.

LANDING SHIPS

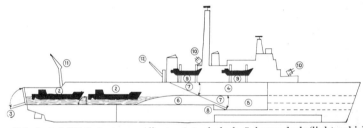

1: well deck; 2: LCM 9; 3: stern wellgate; 4: tank deck; 5: lower deck (light vehicles); 6: half-deck; 7: mobile ramps; 8: fixed ramp; 9: LCA; 10: Sea Cat system; 11, 12: cranes.

Fearless photo

LANDING SHIPS (*continued*)

♦ *5 LCT 8 class*

L 4002	AGHEILA	L 4062	AACHEN
L 4041	ABBEVILLE	L 4097	ANDALNES
L 4061	AUDEMER		

D: 657 tons (895 fl)   **Dim:**   70.18 × 11.90 × 1.80
S: 12 kts (9 cruising)   **Man:**   33 men
M: 4 Paxman diesels; 2 props; 1,840 hp.

REMARKS: Available to the Army's Royal Corps of Transports. The following have been scrapped since 1974:

L 4037 Akyab, L 4074 Antwerp, L 4128 Arezzo and L 4164 Arakan.

♦ *6 LST Sir Lancelot class*

		L			L
L 3004	SIR BEDIVERE	20-7-66	L 3029	SIR LANCELOT	. .-6-63
L 3005	SIR GALAHAD	19-4-66	L 3036	SIR PERCIVAL	4-10-67
L 3027	SIR GERAINT	26-1-67	L 3505	SIR TRISTRAM	12-12-66

Bldr: Fairfield (1), Alexander Stephen (2), Hawthorn Leslie (3).

Sir Geraint   1972 photo

D: 5,550 tons (fl)   **S:**   17 kts   **Dim:**   126.45 × 17.70 × 3.80
Man: 18 officers, 51 men   **M:**   diesels; 2 props; 9,450 hp
A: 12/40-mm   **Fuel:**   811 tons

REMARKS: In 1963 the Ministry of Transportation ordered the first of six specially designed LST-class ships for the Army, chartered in peacetime to various private maritime firms. In 1970 these ships came under the control of the Royal Fleet Auxiliary, although still assigned to a shipping concern. Built into the bow and the stern are ramps and doors for the handling of vehicles (roll-on/roll-off system); quarters are provided in the after superstructure for 402 men; interior ramps connect the two decks; there is a helicopter platform; there are four cranes (½ ton to 4.5 or 8.5 tons) two forward of the bridge; landing craft may be carried in cradles.

LANDING CRAFT

♦ *LCM (9) class*

LCM (9) 700 to 711, LCM (9) 3507 and 3508
The prototype of this new series (*L 3507*) was delivered in 1963. The *Fearless* and the *Intrepid* each carry 4 of these.

Bldr: Vosper (2), Richard Dunston (6), Brooke Marine Ltd., (4) Bolson & Sons (2) 1964–66

1966. Shipbuilding and Shipping Record

D: 75 tons (176 fl)   **Dim:**   25.7 × 6.5 × 1.7
M: 2 Paxman diesels; 312 hp; Kort props.   **Man:**   6 men
Can carry 2 Centurion battle tanks.

REMARKS: Some wooden-hull LCVPs with the same characteristics as the LCVP class from the war; can carry either 30 completely equipped men or a light Land Rover vehicle towing a small-caliber artillery piece. **M:** 2 Foden diesels (6 cylinders). In addition, some series from the last war:
2 LCM (63 tons fl, 7,000 series) — *29 LCVP* (10.5 tons fl, 100 and 1,000 series) — *2 LCP* (10 tons fl, 500 series) — One was fitted with a gas turbine at trials (*LCP 502*).

HYDROGRAPHIC SHIPS

AGS 04 HERALD Bldr: Robb, Caledon — L: 4-10-73 — In serv.: 31-11-74.

D: 2,125 tons (2,945 fl)   **Dim:**   78 × 14.70 × 4.60
S: 14 kts   **Man:**   . . . officers, . . .
Range: 20,000/11
M: diesel-electric propulsion (identical to the *Hecla* class); 1 prop.

REMARKS: Improved version of the *Hecla* class. Replaces the *Vidal*, scrapped in 1972. Wasp helicopter.

♦ **A 133 HECLA** (21-12-64) — **A 137 HECATE** (31-3-65) — **A 144 HYDRA** (14-7-65)
Bldr: Yarrow; two hulls overhauled at the Blythswood Shbldg Co.

D: 1,915 tons (2,733 fl)   **Dim:**   79.25 (71.63 pp) × 14.94 × 4
S: 14 kts   **Range:**   12,000/11
Man: 14 officers, 104 men
M: diesel-electric propulsion; 3 Davey-Paxman-Ventura diesels (12 cyl), each 1,280 hp; 2 electric motors for propulsion (2,000 hp, 190 rpm) linked to a single prop.

REMARKS: Based on the oceanographic research vessel *Discovery*. Air conditioned hull, reinforced against ice; bow propeller for movement in narrow waters. Hangar and platform for 1 Wasp helicopter. Wide range and endurance. Excellent scientific laboratories; usually carries 7 civilian scientists in addition to staff.

HYDROGRAPHIC SHIPS (*continued*)

Hecla (A 133)   1965

♦ *4 Fawn class*

A 317 BULLDOG (12-7-67)   **A 320 FOX** (6-11-67)
A 319 BEAGLE (ex-*Barracuda* (7-9-67)   **A 335 FAWN** (29-2-68)
  Bldr: Brooke Marine (Lowestoft)

Fawn (A 335)   1972 British Crown Copyright

D:	800 tons/990 avg/1,030 (fl)	**Dim:**	60.95 × 11.43 × 3.60
S:	15 kts	**Range:**	4,000/12
Man:	4 officers, 34 men		
M:	4 Lister Blackstone ERS 8 M; 2 Ka-Me-Wa variable pitch props; 2,000 hp		
Electric:	720 kw		

REMARKS: New class coastal ship; operate in pairs; air-conditioned; hulls built with commercial specifications and reinforced against ice damage.

♦ *3 coastal type, specially constructed*

A 70 ECHO (1-5-57) — **A 71 ENTERPRISE** (20-9-58) — **A 72 EGERIA** (13-9-58)
  Bldr: J. Samuel White (Cowes) (1957-59)

Shipbuilding and Shipping Record

D:	160 tons (fl)	**Dim:**	32.55 × 6.98 × 2.10
S:	13/12 kts	**Man:**	2 officers, 16 men
Range:	1,600/10		
M:	Paxman diesels; 2 variable pitch props; 700 hp		
Fuel:	15 tons		

REMARKS: Built of laminated wood. Quarters for 22. Mount for 1/40-mm. Two Fathometers; sonar for detecting shipwrecks.

♦ *2 "-ham" class minesweepers, modified as coastal hydrographic ships*

M 272 WATERWITCH (ex-*Powderham*) (11-57) **M 2780 WOODLARK** (ex-*Yaxham*) (1-58)

Waterwitch   1972 G. Arra

HYDROGRAPHIC SHIPS (continued)

D: 160 tons (fl)   **Dim:** 32.43 (30.48 pp) × 6.45 × 1.70
S: 13/12 kts   **Man:** 2 officers, 16 men
Fuel: 15 tons   **Range:** 1,500/12
M: Diesels; 2 props; 1,100 hp

REMARKS: Weapons removed.

EXPERIMENTAL SHIPS

♦ *1 ship for sonar trials*

D 43 MATAPAN — Bldr: John Brown (Clydebank) L 30-4-45 Modified 1972-73

Matapan (D 43)   1974

D: 2,780 tons (3,400 fl)   **Dim:** . . . × 12.95 × 4.10
S: 30 kts   **Range:** 3,000/20   **Man:** 182 men, 22 scientists
M: Parsons GT; 2 props   **Boilers:** 2 Admiralty   **Fuel:** . . . tons

REMARKS: Former *Battle*-class destroyer. No guns. New bow, decks, superstructure. The forecastle has been extended to the stern, so now is flush-decked. Two stacks instead of original one. Air-conditioned. Based at Portland. Used for the study of sound waves' reflection and resurgence off the sea bottom, using British and American equipment. Powerful bow sonar. Stabilizers.

♦ *1 research vessel*

A 364 WHITEHEAD — Bldr: Scott's (Greenock) — L: 5-5-70
A 367 NEWTON — Bldr: Scott's (Greenock) — L: 26-6-75

D: 3,040 tons (fl)   **S:** 15.5 kts   **Dim:** 95.80 × 14.50 × 5.10
Man: 10 officers, 47 men and scientists   **Range:** 4,000/12
M: 2 Paxman Mk 12 YLCM diesels; 1 prop; 3,400 hp

REMARKS: Will be used to study ballistic missile behavior in the atmosphere and that of newly designed torpedoes. The *Newton* is a bit larger than the *Whitehead* (L:

Whitehead (A 364)   1971 British Crown Copyright

98 m); she will be used in oceanographic research and for the laying and repair of undersea cables. She will have 4 laboratories and 7 winches of various dimensions for deck experiments.

♦ *1 fixed experimental platform (sonars)*

RDV 01 CRYSTAL (1970-72)

D: 3,000 tons   **Dim:** 126 × 16.90 × 1.70

REMARKS: No engines. Assigned to acoustic studies.

LOGISTIC SUPPORT

In the British Navy, the majority of the auxiliary and supply vessels are responsible to the Royal Fleet Auxiliary (R.F.A.), an organization peculiar to the Royal Navy. Built to the specifications of Lloyds of London (compartmenting, security, livability), they also meet the standards of the Shipping Naval Acts of 1911 and of the Ministry of Transportation. Manned by civil service personnel, they do not fly the White Ensign, but the blue flag of the reserve. In addition, about 40 ocean-going tugs, salvage vessels, cable layers, research vessels, etc., are assigned activities called the Royal Maritime Auxiliary Service (R.M.A.S.) and the Port Auxiliary Service (P.A.S.), the personnel of these two groups being civil servants.

♦ *1 ship for helicopter training (R.F.A.)*

Bldr: Henry Robb Ltd.   Laid down 8-65   L 16-9-66   In serv. 12-67

K 08 ENGADINE

D: 9,000 tons (fl)   **Dim:** 129.31 × 17.86 × 6.73
Cargo capacity: 3,640 tons
Man: 61 RFA + 14 RN including 17 officers,
      (+ on occasion 113 RN including 29 officers)
S: 16 kts   **M:** 1 Sulzer diesel 5 RD 68; 5,500 hp

REMARKS: Intended for the training of helicopter crews in ASW; the instructors and students are the only RN personnel on board. Hangar for 4 Wessex helicopters and 2 Wasp or 2 Sea King. Denny-Brown stabilizer. Remote control for propulsion and auxiliary machinery.

♦ *1 destroyer support vessel*

	Bldr	Laid down	L	In serv.
A 108 TRIUMPH	Hawthorn Leslie	1-43	2-10-44	4-46

Triumph (A 108)   1970

LOGISTIC SUPPORT (*continued*)

Engadine (K 08)

D: 13,350 tons (17,000 fl) **Dim:** 211.25 (198 wl) × 24.29 × 7.15
S: 23 kts **Range:** 10,000/14 — 5,500/23
A: 4/40-mm AA
M: Parsons GT; 2 props; 40,000 hp **Man:** 27 officers, 472 men
Boilers: 4 Admiralty; 28 kg/cm² **Fuel:** 3,000 tons

REMARKS: Former *Colossus*-class aircraft carrier; conversion to repair ship finished at
the end of 1964. Landing and take-off platform, 3 Wessex helicopters in one hangar,
4 cranes on the flight deck. Quarters for the relieving crews: 15 officers and 270 men.
Four destroyers can be moored alongside and part of their crews can be quartered
on board. In reserve.

♦ *2 base ships for nuclear submarines*

	Bldr	Laid down	L	In serv.
A 187 FORTH	J. Brown	6-37	11-8-38	5-39
A 185 MAIDSTONE	J. Brown	17-8-36	21-10-37	5-38

D: 10,000 tons (14,000 fl) **S:** 17-mm
Dim: 161.85 (151.50 pp) × 22.25 × 6.10
Man: 45 officers, 650 men, but quarters for 119 officers, 1,040/1,500 men
A: 5/40-mm AA
M: Brown Curtis GT; 2 props; 7,000 hp **Fuel:** 2,310 tons

REMARKS: Rebuilt and recommissioned between 1958 and 1963. Quarters and workshops modernized. Spare parts and stowage for 100 torpedoes. Many compartments
air-conditioned.

Forth (A 187) 1967

LOGISTIC SUPPORT (*continued*)

♦ *3 Store Supply Ships (R.F.A.)*

	Bldr	Laid down	L	In serv.
A 339 LYNESS	Swan Hunter	4-65	7-4-66	12-66
A 344 STROMNESS	Swan Hunter	10-65	16-9-66	3-67
A 345 TARBATNESS	Swan Hunter	4-66	27-2-67	1969

Lyness (A 339)   1972

D: 15,500 tons (fl)   **Dim:** 159.71 (149.36 pp) × 21.95 × 7.70
S: 17 kts   **Man:** 184 men
Cargo capacity: 7,832 tons   **A:** 2/40-mm
M: Sulzer 8 cyl. RD 76 diesel; 1 prop; 11,520 hp

REMARKS: Platform for 2 helicopters. Improved holds with hoists. Closed-circuit TV provided to monitor handling of stores.

♦ *9 Replenishment ships (R.F.A.)*

	Bldr	Laid down	L	In serv.
A 480 RESOURCE	Scott's SB (Greenock)	6-64	11-2-66	5-67
A 486 REGENT	Harland & Wolff	9-64	9-3-66	5-67

Resource (A 480)   1972 J. C. Bellonne

D: 19,000 tons (fl) (18,029 light)   **Dim:** 195.07 (182.88 pp) × 23.47 × 7.95
S: 17 kts   **A:** 2/40-mm AA   **Man:** 182 men (including 11 R.N.)
M: Assoc. Electric gas turbine; 1 prop.
Boilers: 2 Foster-Wheeler, 20,000 hp

REMARKS: Helicopter platform (1 Wessex). Equipped for rapid stores handling and replenishment at sea.

♦ *2 Supply ships*

	Bldr	Laid down	L	In serv.
A 386 FORT AUSTIN	Scott's SB (Greenock)			
A 385 FORT GRANGE	Scott's SB (Greenock)			

Dim: 180.90 × 23.70 × 7.50

REMARKS: Ordered in 11-71. Will have a cargo helicopter and a hangar. Three frames.

♦ *1 Aircraft carrier support ship*

A 84 RELIANT (ex-*Somersby*) (9-9-53) bought and modified in 1958.

Reliant (A 84)   1971 Aldo Fraccaroli

D: 13,730 tons (fl)   **Dim:** 141 × 18.50 × 8
Cargo capacity: 9,290 tons
S: 18 kts   **Man:** 110 men
M: Doxford 6 cyl diesel; 1 prop; 8,250 hp
Endurance: 50 days/16 kts

REMARKS: Supply ship for aircraft carriers. Quarters air-conditioned. Platform for helicopters.

♦ *2 Repair ships*

	L
A 329 RETAINER (ex-*Chungking*)	19-1-50
A 280 RESURGENT (ex-*Changchow*)	31-7-50

Bldr: Scott's — Completed in 1950-51. Bought and modified 1952-1956 — *R.F.A.*

Retainer (A 329)   1972 British Crown Copyright

LOGISTIC SUPPORT (continued)

D: 14,400 tons (fl) **Dim:** 145.80 × 18.92 × 8.83 (fl)
Cargo: 9,400 tons
S: 14 kts **M:** 1 Doxford diesel 6,500 hp
Fuel: 925 tons

REMARKS: Repair ships or tenders. Former mixed cargo ships of the China Line.

A 404 BACCHUS — A 406 HEBE — Bldr: Henry Robb Ltd (1962) R.F.A.

Hebe (A 406)   1974 Guiglini

D: 7,960 tons (fl) **Dim:** 106.70 × 16.76 × 6.40
S: 15 kts **Cargo capacity:** 5,128 tons
M: Sulzer diesel; 1 prop 5,500 hp
Man: 57 men **Fuel:** 720 tons

REMARKS: Chartered for 19 years upon completion. Living spaces and machinery area aft. Transportation of cargo and provisions. 3 holds; refrigerated compartments; carry 800 tons of fuel oil, 200 tons of lubricating oil; 240 tons of fresh water.

♦ *2 modified ex-cargo ships (built in Canada during the war)*. (R.N.)

	Bldr	L
A 134 RAME HEAD	Burrard DD (Vancouver)	4-11-44
A 191 BERRY HEAD	Burrard DD (Vancouver)	21-10-44

D: 8,580 tons, (light) 8,750 (av) 10,200 (fl)
Dim: 134.40 (126.80 pp) × 17.40 × 8.84 (fl)
S: 11 kts **A:** 9 or 11/40-mm AA
M: Triple expans., 2,500 hp **Boilers:** 2 Foster-Wheeler
Fuel: 1,000 tons

REMARKS: "Maintenance ships" for frigates (*134*) and minesweepers (*191*); modernized (1959-60), the *134* was fitted with a trellis mast and four cranes (2/12, 2/5 tons), on a trainable platform. Many workshops, decompression chamber. **Man:** 24 officers, 416 men, including 113 specialists. A *191* is about to be scrapped.

♦ *13 fleet replenishment tankers*
♦ *3 Olwen class*

A 122 OLWEN (ex-*Olynthus*) (10-7-64), **A 123 OLNA** (28-7-65), **A 124 OLMEDA** ex-*Oleander* (19-11-64)

Olmeda (A 124)   1974 M.N.

D: 33,200 tons (fl) **Dim:** 197.51 (185.92 pp) × 25.60 × 10.50
Cargo capacity: 22,300 tons
S: 20 kts **Man:** 115 men
M: Pamatreda GT; 1 prop; 26,500 hp
Boilers: 2 Babcock 60 kg/cm²; superheat: 510°

REMARKS: Reinforced hull against ice, air-conditioned living spaces, advanced automation, excellent replenishment at sea facilities. Helicopter platform. Hangar for 2 Wessex type helicopters.

♦ *5 Tide class*

Tidespring (A 75)

A 75 TIDESPRING (3-5-62), **A 76 TIDEPOOL** (11-12-62), **A 96 TIDEREACH** (2-6-54), **A 97 TIDEFLOW** (30-8-54), **A 98 TIDESURGE** (1-7-54)

D: 25,000 tons (fl) **Dim:** 177.60 (167.65 pp) × 21.64 × 9.75
Cargo capacity: 17,400/700 tons
S: 17 kts **Man:** 115 men
M: Pamatreda GT; 1 prop; 15,000 hp
Boilers: 2 Babcock

REMARKS: *96* and *97* have been air-conditioned and have a hangar installed on each side of the stack, plus a helicopter platform. 15,000 tons of fuel oil, 2,400 tons of various provisions, supplies, ammunition, jet fuel; powerful underway replenishment equipment. *Tideaustral*, the same class, was transferred in 1962 to the Australian Navy and renamed *Supply*.

LOGISTIC SUPPORT (continued)

♦ *5 Rover class*

Blue Rover (A 270)   1970

A 268 GREEN ROVER (19-12-68), **A 269 GREY ROVER** (17-4-69), **A 270 BLUE ROVER** (11-11-69), **A 271 GOLD ROVER** (7-3-73), **A 273 BLACK ROVER** (30-8-73).

Bldr: All constructed by Swan Hunter

  D: 11,500 tons   **Dim:** 140.50 × 19.20 × 7.30
  Cargo capacity: 7,000 tons, of which 5,800 tons of fuel oil
  S: 18 kts   **Man:** 42 men
  M: 2 Ruston and Hornsby diesels, (V-16); 1 variable pitch prop; 8,000 hp

OTHER TANKERS

Seven ocean-going oilers

♦ *Leaf Class (chartered) R.F.A.*

A 79 BAY LEAF (28-10-54)   **A 77 PEAR LEAF** (16-10-59)
A 80 ORANGE LEAF (8-2-55)   **A 82 CHERRY LEAF**

  Merchant tankers chartered for long periods since the spring of 1959. Each has a cargo capacity of 16 to 18,000 tons, a cruising speed of 13.5/14 knots. They are 160 to 180 m. long and have 1 diesel engine for propulsion.

♦ *Dale class (chartered) R.F.A.*

A . . . DEWDALE (5-3-65) (ex-*Edenfield*, 60,200 tons, 17,000 hp)

♦ *Ranger class R.F.A.*

A 169 BROWN RANGER (12-12-40)

  D: 6,630 tons (fl)   **S:** 12 kts   **Dim:** 109 × 14.20 × 6.10

REMARKS: Scheduled for disposal.

♦ *Eddy class*

A 261 EDDYFIRTH R.F.A.

  D: 4,160 tons (fl)   **S:** 12 kts   **Dim:** 85.8 × 12.3 × 5.2

Six coastal tankers. Oil class R.M.A.S.

Y 25 OIL BIRD   **Y 26 OIL MAN**   **Y 22 OIL STONE**
Y 24 OIL FIELD   **Y 21 OIL PRESS**   **Y 23 OIL WELL**

  D: 530 tons (fl)   **Dim:** 41.5 × 9 × 2.50
  S: 10 kts   **Man:** 11 men

Small transports (coastal and naval shipyard service).

A 378 KINTERBURY (1943) R.F.A.

  D: 1,490 tons (1,770 fl)   **Dim:** 56.39 × 10.06 × 4.27
  S: 10 kts
  M: Triple expansion, 1 prop; 900 hp   **Fuel:** 153 tons coal
  Cargo capacity: 770 tons

A 377 MAXIM (1946)

  D: 650 tons   **Dim:** 43 × 7.62 × 5.50
  S: 9 kts   **Cargo capacity:** 240 tons
  M: Triple expansion   **Man:** 13 men

THOMAS GRANT (*Port Auxiliary Service*)

  D: 461 tons (fl)   **Dim:** 34 × 7.60 × 2.70
  S: 9 kts   **M:** 2 diesels

CATAPULT (*R.M.A.S.*)   **BOWSTRING** (*R.M.A.S.*)   **FLINTLOCK** (*R.M.A.S.*)

  D: various

WATER CARRIERS (*R.M.A.S. and Port Auxiliary Service*)

♦ *Water class*

Y . . WATERCOURSE   **Y . . WATERFOWL**
Y 17 WATERFALL   **Y 20 WATERSIDE**
Y 18 WATERSHED   **Y 19 WATERSPOUT**

  D: 300 tons (fl)   **S:** 11 kts   **Dim:** 40 × 7.50 × 2.50

♦ **A 222 SPAPOOL** (1946)   **A 260 SPALAKE** (1946)
  A 257 SPABURN (1946)   **A 224 SPABROOK** (1944)

  D: 1,219 tons   **S:** 10 kts   **Dim:** 38 × 7.70 × 3.15
  Cargo capacity: 500 tons

♦ **FRESHBURN**   **FRESHMERE**   **FRESHPOND**
  FRESHLAKE   **FRESHPOOL**   **FRESHSPRING**

  D: 594 tons   **S:** 9 kts   **Dim:** 49 × 9.50 × 3.70

CABLE SHIPS (*R.M.A.S.*)

A 176 BULLFINCH (8-40)
A 259 St. MARGARETS (10-43) — Bldr — Swan Hunter

  D: 2,500 tons (fl)   **Dim:** 75.70 × 11 × 5
  S: 12 kts   **M:** Triple expansion; 1,250 hp
  A: 1/102-mm — 4/20-mm

Goosander (P 197)   1974 Robb Caledon

MOORING, SALVAGE SHIPS, AND BOOM VESSELS

♦ *2 Pochard class* — Bldr: Robb Caledon (1973-74)

P 196 POCHARD   **P 197 GOOSANDER**

   D: 1,180 tons   **Dim:** 48.80 (pp) × 12.20 × 5.50
   S: 10 kts
   M: Paxman diesel 16 RPHXM; 1 prop.

NETLAYERS — SALVAGE SHIPS

♦ *4 Wild Duck class*

	Bldr	L	In serv.
P 192 MANDARIN	Cammell Laird	17-9-63	2-64
P 193 PINTAIL	Cammell Laird	3-12-63	3-64
P 194 GARGANEY	Brooke Marine Ltd	13-12-65	9-66
P 195 GOLDENEYE DUCK	Brooke Marine Ltd	31-3-66	12-66

Golden Eye (P 195)   1975 G. Arra

   D: 900 tons   **Dim:** 57.86 (47.24 pp) × 13 × 3.20
   S: 13 kts   **Man:** 7 officers, 18 men
   M: 2 Davey-Paxman diesels, 16 cyl.; 550 hp; variable pitch prop

REMARKS: In comparison to the following ships, these are versatile: buoy boats, netlayers, salvage ships. Capable of lifting 200 tons. Electric power, 640 kw (*194, 195*) 405 kw (*192, 193*).

♦ *2 Lay class*

P 190 LAYMOOR (6-8-59)
P 191 LAYBURN (14-4-60) — Bldr: Wm. Simons & Co.

   D: 800 tons (1,050 fl)
   Dim: 58.83 (48.77 pp) × 10.36 × 6.50 × 3.50 (hold depth)
   S: 14 kts
   Man: 2 officers, 29 men
   M: Triple expansion; 2 props
   Boilers: 2 Foster-Wheeler; 1,300 hp.

REMARKS: Excellent quarters comfortable in cold climates and in tropical zones.

Layburn (P 191)

♦ *1 Bar class*

P 202 BARFOOT

Type Bar   Photo A. and J. Pavia

   D: 750 tons (960 fl)   **Dim:** 52.93 × 9.60 × 2.70
   S: 11.75 kts   **A:** 1/76-mm AA
   Man: 32 men   **M:** 1 Triple-expansion; 850 hp
   Boilers: 2 cylindrical boilers

REMARKS: Rigging: 1/10-ton loading mast; bow lift tested at 20 tons; 2/10-ton winches. Several of this class scrapped in 1962 and 1963, 10 in 1964, 17 since then. Others have been transferred (2 to South Africa, 3 to Turkey). About to be scrapped.

VARIOUS

♦ *1 patrol ship for the Antarctic* (hull painted red — 2 helicopters)

H 171 ENDURANCE (ex-*Anita Dan*)
Bldr: Kröger-Werft, Rendsburg (26-5-56)

   D: 2,641 grt/3,600 tons official
   S: 14.5 kts   **Dim:** 93.58 (82.90) × 14.03 × 5.03
   M: 1 B and W 5-cylinder, 2-ton diesel; 1 prop (plus a bow prop); 2,900 hp
   Cargo capacity: 3,235 tons   **Range:** 12,000/14
   Man: 13 officers, 106 men

VARIOUS (continued)

Endurance (A 171)   1975 G. Arra

◆ *1 royal yacht*

	Bldr	Laid down	L	In serv.
BRITANNIA	J. Brown (Clydebank)	7-52	16-4-53	1-54

- **D:** 4,715 tons (fl)   **Dim:** 125.90 (115.82 pp) × 16.76 × 4.86
- **S:** 21 kts   **M:** GT; 2 props   **Boilers:** 2; 12,000 hp
- **Man:** 271 men   **Fuel:** 490 tons

REMARKS: In wartime becomes a hospital ship (200 beds and 60 medical personnel), would have a helicopter platform. Raked bow, 3 masts, gyro-stabilizer. Range: 3,100/20; on trial runs made 22.85 knots; 12,400 hp and 4,320 tons displacement.

A. and J. Pavia

◆ *2 Hovercraft*

1 Winchester class (SNRG)

45 tons, 900 hp — **S:** 60 kts — **Range:** 225. Carries 18 men and 3 tons of freight.

1 Wellington class (BHN 7)

50 tons, 4,250 hp — **S:** 60 kts — **Man:** 14 men.

◆ *1 ship assigned to the Under Water Weapons Establishment*

ICEWHALE (profile of a coastal trader)

- **D:** 289 tons (350 fl)   **Dim:** 36 × 7.2 × 2.7
- **S:** 12 kts   **Man:** 12 men

◆ *1 target vessel for submarines*

A . . . WAKEFUL — Ex-Swedish coastal trader *Dan*, 492 tons

◆ *2 torpedo recovery vessels*

A 127 TORRENT, A 128 TORRID — In serv. 9-71 and 1-72

Torrent   1972 British Crown Copyright

VARIOUS (continued)

Bldr: Swan Hunter, Wallsend

D: 450 tons   **L:** 46
S: 12 kts   **M:** 2 Paxman diesels; 700 hp

♦ *1 experimental vessel for deep diving*

A 231 RECLAIM (3-48)

D: 1,200 tons (1,700 fl)   **Dim:** 64 × 11.50 × . . .
S: 12 kts   **Man:** 84 men
M: Triple expansion; 2,500 hp
Range: 3,000/10

REMARKS: Diving bells and other methods of observation for deep diving experiments.

TENDERS

♦ *7 Insect class* (1970-71) — 450 tons — 600 hp — **S:** 10 kts

BEE, CIGALA, COCKCHAFER, CRICKET, GNAT, LADYBIRD, SCARAB

♦ *9 Aberdovey class* (1963-71) — 70 tons — **S:** 10.5 kts — 210 hp
Can carry 200 passengers (standing) and 25 tons.

♦ *30 Cartmel class* — 143 tons — 320 hp — **S:** 10.5 kts

♦ *5 Ilchester class*

A . . . ILCHESTER, A 309 INSTON, A 310 INVERGORDON, A 311 IRON-BRIDGE, A 312 IXWORTH.

♦ See also "-ham"-class minesweepers

TUGS (R.M.A.S. and P.A.S.)

♦ *19 ocean-going tugs and salvage vessels*

Roysterer   1972

ROYSTERER, ROBUST, ROLLICKER (1970-73) — 1,630 tons (fl) — 4,500 hp
S: 15 kts   **M:** diesels   **Dim:** 53 × 11.60 × 6.50

A 95 TYPHOON (1958)

D: 1,380 tons (fl)   **S:** 17 kts   **Dim:** 60.50 × 12 × 4
M: 2 diesels; 1 variable pitch prop; 2,750 hp

Typhoon (A 95)   1975 G. Arra

♦ *Salvage tugs*

ACCORD, ADVICE, AGILE, A 289 CONFIANCE, A 290 CONFIDENT
D: 760 tons (fl)   **S:** 13 kts   **M:** 4 diesels; 2 props; 1,600 hp

A 288 SEA GIANT (22-6-54),   **SUPERMAN** (23-11-53)
D: 1,000 tons (fl)   **Dim:** 54 × 11.20 × 4.30
S: 15 kts   **M:** 2 Triple-exp, 3,000 hp

A 111 CYCLONE (10-9-42)   **A: 264 REWARD** (13-10-44)
D: 1,630 tons (fl)   **S:** 16 kts   **M:** 2 diesels; 4,000 hp

♦ *45 port tugs*

Diesel-electric (blades)

A 95 DEXTROUS, A 94 DIRECTOR, A 85 FAITHFUL, A 87 FAVOURITE, A 86 FORCEFUL, A 92 GRINDER, A 91 GRIPER

Director

VARIOUS (*continued*)

♦ *Diesel with 2 props*

AIREDALE, ALSATIAN, BASSET, BEAGLE, BOXER, CAIRN, COLLIE, CORGI, DALMATIAN, DEERHOUND, ELKHOUND, HUSKY, LABRADOR, MASTIFF, POINTER, SALUKI, SEALYHAM, SETTER, SHEEPDOG, SPANIEL.

AGATHA, AGNES, ALICE, AUDREY, BARBARA, BETTY, BRENDA, BRIDGET, CELIA, CHARLOTTE, CHRISTINE, CLARE, DAISY, DAPHNE, DORIS, DOROTHY, EDITH, FELICITY, FIONA, GEORGINA, GWENDOLINE, HELEN, IRENE, ISABEL, JOAN, JOYCE, KATHLEEN, KITTY, LESLEY, LILIAN, LILAH, MAY, MARY, MYRTLE, NANCY, NORAH.

REMARKS: *Reward* is going to be assigned to the protection of off-shore oil rigs.

Setter   1975 G. Arra

PERSONNEL: About 17,500 men including 2,000 officers.

NAVAL AVIATION: The Greek navy has signed a contract with SNIAS for the purchase of 4 Alouette III ASW helicopters fitted with AS 12. These machines are the first of the future Greek naval aviation arm which was to begin with the reception of these helicopters in April 1975. The Air Force has a dozen Albatross amphibian planes for ASW warfare.

MERCHANT MARINE (1-7-74): 2,651 ships — 21,759,449 grt
tankers: 389 ships — 7,559,652 grt

NAVAL PROGRAM

The following long and short term projects are planned:

♦ modernization of the *Gearing*-class destroyers;

♦ purchase of 8 additional *Kimothoi*-class missile boats to bring the total number to 12;

♦ purchase of 4 *Combattante* III-class missile boats;

♦ purchase of 4 submarines, bringing the number of modern submarines in the fleet to 8;

♦ purchase of 4 frigates of medium tonnage.

Discussions are continuing between Greece and the German Federal Republic concerning the transfer to the Greek Navy of:
— 7 *Jaguar*-class Type S 141 patrol torpedo boats
— 1 mine transport ship for which the German Navy no longer has any use.
These transfers, undertaken within the framework of German military assistance to Greece, should take place soon.

WARSHIPS IN SERVICE OR UNDER CONSTRUCTION AS OF 1 OCTOBER 1975

	D	L	Main armament
♦ *8 submarines*			
4 GLAVKOS	900	1970-71	8/533-mm TT
1 TRIAINA	1,525	1942-44	10/553-mm TT
2 PAPANIKOLIS	1,500	1944	10/533-mm TT
1 KATSONIS	1,600	1946	10/533-mm TT
♦ *11 destroyers*			
4 THEMISTOKLES	2,425	1944-45	4/6-127-mm. Asroc, 6 ASW TT
2 MIAOULIS	2,200	1944	6/127-mm, 6 ASW TT
5 ASPIS	2,050	1942-45	4/127-mm, 6/76-mm AA, 10/40-mm AA
♦ *12 frigates*			
4 AETOS	1,300	1943-44	3/76-mm AA, ASW weapons
5 ARMATOLOS	990	1942-43	2/76-mm
3 PLOT. ARSANOGLOU	325	1943-44	1/76-mm
♦ *20 guided missile and torpedo patrol boats*			
4 COMBATTANTE III	400	1975-76	4 MM 38, 2/76-mm
4 KIMOTHOI	234	1971	4 MM 38, 4/35-AA
5 ANDROMEDA	69	1966-67	4/533-mm T
1 AIOLOS	75	1961	2/40-mm AA, 2/533-mm T
1 ASTRAPI	75	1962	2/40-mm AA, 2/533-mm T
5 DELPHIN	110	1951-56	1/40-mm AA, 2/533-mm T

♦ *1 minelayer, 15 minesweepers*

GREECE

SUBMARINES

♦ *4 German type 209*

	Bldr	Laid down	L	In serv.
S 110 GLAVKOS	Howaldtswerke, Kiel	1969	1970	1972
S 111 NEREUS	Howaldtswerke, Kiel	1969	1970	1972
S 112 TRITON	Howaldtswerke, Kiel	1969	1971	8-1972
S 113 PROTEUS	Howaldtswerke, Kiel	1970	1971	11-1972

Gafkos (S 110)   1973

D: 980 tons/1,105 surfaced/1,230 submerged   **Dim:** 55 × 6.60 × 5.90
S: 21 kts (max. submerged for 5 min), 12 kts with snorkel
A: 8/533-mm TT fwd (+ 6 reserve torpedoes)   **Man:** 5 officers, 26 men
M: diesel-electric propulsion; 4 Maybach diesels linked to an AEG generator of 420 kw; a single Siemens electric motor of 500 kw; 1 prop

REMARKS: Similar to the submarines ordered by Argentina, Peru, and other countries. Submersion depth superior to 200 m. See remarks under *Salta* class, Argentina section.

♦ *2 ex-U.S. Guppy II class, transferred 30-6-72 and 26-7-72*

	Bldr	L
S 114 PAPANIKOLIS (ex-*Hardhead, SS-365*)	Manitowoc SB	12-12-44
S 115 POSEIDON (ex-*Blackfin, SS-322*)	Electric Boat Co	12-3-44

D: 1,500 tons/1,840 surfaced/2,245 submerged   **Dim:** 93.20 × 8.20 × 5.20
S: 18/15 kts   **Man:** 86 men
A: 10/533-mm TT (6 fwd, 4 aft)   **Range:** 10,000/10
M: diesel-electric propulsion; 3 groups of generators; 2 electric motors; 2 props; 4,800/5,200 hp   **Fuel:** 300 tons diesel

REMARKS: Originally the *Balao* type, but the fourth group of generators has been removed to permit enlarging of the sonar compartment. Two batteries of 126 cells.

SUBMARINES (*continued*)

◆ *1 ex-U.S. Guppy class transferred in 10-73*

	Bldr	L	In serv.
S 115 L. KATSONIS (ex-*Remora, SS-481*)	Portsmouth NSY	12-7-45	3-1-46

- **D:** 1,660 tons/1,975 surfaced/2,540 submerged **Dim:** 99.40 × 8.20 × 5.20
- **S:** 20/13-15 kts
- **A:** 10/533-mm TT (6 fwd, 4 aft)   **Electron Equipt:** Sonar BQG 4
- **M:** diesel-electric propulsion; 4 groups of generators (6,000 hp); 2 electric motors (5,400 hp)

◆ *1 ex-U.S. Gato/Balao class, loaned by the U.S.A.* (*1964*)

	Bldr	Laid down	L	In serv.
S 86 TRIAINA (ex-*Scabbardfish, SS-397*)	Portsmouth NSY	1943	27-1-44	4-44

Triaina (S 86)

- **D:** 1,525 tons/1,825 surfaced/2,300 submerged
- **Dim:** 95 (92.72 pp) × 8.25 × 5.20
- **S:** 20/10 kts   **Man:** 85 men
- **A:** 10/533-mm TT (6 fwd, 4 aft)   **Range:** 12,000/10
- **M:** diesel-electric propulsion surfaced; 2 props; 6,500/5,400 hp

DESTROYERS

◆ *6 ex-U.S. Fletcher class*

	Bldr	L	In serv.
D 06 ASPIS (ex-*Conner, DD-582*)	Boston NSY	18-7-42	6-43
D 16 VELOS (ex-*Charette, DD-581*)	Boston NSY	3-6-42	5-43
D 28 THYELLA (ex-*Bradford, DD-545*)	Bethlehem (San Pedro)	12-12-42	6-43
D 58 LONCHI (ex-*Hall, DD-583*)	Boston NSY	18-7-42	7-43
D 85 SPHENDONI (ex-*Aulick, DD-569*)	Consolidated SB	2-3-42	10-42
D 63 NAVARINON (ex-*Brown, DD-546*)	Bethlehem (San Pedro)	22-2-43	7-43

- **D:** 2,050 tons (2,850 fl)   **Dim:** 114.85 × 12.03 × 5.50
- **S:** 32/30 kts   **Range:** 1,260/350 — 4,400/15   **Man:** 350 men
- **A:** *06, 16, 56, 85:* 4/127-mm, 38-cal (I × 4) — 6/76-mm, 50-cal (II × 3) — 5/533-mm TT (V × 1) — *28, 63:* 5/127-mm AA (I × 5) — 10/40-mm (IV × 2, II × 1). No tubes. All: ASW torpedoes, hedgehog and depth charges.

Thyella (D 28)   1974

- **M:** General Electric GT; 2 props; 60,000 hp
- **Boilers:** 4 Babcock and Wilcox   **Fuel:** 650 tons

REMARKS: Transferred under the Mutual Assistance Pact, three in 1959, the *Lonchi* in 1960, *Thyella* and *Navarinon* in 9-62. Loan renewed in 3-70.

◆ *4 ex-U.S. Gearing class, transferred in 1971* (*210*)*, 1973, 1972* (*212*)

	Bldr	L
D 210 THEMISTOKLES (ex-*Frank Knox, DD-742*)	Bath Iron Works	17-9-44
D 212 KANARIS (ex-*Stickell, DD-888*)	Consolidated Steel	16-6-45
D 213 KONTOURIOTIS (ex-*Rupertus, DD-851*)	Bethlehem (Quincy)	21-9-45
D 214 SACHTOURIS (ex-*Arnold J. Isbell, DD-869*)	Bethlehem (Quincy)	6-8-45

- **D:** 2,425 tons (3,500 fl)   **Dim:** 119.72 × 12.55 × 5.50
- **S:** 30 kts   **Man:** 14 officers, 260 men   **Range:** 2,400/25 — 4,800/15
- **A:** *210:* 6/127-mm 38-cal (II × 3) — 6 ASW Mk 32 TT (III × 2) — 2 Mk 25 TT for wire-guided torpedoes. *212* and *213:* 4/127-mm 38-cal (II × 2) — 1 ASW Asroc system — 6 ASW Mk 32 TT (III × 2)
- **M:** GT; 4 Babcock boilers; 2 props; 60,000 hp   **Fuel:** 650 tons

REMARKS: Modernized under FRAM I (*212, 213, 214*) and II (*210*) programs. Will be fitted with 1/76-mm AA OTO Melara to replace the two 127-mm mounts and a BPDMS, Albatros (Italian version of the Sea Sparrow).

◆ *1 ex-U.S. Allen M. Sumner class transferred 16-7-71*

	Bldr	L
D 211 MIAOULIS (ex-*Ingraham, DD-694*)	Federal SB & DD	16-1-44

- **D:** 2,200 tons (3,320 fl)   **Dim:** 114.75 × 12.45 × 5.80
- **S:** 30 kts   **Man:** 14 officers, 260 men   **Range:** 2,400/25 — 4,800/15
- **A:** 6/127-mm 38-cal (II × 3) — 2 hedgehogs — 6 ASW Mk 32 TT (III × 2)
- **M:** GT; 4 Babcock boilers; 2 props; 60,000 hp   **Fuel:** 650 tons

REMARKS: Modernized under FRAM II program.

FRIGATES

♦ *4 ex-U.S. DE class transferred in 1951*

	Bldr	L
D 01 AETOS (ex-*Ebert, DE-768*)	Tampa Shipbldg	23-5-44
D 31 HIERAX (ex-*Slater, DE-766*)	Tampa Shipbldg	13-2-44
D 54 LEON (ex-*Garfield Thomas, DE-193*)	Federal, Port Newark	12-12-43
D 67 PANTHIR (ex-*Eldridge, DE-173*)	Federal, Port Newark	25-6-43

Aetos (D 01) 1971

D: 1,300 tons (1,750 fl)   **Dim:** 93 (91.50 pp) × 11.17 × 3.25
S: 19 kts   **Range:** 11,500/11 — 5,500/19
Man: 150 men (peace), 185 men (war)
A: 3/76-mm — 6/40-mm AA (II × 3) — 14/20-mm AA — 2 hedgehogs — 8 depth charge projectors — 2 ASW torpedo racks
M: diesel-electric propulsion; 4 General Electric diesels and 2 electric motors; 2 props; 6,000 hp   **Fuel:** 300 tons

♦ *5 ex-British of the Canadian Algerine class*

	Bldr	L
M 12 ARMATOLOS (ex-*Aries*)	Toronto Shipyard	19-9-42
M 58 MACHITIS (ex-*Postillion*)	Redfern Construction Co	18-3-43
M 64 NAVMACHOS (ex-*Lightfoot*)	Redfern Construction Co	14-11-42

Machitis (M 58) 1972 Arra

M 74 POLEMISTIS (ex-*Gozo*)	Redfern Construction Co	27-1-43
M 76 PYRPOLITIS (ex-*Arcturus*)	Redfern Construction Co	31-8-43

D: 990 tons (1,237 fl)   **Dim:** 68.58 × 10.82 × 3.50
S: 16 kts   **Man:** 85/90 men   **Range:** 3,000/15
A: 2/76-mm — 4/20-mm — 2 machine guns — (*Machitis*, training ship, no weapons).
M: Triple expansion; 2 props; 2,000 hp; 2 boilers   **Fuel:** 270 tons

REMARKS: The *Pyrpolitis* is a command ship for amphibious operation; the other four are now designated "fleet auxiliary transports."

♦ *3 ex-U.S. coastal patrol vessels*

Bldr: U.S.A. (1943-44)

P 14 PLOTARCHIS ARSANOGLOU (ex-*PGM 25*, ex-*PC 1556*).
P 70 ANTIPLOIARCHOS PEZOPOULOS (ex-*PGM 21*, ex-*PC 1552*).
P 93 PLOTARCHIS CHADZIKONSTANDIS (ex-*PGM 29*, ex-*PC 1565*).

Plotarchis Arsanoglou (P 14)

D: 325 tons (400 fl)   **Dim:** 52.95 × 7.05 × 3.25
S: 18 kts   **Man:** 65 men   **Range:** 6,000/10 — 2,300/18
A: 1/76-mm — 6/20-mm AA Oerlikons — 1 hedgehog — 2 ASW torpedo racks
M: General Motors diesels; 2 props; 3,600 hp

GUIDED MISSILE PATROL BOATS

♦ *4 Combattante III class*

Bldr: Constr. Méc. de Normandie, Cherbourg — Contract signed 22-5-75.

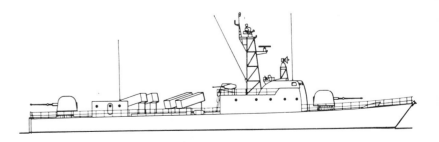

GUIDED MISSILE PATROL BOATS (continued)

	L	In serv.
P . . . N . . .		
P . . . N . . .		
P . . . N . . .		
P . . . N . . .		

D: 400 tons (fl)   **S:** 36.5 kts   **Dim:** 56 × 7.90 × 2.50
A: 4 MM 38 — 2/76-mm AA OTO Melara (I × 2) — 4/35-mm AA (II × 2) —
2/533-mm wireguided TT
Range: 700/32.5   **Man:** 5 officers, 33 men
M: MTU fast diesels; 4 props; 15,000 hp

NOTE: The transfer of the *PG-99 Beacon* and *PG-100 Douglas* has been discussed with
the U.S. Navy.
The 4/35-mm AA (II × 2) of the Combattante III class will be replaced by
2/30-mm AA Emerlec type guns which have a higher firing rate.

♦ 4 Kimothoi class

	L		L
P 53 KIMOTHOI	26-1-71	P 55 EUNIKI	8-9-71
P 54 CALYPSO	27-4-71	P 56 NAVSITHOI	12-71

Bldr: Constr. Méc. de Normandie, Cherbourg

Kimothoi (P 53)   1971 M.N.

D: 234 tons (255 fl)   **S:** 36.5 kts   **Dim:** 47 (44 pp) × 7.10 × 2.50 (fl)
A: 4 MM 38 Exocet missiles — 2 ASW TT aft (wire-guided torpedoes) —
4/35-mm AA (II × 2)
Electron Equipt: Thomson CSF radars: 1 Castor, 1 Pollux, 1 Triton
M: 4 MTU 872 fast diesels; 4 props; 12,000 hp.   **Fuel:** 39 tons
Range: 850/25 — 2,000/15   **Man:** 4 officers, 36 men

REMARKS: *La Combattante II* class; steel hull; superstructure is light steel. In service
in 1972. Eight others are planned.

PATROL TORPEDO BOATS

The Gourlandris shipbuilding group has delivered to the Greek Navy two fast small
boats built in the Island of Syros shipyard. The first was launched 16-6-75.

♦ 5 Norwegian Tjeld class

P 21 ANDROMEDA	P 24 KYKONOS	P 26 TOXOTIS
P 23 KASTOR	P 25 PIGASSOS	

Bldr: Mek. Verks. Mandal, Norway 1966-67

Andromeda (P 21)   1971

D: 69 tons (76 fl)   **Dim:** 24.50 (22.86 pp) × 7.50 × 1.95
S: 43 (40 cruising)   **Man:** 22 men   **Range:** 450/40 — 600/25
A: 2/40-mm AA (I × 2) — 4/533-mm TT (I × 4)
M: 2 Napier-Deltic diesels Mk T 1827K with turbo compressors; 2 props;
6,280 hp   **Fuel:** 10 tons

♦ 2 Vosper type bought in Germany in January 1968

These two small craft have hulls of a composite construction: wood and light metal.
Welded superstructure in light alloys.

(a) *Ferocity* class with 2 Bristol-Siddeley Proteus gas turbines
P 19 AIOLOS (ex-*Pfeil*) — Bldr: Vosper — L: 26-10-61 — In serv. 6-62
D: 75/85 tons (fl)   **Dim:** 28.95 × (28.03 wl) × 7.22 × 2.00
S: 54/50 kts, 7,500 hp   **A:** same as the *Astrapi*.   **Man:** 14 men

Aiolos (P 19)   1971

(b) *Brave* class with 3 Bristol-Siddeley Proteus gas turbines
P 20 ASTRAPI (ex-*Strahl*) — Bldr: Vosper — L: 10-1-62 — In serv. 11-62
D: 75 tons (100 fl)   **Dim:** 30.17 (29.26 wl) × 7.62 × 2.15

PATROL TORPEDO BOATS (continued)

S: 50 kts   **Range:** 400/45   **Man:** 3 officers, 19 men
A: 2/40-mm and 2/533-mm TT or 1/40-mm and 4/533-mm TT — or mines
M: 12,500 hp.

♦ 5 ex-German

P 15 DELPHIN (ex-*Sturmmöwe*)   **P 18 POLYDEYKIS** (ex-*Wildschwan*)
P 16 DRAKON (ex-*Silbermöwe*)   **P 27 PHOINIX** (ex-*Eismöwe*)
P 17 POLIKOS (ex-*Raubmöwe*)   Bldr: Lürssen, Vegesack (1951–56)

Polydeykis (P 18)   1971

D: 110 tons (155 fl)   **S:** 35 kts   **Dim:** 35.40 × 5.10 × 1.80
A: 1/40-mm or 4/20-mm — 2/533-mm TT   **Range:** 600/30
M: 3 Mercedes-Benz diesels, 20 cylinders; 3 props; 9,000 hp
Fuel: 12.5 tons   **Man:** 19 men

REMARKS: Purchased from West Germany in 1968. The following VLT class boats are being acquired from Germany: *Falke, Geier, Greif, Habicht, Kondor, Kormoran,* and *Seeadler.*

MINESWEEPERS

♦ 15 U.S. MSC class transferred beginning in 1964

M 919 ATLANTI (ex-*MSC 169*)   **M 245 DORIS** (ex-*MSC 298*)
M 921 ANTIOPI (ex-*MSC 153*)   **M 246 AIGLI** (ex-*MSC 299*)
M 922 PHEDRA (ex-*MSC 154*)   **M 247 DAPHNI** (ex-*MSC 307*)
M 923 THALIA (ex-*MSC 170*)   **M 248 AIDON** (ex-*MSC 310*)
M 211 ALKYON (ex-*MSC 319*)   **M 213 ARGO** (ex-*MSC 317*)
M 240 PLEIAS (ex-*MSC 314*)   **M 214 AVRA** (ex-*MSC 318*)
M 241 KICHLI (ex-*MSC 308*)   **M 924 NIOVI** (ex-*MSC 171*)
M 242 KISSA (ex-*MSC 309*)

Bldr: U.S.A. 1954–55 (5), 1964–69 (the others)
Pleas and *Alkyone* were transferred in 1970.

D: 300 tons (372 fl)   **Dim:** 43 (41.50 pp) × 7.95 × 2.55
S: 13 (8 sweeping)   **Range:** 2,500/10
A: 2/20-mm (II × 1)   **Man:** 4 officers, 27 men
M: General Motors diesels; 2 props; 880/1,000 hp.   **Fuel:** 40 tons

REMARKS: Transferred under the M.A.P. The *202, 205, 206, 210,* and *254* are the former Belgian ships *St. Truiden, Herne, Malmédy, Blankenbergue,* and *Laroche,* returned to the U.S.A. in 7/9-69 and then transferred to Greece.

Antiopi (M 921 maintenant)   1972 J. C. Bellonne

PATROL BOATS

♦ 2 ex-U.S. LSSL vessels transferred in 1958

L 94 PLOTARCHIS MARIDAKIS (ex-*65*), **L 95 PLOTARCHIS VLACHAVAS** (ex-*45*)

Bldr: U.S.A. 1945
D: 257 tons (395 fl)   **S:** 14 kts   **Dim:** 48 × 7 × 1.75
A: 1/76-mm — 4/40-mm AA (II × 2) — 4/20-mm AA
M: diesels; 2 props; 1,600 hp.   **Fuel:** 87 tons

MINELAYERS

N 04 AKTION (ex-*LSM-301*), **N 05 AMVRAKIA** (ex-*LSM-303*) — Bldr: U.S.A. (1943).

Amvrakia (N 05)

D: 720 tons (1,100 fl)   **Dim:** 61.87 × 10.36 × 2.40
S: 13 kts   **Man:** 65 men   **Range:** 3,500/12
A: 8/40-mm AA (II × 4) — 6/20-mm AA (I × 6) — 100 to 300 mines depending upon the type.
M: 2 Fairbanks-Morse diesels or General Motors; 2 props; 2,800 hp

MINELAYERS (*continued*)

REMARKS: Transferred in 1953; four derricks, 2 forward and two aft, for the embarking of mines. Two minelaying rails. Four 30-cm search lights, 1 of 60 cm. Twin rudders. Three of the same class ships were transferred to Turkey and two to Norway, who in turn passed them on to Turkey in 1961.

HYDROGRAPHIC VESSELS

♦ *1 to be built in Greece. Ordered in 1974.*

N . . .

D:	1,400 tons	**S:**	14 kts	**Dim:**	64 × . . . × . . .	
A:	1 helicopter					

HEPHAISTOS, ex-U.S. *Josiah Willard Gibbs, AGOR-1,* hydrographic ship transferred on 12-71; had been a seaplane tender of the *Barnegat* class in 1942.

D:	2,800 tons (fl)	**S:**	17 kts	**Dim:**	94.70 × 12.52 × 3.65
M:	diesels; 2 props; 6,000 hp	**Man:**	150 men		

A 460 ANEMOS — Bldr: Germany.

D:	112 tons	**S:**	9 kts	**Dim:**	22.60 × 5.80 × 2.50
M:	1 diesel; 135 hp				

REMARKS: Small survey ship commissioned in 1944.

Anemos (A 469)   1971

♦ *1 modified YMS assigned to the hydrographic services.*

A 478 VEGAS (ex-*2078*)

AMPHIBIOUS CRAFT

♦ *1 ex-U.S. LSD transferred 1-71*

L 153 NAFKRATOUSSA (ex-*Fort Mandan, LSD-21*) — Bldr: U.S.A. — L: 2-6-45

D:	4,790 tons (9,375 fl)		**Dim:**	139 × 21.90 × 4.90	
S:	15 kts	**Man:** 254 men	**Range:**	8,000/15	
A:	8/40-mm AA; helicopter platform				
M:	GT; 2 watertube boilers, 3 drums; 2 props; 9,000 hp				

REMARKS: Modernized under the FRAM program (see U.S.A. section). Flagship of the amphibious forces. Well deck: 103 × 13.30; two 35-ton cranes. Can carry 18 LCMs, each with an LCVP nested.

Nafkratoussa (L 153)   A. and J. Pavia

♦ *8 ex-U.S. LST.*

L 144 SYROS* (ex-*LST-325*), transferred by the U.S.A. 29-5-64 after complete refit and modernization.

L 179 SAMOS* (ex-*LST 33*)	**L 154 IKARIA*** (ex-*LST 1068*)
L 195 CHIOS* (ex-*LST 35*)	**L 157 RODOS*** (ex-*LST 391*)
L 158 LEMNOS* (ex-*LST 36*)	**L 172 LESBOS*** (ex-*LST 389*)

L 171 KRITI (ex-*LST 1076*) transferred in 3-71.

    Bldr: U.S.A. 1943

Syros (L 144)   1972

L 171:

D:	4,980 tons (fl)	**Dim:**	105.75 × 16.75 × 4.50	
S:	13 kts	**A:**	10/20-mm AA	
M:	2 Triple expansion; 5,500 hp	**Fuel:**	1,950 tons	

The others:

D:	4,080 tons (fl)	**Dim:**	100.04 × 15.24 × 4.30	
S:	11 kts	**M:**	2 GM diesels; 1,700 hp.	
A:	10/40-mm AA; the 8/40-mm; 6/20-mm; 10/20-mm on the *171*			

REMARKS: Transferred in 1944, 1947, 1960, 1964 and 1971

♦ *7 ex-U.S. LSMs:* numbers *227, 45, 399, 102, 557, 541.* Transferred in 1958.

AMPHIBIOUS CRAFT (*continued*)

♦ **L 161 GRIGOROPOULOS — L 162 TOURNAS — L 163 DANIOLOS — L 164 ROUSEN — L 165 KRYSTALLIDIS**

Same characteristics as the *Aktion* (minelayers).

♦ *6 ex-U.S. LCUs transferred in 1960-72*

L 145 KASSOS	**L 147 KIMONOS**	**L 150 SIFNOS**
L 146 KARPATHOS	**L 149 KYTHNOS**	**L 152 SKYATOS**

D: 143 tons (309 fl) **S:** 8 kts **Dim:** 36.30 × 10.05 × 1.50
A: 2/20-mm **Man:** 13 men **M:** 3 diesels; 440 hp

13 LCM — 34 LCVP

LOGISTIC SUPPORT

♦ *1 net layer*

A 307 THETIS (U.S. *AN-103*) Transferred in 1960.

D: 560 tons (805 fl) **S:** 13 kts **Dim:** 49 × 9.25 × 3.10

♦ *8 oilers and tank ships.*

A 377 ARETHOUSA (ex-U.S. *Natchaug, AOG-54*) — L: 6-12-44; transferred 1959.

Arethousa (A 377)   1968 USN

D: 1,850 tons (4,335 fl) **Dim:** 94 × 14.60 × 4.70
S: 13 kts **Man:** 46 men **Cargo capacity:** 2,040 tons
M: General motors diesels; 2 props; 3,300 hp

A 414 ARIADNI (ex-U.S. *Tombigbee, AOG-11*, transferred in 1972)

D: 4,335 tons (fl) **S:** 14 kts **Dim:** 95 × 14.60 × 4.70
M: diesel-electric propulsion; 2 props; 3,300 hp

A 345 SIRIOS (ex-*Poseidon*, ex-*Empire Faun*) — bought in 1958 — **D:** 850 tons

♦ *6 motorized water vessels*

A 414 ILIKI, A 470 KASTORIA, A 467 VOLVI, A 473 TRICHONIS, A 472 STYMPHALIA, A 407 ANTAIOS.

♦ *1 repair ship*

A 329 SAKIPIS (ex-Norwegian *Ellida*, ex-U.S. *ARB-13*, ex-*LST-50*) (16-10-43)

D: 3,800 tons (5,000 fl) **Dim:** 99.98 × 15.24 × 4.40
A: 12/40-mm AA **S:** 10 kts **Man:** 200 men
M: General Motors diesels; 2 props; 1,800 hp

♦ *11 tugs*

A 408 ATLAS, A 409 ACHILLEUS, A 410 ATROMITOS, A 411 ADAMASTOS, A 418 ROMALEOS, A 421 MINOTAUROS, A 426 KIKLOPS, A 429 PERSEUS, A 430 SAMSON, A 431 TITAN, A 432 GIGAS.

VARIOUS

A 384 SOTIR (ex-HMS *Salventure*) (24-11-42). Salvage ship. **D:** 700 tons (fl)
A 487 SERRAI (buoys and beacons vessel) — **D:** 725 tons

GUATEMALA

PERSONNEL: approx. 300 men

MERCHANT MARINE (1-7-74): 6 ships — 8,222 grt

♦ *1 ex-U.S. Coast Guard vessel transferred in May 1967*

P 851 UTATLAN
Delivered under the Mutual Assistance Pact.

D: 42 tons	**S:** 22 kts	**Dim:** 25.90 × 5.80 × 1	
A: 2 machine guns		**Man:** 12 men	
M: 2 diesels; 2,200 hp		**Range:** 400	

♦ *2 ex-U.S. Coast Guard 19 m in length.*

P 632 MUNAHPU transferred in 1964
P 631 CABRAKAN transferred in 1965

D: 328 tons **S:** 25 kts **Dim:** 19 × 4.70 × 0.90

♦ *4 ex-U.S. Coast Guard small boats of 12 m (a) and 8 m (b).*

(*a*) **P 401 TIKAL — P 402 IXINCHE** — Transferred in 1962.
(*b*) **P 281 XUCUXUY — P 282 CAMALOTE** — Transferred in 1961.

♦ *1 ex-U.S. LCM*

561 CHINALTENANGO — transferred in 12-1965.

♦ *6 small boats*

♦ *1 ex-U.S. repair ship*

YR 40 — transferred in 1952.

GUINEA

PERSONNEL: 350 men

MERCHANT MARINE (1-7-74): 9 ships — 15,558 grt

♦ *4 Shanghai class patrol boats* **P 733** *to* **736** *transferred by the People's Republic of China in 1973.*

♦ *2 Soviet Poluchat class patrol boats*

♦ *4 Soviet P 6 class torpedo boats*

GUYANA

MERCHANT MARINE (1-7-74): 53 ships — 15,689 grt
(tankers: 3 ships — 943 grt)

♦ *3 patrol boats launched 15-2-68*

JAGUAR — MARGAY — OCELOT

D: 10 tons	**S:** 20 kts	**Dim:** 14 × 3.40 × 2
A: 1/7.62-mm machine gun		**Man:** 6 men
M: Cummins D 366 A diesels; 270 hp		**Range:** 150/12

REMARKS: Fiberglass hull; light alloy superstructure.

♦ *3 small patrol boats (33 m) ordered in 1970*

HAITI

PERSONNEL: 250 men

COAST GUARD

GC 1 SAVANNAH (ex-U.S. Coast Guard *56200*) — Bldr: Wheeler SY (Brooklyn) 1944.

D: 47 tons	**Dim:** 25.32 × 4.88 × 1.30
S: 9 kts	**Man:** 12 men
M: 2 diesels; 2 props; 200 hp.	**Fuel:** diesel

GC 2 SEIZE AOUT 1946 (ex-*SC-543*) — Bldr: U.S.A.

D: 110 tons **S:** 14 kts **A:** 2/40-mm — 2/20-mm
M: diesels; 1,000 hp

Former U.S. submarine chaser; in poor condition and not in service.

GC 5 ARTIBONITE (ex-U.S. *LCT* modified — 1944).

D: 134 tons (285 fl)		**Dim:** 36.68 × 9.75 × 1.21 (aft)
S: 8 kts	**Man:** 1 officer, 10 men	**Range:** 700/7
M: 3 Gray diesels; 3 props; 675 hp	**Fuel:** 11.2 tons

GC 7 AMIRAL KILLICK (ex-U.S. CGS *Black Rock*, *WAGL-367*)
Bought in the U.S.A.; ex-tug-buoy tender.

D: 160 tons **Length:** 35 m

GC 8 LA CRÈTE A PIERROT (ex-U.S. *CGS-8*) transferred in 6-60.

D: 100 tons **Dim:** 29 × 5.80 × 1.55

COAST GUARD (*continued*)

S: 21 kts **Man:** 15 men
A: 3/20-mm AA **M:** 4 diesels; 2 props; 2,200 hp

GC 10 DESSALINES (ex-U.S. net layer *Tonawanda, AN-89*) — 14-11-44 — on loan since 1960.

D: 650 tons (785 fl) **Dim:** 51.35 × 10.23 × 3.35
S: 12 kts **A:** 1/76-mm — 2/20-mm **Man:** 48 men
M: diesel-electric; 1 prop; 1,000 hp

1, 2, 3, 4, 5, 6, ex-U.S. Coast Guard small boats — U.S.A. (1942)

D: 45 tons **Dim:** 25 × 4.90 × 1.40
S: 20.5 kts **A:** 1/20-mm AA

VARIOUS

SANS SOUCI (ex-*Captain James Taylor*) — Bldr: U.S.A.
Presidential yacht.

D: 161 tons **Dim:** . . . × . . . × . . .
S: 10 kts **Fuel:** diesel
M: 2 Winton, 8-cyl diesels; 2 props; 300 hp

HONDURAS

MERCHANT MARINE (1-7-74): 56 ships — 69,561 grt
(tankers: 2 ships — 1,223 grt)

♦ *2 small boats in the customs and coast guard service*

PBM 01 BELIZE — PBM 02 BELPOPAN

D: 15 tons **S:** 22 kts **Dim:** 12 × 3.60 × 0.60
A: 3 machine guns **M:** 3 diesels; 370 hp.

HONG KONG

B.C.C.

MERCHANT MARINE (1-7-74): 93 ships — 269,945 grt
(tankers: 14 ships — 7,460 grt)

♦ *7 patrol boats*
Bldr: Vosper Thornycroft Private Ltd, Singapore

D: 80 tons (fl) **S:** 20 kts **Dim:** 24 × 5.30 × 1.70
A: 1/12.7-mm machine gun **Man:** 16 men
M: 2 Cummins diesels; 1,500 hp **Range:** 700/15

REMARKS: Steel hull. Manned by the police.

HUNGARY

♦ *10 river patrol boats*
A: 1/14.5-mm machine gun

♦ *5 LCU*

ICELAND

PERSONNEL: 150 men

MERCHANT MARINE (1-7-74): 350 ships — 148,695 grt
(tankers: 4 ships — 2,434 grt)

FISHERY PROTECTION PATROL BOATS

	L	In serv.	D	Length	HP	S
AEGIR		1968	1,150 tons	63	8,000 (2 props)	19 kts
ODINN		1960	1,000 tons	57	4,400 (2 props)	18 kts
TYR	1974		1,150 tons	63	8,000 (2 props)	19 kts
ARVAKUR	1962		716 tons	32	1,000	12 kts
ALBERT	1957		200 tons	35	650	12 kts

Aegir 1971 J. Meister

ICELAND (*continued*)

FISHERY PROTECTION PATROL BOATS (*continued*)

Odinn   1971 J. Meister

THOR	1951	920 tons	62	3,200 (2 props)	17 kts

REMARKS: All have 1/47-mm or 1/57-mm. **Man:** 15 to 28 men. The *Aegir* has a hangar and a helicopter platform. *Arvakur* purchased in 1969.

INDIA

PERSONNEL: approx. 20,000 men

MERCHANT MARINE (1-7-74): 451 ships — 3,484,751 grt
(tankers: 23 ships — 527,056 grt)

WARSHIPS IN SERVICE OR UNDER CONSTRUCTION AS OF 1 OCTOBER 1975

	L	D	Main armament
♦ *1 aircraft carrier*			
VIKRANT	1945	15,700	15 aircraft
♦ *10 submarines*			
10 KALVARI	1965	1,600	6/533-mm TT, 4/400-mm TT
♦ *2 cruisers* (*obsolete*)			
1 MYSORE	1939	8,700	9/152-mm, 8/102-mm
1 DELHI	1932	7,030	6/152-mm, 8/102-mm
♦ *30 frigates*			
4 NILGIRI	1968–73	2,250	4/114-mm AA — 1 helicopter
3 BRAHMAPUTRA	1957–59	2,300	4/115-mm AA
2 TALWAR	1958	2,150	2/144-mm AA — Limbo
2 KIRPAN	1957	1,180	1/40-mm AA — Limbo
12 KAMORTA	Post 1963	1,000	4/76-mm AA — 5/533-mm TT
3 RANA (*obsolete*)	1942	1,740	4/120-mm — 8/40-mm AA
3 GODAVARI (*obsolete*)	1940–41	1,087	6/102-mm
1 KISTNA (*obsolete*)	1943	1,470	4/102-mm

Vagli (S 42)   1974

♦ *8 OSA-1 guided missile small boats*

♦ *20 small patrol boats*

♦ *9 minesweepers*

NAVAL AVIATION

A few airplanes (Sea Hawk and Bréguet Àlize) on board the carrier *Vikrant* and some helicopters including the *Alouette III* belong to the Navy.

WEAPONS AND SYSTEMS

British equipment, except for the ships recently transferred by the U.S.S.R.

AIRCRAFT CARRIERS — 1 *Vikrant* (*Glory* class bought in Great Britain 1-57)

	Bldr	Laid down	L	In serv.
R 11 VIKRANT (ex-*Hercules*)	Vickers-Armstrongs	10-43	22-9-45	3-61

D:	15,700 tons (19,500 fl)	**Dim:**	211.25 (198 wl) × 24.29 × 7.15
S:	24 kts (fl) (17 cruising)	**Range:**	12,000/14–6,200/23
A:	15/40-mm (II × 4, I × 7) — 15 aircraft (maximum capacity)		
M:	Parsons GT; 2 props; 40,000 hp	**Man:**	1,075 (peace), 1,340 (war).
Boilers:	4 Admiralty, 28-kg pressure.	**Fuel:**	3,000/3,200 tons

REMARKS: Flight deck 210 m long and 34 m wide; 1 hangar; 2 elevators. Fitted with an angled flight deck, steam catapult, air-conditioning, etc.

SUBMARINES

♦ *10 Kalvari* (*Soviet F class bought since 1965*) — Bldr: U.S.S.R. (1960)

S 120 KURJURA	S 40 VELA
S 121 KALVARI	S 41 VAGIR
S 122 KANDHERI	S 42 VAGLI
S 123 KARANJ	S 43 VAGSHEER
S 124 KARSULA	S . . . N . . .
	S . . . N . . .

Karanj (S 123) 1973

D:	2,000 tons surfaced/2,500 submerged	**Dim:**	96.50 × 7.50 × 6
S:	18/16 kts	**Man:**	8 officers, 70 men
A:	6/533-mm TT fwd, 4/400-mm TT aft — 22 torpedoes		
M:	diesels and electric motors; 2 props	**Range:**	20,000

REMARKS: The first two were transferred in 4-68 and 1-69, the next two at the end of 1970, the *S 40* and the *S 41* in 9-73, the *S 42* in 12-73, the *S 43* in 2-75.

CRUISERS

♦ *1 British Fiji class*

	Bldr	Laid down	L	In serv.
C 60 MYSORE (ex-*Nigeria*)	Vickers-Armstrongs	2-38	18-7-39	9-40

Mysore (C 60)

D:	8,700 tons (11,000 fl)	**Dim:**	169.32 × 18.88 × 6.49 (fl)
S:	31 kts	**Man:**	800 men
A:	9/152-mm (III × 3) — 8/102-mm AA (II × 4) — 12/40-mm AA (II × 5, I × 2)		
M:	Parsons GT; 4 props; 72,000 hp.	**Boilers:**	4 Admiralty

REMARKS: Bought in 1954, refitted from 1954-57.

♦ *1 Leander/Ajax class from 1930*

	Bldr	Laid down	L	In serv.
C 74 DELHI (ex-*Achilles*)	Cammell Laird	6-31	1-9-32	10-33

Delhi (C 74) A. and J. Pavia

D:	7,030 tons (9,750 fl)	**Dim:**	169 (161.55 pp) × 16.80 × 4.87
S:	32.5 kts	**Man:**	800 men	**Range:** 12,000/14
A:	6/152-mm (II × 3) — 8/102-mm AA (II × 4) — 14/40-mm Bofors AA		
Armor:	Belt: 76-mm — main deck (partial): 80 — turret: 25 — bridge: 25		
M:	Parsons GT; 4 props; 72,000 hp		
Boilers:	6 Admiralty, 3-drum, 21 kg pressure.	**Fuel:**	1,800 tons

REMARKS: Bought and transferred in October 1948. Modernized in 1960. One of the oldest cruisers still in service.

FRIGATES

♦ *4 Nilgiri* (*British Leander class*) — The construction of two others is being considered.

	Bldr	Laid down	L	In serv.
F 33 NILGIRI	Mazagon, Bombay	10-66	23-10-68	6-72
F 34 HIMGIRI	Mazagon, Bombay	1967	6-5-70	23-11-74
F 35 UDAYGIRI	Mazagon, Bombay	9-70	24-10-72	1975
F 36 DUNAGIRI	Mazagon, Bombay	1-73	9-3-74	1976

Nilgiri (F 33) 1972

D: 2,250 tons (2,800 fl) **Dim:** 113.38 × 13.10 × 4.27 (aver.)
A: 2/114-mm AA (II × 1) — 2 Sea Cat Launchers — 1 ASW Limbo mortar Mk 10 — 1 ASW Alouette III helicopter. **S:** 30 kts

Other characteristics, see Great Britain section.

♦ *3 Brahmaputra* (*British Leopard class*) — characteristics, see Great Britain.

	Bldr	Laid down	L	In serv.
F 31 BRAHMAPUTRA (ex-*Panther*)	J. Brown (Clydebank)	1956	15-3-57	3-58
F 37 BEAS	Vickers-Armstrongs	1957	9-10-58	5-60
F 38 BETWA	Vickers-Armstrongs	1957	15-9-59	12-60

Brahmaputra (F 31) A. and J. Pavia

♦ *2 Talwar* (*British Whitby class*) — characteristics see Great Britain.

F 40 TALWAR	Cammell Laird	1957	18-7-58	4-60
F 43 TRISHUL	Harland & Wolff	1957	18-6-58	1-60

♦ *2 Kirpan* (*British Hardy class*) — characteristics see Great Britain.

F 44 KIRPAN	Alex Stephen & Son	1957	19-8-58	7-59
F 46 KUTHAR	J. Samuel White (Cowes)	1957	14-10-58	1960

REMARKS: *Khukri* sunk by the submarine *Mango* during the Indo-Pakistani conflict.

♦ *12 Kamorta* (*Soviet Petya class*) *Transferred in 1969, 1972, and 1975.*

P 68 ARNALA	P 73 KADMATH	P 82 KANJAR
P 69 ANDROTH	P 79 KILTAN	P 83 AMINDIVI
P 73 ANJADIP	P 80 KAVARATTI	P 74 ANDAMAN
P 77 KAMORTA	P 81 KATCHALL	P 75 ANIMI

Bldr: U.S.S.R. — 1963.

Kavaratti (P 80) 1970

D: 1,200 tons (fl) **S:** 28 kts **Dim:** 80 (76.20 pp) × 9.80 × 3.00
A: 4/76-mm AA — 4 MBU 2500 rocket launchers — 5/533-mm ASW TT (V × 1)
Electron Equipt: Radars: 1/Slim Net, 1/Hawk Screech.
Sonar: 1/Hercules
M: CODOG propulsion; 1 diesel × 4,000 hp + 2 GT × 10,000 hp; 3 props
Man: 130 men

♦ *3 Rana* (*British R class bought in 1948*)

	Bldr	Laid down	L	In serv.
D 115 RANA (ex-*Raider*)	Cammell Laird	4-41	1-4-42	11-42

Rana (D 115) A. and J. Pavia

FRIGATES (*continued*)

D 41 RANJIT (ex-*Redoubt*)   Fairfield (Glasgow)   6-41   2-5-42   10-42

D 209 RAJPUT (ex-*Rotherham*)   J. Brown (Clydebank)   4-41   21-3-42   8-42

D: 1,740 tons (2,465 fl)   **Dim:** 109.20 (109.98 wl) × 10.89 × 4.75
S: 31 kts   **Man:** 200 men   **Range:** 3,300/12 — 900/31
A: 4/120-mm (I × 4) — 8/40-mm AA (II × 4) — 4 depth charge projectors — depth racks
M: Parsons GT; 2 props; 40,000 hp.
Boilers: 2 Admiralty, 3-drum   **Fuel:** 570 tons

REMARKS: Transferred in 1950 after a refit of two years.

♦ *3 Godavari* (*British Hunt class, transferred in 1953*)

	Bldr	Laid down	L	In serv.
D 92 GODAVARI (ex-*Bedale*)	Hawthorn Leslie	5-40	5-9-41	6-42
D 93 GOMATI (ex-*Lamerton*)	Swan Hunter	4-40	14-12-40	8-41
D 94 GANGA (ex-*Chiddingfold*)	Scott's SB (Greenock)	3-40	10-3-41	10-41

Gomati (D 93)   A. and J. Pavia

D: 1,087 tons (1,490 fl)   **Dim:** 85.62 × 9.59 × 3.90
S: 25 kts   **Man:** 146 men   **Range:** 3,700/14 — 1,250/25.
A: 6/102-mm AA (II × 3) — 4/20-mm — depth charge projectors — depth charge racks.
M: Parsons GT; 2 props; 2 boilers; 19,000 hp
Fuel: 280 tons

♦ *2 Kistna* (*British Black Swan class*)

F 46 KRISHNA (22-4-43) — **F 10 KAUVERI** (15-6-43)

D: 1,470 tons (1,925 fl)   **Dim:** 91.30 × 11.70 × 3.40
S: 18 kts   **Range:** 4,500/12
A: 4/102-mm — 2/40-mm AA — 2 depth charge projectors
M: Parsons GT; 2 props; 2 boilers; 4,300 hp   **Man:** 210 men

GUIDED MISSILE PATROL BOATS

♦ *8 Nanuchka class on order from USSR*

♦ *10 Soviet OSA 1 class transferred in 1971*

P 685 NIRBHIK	**P 692 VINASH**
P 686 VEER	**P 693 VIJETA**

P 689 NASHAT   **P 694 VIDYUT**
P 690 NIRGHAT   **P . . . AVZA**
P 691 NIPAT   **P . . . N . . .**

Type OSA I.

D: 190 tons (fl)   **S:** 36 kts   **Dim:** 37 × 7 × 1.80
A: 4 Styx systems — 4/30-mm AA (II × 2)
Electron Equipt: Radars: 1/Square Tie, 1/Drum Tilt
M: 3 diesels; 3 props; 9,000 hp

REMARKS: Three were reportedly stranded during the Indo-Pakistani conflict.

MINESWEEPERS

♦ *4 British "-ton" class*

	L		L
M 1190 CUDDALORE (ex-*Wennington*)	6-4-55	**M 1191 CANNAMORE** (ex-*Whitton*)	30-1-56
M 1197 KARWAR (ex-*Overton*)	28-1-56	**M 1201 KAKINADA** (ex-*Durweston*)	18-8-55

D: 370 tons (425 fl)   **Dim:** 46.33 (42.68 pp) × 8.76 × 2.50
S: 15 kts   **Man:** 27 men
A: 1/40-mm (occasionally) — 2/20-mm AA
M: diesels; 2 props; 2,500 hp   **Fuel:** 45 tons   **Range:** 3,000/8

♦ *4 British "-ham" class*

M 89 BHATKAL (5-67) — **M 90 BULSAR** (17-5-69)
Built in India.

Dim: 30.63 × 6.40   **M:** 2 Davey-Paxman diesels — Teakwood hull.

2705 BIMLIPATHAM (ex-*Hildersham*) (5-2-54) — **2707 BASSEIN** (ex-*Littleham*) (4-5-54) — Transferred in 1955.

D: 120 tons (159 fl)   **Dim:** 32.43 (30.48 pp) × 6.45 × 1.70
S: 14 kts (9 sweeping)   **A:** 1/20-mm AA
Man: 2 officers, + 13 men   **Fuel:** 25 tons diesel
M: Davey-Paxman diesels; 2 props; 1,000 hp

HYDROGRAPHIC SHIPS

A 139 DARSHAK — Bldr: Hindustan SY — L: 2-11-59 — In serv.: 12-64

    D: 2,790 tons   **Dim:** 97.30 × 14.94 × 5.80
    S: 16 kts   **Man:** 150 men
    M: diesel-electric propulsion; 3,000 hp; 1 helicopter

♦ *2 British Pelican class*

F 11 JUMNA (16-11-40) — **F 95 SUTLEJ** (1-10-40)

    D: 1,300 tons (1,735 fl)   **Dim:** 89.15 × 11.43 × 3.10
    S: 18 kts   **Man:** 160 men   **Range:** 4,500/12
    A: (*F 11*): 6/102-mm AA (II × 3) — 6/20-mm AA — 4 depth charge projectors
    M: Parsons GT; 2 props; 2 boilers; 3,600 hp.   **Fuel:** 370 tons

F 243 INVESTIGATOR (ex-*Trent*)

Identical to the training ship *Tir* but without gun battery.

SECURITY VESSELS

♦ *5 Soviet Poluchat class transferred in 1967-69*

P 249 PANAJI, P 246 PANVEL, P 247 PAMBAN, P 248 PURI, P 250 PULICAT

    D: 100 tons   **Dim:** 29.57 × 6.10 × 1.90
    S: 15 kts   **M:** diesels; 2 props; . . . hp

♦ *3 Ajay class*

P 3135 ABHAY (11-61) — **P 3136 AKSHAY** (1-62) — **P 3137 AMAR**

Bldr: G.R.W., Calcutta (*Ajay*), Hooghly D & E, Calcutta (the others).

    D: 120 tons (160 fl)   **S:** 18 kts   **Dim:** 35.75 (33.52 pp) × 6.10 × 1.53
    A: 1/40-mm AA   **M:** 2 diesels; based on the British SDB *Axford* class.

REMARKS: *Ajay* transferred to Bangladesh.

♦ *6 Sharada/Savitri class*

Bldr: Italy (4) — Yugoslavia (*3132-3133*): These ships have **D:** 83 tons; **S:** 18 kts;
Length: 30 m

P 3128 SAVITRI (2-58)	**P 3131 SUVARNA** (8-57)
P 3129 SHARAYU (8-57)	**P 3132 SUKANYA** (12-59)
P 3130 SUBHADRA (10-57)	**P 3133 SHARADA** (12-59)

Shipbuilding and Shipping Record

    D: 66 tons (100 fl)   **Dim:** 27.50 (26 pp) × 6.10 × 1.50
    S: 22 kts (trials) 20 (in service)   **Man:** 4 officers, 12 men
    M: Mercedes-Benz diesels; 2 props; 1,900 hp

♦ *4 ex-British HDML*

SPC 3110 (ex-*HDML 1110*)   **SPC 3117** (ex-*HDML 1117*).
SPC 3112 (ex-*HDML 1112*) 1943   **SPC 3118** (ex-*HMD 1118*). 1943

    D: 48 tons (54 fl)   **Dim:** 21.6 × 4.8 × 1.3
    A: 2/20-mm AA   **Man:** 14 men
    M: diesel; 320 hp   **S:** 12 kts

AMPHIBIOUS SHIPS

♦ *4 Soviet Polnocnyi class transferred in 1967 (2) and 1975 (2). Two more will be transferred later.*

L 3033 GULDAR — **L 3032 GHARIAL** — **L 14 GHORPAD** — **L 15 KESARI** — **L 16 SHARDUL**

    D: 900 tons   **S:** 16 kts   **Dim:** 70 × 10 × 2.50
    A: 2/30-mm AA — 2 fire support rocket launchers
    M: diesels; 4,000 hp   **Practical load:** 350 tons

♦ *1 ex-British LST*

L 3011 MAGAR (ex-HMS *Avenger*, ex-*LST (3) 3011*)

    D: 2,256 tons (4,900 fl)
    A: 2/40-mm AA — 6/20-mm AA
    M: Altern; 2 props; 5,500 hp   **S:** 13 kts

LOGISTIC SUPPORT

♦ *1 Soviet Ougra class submarine support ship*

A 14 AMBA — Bldr: U.S.S.R.

Amba (A 14)   1968 M.N.

    D: 9,500 tons (fl)   **S:** 20/17 kts   **Dim:** 138 × 16.80 × 6.50
    A: 4/76-mm AA (II × 2)
    Electron Equipt: Radars: 1/Slim Net, 2/Hawk Screech
    M: diesels; 2 props; 14,000 hp

REMARKS: Purchased in 1968. Helicopter platform. Quarters for 750 men. 2/6-ton cranes, 1/10-ton crane.

♦ *1 Soviet T 58 class salvage ship (1962-64)*

A 15 NISTAR (former minesweeper)

    D: 850 tons   **S:** 18 kts   **Dim:** 67.70 × 9.10 × 2.30
    Electron Equipt: 1 Don radar
    M: 2 diesels; 2 props; 4,000 hp

LOGISTIC SUPPORT (*continued*)

REMARKS: Purchased at the end of 1971. Two rescue chambers port and starboard sides of the stern. Decompression chamber, diving bells.

♦ *1 repair ship*

A 316 DHARINI (ex-cargo *Hermione*) — Placed in service 5-60.

   D: 4,625 tons   **Dim:** 99 × 13.90
   M: triple expansion   **Fuel:** 620 tons

♦ *4 oilers*

A 136 SHAKTI — Commercial oiler purchased from Italy in 1953.

   D: 3,500 tons   **S:** 13 kts   **Dim:** 97 × 13.50 × 6.60
   M: diesel

A 50 DEEPAK (1967) — **A** . . . **N** . . . (L: 7-75)

   Bldr: Bremer Vulkan Schiffbau, Bremen-Vegesack

   D: 15,000 tons

REMARKS: The ship (as yet unnamed) will have a helicopter platform and a British automatic tension system for replenishment at sea.

A . . . **CHILKA — A** . . . **SAMBHAR** — 1942

   D: 1,350 tons   **S:** 9 kts   **Dim:** 61 × 9.20 × 4
   M: triple expansion; 800 hp

VARIOUS

♦ *1 training ship, former British frigate*

F 256 TIR (ex-*Bann*) — 29-12-42

   D: 1,450 tons (2,100 fl)   **Dim:** 91.90 × 11.07 × 4.10.
   S: 19/18 kts   **Man:** 100/120 men   **Range:** 9,500/12.
   M: Triple expansion; 2 props; 2 boilers; 5,500 hp.   **Fuel:** 540 tons

Andaman

INDONESIA

PERSONNEL: 40,000 men including 5,000 marines.

MERCHANT MARINE (1-7-74): 616 ships — 762,268 grt
(tankers: 43 ships — 76,526 grt)

WARSHIPS IN SERVICE OR UNDER CONSTRUCTION AS OF 1 OCTOBER 1975

	D	L	Main armament
♦ *2 submarines*			
2 W class	1,100	1958	6/533-mm TT
♦ *12 frigates*			
4 SAMADIKUN	1,450	1958	1/76-mm AA — 6 ASW TT
4 NUKU	1,200	1954-57	3/100-mm — 3/533-mm TT
2 IMAN BONDJOL	1,950	1956	4/102-mm — 3/533-mm TT
2 PATTIMURA	950	1956-57	2/76-mm AA

♦ *9 guided missile patrol boats*

♦ *10 patrol torpedo boats*

♦ *14 patrol boats*

♦ *15 minesweepers*

NOTE: The names of the Indonesian ships are now preceded by the three-letter designation KRI (for Kapal perang Republik Indonesia — warship of the Indonesian Republic).

NAVAL PROGRAM

A project from 1974-78 to purchase 4 corvettes of 1,000 tons, and a further project from 1978-82 to acquire 2 or 3 submarines and 36 fast patrol boats which will make up six flotillas of 6 boats each.

SUBMARINES

♦ *2 Soviet W class*

408 NAGAPANDA   **410 PASOPATI**   **403 NAGAPAKSA**

For characteristics see U.S.S.R. section.

REMARKS: The *408* serves as an alongside training ship. The *410* is the only one on active service. The *403* which was thought to have been removed from the active list has been refitted and returned to service.

FRIGATES

During 8-75, the Indonesian Navy signed an agreement with The Netherlands for the construction of 3 corvettes. These ships will have gas turbines and should be delivered at the end of 1979 or early in 1980.

♦ *4 ex-U.S. destroyer escorts transferred in 2-73 and 2-74*

		L	In serv.
341 SAMADIKUN	(ex-*John R. Perry, DE-1034*)	29-7-58	5-5-59
342 MARTADINATA	(ex-*Charles Berry, DE-1035*)	17-3-59	11-60
343 MONGINDISI	(ex-*Claud Jones, DE-1033*)	27-5-58	2-59
344 NGURAH RAI	(ex-*Mc Morris, DE-1036*)	26-5-59	3-60

Bldr: Avondale SY, U.S.A.

D: 1,450 tons (1,750 fl)   **Dim:** 95 × 11.30 × 5.50
Man: 15 officers, 160 men   **S:**   22 kts
A: 1/76-mm AA — 6 ASW Mk 32 TT.

Martadinata (342)   1974

Electron Equipt: Radars: 1/SPS 10 — 1/SPS 6
                          Sonar: 1/SQS 29
M: 4 Fairbanks diesels; 1 prop; 9,200 hp

♦ *4 ex-Soviet Riga class transferred since 1962*

351 JOS SUDARSO   **360 NUKU**   **357 LAMBUNG MANEGURAT**
Bldr: U.S.S.R. 1954-57

FRIGATES (continued)

D: 1,200 tons (1,600 fl)   **Dim:** 89.95 × 10 × 3.90
S: 28 kts   **Man:** 150 men
A: 3/100-mm — 4/37-mm AA — 3/533-mm TT (III × 1) — 1 hedgehog — 4 depth charge projectors — 50 mines (fitted)
M: GT; 2 props; 20,000 hp

REMARKS: The *352 Slamet Rijaja* has been removed from the active list.

♦ *2 Italian class*

	Bldr	Laid down	L	In serv.
355 IMAN BONDJOL	Ansaldo (Genoa)	1-56	5-5-56	5-58
358 SURAPATI	Ansaldo (Genoa)	1-56	5-5-56	5-58

Iman Bondjol (355)   Ansaldo

D: 1,150 tons (1,500 fl)   **Dim:** 97.60 × 10.84 × 2.60
S: 31.5 kts   **Range:** 2,800/22
A: 4/102-mm (II × 2) — 6/30-mm AA (III × 2) — 3/533-mm TT (III × 1) — 2 hedgehogs — 4 depth charge projectors
M: GT; 2 props; 2 Foster Wheeler boilers; 24,000 hp
Fuel: 350 tons black oil   **Man:** 200 men

REMARKS: Similar to the destroyers ordered in Italy by Venezuela. The *355 Iman Bondjol* is now in reserve.

♦ *2 Italian Alcione class*

801 PATTIMURA	Ansaldo (Livorno)	1-56	1-7-56	1-58
802 SULTAN HASANUDIN	Ansaldo (Livorno)	1-56	24-3-57	3-58

Pattimura (371)   1974

D: 950 tons (1,200 fl)   **Dim:** 82.37 × 10.30 × 2.80
S: 21.5 kts   **Man:** 119 men
Range: 2,400/18
A: 2/76-mm AA — 2/30-mm AA (II × 2) — 2 hedgehogs — 4 depth charge projectors
M: diesels; 2 props; 7,000 hp   **Fuel:** 100 tons diesel

REMARKS: Very similar to the Italian *Alcione* class.

TORPEDO PATROL AND GUIDED MISSILE BOATS

♦ *4 German Jaguar class*

P 654 ANOA	P 655 HARIMAU
P 652 BERUANG	P 653 MADJAN KUMBANG

Bldr: Lürssen, Vegesack — 1959-60

D: 140 tons (180 fl)   **Dim:** 42 × 7.60 × 1.80
S: 40 kts   **Man:** 42 men
A: 2/40-mm AA — 4/533-mm TT
M: 4 Mercedes-Benz diesels; 4 props; 12,000 hp

REMARKS: One of this class sank in 1962 and two others were recently stricken.

♦ *9 Soviet Komar class transferred in 1962, 1963, and 1964*

603 SARPAWISESA	612 GRIWIDJAJA	HARDADALI
KOLAPLINTAH	602 KALAMISANI	611 NAGAPASA
608 SAROTAMA	605 PULANGGENI	SARPAMINA

D: 75 tons (100 fl)   **Dim:** 26.80 × 6.40 × 1.70
A: 2 Styx — 2/25-mm AA (II × 1)   **S:** 40 kts
M: 4 diesels; 4,800 hp   **Range:** 400/30

♦ *5 Soviet P 6 class transferred since 1962*

ANGIN TONGGI	ANGIN GRENGGONG	ANGIN WAMANDAIS
ANGIN KUMBANG	ANGIN RIBUT	

D: 75 tons (100 fl)   **Dim:** 26.80 × 6.40 × 1.70

TORPEDO PATROL AND GUIDED MISSILE BOATS (*continued*)

S: 40 kts   **M:** diesels
A: 2/533-mm TT — 4/25-mm AA (II × 2)

REMARKS: Hull numbers in the 1600 series. There are no more than two in active service.

PATROL BOATS

♦ *4 Soviet Kronstadt class transferred in 1958-59*

811 KATULA, 814 PANDRONG — Bldr: U.S.S.R. 1951-52. Ten others have been stricken.

Kronstadt type Patrol boats and their base

D: 300 tons   **Dim:** 51.05 × 5.90 × 2.75
S: 27/26 kts   **Man:** 40 men
A: 1/25-mm — 2/37-mm AA — 3/20-mm — depth charge projectors
M: diesels; 2 props   **Fuel:** 20 tons

REMARKS: The *810 Tjutjut* and *818 Palu* have either been scrapped or put in reserve.

♦ *2 Australian Acute class bought in 1973*

846 SULIMAN (ex-*Archer*), **847 SIBARAU** (ex-*Bandolier*).

D: 146 tons (fl)   **S:** 24/21 kts   **Dim:** 32.76 × 6.20 × 1.90
A: 1/40-mm — 2 machine guns   **Man:** 3 officers, 19 men
M: 2 Davey-Paxman diesels; 3,460 hp   **Fuel:** 20 tons

REMARKS: Superstructure of light alloys; air-conditioned.

♦ *5 ex-Yugoslavian PBR 500 class (1953-57) transferred in the spring of 1959*

822 DORANG   **821 KAPRAY**   **823 TODAK**
819 LAJANG   **820 LEMADANG**

D: 190 tons (235 fl)   **Dim:** 41 × 6.30 × 2.10
S: 20 kts   **Man:** 54 men.
A: 1/76-mm — 1/40-mm AA — 6/20-mm AA
M: diesels; 2 props; 3,300 hp
Range: 1,500/12   **Fuel:** 15 tons diesel

REMARKS: The *810 Kalahitam* and *830 Sembilang* are still in active service.

♦ *3 ex-U.S. PC class (1942-43) transferred in 1959 and 1960*

806 TORANI
(ex-*PC 581*) (8-7-42)
807 TJAKALANG   **805 HUI**
(ex-*Pierre, PC-1141*)   (ex-*Malvern, PC-580*)
(22-6-43)   (29-4-42)

D: 335 tons (400 fl)   **Dim:** 52.95 × 7.25 × 3.25
S: 19 kts   **Man:** 55 men
A: 1/76-mm — 5/30-mm   **Range:** 4,800/9
M: Fairbanks diesels; 2 props; 2,880 hp   **Fuel:** 60 tons

MINESWEEPERS

♦ *5 German Raum Boote class (shallow water minesweepers)*

708 PULAU RUPAT   **715 PULAU RINDJA**
710 PULAU RANGSANG   **712 PULAU RENGAT**
     706 PULAU RAAS

Bldr: Lürssen (Vegesack), and Abeking & Rasmussen (1954-56)

D: 130 tons   **Dim:** 39 × 5.70 × 1.58
S: 24 kts   **Man:** 26 men
A: 1/40-mm AA — 2/20-mm AA
M: M.A.N. diesels; 2 props; 2,800 hp

REMARKS: Frame and inner hullwork of metal alloy; planked in wood. Similar to the *R 55* of the Federal German Navy.

♦ *6 ex-U.S. MSC class transferred in 1971*

717 PULAU ALOR   **720 PULAU IMPALASA**
(ex-*Meadowlark, MSC-196*)   (ex-*Humming Bird, MSC-192*)
718 PULAU ARUAM   **721 PULAU ANTANG**
(ex-*Jacana, MSC-193*)   (ex-*Frigate Bird, MSC-191*)
719 PULAU ANJERC   **722 PULAU ARU**
(ex-*Limpkin, MSC-195*)   (ex-*Falcon, MSC-190*)

Bldr: U.S.A. 1952-55. Similar to the French *Acacia* class

D: 320 tons (370 fl)   **Dim:** 43.90 × 8.23 × 2.55
Man: 39 men   **S:** 13 kts
A: 1/20-mm AA   **Range:** 2,500/10
M: General Motors diesels; 2 props; 1,200 hp   **Fuel:** 25 tons

♦ *4 ex-Soviet T 43 class transferred in 1962-64*

701 PULAU RANI   **704 PULAU RORBAS**
703 PULAU ROON   **715 PULAU RADJA**

See characteristics in the U.S.S.R. section. The *702 Pulau Ratewo* is still in active service.

AMPHIBIOUS SHIPS

503 TELUK AMBOINA — Bldr: Sasebo H.I., Tokyo — (17-3-61)
With a few exceptions, similar to the U.S. LSTs below.

D: 4,145 tons (fl)   **Dim:** 99.90 × 15.24 × 3
Man: 88 + 212 passengers   **A:** 2/85-mm, 4/40-mm AA
Range: 4,000/13   **S:** 13 kts
M: 2 M.A.N. diesels, each 1,425 hp   **Fuel:** 1,200 tons

AMPHIBIOUS SHIPS (continued)

♦ 8 former U.S. LSTs bought since 1961 (510, 511 in 7-70)
Bldr: U.S.A. — 1943

N . . . (ex-Middlesex County, LST-983)
501 TELUK LANGSA (ex-1128)
502 TELUK BAJUR (ex-616)
504 TELUK KAU (ex-652)

N . . . (ex-Polk County, LST-1084)
505 TELUK MENADO (ex-657)
510 TELUK SALEN (ex-601)
511 TELUK BONE (ex-639)

- **D:** 1,650 tons (4,080 fl)
- **S:** 11 kts
- **A:** 7/40-mm
- **M:** General Motors diesels; 2 props; 1,400 hp
- **Dim:** 100.04 × 15.24 × 4.30
- **Man:** 119 men + 264 passengers
- **Fuel:** 600 tons
- **Range:** 7,200/10

Can carry 2,100 tons of cargo. Transferred in 3-60 and 1961 and in 7-70 (510, 511) under the Mutual Assistance Pact.

802 TELUKWEDA, 808 TELUKKATURAI, 801 TELUKWORI

Bldr: U.S. — 1958

- **D:** 110 tons (250 fl)
- **A:** 1/40-mm — 2/20-mm
- **M:** 2 HSA diesels; 375 hp
- **Fuel:** 6 tons
- **Dim:** 50.60 × 6.55 × 1.70
- **Man:** 15 men
- **S:** 7 kts

HYDROGRAPHIC SHIPS

1006 BURUDJULASAD — Bldr: Schlichtingwerft, Travemünde — (1966)

- **D:** 1,470 tons
- **S:** 19 kts
- **M:** 4 M.A.N. fast diesels; 2 props; 6,850 hp. 1 helicopter
- **Dim:** 82 × 11.40 × 3.50
- **Man:** 78 men

1003 BIDUK — Bldr: J. and K. Smit (30-10-51, put in service 7-52) — Buoy and cable tender.

- **D:** 1,250 tons
- **S:** 12 kts
- **Dim:** 65 × 12 × 4.50.
- **M:** triple expansion; 1 prop; 1,600 hp **Man:** 66 men

1002 BURDJAMHAL — Bldr: De Waal Scheepswerf, Nijmegen (6-9-52, manned in 7-53) — hydrographic ship.

- **D:** 1,200 tons
- **S:** 10 kts
- **Dim:** 65 × 12 × 4.50
- **M:** Werkspoor diesels; 2 props; 1,160 hp

1006 ARIES (ex-Samudera) — Bldr: Ferus Smit (28-5-52, manned in 8-52).
Same characteristics as the Bango class patrol craft used by the maritime police (see page 212).

LOGISTIC SUPPORT

♦ 2 ex-Soviet support ships.

4101 RATULANGI — Bldr: U.S.S.R. — 1960
Don class, ex-441 transferred in 1962

- **D:** 6,000 tons (fl)
- **S:** 20 kts
- **A:** 4/100-mm — 12/37-mm AA
- **Dim:** 137.20 × 14.95 × 5.20
- **Man:** 300 men
- **M:** diesels; 2 props

4102 THAMRIN — Bldr: Neptun, Rostock — 1955
Atrek class, transferred in 1962.

- **D:** 3,500 tons
- **S:** 13 kts
- **Range:** 3,500/10
- **Dim:** 102.40 × 14.95 × 6.10
- **M:** Steam expansion and exhaust turbine
- **Boilers:** 2 boilers; 2,450 hp

♦ 1 built in Japan

561 MULTATULI — Bldr: Ishikawajima — (13-6-61)

Multatuli (S 561)   1974

- **D:** 4,500 tons (fl)
- **S:** 18.5 kts
- **A:** 3/40-mm AA
- **M:** 1 Burmeister & Wain diesel; 5,500 hp
- **Dim:** 111.35 (103 pp) × 16 × 6.98
- **Man:** 134 men
- **Range:** 6,000/16
- **Fuel:** 1,400 tons

REMARKS: Replenishment ship: food, ammunition, fuel

♦ 1 ex-U.S. destroyer tender, transferred 2-71.

923 DUMAI (ex-Tidewater, AD-31) — Bldr: U.S.A. — L: 30-6-45

- **D:** 9,250 tons (16,900 fl)
- **S:** 17/16 kts
- **A:** 1/127-mm 38-cal.
- **Dim:** 161.55 × 22.35 × 8.20
- **Man:** 800 men
- **M:** GT; 2 boilers; 8,500 hp; 2 props

♦ 3 small transports

952 NUSA TELU (ex-Casablanca)   **925 BANGGAI** (ex-Biscaya)   **959 N** . . .

- **D:** 750 tons
- **Dim:** 50.50 × 8.30 × 2.30

♦ 3 oilers

903 WONOKROMO

- **D:** 7,115 tons (fl)
- **S:** 17 kts
- **Dim:** 112 × 16 × 6.4
- **M:** 2 diesels; 4,500 hp

960 PAKANBBARU

- **D:** 1,500 tons (fl)
- **S:** 11 kts
- **Dim:** 63 × 11.5 × 4.5
- **M:** 1 diesel; 800 hp

904 BUNJU — Soviet oiler transferred in 6-59

- **D:** 6,170 tons (fl)
- **S:** 10 kts
- **Dim:** 107 × 15 × 6.15
- **M:** 1 diesel; 2,650 hp

LOGISTIC SUPPORT (*continued*)

♦ *Tugs*

922 RAKATA (ex-U.S. *Menominee*, ATF-73) transferred in 1961
  See U.S. *Apache* class for characteristics.
934 LAMPO BATANG — Bldr: Japan (4-61) — 250 tons — 1,200 hp — **S:** 11 kts
935 TAMBORA — **936 BROMO** — Bldr: Japan (6-61) — 150 tons — 600 hp
KARIMAJA

VARIOUS

♦ *1 sail training ship*

DEWARUTJI — Bldr: Stülcken, Hamburg (21-1-52, armed in 7-53)

D:	810 tons (1,500 fl)	**Dim:**	58.30 (41.50 pp) × 9.50 × 4.23
Man:	110 men (78 cadets)	**S:**	9 kts
M:	1 M.A.N. diesel; 575 hp		

Sail area: 1,091 m²

SHIPS MANNED BY THE POLICE

♦ *6 German Raum Boote class (shallow water minesweepers)*

DKN 901 to 906 — Bldr: Lürssen (Vegesack) and Abeking 1958-59.

D:	135 tons (190 fl)	**Dim:**	38.50 × 7.00 × 1.60
S:	21 kts	**Man:**	...
A:	4/20-mm AA (II × 2)	**M:**	diesels; 2 props; 3,000 hp

♦ *4 based on the above*

DKN 908 — 911 KELABANG (22-8-60) — **KALAHITAM** (end of 1960) —
KELALANG MAWER — Bldr: Soerabaya (Indonesia)

D:	147 tons	**S:** 21 kts	**Dim:** ... × ... × ...
A:	1/40-mm AA		**M:** diesels bought in Germany

♦ *8 Soviet T 43 class, transferred since 1962*

D:	600 tons (fl)	**S:** 17 kts	**Dim:** 61 × 8.3 × 2.80
A:	4/37-mm AA — 8/12.7-mm machine guns		**M:** diesels

♦ *1 Soviet T 301 class, transferred in 1962*

D:	130 tons	**S:** 10 kts	**Dim:** 30.50 × 4.90 × 1.40
A:	2/30-mm		**M:** diesels; 2 props; 480 hp

♦ *10 of the 500 series*

Bldr: Ishikawajima Harima, **503, 506/509, 512/516,** Hitachi and Uraga H.I.

D:	390 tons	**Dim:** 48.13 (44 pp) × 7.50 × 2.35
S:	14.75 kts	**Man:** 21 men, 10 police personnel
M:	M.A.N.-Mitsubishi diesels; 2 props; 1,280 hp	

♦ *12 BT 401 class*

BT 401-404, 501-504, 601-604 (1963-64) — Bldr: Lürssen (Vegesack)

D:	60 tons	**S:** 20 kts	**M:** diesels; 2 props

♦ *14 Bango class* (**A: 1952** — **B: 1953**)

Bldr: Holland

(A) **BANGO, BETTET, BABUT, BEKALLA, BEO, BLEKOK, BIDO, BLIBIS.**
(B) **BALAM, BARAU, BEKAKA, BELATIK, BENDALU, BOGA.**

Patrol type 500

D:	194 tons	**S:** 11 kts	**Dim:** 38.18 × 6.53 × 2.95
A:	1/40-mm — 4 machine guns		**M:** 1 Werkspoor diesel; 450 hp

♦ *8 Atang class (1949-50)*

Bldr: Holland

ALKAI (19-12-49)	**ANGKLOENG** (10-2-50)	**ARYAT** (9-2-50)
AMPOK (6-3-50)	**ANTANG** (2-12-49)	**ATTAT** (16-2-50)
ANDIS (16-12-49)	**AROKWES** (8-12-49)	

Andis

D:	143 tons	**S:** 12 kts	**Dim:** 30.60 × 5.65 × 2.28
A:	1/37-mm — 4 machine guns		**Man:** 20 men
M:	diesel; 1 prop; 400/450 hp		

At least 4 have already been taken out of active service.

♦ *6 Durian class (1952)*

DURIAN, DATA, DUATA, DUKU, DAIK, DAMARA.

D:	90 tons (118 fl)	**Dim:** 23.83 × 4.50 × 2.10
S:	12 kts	**M:** 1 Caterpillar diesel; 190 hp

♦ *6 Pat class* (1954 **PAT 1** to **PAT 6**)

D:	60 tons	**Dim:** 20.50 × 5.10 × 1.85
S:	12 kts	**M:** 2 Caterpillar diesels; 340 hp

PERSONNEL: 12,500 men including 1,100 officers.

MARITIME AVIATION: 8 AB 204 or 206 helicopters, 8 Sea King, 6 P 3 F Orion patrol planes.

MERCHANT MARINE (1-7-74): 115 ships — 291,928 grt
(tankers: 14 ships — 58,588 grt)

NAVAL PROGRAM:

It is anticipated that the following will be procured during the next few years: 1 aircraft carrier, U.S. USS type or British *Invincible* class; 6 U.S. *Spruance*-class large destroyers; at least 4 submarines; at least 12 fast missile boats. An agreement has been signed with the United States for the transfer of 3 *Tang*-class submarines.

IRAN

DESTROYERS

♦ *1 ex-British Battle class*

	Bldr	Laid down	L	In serv.
D 5 ARTEMIZ	Cammell Laird	11-43	28-2-45	9-46
(ex-*Sluys*, D-60)				

Artemiz (D 5) 1969 Thornycroft

D:	2,325 tons (3,360 fl)	**S:**	31 kts
Dim:	115.52 (108.20 pp) × 12.95 × 5.20 (fl)	**Man:**	260 men
A:	4/114-mm (II × 2 fwd) — 8/40-mm AA — 1 Seacat (IV × 1) — 1 Squid, 1 mortar.		
Electron Equipt:	Radars: 1 air search, 1 surface search, both Plessey manufact.		
M:	Parsons GT; 2 props	**Boilers:**	2 Admiralty; 50,000 hp
Fuel:	680 tons	**Range:**	3,000/20

REMARKS: Transferred 20-1-67; modernized. To be fitted with 4 anti-surface Tartar missiles.

♦ *6 ex-U.S. Spruance class ordered in 1974*

	L	In serv.		L	In serv.
N . . .	. . .	. . .	N . . .	. . .	. . .
N . . .	. . .	. . .	N . . .	. . .	. . .
N . . .	. . .	. . .	N . . .	. . .	. . .

REMARKS: 31 to 36 of the U.S. series with slightly different armament and fittings.

♦ *2 ex-U.S. Allen M. Sumner class assigned in 3-71 and delivered in 10-1973 and 1974.*

		Bldr	L
D 9 PALANG	(ex-*Stormes*, DD-780)	Federal SB, Kearny	4-11-44
D 7 BABR	(ex-*Zellars*, DD-777)	Todd, Pacific	18-7-44

Babr (D7) D. A. Peszko

D:	2,200 tons (3,320 fl)	**Dim:**	114.75 × 12.45 × 5.60
S:	30 kts **Man:** 14 officers, 260 men	**Range:**	1,260/30 — 4,600/15
A:	4 anti-surface Tartar systems — 4/127-mm (II × 2) — 4 324-mm ASW TT — 2 hedgehogs		
Electron Equipt:	Radars: 1/SPS 10, 1/SPS 37, CT Mk 56 Sonars: 1/SQS 29, 1/SQS 11 towed		
M:	GT; 4 Babcock boilers; 2 props; 60,000 hp	**Fuel:**	650 tons

NOTE: The *Gainard* (DD-706) and the *Kenneth D. Bailey* (DDR-713) transferred for cannibalization.

FRIGATES

♦ *4 Saam Mk 5 class (Vosper-Thornycroft)*

	Bldr	Laid down	L	In serv.
DE 12 SAAM	Thornycroft	5-67	25-7-68	20-5-71
DE 14 ROSTAM	Vickers (Barrow)	12-67	4-3-69	26-5-72
DE 16 ZAAL	Vickers (Newcastle)	3-68	25-7-68	1-3-71
DE 18 FARANARZ	Thornycroft	7-68	30-7-69	28-2-72

FRIGATES (continued)

Rostam (DE 14)   1974

D: 1,100 tons (1,350 fl)   **Dim:** 94.50 (88.40 pp) × 11.07 × 3.25
S: 40/30 kts (17.5 with diesel)   **Range:** 5,000/15
A: 1/114-mm AA (Mk 5 on the 12 and 14, Mk 8 on the 16 and 18) — 2/35-mm AA — 1 surface-surface Seakiller missile — 1 Seacat — 1 ASW Limbo Mk 10
M: CODOG propuls.; 2 Rolls-Royce Olympus TM 2 A gas turbines; 2 Paxman 16-cyl. diesels for cruising; 2 variable pitch props; 48,000 hp (turbines) 3,800 (diesels).   **Fuel:** 150 tons (250 with overload). Quarters for 135 men.

REMARKS: Air-conditioned; retractable stabilizers. Plessey radars. *D 12* and *D 14* to have 114 Mk 8 radars installed.

Rostam (DE 14)   1974

♦ *4 U.S., based on the PF class*

	Bldr	L	In serv.
F 25 BAYANDOR (ex-*PF 103*)	Levingstone SB Co, Orange (Texas)	7-7-63	5-64
F 26 NAGHDI (ex-*PF 104*)		10-10-63	7-64
F 27 MILANIAN (ex-*PF 105*)		4-1-68	12-68
F 28 KAHNAMOIE (ex-*PF106*)		4-4-68	2-69

D: 900 tons (1,135 fl)   **S:** 20 kts   **Dim:** 83.82 × 10.05 × 3.05
A: 2/76-mm, 2/40-mm AA, 1 hedgehog, 4 depth charge projectors.
M: Fairbanks-Morse diesels; 2 props; 5,600 hp   **Crew:** 133 men.
Electron Equipt: Radars: 1/SPS 10, 1/SPS 12.   **Range:** 3,000/15

REMARKS: Transferred under the M.A.P. One of them may receive a 76-mm AA OTO-Melara Compact gun.

Naghdi (F 26)

GUIDED MISSILE PATROL BOATS

♦ *12 Combattante II class* (contracted 19-2 and 14-10-74).

Bldr: Constr. Méc. de Normandie, Cherbourg

	L		L		L
N . . .	. . .	N . . .	. . .	N . . .	. . .
N . . .	. . .	N . . .	. . .	N . . .	. . .
N . . .	. . .	N . . .	. . .	N . . .	. . .
N . . .	. . .	N . . .	. . .	N . . .	. . .

REMARKS: For characteristics, see German Federal Republic section. Will have 1/76-mm AA and, 1/40-mm and 4 Harpoon.

♦ *2 U.S. Asheville class transferred in 1975*

N . . . (ex-*Beacon*, PG-99)
N . . . (ex-*Green Bay*, PG-101)

REMARKS: Other sources indicate that these ships will be transferred to Greece. For characteristics, see U.S.A. section.

NOTE: The 7 patrol boats, PGM class, have been transferred to Sudan.

MINESWEEPERS

♦ *4 coastal*

31 SHAHROKH (ex-*MSC 276*) — 1958.
32 SHABAZ (ex-*MSC 275*) (22-11-58)
33 SIMORGH (ex-*MSC 291*) (3-3-61)
34 KARKAS (ex-*MSC 292*) — 1963.

Shabaz (with her former number)   A. and J. Pavia

MINESWEEPERS (*continued*)

D: 320 tons (378 fl)
S: 12.5 kts (8 sweeping)
A: 1/20-mm AA
M: General Motors diesels; 2 props; 1,200 hp

Dim: 43 (41.50 pp) × 7.95 × 2.55
Range: 2,500/10
Man: 3 officers, 35 men
Fuel: 27 tons

REMARKS: Coastal minesweepers transferred by the U.S.A. in 1959 (2) and 1963-64 (2). Similar to the French *Acacia* class.

♦ *2 river boats — transferred from U.S.A. 1964-65*

301 HARISCHI (ex-*Kahnamuie*, ex-*MSI-13*) — **302 RIAZI** (ex-*MSI-14*)

Bldr: U.S.A. (1962-64).

Riazi (302)

D: 180 tons (235 fl)
S: 13 kts
A: 2/20-mm

Dim: 34 × 7 × 1.80
Man: 5 officers, 18 men
M: 2 diesels; 650 hp

AMPHIBIOUS SHIPS

♦ *2 Hengham class LSTs*

Bldr: Yarrow & Co., Glasgow

	L	In serv.
HENGAM	27-9-73	12-8-74
LARAK	7-5-74	12-11-74

D: 2,500 tons   **S:** ...   **Dim:** 90 × ... × ...
M: 2 diesels; 2 variable pitch props; 5,600 hp

REMARKS: Bow door. Helicopter platform on the stern.

♦ *1 ex-U.S. LSIL and 1 ex-U.S. LCU*

47 GHASM (ex-*LSIL . . .*) transferred 1964 — Bldr: U.S.A. (1943-44)

D: 230 tons (387 fl)
S: 13 kts
A: 4/20-mm AA

Dim: 48.50 × 7 × 1.65
M: 2 GM diesels; 900 hp
Range: 5,000/12

GHESHNE (ex-U.S. *LCU-1431*) transferred in 1964.

D: 160/320 tons (fl)
A: 2/20-mm

S: 10 kts
M: 2 diesels; 675 hp

HOVERCRAFT

(1) *8 SRN 6 Winchester class:* **01** to **08**

D: 10 tons   **S:** 58 kts   **Dim:** 14.40 × 8 × 4.80
M: 1 Gnome Mk 1050 gas turbine

(2) *4 BH 7 Wellington class:* **101** to **104**

D: 50 tons   **Dim:** 23.40 × 12.60 × 12.7 (h)
S: 60 kts   **M:** 1 Proteus gas turbine

4 others (BHC 7 Mk 5) ordered in 1972.

SECURITY PATROL BOATS

♦ *3 fishery protection patrol boats*

ZOREGH, GOHAR, SHAPAR — Ordered in 1971 from Abeking & Rasmussen (German Fed. Rep.)

D: 70 tons   **Dim:** 29 × 5.10 × 1.50   **Man:** 19 men
S: 27 kts   **M:** diesels; 2,200 hp

TOUFAN, TOUSAN — Bldr: I.N.M.A., La Spezia (1954-55)

D: 65 tons (90 fl)   **Dim:** 27.40 × 4.90 × 2.75
S: 22 kts   **A:** machine gun
M: 2 diesels — Used in the Customs Service since 1958.

LOGISTIC SUPPORT

A 42 BANDAR ABBAS (L: 14-8-73) — **A 44 BOOSHER** (L: 22-3-74)

Bldr: Lühring (German Federal Republic)

D: 3,250 tons   **S:** 15 kts   **Dim:** 102 × 16.60 × 4.50
A: 4/40-mm AA (I × 4) — 1 helicopter
M: 2 M.A.N. Ruston Paxman diesels, 2 props; 12,000 hp

IRAN (*continued*)

LOGISTIC SUPPORT (*continued*)

Bandar Abbas (A 42)   1974

♦ *3 oilers*

N . . . — Bldr: Swan Hunter

  D: . . .   **Dim:** . . .
  S: . . .   **M:** . . .

43 HORMUZ — Bldr: Nav. Mec. Castellammare — 1956

  D: 1,700 tons (fl)   **Dim:** 54 × 9.80 × 3.60   **M:** 1 Ansaldo diesel

Hormuz (D 43)   1974

46 HENGEH (ex-U.S. *YW-88*) — purchased in 1964

  D: 1,250 tons   **S:** 10 kts

♦ *2 repair ships*

44 SOHRAB (ex-U.S. *Gordius, ARL-36*) — transferred in 1961

  D: 1,625 tons (4,100 fl)   **S:** 11 kts   **Dim:** 99 × 25.25 × 3.70
  M: 2 GM diesels — 1,800 hp

CHAH BAHAR (ex-U.S. *Amphion, AR-13*) — transferred in 10-71.

  D: 14,450 tons (fl)   **S:** 16 kts   **Dim:** 148 × 21.50 × 3.20
  A: 2/76-mm   **M:** 1 GT; 8,500 hp. Quarters for 921 men.

VARIOUS

CHAH SEVAR (1936) — Bldr: Boele's SW, Bolnes, Neth. — Imperial yacht (In the Caspian Sea)

  D: 530 tons   **S:** 15 kts   **Dim:** 53 × 7.65 × 3.20
  M: Stork diesels; 2 props; 1,300 hp

KISH (1970). Bldr: West Germany — Imperial yacht (In the Persian Gulf)

  D: 175 tons   **Dim:** 37 × 7.60 × 2.20
  M: 2 M.T.U. diesels; 2,920 hp

HARBOR CRAFT

♦ *6 U.S. built, 10 tons*

MAHMAVI-HAMRAZ — MAHMAVI-TEHERI — MAHMAVI-VAHEDI — MARDJAN — MORDARID — SADAF.

  D: 10 tons   **Dim:** 12.40 × 3.40 × 1.20

TUG

45 BAHMAN SHIR (ex-U.S. Army)

  D: 150 tons

IRAQ

PERSONNEL: 1,000 men including 100 officers

MERCHANT MARINE (1-7-74): 49 ships — 229,603 grt
                  (tankers: 9 ships — 150,185 grt)

FRIGATES

♦ *3 ex-Soviet SO 1 class delivered in 1962*

  D: 200 tons (fl)   **S:** 27 kts   **Dim:** 34 × 4 × 1.80
  A: 4/25-mm AA (II × 2) — 4 MR 1800 ASW rocket launchers — 2 depth charge projectors — 2 TT — mines
  Electron Equipt: Radars: 1/Pot Head
                    Sonar: high frequency
  M: 3 diesels; 3 props; 6,000 hp
  Man: 3 officers, 27 men   **Range:** 1,500/12

GUIDED MISSILE AND TORPEDO PATROL BOATS

♦ *8 ex-Soviet OSA I and 4 OSA II class delivered in 1972, 1973, 1974, and 1975*

  D: 200 tons (fl)   **S:** 32 kts   **Dim:** 37 × 9 × 1.80
  A: 4/30-mm AA (II × 2) — 4 Styx   **Man:** 25 men
  Electron Equipt: Radars: 1/Square Tie, 1/Drum Tilt
  M: 3 diesels; 9,000 hp

♦ *3 ex-Soviet Komar class delivered early in 1972*

  D: 78 tons (fl)   **S:** 32 kts   **Dim:** 25.30 × 6.10 × 1.68
  A: 2/25-mm AA (II × 1) — 2 Styx   **Man:** 2 officers, 12 men
  Electron Equipt: Radar: 1/Square Tie
  M: diesels; 4 props; 4,800 hp   **Range:** 700/15

♦ *10 ex-Soviet P 6 class transferred in 1960-62*

14 RAMADAN, AL TAMI, LAMAKI BIN ZIHYAD, TAMOUR, ALEF. AL ADRISI, AL BAHI, AL SHAAB, TAREQ BEN ZOID.

  D: 75 tons (fl)   **S:** 32 kts   **Dim:** 25.30 × 6.10 × 1.68
  A: 4/25-mm AA (II × 2) — 2/533-mm TT (I × 2)   **Man:** 2 officers, 12 men

IRAQ (*continued*)
GUIDED MISSILE AND TORPEDO PATROL BOATS (*continued*)

Electron Equipt: Radar: 1/Skin Head or 1/Pot Head
M: diesels; 4 props; 4,800 hp   **Range:** 700/15

PATROL BOATS

♦ *2 ex-Soviet Poluchat class transferred in 1966*

D: 120 tons   **Dim:** 30 × 6 × 1.80
S: 15 kts   **A:** 2/25-mm AA

Used in coastal patrol and as torpedo recovery boats.

♦ *3 Soviet Zhuk class transferred in 1975*

D: 50 tons   **Dim:** 23 × . . . × . . .
S: 34 kts   **A:** 2/14.5-mm machine guns (II × 1)

SMALL CRAFT

♦ *2/4 ex-Soviet Nyriat class*

Used as diving support boats.

♦ *8 port security boats delivered by Thornycroft in 1961-62*

D: 10 tons   **Length:** 11   **M:** 1/25-hp diesel

VARIOUS

♦ *1 lighthouse supply ship*

FAISAL I (ex-*Sans Peur*, ex-*Restless*) (1923) — Bldr: J. Brown (Clydebank)
Former yacht.

D: 1,025 tons   **S:** 13 kts   **Dim:** 56 × 9 × 4.50
M: Triple expansion; 2 props; 850 hp; 1 boiler

♦ *1 yacht used as a patrol boat*

AL THAWRA

D: 746 tons   **S:** 14 kts   **M:** diesels; 2 props; 1,800 hp

♦ *1 tug*

ALARM (ex-*St. Ewe*) — Tug

D: 820 tons (fl)   **S:** 12 kts   **M:** 1,200 hp

COASTAL MINESWEEPERS

♦ *3 Soviet Eugenia class inshore minesweepers transferred in 1975.*

IRELAND

Eire

PERSONNEL: 500 men

MERCHANT MARINE (1-7-74): 88 ships — 208,700 grt
(tankers: 5 ships — 3,381 grt)

♦ *2 fishery protection ships*

	Bldr	L	In serv.
FP 20 DEIRDRE	Verolme Cork Dockyard	29-12-71	4-72
FP 21 N . . .	Verolme Cork Dockyard		

Deirdre (FP 20)   1972 Photo Batenian

D: 972 tons   **Dim:** 62.50 (56.20 pp) × 10.40 × 4.35
S: 18 kts (15.5 cruising)   **Man:** 42 to 55 men
A: 1/40-mm — 2/52-mm flare launchers
M: 2 Polar Mk SF 112 VS-F diesels driving a variable pitch propeller; 4,200 hp   **Range:** 3,000/15.5 (on one engine)

REMARKS: Vosper-Thornycroft stabilizers.

♦ *3 fishery protection ships, ex-British "-ton" class minesweepers*

CM 10 GRAINNE (ex-*Oulston*)   **CM 12 FOLA** (ex-*Blaxton*)
CM 11 BANBA (ex-*Alverton*)   1954-59, transferred 1971

Grainne (CM 10)   1972

D: 370 tons (425 fl)   **Dim:** 46.33 (42.68 pp) × 8.76 × 2.50
S: 15 kts   **Man:** . . .
A: 1/40-mm   **Range:** 3,000/8 — 2,300/13
M: diesels; 2 props; 2,500/3,000 hp   **Fuel:** 45 tons diesel

PERSONNEL: Active: 3,500, of whom 250 officers and 500 men are especially trained as commandos and frogmen. Reserves: 500 men.

MERCHANT MARINE (1-7-74): 76 ships — 611,300 grt
(tankers: 3 ships — 867 grt)

ISRAEL

SHIPS IN SERVICE OR UNDER CONSTRUCTION AS OF 1 OCTOBER 1975

	L	D	Main armament
♦ *4 submarines*			
2 German type 206	1975	450	8/533-mm TT
2 LEVIATHAN	1944	1,200	6/533-mm TT
♦ *At least 24 guided missile and patrol boats*			
6 SAAR III	1973	415	2/76-mm — Gabriel missile system
12 SAAR I and II	1967-69	220	1/40-mm or 1/76-mm — Gabriel missile system
6 AYAH	1950-56	40	6/450-mm TT
♦ *25 small patrol craft*			

WEAPONS AND SYSTEMS

The Israeli navy uses foreign equipment such as the Italian 76-mm OTO Melara Compact, the Breda 40-mm and the Bofors guns, but has also perfected a rather remarkable missile system named the Gabriel.

This is a 400-kg solid propellant surface-to-surface missile. After firing, it climbs about 100 meters, then sinks slowly to an altitude of 20 meters at 7,500 meters from the launcher. Optical or radar guidance is furnished in azimuth. A radio altimeter determines the altitude. At a distance of 1,200 meters from the target, the missile descends to 3 meters, either under radio command or guided by semi-active homing. The explosive charge consists of a 75-kg conventional warhead. 85% of the Gabriel missiles fired in the 1973 Yom Kippur war reached their target.

In order to be able to offer a surface-to-surface missile for sale on the international market that is even more effective, the Israeli navy is studying an improved version

Trainable, triple Gabriel missile launcher

of the Gabriel system. The Gabriel II will carry a television camera and a transceiver for azimuth and altitude commands. The television will be energized when the missile has attained a certain height and will send to the firing ship a picture of the areas which cannot be picked up by shipboard radar. The operator then can send such corrections as may be necessary during the middle and final phases of the flight of the missile and thus can find a target which cannot be seen either by the naked eye or on radar. The range of the Gabriel II will be about 40,000 meters. The necessity to increase the range of the Gabriel is one of the lessons the Israeli learned from the Yom Kippur war.

SUBMARINES

♦ *2 German 206 class ordered from Vickers-Barrow in 1972, to be delivered in 1976*

N . . .   N . . .

D: 450 tons surfaced/600 submerged   **Dim:** 48.15 × 4.70 × 3.70
S: 17/11 kts   **A:** 8/533-mm TT fwd   **Man:** 22 men
M: diesel-electric; 1 prop; 1,800 hp

REMARKS: will have British SLAM system installed.

♦ *1 ex-British T class, rebuilt, bought and transferred in 6-66*

	Bldr	Laid down	L	In serv.
Z 77 DOLPHIN	HMDY, Devonport	11-42	22-2-44	5-45
(ex-*Truncheon*)				

D: 1,200 tons surfaced/1,650 submerged   **Dim:** 86 × 8.10 × 4.60
S: 15 kts   **Man:** 64 men — Welded hull
A: 6/533-mm TT (4 fwd, 2 aft)   **Fuel:** 132 tons
M: diesels and electric motors; 2 props; 2,500/1,450 hp

REMARKS: Modified for the transport of frogmen for commando type engagements. Used for training.

GUIDED MISSILE PATROL BOATS

♦ *6 Saar III class (Reshef)*

	L			L
. . . **RESHEF**	(19-2-73)		. . . **KIDON**	(74)
. . . **KESHET**	(23-8-73)		. . . **TARSHISH**	(75)
. . . **ROMACH**	(74)		. . . **YAFO**	(75)
Bldr: Haifa NSY				

GUIDED MISSILE PATROL BOATS (*continued*)

Reshef 1974

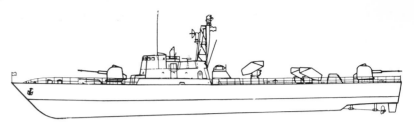

D: 415 tons/450 (fl)   **Dim:** 58.10 × 7.60 × 2.40
S: 32 kts   **Man:** 45 men
A: 7 missile launchers (II × 3, I × 1) or 6 (II × 3) for the Gabriel system —
2/76-mm OTO Melara Compact guns — 4/12.7-mm machine guns (II × 2) or
2/20-mm and 2/12.7-mm machine guns

REMARKS: Quarters air-conditioned. Can fire "chaff" for long distance cluttering of
radar screens and deception. Six others to be built, three for the Union of South
Africa.

♦ *6 Saar I class*

	L		L
311 MIVTACH	11-4-67	**321 EILATH**	14-6-68
312 MIZNAG	1967	**322 HAIFA**	14-6-68
313 MIFGAV	1967	**323 AKKO**	1968

Bldr: Constr. Méc. de Normandie, Cherbourg

D: 220 tons (250 fl)   **Dim:** 44.95 × 7.01 × 1.80 (2.50 fl)
S: 40 kts   **Range:** 1,000/30 — 1,600/20 — 2,500/15
A: see Remarks   **Man:** 5 officers, 30/35 men
M: 4 Maybach MD 871 fast diesels; 4 props; 14,000 hp   **Fuel:** 30 tons

Reshef 1973

Keshet 1974

GUIDED MISSILE PATROL BOATS (*continued*)

Saar I type 1970

REMARKS: Excellent sea qualities and endurance. Two weapon variations have been noted, reading from forward to aft: 1/40-mm AA Breda, 2 single fixed Gabriel launchers, bridge, 1 triple trainable Gabriel launcher, 1/40-mm AA, or, the same but with a second triple trainable Gabriel launcher replacing the after 40-mm AA gun. The *Haifa* and the *Akko* have 2/533-mm torpedo launchers.

♦ *Saar II class*

	L			L
331 SAAR	25-11-69		**341 HEREV**	20-6-69
332 SOUFA	4-2-69		**342 HANIT**	1969
333 GAASCH	24-6-69		**343 HETZ**	14-12-69

Bldr: Constr. Méc. de Normandie, Cherbourg

Type Saar II

REMARKS: Same characteristics as the *SAAR I* but the ships are armed as follows:
— 1/76-mm AA OTO Melara Compact gun; bridge, 2 triple trainable Gabriel launchers or 1 triple trainable and 2 fixed launchers.

PATROL TORPEDO BOATS

T 150 OPHIR — T 151 SHVA

Bldr: Italy — 1956-57

D:	62 tons	**S:**	42 kts	**Dim:**	26 × 6.30 × 1.50
A:	1/40-mm — 4/20-mm — 2/450-mm torpedoes				
Man:	1 officer, 13 men		**Range:**	600/29	
M:	Napier Deltic diesels; 2 props; 4,600 hp				

REMARKS: Probably in poor condition.

♦ *6 Ayah* — Bldr: Meulan 1950-56

T 200 AYAH	**T 202 DAYA**	**T 204 TAHMASS**
T 201 BAZ	**T 203 YAASOUR**	**T 205 YASSOR**

Tahmass (204)

D:	40 tons	**Dim:**	21.35 × 5.20 × 1.55
S:	40 kts	**Range:**	600/29
A:	1/40-mm — 2/20-mm — 2/450-mm torpedoes		
M:	Gasoline engines; 4,600 hp		

PATROL CRAFT

♦ *1 ex-U.S. PC*

P 22 NOGAH (ex-*PC-1188*)

Dr. Le Calve, Toulon

PATROL CRAFT (*continued*)

D: 325 tons (400 fl)   **Dim:** 53 × 7.05 × 3.25
S: 19/18 kts   **Range:** 6,000/10   **Man:** 70 men
A: 1/76-mm — 3/20-mm — 4 depth charge projectors
M: 2 General Motors diesels; 2 props; 3,000 hp   **Fuel:** 62 tons diesel

REMARKS: Used as target for Gabriel missile testing.

♦ *12 Bertram-class small craft (U.S. PBR)*

1971

D: 6.5 tons   **S:** 25 kts   **Dim:** 9.26 × 9.20 × 0.46
A: 1/20-mm — 2 machine guns   **Man:** 5 men

REMARKS: Bought in the U.S.A. in 1968; several may be stationed in the Red Sea.

♦ *6 Swift class (ex-U.S. PCF) transferred in 1972.*

D: 18 tons (fl)   **Dim:** 15.60 × 4.12 × 1.50
A: 3/12.7-mm machine guns (II × 1), 1 combined with an 81-mm mortar
M: Gray 12-V-721 diesel; 2 props; 960 hp   **Endurance:** 24 to 36 hours

♦ *16 Dabur class*

Bldr: Sewart Seacraft (U.S.A.) — 1972-73.

D: 25 tons (30 fl)   **S:** 25 kts   **Dim:** 19.80 × 5.80 × 0.80
A: 6/12.7-mm machine guns (II × 3) or 1/20-mm, 4/12.7-mm machine guns
(II × 2) — ASW depth charges   **Man:** 1 officer, 5 men
M: 3 GM diesels; 3 props   **Range:** 1,200/17

Quarters air-conditioned and spacious. The Dabur class are now built in Israel.

♦ **46 KEDMA, 48 YAMA, 50 TZAFONA, 52 NEGBA** — Bldr: Japan (1968)

D: 32 tons   **S:** 25 kts   **Dim:** 20.50 × 4.60 × 1.45
A: 2/20-mm   **Man:** 10 men   **M:** 2 diesels; 1,540 hp

Dabur type   1973

Negba   1974

♦ *2 ex-British HDML* — **21 DROR** — **25 TIRTSA** — (1944)

D: 46 tons (54 fl)   **S:** 12 kts   **Dim:** 21.95 × 4.88 × 1.70
A: 2/20-mm   **Man:** 12 men   **M:** diesels; 2 props; 320 hp

♦ **TIRAN, SANAFIR,** Egyptian trawlers captured at Eilath (1967)

AMPHIBIOUS SHIPS

♦ **BAT SHEVA,** 1967 — LCT type

D: 1,150 tons   **Dim:** 95 × 11.20 × . . .
A: 4/20-mm — 4/12.7-mm machine guns   **Man:** 26 men
S: 10 kts   **M:** diesels; 2 props

REMARKS: Bought in 1968 in South Africa.

AMPHIBIOUS SHIPS (continued)

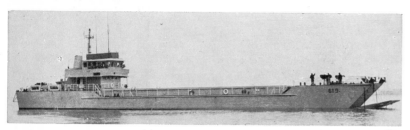

1971

♦ **61 ASHDOD — 63 ASHKELON — 65 AHZIV** — Bldr: Haifa. LCT type.

Ashdod
1969

D:	400 (730 fl)	**Dim:**	61.40 × 10 × 1.80
S:	10.5 kts	**Man:**	20 men
A:	2/20-mm	**Fuel:**	37 tons
M:	3 MWM 1/99-hp diesels		

♦ **51 ETZION GUEBER — 53 SHIKMONA — 55 UNIDENT** — Bldr: Haifa (1965)

Etzion Gueber

D:	182 tons (230 fl)	**Dim:**	30.50 × 5.90 × 1.30
S:	10 kts	**Man:**	10 men
A:	2/20-mm	**M:**	diesels; 2 props; 1,280 hp

♦ *A flotilla of three LCMs (ex-U.S.)* — **D:** 60 tons (fl) — **S:** 11 kts

VARIOUS

♦ *2 small cargo ships fitted out as assault transports* (based at Eilath)

T 81 GALIM, T . . . BAT YAM, former Dutch motorized barges, refitted in Israel (1967).

♦ **NOGAH,** former cargo ship equipped as a training ship for the merchant marine. **NAHARYA** (base ship for the missile craft stationed at Eilath).

Keshet (type Saar III)
1974

Type Saar I
1970

ITALY

	L	D	Main battery
◆ *12 submarines*			
2 NAZARIO SAURO	under const.	1,400	. . .
4 BAGNOLINI	1967–68	524	4/TT
2 PIOMARTA	1951	2,100	8/TT
2 PRIMO LOMBARDO	1944–46	1,650	10/TT
2 CAPPELINI	1944	1,525	10/TT
◆ *3 helicopter carrier cruisers*			
1 VITTORIO VENETO	1967	7,500	2/ML, 8/76-mm, 2 helicopters
2 ANDREA DORIA	1962–63	6,000	2/ML, 8/76-mm, 2 helicopters
◆ *7 destroyers*			
2 AUDACE	1971	3,950	1 Tartar system, 2/127-mm, ASW arms
2 IMPAVIDO	1962	3,201	1 Tartar system, 2/127-mm, ASW arms
2 INDOMITO	1955–56	2,775	4/127-mm, ASW arms
1 SAN GIORGIO	1941	3,950	4/127-mm, ASW arms
◆ *23 frigates and corvettes*			
4 LUPO	1976–78	2,208	8 Otomat, 1/127-mm
2 ALPINO	1967–68	2,000	6/76-mm, ASW arms
4 BERGAMINI	1960–61	1,410	4/76-mm, ASW arms
4 CANOPO	1954–55	1,680	4/76-mm, ASW arms
4 TODARO	1964–65	940	2/76-mm, ASW arms
4 ALBATROS	1954	800	2/76-mm, ASW arms
1 BAIONETTA	1943–44	553	3/40-mm, ASW arms
◆ *58 minesweepers*			
4 STORIONE (ocean.)	1954–55	700	1/40-mm
36 ABETE/BAMBU	1953–55	370	2/20-mm
18 ARAGOSTA	1954–56	120	1/20-mm

◆ *12 fast gunboats and small boats, 2 troop carriers, 3 landing ships*

PERSONNEL (1975): 41,800 including 4,300 officers

MERCHANT MARINE (1-7-74): 1,710 ships — 9,322,015 grt
(tankers: 322 ships — 3,569,566 grt)

NAVAL AVIATION (*Aviazione per la Marina Militare "MARINAVIA"*)

Antisubmarine warfare fixed-wing aircraft belong to the Air Force but are put at the disposal of the Navy. For some time these planes were primarily American two-engine S2A Trackers, but now the BR 1150 Atlantic is the principal aircraft type following a contract of October 1968, the last of 18 machines being delivered in 1973.

Helicopters, on the other hand, are under the control of the Navy. Numbering about 80, there are several types (AB 204 B, Sikorsky, SH3D, etc.). They are essentially for ASW but they could be used in an antiship role; these helicopters carry missiles such as the AS 12. The Italian Navy has preferred for ASW a combination of a light helicopter carrying weapons working with another of the same size equipped with ASW sensors. This limits ships in ASW operations to those properly fitted to carry both type helicopters. Therefore future orientation in ASW operations would appear to be towards the use of a heavy helicopter (SH3D) carrying both weapons and sensors: several of these have been ordered in the U.S.A. These helicopters may be based ashore or on such ships as can handle them (*Vittorio Veneto*, the 2 *Andrea*

Doria ships, the *Audace*). At present the most widely used helo is the Agusta Bell 204B built under American license in Italy.

Its principal characteristics are as follows:

Ceiling: 10,800 feet
Range: 2 hours 5 min w.o. torpedoes
  1 hour 15 min with torpedoes
Crew: 3
Armam: 2 Mk 44 torpedoes or 4 AS 12;
  1 ASQS 13 sonar

Length: 17.40 m
Rotor dimension: 14.60 m
Max. weight at takeoff: 3,600 kg
Motor: 1 turboshaft, 1,200 hp
Max. speed: 120 knots
Cruis. speed: 90 knots

NAVAL PROGRAM:

In 1974 the Italian Navy presented to Parliament a "White Paper on the Navy." The document indicated that 160,000 tons of ships should be available to the Navy if it is to carry out its tasks. However, the present tonnage of the fleet is only about 105,000 tons in aging vessels, especially in the smaller ships. The total funds presently allotted the Navy, up until now, has not permitted any renewal of equipment; if this situation continues, the fleet would be reduced, according to this document, to 45,000 tons by 1984, which would prevent it from carrying out its most essential missions even in peacetime. To correct this situation, the White Paper states that it is vital to begin a 10-year progressive building program of about 1,000 billion lire. Constructed by 1985 would be:

— 2 guided missile (surface-air) frigates of the *Audace* class (4,400 tons) to replace the 3,800-ton class destroyers *Impetuoso* and *Indomito* which, dating from 1958, must be withdrawn from service within this decade;

— 8 frigates, 4 of the improved *Alpino* class in addition to the 4 *Lupo* class, which have been ordered and will enter in service between 1977 and 1979;

— 4/60-ton hydrofoil craft based on the *Sparviero;*

— 4/250-ton hydrofoil craft;

— 2/1,400-ton *Sauro*-class submarines now being built and anticipated in service in 1977-78;

— 10 minehunters;

— 1/8,000-ton logistic support ship;

— 1/1,600-ton hydrographic ship;

— various types of tugs including medium harbor size.

The construction of an amphibious ship capable of carrying landing craft and of a small aircraft carrier will be necessary by the end of the 1980s to replace the amphibious ships now in service, the 2 guided missile cruisers (surface-air) *Andrea Doria* and *Caio Duilio* of 7,900 tons, which entered service in 1964.

In addition, a certain number of ships now in service should be modernized with new radars, new missiles, etc.

As regards naval aviation, the document sees the need for acquisition between now and 1978-80 of:

— 40 helicopters;

— 14 Breguet Atlantic aircraft which will be added to the 18 machines already in service.

The Italian Parliament has approved the project.

WEAPONS AND SYSTEMS OF THE ITALIAN NAVY

A) MISSILES

In this area, Italian engineers have conceived and completed some interesting equipment not all of which will be accepted by the Navy.

♦ *Surface-to-air*

The Navy uses the American systems Terrier, Tartar, SM 1, and SM 1 A (see U.S.A. section).

Sea Indigo
Builder: CONTRAVES

Length: 3.2 m	Diameter: 0.200 m
Wingspan: 0.8 m	Weight: 110 kg
Range: 10,000 m	Guidance system: beam-rider

Albatros (Italian version of the Sea Sparrow)
Builder: SELENIA

Altitude: mini: 15 m, maxi: 5,000 m

Length:	Diameter: 0.2 m
Wingspan:	Weight: 204 kg
Range: 10,000 m	Guidance system: semi-active homing

♦ *Surface-to-surface*

Nettuno (also known as "Sea Killer Mk 1")
Builder: CONTRAVES

Length: 3.9 m	Diameter: 0.2 m
Wingspan: 0.85 m	Weight: 168 kg
Range: 10,000 m	Guidance system: beam-rider

Vulcano (also known as "Sea Killer Mk 2")
Builder: CONTRAVES

Length: 4.5 m	Diameter: 0.2 m
Wingspan: 0.85 m	Weight: 270 kg
Range: 25,000 m	Guidance system: beam-rider

Otomat Mk 1
Builder: OTO MELARA/MATRA

Length: 4.820 m
Diameter: 1,060 m (with boosters) — 0,460 m

Wingspan: 1.19 m	Weight: 750 kg
Range: 60-80 km	Guidance system: Thomson/CSF active homing

The missile flies almost at sea level after firing, then climbs at a steep angle to a predetermined height before striking the target during its descent.

Otomat Mk II

Also known at times under the name of Teseo, it differs from the Mk 1 by its active radar homing head which is Italian (SMA) and not French. This missile is also of the "Sea Skimmer" type, that is, once fired, it can remain near water level. The explosive charge is about 200 kg. The propulsion is by ramjet. This propulsion system allows the missile to be employed at greater ranges limited only by the guidance system and the target designation. It will be mounted in the *Lupo* class of destroyers.

♦ *Air-to-Surface*

Marte (system using the Vulcano missile still in development stage)

The Italian Navy has in the meantime adopted the French AS 12.

B) GUNNERY

With the exception of some old American equipment, such as the 127-mm twin barrel 38-cal. semi-automatic guns, the Italian navy uses the following systems of national design:

♦ **76 Brescia**

Single or twin barrel, automatic, air, surface, and land targets

Length: 62 calibers.
Max. effective range surface fire: 8,000 m
Max. effective range anti-aircraft fire: 4-5,000 m
Muzzle velocity: 850 m/sec. Rate of fire: 60 rounds/min./barrel.

♦ **76 OTO Melara Compact**

Single barrel light anti-aircraft automatic fire; entirely remote control with muzzle brake and cooling system.

Length: 62 calibers
Muzzle velocity: 925 m/sec
Max. effective range surface fire: 8,000 m
Max. effective range anti-aircraft fire: 4-5,000 m
Rate of fire: 85 rounds/min.
Weight of mount: 7.35 tons, owing to the use of light alloys and fiberglass; 80 ready service rounds in the drum, which permits at least one minute of fire before reloading. There are no personnel in the mount; the ammunition handlers in the magazine have only to feed the drum. The gun has been purchased by many navies.

♦ **127 OTO Melara Compact**

Single barreled automatic, triple-purpose, remote control.

Length: 54 calibers
Muzzle velocity: 808 m/sec
Max. effective range surface fire: 15,000 m
Max. effective range anti-aircraft fire: 7,000 m
Rate of fire: 45 rounds/minute, automatic setting.
Weight of the mount: 32 tons because of the use of light alloys and a fiberglass shield. The gun has a muzzle brake; it can fire, if desired, 66 rounds thanks to 3 loading drums, each with 22 rounds. Two hoists serve two loading trays with rounds coming from the magazine and a drum may be loaded even when the gun is firing. An automatic selection system allows a choice of the kind of ammunition (anti-aircraft, surface target, pyrotechnics, "chaff" rounds for cluttering radar). This equipment has been purchased by the Canadian Navy for its DDH destroyers of the *Iroquois* class.

C) ASW WEAPONS

Mortars

The Italian Navy has perfected the following systems:

WEAPONS AND SYSTEMS (*continued*)

♦ *Menon Triple Mortar*

The system has a launcher carrying 3 barrels 320-mm cal, 4.600 m in length. These tubes fire a 160-kg rocket at a fixed elevation of 45°. The range (400 to 900 m.) is reached by varying the quantity of gas admitted into the tubes from three powder chambers. The reloading of the tubes is made at a 90° elevation from a drum containing the projectiles.

♦ *Menon single-barreled Mortar*

The system has a single barrel with automatic loading. Fire control is usually directed in the underwater battery plot. The mortar is fired at a 45° angle with the range fixed by a similar system to the triple barrel Menon; firing 160-kg grenades round by round; the gas relief valves have adjustable vents. The weapon is automatically reloaded from the magazine by hoist and a loading drum.

Torpedoes

The Italian Navy uses American Mk 44 and Mk 46 torpedoes, either on board ship or on board helicopters. A wire-guided torpedo is being studied.

D) ELECTRONICS

Radars

The Italian Navy uses American radars, either bought or built under license.

SPQ 2   Combin. search
SPS 6 ⎫
SPS 12 ⎭ long-range air search
SPS 39 ⎫
SPS 52 ⎭ Height-finding

SPG 51 Tartar guidance system on board *Audace* and *Impavido* class frigates.
SPG 55 B Terrier guidance system on board *Vittorio Veneto* and the 2 *Andrea Doria* class.

For fire control of the 76-mm and 127-mm guns, the Italians used the Argo system made up of an optical target selection and a tracking radar (Orion) of Italian design.

Sonars

The most recent equipment has been in general American or Dutch.

SQS 23	Hull	med. freq.	SQS 4	Hull	med. freq.
SQS 29	Hull	med. freq.	SQA 10	Towed	med. freq.
SQS 11 A	Hull	med. freq.	SQS 36	Towed	high freq.
SQS 10	Hull	med. freq.	CWE 610	Hull	low freq. (Dutch)

Tactical Information System

The Italian Navy has perfected the Sadoc system, compatible with the American NTDS and the French SENIT.

SUBMARINES

♦ *2 Sauro class with diesel propulsion (Italian design)*

	Bldr	Laid down	L	In serv.
S . . . NAZARIO SAURO	C.R.D.A. Monfalcone	1971	. . .	. . .
S . . . COSARE BATTISTI (?)	C.R.D.A. Monfalcone	1973	. . .	. . .

D: 1,300 tons surfaced/1,450 tons submerged   **Dim:** 64 × 6.60 × 4.50
S: 19/11 kts   **A:** 6/533-mm TT   **Man:** 45 men

Virgilio Fasan (F 594)

Lazzaro Mocenigo (S 514)

1974

SUBMARINES (continued)

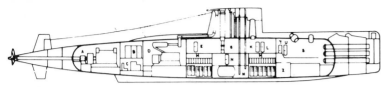

Nazario Sauro

◆ *4 Bagnolini class*

	Bldr	Laid down	L	In serv.
S 505 ATTILIO BAGNOLINI	C.R.D.A. Monfalcone	5-65	25-8-67	5-68
S 506 ENRICO TOTI	C.R.D.A. Monfalcone	5-65	12-3-67	7-68
S 513 ENRICO DANDOLO	C.R.D.A. Monfalcone	1966	16-12-67	9-68
S 514 LAZZARO MOCENIGO	C.R.D.A. Monfalcone	1966	20-4-68	1-69

D: 524 tons surfaced/581 tons submerged **Dim:** 46.20 × 4.75 × 4
S: 20/14 kts **A:** 4/533-mm TT (6 torpedoes)
M: diesel-electric propulsion; 2 diesels, 1 electric motor; 1 prop; 2,200 hp

◆ *ex-U.S. transferred in 1959 (1) and 1966 (2)*

	Bldr	Laid down	L	In serv.
S 507 ALFREDO CAPPELLINI (ex-*Capitaine*, SS-336)	Electric Boat	1943	1-10-44	1-45
S 512 EVANGELISTA TORRICELLI (ex-*Lizardfish*, SS-373)	Manitowoc SB	1943	16-7-44	1944

D: 1,525 tons surfaced/2,450 tons submerged **Dim:** 95 × 8.30 × 4.80
S: 18/10 kts **Range:** 12,000/10
A: 10/533-mm TT (6 fwd, 4 aft) **Man:** 85 men
M: diesel-electric propulsion; 2 props; 6,500/2,750 hp **Fuel:** 300 tons

REMARKS: Transferred after modernization. Three of the same class already stricken.

◆ *2 U.S. Guppy class, transferred in 1972*

	Bldr	Laid down	L	In serv.
S 502 GIANFRANCO GAZZALA PRIAROGGIA (ex-*Volador*, SS-490)	Portsmouth NSY	6-45	17-1-46	1-48
S 501 PRIMO LONGOBARDO (ex-*Pickerel*, SS-524)	Boston NSY	2-44	15-12-44	4-49

D: 1,650 tons/1,975 surfaced/2,540 submerged **Dim:** 99.40 × 8.20 × 5.20
S: 20/13-15 kts **Range:** 10,000/10
A: 10/533-mm TT (6 fwd., 4 aft) **Man:** 86 men
M: diesel-electric propulsion — 4 groups of generators — 2 electric motors — 6,400/5,200 hp

REMARKS: *Balao* class; underwent FRAM II modernization in 1961-63; a 1.50 m compartment was added to the sail to make room for an "attack center" operations area. A 3.50 m battery compartment was added. Two 126-cell batteries. BQR-2 sonar.

Primo Longobardo (S 501) 1972

◆ *2 U.S. Tang class, transferred in 7-73 and 3-74*

	Bldr	Laid down	L	In serv.
S 515 LIVIO PIOMARTA (ex-*Trigger*, SS-564)	Electric Boat	24-2-49	14-6-51	31-3-52
S 516 ROMEO ROMEI (ex-*Harder*, SS-568)	Electric Boat	30-6-50	3-12-51	19-8-52

D: 2,100 tons surfaced/2,700 tons submerged **Dim:** 84.73 × 8.30 × 5.70
S: 20/17 kts **Man:** 8 officers, 73 men
A: 8/533-mm TT (6 fwd, 2 aft)
M: diesel-electric propulsion; 2 props; 5,600 hp

REMARKS: The *S 515* arrived in Italy in 4-75.

CRUISERS

◆ *1 Vittorio Veneto class*

	Bldr	Laid down	L	In serv.
C 550 VITTORIO VENETO	Nav. Mec. Castellammare	6-65	5-2-67	3-69

Vittorio Veneto (C 550) 1972 J. C. Bellonne

CRUISERS (*continued*)

Vittorio Veneto (C 550)   A. Fraccaroli

D: 7,500 tons (8,870 fl)   **Dim:** 179.50 (170.61 pp) × 19.40 × 5.25
S: 30.5 kts   **Range:** 6,000/20 — 3,000/28   **Man:** 72 officers, 493 men
A: 1 Astor system — 8/76-mm OTO Melara AA — 6/324-mm ASW Mk 32 TT
(III × 2) — 9 light ASW helicopters AB/204 B or 6/HSS or 4 SH-3D.
Electron Equipt: Radars: 1/SPS 40, 1/SPS 52, 1/SPQ 2 B,
2/SPG 55 B, 4 Argo systems
Sonar: 1/SQS 23
M: Tosi GT; 2 props   **Boilers:** 4 Foster Wheeler, 43 kg/cm² pressure;
73,000 hp   **Fuel:** 1,200 tons   **Electric:** . . .

REMARKS: The flight deck (40 × 18.50) is on the stern and is served from a hangar
immediately below by two elevators (18 × 5.30). The hangar measures 27.50 ×
15.30 and is two decks in depth. Anti-rolling stabilizers.
The Astor system can launch either Terrier or Asroc.

♦ *2 Andria Doria class*

	Bldr	Laid down	L	In serv.
C 553 ANDREA DORIA	C. Nav. Tirreno,	5-58	27-2-63	2-64
	(Riva Trigoso)			
C 554 CAIO DUILIO	Nav. Mec. Castellammare	5-58	22-12-62	4-64

D: 6,000 tons/(7,300 fl)   **Dim:** 149.30 (144 pp) × 17.25 × 4.70 (7.50 fl)
S: 30 kts   **Range:** 6,000/15   **Man:** 54 officers, 460 men
A: 2 Terrier guided missiles (II × 1 fwd) — 8/76-mm AA (I × 8) — 6/324-mm
ASW TT (III × 2) Mk 32 — 4 A/B 204 B helicopters.
Electron Equipt: Radars: 1/SPS 12 (1/SPS 40 on 554), 1/SPQ 2, 1/SPS 39
(1/SPS 52 on 554), 2/SPG 55, 4 Argo systems
Sonar: 1/SQS 23.
M: GT; 2 props; 60,000 hp.   **Boilers:** 4 Foster Wheeler, 43 kg/cm² pressure
Fuel: 1,100 tons   **Electric:** 4,700 kw

Andrea Doria (C 553)

Andrea Doria (C 553)   1974 Guiglini

REMARKS: Officially designated escort cruisers, the *Andrea Dorias* are really small
helicopter carriers with a 30 × 16 m platform. The AB/204 B helicopters work in
tandem: one carries a sonar system, the other ASW torpedoes (2 Mk 44 torpedoes).
Anti-rolling stabilizers.
The engineering spaces are divided in two groups, forward and aft, each with a
boiler-room with two boilers and a turbine compartment separated by living spaces.
In each turbine space are two turbo-alternators of 1,000 kw each; there are also two
emergency diesel alternators of 350 kw each. Functioning of each engineering
group is automatic and remote-controlled. The *554* will be fitted with SM 1 "Extended Range" missiles and will have the Sadoc system installed.

DESTROYERS

♦ *Audace class*

	Bldr	Laid down	L	In serv.
D 550 ARDITO	Nav. Mec. Castellammare	7-68	27-11-71	9-72
D 551 AUDACE	C. Nav. del Tirreno	4-68	2-10-71	4-72

D: 3,950 tons (4,400 fl)   **Dim:** 136.60 × 14.23 × 4.60 (aver.)

Vittorio Veneto (C 550)

1973

Audace (D 551)

1974

DESTROYERS (continued)

Audace (D 551)   1975 J. C. Bellonne

S: 33/34 kts   **Range:** . . .   **Man:** . . . officers, . . . men
A: 1 Mk 13 missile launcher aft (40 SM 1) — 2/127-mm OTO Melara Compact —
4/76-mm AA OTO Melara Compact — 6/324-mm ASW Mk 32 TT (III × 2)
— 4 single TT for wire-guided torpedoes — 2 ASW helicopters 204 B or 1
SH-3 D Sea King
Electron Equipt: Radars: 1/SPS 12, 1/SPQ 2, 1/SPS 52, 2/SPG 51 B,
                    3 Argo systems
              Sonar: 1/CWE 610
M: GT; 2 props; 73,000 hp   **Boilers:** 4 Foster Wheeler
Electric: . . . kw

REMARKS: Habitability given much attention in design. Very fine ships.

♦ *2 Impavido class*

	Bldr	Laid down	L	In serv.
D 570 IMPAVIDO	C.N. del Tirreno	6-57	25-5-62	11-63
	(Riva Trigoso)			
D 571 INTREPIDO	Ansaldo (Livorno)	5-59	21-10-62	7-64

D: 3,201 tons (3,990 fl)   **Dim:** 131.30 × 13.65 × 5.43
S: 33.5 kts   **Range:** 4,500/20   **Man:** 22 officers, 312 men
A: 1 Mk 13 missile launcher aft (40 missiles Tartar (IT) or SM 1) — 2 U.S.
127-mm 38-cal. (II × 1) fwd — 4/76-mm Brescia AA (I × 4) — 6/324-mm
Mk 32 torpedo tubes (III × 2) — 1 ASW helicopter 204 B.
Electron Equipt: Radars: 1/SPS 12, 1/SPQ 2, 1/SPS 39 (1/SPS 52 on the 570),
                    2/SPG 51, 3 Argo systems
              Sonar: 1/SQS 23
M: Tosi GT; 2 props; 70,000 hp
Boilers: 4 Foster Wheeler 43 kg/cm² pressure

Impavido (D 570)   A. Fraccaroli

Intrepido (D 571)   1972 G. Arra

♦ *2 Indomito class*

	Bldr	Laid down	L	In serv.
D 558 IMPETUOSO	C. Nav. del Tirreno	5-52	16-9-56	1-58
	(Riva Trigoso)			
D 559 INDOMITO	Ansaldo (Livorno)	4-52	9-8-55	2-58

D: 2,775 tons (3,811 fl)   **Dim:** 127.60 (123.40 pp) × 13.15 × 4.60
S: 34 kts (32 fl)   **Range:** 3,460/20   **Man:** 24 officers, 320 men
A: 4/127-mm U.S. (II × 2) — 16/40-mm AA (IV × 2, II × 4) — 1 Menon triple
mortar fwd — 6/324-mm ASW Mk 32 TT (III × 2)
Electron Equipt: Radars: 1/SFS 60, 1/SG 6 B
              Sonar: 1/SQS 11 or 1/SQS 4
M: Tosi GT; 2 props; 65,000 hp
Boilers: 4 Foster Wheeler, 43 kg/cm² pressure
Electric: 3,100 kw

♦ *1 Capitani Romani*

	Bldr	Laid down	L	In serv.
D 562 SAN GIORGIO	C.N. del Tirreno	9-39	28-8-41	6/43/7-55
(ex-*Pompeo Magno*)	(Ancona)			

DESTROYERS (*continued*)

Impetuoso (D 558)   1971 A. Fraccaroli

San Giorgio (D 562)   1972 G. Arra

- **D:** 3,950 tons (4,450 fl)   **Dim:** 142.18 (138.75 pp) × 14.40 × 6.40
- **S:** 27 kts   **Man:** 314 men, 130 midshipmen
- **A:** 4 U.S. 127-mm AA (II × 2) 38-cal — 3/76-mm AA (1 × 3) OTO-Melara — 1 Menon triple mortar — 6 U.S. 324-mm ASW Mk 32 TT (III × 2) with Mk 44 torpedoes)
- **Electron Equipt:** Radar: 1/SPS 6 — Sonar: 1/SQS 10
- **M:** 4 Fiat-Tosi diesels, 4,500 hp each 2 AEI/G 6/2 gas turbines each 7,500 hp; combined on 2 shafts (CODAG apparatus); 2 props; 31,200 hp.

REMARKS: Sister ship of the *San Marco* which was stricken from the active list in 1970. Converted into a school ship for midshipmen from the naval academy at Livorno in 1964-65 (130 midshipmen). New engine fittings; armament renewed.

FRIGATES

♦ *4 Lupo class*

	Bldr	Laid down	L	In serv.
LUPO	C.N. del Tirreno	8-10-74	3-76	12-76
	(Riva Trigoso)			

	Nav. Mec. Castellammare			
N . . .	—	9-75	12-76	6-76
N . . .	—	4-76	6-77	4-78
N . . .	—	2-77	4-78	2-79

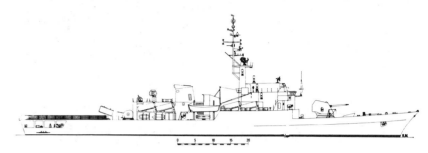

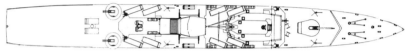

Lupo

- **D:** 2,208 tons (2,304 avg.) 2,900 (fl)   **S:** 34 kts
- **Dim:** 112 (106 pp) × . . . × 3.66
- **A:** 8 Otomat Mk 2 Teseo systems — 1/127-mm OTO Melara Compact AA — 1 Albatros BPDMS — 6/324-mm Mk 32 TT (III × 2)
- **Electron Equipt:** Radars: 1/SPQ 2F combin. search, 1 long-range air search from SELENIA, 1 Argo Mk 10 fire control. Sonar: 1 mid. freq. hull.
- **M:** CODOG system with 2 General Electric gas turbines/Fiat LM 2,500 of 25,000 hp, 2 GMT diesels of 3,900 hp (1,140 rpm), 2 variable pitch props.
- **Electric:** 3,120 kw (4 diesels — altern. of 780 kw).
- **Crew:** 16 officers, 169 men.

REMARKS: Principal mission: surface-to-surface warfare: secondary: fire support. The machinery compartments will be divided in four parts: auxiliaries, turbines, reduction gears, diesels.

Exhaust from the diesels is through two tubes leading to the after section of the stacks, whereas the hot gas turbine exhausts out the forward part of the stack. The air intake for the turbines through ports forward and on the sides of the stacks. Maximum speed on the diesels is 22.5 knots. Four frigates based on the *Lupo* class have been ordered by Peru.

♦ *2 Alpino class*

	Bldr	Laid down	L	In serv.
F 580 ALPINO	C.N. del Tirreno	2-63	14-6-67	1-68
(ex-*Circe*)	(Riva Trigoso)			
F 581 CARABINIERE	C.N. del Tirreno	1-65	30-9-67	4-68
(ex-*Climene*)	(Riva Trigoso)			

- **D:** 2,000 tons (2,700 fl)   **Dim:** 113.50 (106.40 pp) × 13.10 × 3.76
- **S:** 27 kts   **Range:** 4,200/17   **Man:** 20 officers, 244 men
- **A:** 6/76-mm AA, 62-cal. (I × 6) — 1 single-barrel Menon mortar — 6/324-mm

FRIGATES (continued)

Alpino (F 580)   1974

Mk 32 TT (Mk 44 torp) — 2/ASW A/B 204 B helicopters — 2 pyrotechnic launchers
Electron Equipt: Radars: 1/SPS 12, 1/SPQ 2, 3 Argo systems
                Sonars: 1/SQS 29, 1/SQA 10 (towed)
M: CODAG propulsion; 4 Tosi diesels; each 4,200 hp; Tosi-Metrovik gas turbines (7,700 hp each); 2 props; 31,800 hp
Electric: 2,400 kw.

REMARKS: 22 knots cruising speed on diesels. Stabilizers.

♦ *4 Todaro class*

	Bldr	Laid down	L	In serv.
F 540 PIETRO DE CRISTOFARO	C.N. del Tirreno	4-63	29-5-65	12-65

P. de Cristofaro (F 540)   1974

F 541 UMBERTO GROSSO	Ansaldo (Livorno)	10-62	12-12-64	4-66
F 546 LICIO VISINTINI	C.R.D.A. Monfalcone	9-63	30-5-65	8-66
F 550 SALVATORE TODARO	Ansaldo (Livorno)	10-62	24-10-64	4-66

D: 940 tons (1,050 fl)   **Dim:** 80.20 × 10 × 2.50

S: 23/22 kts   **Range:** 4,600/18   **Man:** 8 officers, 123 men
A: 2/76-mm Brescia AA (I × 2) — 1 single-barrel Menon mortar — 6/324-mm Mk 32 TT (III × 2)
Electron Equipt: Radars: 1/SPQ 2, 2 Argo systems
                Sonar: 1/SQS 36 (towed).
M: diesels (see Remarks); 2 props; 8,400 hp.

REMARKS: Fast diesels: Fiat on P de C, ST and UG, Tosi on LV with reducing gears and Tosi-Vulcan hydraulic linkage.

♦ *4 Bergamini class*

	Bldr	Laid down	L	In serv.
F 593 CARLO BERGAMINI	C.R.D.A., Trieste	7-59	16-6-60	6-62
F 594 VIRGILIO FASAN	Castellammare	3-60	9-10-60	6-62
F 595 CARLO MARGOTTINI	Castellammare	5-57	12-6-60	5-62
F 596 LUIGI RIZZO	Castellammare	5-57	6-3-60	12-61

Virgilio Fasan (F 594)   1971 Molinari

D: 1,410 tons/1,650 (av) 2,100 (fl)   **Dim:** 93.95 (86.51 pp) × 11.35 × 3.10
S: 25 kts   **Man:** 155 men   **Range:** 4,500/16 — 3,600/18
A: 2/76-mm automatic, 62-caliber (I × 2) — 1 single-barrel Menon — 6/324-mm Mk 32 ASW TT (III × 2) — 1 ASW helicopter   **Electric:** 204 kw
Electron Equipt: Radars: 1/SPS 12, 1/SPQ 2.
                Sonar: 1/SQS 11.
M: 4 fast Fiat (CB/LR) diesels or Tosi; 2 props; 16,000 hp

REMARKS: Denny-Brown anti-rolling stabilizers. Rolling can be reduced from 20° to 3°. Enlarging the helicopter platform required the removal of the after 76-mm gun. Telescopic hangar.

♦ *4 Canopo class*

	Bldr	Laid down	L	In serv.
F 552 CANOPO	C. Nav. di Taranto	5-52	20-2-55	5-58
F 553 CASTORE	C. Nav. di Taranto	3-55	8-7-56	7-57
F 554 CENTAURO	Ansaldo (Livorno)	5-52	4-4-54	5-57
F 555 CIGNO	C. Nav. di Taranto	2-54	14-3-55	4-57

FRIGATES (continued)

Castore (F 553)   1974 Guiglini

D:	1,680 tons	**Dim:**	93.30 × 12 × 7.80
S:	26 kts **Range:** 2,600/21	**Man:**	160 men

A: 3/76-mm Brescia AA (1 fwd, 2 aft) — 1 Menon triple barrel mortar — 6/324-mm ASW TT

Electron Equipt: Radars: 1/SPS 6, 1/SPQ 2
                  Sonar: 1/SQS 11

M: Tosi GT; 2 props; 22,000 hp.   **Boilers:** 2 Foster-Wheeler, 43 cm²

Fuel: 400 tons   **Electric:** . . . kw.

REMARKS: Refitted after 1965.

♦ *4 Albatros class*

	Bldr	Laid down	L	In serv.
F 542 AQUILA	Breda, Marghera	7-53	31-7-54	10-56
(ex-*Lynx hollandais*)				
F 543 ALBATROS	Nav. Mec. Castellammare	1953	18-7-54	6-55
F 544 ALCIONE	Nav. Mec. Castellammare	1953	19-9-54	15-55
F 545 AIRONE	Nav. Mec. Castellammare	1953	21-11-54	10-55

Alcione (F 544)   1972 G. Arra

D:	800 tons (950 fl)	**Dim:**	76.30 (69.49 pp) × 9.65 × 3.00
S:	19 kts **Range:** 2,980/18	**Man:**	7 officers, 111 men

A: 4/40-mm AA (70-cal) (II × 2) — 6/324-mm ASW TT Mk 32 (III × 2) — 2 hedgehogs — 1 depth charge projector

M: Fiat diesels; 2 props; 5,200 hp   **Fuel:** 100 tons

REMARKS: Ships built "off-shore" (ex-U.S. *PC-1626, 1919, 1920, 1921:* Five similar ships delivered, one to the Netherlands, (returned to Italy in 10-61), four to Denmark.

♦ *1 Baionetta class*

	L	
F 571 GABBIANO	30-1-43	

Bldr: C. Nav. Breda, Porto Marghera

Gabbiano (F 571)   1970

D:	553 tons (670 avg/800 fl)	**Dim:**	64.50 (58.80 pp) × 8.70 × 2.72
S:	15 to 16 kts (operational)	**Range:**	4,000/12 — 2,000/15.5
Man:	108 men		

A: 3/40-mm AA (56-cal) (4 on the *549*) — 1 hedgehog — 4 depth charge projectors.

M: 2/7-cylinder Fiat diesels and 2 electric motors, each 150 hp; 2 props; 3,400 hp (up to 4,300 in trials).   **Fuel:** 63 tons

REMARKS: Electric equipment permits 2 h 30 min of silent cruising at 6 knots in an antisubmarine attack.

GUNBOATS

♦ *2 Frecia class*

	Bldr	Laid down	L	In serv.
P 493 FRECCIA	C. Nav. di Taranto	4-63	9-1-65	7-65
(ex-*MC 590*)				
P 494 SAETTA	C.R.D.A. Monfalcone	6-63	11-4-65	1966
(ex-*MC 591*)				

D:	175 tons (206 fl)	**S:**	40 kts	**Dim:** 46.10 × 7.20 × 1.54

A: as gunboat: 3/40-mm 70-cal AA or 2/40-mm and a missile launcher as a torpedo boat: 1/40-mm, 70-cal AA — 4/533-mm TT

M: 2 Fiat diesels, each 3,800 hp; 1 gas turbine by Metrovik-Nuove Reggiane, 4,250 hp; 3 props; 11,860 hp.

GUNBOATS (continued)

Freccia (P 493)   1972 G. Arra

Two more than had been planned will not be built. *P 494* has served in the Nettuno system experiments.

♦ *1 Folgore class*

	Bldr	Laid down	L	In serv.
P 490 (ex-MC) **FOLGORE**	C.R.D.A. Monfalcone	1953	21-1-54	31-7-55

Folgore (P 490)   1972 G. Arra

  D: 160 tons (190 fl)   **Dim:** 39.40 × 5.80 × 1.70
  S: 36   **A:**   2/40-mm AA — 2/533-mm torpedoes
  M: 4 diesels; 4 props; 10,000 hp; 2 rudders

♦ *2 Lampo class*

	Bldr	Laid down	L	In serv.
P 491 LAMPO	C. Nav. di Taranto	1-58	22-11-60	7-63
P 492 BALENO	C. Nav. di Taranto	1-58	10-5-64	7-65

  D: 197 tons (210 fl)   **S:** 39 kts   **Dim:** 43 × 6.30 × 1.50
  A: as gunboat: 3/40-mm AA (70-cal) or 2/40-mm AA and 1 missile launcher.
      as torpedo boat: 1/40-mm AA (70-cal) — 2/533-mm TT

Lampo (P 491)   1972 G. Arra

  M: 2 Fiat diesels, 3,600 hp each; plus Metrovik-Nuove Reggiane gas turbine, 11,700 hp.

GUIDED MISSILE HYDROFOIL

	Bldr	Laid down	L	In serv.
P 420 SPARVIERO	Alinavi (Naples)	4-71	3-73	1974

Sparviero (P 420)   1974

  D: 62.5 tons (fl)   **Dim:** 23 × 7 × 1.30
  S: 42 kts (heavy sea), 50, (calm sea)   **Man:** 10 men
  Range: 325/42, 1,050/8 (diesel)
  A: 1/76-mm automatic OTO-Melara Compact — 2/Otomat surface-to-surface guided missiles
  M: Water jet Propulsion while foil-borne; 1 Proteus Rolls-Royce gas turbine; 4,500 hp

REMARKS: Prototype studied by the Alinavi Society, formed in 1964 by Boeing (U.S.A.), the I.R.I. of the Italian government, and the builder of commercial hydrofoils, Carlo Rodriguez of Messina. While cruising, the three hydrofoils are raised and the diesel engine is engaged (1 propeller). Project based on U.S. *Tucumcari* experiments but improved.

FAST TORPEDO PATROL BOATS

♦ *3 ex-PT (U.S.) Higgins type (1943)*

MS (ex-GIS) **441, 443, 453** (ex-*841, 843, 853*)

- **D:** 43 tons (51 fl)   **Dim:** 23.77 × 6.09 × 1.83
- **S:** 29 kts (practical max)   **Man:** 12 men
- **A:** 1/40-mm — 2 or 4/20-mm (II or IV × 1) — 2/450-mm torpedoes (no tubes)
- **M:** 3 Isotta-Fraschini, 12-cylinder 4 M 2,500; 3 props; 4,050 hp   **Fuel:** 8 tons gasoline   **Range:** 1,000/20

REMARKS: Accepted in 1951. Four stricken in 1958, four in 1964, transferred to the customs administration.

♦ *3 German Schnellboote type, Italian design*

MS 472, 474, 481 (ex-*MS/MV 612/615*) — Bldr: C.R.D.A. Monfalcone (1942-43)

- **D:** 63 tons (72 fl)   **S:** 27 kts   **Dim:** 28 × 4.30 × 1.50
- **A:** 1 or 2/40-mm AA — 2/450-mm torpedoes without tubes; 471 has neither tubes nor torpedoes   **Man:** 17 men
- **M:** 3 Isotta-Fraschini, 3 props; 3,450 hp   **Range:** 600/16

REMARKS: *MS 473* retained as a memorial.

MINESWEEPERS

♦ *4 ocean-going U.S. MSO class (transferred 1956-57)*

M 5340 SALMONE (ex-*MSO-507*)   **M 5432 SGOMBRO** (ex-*MSO-517*)
M 5431 STORIONE (ex-*MSO-506*)   **M 5433 SQUALO** (ex-*MSO-518*)

Bldr: Martinolich, San Diego (Calif.) 1955-56

Storione (M 5431)   1972 G. Arra

- **D:** 665 tons (750 fl)   **S:** 14 kts   **Dim:** 52.70 × 10.70 × 4 (fl)
- **A:** 1/40-mm AA   **Man:** 104 men   **Range:** 3,000/10
- **M:** diesels; 2 props; 1,600 hp   **Fuel:** 46 tons

American *Agile* type, similar to the French *Alençon* class.

♦ *18 coastal minesweepers Abete series (ex-U.S. AMS/MSC)*

M 5501 ABETE	**M 5507 FAGGIO**	**M 5513 ONTANO**
M 5502 ACACIA	**M 5508 FRASSINO**	**M 5514 PINO**
M 5503 BETULLA	**M 5509 GELSO**	**A 5307 PIOPPO**
M 5504 CASTAGNO	**M 5510 LARICE**	**M 5516 PLATANO**
M 5505 CEDRO	**M 5511 NOCE**	**M 5517 QUERCIA**
M 5506 CILIEGIO	**M 5512 OLMO**	**M 5519 MANDORLO**

Mandorlo (M 5519)   Nani

- **D:** 375 tons (405 fl)   **Dim:** 43.90 × 8.20 × 2.50
- **S:** 13.5 kts   **Range:** 2,500/10
- **A:** 2/20-mm AA   **Fuel:** 25 tons
- **Man:** 36/38 men   **M:** diesels; 2 props; 1,200 hp

Transferred by the U.S.A. in 1953-54. Ex-*AMS 72-77, 79-82, 88-90, 133-138* and *280* in 1960. The *5519* has different detection and sweeping equipment than the others. It also has a large tall stack. *Pioppo* has been converted into a hydrographic ship.

♦ *18 coastal minesweepers, MSC class but Italian built*

M 5521 BAMBU (26-6-55)	**M 5534 GAGGIA** (15-12-55)
M 5522 EBANO (15-4-56)	**M 5535 GELSOMINO** (5-3-55)
M 5523 MANGO (19-4-56)	**M 5536 GIAGGIOLO** (29-1-56)
M 5524 MOGANO (3-5-56)	**M 5537 GILICINE** (25-5-56)
M 5525 PALMA (8-11-56)	**M 5538 LOTO** (19-12-54)
M 5527 SANDALO (9-1-57)	**A 5306 MIRTO** (23-11-54)
M 5531 AGAVE (27-6-55)	**M 5540 TIMO** (19-12-55)
M 5532 ALLORO (11-7-55)	**M 5541 TRIFOGLIO** (10-5-55)
M 5533 EDERA (25-7-55)	**M 5542 VISCHIO** (20-5-56)

Bldr: Monfalcone; Costaguta, Voltri; Baglietto, Varrazze; Picchiotti, Viareggio; Mediterraneo Piera; the last 7, U.S. "off-shore" command assistance program.

Same silhouette and same characteristics as the French *Acacia* class. *Mirto* fitted out as hydrographic ship.

MINESWEEPERS (continued)

Sandalo (P 5527) (see preceding page) — 1972 G. Arra

◆ *18 inshore minesweepers, Aragosta series*

M 5450 ARAGOSTA (8-56) M 5459 MITILO (6-57)
M 5451 ARSELLA (9-56) M 5461 PAGURO (4-57)
M 5452 ASTICE (1-57) M 5462 PINNA (4-57)
M 5453 ATTINIA (2-57) M 5463 POLIPO (5-57)
M 5454 CALAMARO (4-57) M 5464 PORPORA (6-57)
M 5455 CONCHIGLIA (4-57) M 6465 RICCIO (5-57)
M 5456 DROMIA (6-57) M 5466 SCAMPO (5-57)
M 5457 GAMBERO (5-57) M 5467 SEPPIA (5-57)
M 5458 GRANCHIO (5-57) M 5468 TELLINA (4-57)

Bldr: Monfalcone (4); Baglietto, Varraze (3); Viareggio (3); Celle, Venice (2); Costaguta, Voltri, (3); C.N. Carrera (2), Ancona (1) Breda, Venice (2).

Scampo (P 5466) — 1972 G. Arra

D: 119 tons (140 fl) **S:** 14 kts **Dim:** 32.50 × 6.40 × 1.90
A: 1/20-mm AA **Man:** 14 men **Range:** 200/9
M: diesels; 2 props; 550 hp. **Fuel:** 15 tons

REMARKS: Based on British "-ham" class. *Ostrica* and *Totano* scrapped in 1975.

AMPHIBIOUS SHIPS

◆ *2 ex-U.S. LSTs transferred in 7-72*

	Bldr	L
L 9890 GRADO (ex-*de Soto County, LST-1171*)	Boston NSY	28-2-57
L 9891 CAORLE (ex-*York County, LST-1175*)	Newport News SB & DD	5-9-57

Grado (L 9890) — 1972 G. Arra

D: 3,680 tons (7,800 fl) **Dim:** 134.70 × 18.90 × 5.50
S: 16/15 kts **Man:** 15 officers, 173 men
A: 6/76-mm AA (50-cal) (II × 3)
M: 6 Fairbanks Morse diesels; 2 variable pitch props; 14,000 hp

REMARKS: See *Lorain County* class, U.S.A. section. Quarters for 634 troops including 30 officers.

◆ *1 Italian class*

	Bldr	Laid down	L	In serv.
L 9881 QUARTO	C. Nav. di Taranto	3-66	18-3-67	6-68

D: 764 tons (980 fl) **Dim:** 96 × 9.55 × 1.81
S: 13 kts **Range:** 1,300/13
A: 4/40-mm AA (II × 2) **M:** 3 diesels; 2,300 hp

REMARKS: Bow door. Sister ships *Marsala* and *Caprera* were planned but not completed. The *Marsala* hull is used as a pontoon.

◆ *2 assault transport*

A 9871 ANDREA BAFILE (ex-*St. George, AV-16*) — Bldr: Todd, Tacoma (14-2-44).
D: 13,380 tons (fl) **Dim:** 163 × 23 × 8.50
S: 17 kts **Range:** 13,400/13
A: 2/127-mm — 12/40-mm **M:** 1 GT; 2 boilers; 8,500 hp
Former U.S. aviation supply ship, modified and transferred 12-68.

AMPHIBIOUS SHIPS (continued)

Quarto (L 9881)   1972 G. Arra

A 9870 ETNA (ex-*Witley*, *AKA-91*) — Bldr: Moore-Oakland (U.S.A.) (21-9-44)

D:	6,200 tons (12,800 fl)	**Dim:**	140 × 19.20 × 7.40
S:	15.5 kts	**Range:**	18,500/12
A:	8/40-mm AA	**M:**	1 GT; 2 boilers; 6,600 hp

Transferred in 1962; can carry 22 landing craft and 7,400 tons of cargo. Will soon be stricken.

♦ *10 motorized barges*

MTC 1001
MTC 1004/1010
MTC 1101, 1102

D:	240 tons	**S:**	10 kts	**Dim:**	50 × 6.50 × 1.70
A:	3/20-mm AA			**M:**	2 to 3 diesels; 500 hp

Old Italian or German LCT class.

23 MTM 9909/9925 (less *9907, 9910*) — ex-U.S. LCM (1943-44)

D:	20 tons	**S:**	10 kts

39 MTP 9701/9741 (less *9716, 9725*) — ex-U.S. LCVP (1943-44)

D:	8 tons	**S:**	11 kts

HYDROGRAPHIC SHIPS

♦ *1 new class. Program 1972.*

	Bldr	Laid down	L	In serv.
A 5303 AMMIRAGLIO **G.B. MAGNAGHI**	C.N. del Tirreno (Riva Trigoso)	1973	11-9-74	. . .

Magnaghi (A 5303)   1974 Martinelli

D:	1,582 tons (fl)	**S:**	15 kts	**Dim:**	76.80 × 13.70 × 3.60
A:	1/40-mm — 1 helicopter			**Man:**	145 men
M:	2 diesels; 1 prop; 3,400 hp				

NOTE: The minesweepers *Mirto* and *Pioppo* are fitted as survey ships.

LOGISTIC SUPPORT

♦ *1 Stromboli class*

	Bldr	Laid down	L	In serv.
A 5327 STROMBOLI	C.N. del Tirreno (Riva Trigoso)	10-73	. . .	3-75

Stromboli (A 5327)   1975 Martinelli

LOGISTIC SUPPORT (continued)

D: 8,706 tons (fl)   **S:** 15 kts   **Dim:** 129 (118.50 pp) × 18 × 6.50
A: 1/76-mm AA-2/40-mm AA (II × 1)   **Man:** 9 officers, 106 men
M: 2 Fiat diesels; 1 prop; 9,600 hp   **Electric:** 2,490 kw

REMARKS: *Cargo capacity:* fuel oil or diesel: 3,000 tons; diesel oil: 1,000 tons; jet fuel: 400 tons; spare parts: 300 tons. Lifting equipment: double booms, 1 crane.

♦ *1 supply ship for small boats and amphibious ships*

	Bldr	L
A 5301 Pietro CAVEZZALE	Lake Washington SY	23-5-43

(ex-*AGP-6, Oyster Bay, AVP-28*)

P. Cavezzale (A 5301)   1973 Martinelli

D: 1,766 tons (2,800 fl)   **Dim:** 94.60 × 12.58 × 3.70
S: 16 kts   **Man:** 210 men
A: 2/40-mm AA   **Range:** 10,000/11
M: 2 diesels; 2 props; 6,000 hp.   **Fuel:** 400 tons

Transferred at the end of 1957. Air search radar ASP/SN 6 fitted.

♦ *3 buoy tenders*

	Bldr	Laid down	L	In serv.
A 5309 RAMPINO (350 t.).				
A 5304 ALICUDI (AN 99)	Ansaldo (Livorno)	4-54	11-7-54	1955
A 5305 FILICUDI (AN 190)	Ansaldo (Livorno)	5-74	26-7-54	1955

D: 680 tons (834 fl)   **Dim:** 46.28 × 10.26 × 3.20
S: 12 kts   **A:** 1/40-mm AA — 4/20-mm AA
M: diesel-electric propulsion; 1 prop; 1,200 hp.

♦ *1 support ship for frogmen and mine defusing divers*

F 567 APE — Bldr: Nav. Mec. Castellammare — 22-11-42

D: 771 tons (fl)   **S:** 15 kts   **Dim:** 64.80 × 8.70 × 2.72
A: 2/20-mm AA   **Man:** 108 men   **Range:** 2,445/15
M: 2 Fiat diesels; 2 props   **Fuel:** 63 tons

Filicudi (A 5305)   1972 G. Arra

APE (F 567) Former *Baionetta* class corvette.

♦ *1 T 2 tanker bought in 1959*

A 5368 STEROPE — (Bldr: U.S.A. — 1944)

Sterope (A 5368)   A. Fraccaroli

D: 5,830 tons (light) (21,800 fl)   **Dim:** 159.90 × 20.7 × 8

LOGISTIC SUPPORT (*continued*)

S: 14 kts   **Boilers:** 2 — 6,000 hp
M: Turbo-electric propulsion; 1 prop

REMARKS: Will soon be stricken.

♦ *8 water carriers*

A 5354 PIAVE, A 5355 TEVERE — Bldr: Italy — 1970-71.

Piave (A 5354)

D:	4,973 tons	**Dim:**	88 × 13.4 × 5.90
S:	13.6 kts	**Range:**	1,500/12
M:	2 diesels; 2,560 hp	**Cargo capacity:**	3,500 tons

A 5356 BASENTO, A 5357 BRADANO, A 5358 BRENTA — 1970-71

D:	1,914 tons	**Dim:**	66.10 × 10 × 3.90
S:	12.5 kts	**Range:**	1,650/12.5
M:	2 diesels; 1,730 hp	**Cargo capacity:**	1,200 tons

A 5376 TANARO (ex-*YM-99*)   **A 5369 ADIGE** (ex-*YM-92*)
A 5377 TICINO (ex-*YM-79*)

D: 1,517 tons   **S:** 8 kts   **M:** 2 diesels; 315 hp — 300 tons of water

♦ *7 motorized barges MOC class*

MOC 1201/1205, 1207, 1208

D:	640 tons	**Dim:**	48 × 7.7 × 1.7
A:	2/40-mm AA	**S:**	10 kts

REMARKS: *MOC-1207* and *1208* refitted as ammunition carriers. *MOC-1201* small craft supply ship. *MOC-1203* minesweeper supply ship.

TUGS

A 5310 PROTEO — 1944 — Bldr: C.N. del Tirreno (Ancona)

Proteo (A 5310)   1968

D:	1,865 tons (2,178 fl)	**Dim:**	76.70 × 11.70 × 6.10
S:	16 kts	**A:**	1/100-mm — 2/20-mm
M:	2 diesels; 4,800 hp	**Range:**	7,500/13

Used as a salvage ship.

♦ *2 ocean-going tugs (1974-75)*

Bldr: Visintini Donada

A . . . N . . .   **A . . . N . . .**

D:	750 tons	**Dim:**	39 × 9.6 × 4.1
M:	1 diesel; 1 prop; 2,600 hp		

♦ *23 harbor tugs*

A 5319 CICLOPE, A 5325 TITANO (1948) 1,200 tons — 1,000 hp — **M:** triple expansion
A 5318 ATLETA, A 5320 COLOSSO, A 5321 FORTE, A 5324 TENACE (ex-U.S. — 1943) 835 tons — 700 hp — **M:** diesel-electric
A 5326 S. GIUSTO (1941) 486 tons — 900 hp
A 5322 GAGLIARDO, A 5323 ROBUSTO (1939) 506 tons — 1,000 hp
PORTO D'ISCHIA, RIVA TRIGOSO — 296 tons — 850 hp — **S:** 12 kts
AUSONIA, 240 tons — 500 hp — **S:** 9 kts
PANARIA, 240 tons — 500 hp — **S:** 9 kts
MISENO, MONTECRISTO — Bldr: U.S.A. — **D:** 285 tons

PORTO FOSSONE	**PORTO RECANATI**	**PORTO VECCHIO**
PORTO PISANO	**PORTO TORRES**	**SALVORE**
		TINO

D: 226 tons   **S:** 9 kts

TUGS (continued)

Forte (A 5321)   1974 G. Arra

VINTIMIGLA, 230 tons — 500 hp — **S:** 10 kts

♦ *30 small harbor tugs*

RP 101/110

D: 75 tons   **S:** 12 kts   **Dim:** 18.8 × 4.5 × 1.9
M: 1 diesel; 1 prop; 431 hp

ARSACHENA	LISCOSIA ABAZIA	SAN BIAGIO
BOEO	MESCO	SAN BENEDETTO
CABONARA	NISIDA	SAN DANIELE
CIRCEO	SAN ANTIOCHO	TAVOLARA
GORGONA	SAN ANTONIO	TEULADA
ERCOLE	CAPRENA	LEVANZO
VIGOROSO	PIANOSA	

TRAINING SHIPS

                                                 L

A 5312 AMERIGO VESPUCCI — Bldr: Nav. Mec. Castellammare   22-3-30

A. Vespucci (A 5312)   Lionel Fava

D: 3,545 tons (4,186 fl)   **Dim:** 82.38 (70.72 pp) × 15.54 × 6.70
S: 10 kts   **Range:** 5,450/6.5
A: 4/76-mm — 1/20-mm   **Man:** 400 men, 150 cadets
M: 2 Fiat diesels with electric transmission; 1 prop; 1,900 hp — sail area: 2,100 m²

A 5311 PALINURO (ex-*Cdt Louis Richard*) — Bldr: Dubigeon (1920)

Palinuro (A 5311)   Aldo Fraccaroli

     D: 1,042 tons (1,351 fl)   **Dim:** 59 × 9.70 × 4.80
     A: 2/76-mm (saluting battery)   **Range:** 5,300/7.5
     M: 1 diesel; 450 hp

Former French cod fishing craft bought in 1951. Steel hull.

A 5316 CORSARO II — Sailing school ship — Bldr: Costaguta, Genoa — 1960
     D: 41 tons   **Dim:** 20.90 × 4.70 — 1 auxiliary engine 96 hp.
Rigged as a yawl.

A 5313 STELLA POLARE — Sailing school ship — Bldr: Sant. Germ., Chiavari — 1965.
Cruising yacht, RORC class. 47 tons.

VARIOUS

♦ *1 experimental ship, former U.S. destroyer*
A 5302 AVIERE (ex-*Nicholson, DD-442*) — Bldr: Boston NSY — 31-5-40
     D: 2,500 tons (fl)   **S:** 25 kts   **Dim:** 106.07 × 11.80 × 4.70
     M: General Electric GT; 2 props   **Boilers:** 4 Babcock; 50,000 hp

Has served particularly in equipment trials for the 76-mm and 127-mm OTO-Melara Compact of the Albatros system, the Italian version of the BPDMS Sea Sparrow.

♦ *1 "hovercraft," HC 9802 British SNR 6 class,* assigned to the San Marco naval infantry battalion.

IVORY COAST

PERSONNEL: 140 to 150 men

MERCHANT MARINE (1-7-74): 46 ships — 121,276 grt

♦ *2 patrol boats*

	Bldr	Laid down	L	In serv.
VIGILANT	C.N. Franco-Belges	2-67	23-5-67	1968

   D: 240 tons (avg)   **Dim:** 47.50 (45.50 pp) × 7.00 × 2.50
   S: 18.5 kts   **Man:** 3 officers, 22 men
   A: 2/40-mm AA — 8 SS 12 missiles   **Range:** 2,000/15
   M: 2 MGO diesels with Masson reduction gear; 2 props; 2,400 hp

A similar type has been built for Madagascar, two others for Senegal.

PERSEVERANCE (ex-*P 759, VC 9*) (25-2-58)

   D: 70 tons (80 fl)   **S:** 28 kts   **Dim:** 31.77 × 4.70 × 1.70
   A: 2/20-mm AA   **Man:** 15 men   **Range:** 1,500/15
   M: 2 Mercedes-Benz diesels; 12 cylinders 2 props; 2,700 hp.   **Fuel:** 4 tons

♦ *2 LCVP (with Mercedes motors) recently built in Abidjan*

♦ *1 training and support ship*

LOCODJO (1953), 450 tons, built in West Germany, delivered in 1970

♦ *4 small craft of 7 to 10 meters*

♦ *1 Arcoa-class small craft*

♦ *1 small (25 men) Barracuda-type transport*

It is anticipated that an additional patrol boat of the *Vigilant* class and a light transport similar to the *Francis Garnier* of the French Navy will be added. The order for these two ships is expected soon. Later two flotillas of lagoon patrol boats will be established and the number of personnel should be doubled.

JAMAICA

MERCHANT MARINE (1-7-74): 5 ships — 6,740 grt

Has a military unit similar to the U.S. Coast Guard; material furnished by the U.S.A. under the Mutual Assistance Pact; British personnel.

♦ *3 coastal security patrol boats*

P 4 DISCOVERY BAY — P 5 HOLLAND BAY — P 6 MANATEE BAY

   Bldr: Sewart Seacraft (Berwick, La., U.S.A.) 1966-68.

   D: 60 tons   **Dim:** 25.90 × 5.68 × 1.83
   S: 21/20 kts   **Range:** 500/12
   A: 3/12.7-mm machine guns   **Man:** 10 men
   M: General Motors Mk 16 V 71 N diesels; 2 props; 700 hp.

♦ *2 105-foot patrol boats*

P . . .   **P . . .**

   Bldr: Sewart Seacraft (Berwick, La., U.S.A.), 1974.

   D: . . .   **S:** 32 kts   **Dim:** 31.50 × 5.70 × 2.10
   A: 2/20-mm AA — 3/12.7 mm machine guns — 1/81-mm mortar
   M: 2 Maybach diesels; 6,000 hp   **Man:** 15 men

REMARKS: Can carry 24 soldiers and serve as small floating hospitals.

Discovery Bay (P 4)

JAPAN

In addition to the maritime self-defense force, Japan has a maritime agency (Kaijo Hoancho) which differs from the Navy (Kaiso Jeitai) and is comparable to the U.S. Coast Guard. The ships of the Maritime agency are listed in a special section following the Navy.

I. NAVY

THE NAVY IN THE FOURTH DEFENSE PLAN

The Fourth Defense plan covering the period from 1-4-1972 to 31-3-1977, and adopted 9-10-1972, anticipates upon completion:

(a) the construction of 54 combatant and auxiliary ships for a total of 69,600 standard displacement tons, as follows:

— 2 destroyers (DDH) of 5,200 tons each
— 1 destroyer (DDG) of 3,850 tons armed with medium-range, surface-to-air missiles
— 1 destroyer (DDA) all-purpose, 3,500 tons armed with surface-to-surface missiles
— 3 destroyers (DDK) antisubmarine of 2,500 tons
— 3 frigates of 1,500 tons
— 3 frigates of 1,450 tons
— 2 submarines of 2,200 tons
— 3 submarines of 1,800 tons
— 19 minesweepers and minehunters of various classes
— 6 patrol boats
— 1 small fast combat support supply ship (AOE) of 5,000 tons
— 1 small submarine tender of 2,000 tons
— 5 amphibious ships (LST) of 1,500 to 2,000 tons
— 1 hydrographic ship of 2,000 tons

(b) the purchase of
— 43 patrol aircraft P 2J type
— 9 ASW flying boats PS1 type
— 34 ASW helicopters

PERSONNEL: Approximately 45,000 men

NAVAL AVIATION

Part of the Navy; in October 1973 this included 250 aircraft, all built in Japan but most based on U.S. Navy types redesigned to fulfill the requirements of the Japanese Navy: P2J (Neptune, U.S.) patrol planes, SH3D Sea King helicopters or others for ASW, minesweeping, or rescue-at-sea operations. A few flying boats of Japanese design, the ASW PS 1 type, are also included (see *Flottes de Combat 1970*, page 289).

MERCHANT MARINE (1-7-74): 9,974 ships — 38,707,659 grt
(tankers: 1,537 ships — 16,012,234 grt)

WARSHIPS IN SERVICE OR UNDER CONSTRUCTION AS OF 1 OCTOBER 1975

	L	D	Main armament
♦ *18 submarines*			
8 UZUSHIO	1970-75	1,800	6/533-mm TT
5 OSHIO	1964-68	1,650	8/533-mm TT
4 HAYASHIO	1961-62	750	3/533-mm TT
1 OYASHIO	1959	1,000	4/533-mm TT
♦ *5 ASW and guided-missile destroyers*			
2 TACHIKASE	1975-78	3,900	1 Tartar missile launcher, 1/Asroc
2 HARUNA	1971-73	4,700	2/127-mm AA, 1/Asroc, 3 helicopters
1 AMATSUKAZE	1963	3,050	1 Tartar missile launcher, 1/Asroc, 4/76-mm
♦ *45 frigates and escort ships*			
4 KIKUZUKI	1966-69	3,050	2/127-mm AA, 1 Asroc
2 AOKUMO	1972-73	2,150	4/76-mm AA, 6 ASW TT, 2 ML
7 YAMAGUMO	1965-69	2,066	5/76-mm AA, 1/Asroc or 1 helicopter
2 AKIKUZI	1959	2,300	3/127-mm AA, 4/76-mm AA, 1 Weapon Able
3 MURASAME	1958-59	1,800	3/127-mm AA, 4/76-mm AA, 4 ASW TT
7 AYANAMI	1957-60	1,700	6/76-mm AA, 4/533-mm TT, 4 ASW TT
2 HARUKAZE	1955	1,600	3/127-mm AA, 8/40-mm AA, ASW weapons
3 TESHIO	1974-75	1,450	2/76-mm AA, 2/40-mm AA, 1/Asroc
7 CHIKUGO	1970-72	1,470	2/76-mm AA, 2/40-mm AA, 1/Asroc
4 IZUZU	1961-63	1,490	4/76-mm AA, 1 Weapon Able
2 IKAZUCHI	1955	1,080	2/76-mm AA, 2/40-mm AA, ASW weapons
1 AKEBONO	1955	1,075	2/76-mm AA, 2/40-mm AA, ASW weapons
2 ASAHI	1943	1,400	3/76-mm, ASW weapons
♦ *20 coastal escort vessels*			
12 UMIKATA	1959-65	420/440	2/40-mm, 6 ASW TT
1 HAYABUSA	1957	380	2/40-mm, ASW weapons
4 KARI	1956	310	2/40-mm, ASW weapons
3 KAMONE	1956	330	2/40-mm, ASW weapons

♦ *4 minelayers*

♦ *5 LSTs*

♦ *44 minesweepers and minehunters*

WEAPONS AND SYSTEMS

Most of the weapons and detection gear are of American design built under license in Japan. Nevertheless, the latest ships are being equipped with long-range air search radar of Japanese design, with a short pulse feature.

SUBMARINES (SS)

♦ *2 new class submarines (4th plan)*

	Bldr	Laid down	L	In serv.
N ...	Mitsubishi, Kobe	1975	...	...
N ...		1976	...	...

D: 2,200 tons   S: ...   Dim: ...
A: ...
M: diesel-electric propulsion

SUBMARINES (SS) *(continued)*

Makishio (567)   1972

♦ *8 submarines with tear-shaped hulls, 566 to 570 (3rd plan), 571-573 (4th plan)*

	Bldr	Laid down	L	In serv.
566 UZUSHIO	Kawasaki, Kobe	9-68	11-3-70	1-71
567 MAKISHIO	Mitsubishi, Kobe	1969	1-2-71	2-72
568 ISOSHIO	Kawasaki, Kobe	7-70	3-72	2-73
569 NARUSHIO	Mitsubishi, Kobe	1972	24-11-72	2-73
570 KUROSHIO	Kawasaki, Kobe	. . .	22-2-74	2-75
571 TAKASHIO	Kawasaki, Kobe	. . .	7-75	2-76
572 N . . .	Kawasaki, Kobe	1975	. . .	3-78
573 N . . .	Kawasaki, Kobe	. . .	. . .	. . .

Narushio (569)   1974

D: 1,850 tons   **S:** 20/12 kts   **Dim:** 72 × 9.90 × 7.50
A: 6/533-mm TT (fwd)   **Man:** 10 officers, 70 men
M: diesel-electric propulsion; Kawasaki M.A.N. diesels; V8V24/30; 1 prop;
3,400/7,200 hp

REMARKS: Modeled on the U.S. *Barbel* class. Maximum depth: 200 m.

Arashio (565)

SUBMARINES

♦ *5 Oshio class*

	Bldr	Laid down	L	In serv.
561 OSHIO	Shin-Mitsubishi, Kobe	6-63	30-4-64	4-65
562 ASASHIO	Kawasaki, Kobe	10-64	27-10-65	10-66
563 HARUSHIO	Shin-Mitsubishi, Kobe	10-65	25-2-67	3-68
564 MICHISIO	Kawasaki, Kobe	7-66	5-12-67	8-68
565 ARASHIO	Shin-Mitsubishi, Kobe	7-67	27-10-68	9-69

D: 1,650 tons **Dim:** 88 × 8.20 × 4.90
S: 18/14 kts **Man:** 80 men **A:** 8/533-mm TT (6 fwd, 2 aft)
M: 2 Kawasaki diesels, each 2,900 hp; 2 electric motors, each 3,150 hp; 2 props

♦ *4 Hayashio class*

	Bldr	Laid down	L	In serv.
521 HAYASHIO	Shin-Mitsubishi, Kobe	6-60	31-7-61	6-62
522 WAKASHIO	Kasawaki, Kobe	6-60	2-8-61	6-62
523 NATSUSHIO	Shin-Mitsubishi, Kobe	12-61	18-9-62	6-63
524 FUYUSHIO	Kawasaki, Kobe	12-61	14-12-63	1-64

Natsushio (523)   1963 Mitsubishi

D: 750 tons (*521, 522*) 780 tons (*523, 524*) **Man:** 43 men
Dim: 59.20 (61 on the *523, 524*) × 6.50 × 4.10
S: 14/11 kts **A:** 3/533-mm TT
M: 2 Sulzer-Mitsubishi diesels, each 850 hp; 2 electric motors, each 650 hp; 2 props

♦ *1 Oyashio class*

	Bldr	Laid down	L	In serv.
511 OYASHIO	Kawasaki, Kobe	11-57	25-5-59	5-60

Oyashio (511)   1960

D: 1,140 tons surfaced/1,420 tons submerged **Dim:** 78.80 × 7 × 4.60
S: 19/13 kts **Range:** 5,000/10
A: 4/533-mm TT **Man:** 65 men
M: 2 Kawasaki diesels, 2,400 hp each; 2 electric motors, 5,400 hp each

REMARKS: Withdrawn from operational service 1-4-75 to serve as school ship.

DESTROYERS

♦ *2 DDH destroyers (4th plan)*

	Bldr	Laid down	L	In serv.
N . . .	. . .	1974	. . .	. . .
N . . .	. . .	1976	. . .	. . .

D: 5,200 tons **S:** . . . **Dim:** . . .
A: . . .
Electron Equipt: . . .

REMARKS: Modification of the *Haruna* class. Will have BPMDS Sea Sparrow system and 6 HSS2 helicopters.

♦ *2 DDH destroyers Haruna class (3rd plan)*

	Bldr	Laid down	L	In serv.
DDH 141 HARUNA	Mitsubishi, Nagasaki	3-70	12-71	22-2-73
DDH 142 HIEI	Ishikawajima-Harima		13-8-73	27-12-74

Haruna (141)   1973 Ships of the World

Haruna (141)   1973

D: 4,700 tons **S:** 32 kts **Dim:** 153 × 17.60 × 5.10
A: 2/127-mm AA Mk 42 (I × 2) — 6/324-mm Mk 32 ASW TT (III × 2) — 1 Asroc ASW system — 3 HSS2 helicopters
M: GT **Boilers:** . . . ; 2 props; 70,000 hp
Man: 36 officers, 304 men.

DESTROYERS (*continued*)

Hiei (142)   1975

◆ *1 DDA (4th plan)*

	Bldr	Laid down	L	In serv.
N ...	...	1975	17-12-74	...

D: 3,500 tons   **S:** ...   **Dim:** ...
A: ...
Electron Equipt: ...
M: ...

REMARKS: Will be equipped with U.S. Harpoon missiles

◆ *2 guided missile destroyers (1 from the 3rd plan, 1 from the 4th)*

	Bldr	Laid down	L	In serv.
168 TACHIKAZE	Mitsubishi	...	17-12-74	2-76
N ...				1978

Tachikaze (168)

D: 3,850 tons
A: 1 Mk 13 missile launcher (40 Tartar SM1) — 2/127-mm AA Mk 42 (I × 2) — 1 ASW Asroc system
Electron Equipt: Radars: 1 Japanese air search, 1/SPS 52, 2/SPG 51
M: GT; 2 props; 70,000 hp.

◆ *1 guided missile destroyer Amatsukaze class (surface-to-air)*

	Bldr	Laid down	L	In serv.
163 AMATSUKAZE	Mitsubishi, Nagasaki	11-62	5-10-63	2-65

D: 3,050 tons (4,000 fl)   **Dim:** 131 × 13.40 × 4.20
S: 33 kts   **Man:** 290 men
A: 1 Mk 13 missile launcher (40 Tartars) (I × 1 aft) — 4/76-mm AA 50-cal (II × 2) — 1 ASW Asroc system — 2 ASW fixed TT — 2 hedgehogs

Amatsukaze (163)   1974 Ships
of the World

DESTROYERS (continued)

Electron Equipt: Radars: 1/SPS 39, 1/SPS 37, 2/SPG 51
M: Ishikawajima General Electric GT; 2 props
Boilers: 2 Foster-Wheeler; 60,000 hp.   **Fuel:** 900 tons
Electric: 2750 kw

♦ *3 DDK class destroyers (4th plan)*

N . . .   1975
N . . .   1975
N . . .   1975

D: 2,500 tons   **S:** . . .   **Dim:** . . .
A: . . .   **M:** . . .   **Electron Equipt:** . . .

♦ *4 Kikuzuki class destroyers (2nd plan)*
Series named after the phases of the moon.

	Bldr	Laid down	L	In serv.
164 TAKATSUKI	Ishikawajima, Tokyo	10-64	7-1-66	3-67
165 KIKUZUKI	Mitsubishi	3-66	25-3-67	3-68
166 MOCHIZUKI	Ishikawajima, Tokyo	11-66	15-3-68	3-69
167 NAGATSUKI	Ishikawajima, Tokyo	3-67	19-3-69	2-70

Takatsuki (164)

Kikuzuki (165)   1974

D: 3,050 tons (4,000 fl)   **Dim:** 136 (131 pp) × 130 × 4.50
S: 32 kts   **Range:** . . .   **Man:** 270 men
A: 2/127-mm AA 54-cal (I × 2) — 1 Asroc ASW system — 1 Bofors ASW four-barrel rocket launcher (fwd) — 6/324-mm Mk 32 ASW TT (III × 2) — 2 ASW helicopters.
M: General Electric GT; 2 props   **Boilers:** 2 Foster-Wheeler; 60,000 hp
Fuel: 900 tons

REMARKS: The first Japanese destroyers with "macks" (combination of masts and stacks). Same hull and engineering spaces as the *Amatsukase*. American equipment built under license. Japanese search radar; the sonar is a Japanese copy of the U.S. SQS 23. *166* fitted with Tacan.

♦ *Improved Murakumo class destroyers (3rd plan)*

	Bldr	Laid down	L	In serv.
119 AOKUMO	Sumitomo, Uraga	11-70	30-3-72	25-11-72
120 AKIGUMO	Sumitomo, Uraga	7-71	19-10-73	31-4-74

Aokumo (119)   1974 J. C. Bellonne

D: 2,150 tons   **S:** 26 kts   **Dim:** 114.90 × . . . × . . .
A: 4/76-mm AA, 4/324-mm ASW TT — 1 quadruple tube Bofors ASW RL, 1 helicopter
M: 6 Mitsubishi diesels coupled to two props; 26,500 hp

REMARKS: Improvement of the *Murakumo* class; equipped with VDS. Another photo later.

♦ *Series named after clouds*

	Bldr	Laid down	L	In serv.
B. **116 MINEGUMO**	Mitsui, Tamano	3-67	16-12-67	8-68
117 NATSUGUMO	Uraga Dock Co., Yokosuka	6-67	25-7-68	4-69
118 MURAKUMO	Maizuru, H.I.	10-68	15-11-69	8-70
120 YUUGUMO	Mitsui, Tamano	11-72	1-9-73	6-74

	Bldr	Laid down	L	In serv.
A. **113 YAMAGUMO**	Mitsui, Tamano	3-64	27-2-65	3-66
114 MAKIGUMO	Uraga Dock Co., Yokosuka	6-64	26-7-65	3-66
115 ASAGUMO	Maizuru, H.I.	6-65	25-11-66	8-67

D: 2,066 tons (2,204 fl)   **Dim:** 114 × 11.80 × 3.90
S: 28/27 kts   **Range:** . . .   **Man:** 19 officers, 196 men

DESTROYERS (continued)

Murakumo (118)   1970

Asagumo (115)   1974

A: all 4/76-mm AA (II × 2) — 1 quadruple Bofors 375-mm ASW rocket launcher — 6/324-mm ASW TT (III × 2) — the A class: 1 Asroc system ASW, the B class: 2 helicopters — 1 VDS

M: 6 Mitsubishi diesels; 12 VEV 3/40 linked 3 by 3 on two propeller shafts; 26,500 hp

REMARKS: The 76-mm Italian OTO Melara Compact will be tested on the *Murakumo*; if the trials are conclusive, this gun could replace the twin 76-mm on the ships which are so armed.

♦ *2 Akizuki class*

	Bldr	Laid down	L	In serv.
161 AKIZUKI	Mitsubishi, Nagasaki	7-58	26-6-59	2-60
162 TERUZUKI	Shin-Mitsubishi, Kobe	8-58	24-6-59	2-60

D: 2,300 tons (2,890 fl)   **Dim:** 118 (115 pp) × 12 × 4.02

S: 32 kts   **Man:** 330 men

A: 3/127-mm 54-cal AA (I × 3) — 4/76-mm 50-cal AA (II × 2) — 4/533-mm TT (IV × 1) — 2 ASW torpedo launchers — 2 hedgehogs — 1 ASW Weapon Able (Mk 108) rocket launcher — 2 depth charge projectors

M: Mitsubishi-Escher-Wyss GT (*161*), Westinghouse (*162*); 2 props; 4 boilers; 45,000 hp

Akizuki (161)   1970

REMARKS: "Off-shore" assistance program ships ordered by the U.S.A., American plans. Will be used as flotilla leaders or as command ship for the convoy escorts.

♦ *3 Murasame class, series named for the winds*

	Bldr	Laid down	L	In serv.
107 MURASAME	Mitsubishi, Nagasaki	12-57	31-7-58	2-59
108 YUDACHI	Ishikawajima, Tokyo	12-57	29-7-58	3-59
109 HARUSAME	Uraga Dock Co., Yokosuka	6-58	18-6-59	12-59

Harusame (109)   Uraga Dock

D: 1,800 tons (2,400 fl)   **Dim:** 109.73 × 10.97 × 3.70 (light)

S: 30 kts   **Man:** 229 men

A: 3/127-mm AA (I × 3) — 4/76-mm 50-cal (II × 2) — 4 305-mm fixed ASW TT — 1 hedgehog — 2 depth charge projectors

M: Kampon GT (*107, 108*); Mitsubishi-Escher-Wyss (*109*); 2 props; 2 boilers; 35,000 hp

REMARKS: Hull and machinery spaces quite similar to the *Ayanami* class; armament different. Mitsubishi CE boilers (*109*), Foster-Wheeler D (*107, 108*). The *107* will be fitted with a triple TT.

♦ *7 Ayanami class. Series named after the waves*

	Bldr	Laid down	L	In serv.
103 AYANAMI	Misubishi, Nagasaki	11-56	1-6-57	2-58
104 ISONAMI	Mitsubishi, Kobe	12-56	30-9-57	3-58

DESTROYERS (*continued*)

105 URANAMI	Kawasaki, Kobe	2-57	29-8-57	2-58
106 SHIKINAMI	Mitsui, Tamano	12-56	25-9-57	2-58
110 TAKANAMI	Mitsui, Maizuru	11-58	8-8-59	1-60
111 ONAMI	Ishikawajima, Tokyo	3-59	13-2-60	8-60
112 MAKINAMI	Iino, Maizuru	3-59	25-4-60	10-60

Isonami (104)

Onami (111)   Isikawajima

D: 1,700 tons (2,400 fl)   **Dim:** 109 × 10.70 × 8.70 (light)
S: 32 kts   **Man:** 220/230 men
A: 6/76-mm AA (II × 3) — 4/533-mm TT (IV × 1) — 4 fixed ASW TT (2 each
side) — 2 hedgehogs — 2 depth charge projectors.
M: Mitsubishi Escher-Wyss GT; 2 props; 2 boilers; 35,000 hp

REMARKS: The 2 hedgehogs, (forward of the bridge) are trainable. Boilers: Hitachi-
Babcock (*106, 110*), Mitsubishi (the others). *111* has a Hitachi-General Electric
geared turbine. *104* and *106* fitted as training ships; the trainable TT have been
removed and a classroom has replaced them.

♦ *2 Harukaze class. Series named after the winds*

	Bldr	Laid down	L	In serv.
101 HARUKASE	Misubishi, Nagasaki	12-54	20-9-55	4-56
102 YUKIKAZE	Mitsubishi, Kobe	12-54	20-8-55	7-56

Harukaze (101)   Akura Nakumo

D: 1,600 tons (2,300 fl)   **Dim:** 106.30 × 10.50 × 4.40 (fl)
S: 30 kts   **Man:** 187 men   **Range:** 6,000/18
A: 3/127-mm 38-cal AA (I × 3) — 8/40-mm AA (IV × 2) — 2 hedgehogs — 8
depth charge projectors — ASW torpedo launchers
M: Mitsubishi-Escher-Wyss GT (*101*); Westinghouse (*102*); 2 props; 2 Hitachi-
Babcock (*101*) boilers; combustion eng. (*102*); 30,000 hp.   **Fuel:** 557 tons

REMARKS: Hull largely electric-welded, light alloys widely used in superstructure;
American guns; refitted in 1959-60. The *102* will receive a VDS in 1976.

♦ *3 Frigates of a new class (4th plan)*

	Bldr	Laid down	L	In serv.
N . . .	. . .	. . .	. . .	. . .
N . . .	. . .	. . .	. . .	. . .
N . . .	. . .	. . .	. . .	. . .

D: 1,500 tons   **S:** . . .   **Dim:** . . .
A: . . .   **M:** . . .   **Electron Equipt:** . . .

FRIGATES

♦ *3 Teshio-class frigates (4th plan)*

	Bldr	Laid down	L	In serv.
222 TESHIO	Uraga	1973	28-5-74	10-1-75
223 YOSHINO	1973		8-74	6-2-75
224 KUMANO		5-1974	26-2-75	11-75

D: 1,450 tons   **S:** 25 kts   **Dim:** 93 × 10.80 × 3.50
A: 2/76-mm AA (II × 1), 2/40-mm AA (II × 1), 1 Asroc
Electron Equipt: Radars: 1 air search, 1 surface search, 1 fire control
Sonars: 1 hull mounted 1 VDS, medium frequency
M: diesels; 2 props; 1,600 hp

REMARKS: Improvement of *Chikugo* class.

FRIGATES (continued)

Teshio (222) — 1975

♦ *7 Chikugo class*

	Bldr	Laid down	L	In serv.
215 CHIKUGO	Mitsui, Tamano	12-68	13-1-70	7-70
216 AYASE	Ishikawajima, Tokyo	12-69	16-9-70	7-71
217 MIKUMO	Mitsui, Tamano	3-70	2-71	8-71
218 TOKACHI	Mitsui, Tamano	12-70	11-71	5-72
219 IWASE	Mitsui, Tamano	1971	4-72	12-12-72
220 CHITOSE	Hitachi, Maizuru	1971	25-1-73	21-8-73
221 NIYODO	Mitsui, Tamano	1972	28-8-73	8-2-74

Tokachi (218) — 1973 Ships of the World

D: 1,470 tons (1,700 fl) **S:** 25 kts **Dim:** 93 × 10.80 × 3.50
A: 2/76-mm AA (II × 1) — 2/40-mm AA (II × 1) — 6/324-mm ASW TT — 1 Asroc ASW system
M: 4 B & W diesels, Mitsui Mk 1628 V 3B U-38V; 2 props; 16,000 hp

REMARKS: Improvement of the *Isuzu* class; towed sonar.

♦ *4 Isuzu class*

	Bldr	Laid down	L	In serv.
211 ISUZU	Mitsui, Tamano	5-60	17-1-61	7-61
212 MOGAMI	Mitsubishi, Nagasaki	8-60	13-3-61	11-61
213 KITAKAMI	Ishikawajima, Tokyo	1962	21-6-63	2-64

Kitakami (213) — 1970

214 OHI	Iino, Maizuru	1962	15-6-63	2-64

D: 1,490 tons (1,700 fl) **Dim:** 94 × 10.40 × 3.50
S: 25 kts **Man:** 180 men
A: 4/76-mm AA (50-cal) (II × 2) — 1 Weapon Able Mk 108 rocket-launcher on *211, 212,* 1 Bofors 375-mm rocket-launcher (IV × 1) on *213, 214* — 4/305-mm ASW RL (IV × 1) on *211, 212,* — 6 ASW TT (III × 2) on *213, 214* — 1 depth charge projector
M: 4 B & W Mitsubishi diesels; 2 props; 16,000 hp

♦ *2 Ikazuchi class*

	Bldr	Laid down	L	In serv.
202 IKAZUCHI	Kawasaki, Kobe	12-54	6-9-55	2-56
203 INAZUMA	Mitsui, Tamano	12-54	4-8-55	2-56

Inazuma (203) — Mitsui

D: 1,080 tons (1,300 fl) **Dim:** 87.50 × 8.70 × 3.10 (light)
S: 25 kts **Man:** 145 men
A: 2/76-mm AA — 2/40-mm AA (II × 1) — 1 hedgehog — 4 depth charge projectors — 2 depth charge racks.
M: diesels; 2 props; 12,000 hp

	Bldr	Laid down	L	In serv.
201 AKEBONO	Ishikawajima, Tokyo	12-54	15-10-55	3-56

D: 1,075 tons (1,350 fl) **Dim:** 91.75 (87.50 pp) × 8.69 × 3.35
S: 28 kts **Man:** 183 men

FRIGATES (continued)

Akebono (201) 1970

A: 2/76-mm AA (I × 2) — 2/40-mm AA (II × 1) — 1 hedgehog — 8 depth charge projectors — 1 depth charge rack
M: Ishikawajima GT; 2 props; 2 Foster-Wheeler boilers; 18,000 hp

COASTAL ESCORTS

♦ *12 Umitaka class*

309 UMITAKA (25-7-59)	**315 HATSUKARI** (24-6-60)
310 OTAKA (3-9-59)	**316 UMIDORI** (15-10-62)
311 MIZUTORI (22-9-59)	**317 WAKATAKA** (13-11-62)
312 YAMADORI (22-10-59)	**318 KUMATAKA** (21-10-63)
313 OTORI (27-5-60)	**319 SHIRATORI** (8-10-64)
314 KASASAGI (31-5-60)	**320 HIYODORI** (25-9-65)

Bldr: Kawasaki, Kobe; Kure; Fujinagata, Osaka; Sasebo, etc. . . (1959-66).

D: 420/440 tons (450/480 fl) **Dim:** 60 × 7.10 × 2.35
S: 20 kts **Man:** 70 men **Fuel:** 24 tons
A: 2/40-mm AA (II × 1) — 6 ASW TT — 1 hedgehog — 1 depth charge rack
M: diesels (see Remarks); 2 props; 3,800/4,000 hp

REMARKS: Programs 1957 (2), 1958 (2), 1959 (3), 1961 (2), 1962 (2), 1963 (1) 1964 (1). Mitsui-Burmeister & Wain diesels (*309, 310*), Kawasaki M.A.N. V-8-V the others.

Yamadori (312)

♦ *1 gas turbine experimental class*

308 HAYABUSA (10-6-57) — Bldr: Mitsubishi

Hayabusa (308) Mitsubishi

D: 380 tons **Dim:** 58 × 7.80 × 2
S: 26 kts **Range:** 2,000/12
Man: 80 men **Fuel:** 22 tons
A: 4/40-mm AA (II × 2) — 1 hedgehog — 2 depth charge projectors
M: 14,000 hp gas turbine and 2 B. & W. diesels (4,000 hp)

♦ *4 Kari class*

301 KARI (26-9-56), **302 KIJI** (11-9-56), **303 TAKA** (17-11-56), **304 WASHI** (12-11-56).
Bldr: Fujinagata (2), Maizuru (2).

Washi (304)

D: 310 tons **Dim:** 54 × 6.50 × 2
S: 21 kts **Range:** 2,000/12
Man: 74 men **Fuel:** 21.5 tons
A: 2/40-mm AA (II × 1) — 1 hedgehog — 2 depth charge projectors — 2 depth charge racks
M: Kawasaki-M.A.N. diesels; 2 props; 4,000 hp

♦ *3 Kamome class*

305 KAMOME (3-9-56), **306 TSUBAME** (10-10-56), **307 MISAGO** (1-11-56)
Bldr: Uraga (2) Kure Zosen (1)

D: 330 tons **S:** 20 kts **Dim:** 54 × 6.60 × 2.10
A: 2/40-mm AA (II × 1) — 1 hedgehog — 2 depth charge racks
M: Mitsui-Burmeister & Wain diesels; 2 props; 4,000 hp **Fuel:** 21.5 tons

COASTAL ESCORTS (*continued*)

Kamome (305)   Uraga

MINELAYERS

♦ *2 Hayase class*

	Bldr	Laid down	L	In serv.
462 HAYASE (*MST*)	Ishikawajima	9-70	6-70	6-11-71
951 SOYA (*MMC*)	Maizuru, H.I.	7-70	31-3-71	30-9-71

Hayase (462)   1974

D: 2,150 tons **S:** 18 kts **Dim:** 99 × 15 × 4.20
A: 2/76-mm AA (II × 1) — 2/20-mm AA — 6/324-mm ASW TT (III × 2)
M: diesels; 2 props; 6,400 hp

REMARKS: 200 mines. *462* base ship for minesweepers. Minesweeping helicopter (type V 107) platform. See *Soya* photo.

	Bldr	Laid down	L	In serv.	Modernized
481 TSUGARU	Mitsubishi, Yokohama	12-54	19-7-55	12-55	1969-70

Tsugaru (481)   1970 U.S. Navy

D: 1,000 tons **S:** 16 kts **Dim:** 66.80 × 10.40 × 3.35
M: diesels; 2 props; 3,200 hp. **Man:** 105 men
A: 1/76-mm — 2/20-mm — 4 depth charge projectors
Coastal minelayer (4 minelaying rails for 40 mines) and cable-working ship.

491 ERIMO — Bldr: Uraga Dock Co. — L: 12-7-55

Erimo (491)

D: 630 tons **S:** 18 kts **Dim:** 64 × 7.93 × 2.45
A: 2/40-mm AA — 2/20-mm — 1 hedgehog — 1 depth charge projector — mines
M: diesel; 1 prop; 2,500 hp **Man:** 74 men

REMARKS: Will be modified and assigned as a training ship at the gunnery school (hull designation YAS).

MINESWEEPERS

♦ *3 coastal sweepers of a new class (4th plan)*

	L	In serv.
N . . .	. . .	. . .

MINESWEEPERS (continued)

N . . .   .
N . . .   .
D: 420 tons   **S:** . . .   **Dim:** . . . × . . . × . . .
A: . . .
M: . . .

REMARKS: Fitted out as well for minehunting.

♦ *14 Takami class (minehunters)*

630 TAKAMI	15-7-69		**637 MUROTSU**	10-72
631 IOU	12-8-69		**638 TASHIRO**	2-4-73
632 MIYAKE	3-6-70		**639 MIYATO**	3-4-73
633 UTONE	6-4-70		**640 TAKANE**	8-3-74
634 AWAJI	11-12-70		**641 MUZUKI**	5-4-74
635 TOOSHI	13-12-70		**642 YOKOSE**	21-7-75
636 TEURU	10-72		**643 SAKATE**	5-8-75

Bldr: Nippon Kokan, Tsurumi; and Hitachi, Kanagawa

Sakate (643)   Ships of the World

D: 380 tons   **S:** 14 kts   **Dim:** 52 × 8.80 × 2.40
A: 1/20-mm AA   **Man:** 45/47 men
M: Mitsubishi YV 12 ZC diesels; 2 props; 1,440 hp

REMARKS: Also fitted as minehunters.

♦ *20 Kasada class (minesweeper)*. *Hario* photo on following page.

	L			L
605 SHISAKA	20-3-58	**620 CHIBURI**	29-11-63
606 KANAWA	22-4-59	**621 OTSU**	5-11-64
473 KOZU	12-11-59	**622 KUDAKO**	8-12-64
612 MIKURA	14-3-60	**623 RISHIRI**	22-11-65
613 SHIKIME	22-7-60	**624 REBUN**	7-12-65
615 KOSHIKI	6-11-61	**625 AMAMI**	31-10-66
616 HOTAKA	23-10-61	**626 URUME**	12-11-66
617 KARATO	10-12-62	**627 MINASE**	10-1-67
618 HARIO	10-12-62	**628 IBUKI**	2-12-67
619 MUTSURE	16-12-63	**629 KATSURA**	18-9-67

Hario (618)   Shbldg and Sh. Record

Bldr: Nippon Kokan, Tsurumi; and Hitachi, Kanagawa — 1955 and following programs.

D: 330 tons   **S:** 14 kts   **Dim:** 45.70 × 8.38 × 2.30
A: 1/20-mm AA   **Man:** 40 men
M: Mitsubishi YV 10 Z-DE diesels; 2 props; 1,200 hp

REMARKS: *Kozu (473)* used as a tender for the MSB boats described later. *Kasada (640)*, *Habushi (608)*, *Tatara (610)* and *Hirado (614)* modified as auxiliary survey ships. *Sakito (607)* and *Tsukumi (611)* modified as gunnery school boats.

♦ *7 Sokaitei shallow water minesweepers (in service)*

MSB 701	. . .	**MSB 708**	1973	**MSB 712**	3-75
MSB 707	1973	**MSB 711**	3-75		
MSB 710	29-3-74	**MSB 709**	28-3-74		

Bldr: Hitachi and Tsurumi

MSB 8   1973 Ships of the World

D: 30 tons (42 fl)   **Dim:** 19 (17.50 pp) × 4.68 × 1.2
S: 10 kts   **Man:** 10 men   **M:** diesels; 2 props; 640 hp

REMARKS: From *707* on: **Dim:** 22.50 × 5.40 × 1.1 — **D:** 58 tons (fl); 960 hp. *MSB 705* and *706* have been scrapped.

FAST SMALL BOATS

♦ *3 PTL type (4th plan)*

	L	In serv.
N . . .	. . .	. . .
N . . .	. . .	. . .
N . . .	. . .	. . .

D: 160 tons **Dim:** . . . × . . . × . . .
A: . . .
M: . . .

♦ *6 PT type (3rd and 4th plans)* — Bldr: Mitsubishi

	L	In serv.			L	In serv.
811 PT 11	10–70	Yes		**814 PT 14**	. . .	10–7–73
812 PT 12	7–72	8–72		**815 PT 15**	. . .	8–1–75
813 PT 13	7–72	12–72		**816 PT 16**	. . .	

PT 12   1973 Ships of the World

D: 100 tons **S:** 50 kts **Dim:** 35 × 9.20 × 1.20
A: 2/40-mm — 4/533-mm torpedoes **Man:** . . . men
M: CODAG, 2 gas turbines — 2/24W2 diesels — 3 props; 10,500 hp

♦ *1 PT 10 type*

810 PT 10 — Bldr: Mitsubishi, Shimonoseki — L: 28–7–61

D: 90 tons (120 fl) **Dim:** 32 × 8.45 × 1.20
S: 40 kts **A:** 2/40-mm — 4/533-mm TT **Man:** 12 men
M: 3 Napier-Deltic diesels; 9,400 hp

REMARKS: Light metal hull.

♦ *2 Kosoku class*

ASH 01 **ASH 06**
D: 30 tons (*ASH 06*: 40 tons) — **L:** 19 m
S: 33/30 kts — 1,200/3,000 hp

AMPHIBIOUS SHIPS

♦ *2 LST (4th plan)*

	Bldr	Laid down	L	In serv.
4151 MIURA	Ishikawajima	1972	13–8–74	29–1–75
4152 OJIKA	Ishikawajima	1973	2–9–75	3–76

Miura (4151)   1975

D: 2,000 tons **S:** 14 kts **Dim:** 98 × . . . × . . .
A: 2/76-mm AA (II × 2) — 2/40-mm (II × 1) **Range:** . . .
M: 2 diesels; 2 props; 4,400 hp **Man:** 118 men

♦ *3 Atsumi class LST (1 prog. 1970, 1 prog. 1972)*

	Bldr	Laid down	L	In serv.
4101 ATSUMI	Sasebo H.I.	1971	13–6–72	27–11–72
4102 MOTOBU	Sasebo H.I.	1972	3–8–73	21–12–73
4103 NEMURO	. . .	1973	. . .	. . .

D: 1,480 tons **S:** 14 kts **Dim:** 89 × 13 × 2.70
A: 2/40-mm AA **Man:** 100 men **Range:** 4,300/12
M: 2 Kawasaki M.A.N. diesels; 2 props; 4,400 hp

REMARKS: The *Atsumi* is the first LST of Japanese construction. She can carry 20 vehicles and 120 men.

LOGISTIC SUPPORT

♦ *2 salvage ships for submarine rescue*

402 FUSHIMI — Bldr: Sumitomo-Uraga — (10–9–69)
D: 1,430 tons **S:** 16 kts **Dim:** 76 × 12.50 × 3.80

LOGISTIC SUPPORT (*continued*)

Atsumi (4101)   1973

Fushimi (402)   1970

    M: 2 Mitzu V 6 22/30 diesels; 1 prop; 3,000 hp   **Man:**   102 men

401 CHIHAYA — Bldr: Mitsubishi — (4-10-60)
    D: 1,340 tons   **S:**   15 kts   **Dim:**   73 × 12 × 3.90   **Man:**   90 men
    M: diesel; 2,700 hp. Salvage diving-bell for 6 persons. Same profile as the *402*.

♦ *1 support ship* (*personnel training, drone control*)

	Bldr	Laid down	L	In serv.
ATS 4201 AZUMA	Maizuru, H.I.	9-68	14-4-69	11-69

    D: 1,950 tons   **S:**   18 kts   **Dim:**   98 × 13 × 3.80
    A: 1/76-mm AA — 2/324-mm ASW TT   **Man:**   185 men
    M: M.A.N.-Kawasaki diesels; 2 props; 4,000 hp; 10 KD-2R and 3 RQM-34 drones.

♦ *1 oiler-supply ship* (*4th plan*)

	Laid down	L	In serv.
N . . .	1975	. . .	. . .

    D: . . .   **Dim:**   . . .
    M: . . .

Azuma (4201)   1970

♦ *1 oiler-supply ship*
411 HAMANA — Bldr: Uraga (24-10-61)

Hamana (411)   Uraga

    D: 2,900 tons (7,550 fl)   **Dim:**   128 × 15.70 × 6.30
    S: 16 kts   **Man:**   100 men   **A:**   2/40-mm
    M: 1 diesel; 1 prop; 5,000 hp

♦ *1 icebreaker*

	Bldr	Laid down	L	In serv.
5001 FUJI	Nippon Kokan, Tsurumi	8-64	18-3-65	7-65

    D: 8,500 tons (fl)   **S:**   17 kts   **Dim:**   99 × 27.80 × 8.90
    M: Diesel-electric propulsion; 12,000 hp   **Range:**   15,000/15. Carries 3 helicopters. Can make way through ice 5.40 m. thick.

LOGISTIC SUPPORT (*continued*)

Fuji (5001)

♦ *1 submarine tender (4th plan)*

	Bldr	Laid down	L	In serv.
N . . .	. . .	1976	. . .	. . .

   D: . . .   **Dim:** . . .
   M: . . .

♦ *3 support craft, YAS 103 class*

YAS 103 (in service 9-71)   **YAS 104** (in service 9-72)
YAS 105 (in service 1974)

Yas (105)   1974

D: 550 tons (fl)   **S:** 14 kts   **Dim:** 51.50 × 10 × 2.60
M: 2 diesels; 1600 hp; 2 props   **Man:** 26 men + 14 passengers

♦ *2 support ships Atada class*

YAS 56 ATADA (L. 1956)   **YAS 57 ITSUKI** (L. 1956)

   D: 260 tons (fl)   **S:** 13 kts   **Dim:** . . .
   A: 1/20-mm AA   **M:** 1 diesel; 2 props; 1,200 hp

♦ *2 ex-minesweepers modified for service at the gunnery school*

YAS . . . SAKITO (ex-MSC 607)   **YAS . . . TSUKUMI** (ex-MSC 611)

♦ *2 Nasami class support ships*

YAS 59 MIHO (ex-U.S. *FS-524*), **YAS 51 NASAMI** (ex-U.S. *FS-408*)
   D: 706 tons   **S:** 11 kts   **Dim:** . . .
   M: diesels; 2 props; 8,000 hp

♦ **YAS 58 YASHIRO**

former coastal minesweeper

♦ *3 miscellaneous small auxiliaries (ex-torpedo boats)*

YAS 48 (ex-PT 1), **YAS 54** (ex-PT 5), **YAS 55** (ex-PT 6)

♦ *small transports*

YG 01 to 07
   D: 420 tons   **S:** 9 kts   **Dim:** 36.7 × 6.8 × 2.6
   M: 1/350-hp diesel

REMARKS: Inland Sea service.

HYDROGRAPHIC SHIPS

♦ *1 AGS (4th plan)*

	Bldr	Laid down	L	In serv.
N . . .	. . .	. . .	. . .	. . .

   D: . . .   **Dim:** . . .
   M: . . .

5101 AKASHI — Bldr: Nippon Kokan, Tsurumi — 5-69
   D: 1,420 tons   **S:** 16 kts   **Dim:** 74 × 12.90 × 4.30
   M: 2 V8V 20/32 Kawasaki diesels; 2 props (1 bow prop); 3,800 hp. 2 cranes (5-
      and 1-ton)
   Man: 70 men + 10 hydrographic research personnel.

5111 KASADA (ex-*MSC 604*), . . . **KABUSHI** (ex-*MSC 608*), . . . **TATARA** (ex-
MSC 610), and **HIRADO** (ex-*MSC 614*) modified and assigned as auxiliary survey
ships.

VARIOUS

♦ *1 training ship*

	Bldr	Laid down	L	In serv.
3501 KATORI	Ishikawajima	12-67	19-11-68	9-69

   D: 3,372 tons (4,100 fl)   **Dim:** 127.50 (122 pp) × 15 × 4.35
   A: 4/76-mm AA (II × 2) — 1/375-mm Bofors quadruple ASW rocket launcher —
      6/324-mm ASW TT, (III × 2) for Mk 44 Torpedoes.   **S:** 25 kts
   M: Ishikawajima Gt; 2 props; 20,000 hp   **Range:** 7,000/18

REMARKS: Helicopter platform. Can be used as an ASW frigate if required.

♦ *9 small salvage boats PB 901, 903 and 919 to 925*

   D: 18 tons   **S:** 16 kts — 450 hp

VARIOUS (*continued*)

Katori (3501)   1974 J. C. Bellonne

Soya (951)   1973 Ships of the World

II. MARITIME SAFETY AGENCY
(*Kaijo Hoancho*)

The Maritime Safety Agency, a coast guard modeled on the U.S. Coast Guard, is directed by the Department of Transportation in peacetime. Although armed, the ships are not considered as part of the navy and fly only the national colors (red disk on a white background), not the flag reserved for naval ships. In wartime the ships revert to naval control.

PERSONNEL: Approximately 11,000 men

Aokumo (119)   1974

A. Large Patrol Ship (PL)

PL 31 IZU — Bldr: Hitachi Zosen (1-67), **PL 32 MIURA** — Bldr: Maizuru (11-68)

Miura (PL 32)   1970

D: 2,081 tons	**Dim:**	95.50 (86.45 pp) × 11.60 × 3.80
S: 20.3 kts	**Range:**	5,000/20.5 — 14,500/12.7
M: 2 diesels; 2 props; 10,400 hp	**Man:**	72 men

PL 21 KOJIMA (in serv.: 5-64) — Bldr: Kure Zosen — Training ship (50/60 midshipmen)

D: 1,201 tons	**S:** 17.2 kts	**Dim:** 69.60 × 10.30 × 5.40
A: 1/76-mm, 1/40-mm AA, 1/20-mm AA		**Range:** 6,000/13
M: Uraga diesel engine; 1 prop; 2,600 hp		**Man:** 59 men

PL 13 ERIMO (14-8-65) — **PL 14 SATSUMA** (4-66) — **PL 15 DAIO** (19-6-73) **PL 16 MUROTO** (15-3-74. In serv.: 5-8-74).

    Bldr: Hitachi Zosen

VARIOUS (continued)

Kojima (PL 21)   E. Aoki

Daio (PL 15)   1974

D:	1,009 tons	**S:**	19.5 kts	**Dim:**	73 (wl) × 9.20 × 3
A:	1/76-mm — 1/20-mm AA			**Range:**	6,000/18
M:	diesels; 2 props; 4,800 hp				

Hull reinforced against ice.

PL 11 NOJIMA (12-2-62) — **PL 12 OJIKA** (in serv.: 6-64).

Bldr: Uraga Dock Company Ltd — Meteorological frigates

D:	984 tons	**S:**	17.5 kts	**Dim:**	69 × 9.18 × 5.40
A:	...	**Man:**	51 men	**Range:**	6,000 × 14
M:	Uraga Sulzer diesels, 6 MD 42; 2 props; 3,000 hp				

PL 01 MUROTO (5-12-49) — Bldr: Uraga Dock Company Ltd (1950)

D:	750 tons (840 fl)	**S:**	15 kts	**Dim:**	61 (55.50 pp) × 9.30 × 3.15
A:	1/76-mm — 2/20-mm AA			**M:**	diesels; 2 props; 1,500 hp

PL 107 SOYA — refitted in 1956 (supply and buoy ship modified P. and Ch.)

D:	4,818 tons (fl)	**S:**	14 kts	**Dim:**	79 × 15.75 × 5.25
M:	diesels; 2 props; 4,800 hp			**Range:**	10,000/12

Nojima (PL 11)   E. Aoki

Soya (PL 107)   Tsurumi

Hydrographic research ship for the Southern Hemisphere. Reinforced bow for navigation in ice 1-m thick. 4 helicopters.

PM/PS

B. Patrol boats

♦ *3 Miyaka class*

PM 70 MIYAKE — **PM 71 AWAJI** — **PM 72 YAEYAMA** — **PM 73** . . . **PM 74** . . . — **PM 75 FUJI** — **PM 76 KABASHIMA** in serv.: 25-3-75 — **PM 77 SADO** in serv.: 7-2-75

D:	498 tons	**S:**	17.6 kts	**Dim:**	...
A:	2/20-mm AA	**Man:**	40 men	**Range:**	3,000/16.9
M:	2 diesels — 2,600 hp.				

♦ *4 Kunashiri class*

PM 65 KUNASHIRI (12-68)	**PM 69 OKINAWA**
PM 67 SAROBETSU	**PM 3 SADO**

Bldr: Maizuru; Usuki Iron Works — 1968-72

D:	498 tons	**S:**	17.5 kts	**Dim:**	58 × 7.40 × 2.40
A:	1/20-mm AA			**Man:**	40 men
M:	diesels; 2 props; 2,600 hp				

VARIOUS (*continued*)

♦ *5 Matsuura class*

PM 60 MATSUURA (24-12-60) **PM 63 NATORI** (8-65)
PM 61 SENDAI (18-1-62) **PM 64 KARATSU** (1-67)
PM 62 AMAMI (1964)

Bldr: Osaka S.B. Co. (*60, 61*); Hitachi Zosen

D:	420 tons	**S:**	16.5 kts	**Dim:**	55.30 × 7.01 × 2.30
A:	1/20-mm AA	**Man:**	37/40 men	**Range:**	3,500/12
M:	diesels; 2 props; 1,400/1,800 hp				

REMARKS: *Karatsu:* 2,600 hp — **S:** 18 kts

♦ *2 Tokachi class*

PM 52 TATSUTA — **PM 51 TOKACHI** (8-5-54).

D:	370 tons (380 fl)	**S:**	15/16 kts	**Dim:**	. . .
A:	1/40-mm AA	**Man:**	37 men		
M:	2 diesels; 1,400/1,500 hp				

♦ **PM 53 TESHIO** (12-1-55)

Bldr: Uraga

D:	420 tons	**S:**	15.7 kts	**Dim:**	58 × 7.9 × 2.5
A:	1/40-mm AA	**Man:**	37 men	**Range:**	3,800/12
M:	2 diesels; 1,400 hp				

♦ *6 Yahagi class*

PM 54 YAHAGI (19-5-56) **PM 57 SORACHI** (3-59)
PM 55 SUMIDA (6-57) **PM 58 YUBARI** (3-60)
PM 56 CHITOSE (24-2-58) **PM 59 HORONAI** (2-61)

Bldr: Niigata

D:	400/430 tons	**S:**	15 kts	**Dim:**	52 × 6.60 × 3.40 (fl)
A:	1/40-mm AA	**Man:**	37 men	**Range:**	3,600/4,000/12
M:	diesels; 2 props; 1,400 hp				

REMARKS: The above-mentioned ships have a close resemblance to the *Rebun* (PM 04) class, but they carry two tripod lattice masts and have a flush deck hull. They maintain 12/13 knots cruising speed.

♦ *14 Rebun class*

PM 04 REBUN **PM 09 AMAKUSA** **MP 14 HEKURA**
PM 05 IKI **PM 10 OKUSHIRI** **MP 15 MIKURA**
PM 06 OKI **PM 11 KUSAKAKI** **PM 16 KOSHIKI**
PM 07 GENKAI **PM 12 RISHIRI** **PM 17 HIRADO**
PM 08 HACHIJO **PM 13 NOTO**

Bldr: Japan (1950-52)

D:	450/510 tons	**S:**	14.5	**Dim:**	52 (47.50 pp) × 8.10 × 2.90
A:	1/76-mm — 1/20-mm AA			**Range:**	3,000/12
M:	2 diesels; 1,300 hp				

♦ *5 Chifuri class*

PM 18 CHIFURI **PM 21 SHIKINE**
PM 19 KUROKAMI **PM 22 DAITO**
PM 20 KOZU

Genkai (PM 07) Shizuo Fukui

D:	483 tons	**S:**	15.8 kts	**Dim:**	51.10 × 7.60 × 2.60
A:	1/76-mm AA — 1/20-mm AA			**Range:**	3,000/12
M:	2 diesels; 1,300 hp				

♦ *15 Fuji class* — Bldr: Japan

PS 03 TENRYU (4-51) **PS 11 MOGAMI** (9-51)
PS 04 ISUZU (6-51) **PS 12 YOSHINO** (10-51)
PS 05 ISHIKARI (7-51) **PS 13 NOSHIRO** (11-51)
PS 06 SAGAMI (7-51) **PS 14 KISO** (11-51)
PS 07 OYODO (8-51) **PS 15 SHINANO** (12-51)
PS 08 ABUKUMA (9-51) **PS 16 CHIKUGO** (1-52)
PS 09 KUZURYU (8-51) **PS 17 KUMANO** (2-52)
PS 10 KIKUCHI

D:	280 tons	**S:**	13.5 kts	**Dim:**	40.30 × 7 × 2.20
A:	1/40-mm AA			**Man:**	35 men
M:	diesels; 2 props; 800 hp			**Range:**	2,000/12

♦ *13 Hidaka class* — Bldr: Japan

PS 32 HIDAKA (2-3-62) **PS 39 TAKATSUKI** (1966)
PS 33 HIYAMA (3-63) **PS 41 KAMUI** (1966)
PS 34 TSURUGI (3-63) **PS 43 ASHITAKA** (1967)
PS 35 ROKKO (1964) **PS 44 KURAMA** (1968)
PS 36 TAKANAWA (1964) **PS 45 IBUKI** (1969)
PS 37 AKIYOSHI (1964) **PS 46 TOUMI** (1970)
PS 38 KUNIMI (19-12-64)

D:	169.4 tons		**Dim:**	33.72 (30.5 pp) × 6.30 × 1.80
S:	13.5 kts		**Man:**	17 men
M:	one diesel; 700 hp.		**Range:**	1,200/12

♦ *3 Nagara class* — Bldr: Japan (1950-52)

PS 18 NAGARA (1952) — **PS 19 TONE** (1952) — **PS 20 KITAKAMI** (1952)

D:	260 tons	**S:**	13.5 kts	**Dim:**	49.4 × 6.9 × 2.2
A:	1/40-mm AA			**Man:**	35 men
M:	2 diesels; 800 hp			**Range:**	2,000/12

VARIOUS (*continued*)

Akiyoshi (PS 37)   E. Aoki

C. Small boats (PS/PC)

♦ *5 aircraft rescue boats*

PS 42 BIZAN (3-66)
PS 47 ASAMA (2-69)   **PS 48 SHIRAMINE** (12-69)

 Bldr: Mitsubishi-Shimonoseki

D:	83/130 tons	**S:**	21/25 kts	**Dim:** 26 × 5.60 × 1
A:	1 machine gun			**Man:** 14 men
M:	2 diesels; 1,140 hp			**Range:** 400/18

REMARKS: *Shiramine* — **D:** 48 tons — **M:** 2 Benz diesels; 2,200 hp — **Range:** 250/25

PS 40 AKAGI (3-65) — Bldr: Hitachi-Zosen, Kanagawa

 D: 42 tons **S:** 28 kts **Dim:** 23.50 × 5.30 × 1
 M: 2 Mercedes-Benz diesels; 2,200 hp **Range:** 350/21

PS 31 TSUKUBA (3-62) — Bldr: Hitachi-Zosen, Kanagawa

 D: 65 tons **S:** 18 kts **Dim:** 23 × 6.50 × 1
 M: 2 Niigata diesels; 1,800 hp. **Range:** 230/15

♦ *41 Shinonome class*

PC 31 HATAGUMO	**PC 52 HAMANAMI**
PC 32 MAKIGUMO	**PC 53 MATSUNAMI**
PC 33 YAEGUMO	**PC 54 SHIKINAMI**
PC 34 ASAGUMO	**PC 55 TOMONAMI**
PC 35 NATSUGUMO	**PC 56 WAKANAMI**
PC 36 TATSUGUMO	**PC 57 ISONAMI**
PC 37 HANAYUKI	**PC 58 TAKANAMI**
PC 38 MINEYUKI	**PC 59 MUTSUKI**
PC 39 ISOYUKI	**PC 60 MOCHIZUKI**
PC 40 MATSUYUKI	**PC 61 HARUZUKI**
PC 41 SHIMAYUKI	**PC 62 KIYOSUKI**
PC 42 TAMAYUKI	**PC 63 URAZUKI**
PC 43 HAMAYUKI	**PC 64 AKIZUKI**
PC 44 YAMAYUKI	**PC 65 SHINONOME**
PC 45 KOMAYUKI	**PC 66 URANAMI**
PC 46 UMIGIRI	**PC 67 TAMANAMI**

PC 47 ASAGIRI	**PC 68 MINEFUMO**
PC 48 HAMAGIRI	**PC 69 KIYONAMI** (30-10-75)
PC 49 SAGIRI	**PC 70 OKINAMI**
PC 50 SETOGIRI	**PC 71 WAKAGUMO**
PC 51 HAYAGIRI	

 Bldr: Japan 1954-70

 D: 45 tons **S:** 21 kts (*30:* 18) **Dim:** 21 × 5.20 × 2.40
 M: diesels; 2 props; 1,400 hp (*30:* 1,000)
 Man: 9/10 men

 The PC 40/71 have 2,200 hp. — **S:** 25 kts — **A:** 1 machine gun.

D. Hydrographic ships (HL, HM, HU)

HL 01 SHOYO (1972)

 D: 2,000 tons **S:** 17.4 kts **Dim:** 78.60 × 12 × 4.20
 M: 2 diesels; 4,400 hp **Man:** 73 men

HL 02 TAKUYO — Bldr: Niigata (19-12-56) — Hydrographic vessel

 D: 930 tons **S:** 14 kts **Dim:** 58.75 × 9.50 × 3.25
 Man: 42 men   **Range:** 8,000/12.
 M: diesels; 2 props; 1,300 hp

HL 03 MEIYO — Bldr: Nagoya Zosen (in serv.: 3-63)

1964 E. Aoki

 D: 486 tons **S:** 12 kts **Dim:** 40.50 × 8.05 × 3.80
 M: diesel; 1 prop; 700 hp **Range:** 5,280/11

HM 04 HEIYO (1955)

 D: 69.1 tons **S:** 9 kts **Dim:** 22 × 4.40 × 1.60
 Man: 9 men **Range:** 670/9 **M:** diesel; 1 prop; 130 hp

HM 05 TENYO (1961).

 D: 171 tons **S:** 10 kts **Dim:** 28 × 5.80 × 2
 Man: 28 men **Range:** 3,160/10 **M:** 1 diesel; 1 prop; 230 hp

HM 06 KAIYO — Bldr: Isikawajima-Harima (in serv.: 3-64)

JAPAN (*continued*)

VARIOUS (*continued*)

D: 378 tons **S:** 12 kts **Dim:** 44.53 × 8.05 × 3.80
M: 1 diesel; 1 prop; 450 hp **Range:** 6,100/11

HU 06 SHINKAI (5-68) — deep-diving submarine (600 m)

D: 85 tons **S:** 3.5/10 (surfaced) **Dim:** 15.30 × 5.50 × 4
M: 1 electric motor **Man:** 4 men

18 **HS** (hydrographic small craft) + 3 planned.

E. Various

♦ *4 large buoy tenders*

LL 01 WAKAGUSA (1946)

Bldr: Hitachi Zosen
D: 1,815 tons **S:** . . . **Dim:** 61.2 × 9.6 × 5.7
M: diesel; 1,850 hp

LL 11 KOKUTO — LL 12 GINGA — LL 13 KAIO.

D: 500 tons **S:** 11.2 kts **Dim:** 38.6 × 9.4 × 4.2
M: 2 diesels; 420 hp **Range:** 2,800/10

REMARKS: The characteristics of the above-mentioned ships are the same as those of the *Ginga*. Others have slight differences.

LM 11 MIYOJO

Buoy tender with catamaran hull.
D: 318 tons **S:** 11 kts **Dim:** 26.10 × 13.60 × 2.65
M: 2 diesels; 600 hp **Range:** 3,680/10

♦ *12 medium size buoy tenders LM 101 to LM 112 class*

♦ *2 catamarans for measuring radioactive fallout*

MS 01 KINUGASA (9-10), **MS 02 SAIKAI** (9-70)

D: 23 tons **Dim:** 10.02 × 5 × 0.63 (Beam of each hull: 2 m)
S: 8.5 kts **Man:** 3 men — Two 90 hp diesels.

♦ *1 anti-pollution patrol catamaran*

SOKAI

D: . . . **S:** 11 kts **Dim:** 27.40 × 13.60 × 13.60 × 2
M: 2 diesels; 2 props; 1,080 hp

♦ *3 fire boats*

♦ **FL 01 HIRYU** (3-69), **FL 02 SHORYU** (2-70), **FL 03 NANRYU** (3-71):

D: 250 tons **S:** 13 kts Catamaran class

♦ *Port security small craft:* **CL 03** to **CL 97** (95 boats) and **CL 105** to **CL 157** (19 still in service).

D: 18/19 tons **S:** 15 kts **Dim:** 15 × 4.10 × 0.75
Man: 6 men **Range:** 400/15 **M:** 2 diesels; 500 hp

♦ *Port support small craft:* 49 **CS** of 6 to 10 tons.

The most recent, the *Sayuri* class (9 tons), have fiberglass hulls.

JORDAN

PERSONNEL: 300 men including the personnel of the base at Aqaba and the frogmen.

♦ *1/12-m wooden small craft*

HUSSEIN ABDALLAH

♦ *4/7.50-meter small craft*
♦ *4/5 or 6-meter small craft (unarmed)*
♦ *6/14-m U.S. Bertram-class small craft*

D: 6.5 tons **S:** 25 kts **Dim:** 9.26 × 3.26 × 0.46
A: 1/12.7-mm machine gun, 1/7.62-mm machine gun

REMARKS: The first was delivered 8-74.

KENYA

PERSONNEL: 360 men

MERCHANT MARINE (1-7-74): 21 ships — 21,829 grt
(tankers: 4 ships — 3,197 grt)

♦ *3 Simba class coastal security small craft*

P 3110 SIMBA (9-9-65) — **P 3112 CHUI** (25-11-65) — **P 3117 NDOVU** (ex-*Twigg*) (22-12-65) — Bldr: Vosper (1965-66)

D: 96 tons (109 fl) **Dim:** 31.25 (28.95 pp) 5.95 × 1.65
A: 2/40-mm AA (I × 2) Mk 7
M: 2 Paxman Ventura 12-cyl. diesels; 2 props; 2,900 hp
Man: 3 officers, 21 men **S:** 24/23 kts
Range: 1,500/16
Fuel: 14 tons

REMARKS: Welded hull, similar to the Malaysian *SRI* class.

Simba (P 3110) Vosper

KENYA (continued)

♦ *1 37.50-m coastal surveillance small craft*

P 3100 MAMBA
Bldr: Brooke (Gt. Br.) (L: 6-11-73)

Mamba (P 3100) 1975

D:	130 tons (160 fl)	**Dim:**	37.50 × 6.9 × 1.6
S:	25 kts	**Man:**	3 officers, 22 men
A:	2/40-mm AA	**Range:**	3,500/13
M:	2/16-cyl. Ruston diesels; 4,000 hp		

♦ *3 32 m coastal surveillance small craft.*

P 3121 MADARAKA (28-1-75) — **P 3122 JAMHURI** (14-3-76) — **P 3123 HARAMBEE** (2-5-75)

D:	120 tons (145 fl)	**S:**	25.5 kts	**Dim:**	32.6 × 6.1 × 1.7
A:	2/40-mm AA	**Man:**	21 men	**Range:**	2,300/12
M:	2 Ruston Paxman Valenta diesels; 5,400 hp				

♦ *3 small craft, used for port services*

KOREA
North

PERSONNEL: approximately 9,000 men
MERCHANT MARINE (1-7-74): 13 ships — 60,347 grt
(tankers: 1 — 9,791 grt)

With the exception of a small number of patrol boats of local construction, the North Korean navy is composed of ships received from the U.S.S.R. and from the People's Republic of China. See those sections for ship characteristics.

♦ *Submarines:* 4 Soviet W class
2 Soviet R class transferred by China

♦ *Fast Submarine Chasers:* 9 Soviet SO 1 class
6 Sariwon class built in North Korea
D: 160 tons **Length:** 38

♦ *Guided missile boats:* 8 Soviet OSA 1 class, 10 Komar class.

♦ *Torpedo boats:* 3 Soviet Shershen class, 100 to 120 P4 and P6 class.

♦ *Minesweepers:* at least 20 of 20 tons (inshore type).

KOREA
South

PERSONNEL: approximately 27,000 men including Marines
MERCHANT MARINE (1-7-74): 650 ships — 1,225,679 grt
(tankers: 47 — 462,126 grt)

DESTROYERS

♦ *2 ex-U.S. Gearing class, modernized with FRAM II, transferred 7 and 10-72*

95 CHUNG BUK (ex-*Chevalier, DDR-805*)
96 JEON BUK (ex-*Everett F. Larson, DDR-830*)

D:	2,400 tons (3,500 fl)	**Dim:**	119.17 × 12.45 × 5.80
Man:	14 officers, 260 men	**S:**	30 kts
A:	6/127-mm AA (II × 3) — 4/76-mm AA (II × 2) — ASW weapons		
M:	GT; 4 Babcock boilers; 2 props; 60,000 hp		
Fuel:	640 tons	**Range:**	2,400/25 — 4,800/15

♦ *2 ex-U.S. Sumner class modernized with FRAM II, transferred 12-73*

97 DAE GU (ex-*Wallace L. Lind, DD-703*)
98 INCHON (ex-*De Haven, DD-727*)

D:	3,320 tons (fl)	**S:**	34 kts **Dim:** 114.8 × 12.4 × 5.20
A:	6/127-mm AA (II × 3) — 6/324-mm TT (III × 2) Mk 32		
M:	GT; 4 Babcock boilers; 2 props; 60,000 hp		
Electron Equipt:	Radars: 1/SPS 10, 1/SPS 40		
	Sonars: 1/SQS 4 (towed) 1/SQS 11		

♦ *3 ex-U.S. Fletcher class, 1 transferred in 1963 (91), 2 in 1968*

91 CHUNG MU (ex-*Erben, DD-631*) Bath Iron Works — 21-3-43
92 SEOUL (ex-*Halsey Powell, DD-686*) Bethlehem — 30-6-43
93 PUSAN (ex-*Hickox, DD-673*) Federal S.B. — 4-7-43

D:	2,050 tons	**Dim:**	114.85 (wl) × 12.03 × 5.50
S:	35 kts	**Man:**	303 men
Range:	900/35 — 4,500/12		
A:	5/127-mm 38-cal (I × 5) — 6/40-mm AA (II × 3) — 6 ASW TT		
Electron Equipt:	Radars: 1/US SPS 10 and 6		

DESTROYERS (*continued*)

M: General Electric GT; 4 boilers; 2 props
Fuel: 650 tons
Electric: 60,000 kw.

Paek Ku

FRIGATES

♦ *3 ex-U.S. DE*

DE 71 KYONG KI (ex-*Sutton, DE-771*) ⎫ Transferred ⎧ Tampa SB 4-6-44
DE 72 KANG WON (ex-*Muir, DE-770*) ⎭ in 1956   ⎩ Tampa SB 6-8-44

D: 1,900 tons (fl)   **Dim:** 93.20 × 11.20 × 4.30
S: 20/19 kts   **Man:** 208 men
Range: 9,000/12
A: 3/76-mm AA (I × 3) — 3/40-mm AA — 8/20-mm AA — 8 depth charge projectors
M: diesel-electric; 2 props; 6,000 hp

DE 73 CHUNG NAM (ex-*Holt, DE-706*) Transferred 5-63 Defoe SB 15-12-43

D: 2,230 tons (fl)   **Dim:** 92.30 × 11.20 × 4.30
S: 24/23 kts   **Range:** 5,000/15
A: 2/127-mm — 2/40-mm AA — 6/20-mm AA — 6 ASW TT (III × 2)
Electron Equipt: Radars: 1/U.S. SPS 5 and 6
M: turbo-electric; 2 boilers; 2 props; 12,000 hp

♦ *3 Raven/Auk class transferred in 7-63, 5-66 and 1967*

PCE 1001 SHIN SONG (ex-*Ptarmigan, MSF-376*) — 15-7-44
PCE 1002 SUN CHONKE (ex-*Speed, MSF-116*) — 1944
PCE 1003 KOJE HO (ex-*Dextrous, MSF-341*) — 1944

D: 890 tons (1,250 fl)   **Dim:** 67.20 (65 pp) × 9.75 × 3.30
S: 18 kts   **Man:** 100 men
A: 2/76-mm AA — 4/40-mm AA, — 4/20-mm AA — hedgehog — 3-ASW TT (III × 1)
M: diesel-electric propulsion; 2 props; 3,500 hp

PATROL BOATS

♦ *1 ex-U.S. PGM Asheville class, transferred in 1972*

PAEK KU 11 (ex-*Benicia, PG-96*)

D: 225 tons (240 fl)   **S:** 40 kts   **Dim:** 50.14 × 7.28 × 2.90
A: 1/76-mm AA with Mk 64 fire control — 1/40-mm AA — 4/12.7-mm machine guns
M: CODAG propulsion; 1 GE gas turbine; 2 Cummins diesels

♦ *2 PSM class (Patrol Boats Multipurpose)*

	Bldr	L	In serv.
PAEK KU 12	Tacoma Boatbuilding Co.	1-75	1975
PAEK KU 13	Tacoma Boatbuilding Co.	2-75	. . .

D: 220 tons   **Dim:** 49.50 × . . . × . . .
S: 40 kts   **Man:** 5 officers, 7 men
A: 1/76-mm AA, 1/40-mm AA — 2/12.7-mm
M: 6 gas turbines, 2 reversible pitch props.

REMARKS: These boats could be fitted with the anti-surface Tartar missile. Installation of the MM 38 Exocet is also planned.

♦ *8 ex-U.S. PCE class*

PCE 50 KOJIN (ex-*MSF-289*)	PCE 55 OK PO (ex-*PCE-898*)
PCE 51 RO RYANG (ex-*PCE-882*)	PCE 57 PYOK PA (ex-*PCE-870*)
PCE 52 MYONG RYANG (ex-*PCE-896*)	PCE 58 RYUL PO (ex-*PCE-892*)
PCE 53 HAN SAN (ex-*PCE-873*)	PCE 59 SA CHON (ex-*PCE-903*)

Transferred since 1955.

D: 970 tons (fl)   **Dim:** 56.24 × 10.06 × 2.75
S: 17 kts   **Man:** 80/95 men
A: 1/76-mm — 3/40-mm — 8/20-mm
M: General Motors diesels, 2 props, 2,400 hp.
Range: 4,300/10

♦ *2 coastal patrol boats built in Korea*

PK 10 PK 11

D: 120 tons   **S:** 33 kts   **Dim:** 46 × 6.8 × . . .
A: 1/40-mm AA — 1/20-mm AA
M: 2 Mercedes-Benz diesels; 2 props; 10,200 hp

♦ *9 Sewart-class small boats transferred by the U.S.A. in 1967.*

FB 1 to 10

D: 330 tons (fl)   **S:** 25 kts   **Dim:** 20 × 4.90 × . . .
A: 2/20-mm — 3/12.7-mm machine guns
Range: 1,200/17
M: 3 General Motors diesels, 1,590 hp

♦ *Patrol boats of the U.S. CPIC type, ordered in 1972*

D: 70 tons (fl)   **Dim:** 30 × 5.4 × 1.8
A: 2/30-mm AA — 1 recoilless rifle
M: 3 gas turbines; 5,400 hp; 3 props; 40 knots

Several built in Korea

♦ *8 PB Cape-class ex-USCG, transferred in 1968-69*

PB 3 (ex-*Cape Rosier, WPB-95 333*)	PB 9 (ex-*Cape Falcon, WPB-95 330*)
PB 5 (ex-*Cape Sable, WPB-95 334*)	PB 10 (ex-*Cape Trinity, WPB-95 331*)
PB 6 (ex-*Cape Providence, WPB-95-335*)	PB 11 (ex-*Cape Darby, WPB-95 323*)
PB 8 (ex-*Cape Porpoise, WPB-95 327*)	PB 12 (ex-*Cape Kiwanda, WPB-95 329*)

FRIGATES (*continued*)

The **PB 7** (ex-*Cape Florida*) lost in 1971.

D: 101.95 tons (fl)	**S:** 21/20 kts	**Dim:** 28.95 × 5.80 × 1.55
A: 1/40-mm or 2/20-mm AA	**Man:** 15 men
Range: 1,500
M: 4 diesels; 2 props; 2,200 hp

♦ *10 to 20 PB constructed in Korea*

D: 30 tons   **S:** ...   **Dim:** 21.60 × 3.50 × 1.10
A: 2/20-mm AA   **M:** diesels; 2 props; 1,600 hp

MINESWEEPERS

♦ *8 ex-U.S. MSC class*

MSC 522 KUM SAN (ex-*284*)	**MSC 527 HA-DONG** (ex-*296*)
MSC 523 KO HUNG (ex-*285*)	**MSC 528 SHAM CHOK** (ex-*316*)
MSC 525 KUM KOK (ex-*286*)	**MSC 529 YONG-DONG** (ex-*320*)
MSC 526 NAM YANG (ex-*295*)	**MSC 530 OKCHEON** (ex-*321*)

Six transferred in 1959/68 and the last two in 1974. Characteristics of the French *Acacia* class. A: 2/20-mm

♦ *4 ex-U.S. YMS class*

MSC (0) 503 KWANG CHU (ex-*YMS 413*)
MSC (0) 519 KUM HWA (ex-*YMS 218*)
MSC (0) 520 KIM PO (ex-*YMS-375*)
MSC (0) 521 KO CHANG (ex-*YMS 419*)

D: 325 tons (fl)	**S:** 11 kts	**Dim:** 41.45 × 7.45 × 3.60
A: 2/40-mm — 2/20-mm	**Man:** 30/35 men
M: diesels; 2 props; 1,000 hp	**Fuel:** 22 tons

♦ *1 small ex-U.S. minesweeper transferred in 1961*

MSB 1 (ex-U.S. *MSB-2*)

D: 39 tons (fl)   **Dim:** 17.50 × 4.60 × 1.25
M: 2 Packard diesels; 2 props, 600 hp

AMPHIBIOUS SHIPS

♦ *6 ex-U.S. APD type*

PG 81 KYONG NAM (ex-*Cavallaro, APD-128*) — (15-6-44)
PG 82 AH SAN (ex-*Harry L. Corl, APD-108*) — (1-3-44)
PG 83 UNGPO (ex-*Julius A. Raven, APD-110*) — (3-3-44)
PG 85 KYONG PUK (ex-*Kephart, APD-61*) — (6-9-43)
PG 86 CHUN NAM (ex-*Hayter, APD-80*) — (11-2-44)
PG 87 CHE JU (ex-*W. M. Hobby, APD-95*) — (11-11-43)

D: 2,114 tons (fl)   **Range:** 2,300/22 — 4,800/12
A: 1/127-mm — 6/40-mm AA (II × 3)

Transferred in 1960 (1), 1966 (2), 1967 (4)

♦ *8 ex-U.S. LST class, transferred in 1955–58*

LST 807 UN BONG (ex-*U.S. 1010*)
LST 808 TUK BONG (ex-*U.S. 227*)
LST 809 BI BONG (ex-*U.S. 218*)
LST 810 KAE BONG (ex-*U.S. 288*)

Kyong Nam

Tuk Bong

LST 812 WEE BONG (ex-*Johnson County, LST-849*)
LST 813 SU YONG (ex-*Kane County, LST-853*)
LST 815 BUK HAN (ex-*Linn County, LST-900*)
LST 816 HAW SAN (ex-*Pender County, LST-1080*)

D: 1,653 tons (4,080 fl)	**Dim:** 100.04 × 15.24 × 4.30
S: 10 kts	**Man:** 70 men
A: 7/40-mm — 2/20-mm
M: General Motors diesels; 2 props; 1,800 hp

♦ *10 ex-U.S. LSM class, transferred in 1956*

LSM 601 TAE CHO (ex-*U.S. 546*)	**LSM 609 WOLMI** (ex-*U.S. 57*)
LSM 602 TYO TO (ex-*U.S. 268*)	**LSM 610 KI RIN** (ex-*U.S. 19*)
LSM 605 KA TOK (ex-*U.S. 462*)	**LSM 611 NUNG RA** (ex-*U.S. 84*)
LSM 606 KO MUN (ex-*U.S. 30*)	**LSM 612 SIN MI** (ex-*U.S. 316*)
LSM 607 PIAN (ex-*U.S. 96*)	**LSM 613 UL RUNG** (ex-*U.S. 17*)

Bldr: U.S.A., 1943-44

D: 520 tons (1,095 fl)	**Dim:** 62 × 10.52 × 3
S: 13 kts	**Man:** 75 men
A: 1/40-mm AA — 4/20-mm AA
M: diesels; 2 props; 2,880 hp

♦ *1 ex-U.S. LCU*

HYDROGRAPHIC SHIPS

♦ *2 ex-Belgian-U.S. AMI class bought in 1970*

SURO 5 (ex-*Temse*), **SURO 6** (ex-*Tournai*) — 1956-57

KOREA — SOUTH *(continued)*

HYDROGRAPHIC SHIPS *(continued)*

D: 160 tons (190 fl) **Dim:** 34.50 × 6.60 × 2.10
S: 15 kts **Man:** 17 men
A: 2/20-mm AA (II × 1)
Range: 2,300/10 **Fuel:** 18 m³ diesel
M: diesels; 2 props; 630 hp

LOGISTIC SUPPORT

R 1 TUK-SU (ex-*Minotaur, ARL-15*). Repair ship LST class (ex-*645*) loaned by the U.S.A.

D: 2,225 tons (3,640 fl) **Dim:** 99.98 × 15.34 × 4.27
S: 10 kts **Man:** 277 men
A: 2/40-mm AA — 6/20-mm AA
M: diesels; 2 props; 1,000 hp

AO 2 CHUN JI (ex-Norwegian *Birk*). Small oiler bought in 1951.

D: 2,225 tons **Dim:** 84 × 13.50 × 5.60
A: 1/40-mm AA — 2/20-mm AA **Man:** 73 men

The *Puchon* of the same class lost 5-71.

♦ *2 ex-U.S. oilers transferred in 1960*

YO 1 KU RYONG (ex-U.S. *YO-118*).

D: 1,126 tons (fl) **Dim:** 53 × 10 × 4
S: 7 kts **Man:** 36 men
M: diesel; 1 prop; 700 hp

YO 5 HWA CHON (ex-U.S. *YO-59*)

D: 2,700 tons (fl) **Dim:** 72 × 11.60 × 4.60
S: 10 kts **Man:** 46 men
M: diesel; 1 prop; 1,150 hp

♦ *6 ex-U.S. small supply ships, transferred since 1956*

AKL 902 IN CHON (ex-*FS 198*)   **AKL 908 KUN SAN** (ex-*AKL 10*)
AKL 905 CHIN NAM (ex-*FS 356*)   **AKL 909 MA SAN** (ex-*AKL 35*)
AKL 907 MOK PO (ex-*WAK 170*)   **AKL 910 UL SAN** (ex-*AKL 28 Brule*)

D: 520 tons **Dim:** 53.95 × 10.06 × 3.10
S: 12 kts **Man:** 43/49 men
A: 1/40-mm AA — 2/20-mm AA — 2 machine guns
M: diesels; 2 props; 1,000 hp

VARIOUS

♦ *3 ex-U.S. tugs* — 1944 — 835 tons — 1,300 hp

DO BANG (ex-*ATA 206*), **YUNG MUNG** (ex-*ATA 138*), **TAN YUNG** (ex-*ATA 192*) hyd. aux.

KUWAIT

PERSONNEL: 120 men

MERCHANT MARINE (1-7-74): 160 ships — 681,692 grt
(tankers: 6 ships — 423,740 grt)

♦ *10 coastal patrol boats*

				Bldr
AL SALEMI	30-6-66	**MARZOOK**	1969	Thornycroft,
AL MUBARAKI	16-7-66	**MASHHOOR**	1969	Woolston (2);
MAYMOON	..-4-68	**MURSHED**	1970	Vosper-
AMAN	..-3-68	**WATHAH**	1970	Thornycroft (8)
AL SHURTI	1972	**INTISAR**	1972	

Intisar   1972 Vosper

D: 40 tons **Dim:** 27.78 × 4.73 × 1.38
S: 20 kts **Man:** 5 officers, 7 men
M: Rolls-Royce 8-cylinder diesels; 2 props; 1,340 hp
Range: 700/15

♦ *2/56-foot patrol boats*

N . . . N . . .
Bldr: Vosper Thornycroft Private Ltd, Singapore (1974)
D: 25 tons **Dim:** 16.80 × . . . × . . .
S: 21 kts **Man:** 8 men
Range: 320/20
A: 1/20-mm — 2 machine guns
M: 2 MTU MB 6 diesels; 1,350 hp

♦ *7/50-foot small craft*
Bldr: Thornycroft Ltd, Singapore

♦ *8/35-foot small craft*
Bldr: Vosper Thornycroft Private Ltd, Singapore
S: 24 kts **M:** 2 Perkins diesels

♦ *2 small landing craft*
Bldr: Vosper Thornycroft Private Ltd, Singapore (1971)
WAHEED FAREED **Length:** 27

LEBANON

PERSONNEL: 200 men

MERCHANT MARINE: (1-7-74): 88 ships — 120,130 grt

PATROL BOATS

	Bldr	L
TARABLOUS	Esterel NSY	6-59

Tarablous

D:	105 tons	**S:** 27 kts	**Dim:** 38 × 5.50 × 1.75
A:	2/40-mm		**Man:** 3 officers, 16 men
Range:	1,500		
M:	Mercedes-Benz diesels; 2 props; 2,700 hp		

♦ *3 patrol boats ordered from the Hamelin SY, West Germany (1975)*

N . . .   N . . .   N . . .

D: 135 tons   **S:**   **Dim:**
A: 2/40-mm AA
M:

♦ *3 Biblos-class patrol boats*

11 BIBLOS — 13 SIDON — 13 BEYROUTH (ex-*Tir*) — Esterel NSY (1954-55)

D: 28 tons   **Dim:** 20.10 × 4.10 × 1.30
S: 18 kts
A: 1/20-mm AA — 2 machine guns
M: General Motors diesels; 2 props; 530 hp

♦ *1 landing craft*

SOUR (ex-*LCU 1474* transferred by the U.S.A. in 11-58)

D: 180 tons (360 fl)   **Dim:** 35.05 × 10.36 × 1.85
A: 2/20-mm AA   **S:** 10 kts
M: diesels; 3 props; 675 hp

LIBERIA

PERSONNEL: Approximately 120 men

MERCHANT MARINE (1-7-74): 2,332 ships — 55,321,641 grt
(tankers: 877 ships — 33,749,633 grt)

ALERT (ex-*PGM 102*) — Bldr: U.S.A. (1967) — same class as the PGMs transferred to South Vietnam, Thailand, etc.

LIBERIAN (ex-*Virginian*) — Bldr: Wm. Beardmore & Co., Dalmuir (1930)
Yacht with sharply raked bow bought in 1957 and modified.

D: 1,200 tons   **Dim:** 63.70 × 9.05 × 4
S: 14 kts   **M:** 2 diesels

ML 4001 — ML 4002 — (1957) 12-ton former USCG small craft (22 knots).

LIBYA

PERSONNEL: Approximately 1,200 men

MERCHANT MARINE (1-7-74): 25 ships — 160,180 grt
(tankers: 4 ships — 147,060 grt)

NAVAL PROGRAM

The transfer of Soviet submarines and guided missile patrol boats is expected, but the number and classes are not known. In addition, Libya has ordered some Daphne-class submarines from Spain. Two landing craft have been ordered from the Seine Maritime shipyards — delivery in 1976. Ten PR 72 fast patrol boats have been ordered from France, which like the corvettes ordered from Italy will be armed with Otomat SSMs.

FRIGATES

♦ *1 Vosper Mk 7*

	Bldr	Laid down	L	In serv.
DAT ASSAWARI	Vosper-Thornycroft	1968	10–69	1973

1972 Vosper

Dat Assawari   1972

- **D:** 1,325 tons (1,650 fl)   **Dim:** 101.60 (94.50 pp) × 11.08 × 3.36
- **S:** 37 kts (17 cruising)   **Man:** 132 men   **Range:** 5,700/17
- **A:** 1/114-mm AA — 2/40-mm (II × 1) — Sea cat system (III × 1) — 1 helicopter — 1 depth charge projector
- **M:** CODOG Propulsion; 2 TM 2A Olympus Rolls-Royce gas turbines, each 24,000 hp; 2 Paxman-Ventura diesels, each 1,900 hp; 2 variable pitch props.   **Fuel:** 300 tons

♦ A contract for four guided missile corvettes was signed in 4-75 with Cantieri Navali del Tirreno e Riuniti, Genoa, Italy.

- **D:** 550 tons   **S:** 30 kts   **Dim:** 61.70 × 5 × 2.90
- **A:** 2/76-mm Oto Melara Compact — 4 missiles
- **M:** MTU diesels

♦ *1 Vosper Mk 1 B*

TOBRUK — Bldr: Vosper Ltd, Portsmouth (29-4-65).

- **D:** 440 tons (500 fl)   **Dim:** 53.95 (48.77 pp) × 8.68 × 4
- **S:** 18 kts   **Man:** 5 officers, 58 men

Tobruk   Shbldg. and Sh. Record

- **A:** 1/102-mm — 4/40-mm AA   **Range:** 2,900/14
- **M:** 16-cyl. Paxman-Ventura diesels; 1,500 rpm; 2 props; 3,800 hp.
- **Fuel:** 60 tons

REMARKS: Anti-rolling devices, living quarters air-conditioned.

PATROL BOATS

♦ *3 F.P.B.*

	Bldr	L	In serv.
P 01 SUSA	Vosper Ltd, Portsmouth	31-8-67	8-68
P 02 SIRTE	Vosper Ltd, Portsmouth	10-1-68	4-68
P 03 SEBHA (ex-*Sokna*)	Vosper Ltd, Portsmouth	29-2-68	1-69

Susa (P 01)   1968 Vosper

- **D:** 95 tons (115 fl)   **Dim:** 30.38 (27.44 pp) × 7.30 × 2.15
- **S:** 50 kts   **Man:** 20 men   **A:** 8/SS 11 or 12 (II × 4) — 2/40-mm
- **M:** 3 Bristol-Siddeley Proteus gas turbines; 3 props; 12,750 hp; 2 General Motors cruising diesels, 190 hp

These are modeled on the Danish *Soloven* class.

PATROL BOATS (continued)

♦ *6 security small craft (customs and fishing)*

AR RAKIB, FARWA (1966-67), Bldr: John I. Thornycroft, Woolston; **BENINA, MISURATA** (1967-68), **AKRAMA, HOMS** (1968-69). Bldr: Vosper-Thornycroft, Portsmouth.

D:	100 tons	**S:**	20/18 kts	**Dim:**	30.50 × 6.40 × 1.70
A:	1/20-mm	**Range:**	1,800/14	**Man:**	15 men
M:	3 Rolls-Royce diesels; 1,740 hp.				

♦ *3 for fishery protection* (Bldr: Thornycroft)

N . . .   N . . .   N . . .

D: 50 tons   **S:** 20 kts   **Dim:** 17.50 × 3.80 × 1.10
M: 2 diesels; 630 hp

♦ *4 Brooke type*

PC 1 GARIAN, PC 2 KHAWLAN, PC 3 MERAWA, PC 4 SABRATHA.

Khawlan (PC 2)   1970

Bldr: Brooke Marine Ltd, Lowestoft (Gt.Br.) (1968-70)

D: 100 tons (125 fl)   **Dim:** 36.58 × 7.16 × 1.75
S: 23.5 kts   **Man:** 22 men
A: 1/40-mm — 1/20-mm   **Range:** 1,800/13
M: 12-cyl. Paxman-Ventura diesels; 2 props; 3,600 hp

Same engines as the *Tobrouk* and the *Zeltin*.

MINESWEEPERS

♦ *2 ex-British "-ham" class, transferred in 1963*

ZUARA (ex-*Greetham*) (19-4-54), **BRAK** (ex-*Harpham*) (14-9-54)

D: 120 tons (159 fl)   **Dim:** 32.43 (30.48 pp) × 6.45 × 1.70
S: 14 kts (9 sweeping)   **Man:** 15 men   **A:** 1/20-mm AA
M: Davey-Paxman diesels; 2 props; 1,000 hp.   **Fuel:** 25 tons

Zuara   A. et J. Pavia

LOGISTIC SUPPORT

♦ *2 support ships for minesweepers and small craft*

	Bldr	Laid down	L	In serv.
ZELTIN	Vosper-Thornycroft, Woolston	1967	29-2-68	1-69

Zeltin   1968

D: 2,200 tons (2,470 fl)   **Dim:** 98.72 (91.44 wl) × 14.64 × 3.05
S: 15 kts   **Man:** 15 officers, 86 men
A: 2/40-mm AA   **Range:** 3,000/14
M: 2 Davey-Paxman Ventura 16-cyl. diesels, each 1,750 hp (1,350 rpm)

REMARKS: Well deck 41 × 12 able to receive small craft drawing 2.30 m. Hydraulically controlled stern gate. A movable crane (3 tons loading capacity) is available for the well deck and a 9-ton crane on the port side is available for the workshops. Electricity furnished by 4 diesel alternators, 200 kw AC, 450 volts.

ZLEITEN (ex-British *MRC 1013*). Former LCT bought and modified in 1968.

D: 650 tons (900 fl)   **Dim:** 70.40 × 11.80 × 1.60
S: 11/10 kts   **M:** 4 Paxman diesels, 2 props; 1,840 hp

♦ *1 ex-Italian Expresso-class Ro-Ro carrier*

EL TIMSAH

D: 3,100 tons (fl)   **S:** 20 kts   **Dim:** 117.5 (108.7 pp) × 17.5 × 4.9
M: 2 Fiat diesels, 18-cyl. in V; 9,000 hp

REMARKS: Stabilizers.

LIBYA (*continued*)

LOGISTIC SUPPORT (*continued*)

Zeltin   1972

MALAGASY REPUBLIC

PERSONNEL: Approximately 300 men

MERCHANT MARINE (1-7-74): 50 ships — 53,409 grt
(tankers: 5 ships — 20,179 grt)

♦ *1 Batram class transport and support ship*

	Bldr	Laid down	L	In serv.
TOKY	Diego Suarez SY	1972	1973	10-74

D: 810 tons (avg)   **Dim:** 66.37 (56 pp) × 12.50 × 1.90
S: 13 kts   **Range:** 3,000/12   **Electric:** 240 kw
A: 1/76-mm — 2/20-mm AA — 1/81-mm mortar
M: 2 M 60 diesels; 2,400 hp; 2 props   **Man:** 27 men

REMARKS: Ships similar to the French EDIC class. Ramp forward which can be folded upon itself. Transport capacity: 250 tons; quarters for 30 passengers; 120 soldiers can be carried for shorter distances. Financed by the French government under the military cooperation pact.

♦ *1 coastal patrol boat*

	Bldr	Laid down	L	In serv.
MALAIKA	C.N. Franco-Belges	11-66-72	22-3-67	12-67

D: 240 tons (avg)   **Dim:** 47.50 (45.50 pp) × 7.10 × 2.50
S: 18.5 kts   **Range:** 2,000/15
A: 2/40-mm AA — 8/SS 12 missiles   **Man:** 3 officers, 22 men
M: 2 MGO diesels with Masson reduction gears (1/3); 2 props; 2,400 hp

♦ *1 transport patrol boat — Bought and modified in 1966-67*

	Bldr	L
FANANTENANA (ex-trawler *Richelieu*)	A. G. Weser (Bremen)	1959

D: 1,040 tons (1,200 fl)   **Dim:** 62.90 (56 pp) × 9.15 × 4.52
S: 12 kts   **A:** 2/40-mm A   **Man:** ...
M: 2 Deutz diesels ("father-mother" system); 1 prop; 1,060 + 500 hp
Can carry 300 tons of freight and 70 (up to 120) police.

♦ *Maritime Police:* 5 coast surveillance small craft, delivered in 1962 by the West German Republic.

D: 46 tons   **S:** 22 kts   Length: 24 m
A: 1/40-mm   **M:** 2 diesels; 2 props

PERSONNEL: Approximately 4,800 men

MERCHANT MARINE (1-7-74): 122 ships — 337,521 grt
(tankers: 7 ships — 4,864 grt)

MALAYSIA

FRIGATES

	Bldr	Laid down	L	In serv.
F 24 RAHMAT	Yarrow, Glasgow	2-66	18-12-67	3-71

Rahmat (F 24)   1970 Yarrow

D: 1,550 tons (fl)   **Dim:** 93.87 (91.44 pp) × 10.36 × 3.05
S: 27 kts (16.5 on diesels alone)   **Range:** 5,200/16.5 — 1,000/27
A: 1/114-mm AA Mk 4 — 2/40-mm Bofors AA, 70-cal — 1 Quadruple Sea Cat missile launcher — 1 ASW triple Mk 10 mortar — helicopter platform.
Man: 120 men
M: CODOG propulsion: 8-cyl. Pielstick-Crossley diesels, with 3,850 hp. Rolls-Royce Olympus gas turbine, 22,000 hp; 2 Stone Ka-Me-Wa props

REMARKS: Ordered in 9-66; advanced automation. Fire control radar Mk 22 (at the top of the mast) for the 114-mm, and Mk 44 on the stern for the Sea Cat.

♦ *1 British Loch class (transferred at the end of 1964).*

	Bldr	Laid down	L	In serv.
F 433 HANG TUAH (ex-*Loch Insh*)	Henry Robb	11-43	10-5-44	10-44

D: 1,571 tons (2,400 fl)   **Dim:** 93.57 × 11.75 × 4.49.
S: 17 kts   **Range:** 6,400/10 — 2,500/18
Man: 140 men   **Fuel:** 720 tons
A: 2/102-mm (II × 1) — 6/40-mm AA (II × 2) — 2 Squids
M: triple expansion, 2 props, 2 Admiralty boilers; 5,500 hp

Quarters air-conditioned. Helicopter platform

GUIDED MISSILE PATROL BOATS

♦ *4 Serang class*

	L	In serv.		L	In serv.
SERANG	22-12-71	31-2-73	GANYANG	16-3-72	20-3-73
GANAS	26-10-72	28-2-73	PERDANA	31-5-72	31-12-72

Bldr: S.F.C.N. (2). Constr. Méc. de Normandie, Cherbourg (2). Delivered in 1973
D: 234 tons (265 fl)   **Dim:** 47 × 7.10 × 2.50 (fl)
S: 36.5 kts   **Range:** 800/25
Man: 5 officers, 30 men.   **Fuel:** 39 tons
A: 2 MM 38 Exocet missiles — 1/57-mm Bofors — 1/40-mm Bofors L 70
M: 4 MTU diesels, MB 870 class; 4 props; 14,000 hp

Ganyang   1973 M.N.

Serang   1973

REMARKS: *La Combattante II (A4L)* class of the French Navy. Steel hull. Superstructure in alloyed metal. Similar type ships have been ordered by Greece and West Germany.

FAST PATROL BOATS

♦ *4 Perkasa class*

P 150 PERKASA (26-10-65)	P 152 GEMPITA (6-4-66)
P 151 HANDALAN (18-1-66)	P 153 PENDEKAR (24-6-66)

Bldr: Vosper Ltd, Portsmouth

FAST PATROL BOATS (*continued*)

Perkasa (P 150)
Shbldg. and Shipping Record

D:	95 tons (114 fl)	**Dim:**	30.40 (27.43 pp) × 7.30 × 2.15
S:	54 kts (trials 57, *P 150*)	**Man:**	22 men
A:	1/40-mm AA — 1/20-mm AA — 8/SS 12 missiles (IV × 2)		
M:	2 Rolls-Royce gas turbines; 12,750 hp. For cruising at 10 knots, 2 General Motors V 71 diesels.	**Fuel:**	25 tons

REMARKS: Quarters air-conditioned. Can be armed with torpedoes or fitted as mine-layers (10). Equipped with SS 12 missiles in 1972.

♦ Six patrol boats which will replace the *Sri Kedah* class are being built in the Hong Leong shipyards in Singapore based on Lürssen designs.

D:	240 tons (fl)	**S:**	38 kts	**Dim:**	45 × 5 × . . .
A:	1/57-mm AA — 1/40-mm AA			**Man:**	35 men
M:	diesels			**Range:**	. . .

GUNBOATS

♦ *24 103-foot Vosper type*

(a) 6 ordered in September 1961

P 3138 SRI KEDAH (4-6-62)
P 3140 SRI PERAK (30-8-62)
P 3142 SRI KELANTAN (8-1-63)
P 3139 SRI SELANGOR (17-7-62)
P 3141 SRI PAHANG (15-10-62)
P 3143 SRI TRENGGANU (12-12-62)

(b) 4 ordered in March 1963

P 3114 SRI SABAH (30-12-63)
P 3146 SRI NEGRI SEMBILAN (17-9-64)
P 3145 SRI SARAWAK (20-1-64)
P 3147 SRI MELAKA (25-2-64)

(c) 14 ordered in 1965

P 34 KRIS (11-3-66)
P 37 BADEK (8-5-66)
P 39 TOMBAK (20-6-66)
P 41 SERAMPANG (14-9-66)
P 43 KERAMBIT (20-11-66)

P 36 SUNDANG (22-5-66)
P 38 RENCHONG (22-6-66)
P 40 LEMBING (22-8-66)
P 42 PANAH (10-10-66)
P 44 BELADAU (11-1-67)

P 45 KELEWANG (31-1-67)
P 47 SRI PERLIS (26-5-67)
Bldr: Vosper Ltd, Portsmouth

P 46 RENTAKA (15-3-67)
P 48 SRI JOHORE (21-8-67)

Sri Kedah (P 3138)

D:	96 tons (109 fl)	**Dim:**	31.39 × 5.95 × 1.65
S:	27 kts (23 cruising)	**Range:**	1,500/17.5
A:	2/40-mm (I × 3) — 2 machine guns.	**Man:**	3 officers, 20 men
M:	2 Bristol-Siddeley diesels or Maybach MD 655/18; 2 props; 3,550 hp.		

REMARKS: Vosper anti-rolling stabilizers. Decca radar. Welded hull. The Malaysian prototype was delivered in February of 1963 and was quickly followed by many others. Similar fast patrol boats of this class are found in the navies of Peru, Kenya, Libya, Singapore, Trinidad and Tobago. They differ somewhat according to the engines installed — Maybach, Davey-Paxman or Napier-Deltic. A few (Peru and Singapore) are larger than the rest (110 feet instead of 103). This type of fast patrol boat which was produced by the Vosper shipyards has been followed by several other British shipbuilders such as Brooke Marine, for example, who built similar ships for Pakistan. It has also been the prototype for the Royal Australian Navy in its *Acute/Aitape* series, the first unit of which began service early 1968.

POLICE SMALL BOATS

♦ *6 built in Malaysia with the assistance of the Lürssen shipyards (RFA).*

♦ *18 type PX*

ARAU, BENTARA, HULUBULANG, KELANG, KUALA KANGSAR, LAKSAMANA, MAHAKOTA, MAHARAJASETIA, MAHARAJALELA, PAHLAWAN, PEKAN, PERTANDA, PERWIRA, SANGSETIA, SHAHBAN-DAR, SRI GUMANTONG, SRI LABUAN, TEMENGGONG

D:	80 tons	**S:**	29 kts	**Dim:**	26.29 × 5.70 × 1.45
A:	2/20-mm	**Man:**	15 men	**Range:**	700/15
M:	2 Mercedes-Benz diesels; 2 props; 2,700 hp.				

♦ *6 improved type PX*

ALOR STAR, JOHORE BAHRU, KOTA BAHRU, KUALA TRENGGANU, KUCHING, SRI MENANTI

D:	92 tons	**S:**	25 kts	**Dim:**	27.30 × 5.8 × . . .
A:	2/20-mm	**Man:**	18 men	**Range:**	750/15
M:	2 diesels; 2,460 hp				

MALAYSIA (*continued*)
POLICE SMALL BOATS (*continued*)

PX 10 and 11   1975

REMARKS: PX and improved PX were built between 1963 and 1970 and 1972-73 by the Vosper shipyards of Singapore.

MINESWEEPERS

♦ *6 British "-ton"-class coastal minesweepers, transferred in 1963-65*

M 1127 MAHAMIRU (ex-*Darlaston*)	25-9-53	
M 1143 LEDANG (ex-*Keston*)	1954	
M 1134 KINABALU (ex-*Essington*)	9-54	
M 1163 TAHAN (ex-*Lullington*)	31-8-55	
M 1168 JERAI (ex-*Dilston*)	15-11-54	
M 1172 BRINCHANG (ex-*Thankerton*)	4-9-56	

For characteristics, see Great Britain section. **A:** 1/40-mm — 2/20-mm

VARIOUS

♦ *1 hydrographic ship*

A 151 PERANTAU (ex-HMS *Myrmidon*), 1964.

D:	360 tons (420 fl)	**S:** 15 kts	**Dim:** 46.33 × 8.75 × 2.50
M:	2 diesels	**Man:** 26 men	**Range:** 2,300/13

Former "-ton"-class minesweeper modified as a hydrographic ship in 1964.

♦ *1 ex-U.S. LST used as a support ship for small craft*

A 1500 SRI LANGKAWI (ex-*Sutter County, LST-1150*)

D:	1,653 tons (4,080 fl)	**Dim:** 99.85 × 15.25 × 4.36	
A:	8/40-mm AA (II × 2) — I × 4	**S:** 11 kts	
M:	GM diesels; 1,700 hp; 2 props		

REMARKS: Transferred in 7-71.

♦ *1 support ship for divers*
DUYONG (18-8-71)

D:	140 tons (fl)	**Dim:**	33 × 6.3 × 1.7
A:	1/20-mm AA	**Man:**	23 men
M:	2 Cummins diesels; 500 hp	**S:**	10 knots

MALTA

MERCHANT MARINE: 26 ships — 38,011 grt
(tankers: 2 ships — 27,442 grt)

SMALL CRAFT

♦ *2 ex-U.S. PCF Swift class*

C 23 and **C 24** — Bldr: Sewart Seacraft (1967), purchased in 1-1971.

D:	22.5 tons (fl)	**Dim:**	15.60 × 4.12 × 1.50
S:	25 kts	**Range:** 24 to 36 hours	**Man:** 6/8 men
A:	3/12.7-mm machine guns (II × 1, 1 combined with an 81-mm mortar)		
M:	Gary diesels, 12-V-721; 2 props; 960 hp		

♦ *1 ex-customs service small craft*

C 21 — Bldr: Malta Drydock (1969), added in 1973.

C 21

D: 20 tons	**S:** 19 kts	**Dim:** 16.30 × 4.10 × 2.30 (light)
A: 2 mounts for machine guns.	**Man:** 8 men	
M: 2 Fiat diesels 521-SH; 2 props; 500 hp		

MALTA (*continued*)
SMALL CRAFT (*continued*)

♦ *3 ex-German small craft used on border patrol.*
C 27 (ex-*Brunsbüttel 1*) — **D:** 95 tons — **Dim:** 31.70 × 5.18
C 28 (ex-*Geier*) — **D:** 90 tons — **Dim:** 28 × 5.49
C 29 (ex-*Kondor*) — **D:** 85 tons — **Dim:** 28 × 5.25

C 27

A: 1 machine gun   **M:** diesels — added in 1972

♦ *2 support small craft (ex-Libyan 1967-68) added in 1974*
No other information.

MAURETANIA

PERSONNEL:

MERCHANT MARINE (1-7-74): 4 ships — 1,681 grt

PATROL BOATS

♦ *2 ex-Soviet Mirnyi class whaling ships*
IDINI   N . . .
Bldr: Ivan Nosenko, Nikolaev (1956)
  D: 1,200 tons   **S:** 17.5 kts   **Dim:** 63.6 × 9.5 × 4.5
  A: 2/25-mm AA — 1/12.7-mm machine gun
  M: 4 Penza 6-cyl diesel-electric engines; 3,100 hp.

REMARKS: Used as patrol boats for fisheries protection and tenders for the *Tichitt* class and small craft.

♦ *2 Tichitt class*

	Bldr	In serv.
TICHITT	Esterel NSY	4-69
DAR EL BARKA	Esterel NSY	4-69

Tichitt   1969 Ch. de l'Estérel

  D: 80 tons (fl)   **S:** 28 kts   **Dim:** 31.45 × 5.75 × 1.70
  A: 1/20-mm, 1/12.7-mm machine gun   **Range:** 1,500/15
  M: 2 Maybach-Mercedes diesels; 2,700 hp

Identical to the Tunisian *Istiqlal* and Moroccan *El Sabiq*-class patrol boats.

SMALL CRAFT

♦ *2 security small craft*

	Bldr	In serv.
IMRAG'NI	Esterel NSY	11-65
SLOUGHI	Esterel NSY	5-68

  D: 20 tons (fl)   **Dim:** 18.15 (17.03 pp) × 4.03 × 1.10
  S: 21 kts (22.7 trials)   **A:** 1/12.7-mm machine gun
  Man: 8 men   **Range:** 860/12
  M: General Motors diesels (7-71 M); 2 props; 512 hp

♦ *1 coastal patrol small craft*

CHINGUETTI (practically inoperative; used as a support ship).

PERSONNEL: 11,000 men including 1,300 Marines.

MARITIME AVIATION: Approximately 20 machines, helicopters, and flying boats.

MERCHANT MARINE (1-7-74): 261 ships — 514,544 grt
(tankers: 25 ships — 276,747 grt)

MEXICO

DESTROYERS

♦ *2 U.S. Fletcher class, transferred in 8-70*

	Bldr	L
F 1 CUITLAHUAC (ex-*John Rodgers, DD-574*)	Consolidated Steel,	7-5-43
F 2 CUAUHTEMOC (ex-*Harrison, DD-573*)	Orange (Texas)	7-5-43

(Profile, see *Para* — Brazil section).

D: 2,100 tons (3,050 fl)   **Dim:** 114.85 (wl) × 12.03 × 5.50
S: 30 kts   **Man:** 262 men   **Range:** 1,360/30 — 4,400/15
A: 5/127-mm (I × 5) — 14/40-mm — 5/533-mm TT (V × 1) — 2 hedgehogs
M: General Electric GT; 2 props; 60,000 hp   **Boilers:** 4 Babcock
Fuel: 650 tons

FRIGATE

A 06 MANUEL AZUETA (ex-*Swasey, DE-248*)

Bldr: Brown SB Co, Houston, Texas

D: 1,200 tons (1,850 fl)   **S:** 21 kts   **Dim:** 93.3 × 11.3 × 3.4
A: 3/76-mm AA — 2 hedgehogs — 2 depth charge racks
M: 4 diesels; 2 props; 6,000 hp

REMARKS: Transferred 1-10-73.

GUNBOATS

♦ *5 ex-U.S. amphibious transports (APD), transferred in 1964 and 1970.*

	L
B 4 PAPALOAPAN (ex-*Earhart, APD-113*)	12-5-45

	L
B 5 TEHUANTEPEC (ex-*Begor, APD-127*, ex-*DE-711*)	5-2-44
B 6 USUMACINTA (ex-*Don O. Woods, APD-118*, ex-*DE-721*)	19-2-44
B 7 COAMUILA (ex-*Barber, APD-57*)	20-5-43
B 8 CHIHUAHUA (ex-*Rednour, APD-102*)	12-2-44

D: 1,450 tons (2,130 fl)   **Dim:** 93.26 × 11.28 × 4.70
S: 23 kts (fl)   **Man:** 204 men — 162 military
Range: 5,000/15.   **A:** 1/127-mm (fwd) — 6/40-mm AA (II × 3)
M: turbo-electric propulsion; 2 props; 2 boilers; 12,000 hp

REMARKS: Modified destroyer escorts. *B3 California* (ex-*Belet, APD-109*) lost at sea in 1972.

♦ *1 Spanish type*

	Bldr	L
C 7 GUANAJUATO	El Ferrol SY	29-5-34

Guanajuato (C 7)   Terzibaschtisch

D: 1,300 tons (1,950 fl)   **Dim:** 79 × 11.50 × 3.50
S: 14 kts   **Man:** 140 men
A: 3/102-mm — 4/20-mm AA (see Remarks)
M: Enterprise DMR-38 diesels; 2 props; 5,000 hp

REMARKS: Original Parsons turbines replaced (1960-62). Can carry 120 men. *C 8 Queretaro* and *C 9 Potosi* stricken in 1972.

Type Papaloapan

PATROL BOATS

(I) **C 1** (ex-C 3) **VIRGILIO URIBE** (ex-*Tomas Marin*, ex-*PCE 825*). Fitted for oceanography.

(II) 16 ex-U.S. MSF.

D 1 DM-01 (ex-*255*)	**D 10 DM-10** (ex-*252*)	**E 7 DM-17** (ex-*221*)
D 2 DM-02 (ex-*241*)	**E 2 DM-12** (ex-*283*)	**E 8 DM-18** (ex-*254*)
D 3 DM-03 (ex-*232*)	**E 3 DM-13** (ex-*256*)	**E 9 DM-19** (ex-*253*)
D 4 DM-04 (ex-*306*)	**E 4 DM-14** (ex-*284*)	**E 10 DM-20** (ex-*365*)
D 5 DM-05 (ex-*298*)	**E 5 DM-15** (ex-*214*)	
D 6 DM-06 (ex-*224*)	**E 6 DM-16** (ex-*223*)	

Bldr: U.S.A. Launched between 2-43 and 6-44. D and E transferred since 1-10-62.

D 3

D: 650 tons (945 fl)   **S:** 15 kts   **Dim:** 56.24 × 10.06 × 2.80
A: 1/76-mm AA — 2/40-mm AA — 4-6/20-mm AA   **Man:** 80 to 104 men
M: 2 G.M. diesels; 2 props; 1,700/1,800 hp   **Fuel:** diesel

♦ *19 ex-U.S. obsolete minesweepers, Auk-Raven (MSF ex-AM), transferred in 1972 and 1973*

IG 01 Leandro VALLE (ex-*Pioneer, MSF-105*)
IG 02 Guillermo PRIETO (ex-*Symbol, MSF-123*)
IG 03 Mariano ESCOBEDO (ex-*Champion, MSF-314*)
IG 04 Ponciano ARRIAGA (ex-*Competent, MSF-316*)
IG 05 Manuel DOBLADO (ex-*Defense, MSF-317*)
IG 06 Sebastian LEIDO de TEJADA (ex-*Devastator, MSF-318*)
IG 07 Santos DEGOLLADO (ex-*Gladiator, MSF-319*)
IG 08 Ignacio de la LLAVE (ex-*Spear, MSF-322*)
IG 09 Juan N. ALVAREZ (ex-*Ardent, MSF-340*)
IG 10 Melchior OCAMPO (ex-*Roselle, MSF-379*)
IG 11 Valentin G. FARIAS (ex-*Starling, MSF-64*)
IG 12 Ignacio ALTAMIRANO (ex-*Sway, MSF-120*)
IG 13 Francisco ZARCO (ex-*Threat, MSF-124*)
IG 14 Ignacio L. VALLARTA (ex-*Velocity, MSF-128*)
IG 15 Jésus G. ORTEGA (ex-*Chief, MSF-315*)
IG 16 Gutierriez ZAMORA (ex-*Seater, MSF-381*)
IG 17 Mariano MATAMOROS (ex-*Herald, MSF-101*)

IG 18 Juan ALDARMA (ex-*Pilot, MSF-104*)
IG 19 Hermenegildo GALEANA (ex-*Sage, MSF-111*)

Bldr: U.S.A. — 1942-45.

D: 890 tons (1,250 fl)   **Dim:** 67.40 (65 pp) × 9.75 × 4.10
S: 16/15 kts   **Man:** 9 officers, 86 men
A: 1/76-mm — 4/40-mm AA (II × 2) — 4/20-mm (II × 2)
M: diesel-electric propulsion; (2 General Motors diesels); 2 props; 3,500 hp

♦ *21 Azreca class*

	L
P 01 Andres QUINTANA ROO	26-3-74
P 02 . . .	
P 03 Miguel RAMOS ARIZPE	
P 04 Jose Maria IZAZAGO	20-8-74
P 05 Juan Bautista MORALES	5-9-74
P 06 Ignacio LOPEZ RAYON	5-9-74
P 07 Manuel CRESCENCIO REJON	11-74
P 08 Antonio DE LA FUENTE	
P 09 Leon GUZMAN	11-74
P 10 Ignacio RAMIREZ	
P 11 Ignacio MARISCAL	17-2-75
P 12 Heriberto JARA CERONA	
P 13 Jose Maria MATA	
P 14 Felix ROMERO	
P 15 Fernando LIZARDI	
P 16 Francisco J. MUJICA	
P 17 Jose Maria del Castello Yelazco	9-75
P 18 . . .	
P 19 . . .	
P 20 . . .	
P 21 . . .	

Bldr: Ailsa SB, Troon (1); James Lamont, Glasgow (5); Scott Lithgow, Greenock (5).

A. Quintana Roo (P 01)   1975

PATROL BOATS (continued)

D: ...
S: 24 kts
A: 1/40-mm — 1/20-mm
M: 2 Ruston-Paxman-Ventura 12-cyl. diesels; 7,200 hp
Dim: 34.06 × 30.94 pp × ... × ...
Man: 2 officers, 22 men
Electric: 80 kw

♦ **G 6 VILLAPANDO** (1960) — **G 9 AZUETA** (8-59). Bldr: Astilleros, Tampico
D: 80 tons (85 fl)   **S:** 12/10 kts   **Dim:** 26 × 4.90 × 2.50
A: 2/13-mm machine guns (II × 1)   **M:** 1 Superior diesel; 600 hp.

♦ **G 1 to G 4 POLIMAR 1, 2, 3, 4** (1960-68) — Bldr: Astilleros, Tampico.

Polimar (G 1)

D: 57 tons   **Dim:** 20.5 × 4.50 × 1.30
S: 16 kts   **M:** diesel; 2 props; 450 hp

♦ *7 river patrol boats*

AM 4, AM 5, AM 6, AM 7, AM 8, AM 9, AM 10 (1960-62) — Bldr: Astilleros Tampico and Vera Cruz
D: 35 tons   **S:** 10 kts   **M:** diesel

MINESWEEPER

♦ *1 ex-U.S. MSO transferred in 1973*

N ... (ex-*Spector, MSO-406*)
For characteristics see U.S.A. section.

LOGISTIC SUPPORT AND VARIOUS

A 5 AGUASCALIENTES (ex-*YOG-6*) — **A 6 TLAXCALA** (ex-*YO 107*)

D: 440 tons (1,800 fl)   **S:** 8 kts   **Dim:** 52.50 × 10 × 4
M: Fairbanks-Morse diesel; 1 prop; 500 hp   **Man:** 62 men
Ex-U.S. motorized water barges bought in 1964.

♦ *2 ex-U.S. LST transferred in 1971 and 1972.*

RIO PANUCO (ex-*Park County, LST-1077*)
RIO MANZANILLO (ex-*Clearwater County, LST-602*)
D: 4,080 tons (fl)   **S:** 11 kts   **Dim:** 100.04 × 15.24 × 4.30
M: GM diesels; 2 props; 1,800 hp

♦ *1 ex-U.S. repair ship bought in 10-73*

VICENTE GUERRERO (ex-*Megata, ARV-6*)
D: 1,625 tons (4,100 fl)   **Dim:** 98.40 × 15 × 4.20
S: 11.6 kts   **A:** 8/40-mm AA
M: 2 General Motors diesels; 2 props; 1,800 hp

B 1 DURANGO — Bldr: Union Navale, Valende (28-6-35)
D: 1,600 tons (2,000 fl)   **Dim:** 85.50 × 12.20 × 3.60
S: 17 kts   **Man:** 140 men   **Range:** 3,000/12
A: 2/102-mm — 2/57-mm — 2/25-mm AA (II × 2)
M: Parsons GT; 2 props; 6,500 hp   **Boilers:** Yarrow   **Fuel:** 140 tons

REMARKS: Training ship. Refitted in 1967. 2 slender tripod masts, conical stack.

B 2 ZACATECAS — transport — Bldr: Ulua, Vera Cruz (1959)
D: 780 tons   **Dim:** 47.50 × 8.20 × 2.80
S: 10 kts   **A:** 1/40-mm AA — 2/20-mm AA
Man: 50 men   **M:** M.A.N. diesel; 1 prop; 560 hp

A 1 SOTAVENTO — Bldr: Higgins, New Orleans (1947) — Hydrographic ship.
D: 400 tons (fl)   **Dim:** 50.40 × 8.50 × 3
S: 17 kts   **M:** diesel; 2 props; 1,800 hp

REMARKS: Air-conditioned, radar-equipped, flush deck construction, angled bow, cone stack with low profile immediately abaft bridge structure.

♦ *5 ex-tugs transferred in 1971*

R 1 (ex-*Farallon*), **R 2** (ex-*Montauk*), **R 3** (ex-*Point Vicente*), **R 4** (ex-*Moose Teak*), **R 5** (ex-*Burnt Island*).
as well as 2 other tugs, the **PRAGMAR** and **PATRON,** added in 1973.

♦ *1 ex-U.S. dry dock*

N ... (ex-*ARD-11*)

REMARKS: Transferred 17-6-74.

PERSONNEL: 1,800 men including 58 officers and 260 petty officers

MERCHANT MARINE (1-7-74): 43 ships — 52,564 grt
(tankers: 2 ships — 937 grt)

NAVAL PROGRAM: A five-year for the period 1973-77 recommends the construction of:

♦ 4 PR 72 type patrol boats to be built by S.E.C.N. The first was launched on 12-10-75.

♦ about 20 type 92 32-m small craft. Six Osa II class guided missile small craft will be transferred by the U.S.S.R. The first will be delivered at the beginning of 1976.

♦ 3 landing craft based on the *Champlain*-class light transports of the French Navy. The third was ordered in 4-75.

PATROL BOATS

♦ *2 PR 72 type*

	L	In serv.
OKBA	12-10-75	
TRIKI	1-2-76	

Ordered in 6-73 from the Société Française de Construction Navale (ex-C.N. Franco-Belges)

D: 370 tons (440 fl)   **Dim:** 57 (54 pp) × 7.60 × 2.50
S: 28 kts   **Man:** 5 officers, 48 men
A: 1/76-mm OTO-Melara — 1/40-mm Bofors   **Range:** 2,500/16
M: 2 AGO diesels; 2,760 hp; 2 props   **Electric:** 360 kw

REMARKS: The second might be equipped with SSM.

♦ *1 patrol boat based on French Fougueux class*

	Bldr	Laid down	L	In serv.
32 LIEUTENANT RIFFI	Constr. Méc. de Normandie	5-63	1-3-64	5-64

(*Profile, see photo of the Agile.*)

D: 311 tons (light) (374 fl)   **Dim:** 52.95 (51.82 pp) × 7.04 × 2.01
S: 19 kts   **Man:** 4 officers, 55 men
Range: 3,000/12 — 2,000/15
A: 1/76-mm — 2/40-mm — 2 depth charge projectors
M: 2 SEMT-Pielstick diesels; 2 props; 3,600 hp

REMARKS: KMW-CMN variable pitch propellers.

	Bldr	Laid down	L	In serv.
22 AL BACHIR	Constr. Méc. de Normandie	6-65	25-2-67	4-67

D: 124.5 tons (light) (153.50 fl)
Dim: 40.60 (38 pp) × 6.35 × 1.40
S: 25.5 kts   **Man:** 3 officers, 20 men
Range: 2,000/15
A: 2/40-mm — 2 machine guns
M: 2 SEMT-Pielstick 12 PA diesels; 2 props; 3,600 hp
Fuel: 21 tons

	Bldr	L	Transferred
11 EL SABIQ (ex-*P 762*, *VC 12*)	Esterel NSY	13-8-57	1960

(Profile, *VC 11* — Tunisian section)

D: 60 tons (80 fl)   **Dim:** 31.77 × 4.70 × 1.70
S: 28 kts   **Man:** 17 men
A: 2/20-mm AA   **Range:** 1,500/15
M: 2 Mercedes-Benz diesels, 4 tons, 12-cyl; 2 props; 2,700 hp

♦ *6 type P 92*

Bldr: C.N.M. Cherbourg (contract 2-74)

	L	In serv.		L	In serv.
EL WACIL	12-6-75		N . . .	1-2-76	
EL JAIL	10-10-75		N . . .	1-4-76	
EL MIKDAM	1-12-75		N . . .	1-6-76	

D: 89 tons   **S:** 28 kts   **Dim:** 32 × . . . × . . .
A: 2/20-mm AA   **Range:** 1,200/15
M: 2 M GO 12 V BZSHR diesels; 1,270 hp

REMARKS: Hull is of laminated wood.
1 Decca radar. 1 Fathometer.

MINESWEEPER

TAWFIC (ex-*Aries*)

REMARKS: Transferred by the French Navy 28-11-74 for a period of 4 years. Characteristics, see France.

AMPHIBIOUS SHIPS

♦ *2 based on the Champlain*

21 LIEUTENANT MALGHAGH — Bldr: C.N. Franco-Belges — In serv: 1965
D: 292 tons (642 fl)   **Dim:** 59 × 11.95 × 1.30
S: 8 kts   **A:** 2/20-mm AA — 1/120-mm mortar (fwd)
M: MGO diesels; 2 props; 1,000 hp   **Man:** 16 men

REMARKS: Similar to the French EDIC class.

VARIOUS

ESSAOUIRA, 60-ton yacht presented by Italy in 1967; used as training ship for watchstanders.

NETHERLANDS

Model of the *Kortenaer* class frigate.

PERSONNEL: Approximately 20,000 men including 3,000 Marines.

MERCHANT MARINE (1-7-74): 1,358 ships — 5,500,432 grt
(tankers: 109 ships — 2,514,003 grt)

WARSHIPS IN SERVICE OR UNDER CONSTRUCTION AS OF 1 OCTOBER 1975

	L	D	Main armament
◆ *6 submarines*			
2 ZWAARDVIS	1970-71	2,300	6 TT
4 DOLFIJN	1959-60	1,140	8 TT
◆ *1 cruiser*			
1 DE ZEVEN PROVINCIEN	1950	9,850	2 Terrier missile-launchers — 4/152-mm AS — 6/57-mm
◆ *13 conventional and guided missile destroyers*			
2 TROMP	1973-74	3,665	1 Tartar missile-launcher — 8 Harpoon — 8 Sea Sparrow 2/120-mm — 1 ASW helicopter — 6 TT
3 HOLLAND	1953-54	2,215	4/120-mm AA — ASW weapons
8 FRIESLAND	1954-55	2,496	4/120-mm AA — ASW weapons
◆ *14 frigates*			
6 VAN SPEIJK	1965-67	2,200	2/114-mm AA — ASW weapons — 8 Sea Cat — 1 ASW helicopter
8 KORTENAER	Constr.	3,600	8 Harpoon — 2/76-mm AA — 8 Sea Sparrow — 1 ASW helicopter — 6 TT
◆ *11 corvettes*			
6 WOLF	1954	808	1/76-mm AA
5 BALDER	1954	150	1/40-mm AA
◆ *52 minesweepers*			
5 OVERSAAGD	1953	735	1/40-mm AA
24 DOKKUM	1953-56	373	2/40-mm AA
7 BEEMSTER	1953-54	330	2/20-mm AA
16 VAN STRAELEN	1958-61	150	1/20-mm AA

NAVAL AVIATION:

With approximately 80 aircraft, it is made up of P2H Neptune patrol, BR 1150 Atlantic, and S2A Tracker antisubmarine planes, and AH12A Wasp helicopters carried on the *Van Speijk*-class frigates as well as the UH1 Agusta Bell helicopters. Support aircraft of various types are included in this total.

WEAPONS AND SYSTEMS OF THE DUTCH NAVY

A. MISSILES

Surface-to-air: U.S. systems (Terrier on the *DeZeven Provincien*, SM 1 and Sea Sparrow on the *Tromp* and *Kortenaer* classes. Harpoon on the *Tromp* and *Kortenaer* classes, British Sea Cat on the *Van Speijk* class.

B. GUNNERY

The following types are used:
— twin barrelled turret-mounted 152-mm Bofors in the cruiser. Rate of fire: 15 rounds/min. Arc of elevation: −5° to +60°. Maximum effective range in surface mode: 18,000 m, 9,000 m in anti-aircraft mode.
— twin-barrelled, 120-mm automatic in the *Holland* and *Friesland*-class destroyers. Weight: 65 tons. Arc of elevation: −10° to +85°. Muzzle velocity: 850 m/sec. Direction rate: 25°/s in train, 40°/s in elevation. Rate of fire: 45 rounds/min/barrel. Maximum effective range in surface mode: 13,000 m, 7,000 m in anti-aircraft mode.
— 114-mm Mk 6 (see section on Great Britain) on the *Van Speijk* class frigates;
— 76-mm OTO Melara compact;
— 57-mm Bofors automatic in single and twin-barrelled mounts;
— 40-mm Bofors automatic.

C. ASW

The Dutch navy uses:
— the 375-mm Bofors quadruple rocket-launcher;
— the U.S. Mk 44, 46 torpedoes on board ships and aircraft.

D. ELECTRONIC

Radars:
All are of Dutch manufacture (HSA):
LWO 1 height-finding:
LWO 2 long-range air search;
LWO 6 long-range air search
SRG 105 combination search;
SRG 103 surface search.
The *Tromp* class are fitted with a new type of three-dimensional radar
Fire control radars are the M 20 HSA band X type.

Sonars:
The following equipment is of Dutch origin and was ordered at EDO (U.S.A.).
CWE 610 LF hull;
PDE 700 LF towed;
the British 170 B and 162 are also used.

SUBMARINES

♦ *2 Zwaardvis class (ordered 24-12-65 and 14-7-66)*

	Bldr	Laid down	L	In serv.
S 806 ZWAARDVIS	Rotterdam DDM	7-67	2-7-70	1972
S 807 TIJGERHAAI	Rotterdam DDM	7-67	25-5-71	72-73

Tijgerhaai (S 807)   1973

D: 2,300 tons surfaced/2,572 submerged
S: 18/15 kts
A: 6/533-mm TT fwd — 12 torpedoes
M: diesel-electric propulsion; 1 prop linked to 3 diesel generators, each of 900 kw and 1/3,800-kw motor.

Dim: 66.90 × 8.40 × 8
Man: 8 officers, 60 men

REMARKS: In general these submarines are based on the *Barbel* of the U.S. Navy; the hull has a teardrop profile similar to the *Albacore;* diesel-electric propulsion with 3 groups of generators and a single electric motor on the propulsion shaft. Due to economic considerations care was taken to use equipment of Dutch manufacture which necessitated some rather important modifications to the original design. These ships can carry 18 torpedoes. The torpedo firing system uses a digital computer and permits the simultaneous launching of two torpedoes, one of which may be wire-guided. In order to make the ship as quiet as possible, all noise-producing machinery is mounted on a false deck with spring suspension.

♦ *4 Dolfijn class*

Author. 1962	Bldr	Laid down	L	In serv.
S 804 POTVIS	Wilton-Fijenoord	17-9-62	12-1-65	11-65
S 805 TONIJN	Wilton-Fijenoord	28-11-62	14-6-65	2-66

Author. 1949	Bldr	Laid down	L	In serv.
S 808 DOLFIJN	Rotterdam DDM	12-54	20-5-59	12-60
S 809 ZEEHOND	Rotterdam DDM	12-54	20-2-60	3-61

D: 1,140 tons/1,494 surfaced/1,826 submerged
Dim: 79.50 × 8.84 × 4.80
S: 14.5/17 kts   **Man:** 7 officers, 57 men
A: 8/533-mm TT
M: diesel-electric propulsion; 2 M.A.N. 12-cyl. diesels, each 1,550 hp, and 2 electric motors, 2,200 hp; 2 props

REMARKS: Profile and sail similar to the U.S. *Guppy* class. Designed by the engineer M. T. Gunnin; the thick hull is made up of three parallel cylinders: 1 exterior and two others, slightly shorter and placed within and on each side of the outer one. The

Tonijn (S 805)   1968

Dolfijn (S 808)   1974

crew and the armament are retained in the outer cylinder, and the batteries and diesel engines are mounted in the other two.

CRUISER

NOTE: *De Ruyter,* sister ship to *De Zeven Provincien* but not converted to carry Terrier missiles, was sold to Peru (spring of 1973) and renamed *Almirante Grau.*

♦ *1 guided-missile cruiser*

	Bldr	Laid down	L	In serv.
C 802 DE ZEVEN PROVINCIEN	Rotterdam DDM	5-39	22-8-50	12-53

D: 9,850 tons (12,250 fl)
Dim: 185.70 (182.40 pp) × 17.25 × 6.70
S: 32 kts
A: 2/U.S. Mk 10 missile launchers (II × 1) (40 Terrier missiles) — 4/152-mm AA (II × 2) — 6/57-mm AA (II × 3) — 4/40-mm AA
Electron Equipt: Radars: 1/LW 01, 1/LW 02, 1/SRG 103, 1/SRG 104, 1/SPS 39, 2/SPG 55
Armor: Belt: 76 to 102-mm — deck: two of 20-25 mm
M: Parsons GT; 2 props; 80,000 hp
Boilers: 4/3-drum type Yarrow
Man: 940 men
REMARKS: Placed in reserve in January 1976.

CRUISER (continued)

De Zeven Provincien   1974 Guiglini

De Zeven Provincien (C 802)   1974 J. C. Bellonne

♦ *2 guided-missile Tromp class*

	Bldr	Laid down	L	In serv.
F 801 TROMP	Kon. Mij. De Schelde, Flushing	8-71	2-6-73	10-5-75
F 806 DE RUYTER (ex-*Heemskerck*)	Kon. Mij. De Schelde, Flushing	1-71	9-3-74	1975

Tromp (F 801)   1975

D: 3,665 tons (4,300 fl)   **Dim:** 138.60 (130 pp) × 14.80 × 4.60
S: 28 kts   **Man:** 34 officers, 267 men
A: 8 Harpoon missiles — 2/120-mm Bofors AA (II × 1) — 1 Mk 13 missile-launcher (I × 1) (40 SM 1 missiles) aft, 1 U.S. BPDMS Sea Sparrow system [60 missiles] — 6/324-mm ASW Mk 32 (III × 2) TT — 1 WG 13 Lynx ASW helicopter — 2 Corvus
Electron Equipt: Radars: 1/3 D, 2/Decca, 1/M 25 from HSA, 2/SPG 51
    Sonars: 1/CWE 610, 1/162
M: COGOG propulsion: 2 Rolls-Royce Olympus gas turbines, each 27,000 hp; 2 Tyne gas turbines, each 4,100 hp for economical cruising (18 kts); 2 reversible pitch props; 54,000 hp
Electric: 4,000 kw   **Range:** 5,000/18

REMARKS: See profile on page 279. Ship has stabilizers. Excellent sea-keeping qualities.

DESTROYERS

♦ *3 Holland class (type 47 A) authorized in 1947.*

	Bldr	Laid down	L	In serv.
D 808 HOLLAND	Rotterdam DDM	21-4-50	11-4-53	12-54
D 809 ZEELAND	Kon. Mij. De Schelde	12-1-51	27-6-53	3-55

D: 2,215 tons (2,765 fl)   **Dim:** 111.30 × 11.30 × 4.86 (light)
S: 32 kts (trials up to 40.3)   **Man:** 247 men
Range: 4,000/18
A: 4/120-mm (II × 2) — 1/40-mm — 2 Bofors RL — 1 depth charge rack

DESTROYERS (continued)

Holland (D 808)   1972

Electron Equipt: Radars: 1/LW 02, 1/SRG 105, 1/SRG 103, 3/HSA band X for fire control
Sonars: 1/170B, 1/CWE 610 (?), 1/162.
M: Parsons GT; 2 props; 45,000 hp
Boilers: 4 Babcock 28 kg/
Electric: 1,350 kw

REMARKS: Built with 45,000-hp engines ordered in 1939 by the Germans for a new series of destroyers (*Gerard Callenburg* class T 61) that was never built. The *D 810 Noord Brabant* was scrapped in 1974 following severe damage suffered in a collision (19-1-74). The *D 811 Gelderland* is now a harbor training hulk in Amsterdam. Her guns and radars have been removed.

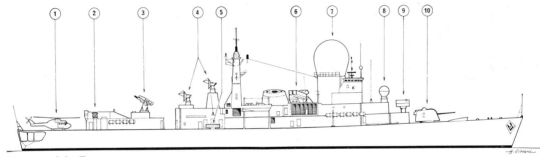

Scale 1/1000

Diagram of the Tromp
1: Lynx helicopter — 2: Corvus — 3: Mk 13 launcher — 4: SPG 51 radars — 5: Mk 32 torpedo tubes — 6: Harpoon launchers — 7: 3 D radar — 8: M 25 fire control radar — 9: Sea Sparrow system — 10: 120-mm mount.

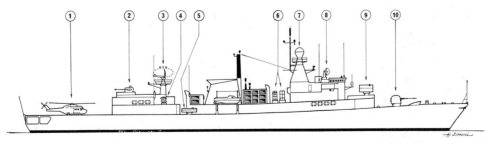

Scale 1/1000

Provisional Diagram of the Kortenaer
1: Lynx helicopter — 2: 35-mm AA twin mount — 3: LW 08 radar — 4: Corvus — 5: Mk 32 torpedo tubes — 6: Harpoon launchers — 7: WW 25 fire control radar — 8: Sea Sparrow system fire control radar — 9: Sea Sparrow — 10: 76-mm OTO Melara compact gun.

Tromp

1975

DESTROYERS (continued)

♦ 8 Friesland class (type 47 B) 2 author. in 1947, 6 in 1949

	Bldr	Laid down	L	In serv.
D 812 FRIESLAND	Nederlandsche DSM	17-12-51	21-2-53	3-56
D 813 GRONINGEN	Nederlandsche DSM	4-2-52	9-1-54	9-56
D 814 LIMBURG	Kon. Mij. De Schelde	28-11-53	5-9-55	10-56
D 815 OVERIJSSEL	Wilton-Fijenoord	15-10-53	8-7-56	10-57
D 816 DRENTHE	Nederlandsche DSM	9-1-54	26-3-55	8-57
D 817 UTRECHT	Kon. Mij. De Schelde	15-2-54	2-6-56	10-57
D 818 ROTTERDAM	Rotterdam DDM	7-4-54	26-1-56	2-57
D 819 AMSTERDAM	Nederlandsche DSM	26-3-55	25-8-56	4-58

Drenthe (D 816)   1972 G. Arra

Friesland (D 812)

D: 2,406 tons (3,150 fl)   **Dim:** 116 × 11.77 × 5.10 (light)
S: 36 kts (trials: up to 42.8 kts)
Man: 280 men   **Range:** 4,000/18
Electron Equipt: Radars: 1/LW 02, 1/SRG 105, 1/SRG 103, 3 HSA band X for fire control
    Sonars: 1/170 B, 1/CWE 610 (?), 1/162
A: 4/120-mm AA (II × 2) — 1/40-mm AA (A), 6/40-mm AA — 2 Bofors RL — 1 depth charge rack
M: Parsons GT; 2 props; 60,000 hp; 3 Babcock boilers
Electric: 1,350 kw

REMARKS: Same building authorization as the Holland class of which the Friesland class is an improved version.

FRIGATES

♦ 8 Banckert class (now the Kortenaer class)

Bldr: Kon. Mij., De Schelde, Flushing

L	In serv.	L	In serv.
F 807 KORTENAER		F . . . WITTE DE WITH	
F 808 CALLENBURGH		F . . . ABRAHAM CRIJNSSEN	
F 809 VAN KINSBERGEN		F . . . PIET HEIN	
F 810 BANCKERT		F . . . PIETER FLORISZ	

D: 3,600 tons   **Dim:** 121.8 × 14.8 × . . .
S: 30 kts   **Man:** 185 men
A: 8 U.S. Harpoon missiles — 2/76-mm AA OTO Melara — 1 BPDMS Sea Sparrow — 6/324-mm Mk 32 (III × 2) ASW TT — 1 WG 13 Lynx ASW helicopter
Electron Equipt: 1/ZWO 6 navigation radar — 1 DO surface search, 1 fire control WW 25 radar, 1/LWO 8 — 2 Corvus

Range: 4,000/18
M: COGOG Propulsion: 2 Rolls-Royce Olympus gas turbines, each 27,000 hp; 2 Tyne gas turbines, each 4,100 hp (for economical cruising); 2 props

REMARKS: See page 279 for profile and page 276 for a photograph of a model of these ships. Four more planned.

♦ 6 Van Speijk class

	Bldr	Laid down	L	In serv.
F 802 VAN SPEIJK	Nederlandsche DSM	10-63	5-3-65	2-67
F 803 VAN GALEN	Kon. Mij. De Schelde	7-63	19-6-65	3-67
F 804 TJERK HIDDES	Nederlandsche DSM	6-64	17-12-65	8-67
F 805 VAN NES	Kon. Mij. De Schelde	7-63	26-3-66	8-67
F 814 ISAAC SWEERS	Nederlandsche DSM	5-65	10-3-67	12-67
F 815 EVERTSEN	Kon. Mij. De Schelde	7-65	18-6-66	5-68

Evertsen (F 815)   1974 J. C. Bellonne

FRIGATES (*continued*)

D: 2,200 tons (2,835 fl)
Dim: 113.58 (109.81 pp) × 12.50 × 4.57 (flank speed)
S: 28.5 kts   **Man:** 19 officers, 228 men
A: 2/114-mm AA Mk 6 (Great Britain) (II × 1) — 2 Sea Cat BPDMS (IV × 2) — 1 Limbo — 1 Wasp ASW helicopter.
Electron Equipt: Radars: 1/Kelvin Hughes, 1/LW 03, 1/SRG 105
Sonars: 1/CWE 610, 1/170 B, 1/PDE 700, 1/162
M: double reduction Werkspoor-English Electric GT; 2 props
Boilers: two; 30,000 hp
Electric: 1,900 kw
Range: 4,500/12

REMARKS: Derived from the British *Leander* class with a few modifications and Dutch electronic equipment. The 114-mm fire control radar is a Mk 45 HSA and for the Sea Cat Mk 44 system. Will be armed with the Harpoon system during refit between 1977 and 1982.

PATROL BOATS

♦ *6 wolf class* (*ex-U.S. PCE*)

	In serv. In Netherlands
F 817 WOLF (ex-*PCE 1607*)	3-54
F 818 FRET (ex-*PCE 1604*)	5-54
F 819 HERMELIJN (ex-*PCE 1605*)	8-54
F 820 VOS (ex-*PC 1606*)	12-54
F 821 PANTHER (ex-*PCE 1608*)	6-54
F 822 JAGUAR (ex-*A 1609*)	6-54

Bldr: U.S.A. (1952-53).

Vos (F 820)

D: 808 tons (945 fl)   **Dim:** 56.20 × 10.30 × 2.95
S: 15 kts   **Man:** 96 men
A: 1/76-mm AA — 6/40-mm — 8/20-mm AA — 1 hedgehog — 2 depth charge projectors
M: diesels; 2 props; 1,600 hp

REMARKS: "Offshore" construction ordered by the U.S.A. (*PCE 1604-1609*). One of them is used as a fisheries protection vessel. *821* and *822* have 4/40-mm AA in place of the listed 6, and 4 DC projectors instead of 2.

♦ *5 Balder class*

Bldr		Laid down	L	In serv.
P 802 BALDER	⎫	8-53	24-2-54	7-54
P 803 BULGIA	⎪	10-53	24-4-54	8-54
P 804 FREYR	⎬ Rijkswerf Willemsoord, Den Helder	2-54	17-7-54	12-54
P 805 HADDA	⎪	4-54	2-10-54	2-55
P 806 HEFRING	⎭	8-54	1-12-54	3-55

Hefring (P 806)   1971 S. Terzibaschitsch

D: 150 tons (170 fl)   **Dim:** 36.35 (35 pp) × 6.21 × 1.80.
S: 15.5 kts   **Man:** 3 officers, 24 men
A: 1/40-mm AA — 3/20-mm AA — 2 mousetrap fwd (4 ASW rockets), 2 depth charge projectors and 1 depth charge rack aft
M: diesels; 2 props; 1,050 hp
Range: 1,000/13

REMARKS: *SC 1627* to *1631* "offshore" construction ordered by the U.S.A. All in reserve except for the last two.

MINESWEEPERS

♦ *5 ex-U.S. AM/MSO ocean minesweepers Onversaagd class*

(   ): transfer date to the Netherlands.

A 854 ONVERSAAGD   A 855 ONBEVREESD   A 856 ONVERSCHROKKEN
(ex-*AM 480*) (5-1954)   (ex-*AM 481*) (9-1954)   (ex-*AM 483*) (7-1954)
A 858 ONVERVAARD   A 859 ONVERDROTEN
(ex-*AM 482*) (3-1955)   (ex-*AM 485*) (11-1954)

Bldr: Astoria Marine Const. Co (*854, 5* and *8*) and Peterson Bldrs (Wis.)

D: 735 tons (790 fl)   **Dim:** 50.29 × 10.67 × 3.15
S: 15.5 kts   **Man:** 67 men
A: 1/40-mm AA   **Range:** 3,000/10
M: 2 General Motors diesels; 2 props; 1,600 hp.
Fuel: 47 tons

MINESWEEPERS (*continued*)

Onvervaard (A 858)   1968

REMARKS: Launched in 1953, transferred by the U.S.A. under the Mutual Assistance Pact. *A 854* provisionally fitted out as a hydrographic ship. *A 857 Overmoied* returned to the U.S.A. All in reserve except the *854*.

♦ *24 coastal minesweepers or minehunters Dokkum class (Western Europe class)*

Bldr: Netherlands

	L
M 801 DOKKUM	12-10-1954
M 802 HOOGEZAND	22-3-1955
M 803 WILDERVANK*	24-2-1955
M 806 ROERMOND	13-8-1955
M 807 WAALWIJK*	6-4-1955
M 809 NAALDWIJK	1-2-1955
M 810 ABCOUDE	2-9-1955
M 812 DRACHTEN	24-3-1955
M 813 OMMEN	5-4-1955
M 814 MEPPEL*	19-7-1956
M 815 GIETHOORN	30-3-1955
M 817 VENLO	21-5-1955
M 818 DRUNEN	24-3-1956
M 819 GOES*	23-3-1956
M 820 WOERDEN	28-11-1956
M 822 LEERSUM*	11-8-1956
M 823 NAARDEN	27-1-1956
M 826 GRIJPSKERK*	10-3-1956
M 827 HOOGEVEEN	8-5-1956
M 828 STAPHORST	21-7-1956
M 830 SITTARD	26-4-1956
M 841 GEMERT	13-3-1956
M 842 VEERE	9-2-1956
M 844 RHENEN	31-5-1956

M 804 Steenwijk, 805 Gieten, 816 Lochum, 824 Sneek, 843 Lisse were deleted from the active list in 1969. The *M 806 Roermond, 807 Waalwijk, 820 Woerden, 822*

Dokkum as a minehunter   1970

Leersum, and *844 Rhenen* are no longer manned as minesweepers and are assigned to the diving school (deep sea diving). The *M 808 Axel* and *811 Aalsmeer* sold to Oman in 1974.

D:	373 tons (417 fl)	**Dim:**	46.62 × 8.78 × 2.28
S:	14 kts	**Man:**	40 men
A:	2/40-mm AA		
M:	2 M.A.N. or Werkspoor (*) diesel engines; 2 props; 2,500 hp		

REMARKS: Similar to the French *Sirius* and British *Coniston* classes. 18 built under the "offshore military assistance program." *Dokkum, Drunen* (1969), *Staphorst*, and *Veere* fitted out as minehunters.

♦ *7 Beemster class ex-U.S. coastal minesweepers, transferred in 1953-54*

M 848 BEILEN (ex-*AMS 110*)	**M 853 BLARICUM** (ex-*AMS 112*)	**M 855 BRESKENS** (ex-*AMS 148*)
M 847 BEDUM (ex-*Beerta*, ex-*AMS 106*)	**M 854 BRIELLE** (ex-*AMS 167*)	**M 857 BOXTEL** (ex-*AMS 149*)
M 850 BORNE (ex-*AMS 108*)		

Bldr: U.S.A. 1953-54

Beilen (M 848)   M.N. 1974

MINESWEEPERS (continued)

D: 330 tons (384 fl) **Dim:** 43.94 × 8.50 × 2.51
S: 13.6 kts (12 sweeping) **Man:** 37 men
A: 2/20-mm AA (I × 2)
M: 2 General Motors diesels; 2 props — 900 hp.

♦ *16 inshore minesweepers Van Straelen class*

	Bldr	Laid down	L	In serv.
M 868 ALBLAS	Noord	2-58	26-9-59	12-3-60
M 869 BUSSEMAKER	DVL	8-58	27-2-60	19-8-60
M 870 LACOMBLE	ASM	9-58	6-2-60	22-8-60
M 871 VAN HAMEL	DVL	4-59	28-5-60	14-10-60
M 872 VAN STRAELEN	ASM	11-58	17-5-60	20-12-60
M 873 VAN MOPPES	Noord	4-59	10-5-60	19-12-60
M 874 CHÖMPFF	Noord	6-59	10-5-60	19-12-60
M 875 VAN WELL GROENEVELD	ASM	12-59	1-10-60	28-4-61
M 876 VAN DER WELL	DVL	5-60	5-61	6-10-61
M 877 VAN VERSENDAAL	Noord	3-61	8-61	11-4-62
M 878 SCHUILING	DVL	6-59	30-6-60	5-4-61
M 879 VAN'T HOFF	Noord	6-60	15-3-61	6-10-61
M 880 MAHU	Noord	6-60	15-3-61	6-10-61
M 881 STAVERMAN	DVL	7-60	7-61	21-2-62
M 882 HOUTEPEN	ASM	9-60	6-61	21-3-62
M 883 ZOMER	ASM	5-60	4-3-61	6-10-61

Bldr: Werf de Noord, Alblasserdam — DVL: De Vries-Lentsch, Amsterdam — ASM: Arnhem Scheepsbouw Mij.

Van't Hoff (M 879)   1971 S. Terzibaschitsch

D: 151 tons (169 fl) **Dim:** 33.10 × 6.65 × 1.75
S: 13 kts **Man:** 12 men
A: 1/20-mm AA
M: Werkspoor diesels; 2 props; 1,100 hp

REMARKS: Eight of these ships were from "offshore" procurement. The Dutch designs differ from the French A.M.I. and the British "-*ham*" classes. Wooden hull and

antimagnetic construction. Named for officers, petty officers, and non-rated men who died for their country during World War II.

AMPHIBIOUS SHIPS

♦ *12 small landing craft (LCA)*

L 9521 and L 9526

  D: 20 tons **S:** 8 kts **M:** 1/150-hp diesel

| L 9510 | L 9512 | L 9514 | L 9517 | L 9520 |
| L 9511 | L 9513 | L 9516 | L 9518 | L 9522 |

  Bldr: Rijkswerf Willemsoord, Den Helder — 1962-64
  D: 8.5 tons (13.6 fl) **Dim:** 14.45 × 3.80 × 1.30
  S: 12 kts
  M: 1 diesel; 300 hp; 1 Schottel prop.

HYDROGRAPHIC SHIPS

♦ *1 Tydeman class*
  Bldr: B.V. De Merwede Hardinxveld

	L	In serv.
A . . . TYDEMAN		

Tydeman   (artist's concept)

  D: 3,000 tons **Dim:** 90 × 14.4 × 4.75
  S: 15 kts **Man:** 63 men — 15 civilians
  M: diesel-electric; 1 prop; 3,690 hp

REMARKS: Assigned to civilian and military research.

♦ *3 Blommendal class (1972-73)*

A 804 BUYSKES (11-7-72),   **A 805 BLOMMENDAL** (22-11-72),
A 806 BREEVEERTIEN (16-2-73)
  Bldr: Boele S. M., Bolnes — 1971-74
  D: 1,050 tons **S:** 13 kts **Dim:** 59 × 11 × 3.70
  M: diesel-electric propulsion (3 engines, each 700 hp.)
  Man: 45 men

HYDROGRAPHIC SHIPS (continued)

Buyskes   1973

REMARKS: Helicopter platform. *804/805* are assigned to the North Sea; the other has oceanographic and meteorological capabilities.

A 920 DREG IV (inland waters)

D:	48 tons (fl)	**Dim:**	20 × 4.58 × 1.55
S:	9.5 kts	**Man:**	10 men
M:	diesel; 1 prop; 120 hp		

LOGISTIC SUPPORT

♦ *2 combat supply ships*

	Bldr	Laid down	L	In serv.
A 835 POOLSTER	author. 1961 Rotterdam DDM	18-9-62	16-10-63	9-64

D: 16,800 (fl)   **Dim:** 168.30 (157 pp) × 20.30 × 8.20

Poolster (A 835)

S: 18 kts (21 trials)   **A:** 2/40-mm AA
M: GT; 1 prop; 22,500 hp
Cargo capacity: 10,300 tons including 8,000 tons of fuel.

REMARKS: Hangar which can shelter three HSS 2 helicopters. In addition to her functions as a replenishment tanker, this ship is a "combat supply ship" which can effectively participate in ASW engagements in the heart of a "hunter-killer group" thanks to the five helicopters that she can put in use. These helicopters can, for example, take the place in the screen of a frigate when the latter has to replenish. The *Poolster* has a widescan sonar and an ASW capability (depth charges). She can carry 300 soldiers as well as her own crew for short distances.

	Bldr	Laid down	L	In serv.
A 832 ZUIDERKRUIS	Verolme, Alblasserdam	16-7-73	15-10-74	27-6-75

D:	16,800 fl	**Dim:**	169.90 × 20.30 × 8.20
S:	18 kts	**Man:**	...
M:	...	**A:**	...
Cargo capacity:	...		

REMARKS: Based on the *Poolster.*

♦ *1 torpedo recovery ship*

	Bldr	Laid down	L	In serv.
A 856 MERCUUR	Rijkswerf Willemsoord, Den Helder	7-35	26-2-36	7-36

D:	273 tons (289 fl)	**Dim:**	41.90 × 7.02 × 2.10
S:	12 kts	**Man:**	35 men
A:	3/20-mm AA		
M:	diesel; 1 prop; 330 hp		

REMARKS: Also designated as a repair ship for torpedoes. In 1960 a diesel engine replaced the reciprocating engine.

♦ *1 barracks ship*

	Bldr	Laid down	L	In serv.
A 907 SNELLIUS	P. Smit, Jr. Rotterdam	1-49	9-12-50	2-52

D:	1,110 tons (1,538 fl)	**Dim:**	71.40 × 10.80 × 3.90
S:	15 kts	**Man:**	108 men
A:	1/40-mm AA — 2/20-mm — 2 depth charge projectors — 1 mousetrap		
M:	4-stroke Stork diesels; 2 props; 2,000 hp		

REMARKS: Tender for Dutch submarines stationed by treaty in Great Britain.

♦ *17 tugs*

Y 8037 BERKEL, Y 8038 DINTEL, Y 8039 DOMMEL, Y 8040 IJSSEL (1956-57)

    D: 139 tons (163 fl)
    Dim: 25 × 6.20 × 2.20 — Werkspoor diesel
    S: 10.5 kts — 500 hp.

A 847 ARGUS (1967) — Training ship for deep sea divers as are the 3 *Triton* class listed below.

A 848 TRITON — A 849 NAUTILUS — A 850 HYDRA (1967)

    D: 69.3 tons (fl)   **Dim:** 23.30 × 5.15 × 1.34 — 105 hp   **S:** 9 kts

LOGISTIC SUPPORT (*continued*)

Snellius

A 870 WAMANDAI (1959-61) — **D:** 155 tons (185 fl) — 500 hp **S:** 10.5 kts.
A 871 WAMBRAU (1955-56) — **D:** 154 tons (184 fl) — 500 hp **S:** 10.5 kts.
A 872 WESTGAT — **A 873 WIELINGEN** (1967-68) — Bldr: Rijkswerf Willemsoord,
Den Helder

> **D:** 185 tons   **Dim:** 27.60 × 6.40 × 2.35 — 720 hp
> **A:** 2/20-mm   **S:** 12 kts

Y 8014, Y 8016, Y 8022, Y 8028 (since 1960).

VARIOUS

♦ *School ships*

A 923 VAN BOCHOVE (1967) — Assigned to the torpedo school.

> **D:**   140 tons fl
> **Dim:** 29.80 × 5.53 × 1.80 — 1 diesel; 140 hp

Y 8101 HOBEIN (ex-*Doornbosch*, ex-*Dornbusch*) — 1937 — Den Helder

> **D:** 140 tons   **Dim:** 27.90 × 5.95 × 1.90
> **S:** 9 kts   **Man:** 10 men
> **A:** 1/40-mm — 1/20-mm
> **M:** diesel; 1 prop; 250 hp

Y 8102 HENDRIK KARSSEN (ex-*De Mok 1*) — 1949 — Den Helder

> **D:** 172 tons (185 fl)   **Dim:** 37.90 × 6.50 × 1.80
> **S:** 11 kts   **Man:** 21 men
> **M:** 2 diesels; 200 hp   **A:** 2/20-mm AA

Y 8101 and *8102* are assigned to the communications school.

Y 8050 URANIA (1928) — Sailing ship assigned to the naval academy.

> **D:** 38 tons   **Dim:** 22 × 5 × 3.10
> **M:** 65 hp   **Man:** 15 men

♦ *2 pilot boats*

A 906 BREEVERTIEN (1973)
A . . . FOMALHAUT (in serv. 14-8-74)

♦ The Dutch navy is retaining the following as repair barges (some without their
machinery):

A 881 NEPTUNUS former coastal defense vessel (ex-cruiser *Jacob van Heems-
kerck*).

A 886 CORNELIS DREBBEL former submarine tender, 800 tons — replaced by a
new tender with quarters for 200 men. Launched in 11-70.

> **D:** 775 tons   **Dim:** 63 × 11.70 × 1.10

A 891 SOEMBA former gunboat, 1,683 tons

REMARKS: *A 881*, captured by Germany in 1940, was used as a floating AA battery
under the name of *Undine*.

PERSONNEL: Approximately 3,000 men.

NAVAL AVIATION: Wasp helicopters on the frigates and 5/P3B Orion aircraft, which are under the command of the Royal New Zealand Air Force.

MERCHANT MARINE (1-7-74): 113 ships — 163,349 grt

FRIGATES

◆ *2 British Leander class*

	Bldr	Laid down	L	In serv.
F 55 WAIKATO	Harland & Wolff	1964	18-2-65	9-66
F 421 CANTERBURY	Yarrow	1969	6-5-70	8-72

Canterbury (F 421)   1972 Wright and Logan

REMARKS: Characteristics of the *Leander* class (see section on Great Britain)

A: 2/114-mm AA — 2/20-mm AA — 1/Sea Cat system — 1/Limbo Mk 10 ASW mortar — 1 Wasp helicopter

◆ *2 British Rothesay class*

	Bldr	Laid down	L	In serv.
F 111 OTAGO	J. Thornycroft	1957	11-12-58	6-60
(ex-*Hastings*)				
F 148 TARANAKI	J. Samuel White	1957	19-8-59	3-61

REMARKS: Characteristics of the *Rothesay* class (see Great Britain section).

A: 2/114-mm AA — 2/40-mm AA — 1 Sea Cat system — 6/ASW 324-mm TT (III × 2) — 2/Limbo Mk 10 ASW mortars

◆ *2 ex-Australian Bathurst class, transferred in 1952 (in reserve)*

M 233 INVERELL (2-5-52)   **M 353 KIAMA** (3-7-43)

D:	815 tons (1,025 fl)	**S:**	15 kts	**Dim:**	56.75 × 9.45 × 3.05
A:	2/40-mm	**Man:**	85 men	**Range:**	2,000/15 — 4,200/10
M:	Triple expansion; 2 props; 1,800 hp; 2 Admiralty boilers				
Fuel:	170 tons				

NEW ZEALAND

PATROL BOATS

◆ *4 Pukaki class* — Bldr: Brooke Marine Ltd (1974-75)

P 3568 PUKAKI	**P 3570 TAUPO**	
P 3569 ROTOITI	**P 3571 HAWEA**	

D:	140 tons	**S:**	12 kts	**Dim:**	32 (30 pp) × 6.10 × 3.50
A:	2/40-mm AA	**Man:**	18 men	**M:**	2 Paxman diesels; 2,500 hp

The *Pukaki* and the *Taupo* reached Auckland early in 1975, the other two in 6-75.

◆ *10 British SDML type (1943)*

P 3551 MAKO	**P 3562 PARORE**	**P 3565 HAKU**
P 3552 PAEA	**P 3563 KUPARU**	**P 3566 TARAPUNKA**
P 3553 KAHAWAI	**P 3564 KOURA**	**P 3567 MANGA**
P 3556 TAKAPU		

D:	54 tons	**Length:**	23	**S:**	12 kts
A:	1/20-mm AA			**M:**	2 diesels; 320 hp

3556 and *3566* are hydrographic ships, *3551, 3552, 3553, 3365* fishery protection vessels, the others are used for reserve training.

HYDROGRAPHIC SHIPS

◆ *1 ex-U.S. bought in 8-70*

A 2 TUI (ex-*Sands, AGOR-6*) — Bldr: U.S.A. — L: 16-9-63

D:	1,020 tons (1,370 fl)	**Dim:**	70 (63.70 pp) × 11.28 × 6.30 fl
S:	12.5 kts	**Range:**	12,000/12
Man:	8 officers, 15 technicians, 18 men		
M:	diesel-electric propulsion; 2 props, one mounted in the bow; 1,100 hp		

◆ **F 364 LACHLAN** — Bldr: Mort's Dock, Sydney, Australia — L: 25-3-44

Australian frigate of the British *River* class bought by New Zealand for hydrographic work in 1962 and fitted with a helicopter platform in 1966. (See section on Australia.) Will be replaced in 1976 by the *Monowai* (ex-*Moana Roa*, 2,900 tons).

VARIOUS

◆ *2 tugs*

ARATAKI   **MANAWANUI**

NIGERIA

PERSONNEL: 120 officers, 1,700 men

MERCHANT MARINE (1-7-74): 78 ships — 121,301 grt
(tankers: 5 ships — 2,247 grt)

FRIGATES

	Bldr	Laid down	L	In serv.
F 87 NIGERIA	Wilton-Fijenoord (Netherlands)	4-64	9-65	9-66

Nigeria (F 87)   1966

D: 1,724 tons (2,000 fl)   **Dim:** 109.85 (104 pp) × 11.30 × 3.35
S: 25 kts   **Man:** 216 men
A: 2/102-mm (II × 1) — 4/40-mm AA — 1/triple ASW mortar
M: 4/M.A.N. V-8 diesels; 2 props; 15,500 hp
Helicopter platform. Refit by Cammell Laird in 1970-71.

♦ *2 Mk 3 Hippopotamus class*
DORINA (16-9-70), **F 82 OTOBO** (25-5-71). Bldr: Vosper-Thornycroft, Portsmouth

Dorina 1972   Vosper

D: 650 tons   **Dim:** 61.57 (55.40 pp) × 7.45 × 3.35
S: 22/23 kts   **Man:** 7 officers, 13 petty officers, 46 men
A: 2/102-mm (II × 1) — 2/40-mm AA 60-cal Bofors — 2/20-mm Mk 7 A — 2/Mk 5 illumination flare projectors
M: M.A.N. V-8 V 24/30 B diesels; 2 props; 3,400 hp (4,430 max)
Fuel: 68 tons   **Range:** 3,500/14   **Electric:** 176 kw

REMARKS: Can carry a flag officer and his staff; living spaces air-conditioned; Vosper stabilizers; the 102-mm guns (Mk 19) are hand-loaded; Dutch HSA 22 fire control with a Plessey Mk AWS 1 radar; 1 Decca TM 626 radar; 12 compartments. Can be fitted with a sonar.

PATROL BOATS

♦ *2 Makurdi class*
Bldr: Brooke Marine Ltd, Lowestoft

	In serv.		In serv.
P 167 MAKURDI	14-8-74	**P 168 HADEIJA**	14-8-74

1975

D: 105 tons   **S:** . . .   **Dim:** . . .
A: 2/40-mm AA   **Man:** 4 officers, 20 men   **Range:** . . .
M: . . .

♦ *4 Argundu class*
Bldr: Brooke Marine Ltd, Lowestoft

	In serv.		In serv.
P 165 ARGUNDU	10-74	**P . . . N . . .**	
P 166 YOLA	10-74	**P . . . N . . .**	

D: . . .   **S:** . . .   **Dim:** . . .
A: 1/40-mm AA — 1/20-mm AA   **Man:** . . .   **Range:** . . .
M: . . .

REMARKS: The first two ships were ordered in 1974.

PATROL BOATS (continued)

Argundu (P 165)   1975

♦ *3 Soviet MO VI type*

EKPEN, EKUN, ELOLE — Purchased in the U.S.S.R. in 1967.

D: 70 tons (80 fl)	**S:** 38 kts	**Dim:** 25.45 × 6.10 × 2.75
M: 4 diesels; 4,800 hp		**Man:** 24 men
A: 4/25-mm (II × 2) — ASW mortars and depth charges		

♦ *6 British SBD type*

ENUGU (1961)	**KADUNA** (ex-*Axford*)
BENIN (ex-*Hinksford*)	**IBADAN II** (ex-*Bryans ford*)
BONNY (ex-*Difford*)	**SAPELE** (ex-*Dubford*)

D: 120 tons (160 fl)	**S:** 15 kts	**Dim:** 35.70 × 6.10 × 2.10
A: 1/40-mm — 2/20-mm — depth charges		**Man:** 19 men
M: 2 Davey-Paxman diesels; 1,100 hp		

REMARKS: The first ship was built specifically for Nigeria; the five others were transferred in September 1966 (three) and in 1968. The *Ibadan* was seized in May of 1967 by the Biafrans and renamed *Vigilance;* she was sunk in September of that year, refloated and later scrapped. *Ibadan II* and *Sapele* were bought in 1967-68 and 1968-69.

HYDROGRAPHIC SHIPS

♦ *1 British Fawn class ordered in 1974*

Bldr: Brooke Marine Ltd, Lowestoft

N . . .

D: 800 tons (1,100 fl)	**Dim:** 57.8 × 11.4 × 3.7	
S: 15 kts	**Range:** 4,000/12	
!M: 4 diesels; 2 props; 2,000 hp	**Man:** 38 men	

♦ *2 of various classes*

P 06 PATHFINDER 544 tons (25-10-53) — **P 11 PENELOPE** 79 tons (30-9-58)

VARIOUS

P 10 CHALLENGER — 114 tons (1955) assigned to customs surveillance.

♦ *1 LCT*

LOKOJO (ex-*LCT 1213*) — **D:** 586 tons — **S:** 10 kts

♦ *1 tug*

RIBADU (1973)

D: 147 tons	**S:** 12 kts	**Dim:** 28.5 × 7.2 × 3.7

♦ *1 yacht*

VALIANT — 280 tons — for lagoon patrol.

The police man 8 small patrol boats (Vosper-Thornycroft 1971-72).

D: 15 tons	**S:** 19 kts	**Dim:** 10.40 × 3.10 × 0.85
A: 1 machine gun	**Man:** . . .	**M:** 2 diesels; 290 hp

PERSONNEL: Approximately 6,000 men, to whom should be added 1,800 men in the Coast Artillery and 2,000 civilians working for the navy.

NAVAL AVIATION: The Norwegian navy does not have a naval air arm as such. However, two Air Force formations are assigned to navy missions, usually reconnaissance and ASW patrol.
The two formations are:
— a large squadron, with about a dozen SH 3 Sea King helicopters and another dozen UH 1 B helicopters;
— a smaller group with about a half dozen P 3 Orion patrol aircraft.

MERCHANT MARINE (1-7-74): 2,689 ships — 24,852,917 grt
(tankers: 297 ships — 12,203,299 grt)

WARSHIPS IN SERVICE OR UNDER CONSTRUCTION AS OF 1 OCTOBER 1975

	In serv.	D	Main armament
♦ *Submarines*			
15 ULA class (German *204* class)	1964-66	370	8/533-mm TT
♦ *Frigates*			
5 OSLO class	1966-67	1,450	4/76-mm AA, 1 Terne sys., 1 Penguin sys., 1 Sea Sparrow sys.
2 SLEIPNER class	1963-65	600	1/76-mm, 1 Terne sys., 6 ASW TT
♦ *Gunboats*			
6 SNÖGG class	1970-71	140 (fl)	1/40-mm AA, 2 Penguin system
20 STORM class	1963-67	100	1/76-mm AA, 2 to 6 Penguin system
♦ *Patrol torpedo boats*			
20 NASTY/TJELD class	1960-64	70	1/40-mm AA, 4/533-mm TT
♦ *Minelayers*			
4 TYR class	1942-44	890	1/76-mm AA, mines
1 BORGEN class	1960	282	Mines
2 of a new class			
♦ *Minesweepers*			
10 ex-U.S. *MSC* class	1954	370	2/20-mm AA

NAVAL PROGRAM:

The long-term program decided upon in 1973 by the Norwegian government forecasts:
— the replacement before the end of the 1980 decade:
♦ of the *Oslo* and *Sleipner*-class frigates;
♦ of the 207-class 350-ton submarines (*S 300/309* — *S 315/319*);
♦ of the *Sauda* and *Tana*-class minesweepers;
♦ of the 20 *Tjeld*-class patrol torpedo boats.

In the light of these projections, the first new construction was scheduled for the period 1974-78. To be built during this period are:
— 2 minelayers (expenses outlined in the 1975-76 budget and contract signed at the end of 1974);
— 2 logistic support ships for small craft and submarines;
— 14 modified *Snögg*-class (Swedish *Jagaren* class) guided missile small craft;
— 1 training ship also assigned to the protection of the Continental plateau;
— 1 fishery protection ship;
— the modification of a minesweeper into a mine hunter.
To ensure the protection of offshore oil installations, recommendations have been made to modernize the fishery protection ships *Noren*, *Farm*, and *Heimdal*, and to procure:
— 7 additional ships, able to make 25 knots, each fitted with a helicopter platform, with anti-pollution systems, and fire-fighting equipment.
— a special ship designed for deep diving and able to carry small submarines which can dive to 500 meters.
— 6 helicopters and 3 Orion-type patrol aircraft.

NORWAY

WEAPONS AND SYSTEMS

The Norwegian navy usually uses British, American, or Swedish weapons and systems, but its engineers have built two interesting weapon systems: the Terne and the Penguin which are described below. Among the guns should be mentioned the 76-mm Bofors which is mounted in the *Storm*-class gunboats.

Terne MK III

This is an automatic ASW defense system (maximum range 900 m) including:
— 1 search sonar;
— 1 attack sonar;
— 1 computer;
— 1 stabilized rocket-launcher mount with a rapid reloading system.
The mount, which weighs a little less than 3 tons, is a sextuple type. Firing is executed between 45° and 75° of elevation with the latter for maximum range. Six rounds are fired at a time. Reloading (40 seconds) is done automatically as the carriage is returned to a vertical position from which ready service racks reload the launchers. The rocket is 1.970 m in length, 0.200 m in diameter, 120 kg in weight (warhead: 48 kg), and with a combination timed and proximity fuze.

Penguin:

— Surface-to-surface missile
— Length: 0.300 m
— Wingspan: 1,400 m
— Diameter: 0.280 m
— Weight: 330 kg
— Maximum range: 20,000 m
— Speed: Mach 0.7
— Infra-red homing guidance
The system is mounted in an enclosure to guard it against the weather.

76-mm Bofors gun:

— Single barrel automatic gun mounted on the *Storm*-class gunboats
— Turret weight (no ammunition) 6.5 tons
— Length: 50 calibers
— Muzzle velocity: 825 m/sec
— Rate of train: 25°/sec
— Rate of elevation: 25°/sec
— Arc of elevation: −10° to +30°
— Rate of fire: 30 rounds/min — 100 rounds immediately available in the ready firing station

— Cartridge weight: 11.3 kg
— Shell weight: 5.9 kg
— Warhead weight: 0.54 kg
— Maximum range, surface mode: 7 to 8,000 m.

SUBMARINES

NOTE: *The JKL firm (Lübeck) has received an order from the West German Navy for the study of a 750-ton submarine to be designated the type 210. This type of submarine is designed to replace the 15 type 207 submarines in the Norwegian Navy and possibly the German type 205 submarines.*

♦ *15 German 207 class (350 tons)*

		L	In serv.
S 300	ULA	19-12-64	7-5-65
S 301	UTSIRA	11-3-65	1-7-65
S 302	UTSTEIN	19-5-65	9-9-65
S 303	UTVAER	30-6-65	1-12-65
S 304	UTHAUG	8-10-65	16-2-66
S 305	SKLINNA	21-1-66	27-5-66
s 306	SKOLPEN	24-3-66	17-8-66
S 307	STADT	10-6-66	15-11-66
S 308	STORD	2-9-66	9-2-67
S 309	SVENNER	27-1-67	1-7-67
S 315	KAURA	16-10-64	5-2-65
S 316	KINN	30-11-63	8-4-64
S 317	KYA	20-2-64	15-6-64
S 318	KOBBEN	25-4-64	17-8-64
S 319	KUNNA	16-7-64	1-10-64

Bldr: Rheinstahl-Nordseewerke (Emden)

Kya (S 317)   1970

D:	370 tons surfaced/482 submerged	**Dim:**	45.41 × 4.60 × 4.58
S:	17/13.5 kts	**Man:**	17 men
A:	8/533-mm TT fwd	**M:**	diesel-electric; 1,200/1,700 hp

REMARKS: These submarines are based on the U 4 class of the West German Navy but they have a stronger hull. They are going to be refitted with new sensors, batteries, and wire-guided torpedoes.

FRIGATES

♦ *5 Oslo class based on the U.S. Dealey class*

	Bldr	Laid down	L	In serv.
F 300 OSLO	Marinens Hovedverft, Horten	1963	17-1-64	29-1-66
F 301 BERGEN	Marinens Hovedverft, Horten	1963	23-8-65	15-6-67
F 302 TRONDHEIM	Marinens Hovedverft, Horten	1963	4-9-64	2-6-66
F 303 STAVANGER	Marinens Hovedverft, Horten	1964	4-2-66	1-12-67
F 304 NARVIK	Marinens Hovedverft, Horten	1964	8-1-65	30-11-66

Penguin launchers and *Sea Sparrow* aboard the *Bergen*

Bergen (F 301)   1975

FRIGATES (continued)

D: 1,450 tons (1,850 fl)   **Dim:**   96.62 (93.87 pp) × 11.17 × 4.40
S: 25 kts   **Range:**   4,500/15
Man: 11 officers, 19 petty officers, 120 men
A: After refit (1972-76): 4/76-mm AA automatic (II × 2) — 6 launchers for
      Penguin missiles, 1 Sea Sparrow BPDMS, 1 Terne ASW RL — 2/Mk 32
      ASW TT for Mk 44 torpedoes
Electron Equipt: Radars: 1/DRBV 22, 1/HSA fire control
                Sonars: 1 Terne III Mk 3 attack, 1/AN SQS 36
M: STAL-Laval PN 20 GT; 1 prop   **Boilers:**   2 Babcock 42.18 kg/cm²
      superheat: 454°; 20,000 hp   **Electric:**   1,100 kw

♦ *2 Sleipner class*

P 950 SLEIPNER (9-11-63) — in serv. 29-4-65
P 951 AEGER (24-9-65) — in serv. 31-3-67
    Bldr: Nylands Verksted, Oslo — (Author. 1960)

Sleipner (P 950)   HLM

D: 600 tons (790 fl)   **S:**   over 20 kts   **Dim:**   69.33 × 7.90 × 2.50
A: 1/76-mm — 1/40-mm AA — 1 ASW Terne RL — 6/324-mm Mk 32 ASW TT
      (III × 2) — depth charges   **Man:**   61 men
Electron Equipt: Radars: 1/V-DO
                Sonars: 1 Terne III Mk 3 attack, 1/AN SQS 36
M: 4 Maybach diesels; 2 props; 9,000 hp

GUNBOATS

♦ *6 Snögg class*

P 980 SNÖGG   **P 982 SNARR**   **P 984 KVIK**
P 981 RAPP   **P 983 RASK**   **P 985 KJAPP**
    Bldr: Båtservice Verft, Mandal (1970-71)
D: 140 tons (fl)   **S:**   36 kts   **Dim:**   36.58 × 6.20 × 1.65
A: 1/40-mm AA — 4/533-mm TT for wire-guided torpedoes and usually 2 single
      missile-launchers, one on each side, for Penguin missiles.   **Range:**
      550/36
M: Maybach diesels; 2 props; 7,200 hp   **Man:**   3 officers, 17 men.

Snarr (P 982)   J. C. Bellonne 1974

♦ *20 Storm class*

	L			L
P 960 STORM	19-3-63	**P 970 BRANN**	3-7-66
P 961 BLINK	28-6-65	**P 971 TROSS**	29-9-66
P 962 GLIMT	27-9-65	**P 972 HVASS**	20-12-66
P 963 SKJOLD	17-2-66	**P 973 TRAUST**	18-11-66
P 964 TRYGG	25-11-65	**P 974 BROTT**	27-1-67
P 965 KJEKK	27-1-66	**P 975 ODD**	7-4-67
P 966 DJERV	28-4-66	**P 976 PIL**	29-3-67
P 967 SKUDD	25-3-66	**P 977 BRASK**	27-5-67
P 968 ARG	24-5-66	**P 978 ROKK**	1-6-67
P 969 STEIL	20-9-66	**P 979 GNIST**	15-8-67

    Bldr: Norway

Blink (P 961)   without her *Penguin* missiles

D: 100 tons (125 fl)   **Dim:**   37 (35.98 pp) × 5.87 × 1.55
S: over 30 kts   **Man:**   4 officers, 9 petty officers, 13 men
A: 1/76-mm Mk TAK 76 automatic — 1/40-mm — 6 Penguin launchers
M: Maybach MB 872 A diesels; 2 props; 7,200 hp

♦ *14 based on the Swedish Jagaren class ordered in 6-75*

    Bldr: Bergens Mekaniske Verksteder; 10 in Bergen and 4 at Alta.
D: 120 tons (155 fl)   **S:**   34 kts   **Dim:**   36.5 × 6.2
A: 1/40-mm AA — 4 Penguin missiles — 4/533-mm TT   **Man:**   20 men
M: 2/3,500-hp diesels   **Range:**   440/43

GUNBOATS (continued)

Traust (P 973) 1970

PATROL TORPEDO BOATS

♦ *20 Nasty/Tjeld class*

	In serv.			In serv.
P 343 TJELD	6-60		P 381 HAI	7-64
P 344 SKARV	11-60		P 382 SEL	5-63
P 345 TEIST	12-60		P 383 HVAL	3-64
P 346 JO	2-61		P 384 LAKS	5-64
P 347 LOM	4-61		P 385 KNURR	1966
P 348 STEGG	6-61		P 386 DELFIN	5-66
P 349 HAUK	8-61		P 387 LYR	1966
P 350 FALK	9-61		P 388 GRIBB	3-62
P 357 RAVN	12-61		P 389 GEIR	8-62
P 380 SKREI			P 390 ERLE	6-62

Bldr: Westermoen, Mandal

D: 70 tons (82 fl)   **Dim:** 24.50 × 7.50 × 1.95
S: 45 kts (40 cruising)   **Range:** 450/40 — 600/25

Lom (P 347)

Teist, Tjeld, Skarv (P 345, 343, 344)   Shbldg. and Sh. Record

A: as a torpedo boat: 1/40-mm AA — 1/20-mm AA — 4/533-mm TT
as a gunboat: 2/40-mm AA — 2/533-mm TT
Can be modified as a minelayer and fitted with an RL as well.
M: 2 Napier-Deltic T 18-37 diesels with turbo-compressors; 2 props; 6,280 hp.   **Man:** 4 officers, 4 petty officers, 12 men   **Fuel:** 10 tons

REMARKS: Designed by the Norwegian engineer Jan H. Linge of Boat Service Ltd. of Oslo. Mahogany hull, engines and fittings imported from Great Britain. Two were delivered in 1962 to the navy of the West German Federal Republic which later sold them to Turkey. Two were transferred to the U.S.A. in 1963. Six have been ordered by Greece.

MINELAYERS

♦ *2 of a new class to be delivered in 1977*

N . . .   N . . .

Bldr: Norway

D: . . .   **S:** 15/16 kts   **Dim:** . . .
A: . . .   **Man:** 32 men
M: 2 diesels; 2 props, 1 bow prop

REMARKS: Will be able to carry out the following missions: minelaying (320 carried on three decks with an automatic hoist — 3 minelaying rails), torpedo recovery, personnel and cargo transport, fishery protection.

♦ *4 ex-U.S. Auk-class minesweepers*

		Bldr	L	In serv.
N 47 TYR (ex-*Strive, MSF-117*)		American SB Co, Lorain	16-5-42	9-11-42
N 48 GOR (ex-*Sustain, MSF-119*)		American SB Co, Lorain	23-6-42	27-10-42

MINELAYERS (continued)

N 49 BRAGE (ex-*Triumph, MMC-3*)	Associated SB, Seattle	25-2-43	3-2-44
N 50 ULLER (ex-*Sneer, MSF-112*)	American SB Co, Lorain	23-5-42	21-10-42

Tyr (N 47)

D: 890 tons (1,250 fl)   **Dim:** 67.20 (65 pp) × 9.75 × 3.40
S: 18 kts   **Man:** 105 men
A: 1/76-mm AA — 4/20-mm AA — 2 hedgehogs — 2 depth charge projectors — mines
M: diesel-electric propulsion with General Motors diesels; 2 props; 2,070 hp

REMARKS: Transferred in 1959-60. *49* has for armament 1/40-mm AA, 1/ASW Terne RL, 6/ASW 324 Mk 32 TT (III × 2).

		Bldr	L
N 51 BORGEN		Marinens Hovedverft, Horten	29-4-60

D: 282 tons   **S:** 9 kts   **Dim:** 31.28 × 8 × 3.35
M: 2 General Motors diesels; Voith-Schneider prop; 330 hp

MINESWEEPERS

♦ *10 ex-U.S. MSC/AMS coastal class*

1)

M 311 SAUDA (ex-*AM-131*)	**M 331 TISTA** (1-6-54)
M 312 SIRA (ex-*AM-132*)	**M 332 KVINA** (21-7-54)
M 315 OGNA (18-6-54)	**M 334 UTLA** (2-3-55)
M 316 VOSSO (16-6-54)	

Bldr: Båtservice Verft, Mandal (*315, 332, 334*); Forenede Båtbyggeri, Risör (*331*); Skåluren, Rosendal (*316*); except *311, 312,* U.S.A.

2)

M 313 TANA (ex-*Roeselaere,* ex-*MSC-103*)	
M 314 ALTA (ex-*Arlon,* ex-*MSC-104*)	Bldr: U.S.A. 1953-54
M 317 GLOMMA (ex-*Bastogne,* ex-*MSC-151*)	

D: 370 tons (465 fl)   **S:** 14/13 kts   **Dim:** 43.90 × 8.23 × 2.55
A: 2/20-mm AA   **Man:** 38 men   **Range:** 2,500/12
M: 2 General Motors diesels; 2 props; 1,600 hp   **Fuel:** 40 tons

REMARKS: *M 313, 314, 317* were transferred by Belgium in 1966 in exchange for two ocean minesweepers, the *Lagen* and the *Namsen.*

AMPHIBIOUS SHIPS

♦ *3 of 200 tons*

A 30 TJELSUND, A 31 KVALSUND, A 32 RAFTSUND
Similar to the French EDIC class.

♦ *4 of 560 tons*

A 33 REINSØYSUND (1-72), **A 34 SØRØYSUND** (6-72), **A 35 MAURSUND** (9-72). **A . . . BORGSUND** (1973), **A . . . ROTSUND** (1973).
Bldr: Mjellem & Karlsen, Bergen
D: 560 tons   **S:** 11 kts   **Dim:** 51.40 × 10.30 × 1.85
A: 3/20-mm, 4/12.7-mm machine guns, minelaying rails for 120 mines — Cargo capacity: 5 Leopard tanks, 80/180 men
M: 2 MTU diesels; 2 props   **Man:** 2 officers, 7 men — Double-folding bow ramp door.

FISHERY PROTECTION VESSELS

♦ *1 new class*

P 950 NORNEN — Bldr: Mjellem & Karlsen, Bergen (20-8-62)

Nornen (P 950)

D: 1,000 tons   **S:** 17 kts   **Dim:** 61.50 × 10 × 3.80
M: 4 diesels; 1 prop; 3,700 hp   **Man:** . . .
A: 1/76-mm fwd — 1/40-mm aft — 1 ASW Terne RL

FARM (22-2-62)   **HEIMDAL** (7-3-62)
Bldr: Bolsones Verft, Molde (*Heimdal*); Ankerlokken Verft, Frederikstad (*Farm*).
D: 488 tons (600 fl)   **S:** 16.5 kts   **Dim:** 54.30 × 8.20 × 2.80
A: 1/76-mm   **M:** 2 diesels; 2 props; 2,400 hp

NORWAY (*continued*)
FISHERY PROTECTION VESSELS (*continued*)

♦ *3 modified former whale hunters*

ANDENES, A 531 NORDKAPP, SENJA — Bldr: Netherlands, 1957; purchased in 1965.

Nordkapp (A 531)   1969

D: 500 tons	**S:** 16 kts	**Dim:** 56.70 × 9.45 × 4.90	
A: 1/76-mm	**Man:** 29 men	**M:** M.A.N. diesel; 2,300 hp	

LOGISTIC SUPPORT

♦ *1 former 1940 River-class frigate*

A 535 VALKYRIEN (18-9-43) (ex-Norwegian *Garm*, ex-Canadian *Toronto*)
  Bldr: Davie SB, Lauzon
    D: 1,570 tons (2,250 fl)   **S:** 18 kts   **Dim:** 91.84 × 11.17 × 4.34
    M: Triple expansion; 2 props; 5,500 hp
    Boilers: 2 three-drum Admiralty
  Support ship for fast small craft.

♦ *2 tenders for combat divers*

DRAUG (2-72)   **SARPEN**
    D: 250 tons   **S:** . . .   **Dim:** . . . × . . . × . . .
    M: . . .

VARIOUS

♦ *1 training ship*

N . . .
    D: . . .   **S:** . . .   **Dim:** . . .
    A: . . .
    M: . . .

REMARKS: Will be used as well for patrolling the continental shelf. While awaiting the commissioning of this ship, the 667-ton *Salten* has been put in service.

♦ **A 533 NORGE** (ex-*Philante*) (1-2-37) — Royal yacht
  Bldr: Camper & Nicholsons Ltd.
    D: 1,686 tons   **Dim:** 76.27 × 8.53 × 4.56
    S: 14 kts   **M:** 8-cyl diesel; 2 props; 2,600 hp

OMAN

MERCHANT MARINE: 4 ships — 2,249 grt

PATROL BOATS

♦ *7 FPBs Neal class*

	In serv.		In serv.
B 1 AL BUSHRA	22-1-73	**B 5 N** . . .	
B 2 AL MANSUR	26-3-73	**B 6 N** . . .	
B 3 AL NEJAH	13-5-73	**B 7 N** . . .	
B 4 N . . .			

  Bldr: Brooke Marine Ltd, Lowestoft 1972-76.
    D: 135 tons (153 fl)   **S:** 25 kts   **Dim:** 37.50 × 6.65 × 1.65
    A: 2/40-mm AA   **Man:** 29 men   **Range:** 3,250/12
    M: 2 Paxman Ventura, 16-cyl diesels; 2 props; 4,800 hp

♦ *1 which can be used as a yacht*

	Bldr	In serv.
AL SAID	Brooke Marine Ltd, Lowestoft	1971

D: 785 tons (930 fl)	**Dim:** 57.40 × 10.70 × 3.05	
S: 17 kts **A:** . . .	**Man:** 11 officers, 23 men	
M: 2 Paxman Mk 12 YJCM diesels (1,500 rpm, 2 props, 3,350 hp)		

REMARKS: Also used as a yacht (quarters for 37).

OMAN (*continued*)

PATROL BOATS (*continued*)

♦ *2 ex-Dutch coastal minesweepers*

P 1 AL NASSIRI	5-3-55	**P 2 AL SALIHI**	23-4-55
(ex-*M 808 Axel*)		(ex-*M 811 Aalsmeer*)	

D:	373 tons (417 fl)	**Dim:**	46.63 × 8.78 × 2.28
S:	14 kts	**A:** 2/40-mm AA	**Man:** 40 men
M:	2 Werkspoor diesels; 2 props; 2,500 hp		

REMARKS: Purchased in 1974, air conditioned and fitted out as patrol boat. Similar to the French *Sirius* and British "*-ton*" class. Their minesweeping equipment has been removed.

VARIOUS

♦ *7 landing craft*

PAKISTAN

PERSONNEL: Approximately 13,000 men

MERCHANT MARINE (1-7-74): 88 ships — 494,065 grt

PRINCIPAL WARSHIPS IN SERVICE OR UNDER CONSTRUCTION AS OF 1 OCTOBER 1975

	L	D	Main armament
♦ *7/8 submarines*			
3 HANGOR	1969–70	869	12/550-mm TT
3/4 midget	1970	70	
♦ *1 cruiser*			
BABUR (obsolete)	1942	5,900	8/135-mm AA
♦ *8 frigates*			
2 British WHITBY class	1954	2,150	2/114-mm AA, 2/40-mm AA
1 BADR	1945	2,325	4/114-mm AA, 8/533-mm TT
3 ALAMGIR	1944–45	1,710	3/114-mm AA, 4/533-mm TT
2 TIPPU SULTAN	1941	1,800	2/102-mm 4/533-mm TT
♦ *7 minesweepers*			
♦ *9 patrol boats*			

NAVAL AVIATION:

— 3 Atlantic patrol aircraft (end of 1975)
— 6 Sea King helicopters (1976) with AM 39
— 4 Alouette III helicopters
— 2 Albatros amphibians
— 2 Cessna liaison aircraft

SUBMARINES

♦ *3 Hangor class (French Daphné class)*

	Bldr	Laid down	L	In serv.
S 131 HANGOR	Arsenal de Brest	12-67	30-6-69	1971
S 132 SHUSHUK	Ch. Nav. Ciotat (le Trait)	12-67	30-7-69	1971
S 133 MANGRO	Ch. Nav. Ciotat (le Trait)	6-68	7-2-70	1971

Shushuk (S 132)   1970 J. C. Bellonne

D:	869 tons surfaced/1,043 submerged	**Dim:**	57.75 × 6.75 × 4.56
S:	15.5/13 kts	**Man:**	5 officers, 45 men
A:	12/550-mm TT (8 fwd, 4 aft)		
M:	diesel-electric propulsion (SEMT-Pielstick engines, 450 kw); 2 props; 1,300/1,600 hp		

Mangro (S 133)   1970

SUBMARINES (*continued*)

REMARKS: See *Daphné* class under French section. The Portuguese submarine *Cachalote* of the same class is to be transferred to the Pakistan Navy.

The *S 131 Hangor* sank the Indian frigate *Kukri* during the Indo-Pakistani conflict.

♦ *3 or 4 small Italian-built, 70-ton submarines (Cosmos class) used for the transport of raiders — no armament*

D:	70 tons	**Dim:**	16 × 1/80 × . . .
S:	11/6.5 kts	**Man:**	4 men
Range:	1,200 surface		

CRUISER

		Laid		
	Bldr	down	L	In serv.
84 BABUR (ex-*Diadem*)	Hawthorn Leslie	11-39	26-8-42	1-44

D:	5,900 tons (7,560 fl)	**Dim:**	156.05 (154.23 pp) × 15.70 × 5.70
S:	18 kts	**Range:**	4,000/13 — 2,900/20 — 1,300/29
A:	8/133.5-mm AA (II × 4) — 14/40-mm AA — 4/47-mm (saluting battery)		
	6/533-mm TT (III × 2).		
Armor:	belt: 52 to 76 — deck: 52 — turret: 25 — conning tower: 25		
Man:	590 men (peace)		
M:	Parsons GT; 4 props; 62,000 hp; 4 Admiralty boilers		
Fuel:	1,000 tons		

REMARKS: Sold to Pakistan in 2-56. Modernized. Used as a floating anti-aircraft battery. Can make way but at a much reduced cruising speed.

FRIGATES

♦ *2 British Whitby class — transferred in 1975*

		Laid		In
	Bldr	down	L	serv.
N . . . (ex-*Whitby*)	Cammell Laird	1953	2-7-54	7-56
N . . . (ex-*Scarborough*)	Vickers-Armstrongs	1953	4-4-55	5-57

PHOTO REQUESTED

D:	2,150 tons (2,560 fl)	**Dim:**	112.77 (109.73 pp) × 12.50 × 5.26
S:	26/25 kts	**Man:**	7 officers, 145 men **Range:** 4,500/12
A:	. . .	**Electron Equipt:**	Radars:
			Sonars: 1/177
M:	English Electric GT; 2 props; 2 Babcock boilers; 30,000 hp		

REMARKS: Will have an Alouette III helicopter.

♦ *1 British Battle class — transferred in 1957*

		Laid		
	Bldr	down	L	In serv.
161 BADR (ex-*Gabbard*)	Swan Hunter	2-44	16-3-45	12-46

Badr (161)   1974

D:	2,325 tons (3,360 fl)	**Dim:**	115.32 (108.20 pp) × 12.95 × 4.10
S:	31 kts	**Man:**	300 men **Range:** 3,000/20
A:	4/114-mm AA (II × 2) — 10/40-mm AA — 8/533-mm TT (IV × 2) — 1		
	Squid — depth charges		
Electron Equipt:	Radars: 1/277, 1/293, 1/US/37		
	Sonars: 1/170, 1/174		
M:	2 Parsons GT; 2 props; two 3-drum Admiralty boilers; 50,000 hp		
Fuel:	680 tons		

REMARKS: *Khaiber* of the same class sunk during the Indo-Pakistani conflict.

♦ *3 British C class transferred in 1958*

		Laid		
	Bldr	down	L	In serv.
160 ALAMGIR (ex-*Creole*)	J. Samuel White (Cowes)	8-44	22-11-45	10-46
162 JAHANGIR (ex-*Crispin*)	J. Samuel White (Cowes)	2-44	23-6-45	7-46
164 SHAH JAHAN (ex-*Charity*)	J.I. Thornycroft (Woolston)	7-43	30-11-44	11-45

Shah Jahan (164)

FRIGATES (*continued*)

D: 1,710 tons (2,500 fl)   **Dim:** 110.55 (106.07 pp) × 10.88 × 3.80
S: 31 kts   **Man:** 200 men   **Range:** 2,800/20 — 1,000/30
A: 3/114-mm AA (I × 3) — 6/40-mm AA — 4/533-mm TT (IV × 1) — 2 Squids
— depth charges
Electron Equipt: Radars: 1/293 — 1/275 fire control
Sonars: 1/174, 1/170
M: 2 Parsons GT; 2 props   **Fuel:** 580 tons
Boilers: two 3-drum Admiralty; 40,000 hp.

♦ *2 British O class, modified as fast type 16 frigates*

	Bldr	Laid down	L	In serv.
260 TIPPU SULTAN (ex-*Onslow*)	John Brown (Clydebank)	7-40	31-3-41	10-41
261 TUGHRIL (ex-*Onslaught*)	Fairfield (Glasgow)	1-41	9-10-41	6-42

Tippu Sultan (260)   1968

D: 1,800 tons (2,300 fl)   **Dim:** 103.20 (wl) × 10.68 × 4.70
S: 35 kts (31 fl)   **Range:** 2,700/12 — 1,700/20
A: 2/102-mm — 5/40-mm AA — 4/533-mm TT (IV × 1) — 2 Squids
Electron Equipt: Radars: 1/293 — Sonars: 1/174, 1/170
M: Parsons GT; 2 props; 40,000 hp
Boilers: two 3-drum Admiralty
Fuel: 430 tons

REMARKS: Transferred at the end of 1949, rebuilt (1958-59). *261* used for instruction of the midshipmen from the naval academy. No longer gets underway.

MINESWEEPERS

♦ *7 ex-U.S. MSC class*

M 160 MAHMOOD (ex-*MSC-267*)	**M 165 MUKHTAR** (ex-*MSC-274*)
M 161 MOMIN (ex-*MSC-293*)	**M 166 MUNSIF** (ex-*MSC-373*)
M 162 MURABAK (ex-*MSC-262*)	**M 167 MOSHAL** (ex-*MSC-294*)
M 164 MUJAHID (ex-*MSC-261*)	

Same characteristics as the French *Acacia* class.
Transferred by the U.S.A. under the M.A.P., in 1956-58 (5) and 1963 (2).
Muhafiz of the same class sunk during the 1971 Indo-Pakistani conflict.

PATROL BOATS

♦ *12 of the Chinese Shanghai II class:* (8 transferred in 1972, 4 in 1973)

P 141 LAHORE   **P 145 PISHIN**   **P 149 SAHIVAL**

Mukhtar (M 165)   1974

Quetta   1974

P 142 MULTAN	**P 146 KALAT**	**P 150 BANNU**
P 143 GUILGIT	**P 147 SUKKUR**	**P 151 LARKANA**
P 144 MARDAN	**P 148 QUETTA**	**P 152 BAHAWALPUR**

Bldr: Peoples Republic of China — transferred in 1972.
D: 120 tons/130 (fl)   **Dim:** 39.6 × 5.50 × 1.70
S: 30 kts   **Man:** 28 men.
A: 4/37-mm AA (II × 2) — 4/25-mm AA (II × 2) athwartships
M: 4 diesels; 4 props

P 140 RAJSHAHI

Bldr: Brooke Marine, Lowestoft (1965). Welded construction, light metal used in the superstructure.
D: 115 tons (143 fl)   **Dim:** 32.62 (30.48 pp) × 6.10 × 1.55.
S: 24 kts   **Man:** 19 men
A: 2/40-mm AA (70-cal)
M: 2 Mercedes-Maybach × 1,700 hp

REMARKS: Three — *Jessore*, *Comilla* and *Sylhet* — were sunk during the 1971 Indo-Pakistani conflict.

♦ *2 ex-British 1943 HDML type*

SDML 3517, 3520 (ex-*1266*)

PAKISTAN (*continued*)
PATROL BOATS (*continued*)

1968

D:	56 tons (fl)	**A:**	1/47-mm — 1/20-mm
S:	12 kts	**Man:**	14 men

HYDROFOIL PATROL BOATS
♦ *6 Chinese Hu Chwan class*

HDF 01, 02, 03, 04, 05, 06.

D:	80 tons	**Dim:**	29 × 4.90 × 1 or .31 × 7.50
S:	50 kts	**M:**	diesels; 3 props
A:	2 torpedoes — 2 machine guns (II × 1)		

HYDROGRAPHIC SHIP

	Bldr	Laid down	L	In serv.
262 ZULFIQUAR (ex-*F-265*)	Smith's Dock (Gt. Br.)	4-42	12-10-42	3-43

D:	1,370 tons (2,100 fl)	**Dim:**	91.84 × 11.17 × 4.34
S:	19 kts	**Man:**	150 men
A:	1/102-mm fwd — 2/40-mm		

Range: 3,000/12
M: Triple expansion; 2 props; 2 boilers; 5,500 hp Former *River*-class frigate.

LOGISTIC SUPPORT

♦ *3 oilers*

A 41 DACCA (ex-U.S. *Mission Santa Clara, AO-132*) Transferred 1-63.

D:	22,380 tons (fl)	**Dim:**	159.40 × 20.73
S:	15 kts	**Cargo:**	20,000 tons

Fleet replenishment oiler.

A 298 ATTOCK (ex-U.S. *YO-249*) — harbor oiler (1960) — 1,225 tons (fl) **S:** 8 kts

♦ *2 tugs*

A 42 MADADGAR (ex-U.S. *ATF-94*) — rescue ship (7-43) — 1,575 tons (fl) — 3,000 hp **S:** 16 kts
. . . **RUSTOM** — tug (Netherlands, 1955) — 1,000 hp **S:** 9 kts

♦ *2 floating docks*

PESHAWAR (ex-U.S. *ARD-6*)
FD II (1974 — RFA) Lifting power: 1,200 tons

♦ *1 water carrier*

YW 15 ZUM ZUM (1957) — Bldr: Italy

PANAMA

MERCHANT MARINE (1-7-74): 1,962 ships — 11,003,227 grt
(tankers: 248 ships — 4,681,757 grt)

♦ *2/103-foot Vosper-Thornycroft patrol boats*

GC 10 PANQUIACO (22-7-70), **GC 11 LIGIA ELENA** (25-8-70)
Manned by the National Guard of Panama; same characteristics and appearance as the 2 *Trinity* class of Trinidad and Tobago.

♦ *2 patrol boats, transferred by the U.S.A. in 1962*

D:	35 tons	**Dim:**	21 × 4.27 × 1.55
S:	13 kts	**Man:**	10 men
A:	1 machine gun	**M:**	400 hp

♦ *3 coastal patrol vessels transferred by the U.S.A. between 1965 and 1966, Air Sea Presence class.*

♦ *2 harbor surveillance boats transferred by the U.S.A. in 1947.*

PAPUA

New Guinea

PATROL BOATS

♦ *Five for the surveillance in the rivers of Papua and New Guinea:*

P 84 AITAPE, P 92 LAVADA, P 92 LAE, P 94 MADANG, P 85 SAMARAI

D:	146 tons (fl)	**S:**	21/24 kts
Dim:	32.76 (30.48 pp) × 6.20 × 1.90		
A:	1/40-mm — 2 machine guns		
M:	2 Davey-Paxman Ventura, 16-cyl. diesels; 3,460 hp		

REMARKS: Transferred by Australia in 1975.

AMPHIBIOUS SHIPS

♦ *2 ex-Australian LCU type transferred in 1975*

L 131 SALAMAUA
L 132 BUNA

D:	180 tons (360 fl)	**Dim:**	44.50 × 12.20 × 1.90
S:	8 kts	**M:**	diesel — 675 hp.

PARAGUAY

MERCHANT MARINE (1-7-74): 26 ships — 21,390 grt
(tankers: 3 ships — 293 grt)

♦ *2 obsolete gunboats* **C 1 PARAGUAY** (ex-*Comodoro Meya*), **C 2 HUMAITA** (ex-*Capitan Cabral*) — Bldr: Odero, Genoa (1930)

D:	636 tons/745 avg (865 fl)	**Dim:**	70.15 × 10.70 × 1.65
S:	17.5 kts	**Range:**	1,700/16
A:	4/120-mm — 3/76-mm AA — 2/40-mm AA — 6 mines	**Man:** 86 men
M:	Parsons GT; 2 props; 3,800 hp	**Fuel:** 170 tons

♦ *3 ex-Argentinian minesweepers, transferred in 1964–67*

CAPITAN MESA (ex-*Parker*)   **TENIENTE FARINA** (ex-*Py*)
NANAVA (ex-*Bouchard*)   Bldr: Argentina (1937–38)

D:	450 tons (650 fl)	**Dim:**	59.50 × 7.30 × 2.60
S:	16 kts	**A:**	4/40-mm AA — 2 machine guns
M:	2 M.A.N. diesels; 2,000 hp	**Range:** 3,000/12 **Man:** 170 men

♦ **P 1** (ex-*U.S. CGS-20417*)   **P 2** (ex-*U.S. CGS-20418*)

D:	16 tons	**Dim:**	14 × 4.10 × 1
A:	2/20-mm AA	**S:**	19 kts
M:	gasoline engines; 190 hp		

♦ **A 1 Capitan CABRAL,** wooden hull, former tug, small boat used for riverine patrol.

D:	206 tons (fl)	**Dim:**	30.50 × 7 × 2.90
S:	9 kts	**Man:**	47 men
A:	1/76-mm — 2/37-mm		
M:	Reciprocating; 300 hp		

♦ *1 transport*

Q 70 CORRIENTES (ex-Argentinian *BDM-2*, ex-U.S. *LSM-86*)

D:	743 tons (1,095 fl)	**S:**	13 kts	**Dim:**	62 × 10.20 × 1.81

♦ *1 tug*

YLT 599 A 4 (ex-U.S. *YTL-211*)

♦ *1 floating dry dock* (ex-U.S. *AFDL-26* — lifting capacity 1,000 tons)

♦ *1 floating workshop* (ex-U.S. *YR-37*)

♦ *1 dredger*

TENIENTE O CARRERAS SAGUIER

♦ *6 small craft*

P 101 to **P 106**

PERU

PERSONNEL: approximately 8,000 men including 700 officers

MERCHANT MARINE (1-7-74): 675 ships — 513,875 grt
(tankers: 13 ships — 80,940 grt)

NAVAL AVIATION: The air arm includes about a dozen helicopters (Bell, Alouette III), and some fixed-wing aircraft (S2 Tracker, DC 3, Cessna)

WARSHIPS IN SERVICE OR UNDER CONSTRUCTION AS OF 1 OCTOBER 1975

	L	D	Main armament
♦ *8 submarines*			
2 ISLAY	1973–74	900	8/533-mm TT
4 DOS DE MAYO	1953–54	825	6/533-mm TT
(obsolete)			

WARSHIPS IN SERVICE (*continued*)

2 PEDRERA (obsolete)	1944	1,870	10/533-mm TT

♦ *3 cruisers*

1 ALMIRANTE GRAU (obsolete)	1944	9,529	8/152-mm AA — 8/57-mm AA
2 CORONEL BOLOGNESI (obsolete)	1941-42	8,800	9/152-mm — 8/102-mm AA

♦ *2 guided missile destroyers*

2 PALACIOS	1949-52	2,800	8 MM 38 missile launchers — 6/114-mm AA

♦ *2 conventional destroyers*

2 VILLAR (obsolete)	1942-43	2,050	4/127-mm AA — 6/76-mm AA — 7 TT

♦ *6 frigates*

4 Italian LUPO class		2,500	4 SS missiles — 1/27-mm
2 CALVEZ	1944-45	890	1/76-mm — 2/40-mm

♦ *2 minesweepers, 10 patrol boats, 6 river gunboats*

SUBMARINES

♦ *Two German type 209*

	Bldr	L	In ser .
S 45 ISLAY	Howaldtswerke Kiel	1973	23-1-75
S 46 ARICA	Howaldtswerke Kiel	8-74	

- **D:** 980 surfaced/1,230 submerged tons **Dim:** 55 × 6.60 × 5.90
- **S:** 21 kts submerged for 5 min., 12 with snorkel
- **A:** 8/533-mm TT (6 torpedoes in reserve).
- **Man:** 5 officers, 26 men
- **M:** 4 MTU diesel engines each linked to an AEG generator (420 kw) with a single Siemens electric motor of 5,000 kw.

REMARKS: The Argentinian *Salta* class are similar.

♦ *2 ex-U.S. Guppy 1 A class purchased in 7 and 1-74.*

Islay (S 45)   1975

	Bldr	L
S 47 PEDRERA (ex-*Sea Poacher, SS-406*)	Portsmouth NSY	20-5-44
S 48 PACOCHA (ex-*Atule, SS-403*)	Portsmouth NSY	6-3-44

- **D:** 1,870 surfaced/2,400 submerged tons   **Dim:** 93.8 × 8.2 × 5.2
- **S:** 18/15 kts   **Man:** 84 men
- **A:** 10/533-mm TT (6 fwd, 4 aft)
- **M:** 3 diesels; 2 electric motors; 2 props; 4,800 hp

REMARKS: Had not yet been transferred to Peru in 6-75.

♦ *4 Dos de Mayo class*

41 DOS DE MAYO	**43 ANGAMOS**	Bldr: U.S.A. — 1953-57
42 ABTAO	**44 IQUIQUE**	Obsolete

- **D:** 825 surfaced/1,400 submerged tons   **Dim:** 74 × 6.70 × 4.20
- **A:** 1/127-mm (except 41, 43)   **S:** 16/10 kts
- **M:** 2 GM diesels and 2 electric motors; 2,400 hp

REMARKS: At least two of these submarines are supposed to be scrapped soon.

CRUISERS

♦ *1 ex-Dutch anti-aircraft cruiser, purchased in spring 1973*

	Bldr	Laid down	L	In serv.
86 ALMIRANTE GRAU (ex-*de Ruyter*)	Wilton-Fijenoord	9-39	24-12-44	11-53

- **D:** 9,529 tons (11,850 fl)
- **Dim:** 187.32 (182.40 pp) × 17.25 × 6.70
- **S:** 32 kts   **Man:** 920 men
- **A:** 8/152-mm AA (II × 4) — 8/57-mm AA (II × 4) — 8/40-mm AA (II × 4)
- **Electron Equipt:** Radars: 1/LW 01, 1/LW 02, 1/SRG 105, 1/SRG 103, 1/SRG 104

CRUISERS (continued)

Almirante Grau (86)   1972 G. Arra

Armor: Belt: 76 to 102 — Deck: two, 20 to 25
M: Parsons GT; 2 props; 80,000 hp   **Boilers:** four 3-drum Yarrow
Electric: . . . kw

◆ *2 ex-British Newfoundland class*

	Bldr	L
83 CAPITAN QUINONES (ex-*Almirante Grau,* ex-*Newfoundland*)	Swan Hunter	19-12-41
82 CORONEL BOLOGNESI (ex-*Ceylon*)	Alex. Stephen & Son	30-7-42

Coronel Bolognesi (82)

D: 8,800 tons (11,100 fl)   **Dim:** 169.31 × 18.31 × 6.30
S: 29 kts (max)   **Man:** 776/800 men
Range: 7,000/14
A: 9/152-mm (III × 3, 2 fwd, 1 aft) — 8/102-mm AA (II × 4) — 12/40-mm AA.
Armor: Belt: 76 to 102 — Deck: 52 — Turret: 25 to 52 — Conning tower: 102
M: Parsons GT; 4 props; 80,000 hp; 4 Admiralty boilers   **Fuel:** 2,000 tons

REMARKS: The 102-mm guns of the *82* have radar direction. Purchased in 1959, transferred in 12-59 and 1-60. *CQ* has 2 trellis masts; *CB* has a tripod mast aft.

DESTROYERS

◆ *2 ex-British guided missile D class*

	Bldr	L	In serv. after refit
73 PALACIOS (ex-*Diana*)	Yarrow, Glasgow	8-5-52	11-73

Palacios (73)   1973 M.N.

74 FERRE (ex-*Decoy*)	Yarrow, Glasgow	29-3-49	7-73

D: 2,800 tons (3,700 fl)
Dim: 118.87 (111.55 pp) × 13.10 × 5.50
S: 30 kts   **Man:** 250/300 men
Range: 4,400/20
A: 8/MM 38 Exocet SSM launchers — 1 Squid — 6/114-mm AA (II × 3) — 2/40-mm AA
Electron Equipt: Radars: 1 combination air-to-surface search, 1 Decca, 1 Plessey AW 8 1 air search.
M: Pamatreda GT; 2 props
Boilers: 2 Foster-Wheeler (60 kg/cm²)

REMARKS: Welded hull. Purchased in 1969; refit by Cammell Laird; completed at the end of 1973.

◆ *2 ex-U.S. Fletcher class*

	Bldr	L	Transferred
71 VILLAR (ex-*Benham, DD-796*)	Bethlehem Steel, Staten Island	29-8-43	12-60
72 GUISE (ex-*Isherwood, DD-520*)	Bethlehem Steel, Staten Island	24-11-42	10-61

D: 2,050 tons (3,050 fl)   **Dim:** 114.85 (wl) × 12.03 × 5.50
S: 30 kts   **Man:** 15 officers, 260 men
Range: 1,260/30 — 4,400/15
A: 4/127-mm 38-cal (I × 4) — 6/76-mm AA 50-cal (II × 3) — 5/533-mm TT (V × 1) — 2 fixed ASW TT — 2 hedgehogs — depth charge rack
M: General Electric GT; 2 props; 60,000 hp
Boilers: 4 Babcock and Wilcox, 42 kg/cm², superheat 455°.
Fuel: 650 tons

REMARKS: Transferred in 1961 under the M.A.P. Two ships of the same class (*448 LaVallette, 513 Terry*) transferred in 1974 for cannibalization.

FRIGATES

◆ *4 based on the Italian Lupo class ordered in 1974*

	L	In serv.		L	In serv.
N . . .			N . . .		
N . . .			N . . .		

FRIGATES (*continued*)

Villar (71)

Bldr: Cantieri Navali del Tirreno, Riva Trigoso

A: 4 SSM — 1/127-mm AA — 1 Sea Sparrow BPDMS — 6/324-mm Mk 32 ASW TT (III × 2) — 1 helicopter

REMARKS: Will be identical to the *Lupo* class except for armament. The SSM type has not as yet been chosen.

♦ *2 ex-U.S. MSF type*

		Bldr	L
68 GALVEZ (ex-*Ruddy, MSF-380*)		Gulf SB Corp.	29-10-44
69 DIEZ CANSECO (ex-*Shoveler, MSF-382*)		Gulf SB Corp.	10-21-45

D: 890 tons (1,250 fl)   **Dim:** 67.36 (65.90 pp) × 10.51 × 3.30
S: 17 kts   **Man:** 100 men
A: 1/76-mm — 2/40-mm AA — 2 depth charge projectors — 1 hedgehog
M: General Motors diesels; diesel-electric propulsion; 2 props; 3,500 hp

REMARKS: Transferred under the M.A.P. in 12-60.

PATROL BOATS

♦ *6 Vosper type*

		L
21 VELARDE		10-7-64
22 SANTILLANA		24-8-64
23 DE LOS HEROES		18-11-64
24 HERRERA		26-10-64
25 LARREA		18-2-65
26 SANCHEZ CARRION		18-2-65

Bldr: Vosper Ltd, Portsmouth

Diez Canseco (69)

Santillana   Shbldg. and Sh. Record

D: 100 tons (130 fl)   **S:** 25 kts
Dim: 33.40 (31.46 wl) × 6.40 × 2.15
A: 2/20-mm AA (II × 1); being fitted with SS 12 missiles
M: 2 Napier Deltic diesels; 6,200 hp
Man: 4 officers, 27 men

REMARKS: Modification of the *Sri* class built for Malaysia; welded hull; superstructure of light metal; living spaces air-conditioned. Fitted for fishery protection and

PATROL BOATS (continued)

rescue missions. Also fitted with a sonar and in time of war can be modified to carry torpedoes (4) or lay mines. Placed in service in 10-65.

♦ *2 ex-U.S. PGM type transferred in 9-66 and 30-6-72. — Bldr: U.S.A. 1965*

PC 11 RIO SAMA (ex-*PGM-78*) **PC 12 RIO CHIRA** (ex-*PGM-111*)

D:	100 tons (147 fl)	**Dim:**	31.10 × 4.90 × 2
S:	18.5 kts	**Man:**	27 men
A:	1/40-mm AA — 2/20-mm AA		
M:	diesels; 2 props; 1,800 hp.		

REMARKS: A large number of this class ship have been transferred to various navies since 1966 by the U.S.A.

01 RIO ZARUMILLA **04 RIO PIURA** Bldr: Viareggio (Italy)
02 RIO TUMBES In serv.: 5-60

Rio Zarumilla

D:	37 tons (fl)	**Dim:**	20.27 × 5.25 × 2.75
S:	18 kts	**A:**	2/40-mm
Range:	1,000/14		
M:	General Motors diesels; 2 props; 1,200 hp		

MINESWEEPERS

♦ *2 ex-U.S. MSO class, transferred in 1975*

N . . . (ex-*Agressive, MSO-422*)
N . . . (ex-*Embattle, MSO-434*)

D:	637 tons (735 fl)	**Dim:**	52.30 × 10.36 × 3.15
S:	13.75 kts	**Range:**	2,000/12 — 3,000/10
A:	1 or 2/20-mm AA	**Man:**	4 officers, 52 men
M:	2 diesels; 2 variable pitch props; 1,600 hp		

♦ *2 ex-U.S. YMS class*

137 BONDY (ex-*YMS-35*) (21-1-43) **138 SAN MARTIN** (ex-*YMS-25*) (1942)

D:	215 tons (325 fl)	**Dim:**	41.15 × 7.47 × 3.65
S:	12 kts	**Range:**	2,500/8 — 1/600/12
A:	1/76-mm — 2/20-mm AA	**Man:**	30 men
M:	General Motors diesels; 2 props; 800 hp		
Fuel:	19 tons		

REMARKS: Purchased in 1948. Wooden hulls. Fitted for mechanical, magnetic and acoustic minesweeping. Two stacks.

RIVER GUNBOATS (Amazon Flotilla)

	Bldr	Laid down	L	In serv.
13 MARAÑON	John I. Thornycroft	4-50	23-4-51	7-51
14 UCAYALI	John I. Thornycroft	4-50	7-3-51	7-51

Marañon Thornycroft

D:	350 tons (365 fl)	**Dim:**	47.22 × 9.75 × 1.22
S:	12 kts	**Range:**	5,000/10
A:	2/76-mm — 7/20-mm	**Man:**	4 officers, 36 men
M:	Polar diesels; 2 props; 800 hp		

REMARKS: Based at Iquitos and in service on the Upper Amazon. Forced ventilation. Superstructure of light metal.

	Bldr	L
11 AMAZONAS	Electric Boat Co, Groton	1934
12 LORETO	Electric Boat Co, Groton	1934

D:	250 tons	**S:**	15 kts	**Dim:**	46.70 × 6.70 × 1.20
A:	4/76-mm — 1/47-mm — 2/20-mm AA				
Range:	4,000/10				
Man:	5 officers, 20 men		**M:**	diesels; 1 prop; 750 hp	

14 AMERICA (1902-04)

D:	185 tons (240 fl)	**Dim:**	40.50 × 5.90 × 1.40
S:	12 kts	**Man:**	26 men
A:	2/47-mm — 4/AA machine guns		
M:	Reciprocating; 1 prop; 350 hp		
Fuel:	42 tons coal		

RIVER GUNBOATS (*continued*)

Amazonas

301 (ex-16) NAPO — Bldr: Yarrow (1920).

D: 98 tons	**S:** 12 kts
A: 3/47-mm — 2/AA machine guns	
M: Reciprocating; 1 prop; 45 hp	
Boilers: Yarrow	

Dim: 29.50 × 3.05 × 0.90
Man: 22 men
Fuel: oil

Modified as a hospital ship.

♦ *2/10-ton lagoon patrol boats*

PA 11 LAVE   **PA 12 RAMIS**

LOGISTIC SUPPORT

♦ *1 transport*

31 INDEPENDENCIA (ex-*Bellatrix, AKA-3*) — 1940

D: 6,200 tons (14,225 fl)   **Dim:** 140 × 19.20 × 7.95
S: 15 kts   **Man:** 19 officers, 220 men
A: 1/127-mm — 4/76-mm AA 50-cal — 10/20-mm AA
M: Nordberg diesel; 1 prop
Range: 18,000/14 — 6,000 hp

REMARKS: Former U.S. C2-T class cargo ship, refitted in 1954, transferred under the M.A.P. in 2-63; fitted as a transport and used as a training ship for midshipmen.

♦ *2 Ilo class transports*

Bldr: Servicio Industrial de la Marina (SIMA), Callao

131 ILO (serv.: 15-12-71)   **132 RIMAC** (L: 12-71)

D: 18,000 tons fl
Dim: 153.85 (144.53 pp) × 20.40 × 9.20
S: 19.4 kts   **A:** 4/40-mm AA (II × 2)
M: 1/BW 6 K-74 EF class diesel; 1 prop; 11,600 hp

♦ *1 ex-U.S. DE used as a submarine tender*

63 RODRIGUEZ (ex-*Waterman, DE-740*) — 20-6-43

D: 1,750 tons fl   **Dim:** 93 (91.50 pp) × 11.17 × 3.25
S: 19 kts   **Range:** 12,500/11
M: diesel-electric propulsion; 2 props; 6,500 hp

REMARKS: Fitted as a submarine tender.

♦ *4 ex-U.S. landing craft*

34 CHIMBOTE (ex-*LST-283*), **35 PAITA** (ex-*LST-512*) (1963) — Bldr: U.S.A.

D: 1,625 tons (4,088 fl)   **A:** 1/76-mm (*C*), 6/40-mm AA (*P*).

Chimbote purchased in 1951, *Paita* in 1957. The latter is assigned to the naval academy.

36 LOMAS (ex-*LSM-396*), **37 ATICO** (ex-*LSM-554*) (1945) — Bldr: U.S.A.

D: 513 tons (913 fl)   **Dim:** 61.50 × 10.40 × 2.15
S: 12 kts   **M:** diesels; 3,600 hp
A: 2/40-mm AA — 4/20-mm AA
Fuel: 165 tons — Living spaces for 116 men. Purchased in the U.S.A. and transferred in 7-59.

♦ *7 tankers*

151 MOLLENDO (1962, bought in 1967) — Bldr: Japan — In reserve.

D: 6,084 tons (25,670 fl)   **Dim:** 163 × 22 × 9.15
M: 1 B & W diesel; 7,500 hp   **S:** 14 kts

153 TALARA (20-10-54) — Bldr: Burmeister & Wain

D: 7,000 tons   **S:** 12 kts   **Cargo capacity:** 4,800 tons
Dim: 102 × 15.20 × 6.70   **M:** B & W diesel; 2,400 hp

155 PARINAS (12-6-67) — **156 PIMENTEL** (5-4-68)

Bldr: Servicio Industrial de la Marina, Callao

Cargo capacity: 7,000 tons   **Dim:** 125 × 18.90 × 7.30
M: B & W diesel; 5,400 hp   **S:** 14 kts

158 ZORRITOS (8-10-58) — **159 LOBITOS**

Bldr: Servicio Industrial de la Marina, Callao

D: 8.700 tons   **Cargo capacity:** 6,000 tons
Dim: 115.37 × 15.85 × 6.50   **M:** B & W diesel; 2,400 hp
S: 12 kts   **Man:** 60 men

Fitted for replenishment at sea.

♦ **TUGS**

123 GUARDIAN RIOS (ex-*Pinto, ATF-90, Apache* class) (5-1-43)

D: 1,235 tons (1,675 fl)   **Dim:** 62.50 × 11.70 × 4.80
S: 16 kts   **Man:** 85 men
M: diesel-electric; 3,000 hp

136 UNANUE (ex-*Wateree, ATA-174*) (1943)

D: 534 tons (835 fl)   **Dim:** 43.58 × 10.30 × 4.10
S: 13 kts   **M:** diesel-electric propulsion; 1,500 hp

PERU (*continued*)

TUGS (*continued*)

SELENDON (1968) — Bldr: West Germany

D: 1,000 tons   **S:**   **Dim:**
M:

CONTRAESTRE NAVARRO

D: 50 tons.
Tug for the Amazon Flotilla. Added to the fleet in 2-73.

VARIOUS

♦ *3 water carriers*

141 MANTILLA (ex-*ACA*, ex-U.S. *YW-122*, modified in 3-63)

D: 1,800 tons   **S:** 8 kts
Dim: 53 × 9.75 × 2.90   **M:** 1 diesel

ABA 113 (330 tons) built in Peru in 1972.
ABA 001 800-ton barge for the Amazon Flotilla. (1972).

♦ *2 floating docks*

ADF 111 (1,900 tons)
ADF 112 (5,000 tons)

♦ *1 floating training center*

61 CASTILLA (ex-*Bangust, DE-739*)

REMARKS: Pontoon ship at Iquitos. Same characteristics as the *Rodriguez*.

CUSTOMS SERVICE

♦ *6 small craft ordered from SIMA, Callao at the end of 1973.*

	L			L
PCGC 50	8-10-74		**PCGC 53**	
PCGC 51			**PCGC 54**	
PCGC 52			**PCGC 55**	

D: 150 tons   **S:** 25 kts   **Dim:**
A: **Man:**

REMARKS: To be used by harbor administrations and for coastal surveillance. — Endurance: 20 days.

PHILIPPINES

PERSONNEL (1975): 11,000 men including a brigade of Marines.

NAVAL AVIATION (1975): To be equipped with helicopters, liaison, and transport aircraft.

MERCHANT MARINE (1-7-74): 379 ships — 766,478 grt
(tankers: 35 ships — 115,719 grt)

FRIGATE

PS 76 DATU KALANTIAN (ex-U.S. *Booth, DE-170*) launched in 6-43, transferred in 12-67

D: 1,240 tons (1,908 fl)   **Dim:** 93.30 (91.50 pp) × 11.22 × 4
S: 21 kts   **Range:** 11,600/11   **Man:** 165 men
A: 3/76-mm — 6/40-mm AA (I × 6) — 2/20-mm AA — 6/533-mm TT
M: diesels; 6,000 hp   **Fuel:** 300 tons

PATROL BOATS

♦ *2 ex-U.S. Raven/Auk class*

	L	Transferred
PS 69 RIZAL (ex-*Murrelet, MSF-372*)	24-12-44	5-65
PS 70 QUEZON (ex-*Vigilance, MSF-324*)	5-4-44	8-67

D: 890 tons (1,250 fl)   **S:** 18 kts   **Dim:** 67.20 (65 pp) × 9.75 × 3.30
A: 2/76-mm AA — 4/40-mm AA — 4/20-mm AA — 1 hedgehog — 3/324-mm TT
M: diesel-electric; 2 props; 3,500 hp.   **Man:** 100 men

♦ *5 ex-U.S. PCE class (transferred in 8-48)*

		L
PS 28 CEBU	(ex-*PCE 881*)	10-11-43
PS 29 NEGROS OCCIDENTAL	(ex-*PCE 884*)	24-02-44
PS 30 LEYTE	(ex-*PCE 885*)	30-04-45
PS 31 PANGASINAN	(ex-*PCE 891*)	15-06-44
PS 32 ILO ILO	(ex-*PCE 897*)	3-08-45

D: 640 (850 fl)   **S:** 15 kts
Dim: 52.95 × 7.05 × 3.25 (feet) = 180 wl; 184.5 oa × 34 × 9.5
A: 1/76-mm — 6/40-mm AA — 4/20-mm AA   **Man:** 100 men
M: diesel; 2 props; 2,000 hp.

♦ *4 ex-U.S. patrol boats (transferred in 1947-48)*

		L
PS 24 BATANGAS	(ex-*PC-1134*)	18-01-43
PS 25 NUEVA ECIJA	(ex-*PC-1241*)	24-12-42
PS 27 CAPIZ	(ex-*PC-1564*)	19-04-44
PS 80 NUEVA VISCAYA	(ex-*PCE-568*)	25-04-42

D: 280 tons (450 fl)   **S:** 18 kts
Dim: 52.95 × 7.05 × 3.25 (feet) = 170 wl; 173.66 oa × 23 × 10.8
A: 1/76-mm — 1/40-mm AA — 3 or 5/20-mm AA   **Man:** 70 men
M: diesel; 2 props; 2,880 hp   **Fuel:** 60 tons

♦ *4 ex-U.S. patrol gunboats*

		L	Transferred
G 61 AGUSAN	(ex-*PGM-39*)	3-60	Between 1960
G 62 CATAN DUANES	(ex-*PGM-40*)	3-60	and 1961
G 63 ROMBEON	(ex-*PGM-41*)	6-60	
G 64 PALAWAN	(ex-*PGM-42*)	6-60	

G 62 manned by the coast guard.

D: 122 tons (fl)   **S:** 17 kts   **Dim:** 30.60 × 6.50 × 2.60
A: 2/20-mm AA   **M:** diesel; 2 props; 950 hp

REMARKS: The PG 48/53 are practically identical. *Camarines Sur, Sulu, La Union, Antique,* and *Misamis Occidental* have been scrapped or are about to be.

PATROL BOATS (continued)

Palawan (G 64) (ex *P GM 42*)   U.S. Navy

HYDROFOIL CRAFT

♦ *2 of Italian construction*

M 72 CAMIGUIN, M 73 SIQUIJOR — Bldr: Cantieri Navali Leopoldo Rodriguez, Messina (1965).

Camiguin

  D: 28 tons   **S:** 38 kts   **Dim:** 27 × 4.70/7.50 × 2.10
  A: 1/20-mm AA   **Man:** 15 men
  M: 1 Mercedes-Benz diesel; 1,250 hp   **Range:** 400

REMARKS: Based on the commercial *PT 20* type

♦ *2 of Japanese construction*

M 74 BONTOC, M 75 BALEK — Bldr: Hitachi Zosen, Osaka (1966)
  D: 32 tons fl   **S:** 38 kts   **Dim:** 21 × 4.80/7.50 × 2.10
  A: 2/AA machine guns   **Man:** 15 men
  M: 1 Mercedes-Benz diesel; 1,100 hp   **Range:** 400

SMALL BOATS

♦ *20 ex-U.S. inshore patrol boats, "Swift" type* (**300** to **317, 333** and **334**).

Bldr: U.S.A. — 1965
  D: 22.5 tons (fl)   **S:** 25 kts   **Dim:** 15.60 × 4.12 × 1.50
  A: 3/12.7-mm machine guns — 1/81-mm mortar   **Man:** 6 men
  M: diesel; 2 props; 960 hp

See photographs in the Viet Nam section. The *PFC 333* and *334* (former river patrol boats *739* and *710*) were delivered 24-4-75.

♦ *6 Sewart type* (**320–325** *?*)
  D: 33 tons (fl)   **S:** 25 kts   **Dim:** 21.70 × 5.25
  M: 3 diesels; 3 props; 1,590 hp

Ordered in the U.S.A. in 1971.

♦ *3 Australian type* (**326/328**)

Hull built in Australia.

MINESWEEPERS

♦ *2 ex-U.S. ocean minesweepers (transferred in 1972)*

	L	Transferred
M 91 DAVAO DEL NORTE (ex-*Firm*, MSO-444)	9-53	9-73
M 92 DAVAO DEL SUR (ex-*Energy*, MSO-436)	9-53	9-72

REMARKS: Characteristics the same as the French MSO type

♦ *2 ex-U.S. coastal minesweepers (transferred in 1956)*

	L	Transferred
M 55 ZAMBALES (ex-*MSC-218*)	1955	1956
M 56 ZAMBOANGA DEL NORTE (ex-*MSC-219*)	1955	1956

REMARKS: Characteristics the same as the French *Acacia* class.

AMPHIBIOUS SHIPS

♦ *9 ex-U.S. LST class*

	L
LT 38 BULACAN (ex-*LST-843*)	29-11-44
LT 39 ALBAY (ex-*LST-865*)	22-11-44
LT 40 MISAMIS ORIENTAL (ex-*LST-875*)	29-11-44
LT 85 BATAAN (ex-*LST-515*)	21-12-43
LT 86 CAGAYAN (ex-*LST-825*)	11-11-44
LT 87 ILOCOS NORTE (ex-*LST-905*)	30-12-44
LT 93 MINDORO OCCIDENTAL (ex-*LST-222*)	17-8-43
LT 94 SURIGAO del NORTE (ex-*LST-488*)	5-3-43
LT 95 SURIGAO del SUR (ex-*LST-546*)	16-2-44

REMARKS: Three were transferred in 7-49 and 3 in 11-69, the last three in 4-72.
  D: 1,620 tons (4,080 fl)   **S:** 11.6 kts   **Dim:** 100.04 × 14.24 × 4.30
  A: 8/40-mm AA — 2/20-mm   **M:** General Motors diesels; 2 props

♦ *3 ex-U.S. LSM class*

	L	Transferred
LP 41 ISABELA (ex-*LSM-463*)	1944-45	3-61
LP 65 BATANES (ex-*LSM-236*)	1944-45	9-60
LP 68 MINDORO ORIENTAL (ex-*LSM-320*)	1944-45	4-62

  D: 743 tons (912 fl)   **S:** 12 kts   **Dim:** 62.18 × 10.52 × 2.60

AMPHIBIOUS SHIPS (continued)

A: 2/40-mm AA — several 20-mm AA   **Man:** 39 men
M: 2 diesels; 2,800 hp

♦ *12 ex-U.S. LCVP boats transferred in 1-70*

♦ *1 ex-U.S. landing craft repair ship*

AKLAN (ex-*Krishna, ARL-38*) — 1943 — transferred 30-10-71
D: 1,650 tons (3,700 fl)   **Dim:** 99.85 × 15.25 × 4.36
S: 10 kts   **M:** 2 diesels; 1,500 hp

HYDROGRAPHIC SHIPS

♦ *2 Arinya class*

ARINYA, ARLUNYA — Bldr: Walkers Ltd, Australia — In serv.: 1962-64
D: 245 tons   **S:** 10 kts   **Dim:** 33 × 6.60 × 3.15
M: 2 diesels; 336 hp

ATYIMBA — In serv.: 1969
D: 611 tons (fl)   **S:** 11 kts   **Dim:** 43.50 × 9.90 × 4.50
M: 2 diesels; 2 props; 720 hp.

LOGISTIC SUPPORT

♦ *2 ex-U.S. tankers, YO and YOG class*

YO 43 LAKE MAUJAN (ex-*YO-173*), **YO 78 LAKE BOHI** (ex-*YOG-73*) — 1943
D: 520 tons (1,400 fl)   **S:** 8 kts   **Dim:** 53 × 9.70 × 4.70
A: 2/20-mm AA   **M:** diesel; 560 hp; 1 prop

♦ *1 ex-U.S. water carrier*

Y 42 LAKE LANAO (ex-*YN-135*)
D: 1,235 tons (fl)   **S:** 11 kts   **Dim:** 53 × 9.70 × 3
M: 2 diesels; 1,000 hp

♦ *1 ex-U.S. cargo ship transferred in 3-72*

TK 90 MACTAN (ex-*AK-174*) — 1945
D: 4,900 tons (5,636 fl)   **S:** 11.5 kts   **M:** diesel; 1,750 hp

TUGS

♦ *1 rescue tug*

AQ 44 IFUGAO (ex-HMS *Emphatic*, ex-U.S. *AKR-96*) transferred in 7-48
D: 852 tons   **S:** 13 kts   **Dim:** 43.60 × 10.06 × 4.15
A: 1/76-mm — 2/20-mm AA   **M:** diesel-electric; 1,800 hp.

♦ *5 ex-U.S. harbor tugs*

YQ 221 MARANAO (ex-*YTL-554*)   **YQ 224 AETA** (ex-*YTL-449*)
YQ 222 IGOROT (ex-*YTL-572*)   **YQ 225 ILONGOT** (ex-*YTL-427*)
YQ 223 TAGBANUA (ex-*YTL-429*)

VARIOUS

TP 777 ANG PANGULO (ex-*The President*, ex-*Rosax*, ex-*Lapu-Lapu*) — Bldr: Japan (1958).

D: 2,000 tons   **S:** 18 kts   **Dim:** 83.90 × 12.95 × 6.40
A: 2/20-mm AA   **Man:** 90 men.
M: B & W diesels; 5,000 hp; 2 props; — former presidential yacht.

TK 21 MOUNT SAMAT (ex-*Pagasa*, ex-*Santa Maria*, ex-*APO-21*, ex-*AM-281 Quest*) — L: 16-3-44 — Transferred in 7-48
D: 650 tons (945 fl)   **S:** 14 kts   **Dim:** 56.24 × 10.06 × 2.75
A: 1/76-mm — 4/40-mm AA   **Man:** 100 men
M: diesel; 2 props; 1,800 hp

Former American minesweeper. The *Samar* of the same class has been transferred to the geodetic survey service.

♦ *4 ex-U.S. buoy ships*

L 45 LAUIS LEDGE (ex-*FS-185*), **L 46 BOJEADUR** (ex-*FS-203*), **L 48 LIMASAWA** (ex-*FS-169*)
D: 470 tons (811 fl)   **S:** 11 kts   **Dim:** 54.50 × 9.60 × 3.10
M: diesel; 2 props

L 47 PEARL BANK (ex-*L-04*) — 1944 — Transferred in 1953
D: 162 tons (300 fl)   **S:** 6 kts   **Dim:** 37 × 7.27 × 2.45
M: diesel; 2 props; 1,000 hp

COAST GUARD

♦ *2 PX class*

FB 83 ABRA — **FB 84 BULKIDNON** — Bldr: Vosper, Singapore — 1970-71
D: 40 tons   **S:** 25 kts   **Dim:** 26.52 × 5.80 × 1.40
A: 2/20-mm AA   **Man:** 15 men
M: 2/MB 820 diesels — 2,460 hp

♦ *14 ex-U.S. CGS (numbers 100 to 114)*
D: 45 tons   **S:** 20 kts   **Length:** 25

♦ *1 built of reinforced cement and constructed in the Philippines (11 tons).*

PERSONNEL (1975): 20,000 including 1,800 officers.

MERCHANT MARINE (1-7-74): 648 ships — 2,392,318 grt
(tankers: 10 ships — 38,244 grt)

WARSHIPS IN SERVICE OR UNDER CONSTRUCTION AS OF 1 OCTOBER 1975

	L	D	Main armament
♦ *4 submarines*			
4 ORZEL	1962	1,100	8/533-mm TT
♦ *2 conventional or guided missile destroyers*			
1 WARSZAWA (guided missile)	1958	2,850	1 SAN 1 system, 2/130-mm AA
1 GROM	1950-52	2,600	4/130-mm AA, 10/533-mm TT
♦ *6 frigates*			
6 CZINNY	1955	310	1/76-mm AA, 2/37-mm AA
♦ *34 guided missile or patrol torpedo boats*			
12 OSA 1	1964	150	4 Styx systems, 4/30-mm AA
12 P 6	1956-61	55	4/25-mm AA, 2/533-mm TT
10/12 WISLA	1970	70	2/25-mm AA, 4 TT
♦ *24 minesweepers*			
12 TUR	1955-60	410	4/37-mm AA
12 KROGULEC	1963-7	450	6/25-mm AA

♦ *30 patrol boats (Oksyvic, Obluze, Gdansk, Pilica) used for border patrol.*

NAVAL AVIATION:

About 40 fixed-wing aircraft including MIG 17 Fresco (attack), IL 28 Beagle (attack) and about 20 Hare and Hound helicopters, all of Soviet origin.

WEAPONS AND SYSTEMS

Nearly all weapons and systems are of Soviet origin.

SUBMARINES

♦ *4 ex-Soviet W class transferred since 1962*

ORZEL — SOKOL — KONDOR — BIELIK.

Orzel

D:	1,100 surfaced/1,600 submerged tons	**Dim:**	74 × 6.60 × 4.38
S:	16/13 kts	**Range:**	13,000
A:	6/533-mm TT (4 fwdm 2 aft, 18 torpedoes)	**Man:**	60 men
M:	diesels and electric motors; 2 props; 4,000/2,500 hp		

REMARKS: Snorkel fixed abaft the sail.

POLAND

GUIDED MISSILE AND CONVENTIONAL DESTROYERS

♦ *1 ex-Soviet Kotlin SAM class, transferred in 1970.*

275 WARSZAWA — Bldr: U.S.S.R. — 1958

Warszawa 1973

D:	2,850 tons (3,800 fl)	**Dim:**	127 × 12.75 × 4	**Man:**	360 men
S:	34 kts	**Range:**	3,000/18 — 5,500/16		

A: 1 missile launcher (II × 1) for SAN 1 AA missiles — 2/130-mm fwd (II × 1) — 4/45-mm AA (IV × 1) — 2/2500 ASW RL — 5/533-mm TT (V × 1)

Electron Equipt: 1/Head Net C, 1/Don, 1/Sun Visor, 1/Hawk Screech, 1/Peel Group — Sonar: Herkules or Pegas

M: GT; 2 props; 4 boilers; 60,000 hp

♦ *1 ex-Soviet Skory class* — Bldr: Leningrad (1950-52);

274 WICHER (ex-*Skory*)   transferred in 12-57 and 6-58

D:	2,600 tons (3,200 fl)	**Dim:**	121.50 × 12.50 × 4.60
S:	35 kts	**Man:**	22 officers, 240/250 men

A: 4/130-mm (II × 2) — 2/85-mm AA (II × 1) — 7/37-mm AA (I × 7) — 10/533-mm TT (V × 2) — 2 depth charge projectors — 60 mines

GUIDED MISSILE AND CONVENTIONAL DESTROYERS (*continued*)

Electron Equipt: Radars: 1/High Sieve, 1/Neptun, 1/Cross Bird, 1/Half Bow, 1/Top Bow — Sonar: 1/Tamir
M: GT; 2 props; 62,000 hp; 4 boilers   **Range:** 4,700/15

REMARKS: The 273 GROM is being scrapped (11-75).

NOTE: The *Blyskawica* (1937) has been converted into a naval museum.

FRIGATES

♦ *8 ex-Soviet Kronstadt class transferred in 1957.*

CZINNY	**NIEUGIETY**	**ZWRZIETY**	**GROZNY**
ZWROTNY	**ZWINNY**	**ZRECZNY**	**WYTRWALY**

Bldr: U.S.S.R. 1952-54

D: 310 tons (380 fl)   **S:** 23 kts   **Dim:** 51 × 5.90 × 2
A: 1/76-mm — 2/37-mm AA — 4 depth charge projectors — 4 machine guns
Electron Equipt: Radar: 1/Don — Sonar: 1/Tamir
M: diesels; 2 props;   **Fuel:** 20 tons   **Man:** 20 men

REMARKS: Have probably been stricken.

GUIDED MISSILE PATROL BOATS

♦ *12 Soviet OSA 1 class transferred since 1966.*

Bldr: U.S.S.R. (1960)
D: 150 tons (210 fl)   **S:** 35 kts   **Dim:** 40.07 (36.95 bp) × 7.00 × 2
A: 4/30-mm AA (II × 2) — 4 Styx missile launchers (I × 4)
Electron Equipt: Radar: 1/Square Tie, 1/Drum Tilt   **Man:** 25 men.
M: diesels; 3 props; 4,800 hp

PATROL TORPEDO BOATS

♦ *12 Soviet P 6 class*

KT 401 to 420 — Bldr: U.S.S.R. (1958-1961)
D: 55 tons (75 fl)   **S:** 40 kts   **Dim:** 26 × 6.10 × 1.70
A: 4/25-mm AA (II × 2) — 2/533-mm TT
Electron Equipt: 1/Pot Head
M: diesels; 2 props; 4,800/5,000 hp

♦ *10/12 Polish Wisla class* — Bldr: Poland

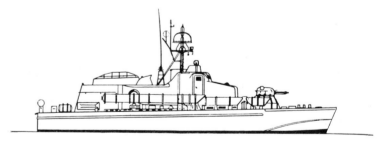

D: 70 tons   **Dim:** 25 × 5.40 × 1.8
S: 34 kts   **Range:** ...
A: 2/25-mm AA — 4 TT   **M:** gas turbines (?)

REMARKS: Will replace the P 6 class torpedo boats.

MINESWEEPERS

♦ *12 Soviet T 43 class.*

T 601 ZUBR	T 605 BIZON	T 609 FOKA
T 602 TUR	T 606 BOBR	T 610 MORS
T 603 LOZ	T 607 ROZMAK	T 611 RYS
T 604 DZIK	T 608 DELFIN	T 612 ZBIK

Bldr: Stocznia Gdynska, Gdynia (1955-60)

D: 410 tons (530 fl)   **S:** 17 kts   **Dim:** 61 × 8.40 × 2.70
A: 4/37-mm AA (II × 2) — 8/15 mm machine guns   **M:** diesels

♦ *12 Polish Krogulec class.*

T 613 N . . .	T 617 JASTRAB	T 621 JASKOLKA
T 614 KROGULEC	T 618 ALBATROS	T 622 ZURAW
T 615 ORLIK	T 619 KANIA	T 623 CZAPLA
T 616 KORMORAN	T 620 TUKAN	T 624 N . . .

Bldr: Stocznia Gdynska, Gdynia (1963-67)

Kormoran (T 616)

D: 450 tons   **S:** 16 kts   **Dim:** 58 × 8.40 × 2.50
A: 6/25-mm AA (II × 3)   **M:** diesels

♦ *28 K8 class inshore minesweepers*

D: 39/41 tons   **S:** 18 kts   **Dim:** 17 × 3.50 × 2.20
M: diesels   **A:** 2/25-mm AA — 2 machine guns

AMPHIBIOUS SHIPS

♦ *20/25 Polnocnyi class built in Poland (see U.S.S.R. section).*

D: 800 to 850 tons   **S:** 18 kts   **Dim:** 75 × 89 × 2.60 (max)
A: 2/30-mm AA (II × 1)   **M:** diesels; 4,000 hp
Electron Equipt: 1/Drum Tilt, 1/Don

REMARKS: Cargo capacity: 350 tons. Some are fitted with 18-barrel land fire support rocket-launchers. There are some variations in the profile (bow and masts).

♦ *15/16 LCVP type.*

HYDROGRAPHIC SHIPS

♦ *2 Soviet Moma class:* **KOPERNIK, HYDROMETR**

D: 1,300 tons   **Dim:** 67 × 10.8   **M:** diesels

LOGISTIC SUPPORT

♦ *5 coastal oilers.*

Z 5, Z 6, Z 7, Z 8, Z 9 (MOSKIT). **D:** 300 tons (fl) — diesel — 4/25-mm AA (II × 2)

Z 8   1973

♦ *3 coastal transports.*

Z 1 KRAB, Z 2 MEDUSA, Z 3 SLIMAK. D: 300 tons (fl)

♦ *2 salvage ships (1974)*

PIAST   LECH

Piast   1974

D: 1,800 tons   **S:** 14.5 kts   **Dim:** 72.6 (67.2 pp) × 11 × 4
A: . . .   **M:** diesel; 1 prop

REMARKS: Carry a diving bell.

VARIOUS

♦ *2 intelligence collectors*

BALTYK

Baltyk 1970

D:	1,200 tons	**S:**	11 kts	**Dim:**	58.30 × 8.75 × 4.20
M:	steam; 1,200 hp				

KOMPAS

D: 183 tons **S:** 16 kts **Dim:** 42 × 6.35 × 1.70
M: diesels; 2 props; 1,000 hp **Man:** 40 men

♦ *1 repair ship* (ex-*Polnocnyi* modified)

♦ *2 torpedo recovery ships*

♦ *18/20 tugs of various classes*

♦ *2 degaussing ships*

♦ *13 diving tenders*

♦ *Approximately 50 small craft*

♦ *1 three-masted sail training ship* (Netherlands 1917)

ISKRA

D: 460 tons **S:** 7.5 kts **Dim:** 39 × 7.60 × 2.95
Man: 38 men **M:** 1 diesel

♦ *3 small Bryza-class training ships.*

BRYZA **PODCHORAZY** **N . . .**
D: . . . **S:** . . . **Dim:** . . .
M: diesels

SURVEILLANCE SHIPS (Manned by frontier guards)

PATROL BOATS (OP/KP)

♦ *4 Oksywic class*

OP 301–304 — Bldr: Poland (1962-64)
D: 170 tons **S:** 20 kts **Dim:** 41 × 6 × 2
A: 2/37-mm AA (I × 2) — 4/25-mm AA (II × 2)
M: diesels

OP 304 1972

♦ *5 Obluze class*

OP . . . — Bldr: Poland (1965)
D: 170 tons **S:** 20 kts **Dim:** 40 × 6 × 2.10
A: 4/30-mm AA (II × 2) **M:** diesels
Electron Equipt: Radars: 1 surface search/Don, 1 fire control/Drum Tilt

Type Obluze 1973

♦ *9 Gdansk class*

OP 311–319 — Bldr: Poland (1960)
D: 120 tons **S:** 20 kts **Dim:** 35 × 5.80 × 1.50
A: 2/37-mm AA **M:** diesels

♦ *3 Pilica class.*

KP 162/163 — Bldr: Poland (1973)
D: . . . **Dim:** . . . **S:** . . .

POLAND (continued)

PATROL BOATS (continued)

OP 315   1970

A: 2/25-mm AA (II × 2)
M: 2 diesels

PORTUGAL

PERSONNEL: Approximately 17,800 men including 3,300 Marines.

NAVAL AVIATION: None as such, but a few Air Force P2V Neptune maritime patrol aircraft are placed at the disposition of the navy.

MERCHANT MARINE (1-7-74): 431 ships — 1,243,128 grt
(tankers: 30 ships — 549,016 grt)

WARSHIPS IN SERVICE OR UNDER CONSTRUCTION AS OF 1 OCTOBER 1975

	L	D	Main armament
♦ 3 submarines			
3 ALBACORA	1966-68	869	12/550-mm TT
♦ 17 frigates			
4 COM. JALO BELO	1966-68	1,650	3/100-mm AA — ASW weapons
3 ALMIR. PEREIRA DA SILVA	1966-68	1,650	4/76-mm AA — ASW weapons
3 JOÃO ROBY	1973-75	1,300	1/100-mm AA — ASW weapons
6 JOÃO COUTINHO	1968-69	1,252	2/76-mm AA — ASW weapons
1 PERO ESCOBAR	1955	1,230	2/76-mm AA — ASW weapons
♦ 40 patrol boats			
3 MAIO	1954-55	325	2/40-mm — 2/20-mm — 1 hedgehog
10 CACINE	1968-70	310 fl	2/40-mm
3 AZEVIA	1951-45	230	2/20-mm
♦ 9 minesweepers			
4 S. ROQUE	1955	370	1/40-mm AA — 2/20-mm AA
5 HORTA	1953-54	357	2/20-mm

ELECTRONIC WEAPONS AND SYSTEMS

The majority of the recently acquired systems are French in origin.

SUBMARINES

♦ 3 French Daphne class

	Bldr	Laid down	L	In serv.
S 163 ALBACORA	Dubigeon-Normandie	9-65	15-10-66	10-67
S 164 BARRACUDA	Dubigeon-Normandie	10-65	24-4-67	5-68
S 166 DELFIM	Dubigeon-Normandie	5-67	23-9-68	10-69

Albacora (S 163)

D: 869 tons surfaced/1,043 submerged   **Dim:** 57.75 × 6.75 × 4.56
S: 13/15.5 kts   **Man:** 5 officers, 45 men
A: 12/550-mm TT (8 fwd, 4 aft)
M: SEMT-Pielstick engines (450 kw) for diesel-electric propulsion; 2 props; 1,300/1,600 hp

REMARKS: See Daphne class in French section. The S 165 Cachalote has been purchased by the Pakistani Navy.

FRIGATES

♦ 4 French Commandant Rivière class

	Bldr	Laid down	L	In serv.
F 480 Com. João BELO	A.C. de Bretagne	5-65	22-3-66	7-67
F 481 Com. Herm. CAPELO	A.C. de Bretagne	5-66	29-11-66	4-68
F 482 Com. Roberto IVENS	A.C. de Bretagne	1-67	11-8-67	11-68
F 483 Com. Sacad. CABRAL	A.C. de Bretagne	8-67	15-3-68	11-69

D: 1,650 tons (2,180 fl)   **Dim:** 103 (98 pp) × 11.50 × 3.80
S: 25 kts (26.5 max)   **Range:** 4,500/15 — 6,000/10-12
A: 3/100-mm AA automatic (I × 3) — 2/40-mm AA — 1 quadruple 305-mm ASW mortar — 6 ASW TT (III × 2)

FRIGATES (*continued*)

Com. João Belo (F 480)

F 480

Man: 214 men
Electron Equipt: Radars: 1/DRBV 22, 1/DRBV 50, 1/DRBR C 31
Sonars: 1/DUBA, 1/SQS 17
M: SEMT-Pielstick diesels; 2 props; 16,200 hp
Electric: kw.

REMARKS: See *Commandant Rivière* class in French section.

♦ *3 U.S. Dealey class*

	Bldr	Laid down	L	In serv.
F 472 Almirante Pereira DA SILVA	Est. Nav. Lisnave, Lisbon	6-62	2-1-64	12-66
F 473 Almirante Gago COUTINHO	Est. Nav. Lisnave, Lisbon	9-63	30-8-65	11-67
F 474 Almirante Magalhaes CORREA	Est. Nav. de Viana do Castelo	1963	26-4-65	11-68

D: 1,450 tons (1,950 fl)
S: 25 kts
Range: 4,500/15
A: 4/76-mm AA (II × 2) — 2/375-mm Bofors ASW RL — 6/ASW TT (III × 2) for Mk 44 torpedoes
Dim: 95.70 × 11.26 × 4.30
Man: 11 officers, 154 men
Electron Equipt: Radars: 1/978 (bank X), 1/MLA 1 B (band L), 1 Mk 34 fire control
Sonars: SQS 29; SQS 35 towed (both U.S.)
M: GT; 1 prop; 2 boilers; 20,000 hp
Fuel: 400 tons

Almir. Gago Coutinho (F 573)   1973 J. C. Bellonne

♦ *1 Italian class*

	Bldr	Laid down	L	In serv.
F 335 PERO ESCOBAR	Nav. Mec. Castellammare	1-55	25-9-55	7-59

Pero Escobar (F 335)   1972 J. C. Bellonne

D: 1,150 tons (trials) 1,230 N/1,600 (fl)
Dim: 93.50 × 10.50 × 3.70
S: 32 kts   **Range:** 2,800/13.5
A: 4/76-mm AA (II × 2) — 6/ASW TT (III × 1) — 2 Squid mortars
Electron Equipt: Radars: 1/MLT 3 A, 1/MLA 1 B, both search
Sonar: 1/SQS 29 (U.S.)
Man: 10 officers, 155 men.
M: GT; 2 props; 24,000 hp
Boilers: 2 Ansaldo-Foster-Wheeler, steam pressure 32 kg/cm²
Fuel: 252 tons

REMARKS: Same hull and machinery as the Venezuelian *Almirante Clemente* class. Will be scrapped soon.

FRIGATES (continued)

♦ *4 João Roby class*

	Bldr	Laid down	L	In serv.
F 486 Baptista DE ANDRADE	Bazan, Cartagena (Spain)	1972	15-3-73	19-11-74
F . . . Alfonso CERQUEIRA	Bazan, Cartagena (Spain)	1973	11-10-73	. . .
F 489 Oliveira ECARMO	Bazan, Cartegena (Spain)	. . .	22-3-74	28-10-75
F 487 João ROBY	Bazan, Cartagena (Spain)	1972	2-6-73	1-3-74

Very similar to the *J. Coutinho* class, but with slightly different armament. Will have the French 100-mm Mk 68 gun, the Vega fire control radar, and possibly the MM 38 Exocet system.

♦ *6 João Coutinho class*

	Bldr	Laid down	L	In serv.
F 475 João COUTINHO	Blohm & Voss	9-68	2-5-69	3-70
F 476 Jacinto CANDIDO	Blohm & Voss	4-68	16-6-69	6-70
F 477 General PEREIRA d'ECA	Blohm & Voss	10-68	26-7-69	10-70
F 484 Augusto CASTILHO	Bazan, Cartagena (Spain)	8-68	5-7-69	11-70
F 485 Honorio BARRETO	Bazan, Cartagena (Spain)	7-68	11-4-70	5-71
F 471 Antonio ENES	Bazan, Cadiz (Spain)	4-68	1-8-69	7-71

João Coutinho (F 475) 1971

D: 1,252 tons (1,348 fl) **Dim:** 84.60 × 10.30 × 3.30.
S: 21 kts **Man:** 9 officers, 84 men
Range: 5,900/18
A: 2/76-mm AA Mk 33 (II × 1) — 2/40-mm AA (II × 1) — 1 hedgehog — 2 depth charge projectors — helicopter platform
Electron Equipt: Radar: 1/MLA 1 B scanning
  Sonar: 1/QCU 2
M: SEMT-Pielstick PA6V-280 diesels; 2 props; 10,960 hp
Electric: 600 kw.

REMARKS: Engines ordered from Chantiers de l'Atlantique, St. Nazaire, France, 1967. Can carry 34 marines. Made more than 22 knots in trials; *F 475* made more than 25 knots; are sometimes called "corvettes."

PATROL AND SURVEILLANCE SMALL CRAFT

♦ *3 French Fougueux class*

	L		L
P 590 BRAVA	2-5-56	P 594 SANTA LUZIA	17-1-57
P 592 BOA VISTA	10-7-56		

Bldr: France or Portugal

Type Brava

D: 366 tons (400 fl) **Dim:** 53.04 × 7.24 × 3
S: 18.7 kts **Man:** 5 officers, 57 men
Range: 3,000/12 — 2,000/15
A: 1 hedgehog — 4 depth charge projectors — 2/40-mm AA — 2/20-mm AA
M: 4 SEMT-Pielstick diesels; 2 props; 3,240 hp
Fuel: 45 tons diesel

REMARKS: Ordered under "offshore" program; the motors were built in the S.G.C.M. factories in Paris. *P 592 Boa Vista* scheduled for disposal list 6-8-75.

♦ *10 Cacine class*

P 1140 CACINE	P 1145 GEBA (21-5-79)
P 1141 CUNENE	P 1146 ZAIRE (28-11-70)
P 1142 MANDOVI	P 1147 ZAMBEZE (1971)

PATROL AND SURVEILLANCE SMALL CRAFT (*continued*)

P 1143 ROMUVA   P 1160 LIMPOPO (9-4-73)
P 1144 QUANZA (30-5-69)   P 1161 SAVE
 Bldr: Arsenal do Alfeite (11-40-43); Est. Nav. do Mondego (the others).

Cacine (P 1140)   1970

D:	310 tons	**S:** 20 kts	**Dim:** 44 × 7.67 × 2.20
A:	2/40-mm AA — 1/37-mm RL		**Man:** 3 officers, 30 men
M:	2 Maybach diesels; 2 props; 4,400 hp		

♦ *3 Azevia class*

P 595 AZEVIA (8-41)   P 597 CORVINA (1942)   P 596 BICUDA (1941)
 Bldr: Arsenal do Alfeite

Azevia (P 595)

D:	230 tons/256 N (270 fl)	**Dim:**	42 (39.75 pp) × 6.50 × 2.15
S:	17 kts	**Man:**	2 officers, 28 men
A:	2/20-mm AA	**Range:**	3,700/11 — 850/17
M:	M.A.N. diesels, 4 tons, 10 cylinders (1 and 2); Sulzer, 2 tons, 7 cylinders (the others); 2 props; 2,400 hp		
Fuel:	25 tons		

REMARKS: Used as fishery protection ships.

♦ P 1148 DOM ALEIXO (12-67) — P 1149 DOM JEREMIAS (12-67).
 Bldr: San Jacintho Aveiro

D:	60 tons	**S:** 16 kts	**Dim:** 25 × 5.20 × 1.60
A:	2 machine guns or 1/20-mm		**Man:** 1 officer, 9 men
M:	Cummins diesels; 2 props; 1,600 hp		

D. Aleixo

♦ P 1156 ALVOR
 Bldr: Arsenal do Alfeite (1966–68)

D:	28 tons (35 fl)	**S:**	12 kts	**Dim:**	20.70 × 5.50 × 2.55
A:	2 machine guns			**Man:**	17 men
M:	Cummins diesels; 2 props; 240 hp				

♦ P 1132 JUPITER   P 1133 VENUS
 Bldr: Est. Nav. do Mondego (1964–65)

D:	31 tons (49 fl)	**S:**	20 kts	**Dim:**	21 × 5 × 1.30
A:	1/20-mm AA	**Man:**	8 men	**Range:**	500/20
M:	2 Cummins diesels; 1,270 hp				

REMARKS: *P 1134 Marte, 1135 Mercurie, 1136 Saturno,* and *1137 Urano* scrapped 21-3/75.

♦ P 1162 ALBATROS   P 1164 AGUIA
 P 1163 ACOR   P 1165 ANDORHINA
 Bldr: Arsenal do Alfeite (1975)

D:	45 tons fl	**S:** 20 kts	**Dim:** 21.88 × 5.25
A:	1/20-mm AA — 1/12.7-mm machine gun		**Range:** 450/18
M:	diesels		

MINESWEEPERS

♦ *4 São Roque* (British design for the Western European coastal class).

M 401 SÃO ROQUE (15-9-55)   M 403 LAGOA (15-9-55)
M 402 RIBEIRA GRANDE (14-10-55)   M 404 ROSARIO (29-11-55)
 Bldr: Ordered early in 1954 (2 as "offshore" commands by the U.S.A.) from Estaleiros Navais da C.U.F., Lisbon.

D:	370 tons (425 fl)	**Dim:**	46.33 (42.68 pp) × 8.75 × 2.50
S:	15 kts	**Man:**	4 officers, 43 men
A:	1/40-mm AA — 2/20-mm AA (II × 1)		
M:	diesels; 2 props; 2,500 hp		

Similar in appearance to the British "*-ton*" class.

♦ *5 ex-U.S. AMS/MSC coastal minesweepers*

M 406 HORTA (ex-*AMS 61*)   M 410 VELAS (ex-*AMS 145*)
M 408 VILA DO PORTO (ex-*AMS 91*)   M 411 LAJES (ex-*AMS 146*)
M 409 SANTA CRUZ (ex-*AMS 92*)
 Bldr: U.S.A. (1951–53); transferred in 1953–54.

MINESWEEPERS (*continued*)

Lajes (Now M 411)

D:	325 tons (387 fl)	**Dim:**	43 (41.50 pp) × 7.95 × 2.85
S:	13 (8 sweeping)	**Range:**	2,500/10
A:	2/20-mm AA	**Man:**	4 officers, 36 men
M:	2 General Motors diesels; 2 props; 900 hp	**Fuel:**	40 tons

Same class as the French *Acacia*.

HYDROGRAPHIC SHIPS

♦ *1 ex-U.S.*

A 527 Commandante Almeida CARVALHO (ex-*Kellar*, AGS-25) 30-7-74

Bldr: Marietta SB (U.S.A.) — Transferred 21-1-72

D:	1,200 tons	**Dim:**	57.50 × 11.70 × 4.50
S:	15 kts	**Man:**	5 officers, 25 men
M:	diesel-electric; 1 prop; 1,200 hp		

Sister ship to the U.S. Navy's *S. P. Lee* (*AGS-31*), hull and machinery characteristics of the *AGOR-3 Robert D. Conrad* class (see U.S.A. section).

♦ *1 former despatch vessel modified in 1956*

	Bldr	Laid down	L	In serv.
A 528 PEDRO NUÑES	Est. Nav. Lisnave, Lisbon	1930	17-3-34	4-35

Pedro Nuñes

D:	1,107 tons (1,238 fl)	**Dim:**	71.42 × 10 × 3.10
S:	16 kts	**Man:**	7 officers, 44 men
A:	1/120-mm (aft) — 4/20-mm AA		
M:	M.A.N. diesels; 2 props; 2,400 hp		
Fuel:	110 tons		
Range:	6,000/13		

♦ *1 ex-British frigate* (serv.: 2-1979).

A 526 ALFONSO DE ALBUQUERQUE

D:	1,590 tons (2,230 fl)	**Dim:**	93.6 (87.2 pp) × 11.7 × 4.3
S:	19.5 kts	**Range:**	7,000/9
M:	triple expansion; 3 boilers; 2 props; 5,500 hp		

♦ *2 small survey vessels*

A 5201 CRUZEIRO DO SUL (ex-*Giroflee*)

D:	100 tons	**Dim:**	27.70 × 5.30 × 2.40
M:	diesels; 320 hp	**S:**	12 kts

REMARKS: In special reserve (13-8-75)

A 5200 MIRA (ex-*Fomalhaut*, ex-*Arrabile*)

D:	23 tons	**S:**	15 kts	**Dim:**	18.9 × 4.60 × 1.20
M:	3 Perkins diesels; 300 hp	**Man:**	16 men		

	Bldr	Laid down	L	In serv.
A 521 XAVIER SCHULTZ	Arsenal do Alfeite	2-70	1972	1973

Xavier Schultz 1973 J. C. Bellonne

D:	900 tons	**Dim:**	
S:	14 kts	**Man:**	**Range:** 3,000/12.5
M:	diesels; 1 prop; 2,400 hp		
Fuel:	diesel		

REMARKS: Fitted for servicing lighthouses.

LANDING CRAFT

Bldr: Est. Nav. do Mondego

♦ *LDG type based on the British LCT-4 type*

LDG 101 ALFANGE	**LDG 201 BOMBARDA**
LDG 102 ARIETE	**LDG 202 ALABARDA** (1969-71).

LANDING CRAFT (*continued*)

D: 500 tons   **S:** 11 kts   **Dim:** 57 × 11.80 × 1.27
M: 2 officers, 18 men   **M:** diesels; 2 props; 1,000 hp

REMARKS: *LDG 103 Cimitarra* was scrapped 31-3-75; *LDG 101, 102,* and *105* were scrapped 10-10-75

♦ 2 LDM 100 class: **LDM 119, LDM 120**

♦ 4 LDM 400 class: **LDM 406, 418** (1971-72), **419, 420**

D: 56 tons (101 fl)   **Dim:** 17 × 5 × 1.20
S: 9 kts   **A:** 1/20-mm
M: diesels; 2 props; 450 hp

REMARKS: The LDM class is based on the U.S.-British LCM class.

LOGISTIC SUPPORT

♦ *1 ex-U.S. landing craft used as a submarine tender*

	Bldr	Laid down	L	In serv.
A 5214 S. RAFAEL (ex-*Medusa*; ex-*Portunus, AGP-4;* ex-*LSM-275*)	Federal SB	8-44	11-9-44	10-44

S. Rafael (A 5214)

D: 743 tons (1,220 fl)   **Dim:** 67.39 × 10.52 × 3.20
S: 12 kts   **Man:** 4 officers, 40 men
Range: 5,000/10
M: General Motors diesels; 2 props; 2,800 hp

REMARKS: Transferred by the U.S.A. under the M.A.P., put in service in November 1959.

♦ *1 modified ex-tanker.*

	Bldr	Laid down		L
A 523 SAM BRAS	Arsenal do Alfeite	1939		17-5-42

D: 5,766 tons (6,374 fl)   **Dim:** 102.50 × 15.60 × 5.50
S: 12 kts   **Man:** 11 officers, 90 men
Range: 11,000/12
A: 1/76-mm — 2/40-mm AA — 1/20-mm AA
M: B & W diesel; 1 prop; 2,700 hp
Fuel: 568 tons

Sam Bras (A 523)   1970

REMARKS: Former tanker. Modified as a logistic support ship. Platform for 3 helicopters. Cargo capacity: *Oil:* 3,000 tons — *Gasoline:* 49 tons — *Lubricating oil:* 50 tons — *Distilled water:* 100 tons. In special reserve (13-8-75).

♦ *1 tanker*

	Bldr	L	In serv.
A 5206 SAO GABRIEL	Est. Nav. de Viana do Castelo	1961	3-63

S. Gabriel (A 5206)

D: 14,200 tons (fl) (**Cargo capacity:** 9,000 tons)
Dim: 146 (138 pp) × 18.22 × 8
S: 17 kts   **Man:** 9 officers, 93 men
Range: 6,000/15
M: Pametrada GT; 1 prop; 2 boilers; 9,500 hp

TRAINING SHIP

A 520 SAGRES (ex-*Guanabara,* ex-*Albert Leo Schlageter*)
Bldr: Blöhm & Voss, Hamburg (30-10-37)

D: 1,425 tons (1,869 fl)   **Dim:** 75.90 × 12 × 4.60
S: 10 kts   **Sail area:** 20,793 sq. ft.
M: M.A.N. diesel; 1 prop; 750 hp   **Fuel:** 52 tons

PORTUGAL (continued)

TRAINING SHIP (continued)

Sagres (A 520)

REMARKS: Former school sailing ship (three-masted schooner) of the German navy. Assigned to the U.S.A. in 1945, sold to Brazil in 1948, sold to Portugal in 1960. Early in 1961 she replaced the training ship *Sagres* (1896), which was removed from the active list of the fleet, renamed *Santo Andre* (A 5207) and now serves as a depot ship.

QATAR

MERCHANT MARINE (1-7-74): 4 ships — 928 grt

COASTAL SURVEILLANCE SMALL CRAFT

♦ *6/103-foot patrol boats (1975-76)*

Bldr: Vosper-Thornycroft

D:	120 tons	**Dim:**	32.40 (31.10 pp) × 6.30 × 1.60
S:	27 kts	**Man:**	25 men
A:	2/40-mm AA	**Range:**	...
M:	2 diesels; 4,000 hp		

♦ *2/75-foot patrol boats (1969)*

Bldr: Whittingham and Mitchell, Chertsey

D:	...	**Dim:**	22.50 × ... × ...
S:	2/20	**M:**	2 diesels; 1,420 hp

♦ *3/45 foot patrol boats*

Bldr: Vosper

ROMANIA

PERSONNEL: 10,000 men, 3,000 on board ship

MERCHANT MARINE (1-7-74): 106 ships — 610,982 grt
(tankers: 5 ships — 150,653 grt)

WARSHIPS IN SERVICE OR UNDER CONSTRUCTION AS OF 1 OCTOBER 1975

NOTE: All recent Romanian ships are of Soviet origin except for those based on Chinese design.

	L	D	Main armament
♦ *6 frigates*			
3 POTI class	1964-67	600 tons	2/57-mm
3 KRONSTADT class	1950	300	1/85-mm — 2/37-mm AA
♦ *11 Shanghai II class patrol boats*			
	1971-72	120	1/57-mm
♦ *10 to 16 guided missile and patrol torpedo boats*			
5/6 OSA 1 class	post-1960	150	4 Styx systems
10/P-4 class	pre-1954	40	2/25-mm AA — 2/450-mm TT
1/3 HUCHWAN-class hydrofoils		40	2/450-mm TT
♦ *32 minesweepers*			
4 DEMOCRATIA class	1943	643	6/37-mm AA
12 T-301 class	pre. 1950	130	1/45-mm AA
8 inshore type			

NAVAL AVIATION:

4/6 ASW helicopters

FRIGATES

♦ *3 Poti class transferred by the U.S.S.R. (1964-67) — V 31, V 32, V 33*

D: 650 tons (fl)   **S:** 34 kts   **Dim:** 60.30 × 7.20 × 3

VLM type OSA I

FRIGATES (*continued*)

A: 2/57-mm AA (II × 1) — 2/MBU 2500 A RL — 4/400-mm ASW TT (II × 2) or 2/400-mm TT (I × 2)

Electron Equipt: Radars: 1/Don, 1/Strut Curve, 1/Muff Cob

M: 2 gas turbines, 2 diesels; 20,000 hp   **Man:** 50 men

♦ *3 Kronstadt class transferred by the U.S.S.R. (1950)* — **V1, V2, V3**

D: 300 tons (350 fl)   **S:** 23 kts (operational)   **Dim:** 51 × 6 × 2.80

M: diesels; 2 props   **Fuel:** 20 tons   **Man:** 40 men

A: 1/85-mm — 2/37-mm AA

PATROL BOATS

♦ *10/11 Chinese Shanghai II class built in Romania (1972-74)*

VP 25 to **VP 33** — **VS 42**

D: 120 tons   **S:** 30 kts   **Dim:** 39.60 × 5.50 × 1.70

A: 1/57-mm — 4/25-mm (II × 2) — 2/MBU 1 500

M: 4 diesels; 5,000 hp

GUIDED MISSILE AND TORPEDO PATROL BOATS

♦ *5/6 OSA 1 class transferred by the U.S.S.R. since 1960*

D: 150 tons (210 fl)   **S:** 35 kts   **Dim:** 40.10 × 7 × 2

A: 4 Styx system — 4/20-mm AA (II × 2)

Electron Equipt: 1/Square Tie, 1/Drum Tilt

M: diesels; 3 props; 15,000 hp

♦ *10 P 4 class transferred by the U.S.S.R. (Launched prior to 1954)*

D: 40 tons   **S:** 40 kts   **Dim:** 22 × 4.70 × 1.50

A: 2/25-mm AA — 2/450-mm torpedoes (one on each side)

M: diesels; 2 props; 4,000 hp

REMARKS: The torpedoes have been removed on some of these ships.

♦ *1 to 3 Huchwan-class hydrofoil ships*

REMARKS: See Pakistan section. Different armament: 4/25-mm AA (II × 2) — 2/450-mm TT.

MINESWEEPERS

♦ *4 Democratia class (German M 40 class)*

DB 13 DEMOCRATIA   **DB 14 DESCATUSARIA**
DB 15 DESROBIREA   **DB 16 DREPTATEA**   Bldr: Galatz (1943)

D: 643 tons (775 fl)   **S:** 17 kts   **Dim:** 62.30 × 8.50 × 2.60

German M 40 class minesweeper

Man: 80 men   **Range:** 4,000/10

A: 6/37-mm AA (II × 3) — 2 depth charge projectors

M: 2 triple expansion engines each driving an exhaust turbine; 2 props; 2 boilers; 2,400 hp   **Fuel:** 152 tons coal

♦ *12 ex-Soviet T 301 coastal minesweepers* — **DR 1** to **DR 20**

D: 130 tons (150 fl)   **S:** 10 kts   **Dim:** 31 × 4.90 × 1.50

M: diesels; 2 props; 480 hp   **Man:** 32 men

A: 1/45-mm AA or 2/20-mm AA — 4 machine guns

♦ *6/8 TR 40 class inshore minesweepers*

AMPHIBIOUS SHIPS

♦ *8/10 Braila-class (LCU type) landing craft*

LOGISTIC SUPPORT

♦ *3 coastal tankers*

♦ *4 auxiliary ocean tugs, 450 tons and 1,200 hp*

VARIOUS

♦ *1 sail training ship* — **MIRCEA** — Bldr: Blohm & Voss. Launched: 9-38.

D: 1,630 tons   **Dim:** 82 × 12 × 5   **S:** 10 kts   **M:** 1 diesel

Sail area: 1,750 m². Refitted in Germany in 1966-67.

♦ *2 to 3 small hydrographic ships*

COASTAL SURVEILLANCE SHIPS

♦ *3 Sontu-class gunboats including the* **GHICULESCU.**

Ghiculescu   1972

D: 330 tons   **S:** 12 kts   **Dim:** 60.90 × 7 × 2.50

A: 2/100-mm (I × 2)   **Man:** 50 men   **M:** 2 Sulzer diesels, 900 hp each

REMARKS: Former World War I French *Friponne*-class gunboats sold to Romania in 1920. Still on active service: appear to be used for coastal surveillance.

DANUBE FLOTILLA

♦ *3 monitors*

A: 1/57-mm — 4/25-mm AA (II × 2) — 2 mortars

♦ *50 patrol boats*

VD series: approx. 30 tons — 4/25-mm AA (II × 2)
VG series: approx. 20 tons — 2 machine guns.

SABAH

PATROL BOATS

♦ *2/55-foot boats* — Bldr: Vosper-Thornycroft, Singapore.

SRI SEMPORNA   SRI BANGJI

D: 50 tons	**S:** 20 kts	**Dim:** 16.50 × 5.50 × 1	
A: 1 machine gun		**Man:** 11 men	
M: diesels; 1,200 hp		**Range:** 300/15	

♦ *2/91-foot boats* — **SRI GUMANGTONG — SRI LABUAN**

D: ...	**S:** ...	**Dim:** ...	
A: ...	**Range:** ...	**Man:** ...	**M:** diesels

♦ *1 ex-yacht* — **PUTRI SABAH**

D: 117 tons	**S:** 22 kts	**Dim:** 27.30 × 9.50 × 1.65

♦ *2 PX class small craft transferred by Malaysia*

ST. LUCIA

MERCHANT MARINE (1-7-74): 2 ships — 904 grt

♦ *1 small craft* — Bldr: Brooke Marine Ltd, Lowestoft (Gt. Br.)

CHATOYER

D: 15 tons	**S:** 22 kts	**Dim:** 12 × 3.60 × 0.65
A: 2 machine guns		**M:** 2 diesels; 370 hp

ST. VINCENT

MERCHANT MARINE (1-7-74): 13 ships — 4,808 grt

♦ *1 small craft* — Bldr: Brooke Marine Ltd, Lowestoft (Gt. Br.)

HELEN

D: 15 tons	**S:** 22 kts	**Dim:** 12 × 3.60 × 0.60
A: 2 machine guns		**M:** 2 diesels; 370 hp

SAUDI ARABIA

PERSONNEL: 750 + 350 coastal surveillance personnel

MERCHANT MARINE (1-7-74): 43 ships — 61,275 grt
(tankers: 4 ships — 19,528 grt)

SURVEILLANCE AND PATROL BOATS

♦ *3 Jaguar-class small craft*

DAMMAM — KHABAR — MACCAH
Bldr: Lürssen, Vegesack (1969)

1975

D: 170 tons	**S:** 40 kts	**Dim:** 42.80 × 7.15 × 2.20
A: 2/40-mm AA		**Man:** 3 officers, 33 men
M: 4 diesels; 4 props; 12,000 hp		

♦ **RIYADH** (ex-U.S. Coast Guard *Cape* class) transferred in 1969

D: 102 tons	**S:** 20 kts	**Dim:** 28.95 × 5.80 × 1.85
A: 1/40-mm	**Man:** 15 men	**Range:** 1,500/12
M: 4 diesels; 2 props; 2,200 hp		

♦ 8 British *SRN-6* air cushion vehicles delivered from 1970 to 1972.

♦ Approximately 30 coastal surveillance ships, most of them in poor condition and with limited effectiveness.

Future project: A framework agreement for the strengthening and development of the Saudi Arabian navy was signed in 1972 by the U.S.A. and Saudi Arabia. It calls for the acquisition within 10 years of 19 ships — 6 fast small craft, 1 training ship, 2 patrol boats, 4 minesweepers, 4 landing craft, and 2 ships for training.

SENEGAL

PERSONNEL: 180 men

MERCHANT MARINE (1-7-74): 48 ships — 20,499 grt
(tankers: 4 ships — 3,876 grt)

♦ *3 coastal patrol boats*

	Bldr	Laid down	L	In serv.
St. LOUIS	Ch. Nav. Franco-Belges	4-70	5-8-70	3-71
POPENGUINE	Ch. Nav. Franco-Belges	1972	1973	1975
FODOR	Ch. Nav. Franco-Belges		6-76	2-77

St. Louis   1971

D:	240 tons (avg.)	**Dim:**	47.50 (45.50 pp) × 7.10 × 2.50
S:	18.5 kts **Range:** 2,000/15	**Man:**	3 officers, 22 men
A:	4/40-mm AA — 8/SS12 missiles	**M:**	2 MGO diesels; 2,400 hp; 2 props

REMARKS: A contract for the construction of a third *St. Louis* class was signed 1-6-75.

♦ *3 coastal surveillance small craft transferred by France*

SINÉ SALOUM (ex-*P 754, VC 4*) (17-8-57) added in 1966
CASAMANCE (ex-*P 755, VC 5*) added in 1963

Bldr: Constr. Méc. de Normandie, Cherbourg

D:	70 tons (80 fl)	**S:** 28 kts	**Dim:** 31.77 × 4.70 × 1.70
A:	2/20-mm AA	**Man:** 15 men	**Range:** 1,500/15
M:	2 Mercedes-Benz diesels — 4 tons, 12 cylinders; 2 props; 2,700 hp.		

LES ALMADIES, former fishery protection vessel

♦ *1 small craft* (1974 — Bldr: Fairey Marine, Gt. Br.)

D:	4.25 tons	**S:** 28 kts	**Dim:** 9 × 2.70 × 0.80
A:	2 machine guns	**Man:** 4 men	**Range:** 200/24
M:	Perkins diesels; 2 props; 200 hp		

♦ *1 Edic class transferred 7-1-74*

FALEME (ex-*Edic 9095*) — 11-4-58

D:	250 tons (470 fl)	**S:** 8 kts	**Dim:** 59 × 11.95 × 4.62

A:	2/20-mm	**Man:** 16 men	
M:	MGO diesels; 2 props; 1,000 hp — can carry 11 trucks or 5 LVT landing craft.		

♦ *2/26-ton LCM-class delivered in 1968 by the U.S.A.*

DIOMBOSS   **DOULOULOU**

♦ *1 training ship*

CRAME JEAN — former fishing vessel (18 tons), put in service in 1970.

SIERRA LEONE

Shanghai II

SIERRA LEONE (*continued*)
PATROL BOATS

♦ *2 Shanghai II class*

001 N . . .   002 N . . .

D: 120 tons	**S:** 30 kts	**Dim:** 39.60 × 5.50 × 1.76
M: 4 diesels; 5,000 hp		**Man:** 28 men
A: 4/37-mm AA (II × 2) — 4/25-mm AA (II × 2)		

SINGAPORE

PERSONNEL: 800 to 1,000 men

MERCHANT MARINE (1-7-74): 511 ships — 2,878,327 grt
(tankers: 68 ships — 729,685 grt)

GUIDED MISSILE PATROL BOATS

♦ *6 Lürssen type* (ordered in 1970)

**P 76 SEA WOLF, P . . . SEA LION, P . . . SEA DRAGON, P . . . SEA HAWK,
P . . . SEA TIGER, P . . . SEA SERPENT.**

Bldr: Designed by Lürssen (Bremen) who built the *Sea Wolf* and *Sea Lion*. The remainder by Jurong shipbuilders (Singapore) with German technical assistance.

D: 230 tons	**S:** 40 kts	**Dim:** 45 × 7 × 2.3
M: 4 diesels; 4 props; 14,400 hp		**Man:** 40 men
A: 5 Israeli Gabriel missiles — 2/57-mm AA		

GUNBOATS AND PATROL BOATS

♦ *6 Vosper-Thornycroft, 110-foot class*

	L		L
P 69 INDEPENDENCE* (A)	15-7-69	**P 72 JUSTICE** (A)	15-5-70
P 70 FREEDOM (A)	18-11-69	**P 73 DARING** (B)	28-11-70
P 71 SOVEREIGNTY* (B)	25-11-69	**P 74 DAUNTLESS** (B)	21-2-71

Bldr: *Vosper-Thornycroft, Portsmouth; the others, Vosper-Thornycroft Private Ltd. (formerly Uniteers), Tanjong Rhu Dockyard, Singapore. (A) (B) see Remarks.

Independence   1970 Vosper

Sovereignty   1971 Thornycroft

D: 100 tons (130 fl)	**Dim:** 33.40 (31.46 pp) × 6.40 × 1.71
S: 30 kts **A:** see Remarks.	**Man:** 4 officers, 27 men
M: 2 Maybach MD 872 diesels, each 3,100 hp (2,400 cruising) with 2,100 or 1,800 rpm respectively.	

REMARKS: Ordered 21-5-68. Very similar to the gunboats delivered to Peru in 1965 and are based on the 103-foot ship built for Malaysia. There are two weapon arrangement groups, (A) and (B). The A type has 1/40-mm Bofors (70-caliber) and 1/20-mm Oerlikon Mk 14 SLA/204 GK (1,000 rounds/min; muzzle velocity 1,050 m/sec), and 2 flares. The B type has 1/76-mm Bofors gun (for characteristics see the Norwegian section) and 1/20-mm AA Oerlikon. Steel welded hull; superstructure in light metal; anti-rolling stabilizers; air-conditioned quarters; Decca radar and navigation equipment. Two diesel-generator groups (Ford 62 CV/Stamford 50 kw).

♦ *1 British Ford class patrol boat*

P 48 PANGLIMA (14-4-56) — Bldr: United Engineers, Singapore
Transferred by Malaysia in 1967.

D: 119 tons (131 fl)	**S:** 14 kts	**Dim:** 35.66 × 6.10 × 1.85
A: 1/40-mm		**Man:** 15 men
M: 2 Paxman diesels		**Fuel:** 15 tons

SINGAPORE (*continued*)

AMPHIBIOUS SHIPS

◆ *4 ex-U.S. LST class transferred, one in 7-71, the last three in 1973.*

A 81 ENDURANCE (ex-*Holmes County*, LST-836)
A 82 N . . . (ex-*LST-276*)
   N . . . (ex-*Chase County*, LST-532)
   N . . . (ex-*LST-117*)

D: 1,653 tons (4,080 fl)	**S:** 11.6 kts	**Dim:** 98.40 × 15 × 4.20
A: 8/40-mm AA (II × 4)		**Man:** 120 men
M: GM diesels; 2 props; 1,700 hp		

SOMALI REPUBLIC

MERCHANT MARINE (1-7-74): 276 ships — 1,916,273 grt
(tankers: 11 ships — 137,529 grt)

◆ *2 ex-Soviet OSA II guided missile boats*

D: 190 tons (fl)	**S:** 36 kts	**Dim:** 37 × 9 × 1.80
A: 4 SS-N-2 Styx system — 4/30-mm AA (II × 1)		
Electron Equipt: 1 Square Tie, 1 Drum Tilt		
M: 3 diesels; 9,000 hp; 3 props	**Range:** 450/34; 700/20

◆ *4 ex-Soviet P 4 type torpedo patrol boats*

D: 30 tons (fl)	**S:** 32 kts	**Dim:** 16.80 × 3.75 × 1.00
A: 2/14.5-mm machine guns — 2/450-mm TT		

◆ *4 ex-Soviet Poluchat class patrol boats*

D: 100 tons	**Dim:** 29.57 × 6.10 × 1.90	
S: 15 kts	**M:** diesels; 2 props	

SOUTH AFRICA

Republic of

PERSONNEL: 4,500 including 420 officers

NAVAL AVIATION: An Air Force detachment is available to the Navy. Shackleton and Piaggio aircraft are used for patrol and Wasp helicopters are found on board ship.

MERCHANT MARINE (1-7-74): 270 ships — 535,322 grt
(tankers: 3 ships — 27,355 grt)

WARSHIPS IN SERVICE OR UNDER CONSTRUCTION AS OF 1 OCTOBER 1975

	L	D	Main armament
◆ *5 submarines*			
3 French Daphne class	1969-70	869	12/550-mm TT
2 French Agosta class		1,200	4/533-mm TT
◆ *11 frigates*			
2 SIMON VAN DER STEL	1943	2,105	4/102-mm AA, 1 helicopter
3 PRESIDENT PRETORIUS	1960-62	2,205	2/114-mm AA, 1 helicopter
1 VRIJSTAAT	1942	2,100	2/102-mm AA, 2 Squids
2 GOOD HOPE	1943-44	1,610	1/102-mm
1 PIETERMARITZBURG	1943	1,040	2/102-mm
2 French A 69 class		1,170	2 MM 38 surface-to-surface missiles, 2/100-mm

◆ *6 guided missile patrol boats*

◆ *6 patrol boats*

◆ *10 minesweepers*

SUBMARINES

◆ *2 French Agosta class*

Two 1,200-ton *Agosta* type submarines have been ordered at the Dubigeon-Normandie shipyards in Nantes. They should be delivered in 11-78 and 8-79. See French *Agosta* class.

◆ *3 French Daphne class*

	Bldr	Laid down	L	In serv.
S 97 MARIA VAN RIEBEECK	Dubigeon, Nantes	3-68	18-3-69	1971
S 98 EMILY HOBHOUSE	Dubigeon, Nantes	12-68	10-69	1971
S 99 JOHANNA VAN DER MERWE	Dubigeon, Nantes	5-69	4-70	1971

Emily Hobhouse (598)   1971 Marius Bar

SUBMARINES (continued)

D: 869 surfaced/1,043 submerged tons
S: 13/15.5 kts
A: 12/550-mm TT (8 fwd, 4 aft)
M: surfaced: diesel-electric propulsion (SEMT-Pielstick, 450 kw each); 2 props; 1,300/1,600 hp

Dim: 57.75 × 6.75 × 4.50
Man: 6 officers, 41 men

REMARKS: See French *Daphne* class.

FRIGATES

♦ *2 French A 69 class*

The *Lieutenant de Vaisseau Le Hénaff* and the *Commandant L'Herminier* are to be transferred to the South African Navy. Trials in November 1977 and May 1978 respectively. Two ships bearing the same names will be ordered for the French Navy.

♦ *2 British W class (transferred in 1950 and 1952)*

	Bldr	Laid down	L	In serv.
D 237 SIMON VAN DER STEL (ex-*Whelp*)	Hawthorn Leslie	2-42	3-6-43	4-44
D 278 JAN VAN RIEBEECK (ex-*Wessex*, ex-*Zenith*)	Fairfield SB&E	10-42	2-9-43	5-44

D: 2,105 tons (2,750 fl)
S: 31 kts
Range: 2,800/20 — 1,000/30
A: 4/102-mm AA (II × 2) — 2/40-mm AA — 4/47-mm (saluting battery) — 4/533-mm TT (IV × 1) — 2 Wasp ASW helicopters — 2 depth charge projectors
M: Parsons GT; 2 props; 2 Admiralty boilers; 40,000 hp
Fuel: 580 tons

Dim: 110.55 × 10.88 × 5.20 (fl)
Man: 186 (peacetime), 215 (war)

REMARKS: *237* refitted in 1962-64; *278* in 1964-66.

♦ *3 British Whitby class*

	Bldr	Laid down	L	In serv.
F 145 PRESIDENT PRETORIUS	Yarrow	1960	28-9-62	3-64
F 147 PRESIDENT STEYN	Alex. Stephen	1960	23-11-61	4-63
F 150 PRESIDENT KRUGER	Yarrow	1959	20-10-60	10-62

D: 2,250 tons (2,800 fl)
Dim: 112.77 (100.73 pp) × 12.50 × 5.20 (fl)
S: 27 kts   **Man:** 190 men
Range: 4,500/12 — 2,100/26
A: 2/114-mm AA Mk 6 (II × 1) — 2/40-mm AA (I × 2) — 6/ASW TT (II × 3) — 1 Mk 10 Limbo mortar — 1 Wasp ASW helicopter (Mk 44 torpedo)
Electron Equipt: Radars: 1/974 GB navigation, 1 air search band L, 1 scan/DO band C, 1/275 fire control
Sonars: 1/177 GB, 1/174 GB.
M: 2 double reduction GT; 2 props; 2 Babcock boilers; 30,000 hp

REMARKS: *F 147* and *F 150* modernized at Simonstown in 1968-70 and 1969-71. Modernization of *F 145* will probably be on schedule.

President Kruger (F 145)   1970

♦ *1 British type 15*

	Bldr	Laid down	L	In serv.
F 157 VRIJSTAAT (ex-*Wrangler*)	Vickers-Armstrongs	9-42	30-12-43	7-44

D: 2,100 tons (2,700 fl). Hull and machinery of the *Jan Van Riebeeck* class.
A: 2/102-mm (II × 1) — 2/40-mm AA (II × 1) — 2 Squids

REMARKS: Modified in 1951-53, transferred in 11-56. Not in service.

♦ *2 British Loch class*

	Bldr	Laid down	L	In serv.
F 432 GOOD HOPE (ex-*Loch Boisdale*)	Blyth DD&SB	11-43	5-7-44	12-44
F 602 TRANSVAAL (ex-*Loch Ard*)	Harland & Wolff	1-44	2-8-44	5-45

D: 1,610 tons (2,400 fl)
S: 19 kts
Range: 6,400/10 — 2,500/19

Dim: 93.57 (87.20 pp) × 11.25 × 4.40
Man: 140 men

Good Hope (432)   1970

FRIGATES (continued)

A: 1/102-mm — 2/40-mm AA, 6 on the *602* — 4 depth charge projectors
M: Triple expansion; 2 props; 5,500 hp; 2 Admiralty boilers
Fuel: 720 tons

REMARKS: Transferred in 1945. These ships are part of a large number of ocean-going frigates built during the war. Both have had refits. *432* has been modified to serve for the staff of the Commander-in-Chief.

♦ *1 British Algerine class bought in 1947*

	Bldr	Laid down	L	In serv.
M 291 PIETERMARITZBURG	Lobnitz & Co,	10-42	13-6-43	10-43.
(ex-*Pelorus*)	Renfrew			

D: 1,040 tons (1,330 fl)   **Dim:** 68.58 (64.80 pp) × 10.82 × 3.50
S: 17 kts   **Man:** 85 men   **Range:** 3,000/15
A: 2/102-mm (II × 1) — 2/40-mm AA — 4 depth charge projectors
Man: 8 officers, 107 men
M: Triple expansion; 1 prop; 3,000 hp; 2 boilers   **Fuel:** 270 tons

REMARKS: Belongs to a minesweeper class built in large numbers during WW II. Used as a training ship.

GUIDED MISSILE PATROL BOATS

♦ *6 based on the Israeli Reshef class*
Bldr: Haifa and Durban.

	L	In serv.		L	In serv.
N . . .			N . . .		
N . . .			N . . .		
N . . .			N . . .		

REMARKS: Could be armed with Gabriel missiles.

PATROL BOATS AND SMALL CRAFT

♦ *5 British Ford class*

P 3105 GELDERLAND (ex-*Brayford*)
P 3120 NAUTILUS (ex-*Glassford*)
P 3125 RIJGER
P 3126 HAERLEM (hydrographic service)
P 3127 OOSTERLAND

Haerlem (converted to a hydrographic ship)

D: 160 tons (fl)   **Dim:** 35.70 × 6.10 × 2.10
S: 15 kts   **Man:** 19 men
A: 1/40-mm
M: 2 Paxman diesels; 1,100 hp
Fuel: 23 tons

♦ *1 British SDML type small craft*

HDML 1204
D: 46 tons (54 fl)   **Dim:** 24.95 × 4.82 × 1.62
S: 11 kts   **Man:** 11 men
M: 2 Gardiner diesels; 130 hp

Haerlem (fitted as a hydrographic ship).

MINESWEEPERS

♦ *10 British "-ton" class*

	L		L
M 1142 KAAPSTAD	6-2-54	**M 1213 MOSSELBAAI**	10-12-58
(ex-*Hazleton*)		(ex-*Oakington*)	
M 1144 PRETORIA	8-3-54	**M 1214 WALVISBAAI**	3-7-58
(ex-*Dunkerton*)		(ex-*Packington*)	
M 1207 JOHANNESBURG	26-8-58	**M 1215 EAST LONDON**	15-7-57
(ex-*Castleton*)		(ex-*Chilton*)	
M 1210 KIMBERLEY	29-7-57	**M 1498 WINDHOEK**	28-6-57
(ex-*Stratton*)			
M 1212 PORT ELIZABETH	8-11-57	**M 1499 DURBAN**	12-6-57
(ex-*Dumbleton*)			

D: 370 tons (425 fl)   **Dim:** 46.33 (42.68 pp) × 8.76 × 2.50
S: 15 kts (cruising)   **Man:** 27 men
A: 1/40-mm AA — 2/20-mm AA   **Range:** 3,000/8 — 2,300/13
M: Mirrlees diesels in *1142* and *1144*, Deltic diesels in others; 2 props; 3,000 hp   **Fuel:** 45 tons

REMARKS: *Kaapstad* and *Pretoria* have an open bridge and a lattice mast; *Durban* and *Windhoek* have a frigate-type bridge and a tripod mast.

HYDROGRAPHIC SHIPS

♦ *1 British Hecla class*

	Bldr	Laid down	L	In serv.
PROTEA	Yarrow	7-70	14-7-71	12-71

D: 2,750 tons (fl)   **Dim:** 71.60 × 14.90 × 4.60
S: 15.5 kts   **Man:** 123 men
M: 4 Paxman-Ventura diesels; 1 variable pitch prop; 4,800 hp
Fuel: 500 tons   **Range:** 12,000/11

REMARKS: Able to navigate in ice fields.

♦ *1 British Loch-class frigate*

	Bldr	Laid down	L	In serv.
A 301 NATAL (ex-*Loch Cree*)	Swan Hunter	10-43	19-6-44	3-43

Good Hope class hull and machinery. Modified in 1958. No guns.

LOGISTIC SUPPORT

♦ *1 fleet replenishment ship*

A 23 TAFELBERG (ex-Danish tanker *Annam*) (20-6-58)
Purchased and refitted in Durban in 1967.

    D: 12,499 grt   **Cargo capacity:** 18,430 tons   **S:** 15 kts
    M: 1 B & W diesel; 8,420 hp   **Man:** 100 men

♦ *1 net tender*

P 285 SOMERSET (ex-*Barcross*) (21-10-41), British "Bar" class

♦ *1 torpedo recovery and diver-training ship*

3148 FLEUR (1969) — Bldr: Dorman Long, Durban

    D: 257 tons (fl)   **Dim:** 35 × 7.50 × 3.40
    M: 2 Paxman-Ventura diesels; 1,400 hp

♦ 2 tugs **DE NEYS** (180 tons), **DE NOORDE** (170 tons)

♦ 5 air-sea rescue boats **P 1551, 1552, 1553, 1555, 1556**
Fairey Marine Corporation (1973) — 19 — 27

Tafelberg (A 243)   1970

Fleur (P 3148)   1970

SPAIN

PROGRAM: The law of 21-7-71 authorized the modernization program of the Spanish Fleet and calls for (after recent budgetary considerations) the construction of:

♦ 1 small aircraft carrier to replace the *Dedalo* which would be named the *Almirante Carrero Blanco*
♦ 2 or 4/1,200-ton submarines
♦ 5 U.S. "Patrol Frigate" type escort vessels
♦ 8/1,500-ton frigates
♦ 6/400-ton patrol craft
♦ 6 light patrol craft

PERSONNEL (1975): 46,000 including 4,000 officers, 650 Marine officers, and 5,850 Marines.

MERCHANT MARINE (1-7-74): 2,520 ships — 4,949,146 grt
(tankers: 108 ships — 2,260, 100 grt)

WARSHIPS IN SERVICE OR UNDER CONSTRUCTION AS OF 1 OCTOBER 1975

	L	D	Main armament
♦ *1 helicopter carrier*			
DEDALO	1943	14,000	26/40-mm, 20 helicopters
♦ *13 submarines*			
2 type AGOSTA	under constr.	1,200	
4 DELFIN	1972-73	870	12/TT
4 ex-Guppies/U.S.	1943-44	1,500	10/TT
1 ALM. G. DE LOS REYES	1942	1,525	10/TT
2 TIBURON	1964-65	76	2/TT
♦ *1 obsolete cruiser*			
CANARIAS	1931	10,670	8/203-mm
♦ *23 destroyers and frigates*			
5 BALEARES	1970-73	2,900	2/127-mm, 1 Asroc system, 1 Tartar system, 6/ASW TT
2 ROGER DE LAURIA	1967-68	3,000	6/127-mm, ASW weapons, 1 helicopter
1 OQUENDO	1956	2,508	4/120-mm, ASW weapons
3 AUDAZ	1951-61	1,227	2/76-mm, ASW weapons
5 CHURRUCA (ex-U.S.)	1945-46	2,400	4/127-mm, 1 Asroc system
5 LEPANTO (ex-U.S.)	1942	2,050	4 or 5/127-mm, 5/TT
2 ALAVA	1946-47	1,841	3/76-mm, ASW weapons
♦ *9 frigates*			
2 LEGAZPI	1945	1,754	2/127-mm, ASW weapons
1 JUPITER	1935	2,100	4/76-mm, 238/254 mines
4 ATREVIDA	1953-58	997	1/76-mm, 3/40-mm, ASW weapons

♦ *23 minesweepers including 4 oceangoing type; 2 fast torpedo boats; 12 patrol craft*

NAVAL AVIATION: ASW fixed-wing aircraft belong to the Air Force. It has about 10 amphibians of the Grumman UH16B Albatros type, to which three 4-engined

Naval Aviation (*continued*)

turboprop P 3 Orions were added by the U.S. Navy in 1973. Whether ASW or transport, the helicopters belong to the navy ("Arma Aera de la Armada"). They include — Bell 47 G (assault), Sikorsky S 55 (training), Agusta Bell 204B, Sikorsky SH3-D, and Hughes 369 HM ASW, for a total of about 40 machines.

Eight Harrier AV-8A VTOL aircraft have been bought in the U.S.A. to be based on board *Dedalo* in 1975. This order may be followed by 8 or 12 other aircraft and could go to 24 if the aircraft carrier considered in the naval program is indeed built. There also exists a proposal to build the Harrier under license as the Matador.

HELICOPTER CARRIER

◆ *1 ex-U.S. light aircraft carrier transferred in 9-1967*

	Bldr	Laid down	L	In serv. for the U.S.A.
PH 01 DEDALO (ex-*Cabot*, CVL-28)	New York SB, Camden	8-42	4-4-43	7-43

Dedalo (PH 01)   MN 1974

D: 14,000 tons (18,000 fl)   **S:** 32 kts (trials)   **Man:** 650 men.

Dim: 188.35 (182.90 wl) { 20.11 (hull) × 7.20 / 31.70 (flight deck)

Range: 11,000/15 (also stated as 7,200/15)

A: 26/40-mm (IV × 2, II × 9) — about 20 helicopters

Electron Equipt: all U.S. radars: 1/SPS 10, 1/SPS 40

Armor: partial belt, 37 to 127-mm

M: GT; 4 props; 8 Babcock and Wilcox boilers   **Fuel:** 1,800 tons

REMARKS: Ended service in U.S. Navy as an aviation transport (AVT 3). Loaned for five years by law of 30-8-67. Loan renewed.

SUBMARINES

◆ *4 French Daphne class*

	Bldr	Laid down	L	In serv.
S 61 DELFIN	E.N. Bazan, Cartagena	8-68	25-3-72	5-73
S 62 TONINA	E.N. Bazan, Cartagena	1969	3-10-72	7-73
S 63 MARSOPA	E.N. Bazan, Cartagena	1971	6-74	12-74
S 64 NARVAL	E.N. Bazan, Cartagena	1972	1-75	7-75

D: 870 tons surfaced/1,040 submerged   **Dim:** 57.75 × 6.75 × 4.56

S: 13/15.5 kts   **A:** 12 TT, (8 fwd, 4 aft)   **Man:** 5 officers, 45 men

M: diesel-electric propulsion (SEMT-Pielstick motors); 2 props; 1,300/1,600 hp

REMARKS: Built with French technical assistance (agreement of 16-7-66).

Tonina (S 62)   1973 J. C. Bellonne

◆ *2 of the 1,200-ton Agosta class*

	Bldr	Laid down	L	In serv.
S . . . N . . .	. . .	1975	. . .	. . .
S . . . N . . .	. . .	1975	. . .	. . .

Bldr: Empresa Nacional Bazan, Cartagena

REMARKS: For characteristics, see the French *Agosta* class. As the *Delfin* class, these ships will be built with French technical assistance (agreement of 6-2-74).

◆ *4 ex-U.S. Guppy II class, transferred in 1971, 1972 and 1974.*

	Bldr	L
S 32 Isaac PERAL (ex-*Ronquil*, SS-396)	Portsmouth NSY	27-1-44
S 33 Narciso MONTURIOL (ex-*Picuda*, SS-382)	Portsmouth NSY	12-7-43
S 34 Cosme GARCIA (ex-*Bang*, SS-385)	Portsmouth NSY	30-8-43
S 35 N . . . (ex-*Jallao*, SS-368)	Manitowoc SY	12-3-44

Isaac Peral (S 32)   1971

D: 1,500 tons/1,840 surfaced/2,240 submerged   **Dim:** 93.20 × 8.20 × 5.20

S: 18/13-15 kts   **Range:** 10,000/10

A: 10/533-mm TT (6 fwd, 4 aft)   **Man:** 86 men

M: diesel-electric propulsion, 3 groups of generators, 2 electric motors; 2 props; 4,800/5,200 hp   **Fuel:** 300 tons

SUBMARINES (*continued*)

REMARKS: Built as the *Balao* class, but the fourth generator group has been removed to enlarge the sonar compartment. Two 126-cell batteries. Modernized in 1952-54. Purchased by Spain.

◆ *1 ex-U.S. Corsair class transferred in 10-59*

	Bldr	L	In serv.
S 31 Almirante Garcia	Manitowoc SY	30-6-44	9-44
DE LOS REYES (ex-*Kraken, SS-370*)			

1971

D:	1,525 tons/1,825 surfaced/2,300 submerged	**S:**	20/10 kts
Dim:	95 (92.72 pp) × 8.25 × 5.20	**Man:**	8/9 officers, 66 men
A:	10 TT (6 for 533-mm torpedoes, 4 for ASW torpedoes)		
M:	diesel-electric propulsion (4 groups of General Electric, each 1,625 hp) and 2 electric motors of 2,700 hp	**Fuel:** 300 tons	**Range:** 10,000/10

REMARKS: Complete modernization in Philadelphia in 1965-66. Probably will be stricken soon because of condition.

Assault submarines

SA 51, SA 52 (*Tiburon* class — 1963-64)

D:	76.8 tons surfaced/79.3 submerged	**Dim:**	21.15 (19.80 pp) × 2.10 × 2.40
S:	9.7/14.5 kts	**A:**	2/533-mm TT
Range:	2,040/6 (surface); 150/2 (submerged)		
M:	Pegaso diesels and electric motors; 2 props; 400 hp	**Man:**	5 men

New batteries in 1966-67.

REMARKS: The Spanish Navy is one of several to operate such small combat craft. Others are operated by the Pakistani, Chinese (Taiwan), and Colombian navies.

SA 51   1972

FRIGATES AND DESTROYERS

◆ *5 based on the U.S. Knox class*

	Bldr	Laid down	L	In serv.
F 71 BALEARES	E.N. Bazan, El Ferrol	10-68	20-8-70	9-73
F 72 ANDALUCIA	E.N. Bazan, El Ferrol	7-69	30-3-71	23-5-74
F 73 CATALUNA	E.N. Bazan, El Ferrol	8-70	3-11-71	15-1-75
F 74 ASTURIAS	E.N. Bazan, El Ferrol	3-71	13-5-72	75
F 75 ESTREMADURA	E.N. Bazan, El Ferrol	11-71	21-11-72	75

Baleares (F 71)   1974

D:	2,900 tons (4,177 fl)
Dim:	133.60 (126.50 pp) × 14.25 × 5.60 (7.50 with sonar)
S:	27/28 kts **Man:** 14 officers, 39 petty officers, 184 men
A:	1/127-mm U.S. Mk 42 — 1 Tartar SAM — 1 ASW Asroc system 4/324-mm ASW TT for Mk 44 torpedoes — 2 fixed TT for Mk 37 torpedoes
Electron Equipt:	Radars: 1/US SPS 52, 1/US SPG 51
	Sonars: 1/SQS 23 hull, 1/SQS 35 towed
M:	1 GT; 1 prop **Boilers:** 2-84 kg/cm² pressure; 35,000 hp

REMARKS: Built with American aid (agreement of 31-5-66). May have 1 or 2 helicopters (ASW). See other photo. The ships have a high pressure steam propulsion plant, like their U.S. counterparts.

◆ *2 modified Oquendo class*

	Bldr	Laid down	L	In serv.
D 42 ROGER DE LAURIA	Cartagena	9-51	22-8-67	5-69
D 43 MARQUES DE LA ENSANADA	Cartagena	9-51	22-2-68	8-70

D:	3,000 tons (3,775 fl)	**Dim:**	119 × 13 × 5.50
S:	30 kts **Range:** 4,500/15	**Man:**	20 officers, 235 men
A:	6/127-mm US (II × 3) — 6/324-mm ASW TT Mk 32 (III × 2) for Mk 44 torpedoes — 2 ASW fixed Mk 25 TT for Mk 37 torpedoes — 1 ASW helicopter		
Electron Equipt:	Radars: 1/US SPS 40, 1/US SPS 10		
	Sonars: 1/US SQS 29, 1/US SQS 10 towed, middle frequency		
M:	Rateau-Bretagne GT; 2 props **Fuel:** 673 tons		
Boilers:	3-35 kg/cm²; superheat 375°		

FRIGATES AND DESTROYERS (*continued*)

Roger de Lauria (D 42)   1970

REMARKS: Modified during construction in order to eliminate defects found in the *Oquendo* prototype (widened and lengthened to make room for the new U.S. semi-automatic, 38-caliber ASW weapons).

	Bldr	Laid down	L	In serv.
D 41 OQUENDO	S.E. Constr. Nav. El Ferrol	15-6-51	5-9-56	1964

Oquendo (D 41)   1972 J. C. Bellonne

D: 2,508 tons (2,895 fl) **Dim:** 116.47 (110.80 pp) × 11 × 3.85
S: 32 kts (fl) **Man:** 15 officers, 252 men
A: 4/120-mm AA (II × 2) — 6/40-mm AA (I × 6) — 2 hedgehogs — 4 depth charge projectors
Electron Equipt: Radars: (British) 1/275 and 1/262 fire control,

1/293 Q and 1/SNW 10
  Sonar: 1/QHB high frequency
M: Rateau-Bretagne GT; 2 props; 60,000 hp
Boilers: 3 at 35 kg/cm² pressure; superheat 375° **Fuel:** 600 tons

REMARKS: Based on the German *Narvik*-class destroyers of 1942. Trials indicated a tendency to instability. Spanish model 120-mm 50-caliber semi-automatic guns.

♦ *5 ex-U.S. Gearing class modernized with FRAM I (2 transferred in 8-72 and 3 in 8-73)*

	Bldr	L
D 61 CHURRUCA (ex-*Eugene A. Greene, DDR-711*)	Federal SB	18-3-45
D 62 GRAVINA (ex-*Furze, DDR-882*)	Consolid. Steel	9-3-45
D 63 MENDEZ NUNEZ (ex-*Leary, DDR-879*)	Consolid. Steel	20-1-45
D 64 LANGARA (ex-*O'Hare, DDR-889*)	Consolid. Steel	22-6-45
D 65 BLAS DE LEZO (ex-*Noa, DD-841*)	Bath Iron Works	30-7-45

Churruca (D 61)   1974

D: 2,400 tons (3,600 fl) **Dim:** 119.17 × 12.45 × 5.80
S: 30 kts **Man:** 14 officers, 260 men **Range:** 2,400/25 — 4,800/15
A: 4/127-mm 38-cal (II × 2) — 1 Asroc ASW system — 6/324-mm ASW TT (III × 2) Mk 32 for Mk 43 or 44 torpedoes
Electron Equipt: Radars: 1/US SPS 10 and 40
  Sonar: 1/US SQS 23
M: GT; 4 Babcock boilers; 2 props; 60,000 hp **Fuel:** 650 tons

♦ *5 ex-U.S. Fletcher class transferred in 1957 (2), 1959 (1), 1960 (2)*

	Bldr	L
D 21 LEPANTO (ex-*Capps, DD-550*)	Gulf SB	31-5-42
D 22 ALMIR. FERRANDIZ (ex-*David W. Taylor, DD-551*)	Gulf SB	4-7-42
D 23 ALMIR. VALDES (ex-*Converse, DD-509*)	Bath Iron Works	30-8-42
D 24 ALCALA GALIANO (ex-*Jarvis, DD-799*)	Todd Pacific	14-2-44
D 25 JORGE JUAN (ex-*McGowan, DD-678*)	Federal SB	14-11-43

D: 2,050 tons, (2,750 fl) **Dim:** 114.85 × 12.03 × 5.50
S: 30/32 kts **Man:** 350 men **Range:** 1,260/32 — 4,400/15
A: *21/22:* 5/127-mm (I × 5) — 6/40-mm AA (II × 3) — 6/20-mm AA — 6/32-mm ASW torpedo tubes (III × 2) — 2 hedgehogs — 6 depth charge projectors
23: 4/127-mm (I × 4) — 6/76-mm AA (II × 3) — 5/533-mm TT (V × 1) —

FRIGATES AND DESTROYERS (*continued*)

Almirante Valdes (D 23)   1971

6/324-mm ASW TT (III × 2) — 4 depth charge projectors
24/25 same weapons as the *23* but 3/533-mm TT (III × 1) — 6/324-mm ASW
TT (III × 2)

Electron Equipt: Radars: 1/US SPS 6, 1/US SPS 10
                      Sonars: 1/US SQS 4 or 1/US SQS 29, or 1/US SQS 32
                                   all middle frequency

M: General Electric GT; 2 props   **Boilers:**   4 — 60,000 hp
Fuel: 650 tons

♦ *3 Audaz of the French Fier class*

	Bldr	Laid down	L	In serv.	Modified
D 37 TEMERARIO	S.E. Constr. Nav. El Ferrol	14-7-45	29-3-60	1960	3-64
D 38 INTREPIDO	S.E. Constr. Nav. El Ferrol	14-7-45	15-2-61	1961	3-65
D 39 RELAMPAGO	S.E. Constr. Nav. El Ferrol	14-7-45	26-9-61	1962	7-65

Temerario (D 37)   1972

D: 1,227 tons (1,484 fl)   **Dim:**   93.93 (90.00 pp) × 9.37 × 3.05
S: 33 kts   **Man:**   7 officers, 138 men
Range: 3,800/15 — 1,500/25 — 900 max.
A: 2/76-mm AA 50-cal (II × 1) — 2/40-mm AA 70-cal — 2 fixed ASW TT (6
        torpedoes) — 8 depth charge projectors.
Electron Equipt: Radars: 1/MLA-lb — 1/SPS 5B — 1/SPG 34 fire control
                       Sonar: 1/QHB-a
M: Rateau-Bretagne GT; 2 props; 30,800 hp (32,500 max.).   **Fuel:**   290 tons
Boilers: 3 F.C.M. rated at 35 kg/cm² pressure; superheat: 375°

REMARKS: Hull and machinery have the same characteristics as the French Le Fier
destroyers of 1939-40, none of which was completed due to the war. The 105-mm
and the 37-mm guns first mounted have been replaced with American weapons. The
boilers are in two compartments separated by the engine compartment; trials
indicated a topheavy superstructure. *D 32 Osado* removed from the active list in
1972, *D 31 Audaz, D 33 Meteoro, D 34 Furor, D 35 Rayo* in 1974. *D 37 Temerario* and
D 39 Relampago will be stricken at the end of December 1975.

♦ *2 Alava class*

	Bldr	Laid down	L	In serv.
D 51 ALAVA	Cartagena NSY	12-44	6-47	1-51
D 52 LINIERS	Cartagena NSY	1-45	5-46	1-51

Alava (D 51)   1970

D: 1,841 tons (2,270 fl)   **Dim:**   101.15 (97.52 pp) × 9.65 × 3.10
S: 28 kts   **Range:**   4,500/14   **Man:**   201 men
A: 3/76-mm AA (I × 3) — 3/40-mm AA — 2 hedgehogs — 8 depth charge
        projectors — 2 fixed ASW TT (6 Mk 32 torpedoes)
Electron Equipt: Radars: 1/SPS 6, 1/MLA-1b
                       Sonar: 1/QHB-a high frequency or 1/SQS 4 (middle fre-
                                quency)
M: Parsons GT; 2 props; 42,000 hp; 4 Yarrow boilers   **Fuel:**   540 tons

REMARKS: Rearmed with U.S. weapons in 1964.

♦ *1 Jupiter class, built as a small minelayer*

	Bldr	Laid down	L	In serv.
F 12 VULCANO	S.E. Constr. Nav. El Ferrol	2-35	18-10-35	3-37

D: 2,100 tons (2,400 fl)   **Dim:**   100 (92.30 pp) × 12.65 × 3.50

FRIGATES AND DESTROYERS (*continued*)

Vulcano (F 12) 1970 Marius Bar

S: 16 kts **Range:** 3,700/12 **Man:** 123 men (peace)
A: 4/76-mm AA (I × 4) — 4/40-mm AA — 2 hedgehogs — 8 depth charge projectors after being refitted as frigates in 1959-60. 238 mines
Electron Equipt: Radars: 1/SPS-5b — 1/MLA-1b — Sonar: QHB-a.
M: Parsons GT — 2 props; 5,000 hp.
Boilers: 2 Yarrow, rated at 24.5 kg/cm² pressure **Fuel:** 280 tons

REMARKS: Mines stowed on the main deck on 4 rails with 4 turning plates similar to loading hatchways. *Neptuno* removed from active service in 1970, *Marte* in 1972, *Jupiter* in 1974.

♦ *8 1,500-ton class*

Bldr: Cartagena NSY

	L	In serv.		L	In serv.
F 81 DESCUBIERTA	8-7-75	...	**F 85 N . . .**	...	...
F 82 DIANA	...	...	**F 86 N . . .**	...	...
F 83 N . . .	...	...	**F 87 N . . .**	...	...
F 84 N . . .	...	...	**F 88 N . . .**	...	...

D: 1,500 tons (fl) **S:** 28 kts **Dim:** 88.8 × 10.6
A: 1/76-mm AA OTO Melara — 2/40-mm AA — 1/BPDMS Sea Sparrow system — 2/375-mm Bofors RL (II × 1) — 6/324-mm TT Mk 32 (III × 2)
Electron Equipt: Radars: 1/LW 04 (Dutch), 1 navigation radar, 1/M 22 fire control radar (Dutch).
M: 4 diesels Bazan-MTU; 4,380 hp; 2 variable pitch props
Electric: 2150 KW

REMARKS: Based on the Portuguese *João Roby* class.

♦ *2 Pizarro class modernized in 1960*

	Bldr	Laid down	L	In serv.
F 41 VICENTE YANEZ PINZON	S.E. Constr. Nav. El Ferrol	9-44	8-8-45	1949
F 42 LEGAZPI	S.E. Constr. Nav. El Ferrol	9-44	8-8-45	8-51

Legazpi (F 42) 1971

D: 1,685 tons (2,123 fl) **Dim:** 95.20 (87.54 pp) × 12.15 × 3.40
S: 18.5 kts (trials: 20) **Man:** 13 officers, 238 men
A: 2 U.S. 127-mm 38-cal — 4/40-mm AA — 2 hedgehogs — 8 depth charge projectors — 2 fixed ASW TT (6 Mk 32 torp)
Electron Equipt: Radars: 1/SPS 5b, 1/MLA-1b — Sonar: QHB-a
M: Parsons GT; 2 props; 5,000 hp **Range:** 3,000/15
Boilers: 2 Yarrow rated at 25 kg/cm² superheat pressure
Fuel: 402 tons (max.) — 386 tons (avg)

REMARKS: Exceptionally seaworthy ships; six which have not been modernized have been taken out of service since 1965; the *F 32 Hernan Cortes* and the *F 36 Sarmiento de Gamboa* in 1971 and 1973.

FRIGATES

♦ *4 Atrevida class*

	Bldr	Laid down	L	In serv.
F 61 ATREVIDA	Cartagena	26-6-50	2-12-52	4-55
F 62 PRINCESA	Cartagena	18-3-53	31-3-55	10-59
F 64 NAUTILUS	Cadiz	27-7-57	23-8-56	12-59
F 65 VILLA DE BILBAO (ex-*Favorita*)	Cadiz	18-3-53	18-3-53	7-60

Princesa (F 62) 1971

FRIGATES (*continued*)

D: 977 tons (1,136 fl) **Dim:** 75.50 (68 pp) × 10.20 × 2.64
S: 18 kts **Man:** 10 officers, 122 men
A: 1/76-mm AA — 3/40-mm AA — 2 hedgehogs — 8 depth charge projectors
Electron Equipt: 1/SPS 5b combination search radar
M: 2 diesels; 2 props; 3,000 hp **Fuel:** 100 tons

REMARKS: Tandem machinery arrangement. Electronic equipment and weapons modernized with U.S. aid. Can carry 20 mines. *Diana* removed from active service in 1972.

♦ *6 patrol boats of 400 tons (full load)*

Bldr: Lürssen (prototype); Bazan, Cadiz

	L	In serv.
P 01 **LAZAGA**	30-9-74	14-7-75
P 02 **ALSEDO**	8-1-75	...
P 03 **CADARSO**	8-1-75	...
P 04 **VILLAAMIL**	24-5-74	...
P 05 **BONIFAZ**	24-5-74	...
P 06 **RECALDE**	...	...

D: 400 tons (fl) **Dim:** 58.10 × 54.40 (wl) × 7.60 × 2.80
S: 28 kts **Man:** 30 men
A: 1/76-mm AA OTO Melara — 1/40-mm AA Breda Bofors — 6/20-mm AA — 6/324-mm ASW TT Mk 32 (III × 2) — 2 depth charge racks
Electron Equipt: Radars: 1 navigation, 1 Dutch M 22 combination air-surface search.
  Sonar: 1 hull mounted high frequency.
M: 2 MTU diesels; 8,760 hp; 2 props **Range:** 2,260/27 — 4,200/17.

REMARKS: Installation of SSM is planned. The *P 01 Lazaga* was commissioned in July 1975 with a provisional armament (2/40-mm AA and 2/20-mm AA) — no missile-launcher.

♦ *6 light Barcelo-class patrol boats.*

Bldr: E.N. Bazan, Cartagena, except *Barcelo* (Lürssen)

	L	In serv.
P 11 **BARCELO**	11-75	...
P 12 **LAYA**	...	...
P 13 **JAVIER QUIROGA**	...	...
P 14 **ORDONEZ**	...	...
P 15 **ACEVEDO**	...	...
P 16 **CANDIDO PEREZ**	...	...

D: 150 tons (fl) **S:** 36 kts **Dim:** 36.20 × 5.80 × 2.50
A: 1/40-mm Breda Bofors — 1/20-mm AA — 2/12.7 mm machine guns
M: diesels

♦ **RR 19, 20, 29.** Tugs classified as patrol boats — 1941-42

D: 454 tons **Dim:** 38 × 8.40 × 3.00
S: 11.5 kts **A:** 1/37-mm AA — 1/20-mm AA
M: triple expansion; 1 prop; 800 hp **Range:** 1,000/10
Boiler: 1 drum type, 13 kg/cm² pressure **Fuel:** 200 tons of coal.

♦ **W 33 CENTINELA, W 34 SERVIOLA** — Bldr: Astano, El Ferrol — 1953 — trawlers.

Centinela

D: 280 tons (fl) **S:** 12 kts **Dim:** 36 × 6.80 × 3
A: 2/37-mm **M:** 450-hp diesel

W 32 SALVORA — purchased in 1952 — (formerly a small trawler, built in 1948)
D: 270 tons (fl) **S:** 12 kts **Dim:** 31 × 6.10 × 2.50
A: 1/20-mm AA **M:** 400-hp diesel

V 18 LANZON (1944)
D: 110 tons **S:** 10 kts **Dim:** 18 × 5.20 × 1.85

V 1, ALCATRAZ (*V 4*), **V 5, V 6, V 9, V 10, V 11, V 17, V 21** and **GAVIOTA** (*W 01*)
Rebuilt fishing vessels: (**D:** 5 to 110 tons — **S:** 6 to 19 kts)

MINESWEEPERS

♦ *4 U.S. MSO class transferred since 7-71*

M 41 GUADELETE (ex-*Dynamic*, MSO-432)
M 42 GUADALMEDINA (ex-*Pivot*, MSO-463)
M 43 GUADALQUIVIR (ex-*Persistent*, MSO-491)
M 44 GUADIANA (ex-*Vigor*, MSO-473)
Bldr: U.S.A. 1952-56.
D: 637 tons (735 fl) **S:** 14 kts **Dim:** 52.30 × 10.36 × 4.15
A: 2/20-mm AA (II × 1) — 2/12.7-mm machine guns
Range: 2,000/12 — 3,000/10. **Man:** 6 officers, 70 men
M: 4 Packard diesels linked to 2 variable pitch props; 2,280 hp

REMARKS: Modernized in 1969-70. Equipped for mechanical, magnetic and acoustic minesweeping. SQQ 14 sonar mine detector.

♦ *12 U.S. ASM/MSC class*

M 21 NALON (ex-*MSC 139*)
M 22 LLOBREGAT (ex-*MSC 143*)
M 23 JUCAR (ex-*MSC 220*) (24-6-55)

MINESWEEPERS (continued)

Guadalette (M 41)

M 24 ULLA (ex-*MSC 265*)
M 25 MIÑO (ex-*MSC 266*)
M 26 EBRO (ex-*MSC 269*)
M 27 TURIA (ex-*MSC 130*)
M 28 DUERO (ex-*MSC 200*)
M 29 SIL (ex-*MSC 202*)
M 30 TAJO (ex-*MSC 287*)
M 31 GENIL (ex-*MSC 279*)
M 32 ODIEL (ex-*MSC 288*)

(8-11-57)

Ulla (M 24)   1971

D: 370 tons (405 fl)   **Dim:** 43 (41.50 pp) × 7.95 × 2.55
S: 13 kts (8 sweeping)   **Range:** 2,500/10
A: 2/20-mm AA (II × 1)   **Man:** 2 officers, 35 men
M: General Motors diesels; 2 props; 1,200 hp   **Fuel:** 40 tons

REMARKS: Transferred under the M.A.P., 2 in 1954, 1 in 1955, 3 in 1956, 1 in 1958, 2 in 1959, 3 in 1960.

♦ *7 based on the wartime German M 40 class*

		L	In serv.
M 11	GUADIARO	26-6-50	4-53
M 12	TINTO	26-6-50	5-53
M 13	EUME	27-7-53	5-54
M 14	ALMANZORA	27-7-53	11-54
M 15	NAVIA	28-7-53	3-55
M 16	GUADALHORCE	18-2-53	1953
M 17	EO	22-9-53	3-55

Bldr: Bazan, Cadiz (12/13); Bazan, Cartagena (all others). Modernized in 1959-61.

Eo (M 17)   1970

D: 670 tons (770 fl)   **S:** 13 kts   **Dim:** 74.26 × 10.17 × 3.70
A: 2/20-mm AA   **Range:** 3,000/10   **Man:** 65 to 80 men
M: reciprocating and BP turbines; 2 props; 2,400 hp
Boilers: 2 tube (3 manifolds) **Fuel:** 192.7 m³ coal (*1 to 6*); oil for the others.

REMARKS: *1948 program.* Each shaft is powered by triple expansion engine with hydraulic linkage to a low pressure turbine. *M 03 Lerez* taken out of service in 1971, *M 02 Nervion, M 06 Ter* in 1972, *M 01 Bidasoa, M 04 Tambre* and *M 05 Segura* in 1974. The M 12 *Tinto* will be condemned on 31-1-76.

FAST SMALL CRAFT

	In serv.		In serv.		In serv.		Bldr
♦ **LT 30**	1954	**LT 31**	1957	**LT 32**	1957		La Caracca, Cadiz

D: 120 tons   **Dim:** 34.80 × 5.10 × 1.40
S: 40 kts   **Range:** 700 to 800/30
A: 2/20-mm AA — 2/533-mm TT (4 torpedoes)   **Man:** 22 men
M: Mercedes-Benz diesels; 3 props; 7,500 hp   **Fuel:** 20 tons

REMARKS: *LT 27, 28, 29* removed from service in 1963-64. Modelled on the wartime German Schnellboote. *LT 32* helicopter target.

AMPHIBIOUS SHIPS

♦ *1 personnel transport*

TA 11 ARAGON (ex-*Noble, APA-218*) (18-10-44)

D: 6,970 tons (14,900 fl)   **S:** 17 kts   **Dim:** 133 × 18.90 × 8.60
A: 1/127-mm — 12/40-mm AA (IV × 1, II × 4)   **Man:** 536 men
Range: 14,700/16

AMPHIBIOUS SHIPS (continued)

Aragon (TA 11)

Castilla (TA 21)   Aguilera

◆ *3 ex-U.S. LST-class tank landing ships. 2 transferred in 10-71, 1 in 1972.*

L 11 VELASCO (ex-*Terrebonne Parish, LST-1156*)
L 12 MARTIN ALVAREZ (ex-*Wahkiakum County, LST-1162*)
L 13 Conde del VENADITO (ex-*Tom Green County, LST-1159*) (19-54)

Martin Alvarez (L 12)   1972

Electron Equipt: Radars: 1/SPS 10, 1/SPS 6
M: GT; 1 prop; 2 Babcock boilers; 8,500 hp

REMARKS: Victory class cargo ships fitted out for troop transport (1,560 men, 3,000 tons of cargo), transferred by the U.S.A. in 1964. Carries 19 LCVPs 2 LCMs, 1 LCPR, 2 LCPs.

◆ *1 cargo carrier.*

TA 21 CASTILLA (ex-*Achernar, AKA-53*) (3-12-43)

D: 7,430 tons (13,050 fl)	**Dim:** 140 × 19.20 × 7.40
S: 15.5 kts	**A:** 1/127-mm — 8/40-mm AA (II × 4)
M: GT; 1 prop	**Boilers:** 2 Foster-Wheeler; 6,000 hp

REMARKS: C-2 cargo ship of the Maritime Commission. Can carry 7,200 tons of cargo including 2,000 tons of oil in ballast; transferred by the U.S.A. early in 1965. Has 14 LCVPs, 8 LCMs, 2 LCPs.

D: 2,590 tons (5,786 fl)	**S:** 13 kts	**Dim:** 117.35 × 16.70 × 3.70
A: 6/76-mm AA (II × 3)	**Range:** 6,000/9	**Man:** 115 men
		Fuel: 1,060 tons

M: 4 General Motors diesels; 2 props; 6,000 hp

Accommodations for 395 troops.

◆ *1 landing ship dock (LSD) transferred 1-7-71*

TA 31 GALICIA (ex-*San Marcos, LSD-25*)   Newport News SB & DD   Bldr 10-1-45   L

D: 4,790 tons (9,375 fl)	**Dim:** 139 × 21.90 × 4.00
S: 15 kts	**Man:** 17 officers, 237 men.
A: 12/40-mm AA (IV × 2, II × 2)	**Range:** 8,000/15.
M: GT; 2 props; 9,000 hp   **Boilers:** 2 drums with 3 shells

REMARKS: Carries 18 LCMs with 1 LCVP inboard each; well deck 103 × 13.30. Platform for 3 helicopters.

AMPHIBIOUS SHIPS (continued)

Galicia (TA 31)   1972

♦ *3 French EDIC class:* **BD K6, 7, 8** — Bldr: E.N. Bazan, El Ferrol — 1965–67

BD K 6 (French type)   1970

> **D:** 279 tons (665 fl)   **Dim:** 59 (52.90 pp) × 11.90 × 1.30
> **S:** 9.5 kts   **A:** 2/12.7-mm machine guns — 1/81-mm mortar
> **M:** diesels; 2 props; 1,040 hp   **Range:** 1,500/9

♦ *3 small LSM class:* **L 01** (ex-U.S. *329*) — **L 02** (ex-U.S. *331*) — **L 03** (ex-U.S. *343*) — 1943, transferred in 1960.

> **D:** 743 tons (1,095 fl)   **A:** 2/40-mm AA   **S:** 12 kts
> **M:** diesels; 2,800 hp

L 02

♦ *3 based on the British LCT:* **BD K3, 4, 5** — Bldr: E.N. Bazan, El Ferrol (1958)

> **D:** 480 tons (894 fl)   **Dim:** 56.60 × 11.60 × 3.20
> **S:** 7 kts   **A:** 1/40-mm AA — 2/20-mm AA   **Range:** 1,000/7
> **M:** diesels; 2 props; 1,000 hp

♦ **BDK 1** (ex-*Foca*), **BDK 2** (ex-*Morsa*) (1943) former British LCT (4) class

> **D:** 440 tons (720 fl)   **S:** 10 kts   **M:** diesels; 2 props
> **A:** 2/20-mm AA

NETLAYERS

CR 1 (ex-*G-6*) — Bldr: Penhoët-Loire — L: 28-9-54

CR 1

> **D:** 770 tons (850 fl)   **Dim:** 46.28 (44.50 pp) × 10.20 × 3.20
> **S:** 12 kts   **Man:** 45 men
> **A:** 1/40-mm AA — 1/20-mm AA   **Range:** 5,200/12
> **M:** diesel-electric propulsion (2 SEMT-Pielstick diesels); 1 prop; 1,600 hp
> **Fuel:** 125 m³ diesel

REMARKS: Same characteristics as the French *Scarabee;* transferred in 1955 under the M.A.P. (*AN 101*).

HYDROGRAPHIC SHIPS

♦ *4 Antares class*

Bldr: E.N. Bazan, Cadiz

	L	In serv.		L	In serv.
A 23 ANTARES	8–73	22-11-74	**A 32 TOFINOS**	...	23-4-75
A 24 RIGEL	8–73	22-11-74	**A 26 MALASPINA**	...	2-2-75

> **D:** 820 tons (1,090 fl)   **S:** 15 kts   **Dim:** 57.60 × 11.70 × 3.64
> **A:** 2/20-mm AA   **Man:** 63 men   **Range:** 4,000/12 – 3,140/14.5
> **M:** 2 diesels; 2 props (variable pitch); 3,240 hp

H 4 CASTOR (11-66), **H 5 POLLUX** (12-66) — Bldr: E.N. Bazan, Le Coruña

> **D:** 355 tons (383.4 fl)   **Dim:** 38.26 (33.84 pp) × 3.85 × 2.75
> **S:** 11.5 kts   **Man:** 36 men   **Range:** 3,600
> **M:** Sulzer diesel; 1 prop; 720 hp

HYDROGRAPHIC SHIPS *(continued)*

Castor (H 4)   1971

LOGISTIC SHIPS AND AUXILIARIES

♦ *6 oilers*

BP 11 TEIDE — Bldr: E.N. Bazan, Cartagena — L: 20-6-55.

Teide (BP 11)

    D: 2,750 tons (8,030 fl)   **Dim:** 117.50 × 14.78 × 6.20
    S: 12 kts   **M:**   diesels
Fitted for underway replenishment.

PP 1 — Bldr: Ast. de Santander (1939)
Small auxiliary tankers

    D: 470 tons   **S:** 10 kts
    M: diesel; 2 props; 220 hp
14 other small auxiliary tankers of 100 to 300 tons including *PP 3, PP 4, PP 5.*

♦ *1 transport*

A 41 ALMIRANTE LOBO (ex-cargo *Torrelaguna*) — Bldr: Ast. Echevarrieta, Cadiz — L: 2-9-53

    D: 7,750 tons   **S:** 12 kts   **Dim:** 103 × 14.60 × 6.80
    A: 2/37-mm   **M:**   1 reciprocating; 1 prop; 2,300 hp

♦ *Fleet ocean tugs*

RA 1, RA 2 — Bldr: E.N. Bazan, Cartagena — 1954

    D: 1,023 tons (fl)   **Dim:** 56.10 (49.80 pp) × 10 × 3.90
    S: 14.5 kts   **Range:** 5,500/14
    A: 2/20-mm (II × 1) — 24 mines   **Man:**   60 men
    M: 2 Sulzer diesels; 1 reversible pitch prop; 3,200 hp   **Fuel:** 142 tons

RA 4, RA 5, BS 1 POSEIDON — Bldr: E.N. Bazan, Cadiz — 1962-63

Poseidon (BS 1)   1971

    D: 1,050 tons (fl) (**BS 1:** 1,098 fl)   **Dim:** 55.90 (49.80 pp) × 10 × 4
Other characteristics those of the *RA 1;* the *Poseidon* is fitted out as a salvage vessel. Can carry and lay 24 mines.

RA 3 (ex-British merchant ship *Metinda III;* joined the fleet in 5-61)

    D: 1,050 tons (fl)   **S:** 10 kts   **Dim:** 41.75 × 10.10 × 3.95.
    M: triple expansion; 1 prop; 3,200 hp.

♦ *Harbor tugs*

RR 15 (800 hp) — **RR 16** (in service 1962 — **RR 50/52** (800 hp)
RR 53/55 (1,400 hp)
RP 1-12 (1965-67, 200 hp) — **RP 18** (1952, 300 hp, Kort injector nozzles)
RP 25, (1947, 300 hp) — **RP 40** (1961, 600 hp)

♦ *Small security patrol boats*

L.A.S. 10, 20, 30, (1963-64) Bldr: E.N. Bazan, Cadiz. Plans of US/CGS 83-ft. patrol craft

    D: 63 tons (fl)   **Dim:** 25.35 (23.78 pp) × 4.90 × . . .
    S: 15 kts   **M:**   diesels, 800 hp. Wooden hull
    A: 1/20-mm — 8-mm AA machine gun — 2 MR-20 (mousetrap) — 8 depth charges

L.P.I. 1, 2, 3, 4, 5 (1964)

LOGISTIC SHIPS AND AUXILIARIES (*continued*)

D: 25 tons   **Dim:** 14.05 × 4.67 × . . .   Small boats for swimmers
S: 16 kts   **A:** 1 or 2 machine guns

CABO FRADERA — Motorized small craft for the Minho river

Bldr: E.N. Bazan, La Caracca (1966)

D: 28 tons (fl)   **S:** 12 kts   **Dim:** 17.80 × 4.20 × 1.60
A: 1 machine gun   **M:** 2 diesels; 760 hp

♦ **AZOR** (1949)

V 1

D: 486 tons (fl)   **Dim:** 47 × 7.70 × 3.80
S: 12 kts   **M:** diesel; 1,200 hp

Used as a yacht for the King of Spain.

TRAINING SHIP

	Bldr	Laid down	L	In serv.
JUAN SEBASTIAN DE ELCANO	Ast. Echevarrieta, Cadiz	1962	5-3-27	8-28

1972

D: 3,420 tons (3,714 fl)   **Dim:** 94.11 × 13.60 × 6.95
S: 11 kts   **Man:** 224 men, 80 cadets
A: 4/57-mm   **Range:** 13,000/8
M: 1 Sulzer diesel; 1 prop; 1,500 hp   **Fuel:** 230 tons

REMARKS: Four-masted schooner, 2,467 m² sail area. School ship for Coast Guard. Same class as the Chilean *Esmeralda*.

VARIOUS

♦ *4 Treasury department small craft, (Vigilencia fiscal)* delivered in 1969–70 by Constr. Méc. de Normandie, at Cherbourg; the *Albatros I* to *IV* could be used as gunboats in a wartime situation.

D: 83 tons   **S:** 7/9 kts   **Dim:** 32.35 × 5.34 × 1.85
S: 29 kts   **A:** 1/20-mm
M: 2 Mercedes-Benz diesels, each 1,300 hp., and a Hispano-Suiza engine for quiet cruising (325 hp)

♦ *1 ex-Treasury Department (Vigilencia fiscal) small craft*

AGUILUCHO — Bldr: Vigo — L: 29-2-73.

D: 45 tons   **Dim:** 26.5 × 5.11 × 1.30
M: diesels; 2,750 hp   **Range:** 750/15

SUDAN

PERSONNEL: 40 officers, 300 men

MERCHANT MARINE (1-7-75): 14 ships — 45,943 grt

PATROL BOATS

♦ *2 Yugoslavian Kraljavica class*

522 EL FASHER — 523 EL KHARTOUM — Bldr: Yugoslavia — 1968-69

Horriya   L. V. Pujo

    D: 190 tons (245 fl)   **S:** 20 kts   **Dim:** 41 × 6.30 × 2.10
    A: 2/40-mm AA — 4/20-mm AA — depth charges.
    M: diesels; 2 props; 3,300 hp
    Range: 1,500/12.

♦ *4 Gihad class*

PB 1 EL GIHAD — PB 2 EL HORRIYA — PB 3 EL ISTIQLAL — PB 4 EL SHAAB

    Bldr: Mosor, Yugoslavia — 1961

    D: 86 tons   **Dim:** 31.40 × 4.90 × 1.45
    S: 20 kts   **Man:** 17 men
    Range: 1,200/12
    A: 1/40-mm — 1/20-mm — 2 machine guns
    M: 2 Mercedes-Benz diesels, each 910 hp

♦ *7 ex-U.S. patrol gunboats transferred by Iran in 1975*

1) **N** . . . (ex-*Parvin*, ex-*PGM-103*) — **N** . . . (ex-*Bahram*, ex-*PGM-112*).
    N . . . (ex-*Nahid*, ex-*PGM-122*)
    Bldr: Peterson (1967-70)
    D: 100 tons (147 fl)   **Dim:** 31.10 × 4.90 × 2
    S: 20 kts   **Man:** 15 men
    A: 1/40-mm — 2/20-mm AA
    M: diesels; 2 props; 1,800 hp

Horriya   LV Pujo

2) **N** . . . (ex-*Veyvan*), **N** . . . (ex-*Tiran*), **N** . . . (ex-*Mahan*), **N** . . . (ex-*Mehran*)
    D: 80 tons (107 fl)   **Dim:** 28.80 × 6.25 × 1.55
    S: 22 kts   **Man:** 15 men
    A: 1/40-mm — depth charges
    M: 4 diesels — 2 props; 2,200 hp
    Range: 1,500/10

REMARKS: Five of these seven PGM have been named *Gadeer, Gohar, Shahpar, Shekan, Zohreh*.

AMPHIBIOUS SHIPS

♦ *2 ex-Yugoslavian DTK 221 type (LCT type) transferred in 1969.* See section on Yugoslavia.

SOBAT   **DINDER**

♦ *3 LCU type transferred by the U.S.S.R. or Yugoslavia at the end of 1970*
    D: 40 tons (80 fl)

VARIOUS

♦ **FASHODA** supply ship — **D:** 200 tons — Bldr: Yugoslavia, delivered in 1969.
    BARAKA self-propelled barge — **D:** 100 tons — Bldr: Yugoslavia, delivered in 1969.
    TIENAGA survey ship

♦ *6 type 108 Yugoslavian-built ships modified as gunboats, delivered 4-70.*
(See section on Yugoslavia.)

SURINAM

The government of Surinam has ordered three small patrol boats from the Schottel Nederlandsche Scheepsbouw in Warmond, Netherlands. Delivery to be in mid-1976.

SWEDEN

PERSONNEL: Peacetime: 9,200 men of the regular navy including officers, petty officers, and civilian personnel with a permanent status, plus 7,000 contingency personnel. In wartime, with the mobilization of the reserve, the number of men could reach 80,000.

NAVAL AVIATION:

Made up entirely of helicopters with about 40 units of which ten Alouette II (HKP2) are for minesweeping, sea rescue and ASW missions, plus a few Agusta Bell 206 A (HKP6) and some Vertol 107 (HKP4).

MERCHANT MARINE (1-7-74): 735 ships — 6,226,659 grt
(tankers: 117 — 2,144,999 grt)

WARSHIPS IN SERVICE (1) OR UNDER CONSTRUCTION AS OF 1 OCTOBER 1975

	L	D	Main armament
♦ *23 submarines*			
4 NACKEN	Under constr.	980	8/533-mm TT
5 SJÖBJÖRNEN	1967-68	800	6/533-mm TT
12 HAGEN	1955-61	770	4/533-mm TT
3 U	1943-44	420	4/533-mm TT
♦ *8 destroyers*			
2 HALLAND	1952	2,650	4/120-mm, SSM system
4 ÖSTERGÖTLAND	1956-57	2,150	4/120-mm — 5/533-mm TT
2 ÖLAND	1945-46	1,990	4/120-mm — 6/533-mm TT
♦ *4 frigates*			
4 VISBY	1942-43	1,150	
♦ *17 missile patrol boats*			
1 JAGAREN	1972	140	1/57-mm
16 JAGAREN mod.	1976		1/57-mm — 4 Penguin
♦ *54 patrol torpedo boats*			
12 SPICA II	1972-75	235	1/57-mm — 6/533-mm TT
6 SPICA	1966-67	190	1/57-mm — 5/533-mm TT
11 PLEJAD	1954-58	155	2/40-mm — 5/533-mm TT
10 T 32	1950-52	40	1/40-mm — 2/533-mm TT
15 T 42	1956-59	44.5	1/40-mm — 2/533-mm TT

(1) Only part of the ships of the fleet are manned in peacetime. The fleet is used primarily for the training of recruits.

Port quarter and bow views of the *Spica* class PT boat

WEAPONS AND SYSTEMS OF THE SWEDISH NAVY

For electronic equipment the Swedish Navy generally uses Dutch products, (for example, radars: air-search LOW 2, fire control HSA, etc.)

Guns:

The Swedish Bofors firm furnishes most of the guns used; the principal equipment has the following characteristics:

◆ *120-mm twin automatic*

— Installed on the *Halland*-class destroyers
— Mount weight: 55 tons — Length of barrel: 46 calibers
— Muzzle velocity: 850 m/sec (projectile weight 23.5 kg)
— Elevation: +80°
— Firing rate: 40 rounds/min/barrel
— Maximum effective range, surface target: 12 to 13,000 m
— Maximum effective range, anti-aircraft fire: 7 to 8,000 m

Each barrel can fire 26 rounds at a time; after which the magazine must then be reloaded. Water cooled. Used with LA 01 fire control radar of Signal Apparaten (HSA).

◆ *120-mm twin semi-automatic*

— Installed on the *Ostergötland* and *Oland* class destroyers
— Mount weight: . . . t — length of barrel: 46 calibers
— Muzzle velocity: 850 m/sec
— Elevation: +80°
— Firing rate: 20 rounds/min/barrel

◆ *57-mm twin automatic*

— Installed on the *Halland*-class destroyers
— Mount weight: 20 tons
— Muzzle velocity: 850 m/sec
— Maximum rate of fire: 120/rounds/barrel
— Maximum effective range, surface target: 13,000 m
— Maximum effective range, anti-aircraft fire: 5,000 m

◆ *57-mm single barrel automatic*

— Installed on *Spica* and *Spica II* patrol torpedo boats
— Mount weight (without ammunition): 6 tons
— Train speed: 55°/sec
— Elevation speed: 20°/sec
— Elevation: −10° + 70°
— Maximum rate of fire: 200/rounds/min

Used on the *Spica I* with an S 62 HSA fire control made up of two radars in a dome, one for search, the other for target designation and, if required, the firing of the gun. On the *Spica II* class these radars are separated.

Missiles:

The Swedish Navy has in service on both the 2 *Halland* class destroyers and in the coastal batteries a surface-surface missile based on the CT 20 of the SNIAS: the Saab 08 A.

Length: 5.70 m, diameter: 0.650 m, wingspan, 3.600 m, weight 9,000 kg, maximum range, 30 miles (on destroyers), 70 miles (coastal batteries).

ASW weapons:

The Swedish Navy uses the 375-mm Bofors ASW RL in triple or quadruple mount. The most recent torpedo models are:
the M 41 400-mm ASW with homing guidance system;
the 500-mm M 61 wire-guided torpedo.

SUBMARINES

◆ *4 A 14 class*

	Bldr	L	In serv.
NACKEN	Kockums (Malmö)	. . .	1977
NAJAD	Kockums (Malmö)	. . .	1978
NEPTUN	Kockums (Malmö)	. . .	1978
N . . .	Kockums (Malmö)		1979

D: 980 tons **Dim:** 49.50 × 5.70 × . . .
S: . . . **Man:** 5 officers, 12 men
A: 8/533-mm TT
M: diesel-electric propulsion: generator group of engines with 2,100 hp; 1/1,100 kw motor; 1 prop

REMARKS: The first 3 were ordered at the end of 1972. The electric battery installation is mounted on shock absorbers. Single periscope; central computer which furnishes in addition to tactical information, main electric motor control, navigation, and cells data. Will be able to lay mines.

◆ *5 Sjöbjörnen (class 11 B)*

SJÖBJÖRNEN	9-1-68	**SJÖHUNDEN**	21-3-68
SJÖHÄSTEN	6-8-68	**SJÖLEJONET**	29-6-67
SJÖORMEN	25-1-67		

Bldr: 3: Kockums (Malmö) — 2: Karlskronavarvet

Sjöormen

D: 800 surfaced/1,125 submerged **Dim:** 51 × 6.10 × 5.10
S: 20 kts submerged **Man:** 7 officers, 11 men
M: Propulsion by an Asea electric motor, 3,500 hp, which runs at slow speeds and is virtually without noise, plus 2 Hedemora-Pielstick diesel-electric groups on the surface (4 generators) and, submerged, four batteries; 1 five-bladed prop.

REMARKS: Hull and sail of the U.S. *Barbel* class; two decks; advanced compartmentation. Endurance 21 days; diving depth of up to 150 m (the Baltic Sea is quite shallow).

SUBMARINES (continued)

♦ *12 Hajen (A 11 class).*

	L		L
A. HAJEN	11-12-54	BÄVERN	3-2-58
SÄLEN	3-10-55	ILLERN	14-11-57
VALEN*	21-4-55	UTTERN	14-11-58
B. DRAKEN	9-1-60	NORDKAPAREN	8-3-61
GRIPEN*	31-5-60	SPRINGAREN	31-8-61
VARGEN	20-5-60	DELFINEN	7-3-61

Bldr: Kockums or (*) Karlskronavarvet

Salen   1972

D: 770 tons/835 normal (720 for the A type)
Dim: 66 (A), 70 (B) × 5.10 × 5.10
S: 14/17 kts   **Man:** 44 men
A: 4/533-mm TT fwd
M: diesel-electric propulsion surfaced (S.E.M.T.-Pielstick diesels); 1,700 hp

REMARKS: Snorkel; streamlined sail; derived from the German XXI type. The A group has 2 props; the more recent B group, 1 prop. The 8 reserve torpedoes are retained in a ready service rack abaft the torpedo tubes.

♦ *3 U (rebuilt 1960-63)*

	L		L
ABBORREN (ex-*U 5*)	8-7-43	MAKRILLEN (ex-*U 9*)	23-5-44
LAXEN (ex-*U 8*)	25-4-44		

Abborren

Bldr: Kockums or Karlskronavarvet

D: 420/430 surfaced/460 submerged tons   **S:** 14/9 kts
Dim: 49.80 (pp) × 5.30 × 4.30   **Man:** 23 men
A: 4/533-mm TT (3 fwd, 1 aft)
M: 2 M.A.N. diesels; electric motor; 1,500/750 hp

REMARKS: One-piece hull, snorkel and streamlined sail. Rebuilt 1960-63. Several fitted for ASW service. *Gaddan* taken out of service in 1974 and the *Siken* in 1975.

NOTE: A salvage submarine is being built at the Kockums shipyards.

DESTROYERS

♦ *2 Halland*

	Bldr	Laid down	L	In serv.
J 18 HALLAND	Götaverken (Göteborg)	1949	16-7-52	4-55
J 19 SMALAND	Eriksbergs (Göteborg)	1949	23-10-52	1-56

Småland (J 19)   1970

Halland (J 18)   1970

DESTROYERS (*continued*)

D: 2,650 tons (3,300 fl)   **Dim:** 121 (116 pp) × 12.60 × 4.50
S: 35 kts   **Man:** 18 officers, 272 men
Range: 3,000/20
A: 1 twin launcher for SAAB 08 A SSM — 4/120-mm AA (II × 2) — 2/57-mm AA (II × 1) — 6/40-mm AA — 8/533-mm TT (IV × 1) — 2 quadruple Bofors ASW RL
Electron Equipt: Radars: 1/LW 02, 1/VC/DO, HSA fire control
                      Sonars: 1 search, 1 attack
M: GT; 2 props; 55,000 hp; 2 Penhoet boilers
Fuel: 500 tons

◆ *4 Östergötland class*

	Bldr	Laid down	L	In serv.
J 20 **ÖSTERGÖTLAND**	Götaverken (Göteborg)	9-55	8-5-56	3-58
J 21 **SÖDERMANLAND**	Eriksbergs (Göteborg)	6-55	28-5-56	6-58
J 22 **GÄSTRIKLAND**	Götaverken (Göteborg)	10-55	6-6-56	1-59
J 23 **HÄLSINGLAND**	Kockums (Malmö)	10-55	14-1-57	6-59

Södermanland (J 21)   1970

D: 2,150 tons (2,600 fl)   **Dim:** 115.80 (112 pp) × 11.20 × 3.70
S: 35 kts   **Man:** 18 officers, 226 men
A: 4/120-mm AA (II × 2) — 5/40-mm AA (7 on the J 20) — 1 Sea Cat system on the 21, 22, and 23 — 5/533-mm TT (V × 1) — 1 Squid — 60 mines
Electron Equipt: Radars: similar to the *Halland* class
                      Sonars: 1 search, 1 attack
M: Laval GT; 2 props; 2 Penhoet boilers; 40,000 hp   **Range:** 2,200/20
Fuel: 330 tons

◆ *2 Öland class*

	Bldr	Laid down	L	In serv.
J 16 **ÖLAND**	Kockums (Malmö)	1943	15-12-45	12-47
J 17 **UPPLAND**	Karlskronavarvet	1943	15-11-46	1-49

D: 1,990 tons (2,400 fl)   **Dim:** 111 (107 pp) × 11.20 × 3.40
S: 35 kts   **Man:** 210 men
Range: 2,500/20
A: 4/120-mm AA (II × 2) — 6/40-mm AA (II × 3) — 6/533-mm TT (III × 2) — 60 mines

Uppland (J 17)

Electron Equipt: Radars: 2 Thomason — CSF Saturn type for air search, 2/M 45 fire control
                      Sonars: 1 search, 1 attack
M: Laval GT; 2 props; 40,000 hp; 2 Penhoet boilers
Fuel: 300 tons
Electric: . . . kw

FRIGATES

	Author	Bldr	L	In serv.
F 11 **VISBY**	*1941*	Götaverken (Göteborg)	16-10-42	10-8-43
F 12 **SUNDSVALL**	*1941*	Götaverken (Göteborg)	20-10-42	17-9-43
F 13 **HÄLSINGBORG**	*1941*	Karlskronavarvet	23-3-43	30-11-43
F 14 **KALMAR**	*1941*	Eriksbergs (Göteborg)	20-7-43	3-2-44

Visby (F 11)

FRIGATES (*continued*)

D: 1,150 tons (1,320 fl) **Dim:** 98 × 9.10 × 3.80.
S: 35 kts **Man:** 140 men
A: 3/120-mm (I × 3) — 3/40-mm AA — 1 depth charge projector
M: 2 Laval GT; 2 props; 36,000 hp; 3 boilers
Range: 1,600/20.

REMARKS: *F 11* and *F 12* have only 2/57-mm AA (I × 2) with HSA fire control radar and a helicopter platform.

GUNBOATS

♦ *17 Norwegian Storm/Snögg class guided missile boats*

P 151 JAGAREN — Bldr: Båtservice Verft, Mandal (Norway) — 8-6-72
P 152/187

Jagaren (P 151) 1974

D: 145 tons **S:** 35 kts **Dim:** 37 × 6 × 1.50
A: 1/57-mm AA — equipped for minelaying.
M: 2 MTU 1082 diesels, 900 hp each at 1,600 rpm and 3,500 hp at 1,700 rpm; 2 props

REMARKS: The *152-167* will be fitted with 4 advanced Penguin systems.

GUIDED MISSILE AND TORPEDO GUNBOATS

♦ *12 Spica II class*

	L	In serv.		L	In serv.
T 131 NÖRRKÖPING	16-11-72	9-73	T 137 UMEA	...	...
T 132 NYNÄSHAMN	24-4-73	...	T 138 PITEA	...	...
T 133 NORTÄLJE	18-9-73	4-74	T 139 LULEA	...	...
T 134 VARBERG	21-3-74	10-74	T 140 HALMSTAD	...	...
T 135 VÄSTERAS	15-5-74	20-10-74	T 141 STRÖMSTAD	...	...
T 136 VÄSTERVIK	3-9-74	2-9-74	T 142 YSTAD	...	...

Bldr: Karlskronavarvet and Götaverken.

D: 230 tons **S:** 40.5 kts **Dim:** 43.60 × 7.10 × 1.60
A: 1/57-mm AA — 6/533-mm wire guided torpedoes — 2 illumination RL — 1 chaff launcher
M: 3 Rolls-Royce GT × 3,800 hp

REMARKS: It is expected that some of this class will have SSM mounted. The fire control system varies from the *Spica I* type. The search radar and the fire control radar are separated and no longer in a dome.

Nörrköping (T 131) 1974

♦ *6 Spica class*

	L		L
T 121 SPICA	26-4-66	T 124 CASTOR	7-6-67
T 122 SIRIUS	26-4-66	T 125 VEGA	7-6-67
T 123 CAPELLA	26-4-66	T 126 VIRGO	7-6-67

Bldr: Karlskronavarvet and Götaverken (*121/123*).

Spica (T 122) 1972

D: 190 tons (235 fl) **S:** 40 kts **Dim:** 42.50 × 7.30 × 1.60
Man: 4 officers, 10 petty officers, 14 men
A: 1/57-mm fwd — 6/533-mm wire-guided torpedoes
M: 3 Bristol-Siddeley Proteus 1274 type gas turbines, each developing 3,860 hp; 3 KaMeWa props

REMARKS: Automatic 57-mm Bofors gun with S 63 fire control radar. Can carry mines.

GUIDED MISSILE AND TORPEDO GUNBOATS (*continued*)

Sirius (T 122)   1970

♦ *11 Plejad class*

	L			L
T 102 PLEJAD	1954		T 108 ALTAIR	1957
T 103 POLARIS	1954		T 109 ANTARES	1958
T 104 POLLUX	1954		T 110 ARCTURUS	1958
T 105 REGULUS	1954		T 111 ARGO	1958
T 106 RIGEL	1954		T 112 ASTREA	1958
T 107 ALDEBARAN	1954			

Bldr: Lürssen-Vegesack (Germany)

Polaris (T 103)   1970

D: 155 tons (170 fl) **Dim:** 48.15 (45 pp) × 5.80 × 1.61
S: 37 kts **Man:** 3 officers, 40 men
Range: 600/30
A: 2/40-mm — 6/533-mm wire-guided torpedoes
M: 3 Mercedes-Benz diesels; 3 props; 7,800 hp (9,000 on the *108/112*)

REMARKS: 40-mm AA have remote control; RL for illumination rockets. Can be fitted for minelaying after the torpedo tubes are removed. The *Jaguar* class of the West German navy is derived from the *Plejad* class.

PATROL TORPEDO BOATS

♦ *10 T 32 and 15 T 42 types* — 1950-1959

T 32 to **T 41** — Bldr: Karlskronavarvet (*T 34-37, T 53-56*) and Kockums (all others).
T 42 to **T 56**

D: *T 32:* 40 tons **S:** 40 kts **Dim:** *T 32:* 23.10 × 5.16 × 1.60
T 42: 44.5 tons   *T 42:* 23.50 × 5.68 × 1.60
A: 1/40-mm — 2/533-mm TT

Steel hull — welded construction — 2 gasoline engines — 1 illumination RL.

Argo (T 111)   1970

(T 46)

MINE LAYERS

♦ *3 Älvsborg class*

	Bldr	Laid down	L	In serv.
M 02 ÄLVSBORG	Karlskronavarvet	11-68	11-11-69	4-71
M 03 VIBORG	Karlskronavarvet	. .-73	22-1-74	1976
M 04 N . . .	. . .		. . .	. . .

MINELAYERS (continued)

Älvsborg (M 02)   1971

D: 2,650 tons   **S:** 15 kts   **Dim:** 92.40 (83.80 pp) × 14.70 × 4
A: 3/40-mm AA — 1 helicopter
M: 2 Nohab-Polar 12-cylinder diesels; 1 Ka-Me-Wa prop; 4,200 hp
Man: 97 men + quarters for 210
Electric: 1,200 kw

REMARKS: Used as a submarine tender. The *M-04* will be a different class.

	Bldr	Laid down	L	In serv.
M 01 ÄLVSNABBEN	Eriksbergs (Göteborg)	11-12	19-1-43	5-43

1970

D: 4,250 tons   **Dim:** 102 (96.80 pp) × 13.60 × 4.90
S: 14 kts   **Man:** 255 men
A: 2/152-mm (aft, I × 2) — 2/57-mm AA — 2/40-mm AA — At least 300 mines
M: diesel; 1 prop; 3,000 hp

REMARKS: Cargo ship modified while under construction. Also used as a supply ship for minesweepers and submarines. Will be replaced by the *M 04*. Used as a training ship.

MINESWEEPERS

♦ *9 minehunters ordered in 1976-77.* The Karlskrona shipyards will build a half-scale model of the ship listed below in fiberglass as a prototype of these ships.

VIKSTEN

D: 140 tons (fl)   **Dim:** 25.3 × 6.64 × 3.65

♦ *6 Hanö (steel hull): 12 Arkö (wooden hull):*

		L			L
M 51	HANÖ	1953	M 60	IGGÖ	1958
M 52	TÄRNÖ	1953	M 61	STYRSÖ	1961
M 53	TJURKÖ	1954	M 62	SKAFTÖ	1961
M 54	STURKÖ	1954	M 63	ASPÖ	1962
M 55	ORNÖ	1954	M 64	HASSLO	1962
M 56	UTÖ	1954	M 65	VINÖ	1962
M 57	ARKÖ	21-1-57	M 68	VALLÖ	1962
M 58	SPÅRÖ	1957	M 67	NÄMDÖ	1964
M 59	KARLSÖ	1957	M 68	BLIDÖ	1964

Tärnö (M 52)   1972

Aspö (M 63)

MINESWEEPERS (*continued*)

M 51/56: **D:** 270 tons   **Dim:** 42 (40 pp) × 7.00 × 2.70
         A: 1/40-mm AA   **S:** 14.5 kts

M 57/69: **D:** 285 tons   **Dim:** 44 × 7.00 × 2.50
         A: 1/40-mm AA   **S:** 14.5 kts
         Man: 25 men
         M: 2 Mercedes-Benz diesels; 1,000 hp — Excellent antimagnetic features.

◆ *8 M 15 class inshore minesweepers*

M 15, 16, M 21/26 (1941)

   D: 70 tons   **Dim:** 26 × 5.05 × 1.40
   S: 13 kts   **Man:** 10 men
   A: 1/20-mm AA
   M: diesels; 1 prop; 600 hp (B) — wooden hull

REMARKS: *M21, 22, 25* used as tenders for divers and demining personnel.

◆ *9 Orust class inshore minesweepers*

A. M 41 ORUST (1948)	**C. M 47 GILLÖGA** (1964)
M 42 TJÖRN (1948)	**M 48 RÖDLÖGA** (1964)
B. M 43 HISINGEN (1960)	**M 49 SVARTLÖGA** (1964)
M 44 BLACKAN (1960)	
M 45 DAMMAN (1960)	
M 46 GALTEN (1960)	

   D: A: 110 tons B/C: 140 tons
   Dim: 18.80 × 5.83 × 1.40 B/C: 22 × 6.40 × 1.40
   S: 9 kts   **M:** diesel; 600 hp
   A: 1/20-mm AA (A) — 1/40-mm AA (B/C)

◆ *3 Gasten class*

M 31 GASTEN (Serv.: 11-73), **M 32 NORSTEN** (Serv.: 10-73), **M 33 VIKSTEN** (L: 18-4-74).

   D: 120 tons   **S:** 9 kts   **Dim:** 23 × 6.60 × 3.70
   A: 1/40-mm AA
   M: diesel. Based on earlier classes.

REMARKS: Plastic and fiberglass hulls.

Hisingen (M 43)

PATROL BOAT

◆ **V 57** (1954)

   D: 115 tons (135 fl)   **Dim:** 29.90 × 5.30 × 2.20
   S: 13.5 kts   **Man:** 12 men
   A: 1/20-mm AA
   M: Nohab-Polar diesel; 1 prop; 500 hp

SMALL PATROL BOATS

   Nos. **61** to **70** (1960-61)
   D: 30 tons   **Dim:** 21 × 4.60 × 1.20
   S: 19 kts   **A:** 1/20-mm AA

SMALL PATROL BOATS (*continued*)

Nos. **71** to **77** (1966-67)
D: 28 tons   **Dim:** 21 × 4.60 × 1.50
S: 18 kts   **A:** 1/20-mm AA

The **SVK 1, SVK 2, SVK 3, SVK 4, SVK 5** (1944) which belonged for a time to the Sjövarnkären naval voluntary militia have been reassigned to the navy list.

D: 19 tons   **Dim:** 17 × 3.65 × 1.20
S: 11 kts   **A:** 1/20-mm

COASTAL ARTILLERY SERVICE

MUL 12-19 1952-56

Mul 19   1970

D: 245   31,18 × 7,62 × 3,10   **A:** 1/40 AA   **V:** 10,5
MUL 11 1946
D: 200   30,10 × 7,21 × 3.65   **A:** 2/20 AA   **V:** 10
MUL 12 to *19* have 1 diesel-electric — 360 hp — Can lay mines.
Photograph of the *MUL 19* on the following page.

HYDROGRAPHIC SHIPS

JOHAAN MÅNSSON (14-1-66)
D: 900 tons   **S:** 15 kts   **Dim:** 56 × 11 × 2.60
M: Nohab-Polar diesel; 3,300 hp

RAN (1945)
D: 285 tons   **S:** 9 kts   **Dim:** 30 × 7 × 2.60
M: diesels; 260 hp

GUSTAF AF KLINT (1941). Rebuilt in 1963.
D: 750 fl   **S:** 10 kts   **Dim:** 52 × 8.70 × 4.70
M: diesel; 640 hp

NILS STROMKRONA (1894). Rebuilt in 1952.
D: 140 tons   **S:** 9 kts   **Dim:** 26.60 × 5.10 × 2.50
M: diesel; 300 hp.

Johaan Mansson

ANDERS BURE (ex-*Rali*)
D: 54 tons   **S:** 11 kts   **Dim:** 24.60 × 5.90 × 2
REMARKS: Former trawler dating from 1968 and bought in 1971.

LOGISTIC SUPPORT

♦ *1 coastal tanker.*

A 228 BRANNAREN (ex-*Indio*) (1965). Small commercial tanker assigned at the end of 1972.
Cargo: 857 tons   **S:** 11 kts   **Dim:** 62 × . . . × . . .

♦ *Salvage and sunken vessel research ship.*

A 211 BELOS (1961)

1970

D: 1,000 tons   **Dim:** 62.30 × 11.20 × 3.65
S: 13 kts   **M:** diesel; 1 prop; 1,200 hp

REMARKS: Carries a helicopter; well fitted out with a decompression chamber, active rudder and a TV for underwater inspection.

AUXILIARY VESSELS

A 251 ACHILLES (1962) — **252 AJAX** (1963). Icebreaker tug.
  D: 450 tons   **Dim:** 33.15 × 8.80 × 4.90.

A 231 LOMMEN (ex-*M 17*), **A 232 SPOVEN** (ex-*M 18*), sister of the *M 15/26*.

A 216 UNDEN — Water carrier (1946).
  D: 500 tons   **S:** 10 kts   **Dim:** 36.50 × 7.10 × 4.30.

A 217 FRYKEN — Water carrier (1959).
  D: 307 tons   **S:** 10 kts   **Dim:** 32 × 5.80 × 2.75.

A 221 FREJA — Fresh water supply ship (1953).
  D: 300 tons (450 fl)   **S:** 11 kts   **Dim:** 49 × 8.40 × 3
  M: 1 diesel.

A 246 HAGERN (1951). Torpedo recovery vessel.
  D: 50 tons   **S:** 10 kts   **Dim:** 28 × 5 × 1.20.

A 247 PELIKANEN (1964). Torpedo recovery vessel.
  D: 100 tons   **S:** 15 kts   **Dim:** 33 × 5.80 × 1.80.

A 248 PINGVINEN. L: 26-9-73. Torpedo recovery vessel.
  D: 189 tons   **S:** 11 kts   **Dim:** 33 × . . . × . . .

A 253 HERMES (1958) — **A 321 HECTOR** — **A 322 HEROS.**
  D: 185 tons   **S:** 11.5 kts   **Dim:** 23 × 6.80 × 4.

A . . . HERA — A 323 HERKULES
  D: 127 tons   **Dim:** 19.60 × 6.40 × 3.70.

A 256 SIGRUN (1961). Laundering ship
  D: 250 tons   **S:** 10 kts   **Dim:** 32 × 6.80 × 2.50.

J 324 ANE — J 325 BALDER — J 326 LOKE — J 327 RING (1943-45).
  Assigned to coastal artillery service. (135 tons — 28 × 8 × 1.80
  S: 8.5 kts   **A:** 1/20).

A 236 FALLAREN — A 237 MINOREN
  D: 165 tons   **S:** 9 kts   **Dim:** 31.50 × 6.10 × 2.10.
  Mine transports

LANDING SHIPS AND BARGES

GRIM — 1961 — **BORE** (9-66) — **HEIMDAL** (12-66)
  D: 380 tons   **S:** 12 kts   **Dim:** 36 × 8.50 × 2.60.

A 333 SKAGUL (1960) — **A 335 SLEIPNER** (1959).
  D: 355 tons   **S:** 12 kts   **Dim:** 36 × 8.50 × 2.60.

L 201/204 — 205/238 — 239/241 — 301/336 (1957-64)
  D: 31 tons   **S:** 18 kts   **Dim:** 20 × 4.20 × 1.30.

L 502/516 under construction
  D: 20 tons   **S:** 18 kts   **L:** 18

L 51, 52, 53, 54, 55 (1948).
  D: 32 tons   **S:** 8 kts   **Dim:** 14 × 4.80 × 0.90.

VARIOUS

♦ *1 flagship*

A 201 MARIEHOLM (1934) — Former small steamship.
  D: 1,445 tons   **Dim:** 62.30 × 9.92 × 4.30

  S: 12 kts   **M:** 1 reciprocating
  A: 2 machine guns — 1 helicopter
  Flagship of the Kustflotte, the official title of the Swedish navy. Will be replaced in 1975 by the *Visborg*.

♦ *1 experimental ship*

A 241 URD (ex-*Capella*)
  D: 63 tons (90 fl)   **Dim:** 22.20 × 5.50 × 2.20.
  M: diesel — 200 hp.   **S:** 8 kts

♦ *2 sail training ships.*

FALKEN, GLADAN (1946-47). (1 auxiliary diesel, 50 hp).
  D: 220 tons   **Dim:** 28.30 × 7.27 × 4.20

ICEBREAKERS

1975

ATLE (L: 27-11-73) — Bldr: Sandviken, Finland.
  D: 7,800 tons   **Dim:** 104 × 99 (pp) × 23.80 × 7.80
  M: Diesel-electric propulsion; 1 prop; 22,000 hp

NJORD — Bldr: Wärtsilä, Helsinki — L: 2-10-68 — In serv.: 10-69
  D: 5,626 tons   **Dim:** 86.45 (79.45 pp) × 21.18 × 6.90.
  S: 18 kts
  M: Diesel-electric propulsion; 4 Sulzer 9 MH 51 diesels; Stromber electric motors, 2 fwd, each 3,400 kw — 2 aft, each 2,200 kw; 4 props; 13,620 hp (330 rpm)

TOR — Bldr: Sandviken, Finland — L: 25-5-63
  D: 5,260 tons   **Dim:** 84.40 × 20.42 × 6.20
  S: 18 kts
  M: Diesel-electric propulsion; 4 props; 11,200 hp — Same machinery as the *Njord*.

ODEN — Bldr: Wärtsilä, Helsinki — L: 16-10-56 — In serv. 1958
  D: 4,950 tons — 3,370 tons (light)
  Dim: 83.35 (78 pp) × 19.40 × 6.90
  S: 17 kts   **A:** No armament
  Man: 75 men
  M: diesel-electric; 4 props (2 fwd, 2 aft); 10,500 hp

SWEDEN (*continued*)
ICEBREAKERS (*continued*)

Njord   1970

Fuel: 740 tons
Similar to the Finnish *Voima* class. — 6 ASEA diesel motors.

THULE (12-51) — Bldr: Karlskronavarvet — In serv. at the end of 1953.

D: 2,200 tons	**Dim:** 57 × 16.07 × 5.90.
S: 16 kts	**Man:** 43 men.
M: diesel-electric — 3 props. (1 fwd., 2 aft) — 4,800 hp	

YMER (1933) — Bldr: Kockums (Malmö)

D: 4,330 tons	**Dim:** 75 (pp) × 19.30 × 6.80.
S: 16 kts	**Man:** 44 men
M: diesel-electric (6 Atlas motors); 3 props (1 fwd); 9,000 hp	

NOTE: The *Ymer* will be replaced by the *Atle*.

SYRIA

PERSONNEL: 1,200 including 100 officers

MERCHANT MARINE (1-7-74): 9 ships — 2,643 grt

FRIGATES

♦ 1 Soviet Petya-class frigate was delivered to the Syrian navy in July 1975. See USSR chapter for characteristics.

GUIDED MISSILE AND TORPEDO PATROL BOATS (ex-Soviet)

♦ *6 OSA I class guided missile boats*
♦ *6 Komar class guided missile boats*
♦ *12 P 4 torpedo patrol boats* transferred by the U.S.S.R. between 1958 and 1960.

D: 30 tons (fl)	**S:** 32 kts	**Dim:** 16.80 × 3.75 × 1.00
A: 2/14.5 mm machine guns (II × 1), 2/TT		

PATROL BOATS

♦ *3 ex-French submarine chasers*

	Bldr	Laid down	L	In serv.
ABDULLAH IBN ARISSI (ex-*Ch 19*)	Seine Maritime	1938	1-40	4-40
TAREK IBN ZAYED (ex-*Ch 13*)	Seine Maritime	1938	1939	1940
AKABEH IBN NEFEH (ex-*Ch 10*)	A & C de France	1938	1939	1940

D: 107 tons (131 fl)	**Dim:** 37.10 (35.50 pp) × 5.34 × 1.95
S: 16 kts	**Man:** 28 men
A: 1/75-mm — 2/20-mm AA — depth charges	
Range: 1,200/8 — 680/13.5	
M: M.A.N. diesels; 2 props; 1,130 hp	
Fuel: 5.4 tons	

REMARKS: Rebuilt in 1955-56. Probably in poor condition.

MINESWEEPERS AND VARIOUS

♦ *1 Soviet T 43 class* — See section on U.S.S.R.

YARMOUK

♦ *2 Soviet Vania class transferred in December 1972.*
♦ *1 Soviet Myriat class diving tender ship.*

TAIWAN

Republic of China

PERSONNEL (1975): 64,000 men including 36,000 Marines

MERCHANT MARINE (1-7-74): 407 ships — 1,416,833 grt
(tankers: 13 ships — 361,741 grt)

SUBMARINES

♦ *2 ex-U.S. Guppy class transferred in 2 and 4-73*

	L		L
S 91 HAI CHIH		**S 92 HAI PAO**	
(ex-*Cutlass, SS-478*)	5-11-44	(ex-*Tusk, SS-426*)	8-7-45

D: 1,517 tons standard/1,870 surfaced/2,240 submerged
Dim: 93.80 × 8.20 × 5.20 **S:** 18-15/13 kts
Man: 82/86 men **A:** 10/533-mm TT **Range:** 10,000/10
M: diesel-electric propulsion; 3 groups of generators; 2 electric motors; 4,800/5,200 hp

♦ *3 Italian Cosmos midgets, used to land Nationalist intelligence agents on the Chinese continent*

DESTROYERS

♦ *5 ex-U.S. Gearing class, transferred 1 in 1971 and 4 in 1973*

a)

	Bldr	L
DD 7 FU YANG		
(ex-*Ernest G. Small, DD-838*)	Bath Iron Wks.	9-6-45
DD 11 DANG YANG		
(ex-*Lloyd Thomas, DD-764*)	Bethlehem (San Fran.)	5-10-45
DD 12 CHIEN YANG		
(ex-*James E. Kyes, DD-787*)	Todd-Seattle	4-8-45
DD 20 LAO YANG		
(ex-*Shelton, DD-790*)	Todd-Seattle	8-3-46
DD 21 LIAO YANG		
(ex-*Hanson, DD-832*)	Bath Iron Wks.	25-2-45

♦ *6 ex-U.S. Allen M. Sumner class, transferred since 1969*

b)

	Bldr	L
DD 1 HSIANG YANG		
(ex-*Brush, DD-745*)	Bethlehem (Staten I.)	28-12-43
DD 2 HENG YANG		
(ex-*Samuel N. Moore, DD-747*)	Bethlehem (Staten I.)	23-2-44
DD 3 HUA YANG		
(ex-*Bristol, DD-857*)	Bethlehem (San Pedro)	29-10-44
DD 5 YUEH YANG		
(ex-*Haynsworth, DD-700*)	Federal SB & DD (Kearny)	15-4-44
DD 6 HUEI YANG		
(ex-*English, DD-696*)	Federal SB & DD (Kearny)	27-2-44
DD 10 PO YANG		
(ex-*Maddox, DD-731*)	Bath Iron Wks.	19-3-44

D: a: 2,425 tons (3,500 fl) **Dim:** 119.17 × 12.55 × 5.50
b: 2,200 tons (3,320 fl) 114.75 × 12.45 × 5.80
S: 30 kts **Man:** 14 officers, 260 men **Range:** a: 2,400/25 — 4,800/15
b: 1,260/30 — 4,800/15
A: 6/127-mm semi-automatic, 38-cal. (II × 3) — 4/76-mm AA — 6/324-mm ASW Mk 32 TT
Electron Equipt: Radars: SPS 6 or SPS 29, 12, and 40 — Sonar: SQS 23

Heng Yang 1972

M: GT; 4 Babcock boilers; 2 props; 60,000 hp. **Fuel:** 650 tons

REMARKS: *DD 7* has received the FRAM 2 modernization, the others FRAM 1. It should be noted that numbers *12, 20,* and *21* were offered to Spain but not accepted. They are in poor condition.

♦ *4 ex-U.S. Fletcher class, transferred in 6-67, 4-68 and 1972*

		Bldr	L
DD 8 KWEI YANG	(ex-*Twining, DD-540*)	Bethlehem (San Fran.)	11-7-43
DD 9 CHING YANG	(ex-*Mullany, DD-528*)	Bethlehem (San Fran.)	12-10-42
DD 18 AN YANG	(ex-*Kimberley, DD-521*)	Bethlehem (Staten I.)	4-2-43
DD 19 KUEN YANG	(ex-*Yarnall, DD-541*)	Bethlehem (San Fran.)	25-7-43

Kuen Yang 1970

DESTROYERS (continued)

D: 2,050 tons (2,850 fl) **Dim:** 114.85 (wl) × 12.03 × 5.50
S: 33 kts **Man:** 350 men **Range:** 1,260/30 — 4,400/15
A: 5/127-mm semiautomatic 38-cal. — 6/40-mm AA — 6/20-mm AA — 5 ASW TT
M: 2 General Electric GT; 4 Babcock boilers; 60,000 hp **Fuel:** 650 tons

♦ *4 ex-U.S. Benson class transferred in 1954 (2), 1955 (1), 1959 (1).*

Two, *Ellyson* (DD-454), and *Macomb* (DD-458), transferred in 8-70 for cannibalization to support the four following ships:

		L
14 LO YANG (ex-*Benson*, DD-421)		15-11-39
15 HAN YANG (ex-*Hilary P. Jones*, DD-427)		14-12-39
16 HSEN YANG (ex-*Rodman*, DD-456)		26-9-41
17 NAN YANG (ex-*Plunkett*, DD-431)		9-3-40

Lo Yang

D: 1,620 tons (2,400 fl) **Dim:** 106.07 × 11.80 × 5.10 (fl)
S: 36 kts **Man:** 250 men **Range:** 6,000/12
A: 4/127-mm (3 on the *16*) — 4/40-mm AA — 4-6/20-mm AA — 5/533-mm TT (V × 1) (on the *17*)
M: GT; 2 props; 50,000 hp; 4 boilers **Fuel:** 600 tons

CANNIBALIZATION — The U.S.A. has transferred several destroyers such as the *Warrington* (DD-843), *Sproston* (DD-577), etc., to help maintain these ships by cannibalization.

FRIGATES

All are ex-U.S. DE class, now obsolete.

♦ *1 Bostwick class transferred in 1946-48.*

	L
25 TAI HU (ex-*Bostwick*, DE-103)	1943

D: 1,300 tons (1,750 fl) **Dim:** 93 (91.50 pp) × 11.17 × 3.25
S: 19 kts **Range:** 11,500/11 — 5,500/19
A: 3/76-mm — 2/40-mm AA — 12/20-mm AA — 3/533-mm TT
M: diesel-electric propulsion; 4 GE diesels and 2 electric motors; 2 props; 6,600 hp. **Fuel:** 300 tons diesel.

REMARKS: *Tai Ho* taken out of service in 1972.

♦ *1 DE class with short hull transferred in 1946.*

	L
27 TAI YUAN (ex-*Riley*, DE-579)	29-12-43

D: 1,150 tons (1,360 fl) **Dim:** 88.22 × 10.69 × 3.25
S: 19 kts **Range:** 5,500/19

Same **A** and **M** as the preceding ships.

♦ *2 ex-U.S. Raven class minesweepers transferred in 1964 and 3-68.*

	L
68 WU CHENG (ex-*Redstart*, MSF-378)	18-10-44
67 CHU YUN (ex-*Waxwing*, MSF-389)	10-3-45
70 MO LING (ex-*Steady*, MSF-118)	

D: 890 tons (1,250 fl) **Dim:** 67.20 (65 pp) × 9.75 × 3.30
S: 18 kts **Man:** 80/100 men
A: 1/76-mm — 4/40-mm AA (II × 2) — depth charge projectors
M: diesel-electric propulsion; 2 props; 3,500 hp

♦ *11 ex-fast transports APD/LPR class (ex-DE) used as escort vessels (PF), transferred between 4-65 and 8-69. — Bldr: U.S.A. 1942-44*

	L		L
315 YU SHAN (ex-*Kinzer*, APD-91)	9-12-43	**321 TAI SHAN** (ex-*Register*, APD-92)	20-1-44
316 HUA SHAN (ex-*Scribner*, APD-122)	22-7-44	**322 HENG SHAN** (ex-*Ray W. Herndon*, APD-121)	15-7-44
317 WEN SHAN (ex-*Gantner*, APD-42)	17-4-43	**323 KANG SHAN** (ex-*George W. Ingram*, APD-43)	8-5-43
318 FU SHAN (ex-*Truxtun*, APD-98)	9-3-44	**324 CHUNG SHAN** (ex-*Blessman*, APD-48)	19-6-43
319 LU SHAN (ex-*Bull*, APD-78)	25-3-43	**325 LUNG SHAN** (ex-*Schmitt*, APD-76)	29-5-43
320 SHOU SHAN (ex-*Kline*, APD-120)	27-6-44		

Hull numbers were changed in 1970; previously, they were *PF 32* to *44*.

Show Shan 1970

D: 1,450 tons (2,049 fl) **Dim:** 93.26 × 11.28 × 4.70
S: 22 kts (fl) **Range:** 5,000/15 **Man:** 214 men
A: 2/127-mm — 6/40-mm AA — 6 ASW 324-mm TT or 1 or 2 hedgehogs
M: turbo-elec. propulsion; 2 props **Boilers:** 2 — 12,000 hp.

FRIGATES (continued)

Hua Shan   1969

PATROL BOATS

♦ *2 of Japanese construction delivered in 6-57 and 11-57*

PT 511 FU CHOU — PT 512 HSUEH CHIH (1957). — Bldr: Mitsubishi Zosen.

    D: 30 tons   **S:** 30 kts   **A:** 1/40-mm AA — 2/457-mm torpedoes

♦ *2 U.S. 71-foot class*

PT 513 FAAN KONG — PT 514 SAO TANG — Bldr: U.S.A. (1957)

    D: 46 tons (fl)   **S:** 32 kts   **A:** 1/20-mm AA — 2 torpedoes

♦ *2 U.S. 79-foot class*

PT 515 FUH KWO — PT 516 TIAN KWO — Bldr: U.S.A. (1957)

    D: 50 tons   **S:** 32 kts   **A:** 1/40-mm AA

NOTE: The ex-minesweepers MST class number *47 Yung Hria, 48 Yung Hsiu, 50 Yung Feng* have been scrapped. (See Flottes de Combat 1974).

MINESWEEPERS

♦ *2 ex-U.S. MSO class transferred in 1975.*

N . . . (ex-*MSO*   ).
N . . . (ex-*MSO*   ).

    D: **V:**   **Dim:**
    A:
    M:

♦ *12 ex-U.S. MSC Bluebird class*

	Transf.		Transf.
155 YUNG PING (ex-*MSC-140*)	6-55	**161 YUNG LO** (ex-*U.S. MSC-306*)	6-66
156 YUNG AN (ex-*U.S. MSC-240*)	6-55	**162 YUNG FU** (ex-*Belg. Diest*)	1970
157 YUNG NIEN (ex-*U.S. MSC-277*)	12-58	**163 YUNG CHING** (ex-*Belg. Eeklo*)	1970
158 YUNG CHOU (ex-*U.S. 278*)	7-59	**164 YUNG SHAN** (ex-*Belg. Lier*)	1970
159 YUNG HSIN (ex-*U.S. 302*)	3-65	**165 YUNG CHENG** (ex-*Belg. Maaseik*)	1970
160 YUNG JU (ex-*U.S. 300*)	4-65	**168 YUNG SUI** (ex-*Belg. Diksmuide*)	1970

Characteristics of the French *Acacia* class.

AMPHIBIOUS SHIPS

♦ *2 Amphibious Command Ships*

AGC 1 KAO HSIUNG (ex-*LST Chung Hai 229*, ex-*U.S. LST-735*)
AGC 2 N . . .   (ex-*LST Chung Chih 226*, ex-*U.S. LST-1071*)

Former U.S. LST class modified in 1968,

    D: 1,650 tons (4,080 fl)   **S:** 11 kts   **Dim:** 160 × 15.20 × 4.30
    M: G. M. diesels; 2 props; 1,700 hp.   **Range:** 15,000/9

♦ *1 ex-U.S. LSD*

191 TUNG HAI (ex-*Whitemarsh, LSD-8*) — Bldr: Moore, Oakland — 19-7-43 — Transferred in 11-60.

Tung Hai (LSD 191)

    D: 4,032 tons (8,700 fl)   **Dim:** 139 × 21.90 × 4.90
    S: 15.5 kts   **A:** 12/40-mm
    M: 2 triple expansion; 2 boilers; 7,000 hp.

AMPHIBIOUS SHIPS (continued)

♦ *22 ex-U.S. LSTs*

	Transf.		Transf.
201 CHUNG HAI (ex-*755*)	4-46	**221 CHUNG CHUAN** (ex-*640*)	2-48
203 CHUNG TING (ex-*537*)	3-46	**222 CHUNG SHENG** (ex-*1033*)	12-47
204 CHUNG HSING (ex-*557*)	3-46	**223 CHUNG FU** (ex-*840*)	7-58
205 CHUNG CHIEN (ex-*716*)	6-46	**224 CHUNG CHENG** (ex-*859*)	8-58
206 CHUNG CHI (ex-*1017*)	12-46	**225 CHUNG CHIANG** (ex-*1110*)	8-58
208 CHUNG SHUN (ex-*732*)	3-46	**226 CHUNG CHIH** (ex-*1091*)	10-58
209 CHUNG LIEN (ex-*1050*)	1-47	**227 CHUNG MING** (ex-*1152*)	10-58
210 CHUNG YUNG (ex-*574*)	3-59	**228 CHUNG SHU** (ex-*520*)	9-58
216 CHUNG KUANG (ex-*503*)	6-60	**229 CHUNG WAN** (ex-*535*)	9-58
217 CHUNG SUO (ex-*400*)	9-58	**230 CHUNG PANG** (ex-*587*)	9-58
218 CHUNG CHIH (ex-*279*)	6-60	**231 CHUNG YEH** (ex-*1144*)	9-61

D: 1,653 tons (4,080 fl)   **Dim:** 100 × 15.24 × 4.36
A: 10/40-mm AA (II × 2, I × 6)   **Man:** 100/125 men
M: G. M. diesels; 2 props; 1,700 hp

♦ *4 ex-U.S. LSMs*

	Transf.		Transf.
341 MEI CHIN (ex-*455*)	9-46	**353 MEI PING** (ex-*471*)	11-56
347 MEI SUNG (ex-*431*)	6-46	**356 MEI LO** (ex-*362*)	5-62

D: 1,095 tons (fl)   **S:** 12.5 kts   **Dim:** 62 × 10.50 × 2.20
A: 2/40-mm AA (II × 1) — 4 to 8/20-mm AA   **Man:** 65/75 men
M: diesels; 2 props; 2,800 hp.   **Range:** 2,500/12

♦ *21 ex-U.S. LCU class*

481 HO CHEN (ex-*892*)	**494 HO CHUN** (ex-*1225*)
482 HO CH'UNG (ex-*1213*)	**495 HO YUNG** (ex-*1271*)
484 HO CHUNG (ex-*849*)	**496 HO CHIEN** (ex-*1278*)
485 HO CHANG (ex-*512*)	**501 HO CHI** (ex-*1212*)
486 HO CHENG (ex-*1145*)	**502 HO HOEI** (ex-*1218*)
488 HO SHAN (ex-*1596*)	**503 HO YAO** (ex-*1244*)
489 HO CHUAN (ex-*489*)	**504 HO DENG** (ex-*1367*)
490 HO SENG (ex-*1598*)	**505 HO FENG** (ex-*1397*)
491 HO MENG (ex-*1599*)	**506 HO CHAO** (ex-*1429*)
492 HO MOU (ex-*1600*)	**507 HO TENG** (ex-*1452*)
493 HO SHOU (ex-*1601*)	

D: 143 tons (285 fl)   **S:** 8 kts   **Dim:** 37 × 9.70 × 1.20
A: 2/20-mm AA   **Man:** 11 men
M: diesels; 3 props; 675 hp.   **Range:** 700/7

HYDROGRAPHIC SHIPS

582 YANG MING (ex-U.S. *MSF-45*) former *PCE/U.S. Admirable* class (1943)
    D: 650 tons   **S:** 15 kts

563 CHIU LIEN (ex-*Geronimo, ATA-207*) former tug
    D: 838 tons (fl)   **S:** 11.5 kts   **M:** 2 diesels: 1,750 hp

564 CHU WA (ex-*Sgt. George Keathley, AGS-35*) (1944).
    D: 2,460 tons   **S:** 10 kts Former auxiliary hydrographic ship.
The last two transferred since 1972.

LOGISTIC SUPPORT

2 repair ships

♦ *1 ex-U.S. ARG class transferred in 1972*

ARG 516 PIEN TAI (ex-*Tutuila, ARG-4*) former Liberty ship (1942).
    D: 4,023/14,250 (fl)   **S:** 10 kts   **Dim:** 134.60 × 17.35 × 8.50
    M: Triple expansion; 1 prop; 2,500 hp.

♦ *1 ex-U.S. AR transferred in 1975*

YU TAI (ex-*Cadmus, AR-14*)
    D: 13,900 tons   **S:** 16 kts   **Dim:** 142.70 × 19 × 8.50
    M: 2 GT; 8,500 hp.

Tankers

♦ *1 Soviet-built added in 10-55*

AOG 506 KUI CHI (ex-*Touapse*)

AOG 506 Kui Chi   1972

    D: 18,000 tons (fl)   **S:** 14.5 kts
    M: diesel; 1 prop; 3,500 hp.
Built for the Soviet merchant marine.

♦ *1 Japanese-built*

AOG 512 WAN SHOU (1969)
    D: 4,150 tons (fl)   **S:** 13 kts   **Dim:** 86 × 16.50 × 5.40
    A: 2/40-mm AA   **M:** diesel; 1 prop; 2,100 hp.

♦ *ex-U.S. AOG 310-foot class transferred in 4-61/6-71 and 1972.*

307 CHANG PEI (ex-*Pecatonica, AOG-57*) — 1945
515 LUNG CHUAN (ex-*Namakagon, AOG-53*) — 1944
517 HSING LUNG (ex-*Elkhorn, AOG-7*) — 1944
    D: 4,335 tons (fl)   **S:** 14 kts   **Dim:** 95 × 14.60 × 4.70
    M: G. M. diesels; 2 props; 3,300 hp.

♦ *2 U.S. YO class*

504 SZU MING (ex-*YO-188*)

TAIWAN — REPUBLIC OF CHINA (*continued*)

LOGISTIC SUPPORT

510 TAI YUN (ex-*YO-175*)

    D: 1,600 tons (fl)   **M:** diesel; 1 prop; 560 hp   **S:** 10.5 kts

♦ *1 ex-U.S. transport transferred in 9-47*

514 YUNG KANG (ex-*Mark, AKL-12*)

    D: 700 tons   **M:** Diesel; 1 prop; 1,000 hp   **S:** 10 kts

TUGS

♦ *2 type U.S. ATF transferred in 1-66 and 4-71*

548 TA TUNG (ex-*Chickasaw, ATF-83*)

    D: 1,700 tons (fl) — 3,000 hp   **S:** 16 kts

550 TA AN (ex-*Cahoka, ATA-186*)

    A: 1/76-mm AA — 4/40-mm AA

♦ *6 ex-U.S. transferred in 4-66 and 4-72*

547 TA SUEH (ex-*Tonkawa, ATA-176*)
549 TA PENG (ex-*Mahopac, ATA-196*)

    Type ATA/U.S.   **D:** 435/835 tons   **M:** 1,500 hp   **S:** 13 kts

542 TA WU
543 TA MING } 570 tons   **S:** 12 kts
545 TA YU   500 tons
546 TA CHING

    All armed with 2/20-mm AA or 2/12.7-mm AA

VARIOUS

♦ *5 ex-U.S. floating docks*

AFDL 1 HAY TAN (ex-*AFDL-36*)
AFDL 2 KIM MEN (ex-*AFDL-5*) } capacity: 1,000 tons
AFDL 3 HAN JIH (ex-*AFDL-34*)
ARD 5 FO WU 5 (ex-*ARD-9*)
ARD 6 FO WU 6 (ex-*Windsor, ARD-22*) } capacity: 3,000 tons

TANZANIA

Personnel:

Merchant Marine (1-7-74): 14 ships — 28,371 grt

FAST SMALL CRAFT AND PATROL BOATS

♦ *7 Shanghai II class transferred in 1970-71*

JW 9861/JW 9867

JW 9862   1975

    D: 120 tons (fl)   **S:** 33 kts   **Dim:** 39.60 × 5.50 × 1.70
    M: 4 diesels — 5,000 hp   **Man:** 28 men
    A: 4/37-mm AA (II × 2) — 2/25-mm (II × 2)

♦ *6 Soviet P 6 (2 without torpedoes)*

SURVEILLANCE SMALL CRAFT

♦ *3 based on the East German Schwalbe class*

ARAKA — SALAAM — N . . . — transferred 1-66 and 1-67 by East Germany

    D: 70 tons (fl)   **S:** 17 kts   **Dim:** 26 × 4.50 × 1.40
    A: 2/37-mm AA — 2/machine guns   **M:** diesel; 300 hp

♦ *4 transferred by the Peoples Republic of China in 11-66*

    D: 20 tons   **S:** 20 kts   **Length:** 13 m
    Man: 10 men   **A:** 1/12.7-mm machine gun

♦ *2 bought in East Germany in 1967*

RAFIKI — UHURU

    D: 50 tons   **A:** 1/40-mm AA — 4/machine guns

♦ *1 Soviet Poluchat class*

PERSONNEL (1975): Navy: approximately 13,800 men — Marines: 7,000 men

MERCHANT MARINE (1-7-74): 80 ships — 176,315 grt
(tankers: 20 ships — 90,503 grt)

THAILAND

FRIGATES

	Bldr	Laid down	L	In serv.
MAKUT RAJAKUMARN	Yarrow	1970	18-11-71	8-73

Makut Rajakumarn   1975 Yarrow

D: 1,900 tons (fl)   **Dim:** 97.56 (93 pp) × 11 × 5.50
Man: 16 officers, 124 men   **S:** 25 kts (gas turbine), 18 kts (diesel)
A: 2/114-mm Mk 8 — 1 Seacat BPDMS aft — 2/40-mm AA — 1 ASW Limbo Mk 10 mortar — 1 depth charge projector
Electron Equipt: Radars: 1/LW 04 (Band L), 1/Decca 626, 1/WM 22 (band X), 1/WM 44 (Band X)
       Sonars: 1/170 high frequency hull mounted, 1/162
M: CODOG system including one Rolls-Royce Olympus TBM 3 B gas turbine (23,125 hp), Crossley-Pielstick diesel (6,000 hp); 2 props
Range: 1,000/25 — 4,000/18

REMARKS: Excellent automatic features; Dutch radars and British sonars.

♦ *1 ex-U.S. transferred in 1959*

	Bldr	L	Delivered
3 PIN KLAO (ex-*Hemminger, DE-746*)	Western Pipe and Steel	12-9-43	5-44

D: 1,240 tons (1,900 fl)   **Dim:** 93.26 × 11.22 × 4.00
S: 19 kts   **Man:** 200 men   **Range:** 11,500/11
A: 3/76-mm (I × 3 — 6/40-mm AA (II × 3) — 6/324-mm ASW TT (III × 2), 8 depth charge projectors
M: diesel-electric propulsion; 2 props; 6,000 hp   **Fuel:** 300 tons

REMARKS: Original armament modified in 1966.

♦ *2 ex-U.S., transferred in 1951*

	Bldr	L	In serv.
1 PRASAE (ex-*Gallup, PF-47*)	Consolidated Steel	17-9-43	2-44
2 TAHCHIN (ex-*Glendale, PF-36*)	Consolidated Steel	28-5-43	10-43

D: 1,430 tons (2,100 fl)   **Dim:** 92.61 × 11.43 × 4.40

Pin Klao

S: 19 kts   **Man:** 180 men   **Range:** 7,800/12 — 5,600/16
A: 3/76-mm (I × 3) — 2/40-mm AA — 9/20-mm AA — 8 ASW mortars
M: Triple expansion; 2 boilers; 2 props; 5,500 hp   **Fuel:** 685 tons

♦ *2 U.S.-built*

	Bldr	L	Delivered
5 TAPI (*PF-107*)	American Shipbuilding	1970	1972
6 KHIRIRAT (*PF-108*)	Toledo, Ohio	18-2-72	10-8-73

D: 900 tons (1,135 fl)   **S:** 20 kts   **Dim:** 83.32 × 10.05 × 3.05
A: 2/76-mm (I × 2) — 2/40-mm AA (II × 1) — ASW mortar and torpedoes — 1 hedgehog   **Man:** 150 men
M: Fairbanks-Morse diesels; 2 props; 5,600 hp

REMARKS: Similar to the Iranian *Bayandor* class.

♦ *1 ex-British Algerine class of 1940*

MSF 1 PHOSAMTON (ex-*Minstrel*) — Bldr: Redfern Constr. Co. — L: 5-10-44
D: 1,040 tons (1,350 fl)   **S:** 16 kts   **Dim:** 68.58 × 10.82 × 2.36
A: 1/102-mm — 6/20-mm AA — 2 depth charge projectors   **Man:** 113 men
Range: 3,000/15 — 5,000/10   **M:** Triple expansion; 2 props; 3,000 hp.
Boilers: 2 to 3 fireboxes   **Fuel:** 270 tons

REMARKS: One of the very few survivors of a long series of escort-minesweepers built in Great Britain during World War II.

FRIGATES (continued)

GUIDED MISSILE BOATS

♦ *3 Sea Hawk class ordered in 1973*

	L		L		L
HANHHAKSATRU	23-10-75	**N** . . .	. . .	**N** . . .	. . .

Bldr: Singapore

D: 230 tons   **S:** 40 kts   **Dim:** 45 × 7 × 2.3

A: 5 Gabriel systems — 1/57-mm AA — 1/40-mm AA   **Range:** . . .

M: 4 diesels; 4 props; 14,400 hp   **Man:** 40 men

REMARKS: Identical to the Singapore class patrol craft.

PATROL BOATS

♦ *10 U.S. PGM export type, transferred in 1966 (1), 1967 (1), 1968 (1), the others 1969/71*

	L			L
T 11 (ex-*PGM-71*)	22-5-65	**T 16** (ex-*PGM-115*)		24-4-69
T 12 (ex-*PGM-79*)	18-12-65	**T 17** (ex-*PGM-116*)		3-6-69
T 13 (ex-*PGM-107*)	13-4-67	**T 18** (ex-*PGM-117*)		24-6-69
T 14 (ex-*PGM-113*)	3-6-69	**T 19** (ex-*PGM-123*)		4-5-70
T 15 (ex-*PGM-117*)	24-6-69	**T 20** (ex-*PGM-124*)		22-6-70

D: 130 tons (147 fl)   **Dim:** 30.80 (30.20 pp) × 6.40 × 1.85

S: 18.5 kts   **M:** diesels; 2 props; 1,800 hp   **Man:** 30 men

A: 1/40-mm AA — 4/20-mm AA — 2/12.7-mm machine guns

♦ *3 of local construction*

♦ **T 91** (1965) — **T 92** and **T 93** (1973) — Bldr: Royal Thai Naval Dockyard, Bangkok

D: 87.5 tons   **Dim:** 30.80 × 6.40 × 1.85

S: 25 kts   **A:** 1/40-mm, 1/20-mm

Man: 21 men   **M:** diesels; 2 props; 1,600 hp

♦ *7 C.R.D.A. type (Italy)*

Bldr: Cantieri Riuniti del Adriatico

	L			L
11 TRAD	26-10-35	**22 CHANDABURI**		6-12-36
12 PHUKET	28-9-35	**23 RAYONG**		11-1-37

	L			L
13 PATTANI	16-10-36	**31 CHUMPORN**		18-13-37
21 SURASDRA	28-11-36			

Trad

D: 318 tons (470 fl)   **S:** 25 kts   **Dim:** 68 × 6.40 × 2.10

Man: 11 officers, 112 men   **Range:** 850/14.5

A: 2/20-mm AA (II × 1) — 4 machine guns — 4/457-mm TT (II × 2)

M: Parsons GT; 2 props; 9,000 hp; Yarrow boilers   **Fuel:** 102 tons

REMARKS: All of these ships are in rather poor condition.

♦ *3 Klongyai class*

	Bldr	Laid down	L	In serv.
5 KLONGYAI	Ishikawajima	1936	26-3-37	6-37
7 KANTANG	Ishikawajima	1936	26-3-37	6-37
8 SATTAHIP	Bangkok NDY	11-56	28-10-57	1958

D: 110 tons (135 fl)   **S:** 18 kts   **Dim:** 42 × 4.60 × 1.50

A: 1/76-mm AA — 2/20-mm AA (II × 1) — 2/457-mm TT

Man: 51 men   **Range:** 475/15

M: GT; 2 props; 1,000 hp; Yarrow boilers   **Fuel:** 18 tons

REMARKS: Poor condition.

PATROL BOATS (continued)

◆ *7 ex-U.S. PC class* (obsolete)

1 SARASIN (ex-*PC-495*)　　　**6 TONGPLIU** (ex-*PC-616*)
2 THAYANCHON (ex-*PC-575*)　　**7 LIULCOM** (ex-*PC-1253*)
4 PHALI (ex-*PC-1185*) (1942–43)　**8 LONGLOM** (ex-*PC-570*)
5 SUKRIP (ex-*PC-1218*)

    D: 400 tons (fl)　　**S:** 19 kts　　**Dim:** 53 × 7 × 3.30
    A: 1/76-mm AA — 1/30-mm AA — 5/20-mm AA　　**Man:** 62 to 71 men
    M: General Motors diesels; 2 props; 3,600 hp　　**Fuel:** 60 tons
    Range: 6,000/10

◆ *1 ex-U.S. SC class* (obsolete)

SC 8 (ex-*8*, ex-U.S. *1633*) — 1945

    D: 125 tons (fl)　　**S:** 16 kts　　**Dim:** 33.85 × 5.20 × 1.85
    A: 1/40-mm — 3/20-mm — 1 hedgehog — ASW depth charges
    M: diesels; 2 props

SMALL CRAFT

◆ *4 ex-U.S.CG Cape class transferred in 1954* (**CGC 3, 4, 5, 6**) — 1953

    D: 105 tons fl　　**S:** 19/18 kts　　**Dim:** 28.95 × 5.80 × 1.55
    A: 1/20-mm — 2 hedgehogs — 2 depth charge racks　　**Man:** 15 men
    M: 4 diesels; 2 props; 2,200 hp　　**Range:** 1,500

◆ *5 ex-U.S. PCF "Swift" type, transferred between 1966 and 1970*

T 23 (ex-*696*)　　　**T 25** (ex-*698*)　　　**T 27** (ex-*691*)
T 24 (ex-*697*)　　　**T 26** (ex-*699*)

    D: 20/22 tons (fl)　　**S:** 25 kts　　**Dim:** 15.60 × 4.12 × 1.50
    A: 3/12.7-mm machine guns (II × 1 and 1 combined with an 81-mm mortar.)
    M: diesels; 2 props; 960 hp　　**Man:** 1 officer, 7 men

◆ *2 ex-U.S. PBR — 1965–67*

T 32, T 36.

    D: 10 tons　　**S:** 14 kts　　**Dim:** 9.75 × 3.53
    A: same as the *T 23* but with a 60-mm mortar.　　**Man:** 1 officer, 6 men
    M: Propulsion by water-jet; two 6V53 Detroit diesels. Ten others were supposed
    to be transferred at the end of 1972.

MINELAYERS

◆ *2 Bangrachan class*

	Bldr	Laid down	L	In serv.
1 BANGRACHAN	C.R. del A., Monfalcone	1936	1936	1937
2 NHONG SARHAI	C.R. del A., Monfalcone	1936	7-36	1936

    D: 319 tons (408 fl)　　**S:** 12 kts　　**Dim:** 49 × 7.96 × 2.20
    A: 1/76-mm AA — 1/40-mm AA — 2/20-mm AA (II × 1) — 142 mines
    M: 2 B & W diesels; 2 props; 540 hp　　**Fuel:** 33.5 tons
    Range: 2,690/10　　**Man:** 55 men

MINESWEEPERS

◆ *2 ex-U.S. MSO class transferred in 1974*

N . . . (ex-*Prime, MSO-466*)
N . . . (ex-*Reaper, MSO-467*)

REMARKS: For characteristics, see section on the U.S.A.

◆ *5 ex-U.S. MSC coastal minesweepers.*

TADINDENG (ex-*301*, 8-65) — **BANGKEO** (ex-*303*, 7-65) — **LADYA** (ex-*297*, 12-63) — **DON CHEDI** (ex-*313*, 1-66), **N** . . . (ex-*Bluebird*, MSC-121)

REMARKS: Transferred after completion. Characteristics of the French *Acacia* class. The *Bluebird* transferred in 1974.

◆ *10 riverine minesweepers* (R.M.S.). *U.S./LCM modified*

MSM 1, 2, 3, 4, 5, 6, 7, 8, 9, 10.

    D: 30 tons　　**S:** 10/9 kts　　**Dim:** 17 × 5.30 × 1.40.
    A: 2/20-mm — 1/12.7-mm machine gun — 2/40-mm grenade launchers
    M: 2 diesels　　**Man:** 7 men

AMPHIBIOUS SHIPS

◆ *5 ex-U.S. LST class*

Bldr: U.S.A.

Pangan (ex-*LST 1134*, transferred in 5-66)

ANTHONG (ex-*LST-294*)
CHANG (ex-*Lincoln County, LST-898*)
PANGAN (ex-*Stark County, LST-1134*)
LANTA (ex-*Stone County, LST-1141*)
N . . . (ex-*Dodge County, LST-772*)

    D: 1,615 tons (4,080 fl)　　**Dim:** 100 × 15.24 × 4.36

AMPHIBIOUS SHIPS (*continued*)

S: 11 kts   **A:**   6/40-mm AA — 4/20-mm
M: General Motors diesels; 1,700 hp.

♦ *3 ex-U.S. LSM*

KUT (ex-*333*), **PHAI** (ex-*338*), **KRAM** (ex-*469*)

D: 743 tons (1,095 fl)	**Dim:** 62 × 10.50 × 2.20
S: 12.5 kts	**A:** 2/40-mm AA
Range: 2,500/12	**M:** diesels; 2 props; 2,800 hp

♦ *6 ex-U.S. LCU class*

1 MATAPHON	**3 ARDANG**	**5 KOLUM**
2 RAWI	**4 PHETRA**	**6 TALIBONG**

D: 134 tons (280 fl)   **S:** 8 kts   **Dim:** 37 × 9.70 × 1.20
M: diesels; 3 props; 675 hp   **Range:** 700/7

♦ *8 LCVP*

HYDROGRAPHIC SHIPS

CHANDHARA — Bldr: Lürssen, Vegesack (West Germany) — L: 17-12-60

D: 870 tons (990 fl)   **S:** 12 kts   **Dim:** 70 (61 pp) × 10.50 × 3
M: Deutz diesels; 2 props; 1,000 hp   **Man:** 90 men (50 cadets)

REMARKS: Used in oceanography but built as a training ship.

♦ *2 small hydrographic ships.*

Bldr: Lürssen (West Germany)
N . . . N . . . 1973-74

D: 96 tons   **S:** 12 kts   **Dim:** 28.50 × 5.50 × 1.50

LOGISTIC SUPPORT

♦ *1 patrol boat tender*

3 NAKA (ex-U.S. *LSSL-102*) — transferred in 1966

D: 287 tons (fl)   **S:** 15 kts   **Dim:** 47.50 × 7 × 1.40
A: 1/76-mm — 4/40-mm — 4/81-mm mortars   **M:** diesels; 2 props; 1,320 hp.

Used as a base for small patrol boats.

♦ *1 minesweeper maintenance ship (former tug)*

RANG KWIEN (ex-*Muhimari Maru*) — Bldr: Japan, 1944 — Purchased in 1967

D: 586 tons   **S:** 10 kts   **Dim:** 49 × 9.50 × 4   **M:** Triple expansion

♦ *6 tankers and fuel oil or gasoline carriers*

AO 2 CHULA (ex-Japanese *Seisyo Maru*) — tanker

D: 2,395 tons   **M:** GT   **Dim:** 100 × 13.20 × 7.60

AO 3 MATRA (ex-Japanese *Waka Kosa Maru*) — tanker

D: 4,750 tons   **M:** GT   **Dim:** 100 × 14 × 6.10

YO 4 SAMUI (ex-U.S. YOG) — 1944 — barge

D: 420 tons   **S:** 8 kts   **Dim:** 53.20 × 9.75 × 4.60
M: Diesels; 2 props; 600 hp   **Man:** 63 men

YO 5 PRONG — 1938 — barge

D: 150 tons   **S:** 10 kts   **Dim:** 29 × 5.49 × 4.50
M: Diesel; 1 prop; 150 hp   **Man:** 26 men

YO 6 PROET — 1970

D: 360 tons (485 fl)   **S:** 9 kts   **Dim:** 37.40 × 6 × 2.65
M: Diesel; 1 prop; 500 hp

YW 6 CHARN — barge   **YW 8 CHUANG**

D: 355 tons   **M:** Diesel   **Dim:** 42 × 7.50 × . . .

♦ *2 small transports*

AKL 1 SICHANG — Bldr: Harima SB&E, Tokyo, Japan — L: 10-11-37

D: 815 tons (1,369 fl)   **S:** 15 kts   **Dim:** 48.77 × 8.54 × 4.90
M: Diesels; 2 props; 550 hp   **Man:** 66 men

AKL 7 KLED KEO

D: 450 tons (fl)   **S:** 11 kts   **Dim:** 46 × 7.60 × 4.30
M: Diesel; 1 prop   **Man:** 54 men

TUGS

YTB SAMAESAN — 503 tons (fl) — 850 hp — 10.5 kts
YTL KLUEN BADAN — **YTL MARN VICHAI** — 63 tons
YTL RAD — 52 tons

TRINIDAD AND TOBAGO

Merchant Marine (1-7-74): 31 ships — 15,574 grt
(tankers: 2 ships — 2,728 grt)

♦ 4 coastal surveillance craft of the Malaysian SRI type

CG 1 TRINITY (14-4-64) — **CG 2 COURLAND** Bay (20-5-64)
CG 3 CHAGUARAMAS (29-3-71) — **CG 4 BUCCO REEF** (1971)
The last two were ordered in 9-70 and delivered in 3-72.

Bldr: Vosper Ltd. — 1964-65, 1971 (3 and 4)

1968

D:	96-100 tons (123/125 fl)	**Dim:**	31.29 (28.95 pp) × 5.94 × 1.68
S:	23 kts **Range:** 1,800/13.5	**Man:**	3 officers, 14 men
A:	1/40-mm or 1/20-mm AA	**Fuel:**	18 tons
M:	Davey-Paxman diesels (12 cylinders); 2 props; 2,300 hp.		

REMARKS: In the Coast Guard service; living spaces air-conditioned. The diesel engines can be pushed to 1,440 hp (1,500 rpm) and speed raised to 25 knots in exceptional cases.

♦ 2 small craft

SEA HAWK — Bldr: J. Taylor, Shoreham; purchased and given a complete overhaul in 1969 — (in reserve)

D:	. . .	**S:** 14.5 kts	**Dim:** 18.30 × 5.25 × 1.07
A:	1 machine gun		**Man:** 1 officer, 5 men
M:	2 Rolls-Royce diesels; 250 hp		**Range:** 400/14

SEA SCOUT — Bldr: J. Taylor, Shoreham (in reserve)
Length: 13.72   **S:** 12 kts   **M:** 2 Perkins diesels

♦ 4 small patrol boats

CG 6 to **CG 9** — **Length:** 12 to 18 m — **S:** 18 kts

TUNISIA

Personnel: 2,000 men

Merchant Marine (1-7-74): 25 ships — 28,561 grt
(tankers: 1 ship — 6,643 grt)

FRIGATE

♦ 1 ex-U.S. transferred in October 1973

President BOURGUIBA — Bldr: Consolidated Steel — L: 27-11-43 (ex-*Thomas J. Gary, DER-326*)

President Bourguiba (E 7)   1974 J. C. Bellonne

FRIGATES (*continued*)

D: 1,590 tons (2,100 fl)   **Dim:** 93.26 (91.50 pp) × 11.22 × 4.00
S: 19 kts   **Man:** 160/170 men   **Range:** 11,500/11
A: 2/76-mm AA — 2/20-mm AA — 1 ASW hedgehog
M: 4 Fairbanks-Morse diesels; 2 props; 6,000 hp

REMARKS: One of the DE class ships that the U.S. Navy modified in 1957 as a radar picket ship.

PATROL BOATS

♦ *3 Bizerte-class patrol boats*

P 301 BIZERTE (20-11-69)   **P 302 EL HORRIA** (19-2-70)
P 303 MONASTIR (L: 25-6-74 — In serv.: 2-75)

Sakiet Sidi Youssef (P 303) 1970

El Horria 1973 J. C. Bellonne

D: 250 tons   **S:** 22 kts   **Dim:** 48 (45.50 pp) × 7.10 × 2.25
S: 22 kts   **Man:** ...
A: 2/40-mm AA (60-cal) — 8/SS 12 missiles
M: 2 MGO MB 839 Bb diesels, each 2,000 hp

♦ *1 French LeHardi class*

P 303 SAKIET Sidi Youssef — Bldr: Dubigeon (1956) (ex-*UW-12* purchased in 12-69)

D: 325 tons (440 fl)   **S:** 18.7 kts   **Dim:** 53.03 × 7.26 × 3.10 fl
Man: 4 officers, 59 men   **Range:** 3,000/12 — 2,000/15
A: 1/40-mm — 2/20-mm — 1 hedgehog — 4 depth charge projectors
M: 4 SEMT-Pielstick diesels; 2 props; 3,240 hp

♦ *1 ex-French MSC type minesweeper loaned in 1973.*

P . . . HANNIBAL (ex-*Coquelicot*, ex-*AMS-84*) 1955.

D: 300 tons (372 fl)   **Dim:** 43.00 (41.50 pp) × 7.95 × 2.55
S: 13 kts   **Range:** 2,500/10
A: 2/20-mm AA (II × 1)   **Man:** 3 officers, 35 men
M: 2 General Motors diesels; 2 props; 1,200 hp   **Fuel:** 40 tons

REMARKS: Minesweeping fittings removed.

Hannibal 1973 J. C. Bellonne

♦ *4 ex-French VC type*

P 201 ISTIKLAL (ex-French *V-11.* L: 25-5-57) (transferred in 3-59)
P 202 JOUMHOURIA (delivered in 1-61) **P 203 AL JALA** (transferred in 11-63)
P 204 REMADA (delivered in 7-67) — Bldr: Estérel

D: 60 tons (80 fl)   **S:** 28 kts   **Dim:** 31.45 × 5.75 × 1.70
A: 2/20-mm AA   **Range:** 1,400/15   **Man:** 3 officers, 14 men
M: 2 supercharged Mercedes-Benz diesels; 2 props; 2,700 hp

REMARKS: Similar to the Moroccan *El Sabiq* class.

SMALL CRAFT

♦ *6 for coastal surveillance*

V 101, 102, 103, 104, 105, 106 — Bldr: Ch. Navals de l'Esterel (1961-63)
Two others, the *V 107* and *108*, were delivered without armament to the fishery administration.

D: 38/39 tons   **S:** 23 kts   **Dim:** 25 × 4.75 × 1.25
A: 1/20-mm   **Man:** 10 men   **Range:** 900/16
M: 2 General Motors twin diesels; 2 props; 940 hp

TUNISIA (*continued*)
PATROL BOATS (*continued*)

VARIOUS

RAS ADAR (ex-*Zeeland*) — Bldr: Netherlands (1939) — Tug.
 D: 450 tons   **Dim:** 43 × 10 × 4

T 1 JAQUEL EL BAHR   T 2 SABBACK EL BAHR

REMARKS: Small tugs built by the Ch. Navals de l'Esterel.

TURKEY

PERSONNEL: 37,000 including 3,000 officers and 5,000 petty officers (1973).

NAVAL AVIATION: A small naval air arm was organized in 1972. It is made up of 16 S2A and S2E Tracker aircraft and 9 AB 204 helicopters.

MERCHANT MARINE (1-7-74): 369 ships — 917,682 grt
(tankers: 51 ships — 334,786 grt)

WARSHIPS IN SERVICE OR UNDER CONSTRUCTION AS OF 1 OCTOBER 1975

	L	D	Main armament
♦ *18 submarines*			
2 German type 209	1971-73	1,100	8 TT
16 ex-U.S. (obsolete)	1943-45	1,525/2,300	10 TT
♦ *11 destroyers*			
4 ADATEPE	1944-46	2,400	4/127-mm — 1 Asroc system — 6 ASW TT
1 MUAVENET	1944	2,250	6/127-mm — mines
1 ZAFER	1944	2,200	6/127-mm — 6 ASW TT
3 IZMIT (obsolete)	1942-43	2,050	4/127-mm — 6/76-mm — 5 TT
2 GELIBOLU (obsolete)	1941-42	1,630	4/127-mm — 5 TT
♦ *16 frigates*			
2 BERK (DE class)	1971-73	1,450	4/76-mm — 6 ASW TT
6 SULTAN HISAR (coastal)	1964	410	1/76-mm — 1/40-mm
6 CARDAK (obsolete)	1942-43	700	1/76-mm — 6/20-mm AA
2 ALANYA (obsolete)	1941-43	650/700	1/102-mm — 1/40-mm AA

♦ *9 guided missile and patrol torpedo boats*

♦ *24 patrol boats*

♦ *9 minelayers (ex-U.S.)*

♦ *25 minesweepers (ex-U.S., Canadian or German)*

WEAPONS AND SYSTEMS

Practically all furnished by the U.S.A. See the section on U.S.A. for characteristics.

SUBMARINES

♦ *2 German type 209*

	Bldr	Laid down	L	In serv.
S 327 ATILAY	Howaldtswerke, Kiel	1972	23-10-74	1975
S ... SALDIRAY	Howaldtswerke, Kiel	1972		1975

 D: 980 tons surfaced/1,230 submerged   **Dim:** 55 × 6.60 × 5.90
 S: 21 kts max. submerged   **Man:** 3 officers, 26 men
 A: 8/533-mm TT (6 torpedoes in reserve)
 M: diesel-electric propulsion; 4 Maybach diesels coupled to an AEG generator with a 420 kw rating; 1 Siemens electric motor; 5,000 kw

REMARKS: For further details see Argentine or Greek sections. Two 209-class submarines will be built in Turkey with German aid. The first was laid down on 24-7-75.

♦ *4 ex-U.S. Guppy III type*

	Bldr	L	In serv.
S 341 CANAKKALE (ex-*Cobbler*, SS-344)	Electric Boat Co	1-4-45	11-73
S 333 IKINCI INONU (ex-*Corporal*, SS-346)	Electric Boat Co	1-4-45	11-73
S ... N ... (ex-*Clamogore*, SS-343)	Electric Boat Co	25-2-45	1975
S ... N ... (ex-*Tiru*, SS-410)	Mare Island NSY	16-9-47	1975

 D: 1,975 tons surfaced/2,540 submerged   **Dim:** 99.4 × 8.2 × 5.2
 S: 20/15 kts   **Range:** 10-12,000/10, 95/5 submerged
 A: 10/533-mm TT (6 fwd, 4 aft)

SUBMARINES *(continued)*

M: diesel-electric propulsion; 4 diesels, each of 1,625 hp, and 2 electric motors of 2,750 hp; 2 props

REMARKS: The last two may not be transferred.

♦ *7 ex-U.S. Guppy II A type*

	Bldr	L	Transf.
S 335 BURAK REIS	Portsmouth NSY	28-3-44	1970
(ex-*Sea Fox, SS-402*)			
S 336 MURAT REIS	Portsmouth NSY	27-1-44	1970
(ex-*Razorback, SS-394*)			
S 337 ORUÇ REIS	Portsmouth NSY	27-10-43	1971
(ex-*Pomfret, SS-391*)			
S 338 ULUÇ ALI REIS	Portsmouth NSY	7-7-44	1971
(ex-*Thornback, SS-418*)			
S 340 CERBE	Portsmouth NSY	18-8-44	7-72
(ex-*Trutta, SS-421*)			
S 345 PREVESE	Electric Boat Co	17-12-44	7-72
(ex-*Entemedor, SS-340*)			
N 346 BIRINCI INÖNÜ	Portsmouth NSY	26-6-44	8-72
(ex-*Threadfin, SS-410*)			

USN 1970

D: 1,525 tons/1,825 surfaced/2,400 submerged
Dim: 95 (92.72 pp) × 8.25 × 5.20   **Man:** 8/9 officers, 66 men
S: 20/10 (19/9 cruising) kts   **Range:** 10-12,000/10, 95/5 submerged
A: 10/533-mm TT (6 fwd, 4 aft) and 24 torpedoes. In place of the torpedoes, 40 mines which can be laid through the tubes may be carried.
M: diesel-electric propulsion (surface): 3 or 4 groups of diesel engines, each 1,625 hp, and 2 electric motors of 2,750 hp; 2 props   **Fuel:** 300 tons

♦ *1 ex-U.S. Guppy 1 A type*

	Bldr	L	Transf.
S 339 DUMLUPINAR (ex-*Caiman*)	Electric Boat Co.	30-3-44	6-72

D: 1,840 tons surfaced/2,445 submerged   **Dim:** 93.2 × 8.2 × 5.2
S: 17/15 kts   **Range:** 12,000/10
A: 10/533-mm TT (6 fwd, 4 aft)   **Man:** 85 men
M: diesel-electric; 3 GM diesels; 4,800 hp; 2 electric motors; 5,400 hp

♦ *4 ex-U.S. Gato class*

	Bldr	L	Transf.
S 332 SAKARYA	Electric Boat Co	18-6-44	1948
(ex-*Boarfish, SS-327*)			
S 334 GÜR	Electric Boat Co	7-5-44	1948
(ex-*Chub, SS-329*)			
S 342 TURGUT REIS	Electric Boat Co	16-2-44	1958
(ex-*Bergall, SS-320*)			
S 344 HIZIR REIS	Manitowoc SB	17-1-45	1960
(ex-*Mero, SS-378*)			

D: 1,525 tons/1,829 surfaced/2,424 submerged   **Dim:** 95 × 8.3 × 4.2
S: 20/10 kts   **Range:** 12,000/10
A: 10/533-mm TT (6 fwd, 4 aft)   **Man:** 85 men
M: diesel-electric; 4 GM diesels; 6,400 hp; 2 electric motors; 5,400 hp

REMARKS: *S 342* may be cannibalized for the benefit of the other submarines.

DESTROYERS

♦ *3 ex-U.S. Fletcher class transferred in 10-69 (342-343) and 3-70 (344)*

	Bldr	L	In serv.
D 342 IZMIT	Bath Iron Works	5-6-43	8-43
(ex-*Cogswell, DD-651*)			
D 343 ISKENDERUN	Bethlehem, San Pedro	29-10-42	5-43
(ex-*Boyd, DD-544*)			
D 344 ICEL	Bethlehem, San Pedro	12-12-43	3-44
(ex-*Preston, DD-795*)			

1970

D: 2,050 tons (3,000 fl)   **Dim:** 114.85 (wl) × 12.03 × 5.50
S: 34 kts   **Man:** 15 officers, 247 men   **Range:** 1,260/30 — 4,400/15
A: 4/127-mm AA (38 cal) (I × 4) — 6/76-mm AA (50-cal) (II × 3) — 5/533-mm TT — 2 fixed ASW TT, depth charges
Electron Equipt: Radars: 1/SPS 10, 1/SPS 6 — Sonars: 1/SQS 4
M: General Electric GT; 2 props; 4 Babcock boilers; 60,000 hp
Fuel: 650 tons

REMARKS: *D 340 Istanbul* and *D 341 Izmir* scrapped in 1972 for spare parts to ensure the maintenance of the other three.

DESTROYERS (continued)

♦ *4 ex-U.S. Gearing class transferred in 1971-72-73*

	Bldr	L	In serv.
D 353 ADATEPE (ex-*Forrest Royal, DD-872*)	Bethlehem, Staten Island	17-1-45	6-46
D 355 TINAZTEPE (ex-*Keppler, DD-765*)	Bethlehem, San Francisco	24-6-46	5-47
D 352 GAYRET (ex-*Eversole, DD-789*)	Todd Pacific	8-1-46	7-46
D 351 M. F. KAKMAK (ex-*Charles H. Roan, DD-853*)	Bethlehem, Staten Island	15-5-46	9-46
D 354 KOKATEPE (ex-*Norris, DD-859*)	Bethlehem, San Pedro	4-2-45	9-6-45

Adatepe (D 353)   1973 J. C. Bellonne

D: 2,400 tons (3,600 fl)   **Dim:** 119.17 × 12.45 × 5.80
S: 30 kts   **Man:** 14 officers, 260 men   **Range:** 2,400/25 — 4,800/15
A: 4/127-mm AA 38-cal (II × 2) — 6/324-mm ASW TT Mk 32 (III × 2) — 1/ASW Mk 108 RL or 2 hedgehogs (except ex-*789*), 1 Asroc system — helicopter platform
Electron Equipt: Radars: SPS 10 and 40 (or 37) — Sonar: SQS 23
M: GT; 2 props; 4 Babcock boilers; 60,000 hp   **Fuel:** 560 tons

REMARKS: A first *D 354 Kokatepe* sunk 21-7-74 during the Cyprus engagement was replaced by the *Norris* (modernized with FRAM 2) which was renamed *Kokatepe*.

♦ *1 A. Sumner class, modified as a minelayer, transferred in 10-71*

	Bldr	L	In serv.
D 357 MUAVENET (ex-*Gwin, DD-772*)	Bethlehem, San Pedro	9-4-44	9-44

D: 2,250 tons (3,375 fl)   **Dim:** 114.74 × 12.45 × 5.80
S: 30 kts   **Man:** 15 officers, 260 men   **Range:** 1,260/30 — 4,600/15
A: 6/127-mm AA (II × 3) — 7/76-mm AA — 80/100 mines
Electron Equipt: Radars: 1/SPS 10, 1/SPS 6 — Sonar: 1/SQS 29.
M: GT; 2 props; 60,000 hp; 4 Babcock boilers   **Fuel:** 650 tons

REMARKS: One of a dozen *A. Sumner* class built in 1945 and modified as minelayers.

♦ *1 ex-U.S. Allen M. Sumner class, transferred in July of 1972*

	Bldr	L	In serv.
D 356 ZAFER (ex-*Hugh Purvis, DD-709*)	Federal SB & DD	17-12-44	3-45

D: 2,200 tons (3,300 fl)   **Dim:** 114.65 × 12.45 × 5.80
S: 30 kts   **Range:** 1,260/30 — 4,600/15
A: 6/127-mm AA (38-cal) (II × 3) — 6/324-mm ASW Mk 32 TT (III × 2)
Electron Equipt: Radars: 1/SPS 10, 1/SPS 40 — Sonar: 1/SQS 29.
M: GT; 2 props; 60,000 hp; 4 Babcock boilers   **Fuel:** 650 tons
Helicopter platform.

♦ *2 ex-U.S. Benson-Gleaves class, transferred in 1949*

	Bldr	Laid down	L	In serv.
D 346 GELIBOLU (ex-*Buchanan, DD-484*)	Federal SB & DD	2-41	22-11-41	3-42
D 347 GEMLIK (ex-*Lardner, DD-487*)	Federal SB & DD	7-41	20-3-42	5-42

FRIGATES

♦ *2 based on the U.S. Claude Jones class*

	Bldr	Laid down	L	In serv.
D 358 BERK	Gölcük	3-67	7-71	2-74
D 359 PEYK	Gölcük	1968	1-72	24-7-75

Berk (D 358)

D: 1,450 tons (1,950 fl)   **Dim:** 95.15 × 11.82 × 4.40
S: 25 kts   **Range:** ...   **Man:** ...
A: 4/76-mm AA (II × 2) — 6 ASW Mk 32 TT (III × 2)
Electron Equipt: Radars: 1/SPS 10, 1/SPS 40 — Sonar: 1/SQS 11
M: 4 Fiat-Tosi fast diesels, 3 016 RSS (800 rpm), linked 2 by 2 on one propeller shaft; 24,000 hp

REMARKS: The diesel engines are 16-cylinder (300 mm × 610 mm) similar to those installed in the Italian *San Giorgio* class. Can carry a helicopter but these ships have no hangar.

FRIGATES (continued)

♦ 6 ex-U.S. Raven class

		L
A 592	EREGLI (ex-*Pique*)	26-10-42
A 593	CANDARLI (ex-*Frolic*)	1943
A 594	CARSAMBA (ex-*Tattoo*)	4-10-42
A 595	CESME (ex-*Elfreda*)	25-1-43
A 596	CARDAK (ex-*Tourmaline, AM-130*)	22-7-43
A 597	EDINCIK (ex-*Grecian*)	1943

Bldr: Gulf SB Co (U.S.A.)

Candarli (A 593)   G. Arra 1972

D: 1,010 tons (1,250 fl)   **Dim:** 67.31 × 9.75 × 2.95 (light)
A: 1/76-mm AA — 6/40-mm AA   **Man:** 105 men
M: diesel-electric propulsion; diesels either Fairbanks or General Motors; 2 props; 3,500 hp.

REMARKS: Transferred while under construction to Great Britain and then given to Turkey in 4-47; command ship for fast small craft (*592*), minesweeper (*595*), hydrographic ships (*593, 594*), logistic support (*596*), and a training ship (*597*).

♦ 2 Australian Bathurst class

	Bldr	L
A 588 AYVALIK (ex-*A 588 Antalya*, ex-*Geraldton*)	Evans Deakin, Brisbane	16-8-41
A 589 ALANYA (ex-*Broome*)	Poole & Steel, Sydney	6-10-41

D: 650/700 tons (1,025 fl)   **Dim:** 56.75 × 9.14 × 3.05
S: 15 kts   **Man:** 85 men   **Range:** 4,280/10 — 2,010/15
A: 1/102-mm AA — 1/40-mm AA — 4/20-mm AA — 2 depth charge projectors
M: Triple expansion; 2 props; 1,750/2,000 hp   **Fuel:** 170 tons

REMARKS: Transferred in 8-46. Used as support ships for minesweepers.

Ayvalik (hull number changed)   A. and J. Pavia

COASTAL ESCORTS

♦ 6 based on the U.S. PC type of World War II

P 111	SULTANHISAR (*PC 1638*)	(1964)
P 112	DEMIRHISAR (*PC 1639*)	(9-7-64)
P 113	YARHISAR (*PC 1640*)	(14-5-64)
P 114	AKHISAR (*PC 1641*)	(14-5-64)
P 115	SIVRIHISAR (*PC 1642*)	(5-11-64)
P 116	KOCHISAR (*PC 1643*)	(12-65)

Bldr: Gunderson, Portland (U.S.A.) 1964-65 except *P 116*: Golcük NSY

Demirhisar (P 112)   1970

D: 280 tons (412 fl)   **S:** 25 kts   **Dim:** 54 × 7 × 3.10
A: 1 trainable hedgehog — 1/40 mm — 4/20 mm (II × 2) — 2 depth charge projectors
M: Alcoa diesels; 2 props; 4,800 hp   **Man:** 5 officers, 60 men

PATROL BOATS AND SMALL CRAFT

♦ 4 PB 57001 type guided missile patrol boats

	L	In serv.
P 341 MARTI (T)	. . .	1976
N . . .	. . .	. . .

Bldr: Lürssen (West Germany) and Tazkizak (T)

D: 400 tons (fl)   **S:** 27 kts   **Dim:** 58.10 (54.60 pp) × 7.62 × 2.79

PATROL BOATS AND SMALL CRAFT (*continued*)

A: 4 Harpoon systems — 1/76-mm AA OTO Melara compact — 2/35-mm AA (II × 1)

M: 2 diesels, each 4,500 hp **Electric:** 500 kw

Range: 2,250/27 — 4,000/16

♦ *2 ex-U.S. Asheville class transferred in 2 and 6-73*

P 339 BORA (ex-*Surprise*, PG-97) — L: 15-11-68.

P 340 YLDIRIM (ex-*Defiance*, PG-95) — L: 24-8-68.

Bldr: Peterson Bldrs, U.S.A.

D: 225 tons (240 fl) **Dim:** 50.14 (46.94 pp) × 7.28 × 2.90

S: 40 kts **Man:** 3 officers, 22 men

A: 1/76-mm fwd — 1/40-mm AA — 4/12.7-mm machine guns

M: CODAG propulsion; 1 General Electric gas turbine; 2 Cummins diesels; 2 props **Fuel:** 50 tons **Range:** 325/35 — 1,700/16

REMARKS: Check U.S.A. section for characteristics of the *Asheville* class as well as several photographs of these ships.

♦ *9 guided missile or patrol torpedo boats*

P 321 DENIZKUSU	**P 324 KARTAL**	**P 327 ALBATROS***
P 322 ATMACA*	**P 325 MELTEN***	**P 329 KASIRGA***
P 323 SAHIN	**P 326 PELIKAN***	**P 332 SIMSEK**

Bldr: Lürssen, Vegesack, 1967-71

Kartal (P 324) 1970

D: 160 tons (180 fl) **S:** 42 kts **Dim:** 42.80 × 7.14 × 2.20

A: 2/40-mm AA (70-cal) — 4/533-mm TT (4 torpedoes), two on each side

M: Maybach diesels (20 cylinders); 4 props; 12,000 hp **Man:** 39 men

REMARKS: Similar to the German *Jaguar-Zobel* class; wooden hull, keels and frames in steel and light metal, superstructure in light metal. Can be fitted as fast gunboats or mine layers (4 mines). The ships marked with an asterisk have 4 Norwegian Penguin missiles and only two TT. Two Jaguar-class torpedo boats were transferred to Turkey by Germany on 19 and 20-6-75. Their hull numbers are *P 330* and *P 331*.

The following German VLT craft, will be transferred to the Turkish navy: *Wolf, Pinguin, Löwe, Hähaer, Tiger, Storch,* and *Pelikan*. The last two have been renamed *P 331 Tufan* and *P 330 Firtina*.

♦ *10 AB 25/34 type* (*Turkey*)

P 1225 AB 25	P 1229 AB 29	P 1232 AB 32
P 1226 AB 26	P 1230 AB 30	P 1233 AB 33
P 1227 AB 27	P 1231 AB 31	P 1234 AB 34
P 1228 AB 28		

Bldr: Gölçük NSY and Turkish merchant shipyard (1967-70)

AB 26 (Hull number changed) 1969

D: 170 tons **S:** 22 kts **Dim:** 40.24 × 6.40 × 1.65

A: 2/40-mm **M:** S.A.C.M.; AGO diesels; 2 props; 4,800 hp

♦ *4 AB 21/24 type U.S.A.*

Bldr: Peterson, Sturgeon Bay (U.S.A.)

D: 130 tons (147 fl) **Dim:** 30.80 (30.20 pp) × 6.40 × 1.85

S: 18.5 kts **A:** 1/40-mm AA — 2 ASW mousetraps

M: diesels; 2 props; 1,800 hp

REMARKS: A gunboat class which has been transferred to several countries by the U.S.A.

PATROL BOATS AND SMALL CRAFT (*continued*)

AB 23 (Hull number changed)   1969

♦ *4 ex-U.S. small craft transferred 25-6-53*

P 1209 LS 9, P 1210 LS 10, P 1211 LS 11, P 1212 LS 12.
Former hull numbers *P 339, 308 to 310.*

LS 12 (Hull number changed)   1969

D: 63 tons	**Dim:**	25.30 × 4.25 × 1.55
S: 18 kts	**A:**	1/20-mm AA — 2 ASW mousetraps
M: 2 Cummins motors; 1,100 hp		

MINELAYERS

	Bldr	Laid down	L	In serv.
N 110 NUSRET (ex-*N 108*, ex-*MMC 16*)	Denmark	1962	1964	1966

D: 1,880 tons	**Dim:**	77 × 12.80 × 3.40
S: 16 kts	**A:**	4/76-mm AA (II × 2) — 400 mines
Man: 130 men	**M:**	diesels; 2 props; 4,800 hp

REMARKS: This is one of the coastal minelayers ordered by the U.S.A. under the M.A.P. Similar to the Danish *Falster* class. General Motors diesels.

Nusret (Hull number changed)

♦ *5 ex-U.S. LSM type (former landing craft)*

N 101 MORDOGAN (ex-*MMC 11*, ex-*484*) — **N 102 MERIC** (ex-*MMC 12*, ex-*481*) — **N 103 MARMARIS** (ex-*MMC 10*, ex-*490*) — **N 104 MERSIN** (ex-*MMC 13*, ex-*42*, ex-*Vale*, Norway) — **N 105 MUREFTE** (ex-*MMC 14*, ex-*493*, ex-*Vidar*, Norway).

Mersin (N 104)

D: 743 tons (1,100 fl)	**Dim:** 61.87 × 10.52 × 2.40 (12)	
S: 13/12 kts	**A:** 2/40-mm AA — 2/20-mm AA	**Range:** 2,500/12
M: 2 diesels; 2 props; 2,800 hp	**Fuel:** 60 tons	**Man:** 70 men

REMARKS: Transferred in 1952 after a complete overhaul; the first three were transferred to Turkey, the other two to Norway. They were returned to the U.S.A. in 1960, then reassigned to Turkey; 4 loading booms, 2 forward, 2 aft, for the loading of mines; two mine-laying rails.

♦ *2 ex-U.S. LST type, later German*

L 403 BAYRAKTAR (ex-*Bottrop*, ex-*LST-1101*)	Bldr: U.S.A. 1942-43.
L 404 SANKAKTAR (ex-*Bochum*, ex-*LST-1089*)	

MINELAYERS (*continued*)

Sankaktar (Hull number changed)

D:	1,650 tons (4,080 fl)	**S:**	11 kts	**Dim:**	100.04 × 15.24 × 4.30	
A:	6/40-mm AA (II × 3)			**Range:**	15,000/9 (max. possible)	
M:	General Motors diesels; 2 props			**Fuel:**	600 tons	

REMARKS: *B* and *S* were transferred in 1964 to the West German Navy and modified as minelayers. Are used by the Turks as amphibious ships.

♦ *1 ex-U.S. coastal minelayer*

N 115 MEHMETCIK (ex-*YMP-3*) — Bldr: Higgins — L: 1958

D:	540 tons fl	**A:**	1/40-mm AA	**Dim:**	39.62 × 10.60 × 1.90
S:	10 kts	**Man:**	22 men	**M:**	diesels; 2 props

REMARKS: Transferred in 1958 under the M.A.P.

MINESWEEPERS

♦ *12 ex-U.S. MSC type coastal minesweepers* — Bldr: U.S.A.

		L
M 507 SEYMEN (ex-Belgian)		1952
M 508 SELÇUK (ex-*MSC-124*)		1952
M 509 SEYHAN (ex-*MSC-142*)		1952
M 510 SAMSUN (ex-*MSC-268*)		6-9-57
M 511 SINOP (ex-*MSC-270*)		4-1-58
M 512 SÜRMENE (ex-*MSC-271*)		1958
M 513 SEDDUL BAHR (ex-*MSC-272*)		1958
M 514 SILIFKE (ex-*MSC-304*)		21-11-64
M 515 SAROS (ex-*MSC-305*)		1-5-65
M 516 SIGAÇIK (ex-*MSC-311*)		12-6-64
M 517 SAPANCA (ex-*MSC-313*)		14-9-64
M 518 SARIYER (ex-*MSC-315*)		21-4-66

D:	300 tons (392 fl)	**Dim:**	43 (41.50 pp) × 7.95 × 2.55
S:	14 kts	**A:** 2/20-mm AA	**Man:** 4 officers, 34 men
M:	2 diesels; 2 props; 1,200 hp	**Range:**	2,500/10

REMARKS: The *508* and *509* are the former French *Pavot* and *Renoncule* returned to the U.S.A. 23-3-70 and then transferred to Turkey. The *507* is a minesweeper returned by Belgium in 1970.

Selçuk (M 508)   1970 J. C. Bellonne

♦ *4 ex-Canadian coastal minesweepers*

		L
M 530 TRABZON (ex-*Gaspe*)		20-5-53
M 531 TERME (ex-*Trinity*)		31-7-53
M 532 TIREBOLU (ex-*Comax*)		24-4-52
M 533 TEKIRDAG (ex-*Ungava*)		12-11-51

Trabzon (Hull number changed)   1969

D:	390 (412 fl)	**S:**	16 kts	**Dim:**	50 × 9.21 × 2.80	
A:	1/40-mm	**Man:**	44 men	**Range:**	4,500/11	
M:	General Motors diesels; 2 props; 2,500 hp			**Fuel:**	52 tons	

REMARKS: Transferred in 1958 under the M.A.P. Same characteristics as the French *Dunkerquoise* class and the Canadian MCB type.

MINESWEEPERS (continued)

♦ *5 ex-German 321 class (French Mercure class)*

M 522 KILIMI (ex-*Vegesack*) **KARAMÜRSEL** (ex-*Worms*)
M 523 KOZLU (ex-*Hameln*) **N . . .** (ex-*Siegen*)
M 521 KEREMPE (ex-*Detmold*)

  D: 362 tons **S:** 15 kts **Dim:** 44.20 × 8 × 2.10
  A: 2/20-mm AA (II × 1) **Man:** 40 men
  M: Mercedes-Benz diesels, M.B. 820 E.B.; 2 props; 4,000 hp

REMARKS: These ships had been in the German navy and were placed in reserve in 1963; with the exception of a sixth, the *Passau*, they were removed from the reserve list at the end of 1973. The Karamürsel and the Kerempe were transferred in 7-75.

C 211   1973

♦ *4 ex-U.S. inshore minesweepers*

                        L

M 500 FOCA (ex-*MSI-15*)   23-8-66
M 501 FETHIYE (ex-*MSI-16*) 7-12-66

Fethiye (M 501)   1970

M 502 FATSA (ex-*MSI-17*)   11-4-67
M 503 FINIKE (ex-*MSI-18*)   11-67
  Bldr: Peterson (U.S.A.)

  D: 180 tons (235 fl)   **S:** 10 kts   **Dim:** 34.10 × 7.14 × 2.40
  A: 1/12.7-mm machine gun **Man:** 20 men **M:** diesels; 2 props; 960 hp.

AMPHIBIOUS SHIPS

♦ *2 ex-U.S. LST class transferred 6-73 and 8-74*

L 402 SERDAR (ex-*Westchester County*, LST-1167).
L 401 ERTOGRUL (ex-*Windham County*, LST-1170) — Bldr: U.S.A. — 22-5-54

  D: 2,590 tons (5,786 fl)   **Dim:** 117.35 × 16.76 × 3.70
  S: 13 kts   **A:** 4/76-mm AA   **Man:** 116 men
  M: 4 G.M. diesels; 2 variable pitch props; 6,000 hp

♦ *17 LCT type (1967-73)*

C 101 to **C 117** — Bldr: Tazkizak, Istambul

♦ *16 LCU type*

C 201 — 204 (ex-U.S. LCU), **205-216** — Bldr: Turkey

  D: 450 tons   **M:** 3 diesels; 900 hp   **Man:** 10 men

♦ *597 LCM*   ♦ *18 LCVP*

C 301 to **337** and **C 601** to **C 622.**

HYDROGRAPHIC SHIPS

NOTE: The frigates *A 593 Candarli* and *A 594 Carsamba* are fitted as hydrographic ships.

LOGISTIC SUPPORT

Support and repair ships.

♦ *2 submarine tenders*

A 591 ERKIN (ex-*Trabzon*, ex-*Imperial*), 1938, former liner, added to the navy list in 1960.

Erkin (A 591)   1972 G. Arra

  D: 10,990 tons (fl)   **Dim:** 133 × 17.50 × 7

LOGISTIC SUPPORT (*continued*)

A 583 DONATAN (ex-*AS 24 Anthedon*) — Bldr: U.S.A. (1943), former C3-S-A2 cargo ship modified as a supply ship for submarines; transferred 7-2-69.

Donatan (A 591)   1970

D:	8,100 tons (16,100 fl)	**S:** 16.6 kts	**Dim:**	149.96 × 21.18 × 8.05
A:	1/127-mm AA — 4/65-mm AA		**M:**	GT; 1 prop; 8,500 hp

♦ *2 ex-German ships*

N . . . (ex-*A 64 Rhin*)
N . . . (ex-*A 62 Weser*)

D:	2,370 tons (2,430 fl)	**S:** 20 kts	**Dim:**	98.80 × 11.80 × 5.20 fl
A:	. . .		**M:**	6 Maybach diesels × 1,900 hp

REMARKS: Transfer planned but had not taken place as of 1-6-75.

♦ *1 assigned to submarines (repair ship)*

A 582 BASARAN (ex-U.S. *LST-955*, ex-*Patroclus*) (22-10-44). Transferred in 1953.

♦ *1 assigned to small craft (repair ship)*

A 581 ONARAN (ex-U.S. *LST-558*, ex-*Alecto* (14-4-44). Transferred in 1948.

Onaran (A 581)   1971 G. Arra

D:	1,490 tons (4,080 fl)	**S:** 10.5 kts	**Dim:** 99.98 × 15.24 × 4.36
A:	2/40-mm AA — 8/20-mm AA		**Range:** 6,000/9
M:	diesels; 2 props; 1,800 hp		**Fuel:** 1,060 tons

♦ *2 ex-U.S. salvage ships*

A 584 KURTARAN (ex-*Bluebird*, *ASR-19*) — Bldr: U.S.A. (3-12-45)

Kurtaran (A 584)   1970

D:	1,735 tons (fl)	**S:** 16 kts	**Dim:** 62.50 × 12.20 × 3
A:	1/76-mm — 2/40-mm AA	**M:** diesel-electric; 1 prop; 3,600 hp	

A 585 AKIN (ex-*Greenlet*, *ASR 10*) (12-7-42) — Transferred in 1970.

D:	1,740 tons (2,140 fl)	**S:** 14 kts	**Dim:** 75.50 × 12.70 × 4.30
M:	diesel-electric; 1 prop; 3,000 hp	**Man:** 85 men	

Tankers

♦ *4 ex-French*

		Bldr	L
A 570 AKAR (ex-*Istanbul*, ex-*Adour*)		Soc. des Ch. Nav. Provençale	9-10-38

Akar (Hull number changed)   A. and J. Pavia

D:	4,289 (12,000 fl)	**S:** 15 kts	**Dim:** 132 (124.75 pp) × 16.36 × 6.40
M:	Parsons GT; 2 props; 5,200 hp; 2 Penhoet boilers		**Fuel:** 1,100 tons

REMARKS: Former tanker of the French navy, interned in 1942 and purchased by the Turkish navy. **Range:** 10,000/10

A 571 YUSBASI TOLÜNAY (ex-*Taskisak*) — Bldr: Istanbul Naval DY — L: 22-8-50

LOGISTIC SUPPORT (*continued*)

D: 3,500 tons (fl)   **Dim:** 79 × 12.40 × 5.90
S: 14 kts   **M:** diesels; 1,900 hp

A 572 ALBAY HAKKI BURAK — Bldr: Gölçük Naval DY — L: 1964.
D: 1,800 tons (3,740 fl)   **Dim:** 83.73 × 12.25 × 5.50
S: 16 kts   **A:** 2/40-mm   **Man:** 18/20 men
M: diesel-electric propulsion; 4,000 hp

A 573 BINBASI SAADETIN GURLAN — Bldr: Taskizak Naval DY
D: 1,505 tons (4,680 fl)   **S:** . . .   **Dim:** 89.70 × 11.80 × 5.40
M: diesels — 4,400 hp.

A 574 AKPINAR (ex-U.S. *AOG-26*) — Bldr: U.S.A. — L: 22-9-44
D: 4,335 tons (fl)   **S:** 14 kts   **Length:** 95 m
M: diesel-electric propulsion; 3,300 hp

Y 1209 ULABAT — **Y 1208 VAN** — Bldr: Gölçük Naval DY — 1968-70
D: 900 tons   **S:** 14.5 kts   **M:** diesels

Y 1207 GÖLÇÜK — Bldr: Gölçük Naval DY L: 4-11-1935
D: 1,250 tons   **S:** 12 kts   **Length:** 57 m   **M:** diesel; 700 hp
Cargo capacity: 750 tons

Netlayers

P 301 AG 1 (ex-*Barbarian*), 21-10-37, **P 302 AG 2** (ex-*Barbette*), 15-12-37, **P 303 AG 3** (ex-*Barfair*), 21-5-38. — Bldr: Blyth DD & SB (Gt.Br.) (*1* and *2*), John Lewis & Sons (Aberdeen) (*3*)
D: 730 tons   **S:** 11.7 kts   **A:** 1/76-mm   **Dim:** 52.93 × 9.40 × 2.70
M: Triple expansion; 1 prop; 850 hp; 2 drum boilers   **Man:** 32 men

REMARKS: Former British Boom Defense vessels, the first one transferred in 1944, the two others in 2-46.

P 304 AG 4 (ex *Larch*, AN-21) — Bldr: American SB Co, Cleveland — L: 2-7-41
D: 500 tons (700 fl)   **Dim:** 49.69 (44.50 pp) × 9.30 × 3.20
S: 12.5 kts   **Man:** 48 men
A: 1/76-mm   **M:** diesel-electric, 1,000 hp

REMARKS: Transferred in 7-1948; identical to the *Scarabee* class of the French navy.

P 305 AG 5 (ex-U.N.A.S. *104*) — Bldr: Kröger (Germany) 20-10-60
D: 680 tons (960 fl)   **Dim:** 52.50 × 10.50 × 4.05
S: 12 kts   **M:** 4 M.A.N. diesels; 2 props, 1,450 hp
Man: 48 men   **A:** 1/40-mm AA — 3/20-mm AA

P 306 KALDIRAY (1938) former French netlayer, added to the Turkish navy in 1964

P 307 AG 6 (ex-Dutch *Cerberus*, ex-U.S. AN-93) (1952). Transferred in 1970
D: 855 tons   **Dim:** 50.80 × 10.40 × 4
S: 12.5 kts   **A:** 1/76-mm — 6/20-mm AA
Man: 48 men   **M:** diesel-electric; 1,500 hp

Y 1201 — Y 1202 — Y 1203
D: 360 tons   **Dim:** 30.80 × 10.2 × 1.30

VARIOUS

♦ *2 cargo carriers* (*ex-German*)

	Bldr	L
A 586 ULKÜ (ex-*Angeln*)	A. & Ch. de Bretagne	9-10-54
A 1409 KANARYA (ex-*Ditmarshen*)	A. & Ch. de Bretagne	7-7-54

Ulku (With German hull number)

D: 2,100 tons (2,600 fl)   **Dim:** 90.50 (84.50 pp) × 13.30 × 6.20
S: 17 kts   **Man:** 57 men
M: 2 SEMT-Pielstick diesels; 1 prop; 3,000 hp

REMARKS: Former small but fast cargo ships (19 knots on trials) of the Société Navale Caennaise bought at the end of 1959 by the West German Navy, then transferred to Turkey in 1972. Bulbous bow.

♦ *2 water barges* **Y 1240** *and* **Y 1241**

♦ *1 fleet ocean tug*

A 587 GAZAL (ex-*Sioux*, ATF-75) — Transferred 30-10-72.
D: 1,700 fl   **S:** 16 kts   **Dim:** 60.70 × 11.60 × 4.70
A: 1/76-mm — 4/40-mm AA   **Man:** 85 men
M: 4 diesel-electric groups; 2 props; 3,000 hp

♦ *5 harbor tugs*

Y 1128 AKBAS	**Y 1129 KEPEZ**
D: 971 tons	**S:** 12 kts **Dim:** 44.70 × 10.17 × 4.20

Y . . . ONCU	**Y 1125 ONDER**
D: 500 tons	**S:** 12 kts

Y 1122 KUVVET
D: 390 tons   **S:** . . .   **Dim:** 32.10 × 7.95 × 3.60

♦ *1 training ship*

A 578 SAVARONA (ex-*Gunes Dil* until 1952)
Bldr: Blohm & Voss — L: 28-2-31 — Purchased: 1938

TURKEY (*continued*)

VARIOUS (*continued*)

Savarona   1973 J. C. Bellonne

D: 5,750 tons   **S:** 18 kts   **Dim:** 123 × 16.10 × 5.60
A: 2/75-mm — 2/40-mm AA — 2/20-mm AA   **Range:** 9,000/15
M: GT; 2 props; 8,000 hp; 4 boilers   **Man:** 132 men, 80 midshipmen

REMARKS: Former state yacht, modified in 1952 as a training ship for student officers.

♦ *7 floating docks:* **Y 1081** (16,000 tons), **Y 1082** (12,000 tons), **Y 1083** (2,500 tons), **Y 1084** (4,500 tons), **Y 1085** (4,000 tons), **Y 1086** (3,000 tons), **Y 1087** (3,500 tons).

POLICE SMALL CRAFT

The Turkish Gendarmerie use a few small craft for patrol including:

J 12 to **J 16** — Bldr: U.S.A. (1960-62). **J 18** to **J 20** — Bldr: Turkey

J 16   1970

D: 70 tons (101.75 fl)   **S:** 25/27 kts   **Dim:** 29 × 5.80 × 1.55
A: 1/40-mm AA — 2/20-mm AA   **Man:** 15 men   **Range:** 1,500/20
M: 4 Mercedes-Benz diesels; 2 props; 5,400 hp

J 21 to **J 28** — AB class of the Turkish Navy.
Bldr: Gölcük Naval DY

   D: 170 tons   **S:** 22 kts   **Dim:** 40.24 × 6.40 × 1.65
   A: 2/40-mm   **M:** S.A.C.M. — A.G.O. diesels; 2 props; 4,800 hp

J 29 to **J 30**, **J 41** to **J 49**

Similar to the preceding ships but with a depth charge rack in place of the 40-mm aft.

URUGUAY

PERSONNEL: 3,400 (including 500 officers) + 300 civilians.

NAVAL AVIATION: There is a small naval air arm directly under the administration of the navy. American equipment.

MERCHANT MARINE (1-7-74): 37 ships — 130,147 grt
                       (tankers: 7 ships — 392,757 grt)

♦ *1 ex-U.S. destroyer escort, transferred in 1972*

	Bldr	Laid down	L	In serv.
DE 3 18 DE JULIO	Bath Iron Works	12-52	8-11-53	6-54
(ex-*Dealey*, DE-1006)				

D: 1,450 tons (1,914 fl)   **S:** 25 kts   **Dim:** 95.70 × 11.26 × 4.30
Man: 11 officers, 150 men   **Range:** 4,500/15
A: 2/76-mm (II × 1) — 1 ASW Mk 108 Weapon Able RL — 2 triple ASW Mk 32 TT
M: Laval GT; 2 Foster Wheeler boilers; 1 prop; 20,000 hp
Fuel: 400 tons

FRIGATES

♦ *2 ex-U.S. DE class, transferred in 1951*

	Bldr	L	In serv.
DE 1 URUGUAY	Federal SB & DD	9-5-43	7-43
(ex-*Baron*, DE-166)	(Newark)		
refit at Norfolk in 1955			
DE 2 ARTIGAS	Federal SB & DD	14-11-43	12-43
(ex-*Bronstein*, DE-189)	(Newark)		
refit in 1954-56.			

Same profile as the Greek *Aetos* class.

D: 1,240 tons (2,000 fl)   **Dim:** 93.16 (91.50 pp) × 11.22 × 3.25 (avg)
S: 19 kts   **Man:** 175 men   **Range:** 11,500/11 — 5,500/19
A: 3/76-mm AA — 2/40-mm AA — 2 depth charge projectors — 2 depth charge racks — 1 hedgehog
M: diesel-electric propulsion; 2 props; 6,000 hp   **Fuel:** 340 tons

REMARKS: Transferred by the U.S.A. in 1951. 1 U/SP 6 radar.

FRIGATES (continued)

♦ *1 former corvette*

	Bldr	Laid down	L	In serv.
PF 1 MONTEVIDEO	Harland & Wolff	6-43	8-2-44	6-44

(ex-HMSC *Arnprior*, ex-HMS *Rising Castle*) — Used as training ship.

D: 1,010 tons (1,630 fl). **Dim:** 76.80 × 11.70 × 4.73
A: 1/76-mm — 2/40-mm AA — 4/20-mm AA — 4 depth charge projectors — 1 hedgehog
S: 16 kts **Man:** 90 men **Range:** 4,600/9 — 3,300/16
M: Triple expansion; 1 prop; 2,740 hp
Boilers: 2 3-drum Admiralty **Fuel:** 320 tons (avg)

♦ *1 ex-U.S. MSF minesweeper*

MSF 1 COMMANDANTE PEDRO CAMPBELL — Bldr: Defoe SB (Michigan) (20-7-42)
(ex-*Chickadee*, MSF-59). Transferred by U.S.A. in 1966

D: 890 tons (1,250 fl) **Dim:** 67.45 (65.53 pp) × 9.82 × 3.45
S: 18 kts **Man:** 100 men **A:** 1/76-mm — 2/40-mm AA
M: diesel-electric, 2 props; 3,200 hp

♦ *1 ex-U.S. MSO ocean minesweeper, transferred in 1970*

MALDONADO (ex-French *Bir Hakeim*, ex-*AM-451*) 1953

D: 780 tons (fl) — Characteristics of the *Narvik* class (France)

PATROL BOATS

♦ *1 ex-U.S. SC coastal minesweeper, transferred in 11-69*

RIO NEGRO (ex-French *Marguerite*, ex-*MSC-94*) 1952

D: 372 tons (fl) — Characteristics of the *Acacia* class (France).

♦ *1 Italian type*

	Bldr	L	In serv.
PR 2 SALTO	Riuniti NSY (Ancona)	11-8-35	1936

D: 150 tons (180 fl) **S:** 17 kts **Dim:** 42.10 × 5.80 × 1.58
A: 1/40-mm AA — ASW depth charges **Man:** 26 men
M: Germania-Krupp diesels; 2 props; 1,000 hp **Range:** 4,000/10

Used as a buoy tender.

Salto   C. de Rysky

♦ *2 security boats*

PR 12 PAYSADU — Bldr: Sewart Seacraft (U.S.A.) — 1968
D: 42 tons (fl) **S:** 22 kts **Dim:** 25.50 × 5.60 × 1.70
A: 3 machine guns **M:** 2 MG; 1,100 hp **Range:** 400/12

PR 11 — Bldr: Lürssen (West Germany) 1957
D: 70 tons **S:** 25 kts **Dim:** 28.50 × 5.90 × 2

LOGISTIC SUPPORT AND VARIOUS

♦ *1 ex-U.S. netlayer delivered in 4-69*

HURACAN (ex-*Nahant*, AN-83) — Bldr: U.S.A. (1945).
D: 775 tons (fl) **S:** 12 kts **Dim:** 51.35 × 10.23 × 3.35
A: 4/20-mm AA **Man:** 48 men

M: diesel-electric; 1 prop; 1,000 hp

REMARKS: Can be used as a netlayer or in salvage operations.

ACS 10 CAPITAN MIRANDA — Bldr: Cadiz NSY (1930) — Hydrographic ship
D: 516 tons (550 fl) **S:** 10 kts **Dim:** 45 × 8.40 × 3
M: M.A.N. diesel; 1 prop; 500 hp **Fuel:** 45 tons
Fine lines, similar to a yacht; large spaces aft.

AO . . . PRESIDENTE RIVERA — Bldr: Spain 1971 — tanker

D: 19,350 tons **S:** 16.5 kts **Dim:** 191 × 25.40 × . . .

	Bldr	L	In serv.
AO 9 PRESIDENTE ORIBE — Oiler	Ishikawajima Harima (Japan)	1962	3-62

D: 17,900 tons **Dim:** 189 (179 pp) × 25.70 × 10.05
S: 16 kts **Cargo:** 28,270 tons **Range:** 16,000/16

M: Ishikawajima-Harima GT; 1 prop; 12,500 hp

TRAINING SHIP
TACOMA — Cargo ship of the merchant marine.

A. Barrilli 1969

U.S.S.R.

Leningrad

1974

Strategic missile forces constitute the base of Soviet military strength. The navy, with its nuclear submarines, surface vessels and aircraft armed with missiles, has the principal weapons with which to contain the aggressor.

Marshal Zakharov

Henceforth the flag of the Soviet Navy will float proudly on all of the oceans of the world. Sooner or later the United States will have to understand that it is no longer master of the sea!

Admiral Gorshkov
Commander in Chief of the
Soviet Navy

At sea one is where one should be.

Admiral Makarov
(1900)

We are advancing step by step on the road towards international détente. The Soviet government is completing this task with wisdom, prudence, thoughtfulness and a complete capability of considering the facets in the light of all eventualities, not anticipating the most likely future but ready for any eventuality. . . . The risk of war remains an unhappy possibility of our life. In this context, the Party and the State consider the task of strengthening the peace to be inextricably associated with the task of defending the country.

Marshal Grechko

SOVIET MARITIME AREAS

The Soviet Union has nearly 20,000 km of coast line, half in the Arctic regions and nearly all of the rest on inland seas. Only from the coast line of the Kola peninsula can ships gain direct access to the Atlantic, the Gulf Stream keeps the coast ice-free. In the Far East the Soviets can have access to the Pacific from the Kuriles and Petropavlovsk on the east coast of Kamchatka.

The climate makes navigation difficult or impossible during the winter; the Northern Sea Route, which would permit the movement of ships between the White Sea and the Pacific, is actually open only from the beginning of July until the end of September, and then only with the help of icebreakers. The White Sea, the Gulf of Finland in the Baltic, and all the interior navigational waterways are closed each year by ice.

In the Pacific, the Bering Sea, the Okhotsk Sea, and the Tartar Channel are icebound during the winter. Even Vladivostok, the great base on the Sea of Japan, must sometimes be opened by icebreakers during bad weather. There is one exception: the Petropavlovsk region on the east coast of Kamchatka is open all year.

The Black Sea is exited by the Turkish Straits and the free passage of ships is controlled by the Montreux Convention.

The Baltic Sea is dominated by the Baltic Straits which are rather shallow (7 m in the Sound (Öresund) and 10 m in the Great Belt), thereby precluding the passage of submerged submarines and limiting the size of surface vessels.

These geographic characteristics of the Soviet maritime areas indicate why it is essential that the country have 4 fleets.

THE SOVIET FLEETS

1. *The Northern Fleet*

This fleet is the most important by far because of its strength in nuclear submarines. Its headquarters are located at Severomorsk. Surface forces are located and supported at numerous bases along the Kola or Murmansk fjord. Murmansk itself is exclusively a commercial and fishing port. Submarines, especially the nuclear types, are scattered in bases at different points along the Murmansk coast in well-protected, and year-around ice-free areas.

For industrial support, the Northern Fleet depends on the great complex of Severodvinsk near Archangel. This is the largest naval shipyard in the Soviet Union, specializing in the construction and no doubt the maintenance of atomic submarines.

2. *The Baltic Fleet*

The forces in this theater of operations are equally important. The Soviets have assured themselves control of this sea by extending their naval bases towards the West.

As a matter of fact, although the Baltic Fleet was originally limited to the Leningrad area and stationed at Kronstadt, it now has bases in the former Baltic states (Tallin, Riga, Liepaja), and former East Prussia (Baltisk, ex-Pillau) and even some facilities on the German-Poland frontier (Świnoujście, ex-Swinemünde).

Numerous specialized shipyards are scattered along the coast but those especially designed for naval ships are concentrated in the Leningrad port area (Zhdanov, Baltic, Admiralty, Sudomekh, etc.) for the maintenance of the fleet.

Of special note are the following conditions:

In general the rather shallow approaches limit submarine activity (they must surface in order to go to sea by the Danish straits).

For at least 2 or 3 months during the winter the eastern part (Gulf of Finland), the northern area (Gulf of Bothnia) and the Gulf of Riga are partially blocked by ice.

3. *The Black Sea Fleet*

Has its headquarters at Sevastopol. Like that of the Baltic area, its strength is greater than the requirements of this particular sea, but this fleet helps to maintain the squadron that the Soviets now have permanently in the Mediterranean. In order to do this, the Soviets have developed expertise for passage through the Turkish Straits as regulated by the Montreux Convention.

There is only one really important naval seaport on the Black Sea: Sevastopol with its submarine base. In addition, the support areas of Odessa and Poti can be used by the fleet.

There are two important shipyards: Nikolaiev at the mouth of the Bug river, specializing in large commercial and naval vessels, and Kamych Burun in the Kerch Strait, with the capacity to build naval ships in series.

4. *The Pacific Fleet*

Nearly as important as that of the Arctic, the Pacific Fleet has essentially two naval bases in the immediate area of Petropavlovsk and Vladivostok (where headquarters are located), these two sectors being the least affected by winter conditions.

Defense of the approaches seems to depend on a strong detection network and a number of aerial bases on various islands of the Kuriles and Sakhalin Island.

Lack of strength in the Pacific area arises from the weakness of port communication facilities and the vulnerability of the Tran-Siberian Railroad. On the other hand, the fleet can be maintained by the heavy industrial shipyards in the Amur Valley and by the large naval shipyards at Komsomolsk at the headwaters of the Amur river.

5. *The river system*

The U.S.S.R. has the most important river system of interior waterways in the world. The most significant unit in this network has been called the "Canal of Five Seas" by the Soviets. It extends from the Volga River, and links together the Black Sea and the Sea of Azov (Rostov-on-the-Don), the Caspian Sea (Astrakhan), the Baltic (Leningrad), and the White Sea (Belomorsk).

Aside from its economic aspect, this system has an obvious military importance. It should be especially noted that it permits passage of small surface ships and — thanks to specially-built facilities — the transfer of submarines including certain nuclear classes, from any one of the three European areas to the other.

Several naval shipyards on the Volga — especially the large naval complex at Gorki — are building or have built warships and even nuclear submarines.

The great weakness of this fine river network is the vulnerability of its locks and the interruption of navigation from the beginning of November until mid-April because of winter weather and the breaking up of drift ice.

6. *The Northern Sea Route*

The Northern Sea Route represents a considerable shortening of the Murmansk to Vladivostok passage (5,700 miles instead of 13,000 or 14,000 by the Suez or Panama canals).

The real reason for this routing, however, is not so much strategic as it is economic. The route has three areas, complete passage being assured only for 4 to 8 weeks — in August and September — because of ice in the most difficult passages (the Straits of Vilkitskii, Sannikov, and Dimitri Laptev).

Navigation of this route requires the use of icebreakers and aerial reconnaissance and can be accomplished by ships of 9,000 tons or less.

Some warships, especially submarines, have made the passage from the White Sea to the Pacific at certain periods of the year.

PERSONNEL (1975): 475,000 men including 62,000 officers and 95,000 petty officers.

THE SOVIET FLEETS (*continued*)

175,000 are on board ship, 65,000 belong to the naval air arm, 235,000 are members of the naval infantry, central administration or coastal defense branches.

MERCHANT MARINE (1-7-74): As of this date the Soviet merchant marine was made up of 7,473 ships — 17,463,882 grt — including 502 tankers (3,756,668 grt) — and a fishing fleet which is extremely modern and well developed, made up of 4,900 ships of more than 100 tons for 5,941,381 grt.

WARSHIPS IN SERVICE OR UNDER CONSTRUCTION AS OF 1 OCTOBER 1975

	L	D	Main armament
♦ **Aircraft carriers**			
2 KIEV	constr.	30,000	Missile-launchers, guns, helicopters, VSTOL aircraft
2 MOSKVA	1967-68	20,000	2 SAN-3 systems, 1 or 2 MBU 2,500 A rocket-launchers, 10 TT, 14 helicopters, 1 long-range ASW system
♦ **Submarines**			
(a) *Fleet ballistic missile*			
6/8 D (nuclear)	1973	9,500	16 SS-N-8, TT
33 Y (nuclear)	1967-7.	7,900	16 SS-N-6, 6 TT
1 H III (nuclear)	1965	4,500	5 SS-N-6, 6 TT
8 H II (nuclear)	1960-63	4,500	3 SS-N-5, 8 TT
19 G II (diesel)	1958-61	2,300	3 SS-N-5, 10 TT
9 G I (diesel)	1958-61	2,300	3 SS-N-4, 10 TT
(b) *Nuclear-powered attack submarines*			
12 C	1968-7.	4,000	8 SS-N-7, 6 TT
25/E II	1960-68	4,800	8 SS-N-3, 8 TT
1/P	1972		8 SS-N-3, 8 TT
1/2 A	1974	3,000	TT
15/16 V I and V II	1967-7.	4,300	8 TT
14 N	1959-64	4,000	12 TT
5 E	1960-63	4,600	TT
(c) *Conventionally-powered attack submarines*			
1. Cruise missile-launching			
16 J	1961-68	2,800	4 SS-N-3, 6 TT
5 W *Long bin*	1961-63	1,200	4 SS-N-3, 4 TT
4 W *Twin cylinder*	1950-57	1,050	2 SS-N-3, 6 TT
2. Torpedo-launching			
56/58 F	1959-7.	1,950	10 TT
24 Z IV	1952-57	2,000	10 TT
8/10 R	1960	1,400	8 TT
110/120 W	1950-57	1,050	6 TT
8/10 Q	1950-57	460	4 TT
4/B	1970-72	2,400	TT
1/T	1973	1,700	TT
♦ **Cruisers**			
(a) *Guided missile*			
2/4 KARA	1971-7	9,500	8 SS-N-10 missile-launchers, 2 SA-N-3 missile-launchers, 2 SA-N-4 4/76-mm AA, 2 MBU 2500 A rocket-launchers, 2 MBU 4500 A rocket-launchers, 10 TT, 1 helicopter
8 KRESTA II	1970-71	6,600	8 SS-N-10 missile-launchers, 2 SA-N-3 missile-launchers, 4/57-mm AA, 2 MBU 2500 A rocket-launchers, 2 MBU 4500 A rocket-launchers, 10 TT, 1 helicopter
4 KRESTA I	1967-69	6,300	4 SS-N 3 missile-launchers, 2 SA-N-1 missile-launchers, 2 MBU 2500 A rocket-launchers, 2 MBU 4500 A rocket-launchers, 4/57-mm AA, 10 TT, 1 helicopter
4 KYNDA	1962-64	5,700	8 SS-N-3 missile-launchers, 1 SA-N-1 missile-launcher, 2 MBU 2500 A rocket-launchers, 4/76-mm AA, 6 TT
1 DZERZHINSKI	1954	19,300	1 SA-N-2 missile-launcher, 9/152-mm, 12/100-mm AA
(b) *Conventional*			
11 SVERDLOV	1951-57	19,300	6, 9, or 12/152-mm
2 CHAPAEV (obsolete)	1944-51	15,000	12/152-mm
1 KIROV (obsolete)	1945-46	12,000	9/180-mm
♦ **Destroyers**			
(a) *Guided missile*			
4/5 KASHIN MOD	1974	4,900	4 SS-N-11 missile-launchers, 5 TT, 2 SA-N-1 missile-launchers, 4/76-mm AA, 2 MBU 2500 A rocket-launchers
14 KASHIN	1963-72	4,600	2 SA-N-1 missile-launchers, 4/76-mm AA, 2 MBU 2500 A rocket-launchers, 2 MBU 4500 A rocket-launchers, 5 TT
8/10 KRIVAK	1970-7.	3,600	4 SS-N-10 missile-launchers, 4/76-mm AA, 2 SA-N-4 missile-launchers, 8 TT, 2 MBU 2500 A rocket-launchers
6 KANIN	1960-61	4,500	2 SA-N-1 missile-launchers, 8/57-mm AA, 3 MBU 2500 A rocket-launchers, 10 TT
2 KRUPNY	1958-60	4,500	2 SS-N-1 missile-launchers, 16/57-mm AA, 2 MBU 2500 rocket-launchers, 6 TT
2 KILDIN	1958-59	3,800	1 SS-N-1 missile-launcher, 16/57-mm AA, 2 MBU 2500 rocket-launchers, 4 TT
2 KILDIN MOD	. . .	3,800	4 SS-N-11 missile-launchers, 4/76-mm AA, 16/45-mm AA
8 KOTLIN SAM	1958-60	2,850	1 SA-N-1 missile-launcher, 2/130-mm AA, 4/45-mm AA or

THE SOVIET FLEETS (continued)

(b) *Conventional*

19 KOTLIN	1955–57	2,850	4/130-mm AA, 16/45-mm AA, 10 TT some with MBU 2500 or 4500 A rocket-launchers
1 TALLINN	1955	4,400	4/130-mm AA, 16/45-mm AA, 2 MBU 2500 rocket-launchers, 10 TT
20/25 SKORY (a)	1950–53	3,200	4/130-mm AA, 2/85-mm AA, 10 TT
(b) modernized	1961	3,200	4/130-mm AA, 5/57-mm AA, 5 TT, 2 MBU 2500 rocket-launchers

(continued from) 8/30-mm AA, 2 MBU 2500 A rocket-launchers, 5 TT

◆ Frigates

20 MIRKA I or II	1964–67	1,100	4/76-mm AA, 2 or 4 MBU 2500 A rocket-launchers, 5 or 10 TT
49/56 PETYA I, II, III	1962–64	1,000	4/76-mm AA, 2 or 4 MBU 2500 A rocket-launchers, 5 or 10 TT
35 RIGA	1955–57	1,450	3/100-mm AA, 3 TT, at times 2 MBU 2500 rocket-launchers
2 KOLA	1950–53	1,700	4/100-mm AA, 3 TT
10/12 GRISHA	1968–73	900	2/57-mm AA, 1 SA-N-4 missile-launcher, 2 MBU 2500 A rocket-launchers, 4 TT
2 GRISHA MOD			4/57 mm, 2 MBU 2500 RL, 4 TT
60/70 POTI	1961–67	650	2/57-mm AA, 2 MBU 2500 A rocket-launchers, 2 or 4 TT
20 KRONSTADT	1950–60	390	1/85-mm, 2/37-mm AA, at times an MBU 1800 rocket-launcher
75/80 SO 1	1960–64	200	4/25-mm AA, 4 MBU 1800 rocket-launchers, 2 ASW TT

◆ Patrol boats

8/10 NANUCHKA	1964–67	700	1 SA-N-4 missile-launcher, 6 SS-N-9 missile-launchers
30/35 STENKA	1968	190	4/30-mm AA
20/30 MO VI	. . .	73	4/25-mm AA
20/25 PCHELA	1964–67	60	2/23-mm AA

◆ Missile and Torpedo Boats

100/115 OSA I and II	1960–7	190	4 SS-N-2 missile-launchers, 4/30-mm AA
3/4 KOMAR	1961–63	80	2 SS-N-2 missile-launcher, 2/25-mm AA
40/45 SHERSHEN	1963–7	190	4/30-mm AA 4 TT
12/15 TURYA	1974	190	2/57-mm AA, TT
50 P 6	1953–59	73	4/25-mm AA, 4 TT
20/30 P 8 and P 10	1960	73	4/25-mm AA, 4 TT
30 P 4	1950	30	2 TT

Without any pretense as to the validity of the figures presented on page 379 they do give an idea of the size of the Soviet navy and the approximate distribution of its strength among the four fleets, this distribution obviously being modified by international circumstances.

NOTE: The Black Sea fleet usually provides surface ships for the Mediterranean "Eskadra" while the submarines in the Mediterranean always come from the Arctic.

The "Eskadra" averages about 30 combat vessels including a dozen submarines plus about a dozen logistic support and auxiliary ships.

The Soviets also maintain a force in the Indian Ocean, usually about 20 ships, 6 or 8 of them fighting ships, coming from the Pacific fleet.

From time to time they send a few ships to the Caribbean area in the Atlantic and they have a permanent small group standing by off Conakry in Africa.

Nikolayev

M.N. 1974

SOVIET NAVAL MISSILES

1

3

1. Top, left: Launching of a surface-air Goa missile (SA-N-1), from a Kynda class cruiser.

2. Below, left: Goa twin launcher with missiles ready.

3. Top right: The MBU 1 800 ASW rocket launcher on board an SO 1 class patrol boat.

4. Below, right: launching of a Styx missile from an Osa I class missile patrol boat.

2

4

	Arctic	Baltic	Black Sea	Pacific	Total*
Nuclear-Powered Fleet Ballistic Missile Submarines	35/40			12 to 16	47 to 56
Helicopter Cruisers			2		2
Guided Missile Cruisers	6	1	5	5	17
Cruisers	2	3	5	4	14
Guided Missile Destroyers	10/12	10/12	14/16	10/12	44 to 52
Destroyers	6/8	10/12	10/12	14/16	40 to 48
Nuclear-Powered Attack Submarines	50	0		25	75
Conventional Submarines	100	45	40	70	255
Naval Air Arm	350	260	250	340	1,200

*Totals do not always agree with figures on pp. 376-7

WEAPONS AND SYSTEMS OF THE SOVIET NAVY

1. — MISSILES

(a) BALLISTIC MISSILES

NOTE: All have propergol liquid propulsion.

SS-N-4 System

300-mile range. Nuclear warhead. Fitted in G I class diesel-powered fleet ballistic missile submarines. Can be launched only from the surface.

SS-N-5 System

700-mile range. Nuclear warhead of about 800 KT. Fitted in H II class nuclear-powered submarines and in G II class diesel-powered strategic submarines. Can be launched while submerged.

SS-N-6 System

1,300-mile range. Nuclear warhead of about 1 megaton. Found on the Y class nuclear submarines. Can be launched while submerged. A more recent version has a 1,600-mile range and has an MRV type warhead.

SS-N-8 System (NATO code name: Sawfly)

4,000-mile range. Nuclear warhead of about 1 megaton. Found on the D class nuclear submarines.

SS-N-13 System

370-mile range. Nuclear warhead. Tactical ballistic missile.

(b) SURFACE-TO-SURFACE CRUISE MISSILES

NOTE: *Propergol liquid propulsion except for SS-N-7 and SS-N-10 systems which have a solid powder propellant engine.*

SS-N-1 System (NATO code name: Scrubber)

Range: 25 miles on surface targets, 120 to 130 on land targets; subsonic ramjet engine. Radio directed for initial trajectory then active radar guidance automatically to the target. Nuclear or conventional warhead. Fitted on Kildin and Krupny-class destroyers. No longer produced.

SS-N-2 System NATO code name: Styx)

Maximum range: 10 miles. Practical range: 10 miles. Liquid propulsion. Active radar guidance in targeting, possibly with infra-red homing in the most recent version. Flight altitude: 100,200,300 m. 400 to 450 kg conventional warhead. Installed in guided missile boats of the Komar, OSA I and OSA II classes.

SS-N-3 System (NATO code name: Shaddock)

Found on surface ships:
Maximum range: 30 miles on a surface target but can reach 170 miles with an aerial relay (aircraft fitted with a Video Data Link system).
Found on submarines:
Maximum range: 30 miles surface targets, 250 miles land targets.
Inertial guidance with mid-course correction by radio, active radar homing to target. Ramjet propulsion. Conventional or nuclear warhead. Fitted on Kynda class (quadruple launcher) and Kresta I class (twin launcher) cruisers and W twin cylinder, Long Bin, J, and E II class submarines. Launched from the surface by submarines.

SS-N-7 System

Maximum range: 30 miles. Conventional warhead, can be launched submerged. Fitted on class C nuclear attack submarines, 8 to a ship.

SS-N-9

Maximum range: 30 miles but can reach 150 miles with an aerial relay (aircraft fitted with a Video Data Link system), inertial guidance and active radar homing to the target. Ramjet propulsion. Conventional or nuclear warhead. Installed in guided missile boats of the Nanuchka class.

SS-N-10 System

Range 15 to 18 miles on a surface target. Conventional warhead (500 kg). Fitted on the Kresta II and Kara-class cruisers as well as on the Krivak-class destroyers.

SS-N-11 System

Maximum range: 20 miles. Improvement of the SS-N-2 Styx. Fitted on the Kashin Mod and Kildin Mod-class destroyers.

SS-N-12 System.

Maximum range: 260 miles. Conventional or nuclear warhead. Will replace the SS-N-3.

(c) SURFACE-TO-AIR MISSILES

SA-N-1 System (NATO code name of the missile: Goa).

Twin launchers. Range: 30,000 m, interception altitudes: 1,000 to 50,000 feet.
Guidance: radar/command. Conventional warhead, 60 kg. Fitted on the Kynda and Kresta I class cruisers, as well as on the destroyers of the Kashin, Kanin and Kotlin classes.

SA-N-2 System (NATO code name of the missile: Guideline).

Twin launchers. Range: 40,000 m, interception altitude: 1,000 to 80,000 feet. Guidance: radar/command. Conventional warhead, 150 kg. Fitted on the cruiser *Dzerzhinski*.

SA-N-3 System (NATO Code name of the missile: Goblet)

Twin launchers. Range: 40,000 m, interception altitudes: 500 to 80,000 feet. Guidance: radar/command. Conventional warhead, 60 kg. Fitted on the Kresta II and Kara-class cruisers as well as the *Moskva*-class helicopter cruisers.

WEAPONS AND SYSTEMS (*continued*)

SA-N-4 System (short-range system)

Twin launcher, retracting into a vertical drum. Range: 9,000 m, interception altitude: 300 to 10,000 feet. Guidance: radar command. Conventional warhead. Fitted on the *Kara* class cruisers, the Krivak guided missile destroyers, the Grisha-class frigates, and the Nanuchka guided missile boats.

(d) AIR-TO-SURFACE MISSILES

AS 1 System (NATO code name of the missile: Kennel).

Range: 50 to 55 miles. Turbojet propulsion. Semi-active radar guidance. Conventional warhead. No longer in service with Soviet naval air arm.

AS 2 System (NATO code name of the missile: Kipper)

Range: 100 miles. Solid propulsion. Inertial guidance or automatic pilot with radar homing head. Conventional or nuclear warhead. Placed in service on the Badger C and G aircraft.

AS 6 System

Range over 100 miles. Conventional or nuclear warhead. Placed in service on the Badger C aircraft, two on each.

2. — GUNNERY

180-mm

Semi-automatic type fitted on the cruiser *Kirov* in a triple turret; the individual barrels cannot be elevated separately.
— barrel length: 56 calibers;
— muzzle velocity: 920 m/sec;
— Altitude arc: −5° to +40°;
— rate of fire: 6 rounds/min;
— maximum effective range: 18 to 20,000 m;
— projectile weight: 100 kg.

152-mm

Fitted in triple turrets on the *Sverdlov* and Chapaev-class cruisers. Individual barrels can be loaded and elevated separately.
— barrel length: 57 calibers;
— muzzle velocity: 915 m/sec;
— altitude arc: −5° to +50°;
— maximum rate of fire: 4 to 5 rounds/min/barrel;
— Maximum range: 27,000 m;
— Effective range: 18,000 m;
— projectile weight; 50 kg;
— fire control: Top Bow and Egg Cup radars in the upper turrets forward and aft;
— 8 m rangefinder in each turret.

130-mm twin

Semi-automatic type fitted on the Skoryi-class destroyers.
— barrel length: 50 calibers;
— muzzle velocity: 875 m/sec;
— altitude arc: −5° to +40°;
— maximum rate of fire: 10 rounds/min/barrel;
— maximum range: 24,000 m;

— effective range: 14 to 15,000 m;
— projectile weight: 27 kg.

130-mm twin AA

Semi-automatic for surface and AA targets. Fitted on the Tallinn, Kotlin, and Kotlin Sam-class destroyers.
Twin mount on three axes with electric or hydraulic-electric pointing system;
— barrel length: 58 calibers;
— muzzle velocity: 900 m/sec;
— arc of elevation: −5° to +50°;
— maximum rate of fire: 15 rounds/min/barrel;
— maximum range surface target: 28,000 m;
— effective range surface target: 16 to 18,000 m;
— maximum vertical range: 13,000 m;
— projectile weight: 27 kg;
— target designation by stabilized director with a Sun Visor radar;
— Egg Cup radar in each mount.

100-mm twin AA

— mounted on three axes installed on *Sverdlov* and Chapaev-class cruisers.
— weight: approx. 40 tons;
— barrel length: 50 calibers;
— muzzle velocity: 900/sec;
— arc of elevation: −15° to +90°;
— maximum rate of fire: 15 rounds/min/barrel:
— maximum range surface target: 20,000 m;
— effective range surface target: 10 to 12,000 m;
— maximum range AA fire: 15,000 m;
— effective range AA fire: 8 to 9,000 m;
— projectile weight: 16 kg;
— target designation by stabilized director with a Top Bow or Post lamp radar.
— Egg Cup radar in each mount (except on the *Sverdlov*).

100-mm single barrel

Installed on the cruiser *Kirov*, the Kola and Riga-class frigates, and the Don-class logistic support ships.
Gun mount with a shield;
— barrel length: 50 calibers;
— muzzle velocity: 850 m/sec;
— arc of elevation: −5° to +40°;
— maximum rate of fire: 15 rounds/min;
— maximum range: 16,000 m;
— effective range: 10,000 m;
— projectile weight: 13.5 kg;
— target designation by stabilized director fitted with Sun Visor radar.

85-mm AA

Twin barrelled gun mount on certain ships of the Skoryi class, single barrel on the Kronstadt-class frigates.
— barrel length: 50 calibers;
— muzzle velocity: 850 m/sec;
— arc of elevation: −5° to +70° (barrels can be fired independently on the Skoryi class);
— maximum rate of fire: 10 rounds/min/barrel;

WEAPONS AND SYSTEMS (*continued*)

— maximum range surface target: 15,000 m;
— effective range surface target: 8 to 9,000 m;
— practical maximum range AA fire: 6,000 m.

76-mm twin barrel effective AA

Installed on the Kara and Kynda class cruisers, the Kashin and Krivak-class destroyers, the Petya and Mirka-class frigates.
— length of barrel: 60 calibers?
— muzzle velocity: 900 m/sec?
— maximum rate of fire: 60 rounds/min/barrel;
— arc of elevation: +80°;
— maximum range in AA fire: 10,000 m;
— effective range in AA fire: 6,000 to 7,000 m;
— projectile: 16 kg;
— target designation with Owl Screech radar and automatic tracking.

57-mm automatic AA

Single barrel gun mount (Skory modified class), twin-barrel (several classes) or quadruple on the Kanin, Kildin, and Krupny-class destroyers. In the latter case the guns are mounted in pairs on a single gun mount.
— length of barrel: 70 calibers;
— muzzle velocity: 900 to 1,000 m/sec;
— arc of elevation: 0° to +90°;
— maximum rate of fire: 300 rounds/min/gun mount;
— effective vertical range: 4,500 m;
— target designation by Hawk Screech tracking radar.

57-mm AA twin barrels in a mount

This equipment appears to be entirely automatic from the ammunition-handling room to the gun mount and is installed on the *Moskva*, the Kresta I and Kresta II class cruisers, and the Poti and Grisha-class frigates, the *Boris Chilikin, Manych*, on Ugra class replenishment ships, as well as the Nanuchka-class guided missile patrol boats, the Turya-class torpedo boats, and the Ropucha-class LST, and the Ugra class BSL.
— length of barrel: 70 calibers?
— water cooling system;
— maximum rate of fire: 120 rounds/min/barrel;
— maximum effective vertical range: 5 to 6,000 m;
— target designation by Muff Cob radar.

45-mm AA

Quadruple barrelled installation installed in the Tallinn, Kotlin Sam, and Kotlin-class destroyers as well as on other ships.
The guns are mounted in two pairs on a single gun mount
— length of barrel: 85 calibers;
— muzzle velocity: 900 m/sec;
— arc of elevation: 0° to +90°;
— rate of fire: 300 rounds/min/gun mount;
— effective maximum vertical range: 4,000 m;
Target designation by Hawk Screech tracking radar.

37-mm AA model 39

Installed in single or twin barrelled gun mounts in the *Sverdlov* and Chapaev-class cruisers, the Skory class, the Riga-class frigates, and various other ships.
— length of barrel: 60 calibers?
— muzzle velocity: 900 m/sec;
— arc of elevation: 0° to +80°?
— maximum rate of fire: 250 rounds/min/gun mount;
— optical tracking.

30-mm AA automatic

Installed in a light mount on several classes of ships — cruisers, destroyers, guided missile boats, supply ships, etc. Water cooling system.
— length of barrel: 60 calibers?
— muzzle velocity: 1,000 m/sec?
— maximum rate of fire: 150 rounds/min/barrel;
— effective maximum range in AA fire: 2,500 to 3,000 m.
Target designation by Drum Tilt tracking radar.

25-mm AA

Found on many ships and made up of two superimposed guns.
— length of barrel: 60 calibers;
— muzzle velocity: 900 m/sec;
— maximum rate of fire: 150 to 200 rounds/min/gun mount;
— optical tracking.

Anti-missile gun

This gun has been placed in service specifically on the Kara and Kresta II class cruisers and is installed in a mount similar to those of the 30-mm AA double barrel automatic guns. It is a kind of "Gatling" machine gun designed to fire at an extremely high rate a great number of rounds in order to intercept a cruise missile at a comparatively short distance from the ship. The gun has 6/20 to 25-mm barrels. Target designation is accomplished with the Bass Tilt radar.

3. — ASW WEAPONS:

(a) MISSILES

SS-N-15

ASW missile similar to the U.S. Navy's Subroc. Maximum range: 25 miles. Nuclear warhead.

FRAS 1

Jet-propelled weapon similar to the U.S. Navy's Asroc. Installed on the *Moskva* and *Leningrad* helicopter carrier cruisers. Maximum range: 16 miles. Nuclear warhead. Twin launcher.

SS-N-14

Similar weapon to the French Malafon. Maximum range: 20 miles. Fras 1 and SS-N-14 are launched from the SUW-N-1 launcher on the *Moskva* class.

(b) ROCKETS

MBU 1800

Made up of two horizontal rows of short barrels superimposed with two below and three in the upper row, tube diameter: 0.250 m; length: 1.400 m; the rocket is some-

WEAPONS AND SYSTEMS (*continued*)

what shorter. Range: 1,800 m. Fixed tubes. Installed in the SO 1 and Kronstadt class patrol boats.

MBU 2500

Made up of two horizontal rows of 8 barrels each, approximately 1.600 m in length. Trainable. Manual reloading. Range: 2,500 m.

MBU 2500 A

Made up of 12 barrels approximately 1.600 m long arranged in a ring and fired in sequence. Vertical automatic loading system, barrel by barrel. Can be trained and elevated. Range: 6,000 m. Installed on the Kynda and the Kresta I and II class cruisers, the *Moskva* class, the guided missile destroyers of the Krivak, Kashin, and Kanin class, and the patrol craft of the Mirka, Poti, Petya, and Grisha classes.

MBU 4500

Made up of 6 barrels 0.300 m in diameter and 1.500 m long superimposed in two rows and fired simultaneously. Trainable. Range: 2,500 m.

MBU 4500 A

Made up of 6 barrels arranged in a ring and fired in order with vertical automatic reloading. Trainable. Tube diameter: approx. 0.300 m; length: approx. 1.800 m. Range: 2,500 m. Installed in the Kara, Kresta I and II class cruisers and the Kashin-class destroyers.

(c) TORPEDOES

The Soviet navy uses anti-surface and ASW torpedoes 533-mm in diameter and short ASW torpedoes 400-mm in diameter.

4. — ELECTRONIC EQUIPMENT:

(a) ELECTROMAGNETIC DETECTION (NATO code names)

Radar Navigation

The most widely used are the "Neptun" (band I) and various "Don" class (also Band I).

Long range Air Search radar

— *Head Net A;*
— *Head Net B* (made up of 2 Head Net A antennae mounted back to back in a horizontal plane);
— *Head Net C* (made up of 2 Head Net A antennae mounted back to back, one in a horizontal plane, the other inclined).

These radars use a band which gives a 60 to 70 mile detection range on an attack bomber flying at high altitude:
— *Big Net.* A large radar (band C) fitted on a few *Sverdlov* class, the Kresta I class cruisers, and some of the Kashin-class destroyers. Its probable detection range on an aircraft is over 100 miles;
— *Slim Net* (band E) early model radar fitted on some cruisers and destroyers;
— *Hair Net* (band E) early model radar being taken out of service;
— *Top Through.* (band C) has replaced Slim Net on some *Sverdlov*-class cruisers;
— *Sea Gull* (band A);
— *Knife Rest* (band A). Antenna resembles a knife rest. Being removed from service;

— *Strut Curve* (band F). Mounted on the Petya, Mirka, Poti, and Grisha class patrol boats; has replaced Slim Net;
— *Plinth Net.* (band E). Mounted on the Kynda class and the Kresta I class.

Heightfinding radars

— *Top Sail.* 3 dimensional radar (band C) installed on the *Moskva* class and the Kresta II and Kara-class cruisers.
— *High Lune.* Probably in band C. Mounted on the *Dzerzhinski.*

Tracking Radars

— *Peel Group.* Radar mounted on the Kynda and Kresta I class cruisers as well as the guided missile Kashin, Kanin, and Kotlin Sam class destroyers. Made up of a tracking radar for high altitudes (band I) and a missile guidance radar at lower altitudes (band E). The assembly is made up of two groups of large and small reflectors in both horizontal and vertical position with parabolic design. Maximum range approximately 30 to 40 miles. Used as a missile guidance radar for the Goa missile in the SA-N-1 system.
— *Head Lights.* Radar in the bands F, G, H, and D mounted in the *Moskva* class and the Kresta II and Kara class cruisers. Similar to the Peel Group with an assembly of tracking radar for the target and guidance radar for the missile. Probably superior in both distance and altitude to the older Peel Group. Used as a missile guidance radar for the surface-to-air Goblet missile of the SA-N-3 system and in its B version for the surface-to-surface missiles of the SS-N-10 system.
— *Scoop Pair.* Missile guidance radar (band E) for the surface-to-surface Shaddock missile of the SS-N-3 system on board Kynda and Kresta I class cruisers.
— *Pop Group.* Missile guidance radar for the SA-N-4 system (bands F, H, I).
— *Eye Bowl.* Smaller version of the Head Lights radar, installed on the Krivak class, missile guidance radar for the SS-N-10 system. Band F.
— *Fan Song E.* Installed on the *Dzerzhinski;* this system is used with the SA-N-2 system (surface-to-air missiles Guide Line) and consists of two antennae made up of parabolic reflectors in the form of troughs, one vertical and one horizontal, plus three circular reflectors, two side by side and a third mounted on an arm at the extreme end of the horizontal reflector. Detection range: at least 80 miles on a bomber size aircraft.

Target designation radar

— *Half Bow*
— *Post Lamp* } Band I, mounted on various classes of ships.
— *Long Bow*
— *Plinth Net.* Band E, mounted on a few cruisers.

Surface search radars

The most common are Pot Head, Square Tie, Snoop Plate (Band I) High Sieve, Low Sieve, Skin Head, and Pot Head in band E.

Fire Control Radar

— *Top Bow,* 152-mm gun fire control;
— *Sun Visor,* 130-mm AA, 100-mm AA guns:
— *Hawk Screech,* 45-mm AA fire control;   Band I
— *Owl Screech,* 76-mm AA fire control;
— *Muff Cob,* Band II radar used as fire control for 57-mm AA twin automatic guns;
— *Egg Cup* (band E), installed in turrets for 152-mm, 130-mm and 100-mm AA;
— *Drum Tilt* (band H, I), installed on the Osa class and the ships fitted with 30-mm twin barrel AA.
— *Bass Tilt,* possibly Pulse Doppler class radar used with the Gatling type gun fitted in the Kara, Kresta II, and Kashin modified classes (band H).

WEAPONS AND SYSTEMS *(continued)*

(b) SUBMARINE DETECTION

Up until the last few years the Soviet navy had evinced little interest in anti-submarine warfare, and, of course, submarine detection. Most of their ships were equipped with high frequency sonar (Tamir, Pegas, Hercules). Now it would appear that the new ships or modernized ships are equipped with better sensors:
— hull sonars of mid-frequency (Krivak, Kanin, Kresta II, Grisha);
— towed sonars of mid-frequency (*Moskva*, Kara, Krivak, Kashin mod., Petya II);
— hull sonars low frequency (*Moskva*, Kara, Krivak);
— helicopter dipping sonars (Stenka, Pchela, Mirka II, Turya).
The submarines are still for the most part equipped with old detection equipment (active-passive Hercules, passive Feniks). On the other hand, the recent nuclear submarines have a modern low frequency sonar (D, Y, C, V I and V II).

(c) ELECTRONIC WARFARE

The Soviet navy seems to be taking a greater interest in electronic warfare. The increasing number of radomes of every description that can be seen on Soviet ships, especially on the newest and most important types (helicopter carriers and guided missile cruisers, for example), indicates the attention and consideration being given to this aspect of modern warfare.

AIRCRAFT CARRIERS

♦ *3 Kiev class*

	Bldr	Laid down	L	In serv.
KIEV	Nikolayev	1971	1973	1976
MINSK	Nikolayev	. . .	. . .	1978
. . . . .	Nikolayev	. . .	. . .	. . .

D: 35–40,000 tons (fl) **S:** 30 kts **Dim:** 275 × . . . × . . .
A: 8/SS-N-12 (II × 4) — 2/SA-N-3 (II × 2) — 2SA-N-4 (II × 2) — 1/SUW-N-1 (II × 1) — 4/76-mm AA (II × 2) — 8/23-mm Gatling guns — 2/RBU-2500 A asw rockets. About 35 Ka-25 ASW helos and VTOL/STOL fixed-wing aircraft.
Electron Equipt: 2 Hawk Screech, 1 Top Sail, 2 Head Light, 4 Drum Tilt, and others; VDS, probable bow sonar.
M: GT, 150/160,000 hp; 4 props.
REMARKS: The VSTOL aircraft are of a new design. No catapults or arresting gear. Angle of flight deck, 5° off centerline. Two elevators. A fourth ship is reportedly planned.

HELICOPTER CRUISERS

♦ *2 Moskva class*

	Bldr	Laid down	L	In serv.
MOSKVA	Nikolayev (Black Sea)	1963	196–	7-67
LENINGRAD	Nikolayev (Black Sea)	1964	196–	1968

Kiev   1976

Kiev   1976

HELICOPTER CRUISERS (*continued*)

Leningrad

M.N. 1974

Moskva

Hormone Helicopter

U.S. Navy 1971

Leningrad

M.N. 1974

HELICOPTER CRUISERS (*continued*)

Leningrad

M.N. 1974

D: 20,000 tons (fl)
S: 30 kts
A: 2 SA-N-3 systems (II × 2) with 44 Goblet missiles — 1 SUW-N-1-4/57-mm
AA (II × 2) — 1 or 2 MBU 2 500 A RL — 10/533-mm TT (V × 2) — 14
Hormone A helicopters
Dim: 190 × 34 (flight deck) 26 (waterline) × 7.60
Man: 800 men
Electron Equipt: Radars: 3 Don 2, 1 Top Sail, 1 Head Net C,
2 Headlights, 2 Muff Cob
Sonars: 1 low frequency hull-fitted and 1 middle
frequency towed type.
M: GT; 100,000 hp; 2 props **Range:** 2,500/30, 7,000/15

REMARKS: Appears to be based on the French *Jeanne d'Arc*. Flight deck 86 × 34; 3
elevators with two on the flight deck and one forward and interior to the super-

structure. The *Moskva* was modified for a time to permit testing of the VTOL
Yak 36 aircraft which were to go aboard the *Kiev* class.
Notice in the photo at left just aft of the bow the ASW S4W-N-1 system, the two
SA-N-3 system mounts used with the Head Lights guidance radars, and the
tri-dimensional Top Sail radar.

NAVAL AVIATION

Dating from 1919, naval aviation is an integral part of the Soviet navy, but its
organization and ranks are those of the Air Force. Land-based aircraft, with the
possible exception of a few helicopters, are part of the four large naval fleets: Baltic,
Arctic, Black Sea, and Pacific, and are directly under the control of the commanders
of these forces. The air arm has approximately 1,200 aircraft including the following:

* 60 Bear, 60 Badger E, F, J, etc. 60 Blinder A, fitted for reconnaissance, electronic
warfare, etc.

* 300 Badger A, C and G for attack.

* 70/80 Badger A or Bison used for inflight refueling.

* 90 ASW Mail flying boats.

* 60 ASW May patrol aircraft.

Bear D (reconnaissance)

M.N. 1972

Badger A (tanker)

M.N. 1972

NAVAL AVIATION (*continued*)

Badger C (bomber)   M.N. 1972

Mail (ASW)   1972

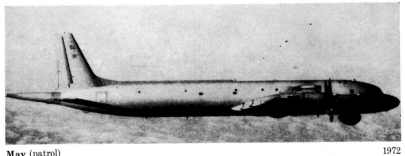

May (patrol)   1972

Tupolev 20 (*Bear D*)   U.S. Navy 1970

Tupolev 16 (*Badger*) armed with KENNEL missiles

CHARACTERISTICS OF THE PRINCIPAL AIRCRAFT OF THE SOVIET NAVAL AIR ARM

♦ A. Fixed-wing including amphibian — The characteristics of the "Backfire" are given on p. 389.

NATO code name builder	Mission	Year put in serv.	Weight	Wing-span	Length	Propulsion	Speed max. cruising	Operational radius (1)	Armament	Fitted with	Remarks
BEAR D **TU 20** (Tupolev)	Reconnaissance and electronic warfare	1955	165 t	50 m	44 m	4 turboprops, 12,500 hp each. 2 props with 4 blades, contrarotating, reversible pitch	550 kts at 25,000 ft 440 kts	8,000 km without refueling, 9,500 km with	6/23-mm cannon	Radomes and tail radar. Well equipped with electronic countermeasures.	There is an ASW Bear F version which is fitted with sonar buoys, depth charges, and torpedoes.
BADGER A **TU 16** (Tupolev)	Bombardment. Ship attack.	1953	75 t	33 m	35 m	2 turbojets. RD 3 M 9,550-kg, thrust each	540 kts at 22,000 ft 445 kts	3,000 km without refueling, 4,500 km with	7/23-mm cannon, 9 tons of bombs	1 navigation/bomb. radar. 1 tail radar. Some electronic warfare equipment.	There is a modified version used for in-flight fueling.
BADGER C **TU 16** (Tupolev)	Ship attack		75 t	33 m	35 m	2 turbojets. RD 3 M 9,550-kg thrust each	540 kts at 22,000 ft 445 kts	3,000 km without refueling, 4,500 km with	6/23-mm cannon, 1 AS 2 "Kipper" or 2 AS 6	1 navigation/bomb. radar. 1 Doppler radar. 1 tail radar.	
BADGER G **TU 16** (Tupolev)	Ship attack		75 t	33 m	35 m	2 turbojets. RD 3 M 9,550-kg thrust each	540 kts at 22,000 ft 455 kts	3,000 km without refueling, 4,500 km with	8/23-mm cannon, 2 AS 5 "Kelt" or 2 AS 6	1 navigation/bomb. radar. 1 Doppler radar. 1 tail radar	
BADGER E, D, E, F, J. **TU 16** (Tupolev)	Reconnaissance and electronic warfare		75 t	33 m	35 m	2 turbojets. RD 3 M 9,550-kg thrust each	540 kts at 22,000 ft 455 kts	3,000 km without refueling, 4,500 km with	6-7/23-mm cannon	1 navigation/bomb. radar. Electronic warfare equipment. 1 tail radar. IFF.	Different versions for ELINT, photo reconnaissance, etc.
BLINDER **TU 22** (Tupolev)	Reconnaissance	1963	84 t	24 m	38 m	2 turbojets. 20,000-kg thrust each, with 13,000-kg thrust without using after burners	Mach 1,6 at 36,000 ft	Supersonic speeds: 1,000 km without refueling, 1,600 km with Subsonic speeds: without refueling, 2,000 km with	1/23-mm cannon	1 navigation radar. 1 tail radar. IFF. 7 cameras.	
BISON **MYA 4** (Myasishchev)	Inflight refueling	1956	165 t	50 m	48 m	4 turbojets. RD 3 M 9,950-kg thrust each	545 kts 440 kts	5,200 km without refueling, 7,400 km with	6/23-mm cannon	1 navigation radar. IFF. Tail radar.	

(1) The operational radius is roughly 60% of half of the full range.
(2) MAD = Magnetic Anomalies Detection.

CHARACTERISTICS OF THE PRINCIPAL AIRCRAFT OF THE SOVIET NAVAL AIR ARM (*cont.*)

♦ A. Fixed-wing including amphibian — The characteristics of the "Backfire" are given below.

NATO code name builder	Mission	Year put in serv.	Weight	Wing-span	Length	Propulsion	Speed max. cruising	Operational radius (1)	Armament	Fitted with	Remarks
MAY (Ilyushin)	ASW	1969	64 t	37 m	40 m	4 turboprops. 4,00 hp each.	380 kts at 30,000 ft 315 kts	3,000 km endurance 12 hours	4 tons of bombs, depth charges, torpedoes	Radomes. MAD (2). Sonar buoys.	
MAIL (Amphibian) **BE 12** (Beriev)	ASW	1967	38 t	27 m	25 m	2 turboprops. AI 20 K 4,000 hp each.	310 kts at 30,000 ft 240 kts	1,300 km land version 1,000 km amphibian	Bombs, charges, mines	Radomes and MAD. Sonar buoys.	

♦ B. Helicopters

HOUND MI 4 (MIL)	ASW	1953	7.2 t	rotor diam. 21 m	17 m	1 piston engine ASH 82 V 1,700 hp.	97 kts 86 kts	230 km	1/12.7-mm machine gun, Depth charges, 4 × 16 depth charges, 57-mm rockets.	Sonar buoys and towed MAD	Land-based
HORMONE KA 25 (Kamov)	ASW	1967	7.3 t	rotor diam. 16 m	10 m	2 turboshafts. GTD 3 F 906 hp each.	120 kts 105 kts	300 km endurance 1.5 to 2 h.	Depth charges or torpedoes 1,000 kg total	Sonar buoys and dipping sonar.	Carried on board *Moskva* and *Leningrad* classes. There is a B version which is fitted with Video Data Link system.

(1) The operational radius is roughly 60% of the radius given by one-half of the range.
(2) MAD = Magnetic Anomalies Detection.

---

* 250 helicopters.

— The Backfire aircraft took part in the sea exercise "Okean 75" and the following characteristics were reported:
— Variable wing bomber
— Weight at takeoff: 129 tons
— Length: 43 m
— Wingspan: 35 m (wings extended), 28 m (wings folded)
— Speed: Mach 1.7 (max)—450/60 kts (cruising)
— Armament: 6,400 kg of bombs or missiles
— Operational action radius: 2,600 to 5,800 km according to altitude of flight
Personnel number about 65,000 men.

I — FLEET BALLISTIC MISSILE SUBMARINES

The nuclear-powered submarines are built or modified in the Severodvinsk (former Molotovsk) naval shipyards on the White Sea near Archangelsk; in the Komsomolsk-on-Amur (Far East), in the Gorki shipyards on the Volga, and at the Admiralty shipyards in Leningrad.

1) **Nuclear-powered**

♦ *At least 6 to 8 of the D or Delta class* — Bldr: Severodvinsk — 1973-7. . .

D: 9,500 surfaced/11,000 submerged tons
A: 12/SS-N-8 missiles — 533-mm TT
M: 1 reactor; steam turbines; 1 prop
Dim: 134 × 12 × 9.50
S: 25 kts

D class   1973

FLEET BALLISTIC MISSILE SUBMARINES (*continued*)

REMARKS: A super Delta with 16 SS-N-8 missiles is possibly being built. Her submerged displacement could reach 14,000 tons.

♦ *33 Y or Yankee class* — Bldr: Severodvinsk — 1967-75

Y class   U.S. Navy 1971

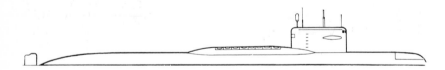

D: 7,900 surfaced/9,500 submerged tons   **Dim:** 128 × 11.50 × 9
S: 30/25 kts   **A:** 16/SS-N-6 — 6/533-mm TT (18 torpedoes or 36 mines)
M: 1 reactor; steam turbines; 2 props

♦ *1 H III or Hotel III class*

Bldr: Severodvinsk
D: 4,500 surfaced/5,500 submerged tons   **Dim:** 116 × 9 × 7
S: 25/20 kts   **A:** 6/SS-N-8 — 6/533-mm TT — 2/400-mm TT
M: 1 reactor; steam turbines; 2 props

REMARKS: Used as trial ship for SS-N-8 missiles.

♦ *8 H II or Hotel II class*
Bldr: Severodvinsk and Komsomolsk/Amur — 1960-63

H II class   M.N. 1972

H II class   M.N. 1972

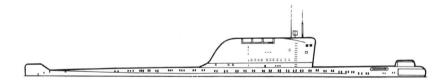

D: 4,500 surfaced/5,500 submerged tons   **Dim:** 116 × 9 × 7
S: 23/20 kts   **A:** 3/SS-N-5 — 6/533-mm TT — 2/400-mm TT
M: 1 reactor; steam turbines; 2 props

2) **Conventionally powered**

♦ *13 G II or Golf II class*
Bldr: Severodvinsk — 1958-61

FLEET BALLISTIC MISSILE SUBMARINES (*continued*)

G II class   Sov. Photo

Sail of a G II class submarine. The missiles are mounted vertically in the after portion of the sail.

D: 2,300 surfaced/2,700 submerged tons   **Dim:** 100 × 8.50 × 6.60
A: 3/SS-N-5 — 10/533-mm TT (6 fwd, 4 aft)
S: 12 kts submerged   **Range:** 9,000/5
M: diesels and electric motors; 3 props   **Endurance:** 70 days
                                           Man: 86 men

♦ *9 G I or Golf I class*

Bldr: Severodvinsk — 1958–61

Same characteristics as the G II class but the armament has 3/SS-N-4 missiles which can be surface fired only in place of the 3/SS-N-5.

II — NUCLEAR-POWERED ATTACK SUBMARINES

A) Guided cruise missiles

♦ *At least 12 C or Charlie class*
  Bldr: Gorki — 1968-7. . .

C class   1971 U.S. Navy

C class   1970 U.S. Navy

D: 4,000 surfaced/4,900 submerged tons   **Dim:** 94 × 10 × 8
S: 30/28 kts   **A:** 8/SS-N-7 — 6/533-mm TT
M: 1 reactor; steam turbines; 1 prop for slow-cruising plus 2 props for normal speeds.

Nuclear attack submarine of the C class

U.S. Navy 1974

Nuclear attack submarine of the V I class

U.S. Navy 1974

F class diesel-driven attack submarine

M.N. 1974

NUCLEAR-POWERED ATTACK SUBMARINES

♦ *25 E I or Echo II class*

Bldr: Severodvinsk and Komsomolsk/Amur — 1960-68

E II class   U.S. Navy

E II class   1968

D: 4,800 surfaced/5,800 submerged tons   **Dim:** 120 × 10 × 7.50
A: 8/SS-N-3 — 8/533-mm TT — 2/400-mm TT   **S:** 20/25 kts
M: 1 reactor, steam turbines; 2 props.

♦ *1 P or Papa class*

    D: . . .   **S:** . . .   **Dim:** . . .
    A: . . .
    M: 1 reactor; steam turbines; 2 props?

REMARKS: Does not seem to have been repeated.

B) Torpedo-launching submarines

♦ *1 or 2 A or Alfa class* — Bldr: Severodvinsk?

    D: 3,900 surfaced/4,250 submerged tons?   **Dim:** 80 × 10 × . . .
    S: . . .   **A:** torpedoes
    M: 1 reactor; steam turbines

REMARKS: Probably has advanced automation.

♦ *15/16 V I and V II or Victor I and II class* — Bldr: Leningrad — 1967-7. . .

V I class   U.S. Navy 1972

D: 4,300 surfaced/5,100 submerged tons   **Dim:** 95 × 10 × 8
A: 8/533-mm TT? — SS-N-15   **S:** 30 kts
M: 1 reactor; steam turbines; 1 prop for slow cruising plus 2 props for normal speeds.

REMARKS: The Victor II class which has been temporarily given the NATO code name of Uniform has a much more advanced hull than the Victor I.

NUCLEAR-POWERED ATTACK SUBMARINES (*continued*)

♦ *14 N or November class*

Bldr: Severodvinsk, 1959–64

N class   U.S. Navy 1970

D: 4,000 surfaced/4,800 submerged tons   **Dim:** 109 × 9 × 7.70
S: 30 kts   **A:** 8/533-mm TT — 4/400-mm TT — (32 torpedoes or mines)
M: 1 reactor; steam turbines; 2 props

♦ *5 E or Echo class* — 1960–68

E class

D: 4,600 surfaced/5,600 submerged tons   **S:** 25/20 kts   **Dim:** . . .
A: 533-mm TT
M: 1 reactor; steam turbines; 2 props

REMARKS: Former guided cruise missile submarines carrying 6/SS-N-3 missiles but converted to a torpedo launching class.

ATTACK SUBMARINES

1) Guided missile launching type

♦ *16 J or Juliett class*

Bldr: Leningrad — 1961–68

D: 2,800 surfaced/3,400 submerged tons   **Dim:** 87 × 10 × 7
S: . . ./14 kts   **A:** 44/SS-N-3 — 6/533-mm TT — 4/400-mm TT
M: diesels and electric motors; 2 props   **Man:** 80 men
Endurance: 70 days   **Range:** 9,000/7

♦ *5 Long Bin class*

Bldr: Leningrad — 1961–63

D: 1,200 surfaced/1,500 submerged tons   **Dim:** 83 × 6.10 × 5

J class   M.N. 1970

J class   M.N. 1972

"Long Bin" class   1968

A: 4/SS-N-3 — 4/533-mm TT   **S:** 13.5/8 kts
M: diesels and electric motors; 2 props
Endurance: 40 days   **Range:** 6,000/5

REMARKS: modified W class. Hull has been lengthened.

♦ *4 Twin Cylinders type.*

Bldr: Various — 1950–57.

D: 1,050 surfaced/1,350 submerged tons   **Dim:** 74 × 6.60 × 4.80.
S: 16/10 kts   **A:** 2/SS-N-3 — 6/533-mm TT (4 fwd, 2 aft)
M: diesels and electric motors; 2 props

REMARKS: Modified W class.

ATTACK SUBMARINES (*continued*)

W "Twin Cylinders"

2) Torpedo launching type

◆ *56/58 F or Foxtrot class*
  Bldr: Leningrad — 1959-7. . .

F class   M.N. 1972

F class   U.S. Navy 1972

F class   U.S. Navy 1970

REMARKS: These are apparently strongly-built submarines. Eight have been transferred to the Indian navy.

◆ *24 Z IV or Zulu class*
  Bldr: Various — 1952-57

Z class   M.N. 1969

Z IV class   M.N. 1969

D: 1,950 surfaced/2,400 submerged tons	**Dim:** 96 × 7.50 × 6
S: 18/16 kts **Endurance:** 70 days	**Range:** 9,000/7
A: 10/533-mm TT (6 fwd, 4 aft) — 22 torpedoes or 44 mines	
M: diesels and electric motors; 3 props	**Man:** Ten officers, 70 men

D: 2,000 surfaced/2,300 submerged tons	**Dim:** 90 × 7.50 × 6
S: 18/16 kts **Endurance:** 70 days	**Range:** 12,000/5
A: 10/533-mm TT (6 fwd, 4 aft) — 22 torpedoes (or 44 mines)	
M: diesels and electric motors; 3 props (?); 10,000/3,500 hp	

SUBMARINES (*continued*)

F class

M.N. 1974

♦ *8 to 10 R or Romeo class*

Bldr: Leningrad — 1960

R class

D:	1,400 surfaced/1,800 submerged tons	**Dim:**	75 × 7 × 5.40
S:	17/15 kts **Endurance:** 45 days	**Range:**	7,000/5
A:	8/533-mm TT (6 fwd, 2 aft) — 18 torpedoes (or 36 mines)		
M:	diesels and electric motors; 2 props; 4,000/2,500 hp		

♦ *4 B or Bravo class* (1970-72)

D:	2,400 surfaced/2,900 submerged tons	**Dim:**	70 × 9.70 × . . .
A:	. . .	**S:**	. . .
M:	diesels and electric motor; 1 prop; 4,000 hp		

REMARKS: Target submarines used for the training of ASW ships.

♦ *1 T or Tango class* (1973)

T class   1973

D:	1,700 surfaced/2,200 submerged tons	**Dim:**	90 × 7.50 × . . .
A:	. . . 533-mm TT	**S:**	. . .
M:	diesels and electric motors		

SUBMARINES (continued)

♦ *110/120 W IV or Whiskey class*

Bldr: Various — 1950-57

W class

D:	1,050 surfaced/1,350 submerged tons	**Dim:**	74 × 6.60 × 4.80
S:	17/16 kts	**Endurance:**	40/45 days
A:	6/533-mm TT (4 fwd, 2 aft) 14 torpedoes (or 28 mines)		
M:	diesels and electric motors; 2 props; 4,000/2,500 hp		

REMARKS: Built in prefabricated sections. Uncomplicated, strongly-built ships which have proven quite satisfactory. Twelve have been converted to guided cruise missile boats. Some of the W class have been transferred to Egypt, Poland, Albania, Communist China and Indonesia. Five have been modified as "radar picket" submarines. Most of the W class are now in reserve; the others are used for training.

W radar picket   U. S. Navy 1970

♦ *8 to 10 Q or Quebec class*

Bldr: Leningrad — 1950-57

Q class

D:	460 surfaced/540 tons	**Dim:**	57 × 5.10 × 3.80
S:	18/16 kts	**Endurance:**	30 days.
A:	4/533-mm TT (fwd) — 18 torpedoes (or 16 mines)	**Range:**	4,500/6
M:	diesels and electric motors; 2 props; 3,000/2,500 hp	**Man:**	40 men

REMARKS: Especially designed for Baltic and Black Sea operations.

GUIDED MISSILE CRUISERS

♦ *2 or 4 Kara class*

	Bldr	Laid down	L	In serv.
NIKOLAYEV	Nikolayev	1969	1971	1973
OCHAKOV	Nikolayev	. . .	. . .	1975
N . . .	Nikolayev	. . .	. . .	1977
N . . .	Nikolayev	. . .	. . .	. . .

Nikolayev   M.N. 1973

D:	9,500 to 10,000 tons (fl)	**S:**	30 kts	**Dim:**	170 × 18.80 × 7

A: 2/SS-N-10 systems (IV × 2) and 8 missiles — 2/SA-N-3 systems (II × 2) with 44 Goblet missiles — 2/SA-N-4 systems (36 missiles) — 4/76-mm AA (II × 2) — 4 Gatling type rapid fire guns — 2/MBU 2500ARL — 2/MBU 4500A RL — 10/533-mm TT (V × 2) — 1 Hormone A or B helicopter

Electron Equipt: Radars: 2 Don, 2 Owl Screech, 1 Top Sail, 1 Head Net C, 2 Headlights, 2 Pop Groups, 2 Bass Tilt

Sonars: 1 low frequency hull-mounted, 1 middle frequency towed — ECM: numerous radomes and "chaff" launchers.

M: gas turbines; 120,000 hp; 2 props   **Man:** 500 men

GUIDED MISSILE CRUISERS (*continued*)

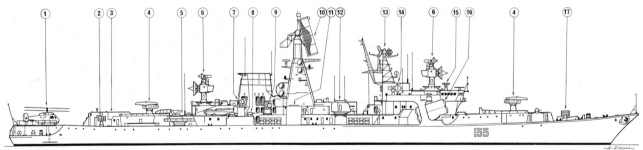

Kara class

1: Hormone — 2: MBU 4500A — 3: helicopter hangar — 4: SA-N-3 — 5: TT (V × 1) — 6: Headlights — 7: Bass Tilt — 8: Gatling-type guns — 9: Pop Group — 10: Top Sail — 11: SA-N-4 — 12: 76-mm guns (II × 1) — 13: Head Net C — 14: Owl Screech — 15: Don — 16: SS-N-10 — 17: MBU 2500A.

Scale 1/1000

Nicolayev   1973

REMARKS: This ship is based on the guided missile cruisers of the Kresta II class and the guided missile destroyers of the Krivak class.

Nicolayev   M.N. 1974

GUIDED MISSILE CRUISERS (*continued*)

Nicolayev

Nicolayev   U.S. Navy 1973

♦ *8 Kresta II class*

	Bldr	In serv.
ADMIRAL NAKHIMOV	Zhdanov (Leningrad)	1970
ADMIRAL MAKAROV	Zhdanov (Leningrad)	1971
KRONSTADT	Zhdanov (Leningrad)	1972
ADMIRAL ISAKOV	Zhdanov (Leningrad)	1973
MARSHAL VOROSHILOV	Zhdanov (Leningrad)	1973
ADMIRAL OKTYABRSKY	Zhdanov (Leningrad)	1974
ADMIRAL ISACHENKOV	Zhdanov (Leningrad)	1975
MARSHAL TIMOCHENKO	Zhdanov (Leningrad)	1976

D: 6,600 tons (fl)   **S:** 34 kts   **Dim:** 158 × 17 × 5.50 (avg)

A: 2/SS-N-10 systems (IV × 2) and 8 missiles — 2/SA-N-3 systems (II × 2) with 44 Goblet missiles — 4/57-mm AA (II × 2) — 2/MBU 2500A RL — 2/MBU 4500A RL — 10/533-mm TT (V × 2) — 1 Hormone A or B helicopter — 4/Gatling type rapid fire guns.

Electron Equipt: Radars: 2 Don Kay, 1 Top Sail, 1 Head Net C, 1 Headlight A and 1 Headlight B, 2 Muff Cob, 2 Bass Tilt

            Sonar: 1 hull-mounted middle frequency

M: GT; 4 boilers; 100,000 hp; 2 props

Range: 1,500/32 — 4,500/17   **Man:** 400 men

GUIDED MISSILE CRUISERS (*continued*)

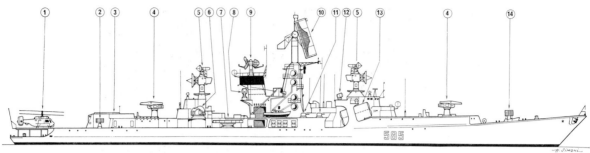

Scale 1/1000

Kresta II class
1: Hormone — 2: MBU 4500A — 3: helicopter hangar — 4: SA-N-3 — 5: Headlights — 6: 57-mm AA (II × 1) — 7: TT (V × 1) — 8: Muff Cob — 9: Head Net C — 10: Top Sail — 11: Gatling type guns — 12: Bass Tilt — 13: SS-N-10 — 14: MBU 2500A.

Admiral Isakov

M.N. 1973

GUIDED MISSILE CRUISERS (*continued*)

Admiral Isakov with Hormone helicopter   M.N. 1973

Admiral Isakov   M.N. 1973

GUIDED MISSILE CRUISERS (*continued*)

Kresta II class   M.N. 1970

Kresta II class   M.N. 1974

GUIDED MISSILE CRUISERS (*continued*)

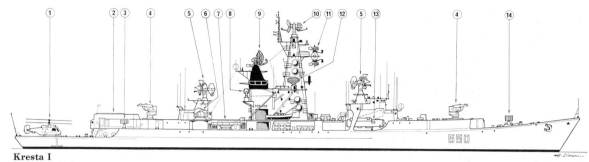

Kresta I

1: Hormone — 2: helicopter hangar — 3: MBU 4500A — 4: SA-N-1 — 5: Peel Group — 6: 57-mm AA (II × 1) — 7: TT (V × 1) — 8: Muff Cob — 9: Big Net — 10: Head Net C — 11: Scoop Pair — 12: Plinth Net — 13: SS-N-3 — 14: MBU 2500A.

Scale: 1/1000

♦ *4 Kresta I class*

	Bldr	In serv.
VICE ADMIRAL DROZD	Zhdanov (Leningrad)	1965
SEVASTOPOL	Zhdanov (Leningrad)	to
ADMIRAL ZOZULYA	Zhdanov (Leningrad)	1968
VLADIVOSTOK	Zhdanov (Leningrad)	

D: 6,300 tons (fl)   **S:** 34 kts   **Dim:** 155 × 17 × 5.50 (avg)

A: 2/SS-N-3 systems (II × 2) with 4 Shaddock missiles — 2/SA-N-1 systems (II × 2) with 44 Goa missiles — 4/57-mm AA (II × 2) — 2/MBU 2500A RL — 2/MBU 4500A RL — 10/533-mm AA (V × 2) — 1 Hormone A helicopter.

Electron Equipt: Radars: 2 Don, 1 Big Net, 1 Head Net, 2 Plinth Net,
1 Scoop Pair, 2 Peel Group, 2 Muff Cob
Sonar: 1 hull-fitted middle freq.

M: GT; 4 boilers; 10,000 hp; 2 props

Range: 1,500/32, 4,500/17   **Man:** 400 men

REMARKS: Based on the Kynda class. Better mixture of weapons. Superstructure is built around the stack. The surface-to-surface launchers are fitted on each side of the superstructure and forward under the bridge wings. Can be elevated, not trained. No Shaddock missiles in reserve.

Kresta I class

GUIDED MISSILE CRUISERS (*continued*)

Kresta I class

Kresta I class

GUIDED MISSILE CRUISERS (*continued*)

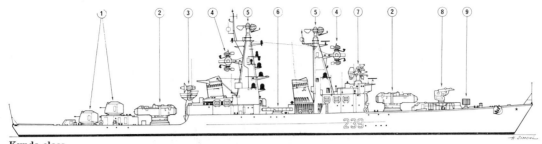

Kynda class
1: 76-mm AA (II × 1) — 2: SS-N-3 — 3: Owl Screech — 4: Scoop Pair — 5: Head Net A — 6: TT (III × 1) — 7: Peel Group — 8: SA-N-1 — 9: MBU 2500A.

Scale 1/1000

♦ *4 Kynda class*

	Bldr	Laid down	L	In serv.
ADMIRAL FOKIN	Zhdanov (Leningrad)	1957	1959	1962
ADMIRAL GOLOVKO	Zhdanov (Leningrad)	1957	1959	1962
GROZNY	Zhdanov (Leningrad)	. . .	. . .	8-62
VARIAG	Zhdanov (Leningrad)	. . .	. . .	4-61

D: 5,700 tons (fl) **S:** 34 kts **Dim:** 142 × 16 × 5 (avg)
A: 2/SS-N-3 systems (IV × 2) with 16 Shaddock missiles — 1/SA-N-1 system (II × 1) with 24 Goa missiles — 4/76-mm AA (II × 2) — 2/MBU 2500A RL — 6/533-mm TT (III × 2)
Electron Equipt: Radars: 2 Don, 2 Head Net, 2 Scoop Pair, 1 Peel Group, 1 Owl Screech
Sonar: 1 hull-mounted high frequency
M: GT; 100,000 hp; 2 props **Range:** 1,100/32 — 4,100/18 **Man:** 400 men

REMARKS: The eight reload missiles are in ready service tubes. Reloading the launchers from the handling rooms requires some time.

Grozny

1973

GUIDED MISSILE CRUISERS (*continued*)

Kynda class

Grozny

1973 J. C. Bellonne

GUIDED MISSILE CRUISERS (*continued*)

♦ *1 modified Sverdlov class*

DZERZHINSKI (1954)

Bldr: Nikolayev

In 1961 the *Dzerzhinski* was fitted with a surface-to-air SA-N-2 system (twin launcher aft) replacing the number 3 152-mm turret.

Characteristics of the hull and machinery: see *Sverdlov*.

A: 1/SA-N-2 system (II × 1) with 30 Guide Line missiles — 9/152-mm guns — 12/100-mm AA (II × 6) — 16/37-mm AA (II × 8)

Electron Equipt: Radars: 1 Neptun, 1 Low Sieve, 1 Big Net, 1 Slim Net, 1 High Lune, 1 Fan Song E, 1 Top Bow, 2 Sun Visor, 6 Egg Cup

Dzerzhinski   USN 1970

Zhdanov   M.N. 1973

COMMAND CRUISERS

Zhdanov   M.N. 1973

♦ *2 modified Sverdlov class*

	Bldr	In serv. after refit
AMIRAL SENYAVIN	Komsomolsk/Amur	1972
ZHDANOV	Nikolayev	1972

Characteristics of hull and machinery: see *Sverdlov*, with the following exceptions:

A: 6 or 9/152-mm (III × 3) — 12/100-mm AA (II × 6) — 1/SA-N-4 system — 16/37-mm AA — 8/30-mm AA (II × 4)

Electron Equipt: Radars: 2 Top Box, 1 Top Through, 2 Sun Visor, 6 Egg Cup, 2 Drum Tilt (*Zhdanov*), 4 Drum Tilt (*Senyavin*), 1 Pop Group.

REMARKS: Excellent means of long-range communications including a Vee Cone antenna, seen on the after tripod mast (photo at left). Also to be seen in this photo to the left of this mast is the hatch cover of the retracting SA-N-4 system. The 30-mm guns are divided on each side of the forward stack on the *Zhdanov* and on the after deck house on the *Senyavin*. The two after turrets on the latter ship have been removed and replaced by a helicopter hangar and platform.

COMMAND CRUISERS (*continued*)

Admiral Ushakov   M.N. 1972

♦ *9 Sverdlov class*

ADMIRAL LAZAREV   **MIKHAIL KUTUZOV** (5–56)
ADMIRAL USHAKOV   **MURMANSK**
ALEXANDER NEVSKI (6–51) **OKTAB. REVOLUTSIYA** (1958)
ALEXANDER SUVOROV   **SVERDLOV** (7–50)
DMITRI POZHARSKI 1950–1958

Bldr: Baltiski (Leningrad), Nikolayev (Black Sea), and Komsomolsk/Amur (Far East).

D: 20,000 tons (fl)   **Dim:** 210 (199.95 pp) × 21.60 × 8.50
S: 33/32 kts   **Range:** 2,200/33 — 8,400/15
A: 12/152-mm (III × 4) — 12/100-mm AA (II × 6) — 32/37-mm AA
(II × 16) — 10/533-mm TT on some of these ships. Can carry 140 mines.
Man: 70 officers, 940 men
Electron Equipt: Radars: 1 Neptun or Don, 1 Low Sieve or High Sieve, 1
Big Net on certain ships, 1 Knife Rest on others,
1 Top Through, 1 Hair Net or Slim Net, 1 Half
Bow, 2 Top Bow, 2 Sun Visor, 8 Egg Cup.

Alexander Suvorov   U.S. Navy 1970

Ok. Revolutsiya   1973

COMMAND CRUISERS (*continued*)

Zhelezniakov 1975

(*Sverdlov class, continued*)

Armor: 152-mm turret: 76/100 — Deck: 25/50 and 50/75 — 100-mm gun shields: 25

M: GT; 2 props; 6 boilers; 10,000 hp   **Fuel:** 4,000 tons

REMARKS: Based on the Chapaev class. 13 put in service from 1952 to 1958; others had been laid down but further construction, which was suspended in 1957, was completely halted in 1960. Slight differences in profile, the merging of the forward stack with the bridge structure being more or less pronounced. In 1962 the *Ordzhonikedze* was transferred to Indonesia and has since been taken off the active list. The *Sverdlov* has 2 Don, 1 Top Through, and no Egg Cup on the 100-mm turrets.

♦ *2 Chapaev class*

	Bldr	Laid down	L	In serv.
ZHELEZNIAKOV	Baltiski (Leningrad)	1946	1948	1950
KOMSOMOLETS	Baltiski (Leningrad)	1947	1949	1951

D: 15,000 tons (fl)   **S:** 34 kts   **Dim:** 201 × 18.90 × 7.30 (mean)

A: 12/152-mm (III × 4), 8/100-mm AA (II × 4), 24/37-mm AA (II × 12), 140 mines.

Electron Equipt: Radars: 1 Neptun, 1 Low Sieve, 1 Slim Net or Knife Rest, 1 Top Bow, 2 Sun Visor, 6 Egg Cup

M: GT; 90,000 hp; 2 props   **Range:** 1,200/34 — 5,400/15

Kirov

♦ *1 Kirov class*

	Bldr	Laid down	L	In serv.
KIROV	Baltiski (Leningrad)	1936	1938	1944

D: 10,000 tons (fl)   **S:** 30 kts   **Dim:** 191.50 × 17.60 × 6.30

A: 9/180-mm (III × 3) — 6/100-mm AA (I × 6) — 12/37-mm AA (II × 6) — 6/533-mm TT (III × 2) — mines

Electron Equipt: 1 Neptun or Don, 1 Hair Net, 1 Sea Gull, 1 Top Bow, 2 Sun Visor

M: GT; 113,000 hp; 2 props   **Range:** 800/29 — 4,100 15

REMARKS: Probably in poor condition. Another of the same class named the *Voroshilov* and stationed in the Black Sea has been used as an experimental ship for missile trials.

GUIDED MISSILE DESTROYERS

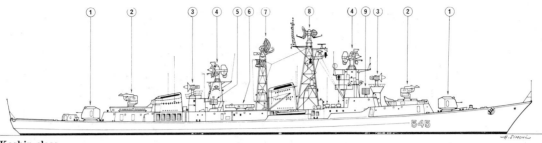

Kashin class

1: 76-mm (II × 1) — 2: SA-N-1 — 3: Owl Screech — 4: Peel Group — 5: MBU 4500A — 6: TT (V × 1) — 7: Big Net — 8: Head Net C — 9: MBU 2500A.

Scale 1/1000

♦ *14 Kashin class*

Bldr: Zhdanov, Leningrad — 1963-66

KOMSOMOLETS LETVY, OBRAZTSOVY, STEREGUSHCHY

Bldr: Nikolayev.

KOMSOMOLETS UKRAINY, KRASNY-KAVKAZ, KRASNY-KRIM, PROVORNY, SKORY, SMELY, SMETLIVY, SOOBRAZITELNY, SPOSOBNY, STOINY, STROGY

Krasnyi Kavkaz

Provorny

1973 J. C. Bellonne

D:	4,750 tons (fl)	**S:** 39 kts	**Dim:**	143 × 15.80 × 5.80 (mean)

A: 2/SA-N-1 system (II × 2) and 40 Goa missiles — 4/76-mm AA (II × 2) — 2/MBU 2500A RL — 2/MBU 4500A RL — 5/533-mm TT (V × 1) — mines

Electron Equipt: Radars: 2 Don, 2 Head Net A or 1 Head Net C and 1 Big Net, 2 Peel Group, 2 Owl Screech
Sonars: 1 hull fitted high frequency.

M: gas turbines; 94,000 hp; 2 props **Range:** 900/35 — 3,500/18

Man: 400 men

REMARKS: 4 to 8 gas turbines. The *Otvagny* of the same class was sunk 31-8-74 following an explosion which has never been explained.

GUIDED MISSILE DESTROYERS (*continued*)

Kashin class   USN 1971

GUIDED MISSILE DESTROYERS (*continued*)

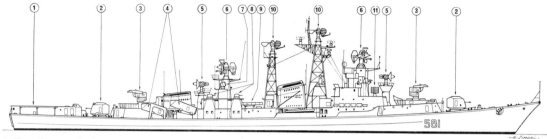

1: Towed sonar fittings — 2: 76-mm (II × 1) — 3: SA-N-1 — 4: SS-N-11 — 5: Owl Screech — 6: Peel Group — 7: Bass Tilt — 8: Gatling type guns — 9: TT (V × 1) — 10: Head Net A — 11: MBU 2500A.

♦ *4/5 modified Kashin class.*

OGNEVOY, (Zhdanov), **SLAVNY** (Zhdanov), **SDERZHANNY, SMYSLENNY** (Black Sea)

  D: 4,900 tons (fl)   **S:** 39 kts   **Dim:** 146 × 15.80 × 6

  A: 4/SS-N-11 systems (I × 4) — 2/SA-N-1 systems (II × 2) with 44 Goa missiles — 4/76-mm AA (II × 2) — 4 Gatling type guns — 5/533-mm TT (V × 1) — 2/MBU 2500A RL

  Electron Equipt: Radars: 2 Don Kay, 2 Head Net A or 1 Head Net C and 1 Big Net, 2 Peel group, 2 Owl Screech, 2 Bass Tilt.
                       Sonars: 1 towed and 1 hull-fitted, middle frequency.

  M: Like the conventional *Kashin* class.

REMARKS: It is possible that all of the conventional *Kashin* class are also modified.

Sderzhanny

M.N. 1975

Srzhannyi

GUIDED MISSILE DESTROYERS (*continued*)

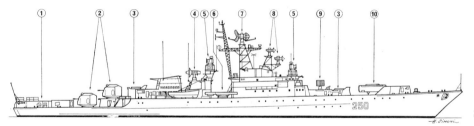

1: Towed sonar fittings — 2: 76-mm (II × 1) — 3: SA-N-4 — 4: Owl Screech — 5: Pop Group — 6: TT (IV × 1) — 7: Head Net C — 8: Eye Bowl — 9: MBU 2500A — 10: SS-N-10.

Scale 1/1000

♦ *8/10 Krivak class*

Bldr: Kaliningrad and Kamish Borun — 1970-7. . .

BDITELNY, BODRY, DOBLESTNY, DOSTOYNY, RAZUMYNI, SILNY, STOROZHEVOI, SVIREPY, N . . . , N . . .

D: 3,600 tons (fl)   **S:** 33 kts   **Dim:** 122 × 14.30 × 5 (avg)
A: 1/SSN-10 system (IV × 1) and 4 missiles — 2/SA-N-4 systems (II × 2) — 4/76-mm AA (II × 2) — 2/MBU 2500A RL — 8/533-mm TT (IV × 2) — mines
Electron Equipt: Radars: 1 Don, 1 Head Net C, 2 Eye Bowl, 2 Pop Group, 1 Owl Screech
Sonars: 1 hull-fitted and 1 middle frequency towed
M: gas turbines; 50,000 hp; 2 props   **Range:** 4,000/18   **Man:** 275 men

REMARKS: Construction rate: 2 ships per year. Extremely handsome ships of great credit to Soviet naval architecture.

Krivak class   M.N. 1971

GUIDED MISSILE DESTROYERS (*continued*)

M.N. 1973

GUIDED MISSILE DESTROYERS (*continued*)

♦ *6 Kanin class*

Bldr: Various 1958-60.

BOYKY, DZERKY, GNEVNY, GREMYASHCHYI, ZHGUCHY, ZORKY

Kanin class   1970

D: 4,500 tons (fl)   **S:** 34 kts   **Dim:** 139.50 × 14.60 × 5 (avg)
A: 1/SA-N-1 system (II × 1) and 20 Goa missiles — 8/57-mm AA (IV × 2) —
8/30-mm AA (II × 4) on some of these ships — 2/MBU 2500A RL —
10/533-mm TT (V × 2)
Electron Equipt: Radars: 2 Don, 1 Head Net C, 1 Peel Group, 1 Hawk Screech,
2 Drum Tilt on those ships with 30-mm AA guns
Sonar: 1 hull-fitted middle frequency.
M: GT; 80,000 hp; 2 props   **Range:** 1,000/30 — 4,500/18   **Man:** 350 men

REMARKS: Modified beginning in 1968 from the Krupny class. Helicopter platform.

Kanin class   1973

♦ *8 Kotlin SAM class*

BRAVY, NAKHODCHIVY, NASTOYCHIVY, NESOKRUSHIMY, SKROMNY, SKRYTNY, SOZNATELNY, VOZBUZHDENNY

Bldr: Various — 1955-57.

Bravy   U.S. Navy 1970

Kotlin SAM class   1974

Kotlin SAM class   M.N. 1971 and 1973

D: 3,500 tons (fl)   **S:** 34 kts   **Dim:** 127 × 12.75 × 4.25 (avg)
A: *Bravy:* 1 SA-N-1 system — 2/130-mm AA (II × 1) — 14/45-mm AA
(IV × 3) — 5/533-mm TT (V × 1) — 2 MBU 2500.
Standard: 1/SA-N-1 system — 2/130-mm AA (II × 1) — 4/45-mm AA
(IV × 1) — 5/533-mm TT (V × 1) — 2/MBU 2500A

GUIDED MISSILE DESTROYERS (*continued*)

Electron Equipt: Radars: 1 Don, 1 Head Net C (standard), 1 Head Net,
1 Peel Group, 1 Sun Visor, 1 Hawk Screech,
1 Egg Cup, 2 Drum Tilt
Sonar: 1 high frequency.
M: GT; 68,000 hp; 2 props   **Range:** 1,200/30 — 4,100/18

REMARKS: *Nesokrushimy, Skrytny* and *Soznatelny* have 8/30-mm AA (II × 4) as well,
with Drum Tilt fire control radar. *Nastochivy* has no Egg Cup radar.

♦ *2 Krupny class*

Bldr: Komsomolsk/Amur — 1958-61

GORDY, UPORNY

Krupny class   U.S. Navy 1971

D: 4,500 tons (fl)   **S:** 34 kts   **Dim:** 138 × 4.50 × 5 (avg)
A: 2/SS-N-1 systems (I × 2) and 20 Scrubber missiles — 16/57-mm AA
(IV × 4) — 2 MBU 2500 RL — 6/533-mm TT (III × 2)
Electron Equipt: Radars: 1 Neptun, 1 Head Net A or C, 1 Top Bow,
2 Hawk Screech
Sonar: 1 hull-fitted high frequency.
M: GT; 2 props; 80,000 hp; 3 boilers   **Man:** 360 men
Range: 1,000/30 — 4,500/18

REMARKS: Will be modified to conform to the Kanin class. The launching ramps have
a semi-cylindrical armored shelter on their after part. The entire system moves in
train and elevation. Each launcher has a magazine containing 10 missiles.

♦ *2 modified Kildin class*

BEDOVY, NEUDERZHIMY

Bldr: Zhdanov (Leningrad) and Nikolayev, 1958.

Bedovy   1974

D: 3,500 tons (fl)   **S:** 34 kts   **Dim:** 126.50 × 12.90 × 4.60 (avg)
A: 4/SS-N-11 systems (I × 4) — 4/76-mm AA (II × 2) — 16/45-mm AA
(IV × 4)
Electron Equipt: Radars: 1 Head Net C, 1 Owl Screech, 2 Hawk Screech
Sonar: 1 hull-fitted high frequency.
M: GT; 72,000 hp; 2 props   **Range:** 1,200/30 — 4,100/18

REMARKS: The *Bedovy* now has 2 Strut Curve radars attached back-to-back in place of
her Head Net C radar.

♦ *2 Kildin class*

NEULOVIMY, PROZORLIVY

Kildin class   1968

D: 3,500 tons (fl)   **S:** 34 kts   **Dim:** 126.50 × 12.90 × 4.60 (avg)
A: 1/SS-N-1 system (I × 1) and 6 Scrubber missiles — 16/45-mm AA (IV × 4)
— 2/MBU 2500 RL — 4/533-mm TT (II × 2)
Electron Equipt: Radars: 1 Slim Net or Flat Spin, 1 Top Bow, 1 Sun Visor,
2 Hawk Screech.
M: GT; 72,000 hp; 2 props   **Range:** 1,200/30 — 4,100/18

REMARKS: A modification of the Kotlin which is very similar in hull and machinery
fittings. Probably will be converted into Kildin modified class.

GUIDED MISSILE DESTROYERS (*continued*)

Kildin class 1967

CONVENTIONAL DESTROYERS

◆ *19 Kotlin class*

BESSLEDNY, BLAGORODNY, BLESTIASHCHY, BURLIVY, BYVALY, DALNEVOSTOCHNY KOMSOMOLETS, MOSKOVSKY KOMSOMOLETS, NAPORISTY, PLAMENNY, SMESHNY, SPESHNY, SPOKOYNYI, SVEDUSHCHY, SVETLY, VESKY, VLIATELNY, VOZMUSHCHENNY, VIDERZHANNY, VYZYVAAYUSHCHY.

Bldr: Leningrad and Nikolayev — 1955-57.

Svetly M.N. 1974

Kotlin class 1970

Dalnevostochny Komsomolets M.N. 1975

D:	2,850 tons (3,800 fl)
S:	35 kts **Man:** 36 officers, 300 men
A:	4/130-mm (II × 2) — 16/45-mm AA (IV × 4) — 10/533-mm TT (V × 2) — 6 depth charge projectors — 2 depth charge racks — 70 mines may be carried.
Dim:	129 × 12.80 × 4.50
Range:	1,000/32 — 4,000/18

Electron Equipt: Radars: 1 Neptun or Don, 1 Slim Net, 1 Sun Visor, 2 Hawk Screech (45-mm AA), 2 Egg Cup
        Sonar: 1 high frequency.

M: GT; 2 props; 4 boilers; 68,000 hp

Speshny M.N. 1974

REMARKS: Destroyer class which went into service during the winter of 1955-56. There are several variations in the armament: 5/533-mm TT + 2 MBU 2500 RL; 5/533- mm TT + 2 MBU 2500 RL + 2 MBU 4500 RL; a few of them have a helicopter platform aft. Others have been fitted with 4 twin 25-mm AA gun mounts.

CONVENTIONAL DESTROYERS (*continued*)

♦ *1 Tallin class*

NEUSTRASHIMY (ex-**NASTOYCHIVY**) — Bldr: Leningrad — 1953-55.

Neustrashimyi   1972

D:	4,400 tons (fl)	**Dim:**	130 × 13.40 × 5.50.
S:	38 kts **Man:** 350 men	**Range:**	1,000/32 — 4,000/18.

A: 4/130-mm AA (II × 2) — 16/45-mm AA (IV × 4) — 2 MBU 2500 RL — 10/533-mm TT (V × 2) — 80 mines.

Electron Equipt: Radars: 1 Don, 1 Slim Net, 1 Knife Rest, 1 Sun Visor, 2 Hawk Screech, 2 Egg Cup
Sonar: 1 high frequency.

M: GT; 4 boilers; 2 props; 100,000 hp. **Fuel:** 1,000 tons

REMARKS: This ship is the only one of her class; she is similar to the *Tashkent* built in Italy before the war.

♦ *20/25 Skory class*

Possible names:

BERNADEZDY	OZHESTOCHENNY	SUROVY
BESPOCHTCHADNY	OZHIVLENNY	STATNY
BESSMENNY	OSTOROZHNY	STEPENNY
BESSMERTNY	OTTCHETLZVY	STOIKY
BEZUDERZNY	OTVETSTVENNY	STREMITELNY
BEZUKORIZNENNY	SERDITY	SVOBODNY
BEZUTVETNY	SERIOZNY	VDUMCHIVY
BOUINY	SMOTRYASTCHY	VNIMATELNY
OTCHAYANNY	SOKRUSHITELNY	VRAZUMITELNY
OGNENNY	SOLIDNY	

In service: 1949-1954.

Bldr: Molotovsk and Zhdanov (Leningrad). Nikolayev (Black Sea). Komsomolsk (Far East).

D: 3,200 tons (fl) **S:** 34 kts **Dim:** 121.50 × 12.50 × 4.60

A: 4/130-mm (II × 2) — 2/85-mm AA (II × 1) — 7 (I × 7) or 8 (II × 4)/ 37-mm AA — 10/533-mm TT (V × 2) — 2 depth charge projectors — 2 depth charge racks — 50 mines.
Or on the modernized Skory class: 4/130-mm (II × 2) — 5/57-mm AA (I × 5) — 2/MBU 2500 RL — 5/533-mm TT (V × 1) — 50 mines

Man: 280 men.

Modernized Skory class

Modernized Skory class

Skory class   M.N. 1968

Electron Equipt: Radars: 1 Don, 1 Slim Net on the modernized Skory, 1 Knife Rest or Cross Bird on those not modernized — 2 Hawk Screech on the Modernized.
Sonar: 1 high frequency.

M: GT; 62,000 hp; 2 props **Range:** 1,100/34 — 4,000/18

REMARKS: Several Skory class have been transferred to Egypt and Poland.

FRIGATES

♦ *35 Riga class* — Bldr: Various — 1955-58.

Possible names: **BUIVOL, BYK, SHAKAL, GEPARD, HIENA, JAGUAR, LEOP-ARD, LEV, LISA, MEDVED, PANTERA, TIGR, VOLK, KOMSOMOLETS ASTRKHANSKY,** etc.

Riga class   1974

Riga class   M.N. 1972

D: 1,450 tons (fl)   **S:** 28 kts   **Dim:** 88 × 10 × 3.90

A: 3/100-mm AA (I × 3) — 4/37-mm AA (II × 2) — 3/533-mm TT (III × 1) — 1 hedgehog, 4 depth charge projectors, 2 depth charge racks or 2/MBU 2500 RL and 2 depth charge racks

Electron Equipt: Radars: 1 Neptun or 1 Don, 1 Slim Net, 1 Sun Visor
                Sonar: 1 high frequency

M: GT; 20,000 hp; 2 props   **Range:** 2,400/15

REMARKS: There are variations in the mounting of the rangefinder for the 100-mm gun. Some of the Riga class have been transferred to other navies (Indonesia particularly).

♦ *2 Kola class*

Bldr: Kaliningrad — 1953-57

D: 1,700 tons (fl)   **Dim:** 100 × 10.70 × 3.50
S: 27 kts   **Man:** 213 men

Kola class

A: 4/100-mm AA — 4/37-mm AA (II × 2) — 3/533-mm TT (III × 1) — 2 mouse traps — 4 depth charge projectors — 2 depth charge racks
M: GT; 24,000 hp; 2 props; 2 boilers

REMARKS: Based on the German *Elbing* class of the war. Will be stricken soon.

♦ *20 Petya I class.*

Bldr: Various — 1962-64

Petya I

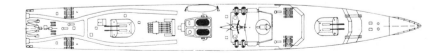

Petya I class   1973

FRIGATES (continued)

♦ *25/30 Petya II*

Profile by Siegfried Breyer.
Petya II

D: 1,100 tons (fl)   **S:** 30 kts   **Dim:** 78 × 11 × 3
A: 4/76-mm AA (II × 2) — 4/MBU 2500 RL and 5/ASW TT (V × 1) on the
Petya I — 4/76-mm AA (II × 2) — 2/MBU 2500A RL and 10/ASW TT
(V × 2) on the Petya II.
Electron Equipt: Radars: 1 Neptun or Don, 1 Slim Net or Strut Curve,
1 Hawk Screech
Sonar: 1 high frequency.
M: CODAG system: 2 gas turbines + 1 diesel — 20,000 hp — 3 props
Range: 4,000/20 (diesel) — 850/30 (diesel + gas turbine).   A few can lay mines.

Petya II class   U.S. Navy 1970

Petya II class   1974

♦ *4/6 Petya III*
REMARKS: The Petya III class has only 5 ASW TT, but has a medium frequency towed
sonar.

Petya III class   1973

♦ *20 Mirka I and II class*
Bldr: Various — 1964-66

Mirka class   M.N. 1966

Mirka class   1970

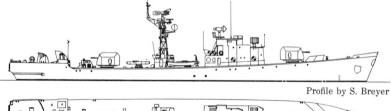

Profile by S. Breyer

FRIGATES (continued)

D: 1,100 tons (fl) **S:** 34 kts **Dim:** 82 × 9.20 × 3
A: 4/76-mm AA (II × 2) — 2 or 4/MBU 2500A RL — 5 or 10 ASW TT (V × 1 or V × 2)
Electron Equipt: Radars: 1 Don, 1 Slim Net or Strut Curve, 1 Hawk Screech
Sonar: 1 high frequency plus a dipping sonar used by the Hormone helicopter on the Mirka II class.
M: CODAG system; 2 gas turbines + 2 diesels; 20,000 hp; 2 props
Range: 4,000/20 (diesel) — 850/30 (gas turbine). **Man:** 130 men

♦ *10 or 12 Grisha class*

Bldr: Nikolayev? — 1968-7. . .

Grisha class M.N. 1971

Grisha class M.N. 1972

D: 900 tons (fl) **S:** 33 kts **Dim:** 75 × 9 × 2.80
A: 1 SA-N-4 system (18/20 missiles) — 2/57-mm AA (II × 1) — 2/MBU 2500A RL — 4/533-mm TT (II × 2) — mines

Electron Equipt: Radars: 1 Don, 1 Strut Curve, 1 Pop Group, 1 Muff Cob
Sonar: 1 medium frequency?
M: CODAG system; 2 diesels + 1 gas turbine; 24,000 hp; 3 props
Range: 450/30 — 4/000/12

♦ *2 modified Grisha class*

Modified Grisha class U.S. Navy 1974

Identical to the Grisha class but with a second 57-mm AA mount in place of the SA-N-4 system and no Pop Group radar. The armament thus consists of 4/57-mm AA (II × 2) and 2/MBU 2500A RL. They may be manned by the naval section of the KGB.

♦ *60 to 70 Poti class*

Bldr: Various — 1961-67

Poti class

D: 650 tons (fl) **S:** 34 kts **Dim:** 60.30 × 7.20 × 3
A: 2/57-mm AA (II × 1) — 2/MBU 2500A RL — 2 (I × 2) or 4 (II × 2) 533-mm TT.
Electron Equipt: Radars: 1 Don, 1 Strut Curve, 1 Muff Cob
Sonar: 1 high frequency
M: CODAG system; 2 M503A diesels (4,000 hp) + 2 gas turbines; 20,000 hp; 4 props

♦ *20 Kronstadt class* (1950-60)

D: 390 tons (fl) **S:** 18 kts (cruising) **Dim:** 51.80 × 6.70 × 2.50
A: 1/85-mm — 2/37-mm AA — mines **Range:** 3,500/14
Man: 80 men **M:** diesels; 2 props; 2,200 hp **Fuel:** 20 tons

FRIGATES (continued)

REMARKS: Certain of this class have been modified as command ships for fast small boats and other small gunboats. (See Libau class further in this section). In this case their armament is made up of 4/25-mm AA (II × 2). Further, they have no stack. Several Kronstadt class have been transferred (Poland, East Germany, Indonesia, People's Republic of China, and Albania). Many have been removed from active service in these navies.

♦ *75 to 80 SO 1 class*

Bldr: Various — 1960–64

S. Breyer

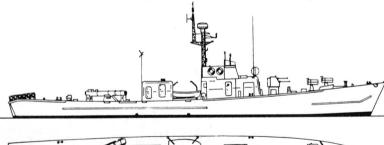

Profile Siegfried Breyer.

D: 200 tons (fl) **S:** 25 kts **Dim:** 34 × 4 × 1.80
Man: 3 officers, 27 men **M:** 3 diesels; 3 props; 6,000 hp
A: 4/25-mm AA (II × 2) — 4 ASW MBU 1800 RL — some have 2/400-mm TT to replace the 25-mm gun mount aft (see profile drawing) — 2 depth charge racks **Range:** 1 Pot Head — May be able to lay mines.

REMARKS: Several have been transferred to East Germany, North Vietnam, Algeria, and Cuba.

GUIDED MISSILE PATROL BOATS

♦ *8 to 10 Nanuchka class*

Bldr: Petrovski, Leningrad — 1969–7. . .

Nanuchka class guided missile patrol boat 1975

D: 700 tons **S:** 28 kts **Dim:** 60 × 12 × 2.50
A: 1/SA-N-4 system — 1/SS-N-9 system (6 missiles) — 2/57-mm AA (II × 1)
Electron Equipt: 1 Don, 1 Pop Group, 1 Muff Cob, 1 guidance system
M: 4 diesels; 20,000 hp; 2 props

PATROL BOATS

♦ *30 to 35 Stenka class* — Bldr: Various — 1967–7. . .

Stenka Siegfried Breyer

D: 190 tons (fl) **S:** 38 kts **Dim:** 37.50 × 8.50 × 1.80
M: 3 diesels; 3 props; 13,000 hp **A:** 4/30-mm AA (II × 2)
Radars: 1 Pot Drum, 1 Drum Tilt — 1 dipping sonar from a Hormone helicopter.

PATROL BOATS (continued)

♦ *20 to 30 MO VI class*

MO VI type patrol boat

D: 73 tons   **S:** 30 kts   **Dim:** 25.30 × 6.10 × 1.70
A: 4/25-mm AA (II × 2) — 4 depth charge projectors
Electron Equipt: 1 Pot Head
M: diesels; 4,000 hp; 4 props

REMARKS: A variation on the *P6* class torpedo boats.

♦ *20 to 25 Pchela class* — since 1964.

D: 60 tons   **S:** 50 kts   **Dim:** 27.50 × 4.20 × 1.55
A: 2/23-mm AA (II × 1)   **M:** diesels; 6,000 hp
Electron Equipt: Radar: 1 Pot Drum
            Sonar: 1 dipping sonar from a Hormone helicopter.

GUIDED MISSILE BOATS

♦ *60 to 70 Osa I class* — since 1960

Osa I class   1970

Profile Siegfried Breyer.

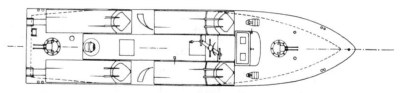

Osa I

D: 190 tons (fl)   **S:** 36 kts max.   **Dim:** 37 × 9 × 1.80
A: 4/SS-N-2 Styx — 4/30-mm AA (II × 2)
Electron Equipt: 1 Square Tie, 1 Drum Tilt
M: 3 diesels; 9,000 hp; 3 props   **Range:** 450/34, 700/20

GUIDED MISSILE BOATS (*continued*)

♦ *40 to 45 Osa II class*

Osa II class   1971

Osa II   1971

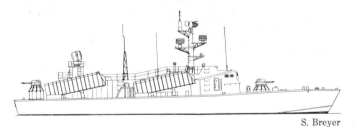

           S. Breyer

These small craft can launch their missiles in a Force 4 sea (2 m waves). Many OSA I class have been transferred to various navies. Iraq has received some OSA II. No doubt the Osa II are fitted with SS-N-2 missiles which carry an infra-red homing device.

♦ *3 to 4 Komar class* — since 1961-63.

Komar class

D:	80/110 tons (fl)	**S:** 40 kts	**Dim:**	26.80 × 6.40 × 1.85
A:	2 SS-N-2 Styx — 2/25-mm AA (II × 1)		**Man:**	20 men
M:	diesels; 4,800 hp; 4 props		**Radar:**	1 Square Tie

REMARKS: Being taken out of service in the Soviet navy.

TORPEDO BOATS

♦ *40 to 45 Shershen class* — since 1963.

Shershen class   1970

D: 190 tons (fl)	**S:** 45 kts	**Dim:** 34 × 8 × 1.50
M: 3 diesels; 3 props; 9,000 hp		**Range:** 450/34, 700/20
A: 4/533-mm torpedoes (I × 4 — 2 on each side) — 4/30-mm AA (II × 2)		
Radars: 1 Pot Drum, 1 Drum Tilt		

TORPEDO BOATS (continued)

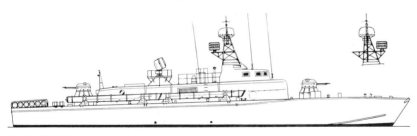

Profile Siegfried Breyer.

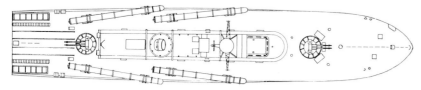

REMARKS: These are similar to the Osa class, but capable of launching torpedoes. Boats of this class have been transferred to Yugoslavia, Poland, Egypt, and East Germany.

♦ *12 to 15 Turya class semi-hydrofoils (1974)*

D: 190 tons (fl)   **S:** 50 kts   **Dim:** 34 × 8 × 1.50
A: 2/57-mm AA aft (II × 1) — 2/25-mm AA (II × 1) — 4/533-mm TT (I × 4).
Electron Equipt: Radars: 1 Pot Drum, 1 Muff Cob
             Sonar: 1 dipping sonar from a Hormone helicopter
M: 3 diesels; 3 props; 9,000 hp

REMARKS: Fitted with folding foils forward.

♦ *About 50 P 6 class*
Bldr: Various — 1953-59.

P 6 torpedo boat   1969

D: 73 tons   **S:** 34 kts   **Dim:** 25.30 × 6.10 × 1.70
A: 4/25-mm AA (II × 2) — 2/533-mm TT (I × 2) — Sometimes 2 depth charge projectors or racks.
Radars: 1 Skin Head or 1 Pot Head
M: diesels; 4,800 hp; 4 props   **Range:** 400/32 — 700/15

♦ *About 20 to 30 P 8 and P 10 class.*

P 8 torpedo boat

P 10 torpedo boat

Same characteristics as the *P 6* but with mixed propulsion (gas turbine and diesels) and folding foils on the *P 8* version.

TORPEDO BOATS (*continued*)

♦ *About 30 P 4 class* (1950).

> **D:** 30 tons (fl)　　**S:** 32 kts　　**Dim:** 16.80 × 3.73 × 1.05
> **A:** 2/14.5-mm machine guns (II × 1) — 2/450-mm TT (I × 2)

Many P 4 and P 6 class have been transferred to friendly navies.

RIVERINE FLOTILLAS

The U.S.S.R. maintains river gunboats which appear to have different missions. There are at least four classes of ships:

— ships carrying the pennant of the commandant of the flotilla (POK) with the appearance of a large, squatty yacht (L: about 20 m) with a raked bow, two bridges, a small angled mast, and a small rangefinder;

— supply ships (PS 10): flush deck hull with a high forecastle and a large superstructure (3 levels) with a small mast. Near midships a large, tall stack and just aft of the stack a small caliber gun with a shield (L: 25 m);

— shallow water minesweepers (RT 40): flush deck hull

> **D:** 70 tons　　**L:** 28　　**A:** 3/25-mm AA (II × 1 fwd, 1 aft)
> **S:** 16 kts — Winch and drum on the stern;

and especially, 75 to 80 patrol gunboats (BKL) of the Schmel class (50/60).

Schmel class　　　　　　　　　　　　　　Jurg Meister 1975

> **D:** 70/100 tons (fl)　　**S:** 20 kts　　**Dim:** 27 × 4 × 1.20
> **A:** 1/76-mm 48-cal fwd in a tank turret — 2/25-mm AA 70-cal (II × 1) aft — a multitube rocket launcher
> **M:** diesels　　**Man:** 15 men

MINESWEEPERS

♦ *20 T-38 class ocean minesweepers* (1962-64).

T 38 class　　　　　　　　　　　　　　　M.N. 1974

> **D:** 900 tons (fl)　　**S:** 18 kts　　**Dim:** 72 × 9.80 × 2.50
> **A:** 4/57-mm AA (II × 2) — 4/25-mm AA (II × 2) — 2/MBU 1800 RL — 2 depth charge racks
> **M:** diesels; 2 props; 4,000 hp

Steel hull; can be used as coastal escorts. Several others are hydrographic and salvage ships.

♦ *16 to 20 Natya-class ocean minesweepers* (1970-7. . .)

Natya class　　　　　　　　　　　　　　M.N. 1972

> **D:** 650 tons (fl)　　**S:** 18 kts　　**Dim:** 59 × . . . × . . .
> **A:** 4/30-mm AA (II × 2) — 4/25-mm AA (II × 2) — 2/MBU 1800 RL
> **Electron Equipt:** Radars: 1 Don, 1 Drum Tilt
> **M:** diesels; 2 props

♦ *40 to 45 Yurka-class ocean minesweepers* (1964-70)

> **D:** 550 tons (fl)　　**S:** 18 kts　　**Dim:** 55 × 9.70 × 2.00
> **A:** 4/30-mm AA (II × 2)　　**M:** diesel
> **Radars:** 1 Don, 1 Drum Tilt

MINESWEEPERS (*continued*)

Yurka class

M.N. 1972

♦ *4 to 6 Sonia-class ocean minesweepers* (1973)

D: . . .   **S:** . . .   **Dim:** 47 × . . . × . . .
A: 2/30-mm AA (II × 1) — 2/25-mm AA (II × 1)
Radars: . . .   **M:** diesels

♦ *80 T-43 class ocean minesweepers* (1947-61)

D: 700 tons (fl)   **S:** 17 kts   **Dim:** 60 × 9 × 2.00
A: 4/37-mm AA (II × 2) — 4/25-mm AA (II × 2)
M: diesel; 2,000 hp

Some of the T 43 class have been transferred to Poland, Egypt, Algeria, China, etc.
Certain of them are used as hydrographic ships.

♦ *70 to 80 Vanya-class coastal minesweepers* (1961-63)

D: 280 tons (fl)   **S:** 18 kts   **Dim:** 40 × 6.00 × 2
A: 2/30-mm AA   **M:** diesel; 2,200 hp

REMARKS: Wooden hull. Certain ships may be fitted out as minehunters.

♦ *5 or 6 Zhenia-class coastal minesweepers* (1972-7. . .)

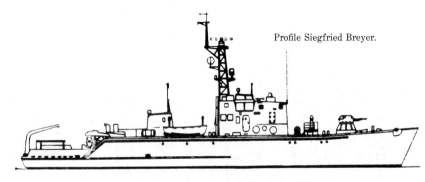

Profile Siegfried Breyer.

D: 300 tons   **S:** 18 kts   **Dim:** 42.7 × 7.6 × 1.8
A: 2/30-mm AA (II × 1)   **Radars:** 1 Spin Trough
M: 2 diesels, 1,200 hp each.

♦ *25 to 30 Sasha-class coastal minesweepers* (1957-61)
Shallow water minesweepers.

D: 180 tons (250 fl)   **S:** 18 kts   **Dim:** 45.70 × 6.50 × 2.00
A: 1/57-mm fwd — 4/25-mm AA (II × 2)
M: diesels; 2 props; 2,200 hp.

MINESWEEPERS (*continued*)

♦ *8 to 10 Evguenia-class shallow water minesweepers*

D: 80 tons   **S:** 16 kts   **Dim:** 21.7 × 5.8 × 1.2
A: 2/14.5-mm machine guns (II × 1) — Fitted for minelaying.
M: 2/600-hp diesels

♦ *4 to 6 Ilyusha-class shallow water minesweepers*

D: 70 tons   **S:** ...   **Dim:** 24.4 × 4.9 × 1.4
A: ...   **M:** ...

♦ *80 K-8 TR-40 class inshore minesweepers*

SPECIAL SHIPS

♦ *5 or 6 T 43 class picket radar ships*

T 43 class radar picket with two *Knife Rest*

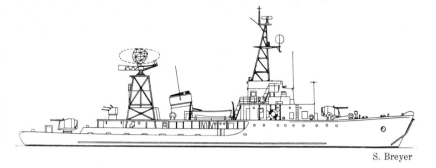

S. Breyer

These are fitted with (as is seen in the profile) an air-search Big Net radar or (as seen in the photo) two Knife Rest radars.

♦ *20 Libau class communication ships*

D: 310 tons   **S:** 18 kts   **Dim:** 51.80 × 6.70 × 1.50
A: 4/25-mm AA

REMARKS: Command ships for fast small boats.

Libau class

♦ *Several former P 6 class small craft. Used for radar targets.*

AMPHIBIOUS SHIPS

♦ *13/14 L 5 Alligator class*
Bldr: U.S.S.R. — 1964-197. . .

Alligator class   1969 M.N.

D: 4,000 tons   **S:** 18 kts   **Dim:** 114 × 15.60 × 3.70 (aft)
A: 2/57-mm AA (II × 1)   **M:** diesels; 8,000 hp
Radars: 1 Don, 1 Muff Cob on certain ships   **Range:** 6,000/16

Ramps fore and aft. Variations in armament and hoisting equipment (1 or 2 cranes

AMPHIBIOUS SHIPS (*continued*)

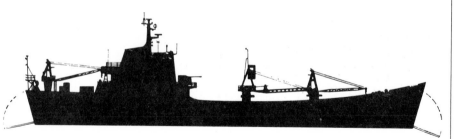

of 5 tons, 1 crane of 15 tons). Certain ships also have a rocket-launcher forward for shore bombardment and 2/25-mm AA on the after part of the ship. Some are armed with SAM missiles. 7 belong to the Army.

Alligator class 1975

Alligator class U.S. Navy 1971

♦ *6 to 8 LST Ropucha class*
  Bldr: Gdansk, Poland.

Ropucha class

A: 2,500 tons (3,500 fl)	**S:** 17 kts	**Dim:** . . .	
A: 4/57-mm AA (II × 2)		**M:** 2 diesels	
Radars: 1 Muff Cob, 1 Strut Curve, 1 Don			

♦ *60 to 65 LSM Polnocny class*

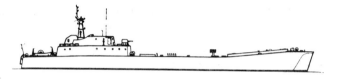

I class

D: 900 tons	**S:** 20 kts	**Dim:** 72.50 × 8.50 × 2 (fl)
A: 2/25-mm (II × 1) or 2/30-mm AA (II × 1) — 2/140-mm multiple RL (XVIII × 2)		
M: diesels		

Alligator class U.S. Navy 1971

SURFACE EFFECT SHIPS

After having experimented with several ships of this type, the Soviet navy has decided to use the following classes for landing operations: Aist, Gus, Lebed. Their characteristics are not known.

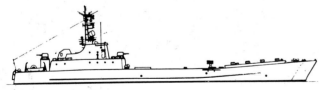

II class

D: 950 tons   **S:** 20 kts   **Dim:** $76 \times 9 \times 2$
A: 2 or 4/30-mm AA — 2/140-mm multiple RL (XVIII × 2)
M: diesels

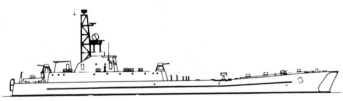

III class

D: 1,150 tons   **S:** 20 kts   **Dim:** $82 \times 10 \times 2$
A: 4/30-mm AA (II × 2) — 2/140-mm multiple RL (XVIII × 2)

Polnocny type I   1974

Polnocny type II   1974

Polnocny type III   1974

	D	S	Dim.	A
◆ *12 MP 8 class* (1958–61)	1,300	15	$74 \times 10 \times 2.70$	4/57-mm (II × 2)
◆ *6 MP 6 class* (1958–61)	2,100	10	$72 \times 12.5 \times 3.80$	4/45-mm (II × 2)
◆ *15 MP 4 class* (1957)	700	10	$56 \times 9 \times 3.50$	4/25-mm (II × 2)
◆ *6 MP 2 class* (1957)	700	15	$55.80 \times 7 \times 2.50$	6/25-mm (II × 3)

Siegfried Breyer

AMPHIBIOUS SHIPS (*continued*)

MP 8 class

Approximately 100 landing craft.

♦ *40 SMB 1 class*

SMB 1 class   Siegf. Breyer

D: 400 tons (fl)   **S:** 10 kts   **Dim:** 48.50 × 6.50 × 2
M: 2 diesels; 400 hp; 2 props
Cargo: 200 tons

♦ *60 Vydra class* (1967)

D: 475 tons (fl)   **S:** 10.5 kts   **Dim:** 50 × 7.80 × . . .
M: diesels; 500 hp; 2 props
Cargo: 4 medium tanks

LOGISTIC SUPPORT

1) SUBMARINE TENDERS

♦ *Don class* (1958-61)

MAHOMET GADZHIEV   MIKHAIL TUKACHEVSKI
DMITRI GALKIN   FEDOR VIDIAEV
VIKTOR KOTELNIKOV

Don class   1970

Don class with Veecone antenna   1974

D: 6,700 tons (9,000 fl)   **S:** 21 kts   **Dim:** 137 × 16.80 × 5.20
A: 4/100-mm AA (I × 4) — 4/57-mm AA (II × 2)   **Man:** 300 men
Radars: 1 Slim Net, 1 Sun Visor (100)
M: 4 diesels; 2 props; 14,000 hp

REMARKS: Can serve as logistic support for a flotilla of 8 to 12 submarines; on two of
them the after 100-mm has been removed and replaced with a helicopter platform.
Two or three have been fitted with a Veecone radar for long-range communication
and are used as flagships.

♦ *6/8 Ugra class* — 1963-64

BORODINO, GANGUT, IVAN KOLYSHKIN, IVAN KUCHERENKO, TOBOL,
VOLGA, N . . ., N . . .

D: 9,000 tons (fl)   **S:** 20 kts   **Dim:** 145 × 8.10 × 5.10
A: 8/57-mm AA (II × 4)

LOGISTIC SUPPORT (*continued*)

Ugra class   U.S. Navy 1971

Radars: 1 Don, 1 Strut Curve, 2 Muff Cob
M: 4 diesels; 2 props; 14,000 hp   **Range:** 10,000/12

REMARKS: Same mission as the Don class but carry special workshops for nuclear
submarines. One ship based on this class was bought by India and was named the
Amba. The *Ivan Kolyshin* has a helicopter hangar.

Ivan Kolyshin   1974

♦ *6 Atrek class*

ATREK, AYACHA, DVINA, MURMAT, N . . ., N . . .

Bldr: Germany — 1955-57

D: 3,300 tons (6,700 fl)   **S:** 13 kts   **Dim:** 103 × 14.40 × 6.60
M: 1 triple expansion engine and 1 turbine; 1 prop; 2,500 hp   **Range:** 3,500
or 4,000/13

REMARKS: Modified cargo ships. Bow reinforced against ice.

♦ *3 Tovda class:* **TOVDA, N . . ., N . . .**

Bldr: Danzig — hulls of modified coal carriers.

D: 2,600 tons   **S:** 12 kts   **Dim:** 87 × 12.40 × 5.40
A: 6/57-mm AA (II × 3)   **M:** diesels

Atrek   1970

Tovda class

♦ *2 Kuban class*

KUBAN, PECHORA — Bldr: Germany — 1939-41

D: 4,725 tons   **S:** 18 kts   **Dim:** 133 × 16 × 4.30
M: 4 diesels; 2 props — No armament.

REMARKS: No longer in service.

2) MISSILE CARGO SHIPS

♦ *5 Lama class* — 1960-63

D: 6,000 tons   **S:** 20 kts   **Dim:** 112.80 × 15 × 4.40
A: 4/45-mm AA (IV × 1) or 8/57-mm AA (IV × 2)
Radars: 1 Don, 1 Slim Net, or 1 Strut Curve, 1 or 2 Hawk Screech

Lama class

LOGISTIC SUPPORT (*continued*)

M: 2 diesels; 4,000 hp; 2 props

REMARKS: 3/20-ton cranes.

♦ *1 Amga class* — 1973

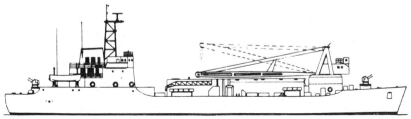

S. Breyer

D: 5,000 tons   **S:** 18 kts   **Dim:** 110 × 17 × . . .
A: 4/25-mm AA (II × 2)   **M:** diesels

REMARKS: 1/50-ton crane (boom: 34 m): can serve as a transport and install the SSN 8 missiles on the Delta-class submarines.

3) REPAIR SHIPS

♦ *5 Dniepr class* — 1960-64

D: 4,500 tons   **S:** 12 kts   **Dim:** 113.20 × 15.50 × 4.30
M: diesels; 2,000 hp

Similar to the merchant marine Neva-class repair ships.
Hoisting equipment: 1/150-ton bow hoist, 1 kingpost, 1 crane; equipment varies from ship to ship.

♦ *10 Amur class* — Bldr: Poland — 1968-7. . .

D: 6,000 tons   **S:** 18 kts   **Dim:** 115 × 16.20 × 5.20
M: diesels; 2 props   **A:** Varies   **Equip:** 2 cranes

♦ *11 Oskol class* — 1964-67 — Bldr: Poland

D: 3,000 tons (fl)   **S:** 16 kts   **Dim:** 86 × 11.50 × 4.40
A: 2/57-mm AA (II × 1) — 4/25-mm AA (II × 2) on some.

1970

1970

Radars: 1 Don, 1 Muff Cob   **Equip:** 2/3-ton cranes
M: 2 diesels; 2 props

♦ *1 Tomba class*

Bldr: Stettin, Poland

D: 3,500 tons   **S:** 18 kts   **Dim:** 100 × 14 × 5
A: . . .   **M:** diesels
Electron Equipt: Radar: 1 Don 2

REMARKS: 2 cargo masts (one very short on the forward part of the forecastle, 1 above the bridge), 2/3-ton cranes.

4) SUBMARINE RESCUE SHIPS

♦ *1 Nepa class* — **KARPATY** — 1970

D: 2,500 tons   **S:** . . .   **Dim:** 105 × 13 × 4.30
M: diesels; 2 props — Based on the *Prut* class

1971

LOGISTIC SUPPORT (*continued*)

♦ *8 to 10 Prut class*, including **ALTAI, BESHTAV, ZHIGULYI** — since 1960.

Prut class   1969

  D: 3,500 tons   **S:** 18 kts   **Dim:** 105 × 13 × 4.30
  M: diesels; 2 props

REMARKS: 1 kingpost, 2 special carriers for diving bells.

♦ *12 modified T 58 class*

Same characteristics as the *T 58* class minesweepers but with salvage equipment (diving bells, decompression chambers).

♦ *10 modified T 43 class.*

Same characteristics as the *T 43* class minesweepers but with the same equipment as the modified T 58 class.

5) FLEET REPLENISHMENT SHIPS

♦ *4 Boris Chilikin class*

Bldr: Leningrad — 1971-73

Ivan BUBNOV, Boris CHILIKIN, DNIESTR, Vladimir KOLECHITSKY

  D: 22,200 tons (fl)   **S:** 16.5 kts   **Dim:** 162.30 × 21.40 × 8.50

Boris Chilikin   M.N. 1972

  A: 4/57-mm AA (II × 2)   **Radars:** 2 Don, 1 Muff Cob
  M: diesels; 9,000 hp; 1 prop

REMARKS: 2/5-ton cranes, 1 of 3 tons, 1 replenishment-at-sea station for heavy loads with automatic tension equipment, 1 kingpost, 1 double kingpost. Carry 13,000 tons fuel oil—400 tons ammunition—400 tons victualling stores—400 tons spares.

Boris Chilikin   M.N. 1975

Boris Chilikin   M.N. 1975

6) OILERS

♦ *1 Manych class*

MANYCH — Bldr: Leningrad — 1971-72

  D: 8,600 tons   **S:** 18 kts   **Dim:** 115 × 15.50 × 7
  A: 4/57-mm AA (II × 2)
  Radars: 1 Don, 1 Strut Curve, 2 Muff Cob

REMARKS: 1 kingpost with two replenishment-at-sea stations (liquids and solids).

♦ *8 Dubna class*

DUBNA

  D: 6,022 tons (6,692 fl)   **Dim:** 102 × 20 × 9.5
  M: 1 BW diesel; 1 prop   **S:** 16 kts

REMARKS: The *Dubna* is one of 8 merchant tankers ordered from the Rauma-Repola Oy in Finland. She flies the flag of the Auxiliary Fleet and is fitted with fueling-at-sea equipment.

LOGISTIC SUPPORT (*continued*)

Manych   1972

♦ *6 to 8 Uda class* (1962-64) including **DUNAI, KOIDA, LENA, SHEKSNA, TEREK, VISHERA.**

Uda class

D: 2,500 tons (6,500 fl)   **S:** 15 kts   **Dim:** 120 × 15 × 6.
A: 6/25-mm AA (II × 3)   **M:** diesels

Only the most important of the known classes are indicated below. Most are attached to the merchant marine.

♦ *Kazbek class*

ALATYR, DESNA, ELBRUS, KASBEK, KURSK, KAUNAS, LENINGRAD, etc.

D: 10,000 tons (fl)   **S:** 14 kts   **Dim:** 145.50 × 19.20 × 8.50
Cargo: 8,229 tons   **M:** diesels; 2 props; 4,000 hp

REMARKS: Some have a replenishment station forward.

The *Desna* replenishing the cruiser *Nikolayev* and, aft, a Kashin-class destroyer 1973

Desna, a fleet oiler   1971

♦ *Altai class*

EGORLYK, ELNIA, IORA, ILIM, KOLA, PRUT, etc.

D: 6,000 tons   **S:** 14 kts   **Dim:** 106 × 15.60 × 6.50
M: 1 diesel; 2,900 hp; 1 prop

Altai class   U.S. Navy 1975

LOGISTIC SUPPORT (*continued*)

♦ *2 Pevek class*

ZOLOTO ROG, PEVEK

D: 3,330 tons   **S:** 14 kts   **Dim:** 105 × 14.80 × 6
M: diesel; 1 prop; 2,900 hp

♦ *Nercha class* (1952)

KLIASMA, NERA, N . . .

D: 1,500 tons   **S:** 11.5 kts   **Dim:** 62 × 9.90 × 4.20
M: 1 diesel; 1,000 hp

♦ *Olekma class*

OLEKMA, N . . ., N . . .

D: 5,500 tons   **Dim:** 103 × 14.70 × 6
M: 1 B & W diesel; 2,900 hp.

♦ *Neftogorsk class*

AKTASH, ALEXIN, INKERMAN, etc., etc.

D: 3,300 tons   **S:** 13.5 kts   **Dim:** 105.10 × 14.8 × 6.8
M: 1 diesel; 2,900 hp.

♦ *4 Konda class* **IAKHROMA, KONDA, NARA, NERTCHA**

D: 1,178 tons   **M:** 1,100 hp   **S:** 13 kts   **Dim:** 69 × 10 × 4.20

♦ *1 Polyarnik class*

POLYARNIK (1945).

D: 5,600 tons   **S:** 17 kts   **Dim:** 132 × 16.15 × 6.10
M: 2 Werkspoor diesels

♦ *20 Khobi class* (1957-59) including **ALAZAN, GORYN, INDIGA, KHOBI, LINDA, LOVAT, SASHA, SEIMA, SHELON, TITAN,** etc.

D: 795 tons   **S:** 10   **Dim:** 68 × 10 × 4.50

7) WATER AND FUEL BARGES

♦ *2 to 4 Toplevo class*

D: 423 tons   **Cargo:** 500 tons   **Dim:** 52.90 × 9.50 × . . .

♦ *8 to 10 Luza class* including **BARGORIN, ENISSEI, SELENGA**

D: 1,500 tons (fl)   **Dim:** 62 × 10 × 4.50

Voda class   1972

♦ *10 to 15 Voda class*

D: 2,615 tons (fl)   **Cargo:** 3,100 tons   **Dim:** 82 × 11.70 × 4.40

8) BOOM VESSELS

♦ *2 Alesha class* — 1967-1969

Alesha class   1969

D: 3,500 tons   **S:** . . .   **Dim:** 107 × 13 × 5
A: 2/57-mm AA fwd (II × 1)   **Man:** . . . men
Radars: 1 Don, 1 Strut Curve, 1 Muff Cob
M: diesel
Minelaying potential.

♦ *4 or 5 Sura class*

D: 3,150 tons   **S:** 12 kts   **Dim:** 80.80 × 14.80 × 5
M: Diesel-electric propulsion; 2,250 hp

LOGISTIC SUPPORT (*continued*)

Profile S. Breyer.

Alesha class

Sura class

♦ *10 to 12 Neptun class* — Bldr: Germany — 1957-60

D: 700 tons   **S:** 12 kts   **Dim:** 52 × 11 × 3.80
M: 2 triple expansion

Neptun class

9) CABLE LAYERS

♦ *3 or 4 Kalar class*

D: 2,600 tons   **S:** 11 kts   **Dim:** 87 × 12.30 × 5.40
M: diesel; 1 prop; 1,100 hp

♦ *5 or 6 Kliazma class* (1962) including **DUNETS, IANA, INGUL, KATUN, ZEYA**

D: 6,200 tons (fl)   **S:** 14 kts   **Dim:** 130.50 × 16 × 5
M: diesels? — 5,000 hp.

10) FLEET OCEAN TUGS

♦ *4 Pamir class*

AGATAN, ALDAN, GUIDOGRAPH*, PELENG*. Bldr: Gävle Varv (Sweden) — 1958

D: 1,443 tons   **S:** 17 kts   **Dim:** 72.65 (66.90 pp) × 11.64 × 3.70.
M: M.A.N. 4-t diesels; 2 KaMeWa variable pitch props; 4,200 hp

LOGISTIC SUPPORT (*continued*)

One 10-ton cargo mast, 2 of 1.5 tons, excellent pumping facilities and fire fighting equipment. Several diving stations (equipment for 90 m dives). Decompression chambers. Can furnish compressed air and AC or DC electric current to other ships. *Fitted as intelligence collectors.

♦ *Okhtenshiy class* — 1959-59

D: 1,000 tons (fl)   **S:** 12 kts   **Dim:** 46.50 × 9.50 × 3.90
M: diesel; 2,000 hp; 2 props

♦ *1 Ingul class*

D: 3,600/3,700 tons   **S:** 15 kts   **Dim:** 90 × 15 × 5.5

♦ *Stereggushchy or Orel class* — 1957-59

D: 1,800 tons (fl)   **S:** 14 kts   **Dim:** 61.60 × 11.60 × 4.50
M: diesel; 1,800 hp; 2 props

INTELLIGENCE COLLECTOR SHIPS

The Soviets man many ships, often designated ELINT (Electrical Intelligence) or SIGINT (Signal Intelligence) trawlers, which have merely the appearance of trawlers. They carry out detection and analysis of radio-electric and electro-magnetic signals. Some patrol the offshore stations of strategic submarines; others follow the Western fleets. Only the most important of these ships are mentioned below.

♦ *6 Primorye class*

including **KAVKAZ, KRYM, PRIMORYE, ZAKARPATYE, ZAPOROZYE, ZABAIKALYE**

D: 3,000 tons   **S:** ...   **Dim:** ...
M: diesel

REMARKS: Has the appearance of a small passenger ship or liner. Ships built and designed for ELINT missions.

Primorie

♦ *2 Sekstan class*

GALS, VIZIR, former trawlers.

D: 370 tons   **S:** 10 kts   **Dim:** 40.50 × 7 × 3.50
M: diesel

♦ *8 to 10 Lentra class*

including **BUJ, GUIROSKOP,** small trawlers.

D: 250 tons   **S:** 9 kts   **M:** diesel; 300 hp

REMARKS: Several are used as hydrographic ships.

INTELLIGENCE COLLECTOR SHIPS (*continued*)

U.S. Navy 1970

♦ *4 Mirnyi class*

BAKAN, LOTSMAN, VAL, VERTIKAL, former whaling ships.

Mirnyi class

M.N. 1972

D: 850 tons   **S:** 16 kts   **Dim:** 63.60 × 9.50 × 4.20
M: diesel; 1 prop

♦ *10 to 12 Mayak class.*

including **ANEROID, GUIRORULEVOI, KURS, KURSOGRAF, LADOGA, MAYAK.**
trawler class.

Mayak class

D: 700 tons   **S:** 12 kts   **Dim:** 54.20 × 9.30 × 3.55
M: diesel

♦ *15 to 16 Okean class including:*

ALIDADA	**DEFLEKTOR**	**LINZA**	**TEODOLIT**
AMPERMETR	**EKHOLOT**	**LOTLIN**	**TRAVERZ**
BAROGRAF	**GIDROFON**	**REDUKTOR**	**ZOND**
BAROMETR	**KRENOMETR**	**REPITER**	(since 1958)

trawler class.

Alidada

D: 700 tons   **S:** 12 kts   **Dim:** 50.80 × 8.80 × 3.40
M: diesel; 1 prop; 700 hp

HYDROGRAPHIC AND OCEANOGRAPHIC SHIPS

The Soviets have concentrated on numerous oceanographic and hydrographic research projects on oceans worldwide. The Soviet Navy has in its own right more than sixty hydrographic and oceanographic ships. On the other hand the Academy of Sciences has a large number of such ships of this category which, it is believed, work for the navy. Listed here are only the better known ships.

HYDROGRAPHIC AND OCEANOGRAPHIC SHIPS (*continued*)

♦ *11 Nikolai Zubov class*

Nikolai ZUBOV	Taddei BELLINGSHAUSEN*	Semen DEZHNEV
Gavril SARITSHEV*	Andrei VILKITSKI	Vladimir OBRUCHEV
Fedor LITKE	Basili GOLOVNIN	Khariton LAPTEV
Aleksei CHIRIKOV	Boris DAVIDOV	

Bldr: Poland 1963-68

Gavril Saritshev　　　　　　　　　　　　　　　　U.S. Navy 1970

♦ *4 Abkhasia class*

ABKHAZIA	**BASHKIRIA**
ADJARIA	**MOLDAVIA**

　D: 5,600 tons　　**S:** 18 kts　　**Dim:** 124.2 × 17 × 6.1
　M: 2 M.A.N. diesels; 2 props

　D: 3,020 tons　　**S:** 18.5 kts　　**Dim:** 87.50 × 13 × 4.60
　M: diesel; 4,800 hp　　　　　　　**Man:** 108/120 men

REMARKS: *Used as intelligence collectors. These ships are fitted with a platform and
hangar for a helicopter.

♦ *7 Akademik Kurchatov class*

AKADEMIK KOROLEV (1967)	**AKADEMIK KURCHATOV** (1965)
AKADEMIK SHIRSHOV (1967)	**AKADEMIK VERNADSKI** (1967)
DMITRI MENDELEYEV (1968)	**PROFESSOR ZUBOV** (1967)
PROFESSOR VIZE (1967)	

Bldr: Thesen Werft (East Germany)

　D: 5,460 tons　　**S:** 19 kts　　**Dim:** 123.50 × 17 × . . .
　M: 6-cyl. Halberstadt diesels; 2 props; 8,000 hp
　Range: 20,000

Akademik Vernadsky　　　　　　　　　　　　　　1971 Maurice Lucas

♦ *3 Andijan (or Polyus) class*

BAIKAL, BALKHASH, POLYUS

　Bldr: East Germany — 1962-64

　D: 6,900 tons　　**S:** 16 kts　　**Dim:** 111.50 × 14.40 × 8
　M: diesel-electric propulsion; 4,000 hp

♦ *1 Vitiaz class*

VITIAZ

　D: 5,700 tons　　**S:** 14.5 kts　　**Dim:** . . .
　M: diesels; 3,000 hp　　　　　　　**Range:** 18,400/14

♦ *14 to 18 Samara class*

**AZIMUT, DEVIATOR, GLOBUS, GLUBOMETR, GORIZONT, GRADUS,
GIDROLOG, GIGROMETR, YUG, KOMPAS, PAMIAT MERKURIA, TROPIK,
ZENIT**

　Bldr: Poland 1962-64.

　D: 1,200 tons (fl)　　**S:** 18 kts　　**Dim:** 60 × 10.80 × 4.40
　M: diesels; 3,000 hp; 2 variable pitch props

HYDROGRAPHIC AND OCEANOGRAPHIC SHIPS (continued)

◆ 25 to 30 Moma class

including **ALTAIR, ANADYR, BEREZAN, ELTON, PELORUS, CHELEKEN, EKVATOR, SEVER, ANDROMEDA, LIMAN, KOLGUEV, N . . .**

Seliger   M.N. 1973

   D: 1,475 tons (fl)   **S:** 16 kts   **Dim:** 67 × 10.80 × 4.00
   M: diesel; 2 props

REMARKS: Some are intelligence collectors.

◆ 4 to 6 Magnit class

BRIZ, MAGNIT, REOSTAT, N . . ., N . . .
   D: . . .   **S:** . . .   **Dim:** . . .
   M: diesel;

◆ 2 ex Z V class submarines

LIRA   **VEGA**

Lyra   1972

   D: 1,900/2,300 tons   **S:** 18/15 kts   **Dim:** 90 × 8 × 5.60
   M: diesels and electric motor; 10,000/3,500 hp; 3 props

REMARKS: Former ballistic guided missile submarines modified as hydrographic ships. Armament removed.

◆ 4 to 5 Telnovsk class

AITADOR, SIRENA SVIAGA
   D: 1,215 tons   **S:** 10 kts   **Dim:** 68.7 × 9.80 × 3.5

◆ 18 to 20 ex-T 43 class minesweepers

SHIPS FOR THE CONTROL OF EXPERIMENTAL MISSILES AND SATELLITES

◆ 1 Kosmonaut Yuri Gagarin class

KOSMONAUT YURI GAGARIN (1971)

Kosmonaut Yuri Gagarin   1975

   D: 45,000 tons (fl)   **S:** 18 kts   **Dim:** 235.60 × 31.10 × . . .
   M: 2 GT; 2 props; 20,000 hp

◆ 1 Komarov class

Kosmonaut Vladimir KOMAROV (1967-68)

Kosmonaut Vladimir Komarov   1968

   D: 17,500 tons (fl)   **S:** 22 kts   **Dim:** 155.70 × 20.60 × 9.10
   M: diesels; 2 props; 24,000 hp

◆ 2 Desna class

CHAZMA   **CHUMIKAN** (1963)
   D: 14,065 tons (fl)   **S:** 14 kts   **Dim:** 153 × 20 × 8.50
   Radars: 2 Don, 1 Head Net B.
   M: triple expansion; 4,000 hp

MISSILE AND SATELLITE TRACKING SHIPS *(continued)*

REMARKS: Veecone antennae and telemetering equipment.

♦ *8 Vytegrales class*

APSHERON, BASKUNSHAK, DIKSON, DAURIYA, DONBASS, SEVAN, TAMAN, YAMAL (1966).

Baskunchak class   M.N. 1972

D: 9,650 tons (fl)   **S:** 15 kts   **Dim:** 120.70 × 16.70 × 7.30
M: 1 diesel; 5,000 hp; 1 prop; 1 helicopter

♦ *4 Sibir class*

SAKHALIN, SIBIR, SPASSKI, CHUKOTKA (in service since 1956).

D: 3,800 tons (fl)   **S:** 12.5 kts   **Dim:** 181 × 24.60 × 6.65
Radars: 1 Neptun, 1 Big Net   **M:** Steam, 2,500 hp; 1 prop

REMARKS: Fitted with a great deal of telemetering equipment.

Sibir

♦ *1 Akademik Sergei Korolev class*

AKADEMIK SERGEI KOROLEV (1971)
D: 21,500 tons (fl)   **S:** 17 kts   **Dim:** 182 × 25 × 8
M: diesel; 12,000 hp

SCIENTIFIC SHIPS

♦ *7 Morzhovets class*

including **BOROVITCHYI, BEZHITSA DOLINSK, KEGOSTROV, MORZHO-VETS, NEVEL** (since 1966).

Nevel   1972

D: 9,000 tons   **S:** 15 kts   **Dim:** 120.70 × 16.70 × 7.30
Radars: 2 Don   **M:** 1 diesel; 5,200 hp; 1 prop

REMARKS: Veecone antennae plus telemetering equipment.

SCIENTIFIC SHIPS (*continued*)

♦ *10 to 12 Passat class*

E. KRENKEL, MUSSON, OKEAN, PASSAT, PRIBOY, PORIV, PRILIV, VOLNA, N . . ., N . . . (1967).

E. Krenkel   1974

D:	7,000 tons (fl)	**S:**	14 kts	**Dim:**	97 × 13.90 × 5
Radars:	2 Don	**M:**			2 8-cyl. Sulzer diesels; 4,800 hp; 2 props

REMARKS: Veecone Antennae.

♦ *2 Lebedev class*

PETR LEBEDEV   **SERGEI VAVILOV**

D:	3,561 tons	**S:**	. . .	**Dim:**	. . . × . . . × . . .
M:	diesels				

♦ *1 Povonets class*

RISTNA

D:	4,200 tons (fl) — 3,724 grt	**Dim:**	114.40 × 14.40 × 4.20
M:	6-cyl. M.A.N. diesels	**S:**	15 kts

REMARKS: Former cargo ship.

ICEBREAKERS

The majority of the ships of this class are based on the *Yermak*, the first large icebreaker built by the Russian navy from the plans of Admiral Makarov (1898) and removed from active service in 1968. Among the ships of this class are the *Lenin* and the *Arktika*, both with nuclear propulsion, and the three *Moskva*-class with diesel-electric propulsion, all of them the newest and most powerful ships with this mission.

Although these ships do operate with the fleet, they are not really a part of the navy; they are under the control of the Northern Sea Route administration in the Arctic Ocean.

It should be noted that the *Arktika* has excellent communication facilities including a Veecone antenna.

The following ships are manned by the navy:

PURGA

Purga

D:	3,000 tons	**S:**	18 kts	**Dim:**	99 × 12.20 × 5.20
A:	4/100-mm — 8/37-mm AA (II × 4)			**M:**	diesels; 2 props; 6,500 hp

IVAN SUSANIN

Ivan Susanin   1975

D:	3,200 tons	**S:**	14.5 kts	**Dim:**	67.6 × 18.1 × 5.5
A:	2/76-mm AA (II × 2) — 2 Gatling gun systems				

Electron Equipt: Radars: 2 Don Kay, 1 Strut Curve, 1 Owl Screech, 2 Bass Tilt.

PERSONNEL: Active duty personnel as provided in successive budgets since 1-7-72:

	1-7-72	1-7-74	1-7-75	1-7-76 (planned)
Navy	588,100	545,900	536,200 (1)	528,700 (3)
Marine Corps	198,200	188,800	196,400 (2)	196,300 (4)
Total	786,300	734,700	732,600	725,000

(1) 65,900 officers (3) 64,400 officers
(2) 18,600 officers (4) 18,600 officers

On 1-7-76 the number of personnel in the Naval Reserve will rise to 434,800. They are divided as follows: Extended Active Duty: 56,300 — Ready Reserve: 215,000 — Other categories: 178,000. The Marine Corps Reserve will reach 135,600 with 69,100 on Extended Active Duty.

NAVAL PROGRAM.

Projects approved under the 1974-75 budget include:

♦ *New construction:* 2 *Trident* SSBN; 2 *Los Angeles* SSN; 7 *Spruance*-class destroyers; 1 CGN-41 nuclear-powered cruiser; 3 FFG (former Patrol Frigates); 4 PHM; 1 ATF tug. Rejected by Congress: the prototype of the Sea Control Ships, a destroyer tender (AD-41), an oiler (AO-166), and 4 FFG.
Congress has not voted for FY 1975-76 the money requested for construction of the CGN-42 and has reduced the number of FFGs authorized from 10 to 9. It has further refused the 60 million dollars requested by the Navy for study of the CSGN cruiser.

♦ *Conversions:* continuation of the *Poseidon* refit on the *Lafayette* class SSBNs.

Projects approved under the 1975-76 budget:
♦ *New construction:* 1 *Trident* SSBN, 2 *Los Angeles* SSN, 9 FFG, 2 PHM, 2 AD (41, 42), 2 AO (166 and 167), 1 ATF tug.

♦ *Naval aircraft:* 24 A-4M Skyhawk, 12 A-6E Intruder, 6 EA-6B Prowler, 30 A-7E Corsair II, 6 E-2C Hawkeye, 41 S-3A Viking, 12 P-3C Orion, 36 F-14A Tomcat, 16 AH-1J Sea Cobra, 24 UH-1N Iroquois.

MERCHANT MARINE (1-7-74) — 4,086 ships — 14,429,076 grt — (Tankers 314 ships — 4,882,598 grt). It should be remembered that ships flying flags of convenience (Liberia, Panama, etc.) carry a great deal of cargo and many are owned by American companies.

ACTIVE FLEET STATISTICS

	1974-75	1975-76
Strategic naval forces:		
SSBN	41	41
General purpose forces:		
Aircraft carriers (CVN, CV)	14	13
Cruisers (CG, CGN, CA)	9	27
Destroyer Leaders (DLGN, DLG, DL)	29	0
Guided missile destroyers (DDG)	29	39
Destroyers (DD)	32	29
Destroyer escorts (now *frigates*) (FF, FFG)	68	64
Nuclear-powered attack submarines (SSN)	64	68
Conventionally-powered submarines (SS)	12	12
Patrol boats	14	13
Amphibious Warfare Ships:		
Amphibious Command ships (LCC)	2	2
Amphibious Transports dock (LPD)	14	14
Amphibious Assault Ships (LPH)	7	7
Tank Landing Ships (LST)	20	20
Other amphibious ships (LKA, LPA, LSD)	21	18
Mine Warfare Ships:	3	3
Logistic supply and auxiliary:	129	117

In general, roughly half of these ships are in the Pacific (Third and Seventh Fleets) and half in the Atlantic (Second and Sixth Fleets). Only the Seventh and the Sixth Fleets — the latter assigned to the Mediterranean — are fully operational. The table does not include units assigned to Naval Reserve training.

MARINE CORPS:

Created in 1775, the Marine Corps gives the U.S. Navy a distinctive quality of its own. Its three assigned missions are the following:

— to seize and/or defend advanced bases necessary for the operation of the fleet;
— to furnish security detachments on board ships and land bases;
— to carry out any other operations that the President of the United States may assign. This third category permits the use of the Corps outside purely naval operations (e.g., Belleau Wood in 1918, Vietnam).

Its total strength is about 196,000 men divided into three divisions (1 stationed in Okinawa/Japan and 2 in the United States, each of 18,000 men), 3 Marine Air Wings, and 2 Force Troops. This last group makes up the heavy support elements of the divisions. There also is a "reserve cadre" division, the fourth.

The Marine Corps has approximately 400 fighter and attack aircraft (A-4M, A-6, AV-8, F-14, F-4) and 600 assault and utility helicopters, 400 tanks, 120 heavy guns and some 450 amphibious landing vehicles.

In both the Atlantic and Pacific theaters the principal organizational unit is called the Marine Amphibious Force (MAF).

The MAF is made up of:
— a Marine Division;
— a Marine Air Wing;
— Force Troops;
which total about 45,000 men.

The amphibious ships presently in service do not permit the rapid overseas deployment of these MAF but only two Marine Amphibious Brigades in both the Atlantic and Pacific theaters. An MAB is made up of:
— 1 Regimental Landing Team, a strong unit with 2 to 6 battalions of about 6,000 men;
— 1 Marine Air Group made up of fighter, attack and/or helicopter squadrons;
— some elements of the Force Troops.

When the *Tarawa* class LHA joins the *Newport* class of LSTs, the Marines hope to be able to make up, once again, three reduced Marine Amphibious Forces (18,000 men and 330 aircraft) which can be shipped overseas quickly at an average speed of 20 knots.

One of these MAF groups will be based in the United States, a second divided among ships in the Atlantic, the Mediterranean, and the Caribbean area, while the third will remain in forward deployment in the Western Pacific.

Thus between three and five battalions will always be at sea, on board the LST, LPH, and LHA class ships in 3 or 4 Task Forces and ready to intervene rapidly in case of necessity.

WARSHIPS IN SERVICE, UNDER CONSTRUCTION OR PROJECTED AS OF 1 OCTOBER 1975

N: nuclear propulsion

AIRCRAFT CARRIERS

(a) *17 attack carriers (CVN, CV)*

	L	D	Main armament
3 NIMITZ	1971-77	77,400	70/90 aircraft 3 missile-launchers
1 ENTERPRISE	1960	75,700	70/90 aircraft 2 missile-launchers
2 AMERICA/KENNEDY	1964-67	61,000	70/90 aircraft 2 or 3 missile-launchers
2 KITTY HAWK	1956-57	60,100	70/90 aircraft 4 missile-launchers
3 SARATOGA	1952-55	60,000	70/90 aircraft 2/127-mm or 3 ML
1 FORRESTAL	1952	59,650	70/90 aircraft 3 ML
3 MIDWAY	1945-46	51,000	60/75 aircraft 3/127-mm AA

(b) *4 antisubmarine aircraft carriers (CVS)*
(c) *12 helicopter carrier and amphibious assault ships (LHA and LPH)*

5 TARAWA (LHA)	1972-73	39,900 fl	3/127-mm AA — 2 ML-30 helicopters
7 IWO JIMA (LPH)	1960-69	17,000	4/76-mm — 2 missile-launchers — 20 heavy helicopters

CRUISERS

(a) *guided missile nuclear propulsion (CGN)*

1 LONG BEACH	1959	14,200	3 missile-launchers — 2/127-mm
4 VIRGINIA	1974-77	11,000 fl	2 missile-launchers — 2/127-mm
2 CALIFORNIA	1971-72	10,150 fl	2 missile-launchers — 2/127-mm
1 TRUXTUN	1964	8,250	1 missile-launcher — 1/127-mm
1 BAINBRIDGE	1961	7,850	2 missile-launchers — 4/76-mm

(b) *guided missile (CG)*

2 ALBANY	1944-45	13,700	4 missile-launchers — 2/127-mm
2 GALVESTON	1944-45	10,670	1 missile-launcher — 3/152-mm
9 BELKNAP	1963-65	6,570	1 missile-launcher — 1/127-mm
9 LEAHY	1961-62	5,670	2 missile-launchers — 4/76-mm

DESTROYERS (DDG and DD), FRIGATES (FF, FFG)

♦ In this category, the letter G indicates that the armament includes one or several missile-launchers.
⁰*: Asroc system included in the armament.

DESTROYERS (DDG and DD), FRIGATES (FF, FFG) (continued)

♦ H: hangar and platform for ASW helicopters, but helicopters are not necessarily carried at all times.

Main armament only for destroyers

(1) *Destroyers (DDG and DD)*.

		L	D	
10	COONTZ (DDG)	1958-60	4,700	1 missile-launcher — 1/127-mm — 0*
23	CHARLES F. ADAMS (DDG)	1959-63	3,370	1 missile-launcher — 2/127-mm — 0*
2	MITSCHER (DDG)	1952	3,680	1 missile-launcher — 2/127-mm — 0*
4	DECATUR (DDG)	1955-58	2,850	1 missile-launcher — 1/127-mm — 0*
8	BARRY (DD ASM)	1955-58	2,850	2/127-mm — 0*
6	FORREST SHERMAN (DD)	1955-58	2,780	3/127-mm — ASW weapons
45	GEARING (DD Fram I)	1944-46	2,400	4/127-mm — 0*
2	CARPENTER (DD Fram I)	1945-46	2,400	2/127-mm — 0*
30	SPRUANCE (DD) H	1974-78	7,800 (fl)	1 missile-launcher — 2 127-mm — 0*

(2) *Frigates (FFG and FF)*

		L	D	
1	GLOVER (AGFF)	1965	2,650	1/127-mm — 0*
6	BROOKE (FFG) H	1963-66	2,643	1 missile-launcher — 1/127-mm — 0*
10	GARCIA (FF) H	1963-65	2,624	2/127-mm — 0*
46	KNOX (FF) H	1966-73	3,011	1 missile-launcher — 1/127-mm — 0*
2	BRONSTEIN (FF)	1962	1,640	2/76-mm AA — 0*
15	FFG (ex-PF) H	1976	3,400	1-missile-launcher — 1/76-mm — 0* ASW weapons

SUBMARINES (* have "tear drop" hulls and a single propeller).

(1) *nuclear propulsion*

		L	D	Main armament
4	SSBN*	1977-8.	12,000	24 Trident 1
31	SSBN LAFAYETTE*	1962-66	7,320	16 Polaris or Poseidon, 4/TT
5	SSBN ETHAN ALLEN*	1960-62	6,900	16 Polaris, 4/TT
5	SSBN GEORGE WASHINGTON*	1959-60	5,900	16 Polaris, 6/TT
29	SSN LOS ANGELES*	1973-80	6,900†	TT (Subroc) (a)
1	SSN GLENARD P. LIPSCOMB*	1973	5,800	TT
1	SSN NARWHAL*	1967	4,650	4/TT (Subroc) (a)
37	SSN STURGEON*	1966-73	3,836	4/TT (Subroc) (a)
13	SSN THRESHER/PERMIT*	1961-66	3,526	4/TT (Subroc) (a)

5	SSN SKIPJACK*	1958-60	3,075	6/TT
1	SSN HALIBUT	1959	3,850	4/TT
1	SSN TULLIBEE*	1960	2,317	4/TT
4	SSN SKATE	1957-58	2,570	6/TT
1	SSN SEAWOLF	1955	3,721	6/TT
1	SSN NAUTILUS	1954	3,532	6/TT

(a) Can also launch conventional 533-mm torpedoes.

(2) *diesel-electric propulsion on surface*

3	SS BARBEL	1959-58	2,150	6/TT
1	SS DARTER	1956	1,870	8/TT
2	SS SAILFISH	1955-56	2,485	6/TT
4	SS TANG	1951-52	2,100	8/TT
1	LPSS GRAYBACK (b)	1957	2,174	4/TT

(b) amphibious transport submarine.

(3) *auxiliary submarines (trials, target, etc.)*

1	AGSS DOLPHIN*	1968	800	. . .

Several small submarines (DSRV) and other craft for deep depth research and salvage.

WEAPONS AND SYSTEMS OF THE U.S. NAVY

FLEET BALLISTIC MISSILE WEAPON SYSTEMS

All are launched from submerged submarines

♦ **Polaris A2 (UGM 27B A2).** — **Length:** 9.340 m. **Diam.:** 1.370 m. **Weight:** 14,500 kg at launch. **Propulsion:** solid propellant grains, two stages. **Inertial guidance. Warhead:** 800 kt. **Range:** 1,500 miles.

♦ **Polaris A3 (UGM 27C A3).** — **Length:** 9.520 m. **Diam.:** 1.370 m. **Weight:** 15,860 kg at launch. **Propulsion:** solid propellant grains, two stages. **Inertial guidance:** (same precision as the Polaris A2 but at a longer range). **Range:** 2,500 miles. **Warhead:** 1 MT or 3 independent but not individually controllable (MRV) of 200 KT each.

♦ **Poseidon.** — **Length:** 10.400 m. **Diam.:** 1.830 m. **Weight:** about 30 tons at launch. **Propulsion:** solid propellant grains, two stages. **Inertial guidance. Range:** 2,500 miles. **Warhead:** 10 warheads with independent and controllable trajectory, each of 50 KT (MIRV).

♦ **Trident 1.** — New type missile, operational in 1978 and designed for a new class SSBN which will carry 24 missiles of this type. **Length:** 10.400 m. **Weight:** more than 30 tons at launch. **Propulsion:** solid propellant grains, three stages. **Inertial guidance. Range:** about 4,000 miles. **Warhead:** 10-14 MIRV of 50 KT. The Trident 2 class now being studied will have a 6,000-mile range.

† submerged

SURFACE-TO-SURFACE MISSILES

♦ **Harpoon.** — An all-weather cruise missile which can be launched by aircraft, surface ship or submarine. **Propulsion:** ramjet with a rocket booster added to the ship and submarine version **Weight:** 225 kg. **Length:** 3.20 m. **Diam.:** 0.350 m. **Rocket booster:** weight 118 kg. **Length:** 0.75 m. **Trajectory:** between 60 and 15 m., descending to a few m. prior to impact. **Guidance system:** inertial, then active homing on band J in the final trajectory. **Range:** 70 miles. **Warhead:** 225 kg. The submarine version is shrouded and may be launched while submerged from the TT. In order to reach the maximum range, it is necessary to use designation guidance systems external to the launching unit, helicopters, for example.

♦ **Standard.** — In order to give small ships such as the *Asheville*-class PG (patrol gunboats) and also to give escort ships of the *Knox* class an anti-surface capability the U.S. Navy has developed a surface-to-surface missile based on the Tartar RIM 24; it can also be fired from the Mk 112 ASROC system launcher.

♦ **SLCM.** — The Sea Launched Cruise Missile (SLCM) is a sea-surface missile and not a surface-to-air missile. It can be launched by a submarine or surface ship and has a nuclear warhead. It is capable of a 2,000-mile range on a land target; for sea targets, it has a shorter range (350 nautical miles). The flight pattern is low altitude in each case. The system is still being developed. It will be fitted on nuclear attack submarines, and a surface-to-surface version with a 350-mile range is being designed for the CSGN class ship.

SURFACE-TO-AIR MISSILES

♦ **Talos.** — (Bldr: Bendix and RCA). Propulsion system on launch is by a 4,000-pound solid booster; then by a McDonnell ramjet sustainer engine. **Weight:** 2.7 tons; **Length:** 9.70 m. **S:** Mach 3; **Range:** 65 miles. Beam-riding guidance system, then semi-active homing. Proximity fuse. Can carry a nuclear warhead. Produced in series until 1968. Twin launcher with the number of missile reloads varying with the ship class. Guidance system components include an airsearch radar, an elevation radar, two SPW 2 radars for target acquisition, and two SPG/49 tracking radars.

♦ **Terrier.** — (Bldr: Convair and Standard). Solid-propellant booster; **Length:** 4.57 m. without the booster, 8 m. with; **Diam.:** 0.356 m; **Weight:** at launch 500 kg + 1,350 kg with booster. **S:** Mach 2.5. **Range:** 20 miles and 60,000 feet. Built in series until 1968. One version of the Terrier missile enables it to attack low-flying aircraft and surface-to-surface missiles. System consists of twin Mk 10 launcher with two horizontal ready service magazines, each with 20 missiles, a computer, an air-search radar, a tri-dimensional radar SPS/39, SPS/48, or SPS/52 on modernized or recently built ships, and two guidance radars SPG/55 or 55 B.

♦ **Tartar.** — (Bldr: Convair) and **Standard** (built by General Dynamics). Dual thrust rocket motor with solid propellant grains. **Length:** 4.54 m; **Diam.:** 0.356 m; **Weight:** 590 kg. Semiactive homing guidance system. System comprises Mk 11 twin launcher or Mk 13 single launcher with a vertical ready service magazine containing 40 missiles, a computer, an air search radar, a tridimensional SPS/39, 48 or 52 radar, and two SP G/51 guidance radars. A series of missiles of approximately the same size as the first RIM 24 Mod 0 (U.S. military designation) but they have been constantly improved with better propulsion, miniaturisation of components, and missile flight profile.

Systems	Range (miles)	Ceiling (feet)	Remarks
RIM 24 *Tartar Md 0*	14	300/50,000	No longer made
RIM 24 B *Improved Tartar (IT)*	15	150/60,000	Analog fire control
RIM 24 C *Tartar Retrofit (ITR)*	15	150/60,000	Analog fire control Anti-surface potential
RIM 66 A *Standard SM 1A*	15	150/65,000	Analog fire control Anti-surface potential
RIM 66 B *Standard SM 1*	25	150/80,000	Digital fire control
SM 2	40?	150/80,000	Being studied and developed

The SM 1 can be installed on ships fitted with the Terrier system, the Mk 12 booster being added and its length becoming that of the Terrier. It can thereupon be retained in the horizontal ready service magazines used in this system and launched by the Mk 10. The SM 1 then becomes the SM 1 ER (Extended Range) and its range is extended some 10 miles.

The range of the SM 2 ER will exceed 100 miles.

♦ **Aegis** (*ex-Advanced Surface Missile System*) (ASMS). — Under study since 1964. The system is based on a fixed array radar to provide 360° coverage ("billboard radar"). It also consists of a weapon repelling simultaneously a number of targets under the most adverse electronic countermeasures and especially against targets at extremely low altitude (Sea Skimmer type). For precise response to threats the Aegis system will be made of various components permitting the control of all necessary steps from the target acquisition stage until missile detonation against the target. A cluster of three computer systems will direct all these functions automatically, especially the detection and tracking of the closing targets, data distribution for target evaluation and designation through pre-programmed information retained in the system, integration of radar and other information sources in the ship, and the selection of missiles and distribution of fire.

The AN/SPY 1 radar is the most important single element in the system. The missile to be used is probably the Standard SM 2, although the SM 1 may be used until it is operational. A Mk 26 twin launcher will be used for launching. This launcher can also handle the ASW Asroc system and Harpoon surface-to-surface missile. The various types of missiles will be stowed vertically in ready service magazines below the launcher. The Aegis system is undergoing trials in the USS *Norton Sound*.

♦ **Sea Sparrow.** — (Bldr: Raytheon-Northrop). Surface-to-air system in three versions: BPDMS (Basic Point Defense Missile System) in use by the U.S. Navy.

NATO Sea Sparrow in use in several navies.

Improved Sea Sparrow under study by the U.S. Navy.

The system is based on the Sparrow III air-to-air missile which is described later.

SURFACE-TO-AIR MISSILES (*continued*)

The missile has an optical guidance system in BPDMS version, and radar in the other two versions making it an all-weather system with a digital computer for fire control. Maximum range is about 6 miles and it has an interception point altitude of between 500 and 16,000 feet. The eight-cell box launcher on a mount is capable of rotating in train and elevation.

♦ **APDMS** (Advanced Point Defense Missile System).
This system is still under study and will use a new missile.

ANTISUBMARINE WARFARE MISSILES

♦ **Weapon Alpha (RUR-4A).** — Formerly designated under the title Weapon Able Mk 108, this is a rocket-launching system with a 227-kg rocket and 800 m range. It consists of a single launch tube .305 m in diameter and with an automatic reloading system (15 rounds/minute).

♦ **Asroc.** — This is an ASW solid fuel rocket. It may be used with a Mk 44 or Mk 46 torpedo with a parachute to decelerate the torpedo to a safe re-entry speed to avoid damaging its highly sensitive transducer head. Range is regulated by the combustion time of the rocket motor. Rocket-torpedo separation is timed. The Mk 112 launcher carries eight rockets which may be trained together and elevated in pairs. The launcher has an arc of elevation from 3° to 85° but the rocket is usually launched at 45°. Rate of fire: 2 rockets per minute.

Fire control is made up of a computer linked with an SQS/23 or SQS/26 sonar. An advanced version of Asroc is the E.R.A. (Extended Range Asroc).
Characteristics:

	ASROC	E.R.A.
L:	4.70 m	5 m.
Diam:	0.300 m	0.350 m
Weight:	450 kg	615 kg
Warhead:	Mk 44 or Mk 46	Mk 46
Range:	9,800 m (Mk 44)	
	9,200 m (Mk 46)	18,000 m.

A nuclear depth charge can replace the torpedo. On the *Knox*-class escorts the launcher has been modified to permit the launching of Tartar SSM missiles in place of ASW weapons. The loading system of the Asroc missile is slow because the rockets must be hoisted from the magazines; however, on the most recently built escort class ships a hoist brings the rocket up forward of the bridge structure for semi-automatic loading.

♦ **Astor.** — This system uses the Terrier Mk 10 ramp for the launching of Asroc.

♦ **Subroc.** — This missile has a nuclear warhead and is fired under water by a submarine through the torpedo tubes. After having been launched, the missile follows an aerial trajectory which is regulated by the range to the target. The second stage of the rocket carries the warhead. This stage follows a ballistic trajectory and enters the water where the warhead explodes at a pre-determined depth.
The Mk 113 fire control system is used with BQQ2 and BQQ5 sonars.
Characteristics: **Length:** 5.950 m. **Diam.:** 0.533 m. **Weight:** 1,800 kg. **Maximum range:** 35 miles. **Supersonic speed.** First stage: solid fuel missile motor with 3,400 m firing distance. Second stage: nuclear depth charge with feathering vanes and a protection cone for re-entry into the water.
The nuclear depth charge may be replaced by an ASW torpedo.

AIR-TO-SURFACE MISSILES

♦ **Bullpup.** — (Bldr: Martin Marietta) with fixed cruciform wings and 4 control ailerons forward. There are several versions and the most common are the AGM 12 B or Bullpup A and the AGM 12 C or Bullpup B.
Bullpup A. — Propulsion solid propellant grains
Length: 3.200 m. **Diam.:** 0.305 m. **Wingspan:** 0.952 m. **Weight** at launch: 258 kg. **Range:** 11,000 m. **Warhead:** 115 kg.
Bullpup B. — Propulsion liquid propellant. **Length:** 4.070 m. **Diam.:** 0.439 m. **Wingspan:** 1.177 m. **Weight** at launch: 812 kg. **Range:** 17,000 m. **Warhead:** 453.6 kg.

♦ **Condor.** — The characteristics of this missile, which is still under study, are not well known. It is known that it will be supersonic and carry a nose-mounted TV camera similar to the British Martel system. Its range is expected to be 60 to 80,000 m. During trials in 1971 a Condor missile was fired successfully from an A-7 on an old destroyer type ship anchored some 56,000 meters from the aircraft.

♦ **Shrike.** — An anti-radar missile with the following characteristics: **Length:** 3.048 m. **Diam.:** 0.200 m. **Wingspan:** 0.914 m. **Weight:** 177 kg. Solid propellant rocket motor. **Speed:** Mach 2. **Range:** 12,000 to 16,000 m.

♦ **Walleye.** — Glide bomb guided by television. **Length:** 0.344 m. **Diam:** 0.325 m. **Wingspan:** 1.160 m. **Weight:** 499 kg. Conventional warhead.

AIR-TO-AIR MISSILES

♦ **Sparrow III (AIM 7).** — (Bldr: Raytheon-Northrop.) **Propulsion:** solid propellant grains. **Length:** 3.650 m. **Diam.:** 0.200 m. **Weight:** 204 kg. **S:** Mach 2.5. **Range:** 15,000 m (AIM 7 D version), 26,000 m (AIM 7 E) version. **Warhead:** 27 kg, proximity fuze. A semiactive homing guided missile.

♦ **Sidewinder (AIM 9).** — (Bldr: Raytheon-Northrop.) Several versions:
— *Sidewinder 1 A.* **Propulsion:** solid propellant grains. **Length:** 2.840 m. **Diam.:** 0.127 m. **Wingspan:** 0.609 m. **Weight:** 75 kg. **S:** Mach 2.5. **Range:** 6,000 m (3,500 m practical). Infrared guidance.
— *Sidewinder 1 C.* **Propulsion:** solid propellant grains. **Length:** 2.950 m **Weight:** 85 kg. **S:** Mach 3. **Range:** 18,000 m. Semiactive homing guided missile.

♦ **Phoenix (AIM 54 A).** — (Bldr: Hughes Aircraft Co) **Propulsion:** solid propellant grains. **Length:** 3.960 m. **Diam.:** 0.380 m. **Wingspan:** 0.914 m. **Weight:** 380 kg. **Range:** over 80,000 m.

♦ **Zuni.** — Stabilized unguided rocket. Attack aircraft can carry as many as 48 of this type. Can be fired singly or in salvos of four. **Length:** 2.750 m., **Weight:** 48.5 kg. **Range:** 8,000/9,000 m.

GUNNERY

♦ **406-mm model 1936**
Fitted in triple turrets in *New Jersey*-class battleships. **Length:** 50 calibers. **Muzzle velocity:** 850 m/sec. **Rate of fire:** 2 rounds/minute/barrel. **Max. Range:** 39,000 m. **Weight of projectile:** 1,230 kg. **Cartridge bags:** 6 weighing 300 kg.

♦ **203-mm model 1944 (Mk 16)**
Automatic weapon fitted in triple turrets on the *Des Moines*-class cruisers. **Length:** 55-cal. **Muzzle velocity:** 900 m/sec. **Gun elevation:** −5° to +41°. **Rate of fire:** 10 rounds/min/barrel. **Maximum range:** 30,000 m. **Maximum effective range:** 23 to 24,000 m. **Projectile:** 125 kg. **Fire control:** Mk 54 director with Mk 13 radar.

GUNNERY (continued)

♦ **203-mm model 1927 (Mk 15)**
Fitted in triple turrets in *Baltimore*-class cruisers. **Length:** 55 cal. **Muzzle velocity:** 830 m/sec. **Gun elevation:** −5° to +30°. **Rate of fire:** 2 rounds/minute/barrel. **Maximum range:** 30,000 m. **Maximum effective range:** 23 to 24,000 m. **Projectile:** 127 kg. A 51-kg projectile fitted with a rocket was fired in Vietnam by the **Saint Paul** (CA-73) reaching a target 51 km away. **Fire control:** Mk 54 director with Mk 13 radar.

♦ **203-mm model 1971 (Mk 71)**
This model which is still undergoing tests can fire 75 projectiles in sequence without interference at a firing rate of 12 rounds per minute. Evaluation ship is destroyer *Hull*. Planned for installation in some *Spruance* class.

♦ **152-mm model 1933 (MK 16)**
Weapons: Fitted in triple turrets on the *Galveston* and *Springfield*-class cruisers. **Length:** 47 cal. **Muzzle velocity:** 915 m/sec. **Rate of fire:** 3 rounds/min/barrel. **Maximum range:** 23,500 m. **Maximum effective range:** 19,000 m. **Projectile:** 46.4 kg.

♦ **127-mm twin barrel model 1935**
Semi-automatic triple purpose (air, sea and land targets) gun fitted in the mounts of the *New Jersey*, the *Galveston, Springfield, Des Moines* and *Baltimore*-class cruisers, and the *Gearing*-class destroyers. **Length:** 38 cal. **Muzzle velocity:** 792 m/sec. **Gun elevation:** −15° + 85°. **Rate of fire:** 17 rounds/min/barrel with a well-trained crew. **Maximum range on a surface target:** 16,500 m. **Maximum effective range on a ship target:** 12 to 13,000 m. **Maximum range in anti-aircraft fire:** 11,400 m. **Maximum effective range in anti-aircraft fire:** 8,000 m. **Projectile:** 25 kg. **Fire control:** usually Mk 37 director with Mk 25 radar.

♦ **127-mm Mk 39**
Single barrel semi-automatic triple purpose (air, sea and land targets) gun installed on the *Midway*-class aircraft carriers. **Length:** 54 cal. **Muzzle velocity:** 900 m/sec. **Gun elevation:** Similar to the Mk 32. **Rate of fire:** 17 rounds/min. **Maximum range on a surface target:** 22,000 m. **Maximum effective range on a surface target:** 20,000 m. **Maximum effective range in anti-aircraft fire:** 10,000 m. **Projectile:** 32 kg.

♦ **127-mm Mk 42**
Single barrel triple purpose (air, sea and land targets) gun fitted on board most recently built ships of the U.S. Navy.
Mount weight: 58.7 tons. **Length:** 45 cal. **Muzzle velocity:** 810 m/sec. **Arc of elevation:** −5° + 80°. **Rate of train:** 50°/sec. **Rate of elevation:** 80°/sec. **Rate of fire:** 40 rounds/minute. **Projectile:** 46 kg.
Loading entirely automatic from two ammunition drums located in the handling room up to the loading tray by means of a rotating hoist. Each ammunition drum contains 20 rounds. The rate of fire can be maintained for only one minute inasmuch as it is necessary to reload the drums.
Crew: 13 with 2 in the turret.

♦ **127-mm Mk 45**
Single barrel mount fitted on the *California* and *Virginia*-class cruisers and the *Spruance*-class destroyers.
Weight of the turret: 20 tons. **Length:** 54 cal. **Muzzle velocity:** 810 m/sec. **Gun elevation:** −5° + 65°. **Rate of fire:** 20 rounds/min. **Personnel:** none except in the handling room to reload the ammunition drums. **Fire control:** 1/SPQ 9 search radar, 1/SPQ 60 tracking radar.

♦ **76-mm (Mk 33 and 34)**
Automatic anti-aircraft gun in single (Mk 34) or twin (Mk 27 and 33) mounts. **Length:** 50 cal. **Rate of fire:** 45 rounds/min/barrel. **Maximum effective range on surface target:** 7,000 m. **Maximum effective range on aerial target:** 6,000 m.

♦ **76-mm Mk 75**
Single-barrelled license-built version of OTO Melara Compact, tested in **Talbot** and used in PHM and FFG 7 classes. **Rate of fire:** 85 rounds/min.

♦ **Vulcan Phalanx System**
The "Close-In Weapon System" designed to destroy such missiles as the Styx but not the Sea Skimmer class missile such as the French Exocet or the Israeli Gabriel.
It consists of a multibarrel 20-mm gun with a very high rate of fire (3,000 rounds/minute). The gun is linked with two radars, one of which follows the target and the other the projectile burst. A computer furnishes the necessary corrections for train and elevation so that two radar targets coincide, bringing heavy fire to bear on the target.

TORPEDOES

(a) *Submarine Torpedoes*

♦ **Mk 14 Mod 5** (1935):
Length: 5.250 m. **Diam:** 0.533 m. **Propulsion:** air/alcohol. **Max range:** 9,000 m (30 knots). No longer used except as an exercise torpedo.

♦ **Mk 16 Mod 8:**
Length: 6.250 m. **Diam:** 0.533 m. **Weight:** 2,180 kg. **Propulsion:** hydrogen peroxide (Navol). No guidance system. Designed for surface ship attack.

♦ **Mk 27 Mod 4:**
Length: 3.200 m. **Diam:** 0.533 m. **Weight:** 590 kg. **Propulsion:** electric. Passive guidance system. Can be used against surface targets and submarines.

♦ **M 35 Mod 0:**
Electric torpedo with an active guidance system used against submarines. Seldom used.

♦ **Mk 37 Mod 0:**
Electric torpedo with an active-passive guidance system. Used against surface and submarine targets. **Length:** 3.450 m. **Diam:** 0.485 m. **Weight:** 650 kg. **S:** 25 knots. **Run duration:** 20,000 m.

♦ **Mk 37 Mod 1**
Similar to the Mk 37 Mod 0 but is guided by wire. Can be used against submarines. **Length:** 4,100 m. **Weight:** 770 kg.

♦ **Mk 45 Mod 0**
Heavy wireguided torpedo with corrective commands being transmitted through the wire to the torpedo. Can be used against surface targets or submarines.
Length: 5.760 m. **Weight:** 1,090 kg. **S:** 40 knots (?) **Run duration:** 20,000 m (?). Carried by the SSN class.

♦ **Mk 48**
Will replace the Mk 37 Mod 0 and 1, the Mk 14 Mod 5, and the Mk 16 Mod 8

TORPEDOES (*continued*)

torpedoes. Can be launched from a destroyer or a submarine against a surface target or a submarine.
   Length: 5.800 m. **Diam:** 0.533 m. **Weight:** 1,250 kg. Can be launched under its own guidance system or with a wireguidance system. High speed (40 knots?) and long run duration (25,000 m). Active-passive guidance system.

b) *destroyer torpedoes*

♦ **Mk 43 Mod 1**
Electric torpedo with an active guidance system which can be used against slow submarines (used by French naval aircraft). **Length:** 2.330 m. **Weight:** 120 kg.

♦ **Mk 44 Mod 0 and 1**
Electric torpedo with an active guidance system which can be used against submarines.
   Length: 2.540 m. **Diam:** 0.324 m. **Weight:** 192 kg.

♦ **Mk 46 Mod 0 and Mk 1**
ASW torpedo using solid fuel (Monergol) with an active-passive guidance system. **Length:** 2.570 m. **Diam:** 0.324 m. **Weight:** 258 kg.

c) *aircraft torpedoes*

♦ **Mk 43 Mod 1**

♦ **Mk 44 Mod 0**

♦ **Mk 46 Mod 0 and 1**

d) special torpedoes

♦ **Captor (Captured Torpedo)**
This is a mine laid on the sea bottom enclosing a torpedo (Mk 46 probably) which is automatically fired on a target passing close aboard.

MINES

The most recent mines are:
— the Mk 52 Mod 2 weighing 500 kg with 315 kg of explosive. Its magnetic adjustment is very sensitive which makes it a very difficult mine to sweep.
— the Mk 36 "Destructor" which weighs 226 kg with 87 kg of explosive, also a magnetic mine and very difficult to sweep.
These mines have automatic devices which neutralize them at the end of a preselected period.

RADARS

Many models are in use, the most recent of which are:

(a) *Surface search and target designation*

♦ **SPS 10**

♦ **SPS 55.** On the *Spruance* class and planned for the FFG-7 and others of this class; will eventually replace the SPS 10.

(b) *Air search*

♦ **SPS 6.** Being replaced.

♦ **SPS 12.** On CGN-9, CVN 65

♦ **SPS 37.** (CGN-25, certain CG class ships, and DDG class). Band A

♦ **SPS 32.** "Billboard" fixed array radar (bearing/range) first used on the *Enterprise* (*CVAN-65*) and the *Long Beach* (*CGN-9*). Has the appearance of four rectangular surfaces mounted on the superstructure of these ships. Band A.

♦ **SPS 40.** The most widely used air search radar. Range against medium bombers: 150 to 180 miles. Band B.

♦ **SPS 43.** Mounted in aircraft carriers and cruisers. Band A.

♦ **SPS 49.** New type of search radar planned for the FFG-7 class and others. Band C.

♦ **SPS 58.** Combined air-surface search radar.

(c) *Height-finding*

♦ **SPS 8 A**

♦ **SPS 30.** Mounted on aircraft carriers and cruisers. Band F.

♦ **SPS 33.** "Billboard" fixed array radar.
   Mounted on the *Enterprise* (*CVN-65*) and the *Long Beach* (*CG-9*). Has the appearance of four square surfaces mounted on the superstructure of these ships. Band E.

♦ **SPS 39.** Band E.

♦ **SPS 39 A** (MT1 digital) mounted on selected aircraft carriers, cruisers and DDG.

♦ **SPS 48 A** (Mounted on the CG class). Band E.

♦ **SPS 48 B** (Electronic frequency sweeping radar). Will replace the SPS 48 A.

♦ **SPS 52 A** (Mounted on the DDG class). Band E/F.

♦ **SPS 52 B.** (Electronic frequency sweeping radar). Will replace the SPS 52 A.

♦ **SPY 1.** Also called the M.F.A.R. (Multi Function Array Radar). It will be the most important segment of the Aegis system. Obtaining a directional effect by dipole radiation to secure an electronic sweep, it will have four fixed aerials which will provide an instant 360° coverage. Long-range air search, target tracking and missile guidance. Band F.

(d) *Guidance radars*

♦ **SPG 49 + SW 2.** Guidance for Talos missiles. Mounted on the *Long Beach* (*CG-9*) and the guided missile cruisers *Columbus* and *Galveston*. Band I.

♦ **SPG 51.** Guidance for Tartar, SM 1 A and SM 1 missiles. Band G.

♦ **SPG 55.** Guidance for Terrier missiles. Band G.

SONARS

The principal types of sonar in service are:

(a) *On surface ships:*

♦ **SQS 4.** MF.

♦ **SQS 29.** MF.

SONARS (continued)

♦ **SQS 23.** Bow sonar, LF, mounted on many destroyers and guided-missile destroyers.

♦ **SQS 26.** The newest and most widely used LF sonar. Several types. It is mounted in a dome in the stem of the cruisers and the guided missile destroyers as well as in the *Garcia, Brooke,* and *Knox*-class escort ships. An improved SQS 26, the SQS 53, is used in the *Spruance*-class destroyer.

♦ **SQS 35.** Towed sonar, MF.

♦ **SQS 56.** New sonar designed for Patrol Frigates.

♦ **SQR 15.** Passive towed sonar.

(b) *On submarines:*

Active-passive sonars: BQS 4 and 6; BQS 11, 12 and 13.
Passive sonars: BQR 2m BQR 7, BQR 15 towed, BQH 4 replacing BQR 15.

♦ **BQQ 1** (1958). Multi-function sonar including: BQR 2, BQR 7, BQS 4 or 6. Mounted in the SSN *Skate* and *Skipjack* class.

♦ **BQQ 1.** Retrofit III (1964): Multi-function sonar including new versions of the BQR 2 and BQR 7, BQS 11 or 12. Mounted in the SSN *Permit* and *Sturgeon* class.

♦ **SSBN Sonar Unit** (1973). Multi-function sonar of the SSBN class; BQR 15 included.

♦ **BQQ 5** (1975). Multi-function sonar including especially the BQH 4 and BQS 13. Mounted in the *Los Angeles.*

(c) *Fixed listening systems for submarine detection:*

♦ **SOSUS** (Sound Surveillance System). This system has 2 networks:
  • **CAESAR.** Surveillance of the Northwest Atlantic.
  • **COLOSSUS.** Surveillance of the Northeast Pacific along the coast of the U.S.A.
These networks are made up of fixed hydrophones suspended under water and connected by cable to about 20 land stations which receive and interpret the signals.

♦ **MSS** (Moored Surveillance System). This is a semi-fixed system now under study made up of long life buoys transmitting to patrol aircraft.

♦ **SASS** (Suspended Array Surveillance System). This is a tremendous project which plans to install in each ocean a single large passive sonar, very deeply sunk (about 6,000 m.) using fixed equipment at this depth.

PROCESSING OF TACTICAL DATA

The system now in use is the NTDS (Naval Tactical Data System). Thanks to its digital calculators (AN/USQ 20 and Univac AN/UYK 7) it gives an instantaneous overall picture of the tactical situation — air, surface, and underwater — and permits the commander to see its development and employ the appropriate means necessary to oppose the enemy. Excellent automatic transmission systems permit the exchange of tactical information with similarly equipped ships and aircraft carrying the ATDS (P3C Orion and S3A Viking) and amphibious landing forces equipped with NTDS.

AIRCRAFT CARRIERS

♦ *3 Nimitz class*

	Laid down	L	In serv.
CVN 68 NIMITZ	6-68	13-5-72	7-75
CVN 69 DWIGHT D. EISENHOWER	8-70	11-10-75	77
CVN 70 CARL VINSON	11-10-75	. . .	1980-81

Author: 1966-67 (*68*), 1970-71 (*69*), 1973-74 (*70*).
Bldr: Newport News SB & DD

D: 77,400 tons (91,400 tons fl) **S:** 30 kts
Dim: 326 (317 pp) (*1*) × 40.85 × 11.30 × 76.80 (flight deck)
Man: 5,193 (403 officers) including aviation personnel (2,366 with 271 officers)
A: about 100 aircraft and helicopters distributed among 6 squadrons — 3 BPDMS Sea Sparrow systems.
Electron Equipt: Radars: 1/SPS 10 F, 1/SPS 43 A, 1/SPS 48 B, 1/SPN 42, 1/SPN 43 A, 1/SPN 44 — NTDS.
M: 2 pressurized water nuclear reactors; 4 sets GT; 4 props; 260,000 hp
Electric: 64,000 kw + 4 emergency generators (8,000 kw).
  (1) 338.85 m. including aircraft arresting gear.

REMARKS: The offensive potential of these ships is remarkable; they carry on board 90% more aviation fuel than the *Forrestal* class and 50% more ammunition (3,000 tons).

Armor: the decks and the hull are of extra-strong high tensile steel which can limit the impact of semi-armor piercing bombs. Independent of the longitudinal bulkheads, there are 23 watertight transverse bulkheads (more than 2,000 compartments) as well as 10 firewall bulkheads which rise to the flight deck. Fire fighting means with foam devices are very well developed, and pumping equipment is excellent, a 1.5° list being correctable in 20 minutes. There are 30 damage control teams available at all times. *Nimitz*-class ships can withstand three times the severe pounding given the *Essex*-class aircraft carrier during 1944-45 and they can take impacts and shock waves in the same proportion.

M: The cores of these ships are expected to last 13 years in normal usage for a cruising distance of 800,000 to 1,000,000 miles.

Aircraft handling installations: four side elevators divided as follows: two forward, one aft of the island structure to starboard, one on the stern to port. Four Mk C13 Mod 1 steam catapults, 94.50 m. long.

NUCLEAR-POWERED CARRIERS

♦ *1 SCB 160 type*

	Author	Bldr	Laid down	L	In serv.
CVN 65 ENTERPRISE	*1957-58*	Newport News SB	2-58	24-9-60	25-11-61

D: 75,700 tons (89,600 fl)
Dim: $\begin{cases} 335.75 \ (1) \\ 317 \ (pp) \end{cases} \times \begin{cases} 40.54 \ (hull) \\ 78.40 \ (flight\ deck) \end{cases} \times 11.30 \ (draft) \ 19.60 \ (freeboard)$
S: 33 kts
A: Carries 80 to 100 airplanes and helicopters among the two interception squadrons (VF), three attack squadrons (VA), 1 heavy attack squadron (VAH), 1 ASW squadron, 1 photo reconnaissance squadron (VPF), AEW

NUCLEAR-POWERED CARRIERS (*continued*)

Nimitz (CVN 68) 1975

(Airborne Early Warning) aircraft, and several liaison helicopters. Two BPDMS Sea Sparrow systems.

Electron Equipt: Radars: 1/SPS 10, 1/SPS 32, 1/SPS 33, 1/SPS 12, 1/SPS 58, 2 aircraft landing radars SPN 12. NTDS.

M: 8 Westinghouse A2 nuclear reactors, 35,000 hp each (max.: 45,000 hp), supplying in pairs 32 Foster-Wheeler heat exchangers; 4 Westinghouse GT; 4 props

Electric: 40,000 kw

Range: 140,000/30 — 400,000/20. (From 21-7 to 2-10-64 circumnavigated the Globe without replenishment, a total of 30,126 miles)

Man: 427 officers, 4,372 men (including aviation personnel: 265/2,133)

(1) 342.30 outboard arresting gear.

REMARKS: The island superstructure is comparatively small; four steam catapults; four elevators, one on the port side aft of the angled deck, three to starboard, two forward of the island, one aft. Carries half again as much aviation fuel as the *Forrestal* class which permits 12 days of intensive aerial operations without replenishment. Carries fuel oil as ballast to replenish other ships. Elevators are steel and alloy and weigh 105 rather than 135 tons, 26 m. long, 16 m. wide, lift 45 tons. The hangar is 7.62 m. high and the flight deck area is over 20,000 m². Electricity: 16 turbo-dynamo generators, each 2,500 kw.

♦ *3 SCB 127 A and B type Kitty Hawk class*

	Author	Bldr	Laid down	L	In serv.
CV 63					
KITTY HAWK	*1955–56*	New York SB Co	27-12-56	21-5-60	29-4-61
CV 64					
CONSTELLATION	*1956–57*	Brooklyn NSY	14-9-57	8-10-60	27-10-61
CV 66					
AMERICA	*1960–61*	Newport News SB	9-1-61	1-2-64	23-1-65

D: 61,000 tons (80,000 fl)   **Dim:** L: 319.25 (wl)
38.5 (wl) — 76 flight deck
10.9 draft

S: 33 kts   **Range:** 4,000/30
8,000/20

A: 2 Terrier systems installed on sponsons aft (80 missiles). Carries from 70 to 90 planes.

NUCLEAR-POWERED CARRIERS (*continued*)

Nimitz (CVN 68)   1975

NUCLEAR-POWERED CARRIERS (*continued*)

The carrier **CVN 65 Enterprise** in company with **FF 1069 Bagley** and the **AE 33 Shasta**

NUCLEAR-POWERED CARRIERS (*continued*)

Enterprise (CVN 65)

CONVENTIONALLY-POWERED CARRIERS

America (CV 66)

The vertical rectangular surfaces are the antennae of the height-finding radar AN/SPS 33, the horizontal those of the air search radar AN/SPS 32.

Enterprise (CVN 65)

Electron Equipt: Radars: 1/SPS 10, 1/SPS 58, 1/SPS 43, 1/SPS 30, 1/SPS 52, 1/SPN 10, 4 SPG 55 — NTDS
Sonars: 1/SQS 23 (*America* only)
M: 280/300,000 hp Westinghouse GT, 4 props (2 × 4 blades, 2 × 5 on *Kitty Hawk*, 4 × 5 on *Constellation*)
Electric: . . . kw
Boilers: 8 Foster-Wheeler 83.4/cm²
Fuel: 7,800 tons

Kitty Hawk (CV 63)

1969

CONVENTIONALLY-POWERED CARRIERS (*continued*)

Constellation (CV 64) 1974

Man: Same as *Forrestal* class.
Aviation fuel: 5,882 tons

REMARKS: Compared to the four *Forrestal*-class predecessors on which these are
based, these ships are greatly improved and have one essential difference: the
elevators are divided with two starboard, forward of the island, one on the port side
abaft island, and one aft and outboard the angled flight deck. Aircraft can be
landed or catapulted simultaneously, a difficult operation on the earlier ships. Four
steam catapults. An 18 m × 5 m removable section can be added to the flight deck
parking area.

♦ *1 SCB 127C type*

	Laid down	L	In serv.
CV 67 JOHN F. KENNEDY	22-10-64	27-5-67	7-9-68

Bldr: Newport News SB & DD Co.

D: 61,000 tons (87,000 fl) **S:** 30 kts

Dim: 319.25 (wl) × 39.60 (wl) × 10.90 draft (76.90 flight deck)
Man: 404 officers, 4,548 men (including 253/1903 aviation)
A: 3 BPDMS Sea Sparrow systems 70 to 90 aircraft
Electron Equipt: Radars: 1/SPS 10, 1/SPS 43, 1/SPS 48, 1/SPS 58, 1/SPN 10,
2/SPN 42
Sonar: 1/SQS 23 — NTDS
M: General Electric GT; 4 props; 280,000 hp **Electric:** . . . kw
Boiler: 8 Foster Wheeler, 83.4 kg/cm²

REMARKS: Four side elevators, three to starboard (two forward and one aft of the
island), the fourth on the port quarter. Complete automatic landing system,
permitting all-weather operation. Four 90-m steam catapults. Flight deck can
permit 40-ton plane operation. Has P.L.A.T. (Pilot Landing Air Television) facili-
tating the control of launching and recovery operations.

CONVENTIONALLY-POWERED CARRIERS (*continued*)

Island of the America   Guiglini 1974

Seen from left to right: the radome containing the SPN 42 landing radars; the SPS 30 heightfinding radar at the top of the trellis mast; starboard of the stack one of the four SPG 55 radars for Terrier missile guidance; at the top of the mainmast the

John F. Kennedy (CV 67)

Tacan as well as the IFF antennae and various counter-measure systems; at the foot of the mainmast and towards the stern a stand supporting the SPN 10 radar and forward another for the SPS 52; and finally, above the bridge, the SPS 43 search radar.

John F. Kennedy (CV 67). Note the angle of the stack on the starboard side.   1968

CONVENTIONALLY-POWERED CARRIERS (*continued*)

♦ 4 conventional carriers, *Forrestal* class SCB 80 (*59*) and SCB 80 M (*60-62*) types.

	Author	Bldr	Laid down	L	In serv.
A. CV					
59 FORRESTAL	*1951-52*	Newport News SB	14-7-52	11-12-54	1-10-55
B. CV					
69 SARATOGA	*1952-53*	Brooklyn NSY	16-12-52	8-10-55	14-4-56
CV					
61 RANGER	*1953-54*	Newport News SB	2-8-54	29-9-54	10-8-57
CV					
62 INDEPENDENCE	*1954-55*	Brooklyn NSY	1-7-55	9-6-58	10-1-59

D: $\begin{cases} 59,650 \text{ tons } (78,000 \text{ fl}) \ 59 \\ 60,000 \text{ tons } (78,700 \text{ fl}) \ 60\text{-}62 \end{cases}$

Dim: $\begin{cases} 316.7 \times 38.5 \text{ (wl)} \times 76.8 \text{ (max} - CV\text{-}61: 79.2) \times 11.3 \\ (319 - CV\ 62) \end{cases}$

Forrestal (CV 59)   1968

Saratoga (CV 60)   Arra 1967

Ranger (CV 61)   1974

S: 33 kts   **Range:** 4,000/30 — 8,000/20

A: 2/127-mm AA automatic 54-cal (I × 2) only in CV 61; they have been replaced by 3 BPDMS Sea Sparrow systems in others. Carry 70 to 90 planes and helicopters (CV).

Electron Equipt: Radars: 1/SPS 10, 1/SPS 43, 1/SPS 30, 1/SPN 10, 1/SPS 58 — NTDS

M: General Electric or Westinghouse GT; 4 props; 260,000 hp (A); 300,000 hp (B)

Boilers: 8 Babcock and Wilcox, 41.7 kg/cm² on the *59*, 84 kg/cm² on the others, superheat: 520°C

Fuel: 12,000 tons

Man: 400 officers, 4,548 men including 253/1903 aviation personnel

REMARKS: Hangar 7.60 m. in height, 234 to 240 m in length, flight deck 315.75 m long. The landing system permits safe landing in the darkest of nights. Four side elevators (15.95 × 18.90) and four steam catapults 65 to 75 m long (C 13 type), 2 forward on the main flight deck, 2 on the angled flight deck. With the four catapults, 32 planes can be launched in four minutes. Deck angled at 8°. Armored flight deck. Six-cable arresting gear.

The *Forrestal* has three rudders and 4 propellers, the two outboard with five blades and the two inboard with four blades. The deck protection and the internal compartmentation are extensive (1,200 watertight compartments): 2 longitudinal bulkheads are fitted from keel to waterline from stem to stern; there are transverse bulkheads at about every 10 meters.

The *60-62* are slightly larger and faster than the *59*. The machinery is the same, reaching about 300,000 hp. They carry 5,880 tons of jet fuel.

♦ *3 SCB-110 (110A Coral Sea) type Midway class*

	Bldr	Laid down	L	In serv.
CV				
A. 41 MIDWAY	Newport News SB & DD	27-10-43	20-3-45	10-9-45
42 F. D. ROOSEVELT	New York NSY	1-12-43	29-4-45	27-10-45

CONVENTIONALLY-POWERED CARRIERS (*continued*)

F. D. Roosevelt (CV 42)   St. Terzibaschitsch 1970

F. D. Roosevelt (CV 42)   G. Arra 1972

B. 43 CORAL SEA	Newport News SB & DD	10-7-44	2-4-46	1-10-47

D:
- *M*   51,000 tons (64,000 fl)
- *FDR*   51,000 tons (62,700 fl)
- *CS*   52,000 tons (63,400 fl)

Dim: 298.39 (293.91 pp) × $\begin{cases} 41.45 \text{ (wl)} \times 10.90 \\ 72.54 \text{ (flight deck) } CS \text{ and } M \\ 64.60 \text{ (flight deck) } FDR \end{cases}$

S: 33 kts
A: 3/127-mm AA of 54-cal (I × 3) (4 on *42*). Carry 60 to 75 planes.
Electron Equipt: 1/SPS 10, 1/SPS 43, 1/SPS 30 1/SPS 58 (*Midway*)
      1/SPN 6, 1/SPN 10 — NTDS (*41* and *43*)
Armor: Horizontal protection on several decks for a total of about 40 cm; excellent compartmentation.
Man: 362 officers, 4,065 men (including aviation personnel: 223/1,591).
M: Westinghouse GT (General Electric in the *FDR*); 212,000 hp
Electric: . . . kw
Boilers: 12 Babcock and Wilcox, 41.7 kg/cm² pressure

Coral Sea (CV 43)   1968

REMARKS: Machinery and ships bottoms very similar to the *Iowa*-class battleship. The original AA guns have been considerably reduced: the 127-mm are semi-automatic, Mk 39.

ELEVATORS: Divided as follows: *F.D.R.* — a side elevator abaft the island, a side elevator to port forward of the angled flight deck. The forward elevator on the center line of the ship was removed in 1969. *Coral Sea* and *Midway* — two side elevators to starboard, one forward and one aft the island, one side elevator to port aft of the angled flight deck. The platforms of these elevators are of alloy construction.

REFITS: From 1954 to 1963 the ships underwent several overhauls: angled flight deck, lengthening of the flight deck, replacing hydraulic with steam catapults, the removal of side armor and addition of "bulges," installation of reinforced arresting gear and barriers, removal and replacing of the centerline elevators (now side elevators), increase of aviation gasoline bunkers, new jet fuel bunkers.

In October 1967 *Midway* entered once again a major overhaul period. She was returned to service in 1-70. The angled flight deck was extended to port, the three elevators were enlarged, the forward port elevator was shifted aft, the catapults

CONVENTIONALLY-POWERED CARRIERS (*continued*)

replaced by a more powerful model; all the electronic equipment was replaced. The *Midway* can launch the all-weather F 14 Tomcat interceptor. It has been decided not to overhaul the other two ships in the same way because of their age and the fact that they cannot maintain earlier speeds. The *F. D. Roosevelt*, which can barely make 27 knots, is going to be used as a reserve training ship.

USS Midway (CV-41)   Top: 1971
                                                             Bottom: 1973

USS Coral Sea (CV-43)   1970

SEA CONTROL SHIP
AND
V/STOL SUPPORT SHIP

The U.S. Navy has completed a study on a small and inexpensive aircraft carrier which is designed principally for convoy and replenishment-at-sea protection but could if necessary render aerial support during an amphibious operation: this is the Sea Control Ship. The first of these ships had been written into the projected 1974-75 budget, but Congress refused to fund its construction. As envisioned, the ship would be about 14,000 tons and could reach a speed of 27 knots with its two 20,000 hp (each) gas turbines. It could put into action about 20 aircraft (ASW helicopters and a few fixed-wing planes with vertical or short takeoff characteristics).

To overcome congressional objections, the Navy revised the project, producing the VSS concept. This Vertical Support Ship would be fitted with arresting gear and catapults and would be able to carry the F 18, ASW S-3 A Viking airplanes as well as helicopters or VTOL/STOL aircraft. In addition to the missions outlined above, the new ship could carry minesweeping helicopters and could support limited aerial defense operations. Although nothing has been decided, the Navy will probably ask for funds for the start of this project in the 1976-77 budget.

NAVAL AVIATION

All weather fighter, F-14 "Tomcat"

Attack aircraft AV-8 A "Harrier" (Marine Corps)   1971

All weather fighter, F-4 B "Phantom"

Attack aircraft A-4 E "Skyhawk"   1974

Attack aircraft, A-6 A "Intruder"

ASW aircraft, S-3 A "Viking"

NAVAL AVIATION

General

American naval aviation is an integral part of the U.S. Navy. Approximately 6,100 aircraft (budget 1975-76) including those of the Marine Corps are assigned to naval aviation, as follows:

1,228 attack planes
  732 fighters
  133 ship-based ASW planes
  376 patrol aircraft
1,166 helicopters
1,113 training planes

The aircraft are divided between:

the U.S. Navy —

65 attack and fighter squadrons (VA/VF)
 8 reconnaissance squadrons
 4 helicopter squadrons
20 ASW (VS/HS) squadrons
41 various classes
24 patrol squadrons

and the Marine Corps

25 attack and fighter squadrons (VMA/VMF)
24 helicopter squadrons
 8 various types (transport, liaison, etc.)

In addition to its fleet of heavy, sophisticated aircraft, the U.S. Navy has just chosen as a light interceptor aircraft the YF-18 (formerly the YF-17). This choice of the Navy has not as yet been acted on by Congress.

The YF-18 is a twin engine jet plane able to fly at a speed of Mach 2 and is built by Northrop. It has two YS 101-GE-100 jet engines with 6,800-kg thrust. *Combat radius:* 945 km. *Convoy range:* 4,800 km. *Armament:* 1/20-mm (1961 model) and 2 Sidewinder rockets.

SHIP-BASED AVIATION

The various aircraft squadrons based on an aircraft carrier comprise the "Carrier Air Wing" (C.A.W.). It is made up of different components depending on the carrier class. Thus a ship of the *Forrestal* class will generally carry:

2 fighter squadrons (VF)
1 heavy attack squadron (VAH)
2 attack squadrons (VA)
1 ASW squadron
1 composite squadron made up of observation, electronic warfare, search radar, transport planes, etc.

♦ The squadron is the basic tactical and administrative unit for the ship-based and land-based groups.

The VF, VA and VAH squadrons usually have 12 planes each.

It should be noted that the *Enterprise* (CVN-65) carries an extra squadron of attack aircraft and that the *Hancock*-class carrier cannot operate all of the aircraft types now in service, especially the F14, F4 and A6.

Reconnaissance configured RF-4B "Phantom"

To make up for the loss of the ASW aircraft carrier (CVS) it has been decided to station on board each large carrier an ASW squadron in place of an attack squadron. How the division between fixed-wing aircraft and helicopters is made in this squadron is not known. Four carriers have already been configured in this manner: the *Saratoga* (CV-60), *Independence* (CV-62), *Kitty Hawk* (CV-63), and *John F. Kennedy* (CV-67). Two others, including the *Constellation* (CV-64), convert during Fiscal Year 1975-76 and all will have an ASW capability by 1980.

LAND-BASED AVIATION (search, ASW patrol, minelaying, radar observation, and so forth.)

Organized in active squadrons of 9 aircraft (Orion P3B and C). In addition, reserve formations are equipped with the Orion P3. These squadrons are divided among the Fleet Air Wings, usually 3 in the Atlantic and 6 in the Pacific; they are operational and administrative commands.

MARINE CORPS AVIATION

The Marines have their own aviation, divided among three Marine Air Wings (M.A.W.); they fully man the aircraft of the LPH (Landing Amphibious Assault Ships) class and their pilots are trained to operate from aircraft carriers. Each M.A.W. is divided in several groups. A group of planes may be made up of one attack squadron (VMA) of 20 aircraft, 1 all-weather attack squadron VMA (AW) of 12 aircraft, 1 squadron of fighter-bombers VMFA of 15 aircraft, 1 squadron of all-

Attack aircraft, A-7A "Corsair"

NAVAL AVIATION (continued)

Tactical reconnaissance aircraft RA-5C "Vigilante"   1970

"Skywarrior" refueling in flight from an RA-5C "Vigilante"

All-weather ASW helicopter, SH-3D "Sea King"

ASW Helicopter SH-3G "Sea King"

ASW Helicopter SH-2D "Sea Sprite"

weather fighters VMF (AW) of 15 aircraft. A helicopter group is made up of one observation squadron, 2 medium helicopter squadrons, and 2 heavy helicopter squadrons.

Designation of aircraft:

Independently of the name given to the aircraft — Phantom, Intruder, Orion, etc. — each class is designated by a group of initials and numbers divided by a hyphen and made up in the following manner:

1. The capital letter immediately preceding the hyphen always indicates the principal mission: A: attack — B: bomber — C: cargo/transport — E: airborne early warning — F: fighter — H: helicopter — K: tanker, inflight refueling — O: observation — P: patrol — S: antisubmarine — T: training — U: utility — V: VTOL/STOL: vertical or short takeoff or landing — X: research

NAVAL AVIATION (continued)

ASW Helicopter SH-2D "Sea Sprite"   1971

2. The number which comes immediately after the hyphen indicates that this is the first or the sequence number of this plane. In this case the figure is itself followed by a letter whose place in the alphabet indicates the number of the latest modification to the aircraft.

3. In the case where an aircraft of a particular class (see para. 1 above) is assigned to a different duty than its principal mission, a second capital letter will precede the letter of that mission: A: attack — C: cargo/transport — D: direct or control drones or aircraft or missiles — E: special electronic installation — H: search/rescue — K: tanker; inflight refueling — L: cold weather; for the Arctic regions — M: missile carrier — Q: drone aircraft — R: reconnaissance — S: antisubmarine — T: trainer — U: utility/general service — V: staff — W: weather, meteorology.

In addition, the following initials may be placed in front of the letter or letters which indicate the mission: G: permanently grounded — J: special test temporarily — N: special test permanently — X: experimental — Y: prototype — Z: planning.

Note: The builder is no longer indicated by a capital letter.

Example: A-1 E indicates an attack aircraft, number 1 type, already modified five times.

Attack aircraft, A-6A "Intruder"

ASW aircraft, S-2E "Tracker"

EA-6B "Prowler"

E-2A "Hawkeye"

♦ Markings on the aircraft.

On each side of the fuselage a five-pointed white star on a blue background. Aircraft assigned to a reserve base carry as well a large orange band which connects the two stars, passing under the fuselage.

PRINCIPAL COMBAT AIRCRAFT OF THE U.S. NAVY AND MARINE CORPS

A. — *SHIP-BASED FIXED WING AIRCRAFT:*

Class, builder	Missions	Wingspan in m	Length in m	Height in m	Weight in kg	Motor	Max speed mach/knots	Ceiling in feet	1) Ferry range (miles) 2) Combat radius (miles) 3) Range (hours)
F-14 TOMCAT (Grumman)	Two-man, All-weather fighter with variable-geometry wing (Navy and Marine Corps)	19.60/ 10.10	18.85	4.87	30,000 26,000	2 PW TF 30 P 412 double flux, 9,350 kg thrust with afterburners	M 2.34	60,000	1) 2,000 2) 500 3) 2½ to 3 h

A: 1/20-mm Vulcan gun. 6 Phoenix, 2 Sidewinder missiles (standard weapons) or 8,500 pounds of Sparrow and Sidewinder missiles or bombs, including tactical atomic bombs.

REMARKS: Max. landing speed: 120 knots. In the attack version, the F 14 could, for certain missions, be equipped with the air-to-surface anti-radar Shrike.

Class, builder	Missions	Wingspan in m	Length in m	Height in m	Weight in kg	Motor	Max speed mach/knots	Ceiling in feet	Range
F-4 PHANTOM (McDonnell-Douglas)	All-weather fighter (Navy) Fighter-bomber (Marine Corps)	11.70	17.75	4.95	24,750	2 J 79 GE 10 8,120 kg thrust with afterburners	M 2.3	60,000	1) 1,800 2) 520 3) 2¼ h

A: 4 Sparrow III and 4 Sidewinder missiles (standard weapons) or 6 Sparrow III or 16,000 pounds of missiles, rockets or bombs, usually 18 bombs of 750 pounds; 15 of 680 pounds; 11 of 1,000 pounds; 7 smoke bombs; 11 napalm bombs; 4 Bullpup missiles; 15 pods of air-to-surface rockets. Can carry an atomic bomb.

REMARKS: Max. landing speed: 140 knots. Several versions: F-4 B, J, G including an RF-4 B fitted for reconnaissance. Cannot, like the F-14, be flown from any other than the large carriers.

Class, builder	Missions	Wingspan	Length	Height	Weight	Motor	Max speed	Ceiling	Range
F-8 CRUSADER (Ling-Temco-Vought)	All-weather interceptor	10.90	16.60	4.80	13,500	1 PW J 57 P 20 8,100 kg thrust with afterburner	M 1.7	53,000	1) . . . 2) 400 3) 2 h

A: 4/20-mm guns, 4 Sidewinder missiles. Several versions E, H, I, J, K, L and RF 8 (reconnaissance).

Class, builder	Missions	Wingspan	Length	Height	Weight	Motor	Max speed	Ceiling	Range
A-4 SKYHAWK (McDonnell-Douglas)	Attack (Navy and Marine Corps)	8.40	12	4.60	8,000	1 PW J 52 P 408 A 5,000 kg thrust	560 kts	42,000	1) 1,600 2) 400 3) 2 h 5

A: 2/20-mm Mk 12 guns. 6,500 pounds of bombs or 127-mm rockets or Mighty Mouse, Sidewinder or Bullpup missiles.

REMARKS: Non-folding wings. Very strong; versatile. Can carry a tactical atomic bomb. Several versions A-4 A, B, C, E, F, M.

Class, builder	Missions	Wingspan	Length	Height	Weight	Motor	Max speed	Ceiling	Range
A-6 INTRUDER (Grumman)	All-weather attack (Navy and Marine Corps)	16.15	16.65	4.75	27,350	2 PW J 52 P 8 A 4,200 kg thrust	530 kts	42,000	1) 2,400 2) 300 3) 2 h

A: 18,000 pounds of conventional bombs or tactical atomic bombs, rockets, etc. Examples of ordnance: 46 bombs of 250 pounds; 30 of 450 pounds; 15 of 900 pounds; 5 of 2,000 pounds; 13 pods with 247 rockets; 52 Zuni rockets; 4 Sidewinder or 4 Bullpup missiles.

REMARKS: Very strong; versatile. Several versions A-6 A, B and C — two classes EA-6, A and B are fitted for electronic warfare. In this case they have a four-man crew (EA-6B) and a minimum of 30 sensors of various types.

Class, builder	Missions	Wingspan in m	Length in m	Height in m	Weight in kg	Motor	Max speed mach/knots	Ceiling in feet	1) Ferry range (miles) 2) Combat radius (miles) 3) Range (hours)
A-7 CORSAIR II (Ling-Temco-Vought)	Attack	11.80	14.05	4.90	19,000	1 Allison TF 41.A.1 6,800-kg thrust	595 kts	40,000	1) 3,050 2) 500 3) 2 h 15

A: 2/20-mm guns. 4,000 to 15,000 pounds of bombs, rockets or missiles according to the mission and the target distance. Examples of weapons: 24 Mk 81 bombs 250 pounds; 4 Zuni rockets and 28/2.75-inch rockets; 1 Shrike missile and one Walleye diffusion bomb; 12 Snakeye bombs; 4 Bullpup A missiles; 2 Shrike missiles; 2 bombs of 2,000 pounds.

REMARKS: Excellent machine, very strong and versatile. Several versions A 7A, B, C, D, E.

Class, builder	Missions	Wingspan in m	Length in m	Height in m	Weight in kg	Motor	Max speed mach/knots	Ceiling in feet	1) 2) 3)
S-2 TRACKER (Grumman)	ASW	22.10	13.25	5.05	11,800	2 Wright R 1 820-82 A 1,525 hp	Max 210 kts Cruise 140 kts Patrol 130 kts	22,000	1) 1,150 2) . . . 3) 8 h 15

A: 10 sono buoys, 6/127-mm rockets, conventional or atomic ASW depth charges or 1 Mk 13 torpedo or 2 Mk 44 or Mk 46 torpedoes.

REMARKS: Retracting belly radome aft, radome in the nose; MAD.   **Man:** 4 men.

Class, builder	Missions	Wingspan	Length	Height	Weight	Motor	Max speed	Ceiling	1) 2) 3)
S-3 VIKING (Lockheed)	ASW	20.90	16.25	6.95	19,700	2 TF 34. GE2 4,080-kg thrust	Max 440 kts Cruise 350 kts Patrol 160 kts	35,000	1) 3,000 2) . . . 3) 6 h

A: 60 sono buoys, LOFAR (SSQ 41), R/O (SSQ 47), DIFAR (SSQ 53), CASS (SSQ 50), DICASS (SSQ 62) or BT (SSQ 36) types. 4 Mk 32 bombs, 4 Mk 57 depth charges, 4 Mk 53 depth charges or 4 Mk 53 mines or 2 Mk 46 torpedoes.

REMARKS: Fitted with a Univac digital computer to apply the information from the different sensors on board.   **Man:** 4 men.

Class, builder	Missions	Wingspan	Length	Height	Weight	Motor	Max speed	Ceiling	1) 2) 3)
RA-5 C VIGILANTE (North American)	Reconnaissance	16.15	23.25	5.90	30,000	2 J 79 GE 10 5,395-kg thrust and 8,120 with afterburner	M 2	64,000	1) . . . 2) 1,000 3) 4 h

REMARKS: Photo equipment, cameras, etc.

Class, builder	Missions	Wingspan	Length	Height	Weight	Motor	Max speed	Ceiling	1) 2) 3)
AV-8 HARRIER (Hawker Siddeley)	Attack	7.70	13.87	3.43	VTOL 8,200 STOL 11,900	1 RR Pegasus 108 9,750-kg thrust	640 kts	50,000	1) 2,000 2) VTOL 50 STOL 200

A: 2/30-mm guns. Bombs to a total of 5,000 pounds.

REMARKS: Used by the Marine Corps. Improved B version in development.

Class, builder	Missions	Wingspan	Length	Height	Weight	Motor	Max speed	Ceiling	1) 2) 3)
A-3 SKYWARRIOR (McDonnell-Douglas)	Inflight fueling	22.10	22.65	7.28	38,000	2 PW-J 57-P 10 4,535-kg thrust	500 kts	45,000	1) 5,000 2) 1,200 3) 6 h

Class, builder	Missions	Wingspan	Length	Height	Weight	Motor	Max speed	Ceiling	1) 2) 3)
E-2 HAWKEYE (Grumman)	Radar search Electronic warfare, Airborne	24.55	17.55	5.60	23,000	2 Allison T 56 A 8 turboprops 4,050 hp	315 kts	28,000	1) 1,500 2) . . . 3) 6 h

REMARKS: In the A version it has a radome and a Air Tactical Data System (for the transmission of tactical information); in the B version it has an L304F computer as well, and in Version C a CAINS inertial navigation computer is fitted.

Class, builder	Missions	Wingspan	Length	Height	Weight	Motor	Max speed	Ceiling	1) 2) 3)
E-1 TRACER (Grumman)	Radar search Electronic warfare	22.05	13.80	5.13	12,250	2 Wright R 1 820-82 A 1,525 hp	230 kts max 140 cruis.	16,000	1) . . . 2) . . . 3) 6.8 h

REMARKS: Fitted with a fixed radome (APS 32).

NAVAL AVIATION (*continued*)

Minesweeping helicopter, CH-53 "Sea Stallion", preparing to take off with the
MK 105 mine sled attached from the Raleigh (LPD 1)   1975

Utility Helicopter, UH-46 "Sea Knight"

ASW patrol aircraft, P3 "Orion"

B. — *PATROL AIRCRAFT:*

Class, builder	Missions	Wingspan in m	Length in m	Height in m	Weight in kg	Motor	Max speed mach/knots	Ceiling in feet	1) Ferry range (miles) 2) Combat radius (miles) 3) Range (hours)
P-3 ORION (Lockheed)	ASW	30.35	35.60	10.29	64,000	4 Allison T 56 A 14 turboprops, 4,910 hp.	410 kts max 205 kts patrol	27,000	1) . . . 2) 2,000 without patrol time 3) 16 h

A: 6 mines of 2,000 pounds, 2 Mk 101 nuclear depth charges, 4 Mk 44 or 46 torpedoes, 87 sono buoys, etc. These weapons can vary and be made up, for instance, of 1 mine of 2,000 pounds, 3 of 1,000 pounds, 3 Mk 57 depth charges, 8 Mk 54 depth charges, 8 Mk 44 or 46 torpedoes, sono buoys and markers. The P-3 Orion can carry a total of 17,000 pounds of arms and equipment which can be dropped.

REMARKS: Several versions. The P3C is fitted with the A-NEW which is a sort of central operations module built around a miniaturized computer ASQ 114 and the ATDS.

C. — *HELICOPTERS:*

Class, builder	Missions	Diameter (rotor)	Length	Height	Weight in kg	Motor	Max speed in knots	Ceiling in feet	1) Range (miles) 2) Endurance (hours)
SH-3 A, D SEA KING (Sikorsky)	ASW	18.90	22.15	4.72	8,450	2 T 58 GE 10 turboshaft, 1,400 hp	144	14,700	1) 542 2) . . .

A: Depth charges or Mk 44 or 46 torpedoes, 840 pounds.

REMARKS: On the CV or CVS aircraft carriers or land-based. Fitted with a dipping sonar AQS 10. There is an RH-3 A version for minesweeping; HH-3 A, 3F and 3G (salvage).

SH-2 D SEA SPRITE (Kaman)	ASW	13.41	16.05	4.72	5,700	1 T 58 GE 8B turboshaft, 1,250 hp	146	22,500	1) 387 2) 2½ h

A: Sono buoys, 1 torpedo.

REMARKS: Found on FF, DD and CG types. Has replaced the DASH.

CH-46 A/D SEA KNIGHT (Boeing Vertol)	Troop-carrying assault helicopter (Marine Corps)	15.25	15.50	5.10	10,400	2 T 58 GE 8 turboshaft, 1,250 hp	155 (CH-46 A) 161 (CH-46 D)	14,000	1) 230 (CH-46 A), 248 (CH-46 D) 2) . . .

REMARKS: Can carry 33 fully-equipped troops. There are two cargo versions (UH-46 A and 46D) usually assigned to vertical replenishment duties on board the AOE and AKS class ships.

CH-53 SEA STALLION (Sikorsky)	Minesweeping (Navy). Assault transport (Marine Corps)	22.02	26.90	5.22	22,650	2 T 64 GE 6 turboshaft, 2,850 hp	170	21,000	1) 223 2) . . .

REMARKS: In version A can carry 38 fully equipped troops or 24 occupied stretchers with 4 hospital corpsmen or 4 tons of freight (2 Hawk missiles for example). CH-53E (three turboshafts) will enter service in 1976.

HELICOPTERS: (cont.)

		Diameter (rotor)	Length	Height	Weight in kg	Motor	Max speed in knots	Ceiling in feet	1) Range (miles) 2) Endurance (hours)
UH-1E IROQUOIS (Bell)	Assault and attack (Marine Corps)	13.41	12.98	3.87	2,155 (empty)	1 Lycoming T 53 L 5 turbine, 1,100 hp	140	14,000	1) 240 2) . . .

A: 2/7.62 machine guns and rockets.

REMARKS: Can carry 7 troops. The AH-IG Huey Cobra (diff. design) is especially armed for ground support (3-barrel 20-mm cannon, 76/2.75 in. rockets or six TOW anti-tank missiles).

HELICOPTERS FOR THE CG, DD AND FF CLASS SHIPS

Since 1961 the DASH-GYRODINE QH-50 C (300 hp) or D with remote control but without crew had been carried (1 or 2) on the destroyers which had been overhauled under the FRAM program. They could carry depth charges or ASW homing torpedoes and they had a 50-km radius. **Wingspan:** 6.10 m **Length:** 4 m. **Height:** 2.90 m.

However, DASH has not lived up to the high hopes placed in it and was to be replaced on cruisers, destroyers and frigates by another ASW system using the LAMPS (Light Airborne Multi Purpose System) helicopter. While still awaiting the completion of this new helicopter, the U.S. Navy is using the SH-2D Sea Sprite as an Interum LAMPS.

DIRIGIBLES

Since 1962 the U.S. Navy has not used any dirigibles and has put in reserve its hangar facilities and the craft. The latter, however, have been preserved in such a way that they could be brought back in service.

NUCLEAR-POWERED SUBMARINES

The nuclear reactor maintains (by means of a heat exchanger, circulating water under pressure) a steam cycle driving one or several conventional turbines, or, in certain submarines, turbo-generators which furnish the current required for an electric motor directly linked to the propeller.

Henry L. Stimson (SSBN 655)   1966

The American nuclear submarines belong to one or the other of the following classes:

♦ SSBN strategic submarines armed with Polaris A2 and A3 type ballistic missiles, Poseidon (since 1971), and eventually Trident.

♦ SSN attack submarines armed with torpedoes and/or Subroc.

The ballistic missiles are launched at very slow speed — less than 3 knots — while submerged, by means of a steam apparatus. The missile is automatically armed after emergence from the sea, about 30 m above the surface.

Fitted on the SSBN class is the DATICO (Digital Automatic Tape Intelligence Checkout) system for trial and control. DATICO is controlled by a magnetic tape carrying an arithmetic code which is constantly testing the 16 missiles to check their circuits and to reject unsuitable missiles. It would appear that this is the system which maintains continually required data on the target and the launching ship; thus one may always be certain that the weapons are ready to be fired towards the assigned target or targets.

Although the SSBN class can cruise at 20 knots submerged, they usually maintain a 5-knot speed on station. At this slow speed they can fire approximately one missile per minute. A much slower firing rate is attained on the surface due to the necessity of ballasting ship by pumping water into each of the sixteen missile wells.

The SSBN class submarine is fitted with the SINS (Ship Inertial Navigation System); this class can also use the Transit satellite navigation system. Signals sent by the satellite are received by a special computer at a regular interval; these signals are then compared with information received from other navigational systems.

NUCLEAR-POWERED SUBMARINES (*continued*)

The Thomas A. Edison (SSBN 610), alongside the *Hunley* receiving a *Polaris* missile

John C. Calhoun (SSBN 630)   1972

Dan Webster (SSBN 526). — Note the experimental position of the diving planes in the sonar dome on the bow at the extreme lower right of the photograph.

The 16 missile tubes of an SSBN

THE TRIDENT PROJECT

In keeping with the development demanded by technological progress, the United States has been studying for some years a strategic missile of extremely long range, launched from a submerged nuclear submarine.

Known in the beginning by the title ULMS (Under Sea Long Range Missile System), the project has made great strides in the perfection of a missile known as "Trident."

The Trident will have two models, I and II.

Trident I, with three propulsion stages, will have a range of 4,000 miles and a "bus" re-entry system carrying 12 or possibly 14 nuclear warheads. This is called the MIRV system for Multiple Independent Re-entry Vehicles. It will be fitted on very large SSBN submarines whose characteristics are outlined below, 24 to a ship. Thanks to its range, the Trident I will have a great advantage over those submarines carrying the Poseidon missile for it can be launched from a much greater distance, 4,000 miles in place of 2,500.

The Trident II which will follow will be able, it is hoped, to reach a target 6,000 miles from the launching submarine. It will be possibly fitted with MARV vehicles. The acceptance of the system towards the end of the 1980s will permit the phase-out of the Minuteman ICBM system.

The principal advantages of the Trident II would be:

— exceptional increase of the patrol sectors from which it would be possible to reach the entire enemy area, making detection of the launching submarine extremely difficult;

— extension of the patrol areas off enemy coasts which would permit phase-out of the present advanced bases for SSBM submarines (Holy Loch, Rota, Guam):

— finally and especially, removal of danger for American cities near Minuteman sites.

In its final version, the Trident system, fitted with 24 missiles per submarine on about 20 ships quite different from those carrying the Trident I system, will be the replacement of all weapons contributing to American deterrent strategy. It will add flexibility to American strength and a nearly total invulnerability.

FLEET BALLISTIC MISSILE SUBMARINES (SSBN)

♦ *4 Trident class (author. 1973-74 (1), 1974-75 (2), 1975-76 (1))*

SSBN	Bldr	Laid down	L	In serv.
726 OHIO	General Dynamics	1974		1978
727 N . . .	General Dynamics	1975		
728 N . . .	General Dynamics	1976		
729 N . . .	General Dynamics			

D: 12,000 surfaced/15,000 tons submerged **Dim:** 165 × . . . × . . .
S: 25 kts (submerged)
A: 24 Trident I missiles (see preceding page).
Electron Equipt: Sonar: *BQQ 6.*
M: 1 natural circulation water cooled reactor

REMARKS: Double hull (ballast tanks surround the entire length of the hull). The NCR reactor will have a 20-year life span, the same as the submarine. A more advanced and more precise inertial navigation system than the SINS of the SSBN now in service. Very quiet operation. Submersion depth: over 300 m.

Ten are planned, ordered according to the following sequence: 1 in FY 74, 2 in FY 75, 1 in FY 76, 2 in FY 77, 1 in FY 78, 2 in FY 79, 1 in FY 80.

♦ *31 SCB 216* and *216 A* type (After the *627*).
Lafayette and *Benjamin Franklin* classes.
Author. *1960-61 (616 to 626), 1961-62 (627 to 636), 1962-63 (6 + 6.)*

SSBN	Bldr	Laid down	L	In serv.
616 LAFAYETTE	Gen. Dynamics	1-61	8-5-62	23-4-63
617 ALEXANDER HAMILTON	Gen. Dynamics	6-61	18-8-62	27-6-63
619 ANDREW JACKSON	Mare Island NSY	4-61	15-9-62	3-7-63
620 JOHN ADAMS	Portsmouth NSY	1-62	12-1-63	12-5-64
622 JAMES MONROE	Newport News	7-61	4-8-62	7-12-63
623 NATHAN HALE	Gen. Dynamics	10-61	12-1-63	23-11-63
624 WOODROW WILSON	Mare Island NSY	9-61	22-2-63	27-12-63
625 HENRY CLAY	Newport News	10-61	30-11-62	20-2-64
626 DANIEL WEBSTER	Gen. Dynamics	12-61	27-4-63	9-4-64
627 JAMES MADISON	Newport News	2-62	15-3-63	28-7-64
628 TECUMSEH	Gen. Dynamics	6-62	22-6-63	29-5-64
629 DANIEL BOONE	Mare Island NSY	2-62	22-6-63	23-4-64
630 JOHN C. CALHOUN	Newport News	6-62	22-6-63	15-9-64
631 ULYSSES S. GRANT	Gen. Dynamics	8-62	2-11-63	17-7-64
632 VON STEUBEN	Newport News	9-62	18-10-63	30-9-64
633 CASIMIR PULASKI	Gen. Dynamics	1-63	1-2-64	14-8-64
634 STONEWALL JACKSON	Mare Island NSY	7-62	30-11-63	26-8-64
635 SAM RAYBURN	Newport News	12-62	20-12-63	2-12-64
636 NATHANAEL GREENE	Portsmouth NSY	5-62	12-5-64	19-12-64
640 BENJAMIN FRANKLIN	Gen. Dynamics	5-63	5-12-64	22-10-65
641 SIMON BOLIVAR	Newport News	4-63	22-8-64	29-10-65
642 KAMEHAMEHA	Mare Island NSY	5-63	16-1-65	10-12-65
643 GEORGE BANCROFT	Gen. Dynamics	8-63	20-3-65	22-1-66
644 LEWIS AND CLARK	Newport News	7-63	21-11-64	22-12-65
645 JAMES K. POLK	Gen. Dynamics	11-63	22-5-65	16-4-66
654 GEORGE C. MARSHALL	Newport News	3-64	21-5-65	29-4-66
655 HENRY L. STIMSON	Gen. Dynamics	4-64	13-11-65	20-8-66
656 GEORGE WASHINGTON CARVER	Newport News	8-64	14-8-65	15-6-66
657 FRANCIS SCOTT KEY	Gen. Dynamics	8-64	23-4-66	3-12-66
658 MARIANO G. VALLEJO	Mare Island NSY	7-64	23-10-65	16-12-66
659 WILL ROGERS	Gen. Dynamics	3-65	21-7-66	1-4-67

FLEET BALLISTIC MISSILE SUBMARINES (SSBN) *(continued)*

D: 7,320 surfaced tons/8,250 submerged
Dim: 129.54 × 10.05 × 9.00
S: 25 kts (submerged)   **Man:** 14 officers, 126 men
A: Originally 16 Polaris A 2 616/617, 619/625, 16 Polaris A 3 on the following ships
All have been refitted with the Poseidon missile — 4/533-mm TT fwd (can launch Subroc missile)
Electron Equipt: Sonar: SSBN Unit
M: 1 SW 5 Westinghouse pressurized water reactor, 1/7-bladed prop; 15,000 hp.

REMARKS: Submersion depth over 250 m. Mk 84 computer for analysis, display and transmission of tactical information. After the *640*, a more silent propulsion machinery and a larger crew, 20 officers and 148 men. Poseidon missile will be replaced by Trident I. Funds will be requested FY 1979 for conversion of the first SSBN and for 3 each year thereafter until FY 1982 inclusive.

♦ *SCB 180 type Ethan Allen class*
Author: 1958-59 (608 to 611) 1960-61 (618)

SSBN		Bldr	Laid down	L	In serv.
608	ETHAN ALLEN	Gen Dynamics	9-59	22-11-60	8-8-61
609	SAM HOUSTON	Newport News	12-59	2-2-61	6-3-62
610	THOMAS A. EDISON	Gen. Dynamics	3-60	15-6-61	10-3-62
611	JOHN MARSHALL	Newport News	4-60	15-7-61	21-5-62
618	THOMAS JEFFERSON	Newport News	2-61	24-2-62	4-1-63

D: 6,300 surfaced tons (6,955 avg)   **Dim:** 124.96 × 10.05 × 9.00
(7,880 submerged)
S: 20 kts (submerged)   **Man:** 10/12 officers, 120 men
A: 16 Polaris A 2 — 4/533-mm TT fwd, four conventional or eight ASW torpedoes as reloads.   **M:** as above
Electron Equipt: SSBN Sonar Unit

REMARKS: Mk 80 computer

♦ *5 SCB 180A type George Washington class*
Author: 1957-58 (598 to 600), 1958-59 (601/02).

SSBN		Bldr	Laid down	L	In serv.
598	GEORGE WASHINGTON	Gen Dynamics	1-57	9-6-59	30-12-59
599	PATRICK HENRY	Gen. Dynamics	6-58	22-9-59	9-4-60
600	THEODORE ROOSEVELT	Mare Island NSY	5-58	3-10-59	13-2-61
601	ROBERT E. LEE	Newport News SB	8-58	18-12-59	16-9-60
602	ABRAHAM LINCOLN	Portsmouth NSY	11-58	14-5-60	11-3-61

D: 5,400 surfaced tons, (5,900 avg), 6,700 (submerged)
Dim: 115.82 × 10.05 × 8.80   **Man:** 10/12 officers, 90/100 men
S: 20 kts (submerged)   **M:** as the preceding
A: 16 Polaris A 3, 6/533-mm TT fwd
Electron Equipt: Sonar: SSBN Sonar Unit

REMARKS: During her first cruise (30-12-60 to 8-3-61) the *599* stayed submerged for 66 days, 22 hours, traveled 11,000 miles (20,400 km) and, in exercises, successfully launched 8 Polaris missiles. The *598* cruised from 12-59 to 3-65 with her original nuclear core. From 6-64 to 6-67 the *598* to the *602* were overhauled: a new core, launching wells modified to permit launch by steam of the A 3 missiles in place of the original A 1, and a Mk 84 computer were added.

Permit (SSN 594)

NUCLEAR-POWERED ATTACK SUBMARINES (SSN)

♦ *23 type 688 Los Angeles class*

		Author	Bldr	Laid down	L	In serv.
688	LOS ANGELES	*69-70*	Newport News	8-1-72	6-4-74	6-76
689	BATON ROUGE	*69-70*	Newport News	18-11-72	18-4-75	7-76
690	PHILADELPHIA	*69-70*	Gen. Dynamics	12-8-72	19-10-74	1-77
691	MEMPHIS	*70-71*	Newport News	23-6-73	3-4-76	1-77
692	OMAHA	*70-71*	Gen. Dynamics	27-1-73	. . .	1-77
693	CINCINNATI	*70-71*	Newport News	6-4-74	. . .	7-77
694	GROTON	*70-71*	Gen. Dynamics	3-8-73	. . .	1-78
695	BIRMINGHAM	*71-72*	Newport News	26-4-75	. . .	10-77

NUCLEAR-POWERED ATTACK SUBMARINES (SSN) *(continued)*

			Laid down	L	In serv.
696 NEW YORK CITY	71-72	Gen. Dynamics	15-12-73	...	78
697 INDIANAPOLIS	71-72	Gen. Dynamics	19-10-74	...	78
698 BREMERTON	71-72	Gen. Dynamics	8-74	...	79
699 JACKSONVILLE	71-72	Gen. Dynamics	12-74	...	79
700 N ...	71-72	Gen. Dynamics	...	...	...
701 N ...	72-73	Gen. Dynamics	...	...	...
702 N ...	72-73	Gen. Dynamics	...	...	...
703 N ...	72-73	Gen. Dynamics	...	...	...
704 N ...	72-73	Gen. Dynamics	...	...	...
705 N ...	72-73	Gen. Dynamics	...	...	...
706 N ...	73-74	...	...	...	...
707 N ...	73-74	...	...	...	...
708 N ...	73-74	...	...	...	...
709 N ...	73-74	...	...	...	...
710 N ...	73-74	...	...	...	...
711 N ...	74-75	...	...	...	...
712 N ...	74-75	...	...	...	...
713 N ...	74-75	...	...	...	...

D: .../(6,900 tons submerged)   **Dim:** 109.73 × 10.06 × 9.75
S: .../35-40 kts   **Man:** ... officers, ... men
A: TT (Mk 48) — Subroc
Electron Equipt: Radar: 1/BPS 15
                    Sonars: 1/BQQ 5. Computer: UYK-7
M: 1 D2G (?) reactor; 2 GT; 1 prop; 30,000 hp

♦ *1 TEDS class author. 1968*

		Bldr	Laid down	L	In serv.
685 GLENARD P LIPSCOMB		General Dyn	5-6-71	4-8-73	21-12-74

D: 5,800 standard; 6,480 submerged
Dim: 110 × 9.6 × 8.8
S: 25 kts   **A:** 4/533-mm TT, Subroc
M: 1 S5WA reactor and turbo-electric drive

♦ *37 SCB 188 M and 188 A type Sturgeon class*

SSN	Author	Bldr	Laid down	L	In serv.
637 STURGEON	61-62	Gen. Dynamics	8-63	26-2-66	3-3-67
638 WHALE	61-62	Gen. Dynamics	5-64	14-20-66	12-10-68
639 TAUTOG	61-62	Ingalls, Pascagoula	1-64	15-4-67	17-8-68
646 GRAYLING	62-63	Portsmouth NSY	5-64	22-6-67	11-10-69
647 POGY (see note)	62-63	New York SB, Camden	5-64	3-6-67	15-5-71
648 ASPRO	62-63	Ingalls, Pascagoula	11-64	29-11-67	20-2-69
649 SUNFISH	62-63	Gen. Dynamics	1-65	14-10-66	15-3-69
650 PARGO	62-63	Gen. Dynamics	6-64	17-9-66	1-5-68
651 QUEENFISH	62-63	Newport News	5-64	25-2-66	6-12-66
652 PUFFER	62-63	Ingalls, Pascagoula	2-65	30-3-68	9-8-69
653 RAY	62-63	Newport News	1-65	21-6-66	12-4-67

660 SANDLANCE	63-64	Portsmouth NSY	1-65	11-11-69	25-9-71
661 LAPON	63-64	Newport News	7-65	16-12-66	14-12-67
662 GURNARD	63-64	Mare Island NSY	12-64	20-5-67	6-12-68
663 HAMMERHEAD	63-64	Newport News	11-65	14-4-67	28-6-68
664 SEA DEVIL	63-64	Newport News	4-66	5-10-67	30-1-69
665 GUITARRO	64-65	Mare Island NSY	12-65	27-7-68	9-9-72
666 HAWKBILL	64-65	Mare Island NSY	9-66	12-4-69	4-2-71
667 BERGALL	64-65	Gen. Dynamics	4-66	17-2-69	13-6-69
668 SPADEFISH	64-65	Newport News	12-66	15-5-68	14-8-69
669 SEA HORSE	64-65	Gen. Dynamics	8-66	15-6-68	19-9-69
670 FINBACK	64-65	Newport News	6-67	7-12-68	4-2-70
672 PINTADO	65-66	Mare Island NSY	10-67	16-8-69	11-9-71
673 FLYING FISH	65-66	Gen. Dynamics	10-67	17-5-69	29-4-70
674 TREPANG	65-66	Gen. Dynamics	3-68	27-9-69	14-8-70
675 BLUEFISH	65-66	Gen. Dynamics	3-68	10-1-70	8-1-71
676 BILLFISH	65-66	Gen. Dynamics	9-68	1-5-70	12-3-71
677 DRUM	65-66	Mare Island NSY	8-68	23-5-70	15-4-72
678 ARCHERFISH	66-67	Gen. Dynamics	6-69	16-1-71	24-12-71
679 SILVERSIDES	66-67	Gen. Dynamics	12-69	4-6-71	5-5-72
680 Wm. H. BATES	66-67	Ingalls, Pascagoula	8-69	12-71	5-5-73
681 BATFISH	66-67	Gen. Dynamics	2-70	9-10-71	1-9-72
682 TUNNY	66-67	Ingalls, Pascagoula	5-70	10-6-72	26-1-74
683 PARCHE	67-68	Ingalls, Pascagoula	12-70	12-72	17-8-74
684 CAVALLA	67-68	Gen. Dynamics	6-70	19-2-72	9-2-73
686 L. MENDEL RIVERS	68-69	Newport News	6-71	2-6-73	31-12-74
687 RICHARD B. RUSSELL	68-69	Newport News	10-71	12-1-74	9-75

REMARKS: The construction contract of the *647* with N.Y. Shipbuilding, Camden, was cancelled in 4-67 and the completion of the ship given to Ingalls, Pascagoula. The *SSN-665* was delayed 28 months in completion because of negligence in the yard.

Drum (SSN 677)   1972

NUCLEAR-POWERED ATTACK SUBMARINES (SSN) (*continued*)

Archerfish (SSN 678)   1972

D: 3,640 tons surfaced/4,640 submerged
Dim: 89 × 9.65 × 8.80
S: 15/30 kts   **A:**   4/533-mm TT, Subroc
Range: 90-100,000
Man: 9 or 10 officers, 85 to 95 men
Electron Equipt: Radar: 1/BPS 14
                Sonars: BQQ 1 System, Retrofit III: 1/BQS 8, 1/BQS 13
M: 1/S5W2 Westinghouse reactor; General Electric or de Laval GT; 1 prop; 20,000 hp

Hawkbill (SSN 666) with a DSRV   1971

REMARKS: The attack center is fitted with analog and digital computers. Two counter-rotating propellers mounted on a single shaft. The torpedo tubes are amidships. The width of the diving planes is 11.60 m. Maximum depth about 500 m.

The *Hawkbill* (*SSN-666*) has been modified to carry a DSRV (salvage submarine) so that she can launch and recover while submerged. The after hatch is so constructed that personnel transfer can take place between the two ships while submerged.

♦ *13 SLB 188 type (594/612/621) SCB 188 M type (613/615) Thresher-Permit class*

	Author	Bldr	Laid down	L	In serv.
594 PERMIT	*57-58*	Mare Island NSY	7-59	1-7-61	29-5-62
595 PLUNGER	*57-58*	Mare Island NSY	3-60	12-9-61	21-11-62
596 BARB (ex-*Pollack*)	*57-58*	Ingalls, Pascagoula	11-59	12-2-62	24-8-63
603 POLLACK (ex-*Barb*)	*58-59*	New York SB, Camden	3-60	17-3-62	26-5-64
604 HADDO	*58-59*	New York SB, Camden	9-60	18-8-62	16-12-64
605 JACK	*58-59*	Portsmouth NSY	9-60	24-4-63	31-3-67
606 TINOSA	*58-59*	Portsmouth NSY	11-59	9-12-61	17-10-64
607 DACE	*58-59*	Ingalls, Pascagoula	6-60	18-8-62	4-4-64
612 GUARDFISH	*59-60*	New York SB, Camden	2-61	15-5-65	20-12-66
613 FLASHER	*59-60*	Gen. Dynamics	4-61	22-6-63	22-7-66
614 GREENLING	*59-60*	Gen. Dynamics	8-61	4-4-64	3-11-67
615 GATO	*59-60*	Gen. Dynamics	12-61	14-5-64	25-1-68
621 HADDOCK	*60-61*	Ingalls, Pascagoula	4-61	21-5-66	22-12-67

Plunger (SSN 595)

1) Up to *612* inclusive plus *621*
    D: 3,526 tons surfaced/4,310 submerged   **Dim:**   84.88 × 9.75 × 8.80
2) *605*
    D: 3,526 tons surfaced/4,465 submerged   **Dim:**   90.11 × 9.65 × 8.80
3) *613, 614, 615*
    D: 3,836 tons surfaced/4,650 submerged   **Dim:**   89 × 9.65 × 8.80
    A: 4/533-mm TT, Subroc   **S:**   30/15 kts   **Man:**   12 officers, 91 men
    Electron Equipt: Sonar: BQQ 1, Retrofit III
    M: 1 S5W2 Westinghouse reactor; General Electric or de Laval GT; 1 prop.

REMARKS: see *Sturgeon* class

NUCLEAR-POWERED ATTACK SUBMARINES (SSN) *(continued)*

♦ *1 prototype based on the Permit class (project SCB-245)*
  Author. 63-64

	Bldr	Laid down	L	In serv.
SSN 671 NARWHAL	Gen. Dynamics	1-66	9-9-67	12-7-69

Narwhal (SSN 671)   1967

D: 4,550 tons surfaced, 5,350 submerged   **Dim:** 95.70 × 11.50 × 7.90
S: 25/20 kts   **Man:** 12 officers, 95 men
A: 4/533-mm TT, Subroc
Electron Equipt: Sonar: BQQ 1
M: 1 S5G General Electric reactor; 17,000 hp; 1 prop

REMARKS: Prototype seagoing reactor designed to study the cooling of the S5G reactor by free circulation, thus eliminating circulation pumps and their noise.

♦ *1 special (SCB 178) type*

	Author	Bldr	Laid down	L	In serv.
SSN 597 TULLIBEE	57-58	General Dynamics	5-58	27-4-60	8-60

D: 2,317 tons surfaced (2,490 normal), 2,640 submerged
Dim: 83.15 × 7.31 × 6.10   **S:** 20/15 kts
A: 4/533-mm TT   **Man:** 6 officers, 50 men
Electron Equipt: Sonar: BQQ 1
M: 1 Combustion Engineering S2C reactor: turbo-electric propulsion; 1 prop.

REMARKS: Used as experimental vessel. The torpedo tubes (amidships) have a 10° angle from the center line. Turbo-electric propulsion with GTs. Original nuclear core changed in 1965.

♦ *1 SCB 137 A (ex-SSGN) type*

	Author	Bldr	Laid down	L	In serv.
SSN 587 HALIBUT	56-57	Mare Island NSY	4-57	9-1-59	4-1-60

D: 3,850 tons surfaced/5,000 submerged   **Dim:** 106.70 × 8.85 × 8.80
S: 20/15 kts

Tullibee (SSN 597)

Halibut (SSN 587)   1968

A: 4/533-mm TT (see remarks)   **Man:** 9 officers, 88 men
M: 1 S3W Westinghouse reactor; 2 GT; 12,000 hp; 2 props

REMARKS: Forward compartment 27 meters long and 7.60 in height where four Regulus missiles were stowed; these missiles as well as their launchers were removed in 1965 when the ship was reclassified as an SSN. To enter reserve 6-76.

♦ *1 SCB 132 (ex-SSRN) type*

	Author	Bldr	Laid down	L	In serv.
SSN 586 TRITON	56-57	General Dynamics	5-56	19-8-58	10-11-59

D: 5,940 tons surfaced/7,780 submerged
Dim: 136.25 × 11.30 × 7.60
S: 27/20 kts   **A:** 6/533-mm TT (4 fwd, 2 aft)
M: 2 S4G Gen. Dynamics reactors; 2 props
Man: 16 officers, 156 men

REMARKS: First submarine with three decks. In 1960 made a round-the-world cruise

NUCLEAR-POWERED ATTACK SUBMARINES (SSN) *(continued)*

Triton (SSN 586)

submerged, sailing 41,519 miles in 84 days at an average speed of 18 knots. In 1962 the original nuclear core with which the *Triton* had run 125,000 miles (231,500 km) was replaced. Contrary to other nuclear submarines, her speed is much greater on the surface than submerged and because of her conventional hull configuration she has good seagoing qualities. It had been hoped that she would be able to operate easily with the large surface ship task forces as a radar picket. Decommissioned since 3-69.

♦ 5 SCB 154 type Skipjack class

SSN	Author	Bldr	Laid down	L	In serv.
585 SKIPJACK	55-56	Gen. Dynamics	5-56	26-5-58	15-4-59
588 SCAMP	56-57	Mare I., NSY	1-59	15-2-60	5-6-61
590 SCULPIN	56-57	Ingalls, Pascagoula	2-58	31-3-60	1-6-61
591 SHARK	56-57	Newport News SB	2-56	16-3-60	9-2-61
592 SNOOK	56-57	Ingalls, Pascagoula	4-58	31-10-60	24-10-61

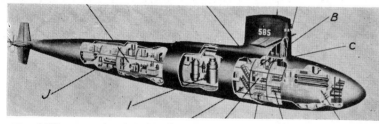

D: 3,075 tons surfaced/3,500 submerged   **Dim:** 76.80 × 9.75 × 8.50
S: 25/15 kts   **Man:** 8 officers, 85 men
A: 6/533-mm TT, 24 torpedoes
M: 1 S5W Westinghouse reactor; 1 Westinghouse GT (*585*) or General Electric (the others)
Range: 100,000

REMARKS: The reactor compartment takes up 6.10 m. Between the reactor and the propeller, all engine fittings are duplicated (two heat exchangers, two pressurized water coolers, two groups of turbines, two groups of turbo-generators). In case of emergency, submerged propulsion can take place by means of two electric motors linked directly on the propeller shaft and feeding off two electric batteries or two small diesel generators. The *Scorpion* (SS-589) disappeared in the Atlantic about 27-5-1968.

♦ 4 SCB 121 Skate class

SSN	Author	Bldr	Laid down	L	In serv.
578 SKATE	54-55	Gen. Dynamics	7-55	16-5-57	22-12-57
579 SWORDFISH	54-55	Portsmouth NSY	1-56	27-8-57	15-9-58
583 SARGO	55-56	Mare Island NSY	2-56	10-10-57	1-10-58
584 SEADRAGON	55-56	Portsmouth NSY	6-56	16-8-58	5-12-59

Skate (SSN 578)

D: 2,570 tons surfaced/2,860 submerged   **Dim:** 81.40 × 7.62 × 6.10
S: 19/15 kts   **Man:** 9 officers, 87 men
A: 6/533-mm TT (4 fwd, 2 aft)
M: 1 Westinghouse S3W reactor in *578, 582, 582*; S4W reactor in *579, 584*; 2 GT; 2 props; 13,200 hp

REMARKS: The *Skate* passed under the North Pole twice (8-58) coming to the surface nine times while in the ice-capped waters during this cruise. *579, 583* have missile guidance apparatus. The *578* ran 120,862 miles in 39 months with her first core.

♦ 1 SCB 64 A type

SSN	Author	Bldr	Laid down	L	In serv.
575 SEAWOLF	52-53	Gen. Dynamics	9-53	21-7-55	30-3-57

D: 3,721 tons surfaced/4,287 submerged   **Dim:** 103.17 × 8.45 × 6.70
S: 20/20 kts   **Man:** 10 officers, 95 men

Sea Wolf (SSN 575)

A: 6/533-mm TT fwd
M: (1959-60) 1 S2WA Westinghouse reactor; 2 GT; 15,000 hp; 2 props

NUCLEAR-POWERED ATTACK SUBMARINES (SSN) *(continued)*

REMARKS: Original propulsion by a S2G reactor with sodium cooling. Not having been satisfactory, it was replaced by 1 S2W A.

♦ *SCB 64 type*

	Author	Bldr	Laid down	L	In serv.
SSN 571 NAUTILUS	51-52	Gen. Dynamics	6-52	21-1-54	30-9-54

Nautilus (SSN 571)   1975

D: 3,532 tons surfaced/4,091 submerged
Dim: 98.65 × 8.45 × 6.70
S: 20/20 kts   **Man:**   10 officers, 95 men
A: 6/533-mm TT fwd.
M: 1 S3W Westinghouse reactor; 2 GT; 25,000 hp; 2 props

REMARKS: First nuclear submarine in the world. Overhaul from 1974-75.

CONVENTIONAL SUBMARINES (SS)

♦ *3 SCB 150*

SS	Bldr	Laid down	L	In serv.
580 BARBEL	Portsmouth NSY	18-5-56	19-7-58	17-1-59
581 BLUEBACK	Ingalls (Pascagoula)	15-4-57	16-5-59	15-10-59
582 BONEFISH	New York SB Corp	3-6-57	22-11-58	9-7-59

D: 1,740 tons standard/2,150 surfaced/2,895 submerged
Dim: 66.75 × 8.84 × 5.80
S: 25/15 kts   **Man:**   8 officers, 70 men
A: 6/533-mm TT fwd
M: Diesel-electric drive (3 Fairbanks Morse, 1 Westinghouse electric motor); 1 prop; 4,800 hp

REMARKS: Teardrop hull design as on the *Albacore*. Diving planes have been relocated to the sail structure.

Barbel (SS 580)   1969

♦ *2 "ex-radar picket"* (author. 51-52) *SCB 84-282 type Sailfish class*

	Bldr	Laid down	L	In serv.
SS 572 SAILFISH	Portsmouth NSY	8-12-53	7-9-55	14-4-56
SS 573 SALMON	Portsmouth NSY	10-3-54	25-2-56	25-8-56

Sailfish (SS 572)   1968

D: 2,045 tons standard/2,485 surfaced/3,168 submerged
Dim: 106.80 × 8.84 × 4.98
S: 20/15 kts   **Man:**   95 men
A: 6/533-mm TT (fwd)
M: 4 Fairbanks-Morse diesels; 2 props; 8,200 hp

REMARKS: Modernized by FRAM.

♦ *1 SCB 116 type* (author. 53-54)

	Bldr	Laid down	L	In serv.
SS 576 DARTER	Electric Boat Co.	1-11-54	28-5-56	20-1-56

D: 1,590 tons standard/1,870 aver./2,372 submerged
Dim: 81.68 × 8.23 × 5.80
S: 20/20 kts   **Man:**   85 men
A: 8/533-mm TT (6 fwd, 2 aft)
M: Diesel electric (3 Fairbanks diesels, 2 electric Westinghouse motors); 2 props; 6,000 hp

CONVENTIONAL SUBMARINES (SS) (*continued*)

Darter (SS 576)

REMARKS: Derived from the *Tang* class; conventional hull form

♦ *4 SCB-2A type Tang class*

SS	Author	Bldr	Laid down	L	In serv.
563 TANG	*1948-49*	Portsmouth NSY	4-49	19-6-51	4-52
565 WAHOO	*1948-49*	Portsmouth NSY	10-49	16-10-51	30-5-52
566 TROUT	*1948-49*	Electric Boat Co.	12-49	21-8-51	27-6-52
567 GUDGEON	*1949-50*	Portsmouth NSY	5-50	11-6-62	21-11-52

Tang (SS 563) The BQS 4 sonars are visible on the deck

Gudgeon (SS 567)   1971

> **D:** 2,100 tons surfaced/2,700 submerged
> **Dim:** 84.73 × 8.30 × 5.70
> **S:** 20/17 kts   **Man:** 8 officers, 75 men
> **A:** 8/533-mm TT (6 fwd, 2 aft)
> **M:** diesel-electric propulsion (see remarks); 2 props; 5,600 hp
> **Fuel:** 350 tons

REMARKS: Based on the German type XXI of 1944. Forward diving planes retractable. The pancake engines of the first four having proved unsatisfactory, they were replaced by the same Fairbanks-Morse rapid diesels that were used in the last two built, which necessitated an additional 2.75 m lengthening of the ship (1957-58). *567*

was used for trials of a plastic bridge in the sail structure (1964-65). FRAM modernization. *Trigger* (SS-564) and *Harder* (SS-568) were transferred to Italy in 7-73 and 3-74 respectively. *Tang* replaced the AGSS *Tigrone* in 1975 as a trials ship. Three submarines of this class will be transferred to the Iranian Navy.

♦ *1 SCB 161 type*

	Bldr	Laid down	L	In serv.
SS 574 GRAYBACK	Mare Island NSY	1-7-54	2-7-57	5-58
SSG 577 GROWLER	Portsmouth NSY	10-11-54	28-5-56	4-58

Grayback (SS 574)   1969

> **D:** 2,174 tons surfaced/3,390 submerged   **Dim:** 96.8 × 9.14 × 5.20
> **S:** 16/12 kts   **A:** 4/533-mm TT   **Man:** 7 officers, 60 men
> **M:** diesel-electric propulsion, (3 Fairbanks-Morse); 2 props; 3,120 hp

REMARKS: Designed as SSG carrying Regulus surface-to-surface missiles. LPSS conversion finished in 1970 took 6 years. In that year the conversion of the *Growler* was cancelled and the ship was decommissioned. 574 redesignated SS in 1975, is 101.8 meters overall.

♦ *1 Balao class modified as a troop transport submarine (1948-49)*

	Bldr	Laid down	L	In serv.
LPSS 315 SEALION	Electric Boat Co.	2-43	31-10-43	3-44

CONVENTIONAL SUBMARINES (SS) *(continued)*

D: 2,145 tons surfaced/2,500 submerged. Hull from the *Balao* class, 2 diesels instead of 4

S: 13/9 kts **A:** TT removed

Man: 74 men; can accommodate 160 additional troops, weapons, craft, etc. In reserve. (1969).

♦ *1 SCB 207 experimental type (author. 60-61)*

	Bldr	Laid down	L	In serv.
AGSS 555 DOLPHIN	Portsmouth NSY	11-62	8-6-68	8-69

1969

D: 800 tons surfaced/930 submerged **Dim:** 46.33 × 5.79 × 4.90

S: .../12 kts **Man:** 23 men

M: diesel-electric propulsion; 1,650 hp; 1 prop

REMARKS: The hull is a perfect cylinder 5.49 m in diameter, strongly braced and closed at the forward and after ends by two hemispheric bulkheads, with minimum compartmentation. Used for deep diving tests as well as acoustic and oceanographic experiments. Extensive use of alloys and plastics. Can be used as a target ship.

♦ *1 Experimental submarine class, SCB 182 A (Author: 51-52)*

	Bldr	Laid down	L	In serv.
AGSS 569 ALBACORE	Portsmouth NSY	15-3-52	1-8-53	12-53

D: 1,265 tons surfaced/1,517 normal/1,810 submerged

Dim: 60.95 × 8.33 × 5.65

S: 25/15 kts without weapons **Man:** 5 officers, 47 men

M: 1 diesel; 1,700 hp; 1 electric motor (see remarks); 1/5-bladed prop

REMARKS: Hydrodynamic (teardrop) hull. Fittings reduced to a minimum. Tall, straight sail with vertical lines. Forward planes non-retractable; after diving planes and rudder forward of the propeller. At 18 knots and an angle of 20° can submerge 105 m per minute.

The *565* was fitted in 1963 with a new type electric motor which drives counter-rotating propellers. New type batteries have permitted higher speed and greater distances while submerged. In reserve 9-72.

RESEARCH AND SALVAGE SUBMARINES

♦ *1 nuclear research submarine for deep diving*

	Author	Bldr	Laid down	L	In serv.
NR 1	1965-66	Electric Boat Co.	6-67	21-1-69	27-10-69

NR 1

D: 400 tons surfaced/700 submerged **Dim:** 42.67 × 3.75 × 4.45

Man: 3 officers, 9 men + 2 scientists

M: 1 reactor; turbo-electric drive; 2 props

REMARKS: Project approved 18-4-65. Designated as a Deep Submergence Research Vessel; fitted for all oceanographic missions whether military or civil. Thick cylindrical hull. Wheels for moving on the ocean bottom. A very successful ship.

RESEARCH AND SALVAGE SUBMARINES

The impossibility of bringing help to the submarine *Thresher* which disappeared 10-4-63 in 1,400 fathoms and an interest in certain oceanographic studies have led the United States to develop small submersibles which are able to operate at great depths and can rescue the crews of sunken submarines.

Since 1963 different types have been tried and the U.S. Navy has undertaken a project called DSSP (Deep Submergence System Project) which should bring into service several ships designated DSRV (Deep Submergence Rescue Vehicles). Built by the Lockheed Missile and Space Company of Sunnyvale, California, they can:

— operate at a maximum depth of 3,500 feet (1,070 m)

— stand a pressure equal to 9,000 feet (2,750 m)

— dive or rise at 100 feet a minute

— have a maximum speed of 5 knots while submerged

— have a submerged endurance of 30 hours at 3 knots

— maintain station in a 1-knot current

— have all machinery operate submerged at a 45° angle.

DSRV 1 — DSRV 2 — Bldr: Lockheed Missile and Space Co. — 1970-71

D: 35 tons **Dim:** 15 × 2.50 × ...

M: electric **S:** 5 kts

REMARKS: Three men including one hospital corpsman are carried by these DSRV which can bring up to 24 men to the surface at one time. Motors energized by a

RESEARCH AND SALVAGE SUBMARINES (*continued*)

DSRV 1   1970

zinc-battery can turn a regular propulsion propeller and two types of rotor (one fwd, one aft) or two variable pitch propellers which can be positioned (one fwd, one aft) permitting a close approach to a sunken object. They have an articulated arm with pincers for removing debris. Size and weight have been determined by the necessity, should the case arise, of transporting these machines by air in the Starlifter (Lockheed C-141 A) cargo airplane. Additional equipment, especially a truck transport for the DSRV, would be carried in a second Starlifter. In addition, the SSN nuclear submarines have received or will receive the equipment necessary to fasten the DSRV to their deck (see photograph of the *Hawkbill* (*SS-666*) with a DSRV secured to its deck) and carry it at 15 knots. The SSN will serve as a base for the DSRV while awaiting the arrival of a submarine rescue ship (ASR). A new class ASR with a double (catamaran) hull has been designed for use with the DSRV. See also the *Halibut* (*SSN-857*).

OTHER SMALL DEEP DIVING SUBMARINES

♦ DSV 1 TRIESTE II

D:	220 tons (submerged)	**Dim:**	22.86 × 4.58
S:	2 kts	**Man:**	3 men
M:	Propulsion electric	**Range:**	5 hrs × 2 kts

REMARKS: U.S. Navy bought Prof. Picard's *Trieste*, modified and renamed it *Trieste II*. Can dive as deep as 6,100 m.

DSV 4 Sea Cliff and DSV 3 Turtle   1970

♦ DSV 3 TURTLE — DSV 4 SEA CLIFF — DSV 5 NEMO

D:	32 tons dw	**Dim:**	14.95 × 2.43
M:	1 electric motor	**S:**	5 kts

REMARKS: The *Aluminaut* was built by a private concern and does not belong to the Navy; the DSV 1 *Alvin* (weight 13 tons dw — **Dim:** 6.70 × 7.44 — **S:** 4) sank accidentally in 1,500 m of water.

BATTLESHIP FIRE SUPPORT SHIPS

♦ 1 former ship of the line

The U.S. Navy is maintaining in inactive reserve (2 at Philadelphia and 2 at Bremerton) as potential fire support ships the four battleships *Iowa* (*BB-61*), *Wisconsin* (*BB-64*), *New Jersey* (*BB-62*), and *Missouri* (*BB-63*) now in reserve since 1955. The *New Jersey*, reactivated from 1966 to December of 1969, underwent a partial overhaul which permitted her to be used in Vietnam in bombardment operations where her large 406-mm guns were very effective. The only survivors of a long line of Dreadnought battleships which for several decades had been the keystone of the fleet, they could not be returned to service, with the exception of the *New Jersey*, without a long overhaul. The *Missouri* having gone aground in 1950 was never restored to her original condition and speed, and even if her propulsion machinery were restored, it would always be quite reduced. A fire broke out in the *Wisconsin* near the 406-mm number 1 and 2 turrets during her last inactivation overhaul and the circuitry was not repaired. The electronic equipment of the *Iowa* is completely out of date, and she and the *Wisconsin* have been more or less cannibalized to refurbish the *New Jersey*. The superstructure and fittings of the latter have been completely overhauled and the most modern electronic warfare equipment has been installed. All the original anti-aircraft guns — about 40/40-mm — have been removed and only the 406-mm and 127-mm turrets were manned during her reactivation.

		Bldr	Laid down	L	In serv.
62 NEW JERSEY		Philadelphia NSY	16-9-40	7-12-42	23-5-43

D:	45,000 tons (58,000 fl)	**Dim:**	271.25 (262.50 pp) × 32.95 × 11
S:	25/27 kts after reactivation		

New Jersey (BB 62)   1968

BATTLESHIP FIRE SUPPORT SHIPS (*continued*)

New Jersey (BB 62)   1969

Man: 70 officers — 1,556 men after reactivation
A: 9/406-mm (III × 3) — 20/127-mm AA (II × 10)
M: 4 GT; 4 props; 212,000 hp
Armor: Belt: 406 — 3 armored decks with a total of 285 (one of 200)
       Turrets and bridge: 457
Boilers: 8 Babcock and Wilcox   **Fuel:** 8,800 tons

CRUISERS

Five heavy cruisers are still in reserve: *Des Moines* (*CA-134*), *Salem*, (*CA-139*), *Newport News*, (*CA-148*), *Saint Paul* (*CA-73*), *Canberra* (*CA-70*). The *Newport News* which is the most recent and the last placed in reserve (27-6-75) has the following characteristics:

D: 16,000 tons (21,500 fl)   **Dim:** 218.42 × 22.96 × 7.50
S: 32 kts   **Range:** 8,000/15
Man: 105 officers, 1,745 men (war) — 1,400 men (peace).
A: 8/203-mm AA (III × 2, II × 2) — 12/127-mm AA (II × 6) — 16/76-mm
    AA automatics (II × 8) (4 on the *148*) — 1 helicopter
Electron Equipt: Radars: 2/SPS 10, 1/SPS 6E, 1/SPS 8A, 1/SPS 39.
Armor: Belt: 152/203 — upper deck: 76 — lower deck: 52
M: GT; 4 props; 120,000 hp; Babcock and Wilcox boilers
Fuel: 2,600 tons

REMARKS: Fitted out as a flagship. The number 2 turret has only two barrels, the central gun having been destroyed in an explosion and not replaced; its gun embrasure has been plated over.

NUCLEAR-POWERED GUIDED MISSILE CRUISERS

Project CSGN

In order to be able to counter the large Soviet cruisers of the Kara class, the U.S. Navy has under study at the present time a heavy cruiser with nuclear propulsion, the CSGN. This 12,000 to 15,000-ton ship would carry helicopters. Her armament would include missiles based on the SLCM type, the Harpoon system, the SM 2 with Aegis system, and the 203-mm Mk 71 gun.

♦ *1 SCB-169 type* (*author: 1956-57*).

CGN	Bldr	Laid down	L	In serv.
9 LONG BEACH	Bethlehem Steel (Quincy)	12-57	14-7-59	9-9-61

Long Beach (CGN 9)

D: 14,200 tons (17,350 fl)   **Dim:** 219.75 × 22.35 × 7.90
S: 30.5 kts (trials: 33)   **Range:** 140,000/20
Man: 77 officers, 979 men (peacetime), 1,700 (war).
A: 2 Talos Mk 12 (II × 1 aft) — 4 ML Terrier (II × 2 fwd) — 2/127-mm AA
    of 38-cal (I × 2) — ASW Asroc Syst — 6/ASW TT Mk 32 (III × 2)
Electron Equipt: Radars: 1/SPS 10, 1/SPS 12, 1/SPS 32, 1/SPS 33, 4/SPG 55,
       2/SPG 49, 2/SPG 35
       Sonar: 1/SQS 23. — NTDS
M: 2 C1W Westinghouse reactors — 8 Foster-Wheeler heat exchangers and 2
    General Electric GT; 2 props; 80,000 hp   **Electric:** 15,000 kw

REMARKS: The *Long Beach* was the first U.S. surface ship with nuclear propulsion. She was planned at first as a frigate of 7,800 tons, but the plans were revised to increase the armament and to install extremely sophisticated radar and sonar equipment. She is fitted with a modular type ClC and the NTDS, and therefore she has the qualifications for a command ship of a large fleet. The plan to mount eight Polaris missiles was cancelled. She has a bow freeboard of 9.20 m. The Talos missile-launching system weighs 350 tons and the *Long Beach* carries 40 Talos and 240 Terrier missiles. The armament was augmented with 2/127-mm AA guns in single mounts, one on each side, amidships.

NUCLEAR-POWERED GUIDED MISSILE CRUISERS (continued)

♦ 5 Virginia class (1 author. 1969-70, 1 author. 1970-71, 1 author. 1971-72, 1 author. 1974-75, 1 author. 1975-76).

	Bldr	Laid down	L	In serv.
CGN 38 VIRGINIA	Newport News SB	19-8-72	14-12-74	8-76
CGN 39 TEXAS	Newport News SB	18-8-73	9-8-75	78
CGN 40 MISSISSIPPI	Newport News SB	22-2-75	. . .	79
CGN 41 ARKANSAS	Newport News SB	. . .	. . .	. . .

Long Beach (CGN 9)

Virginia (CGN 38)

D: 11,000 tons (fl)   **Dim:** 177.30 × 18.50 × 9 × . . .
S: 30 kts   **Man:** 27 officers, 215 men
A: 2 Mk 26 twin launchers (1 fwd, 1 aft) permits the selection at will of SM 2 surface-to-air missiles or Asroc ASW missiles — 2/127-mm AA Mk 45 (I × 2) — 2/Mk 32 triple TT (Mk 46 torpedoes) — 2 ASW helicopters
Electron Equipt: Radars: 1/SPS 40, 1/SPS 48 A, 1/SPS 55, 2 SPG 51, 1 Mk 86 fire control (1/SPQ 9/1 SPG 60).
        Sonar: 1/SQS 53 A — NTDS.

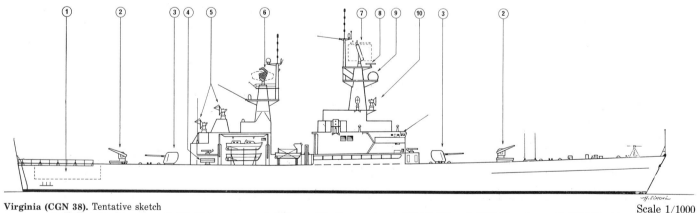

Virginia (CGN 38). Tentative sketch   Scale 1/1000
    1: Helicopter hangar — 2: Mk 26 launcher — 3: 127-mm Mk 45 mount — 4: Mk 32 TT — 5: SPG 51 radar — 6: SPS 40 radar —
    7: SPS 48 A radar — 8: SPS 55 radar — 9: SPQ 9 radar — 10: SPG 60 radar.

NUCLEAR-POWERED GUIDED MISSILE CRUISERS (*continued*)

REMARKS: Designed to carry the Aegis system (see note on this system) but because it has not been sufficiently developed it appears to have been dropped from the plans The Mk 26 can also launch the Harpoon anti-surface missiles, which are retained like the SM 2 and the Asroc in the ready service magazines which feed the launcher. The helicopters may be stowed in a hangar in the stern with an elevator. The SQS 53A sonar is the latest version of the SQS 26.

♦ *2 California class (1 author. 1966-67, 1 author. 1967-68)*

	Bldr	Laid down	L	In serv.
CGN 36	Newport News	21-1-70	22-9-71	16-2-74
CALIFORNIA	SB			
CGN 37	Newport News	1-12-70	1-7-72	25-1-75
SOUTH CAROLINA	SB			

D: 10,150 tons (fl) **Dim:** 181.66 × 18.60 × 8.96
S: 35 kts **Man:** 28 officers, 540 men
A: 2 missile-launchers Mk 13 (II × 1) for SM 1 (80 missiles) with digital fire control — 2/127-mm AA Mk 45 automatic — 1 ASW Asroc system — 4/324-mm ASW TT Mk 32 (II × 2)
Electron Equipt: Radars: 1/SPS 10, 1/SPS 40, 1/SPS 48 A, 4/SPG 51, 1 fire control/M 86 (1/SPQ 9 + 1/SPG 60).
Sonar: 1/SQS 26 — NTDS.
M: 2 D2G General Electric reactors; 2 GT; 2 props; 100,000 hp
Electric: . . . kw

REMARKS: According to photographs, the stern tubes for the wire-guided torpedoes do not appear to have been installed. Eventually will have the SM 2 missile system and probably some Harpoon missiles in the Asroc launcher.

California (CGN 36) 1975

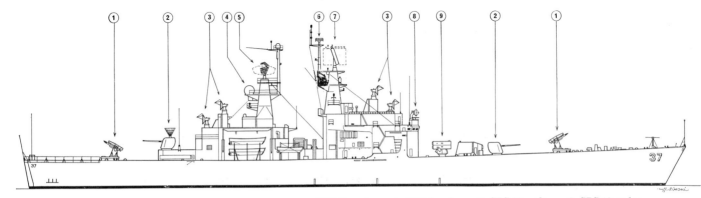

1: Mk 13 launcher — 2: 127-mm Mk 45 mount — 3: SPG 51 radar — 4: SPQ 9 radar — 5: SPS 40 radar — 6: SPS 10 radar — 7: SPS 48 A radar — 8: SPG 60 radar — 9: Asroc

Scale 1/1000

NUCLEAR-POWERED GUIDED MISSILE CRUISERS (*continued*)

South Carolina (CGN 37)

1975

NUCLEAR-POWERED GUIDED MISSILE CRUISERS (*continued*)

♦ *1 Truxtun class*

	Bldr	Author	Laid down	L	In serv.
CGN 35 TRUXTUN	New York SB (Camden)	1961–62	6-63	19-12-64	27-5-67

Truxtun (CGN 35)   1972

D: 8,250 tons (9,050 fl)   **Dim:** 172.20 × 17.67 × 8.80
S: 34 kts   **Man:** 36 officers, 465 men
A: 1 Astor system [Mk 10 launcher for Terrier (40) and Asroc (20)] — 1/127-mm
  AA fwd (54-cal) Mk 42 — 2/76-mm AA Mk 34 automatic (I × 2) — 4/324-mm
  ASW TT Mk 32 (II × 2) — 1 piloted ASW helicopter
Electron Equipt: Radars: 1/SPS 10, 1/SPS 40, 1/SPS 48, 2/SPG 55
  Sonar: 1/SQS 26 — NTDS
M: 2 D2G General Electric reactors; 2 GT; 2 props; 100,000 hp
Electric: 10,000 kw

REMARKS: Two single fixed tubes for Mk 25 torpedoes that had been planned have
  been removed. Eventually will carry the SM 2 ER type missile. Probably will receive
  the Harpoon system as well.

♦ *1 Bainbridge class*

	Bldr	Author	Laid down	L	In serv.
CGN 25 BAINBRIDGE	Bethlehem Steel (Quincy)	1958–59	5-59	15-4-61	6-10-62

D: 7,850 tons (8,700 fl)   **Dim:** 171.90 (167.65 wl) × 17.57 × 8.00
S: 34 kts   **Man:** 34 officers, 463 men
A: 4 Terrier missile-launchers (II × 2, 1 fwd, 1 aft) (80 missiles) — 4/76-mm AA
  (II × 2) — 1 ASW Asroc system — 6/324-mm ASW TT Mk 32 (III × 2)
Electron Equipt: Radars: 1/SPS 10, 1/SPS 39, 1/SPS 37, 4/SPG 55.
  Sonar: 1/SQS 26. — NTDS. (eventually)
M: 2 D2G General Electric reactors; 2 GT; 2 props; 100,000 hp
Electric: 10,000 kw

Truxtun (CGN 35)   1975

GUIDED MISSILE CRUISERS

Bainbridge (CGN 25)

REMARKS: In June of 1974 began refit at the Puget Sound Shipyard for modernization of electronic equipment (SPS 40 radar) and will have an NTDS installed as well as the SM 2 ER missile system. Probably will receive the Harpoon system.

♦ *3 (SCB-002-66) type Albany class*

CG	Bldr	L	In serv. after conv.
10 ALBANY (ex-*CA-123*)	Bethlehem Steel (Quincy)	30-6-45	2-11-62
11 CHICAGO (ex-*CA-136*)	Philadelphia NSY	20-8-44	2-5-64

D: 13,700 tons (17,800 fl)   **Dim:** 205.25 × 21.27 × 7.80
S: 33 kts   **Range:** 7,000/15
A: 4 Talos missile-launchers (II × 1 fwd, II × 1 aft) — 2 twin Tartar Mk 11 launchers on each side of the superstructure — 2 helicopters — 1/Asroc ASW system — 6/ASW TT Mk 32 (III × 2) — 2/127-mm AA (I × 2)

USS Chicago (CG-11)

Bainbridge (CGN 25)

GUIDED MISSILE CRUISERS (continued)

Albany (CG 10)

Electron Equipt: Radars: *CG 10:* 1/SPS 10, 1/SPS 48, 1/SPS 30, 1/SPS 43,
4/SPG 49 + SW 2, 4/SPG 51
CG 11: 1/SPS 10, 1/SPS 52, 1/SPS 43, 2/SPS 30,
4/SPG 49 + SW 2, 4/SPG 51
CG 12: 1/SPS 10, 2/SPS 30, 1/SPS 43,
4/SPG 49 + SW 2, 4/SPG 51
Sonar: 1/SQS 23 — NTDS.
Armor: Belt: 152 to 203 — Upper deck: 100 — Lower deck: 62
Man: 70 officers, 1,000 men   **Fuel:** 2,500 tons
M: Westinghouse or General Electric GT; 4 props; 120,000 hp
Boilers: 8 Babcock and Wilcox, 43 kg/cm³; superheat: 465°

REMARKS: Former heavy cruisers of the *Baltimore* class. Reconversion modifications
lasted four years. Alloy superstructure; living spaces entirely air-conditioned; carry
92 Talos and 80 Tartar missiles. The old masts and stacks replaced by "macks,"
which allow the stack gases to vent through lateral conduits in the same structures
on which the radar antennae are mounted; through this method the corrosion of the
radars by hot gases is avoided. Two single barrel 127-mm AA semi-automatic
38-caliber gun mounts were added in 1963, one on each side. The *Columbus* was
decommissioned at Norfolk on 31 January 1975.

♦ *2 (SCB 140 and 140 A) type Galveston class*

CG	Bldr	Laid down	In serv. after conv.
4 LITTLE ROCK (ex-*CL-92*)	Wm. Cramp (Philadelphia)	27-8-44	6-5-60
5 OKLAHOMA CITY (ex-*CL-91*)	Wm. Cramp (Philadelphia)	28-2-44	7-9-60

D: 10,670 tons (14,400 fl)   **Dim:** 185.93 × 20.11 × 7.31
S: 31 kts   **Range:** 7,000/15

On the left, the **Chicago (CG 11)**, on the right, the **Oklahoma City (CG 5)**

A: 2 Talos missile-launchers (II × 1 aft) — 3/152-mm AA (III × 1 fwd) —
2/127-mm AA (II × 1 fwd)
Electron Equipt: Radars: 1/SPS 10, 1/SPS 43, 1/SPS 30, 2/SPG 49 + SW 2
Armor: Belt: 37 to 127 — Decks: 76 + 52 — Turret: 127/76
Man: 1,000 men (including 59 officers). *CG-4:* 119 officers, 1,197 men
M: General Electric GT; 4 props; 100,000 hp; 8 Babcock and Wilcox boilers
Fuel: 2,000 tons

REMARKS: Former *Cleveland*-class light cruisers. 46 Talos missiles in stowage. These
ships have had the majority of their original guns removed, have spacious command
bridges and are fitted with the communication systems required for the flagship of

GUIDED MISSILE CRUISERS (*continued*)

Oklahoma City (CG 5)   1971

a naval force. Carry a helicopter (liaison). *Little Rock* is the flagship of the Sixth Fleet. Reclassified *CG* 1-7-75. The *Galveston* (*CLG-3*) decommissioned 21-12-1973. *CG-5* has 1/SPS 39.

♦ *2 Providence class*

CG	Bldr	L	In serv. after refit
6 PROVIDENCE (ex-*CL-82*)	Bethlehem Steel (Quincy)	28-12-44	17-9-59
7 SPRINGFIELD (ex-*CL-66*)	Bethlehem Steel (Quincy)	9-3-44	2-7-60

Springfield (CG 7)   1971

D: 10,670 tons (14,400 fl)   **Dim:**   185.93 (189.90 wl) × 20.11 × 7.60
S: 31 kts   **Range:**   7,000/15
A: 2 Terrier missile-launchers, Mk 10 (II × 1 aft) — 3/152-mm AA (III × 1) — 2/127-mm AA (II × 1)

Springfield (CG 7)   G. Arra 1972

Electron Equipt: 1/SPS 10, 1/SPS 43, 1/SPS 30, 1/SPS 52, 2/SPG 51
Armor: Belt: 35 to 127 — Decks: 76 + 52 — Turret: 127/76
Man: 1,680 with flagship personnel (*CLG-6* and *7*)
M: General Electric; 8 Babcock and Wilcox boilers
Fuel: 2,000 tons

REMARKS: Stowage for 120 Terrier missiles. It had been considered to position 4 Terrier missile-launchers (II × 2) on the stern. *6* and *7* fitted as flagships. Carry a liaison and support helicopter. In reserve. Reclassified CG 1-7-75. *Topeka* (*CLG-8*) decommissioned in 12-73.

♦ *9 SLB 212 type* (*172 modified Belknap class*) (3 author. 1960-61, 6 author. 1961-62)

CG	Bldr	Laid down	L	In serv.
26 BELKNAP	Bath Iron Works	2-62	20-7-63	7-11-64
27 JOSEPHUS DANIELS	Bath Iron Works	4-62	2-12-63	8-5-65
28 WAINWRIGHT	Bath Iron Works	7-62	25-4-64	8-1-66
29 JOUETT	Puget Sound NSY	9-62	30-6-64	3-12-66
30 HORNE	San Francisco NSY	9-62	30-10-64	15-4-67
31 STERRETT	Puget Sound NSY	9-62	30-6-64	8-4-67
32 WILLIAM H. STANDLEY	Bath Iron Works	7-63	19-12-64	9-7-66
33 FOX	Todd SY (San Pedro)	1-63	21-11-64	28-5-66
34 BIDDLE	Bath Iron Works	12-63	2-7-65	21-1-67

William H. Standley (CG 32)   G. Arra 1972

GUIDED MISSILE CRUISERS (*continued*)

William H. Standley (CG 32)   Martinelli 1974

D: 6,570 tons (7,930 fl)   **Dim:** 166.72 × 16.76 × 8.80 (fwd)
S: 34 kts   **Man:** 31 officers, 387 men
A: 1 Astor system (Terrier/Asroc) (II × 1 aft) (60 missiles including 20 Asroc) — 1/127-mm Mk 42 aft — 2/76-mm AA (II × 1) — 6/324-mm ASW TT Mk 32 (II × 2) — 1 piloted ASW helicopter (SH-2D Sea Sprite)
Electron Equipt: Radars: 1/SPS 10, 1/SPS 40 (except 26, 27 and 28 which have 1/SPS 37), 1/SPS 48, 2/SPG 55
          Sonar: 1/SQS 26 — NTDS
Range: 2,500/30, 8,000/14
M: 2 GT; 2/6-bladed props

Belknap (CG 26)   1973

Wainwright (CG 28)   1972

Boiler: 4 Foster-Wheeler, 84 kg/cm² pressure, superheat: 520°; 85,000 hp
Electric: 6,900 kw

REMARKS: First ships equipped with the Astor system (see note on equipments) Ex-frigates DLG reclassified CG 1-7-75, are going to be the first to receive the SM2 system. *Belknap* severely damaged in collision with *CV-67* in Mediterranean, November 1975; may be scrapped or at least remain out of service for lengthy repairs.

♦ *9 SCB 172 Leahy class* — (*3 author. 1957-58, 6 author. 1959-60*)

CG	Bldr	Laid down	L	In serv.
16 LEAHY	Bath Iron Works	12-59	1-7-61	4-8-62
17 HARRY E. YARNELL	Bath Iron Works	5-60	9-12-61	2-2-63
18 WORDEN	Bath Iron Works	9-60	2-6-62	3-8-63
19 DALE	New York SB (Camden)	9-60	28-7-62	23-11-63
20 RICHMOND K. TURNER	New York SB (Camden)	1-61	6-4-63	13-6-64
21 GRIDLEY	Puget Sound B & DD Co.	7-60	31-7-61	25-5-63
22 ENGLAND	Todd SY (Los Angeles)	10-60	6-3-62	7-12-63
23 HALSEY	San Francisco NSY	8-60	15-1-62	20-7-63
24 REEVES	Puget Sound NSY	7-60	12-5-62	15-5-64

D: 5,670 tons (7,800 fl)
Dim: 163.07 × 16.15 × 5.80 (7.50 fwd)
S: 34 kts   **Man:** 31 officers, 365 men
A: 4 Terrier missile-launchers (II × 2), (1 fwd, 1 aft) (80 missiles) — 4/76-mm AA (II × 2) — 1 ASW Asroc system — 6/324-mm ASW TT Mk 32 (III × 2)

GUIDED MISSILE CRUISERS (continued)

Yarnell (CG 17)   G. Arra 1972

Reeves (CG 24)   1972

Electron Equipt: Radars: 1/SPS 10, 1/SPS 37, 1/SPS 48, 4/SPG 55
Sonars: 1/SQS 23 — NTDS
M: 2 General Electric; de Laval (20/22) or Allis Chalmers (23-24) GT; 2/5-bladed props
Boilers: 4/84 kg/cm² pressure, superheat: 520°C; 85,000 hp
Electric: 5,100 kw   **Range:** 2,500/30 — 8,000/14

REMARKS: The stacks are inside the radar supporting towers (macks). 80 Terrier missiles are carried on board, 2 ready service magazines of 20 each per launcher. During their overhaul, the *Leahy* class ships received an advanced version of the Mk 76 fire control radar which permits the SM 1 missile in its Extended Range

version to be fired. The *Leahy*, the first ship ready after this overhaul, returned to active service 17-8-68. These are former DLG frigates reclassified CG 1-7-75.

GUIDED MISSILE DESTROYERS

DDG 47 Class

To replace the guided missile destroyers of the *Charles F. Adams* class which will reach their age limit at the beginning of the 1980s, the U.S. Navy hopes to launch a construction program having for its first objective 16 ships of 8,000-10,000 tons with gas turbine propulsion. These ships would carry the Aegis system and the multi-use Mk 26 launcher in its definitive version, permitting the launching as desired of anti-aircraft SM 2 missiles, the Harpoon or the Asroc system.

♦ *10 SCB 142/129 type, Coontz class*
   (6 to 11, author. 1955-56 — 12 to 15, author. 1956-57).

DDG	Bldr	Laid down	L	In serv.
37 FARRAGUT	Bethlehem Steel (Quincy)	6-57	18-7-58	12-10-60
38 LUCE	Bethlehem Steel (Quincy)	10-57	11-12-58	20-5-61
39 MACDONOUGH	Bethlehem Steel (Quincy)	4-58	9-7-59	4-11-61
40 COONTZ	Puget Sound NSY	1-57	18-11-58	10-60
41 KING	Puget Sound NSY	1-57	18-11-58	15-7-60
42 MAHAN	San Francisco NSY	7-57	7-10-59	25-8-60
43 DAHLGREN	Philadelphia NSY	3-58	16-3-60	8-4-61
44 WILLIAM V. PRATT	Philadelphia NSY	3-58	16-3-60	4-11-61
45 DEWEY	Bath Iron Works	8-57	30-11-58	7-12-59
46 PREBLE	Bath Iron Works	12-57	23-5-59	9-5-60

D: 4,700 tons (5,800 fl)   **Dim:** 156.05 × 15.24 × 6.10
S: 34 kts   **Man:** 28 officers, 350 men
A: 2 Terrier missile launchers (II × 1 aft) (40 missiles) — 1/127-mm AA automatic, Mk 42 fwd — 1 ASW Asroc system — 6/324-mm ASW TT (III × 2) Mk 32
Electron Equipt: Radars: 1/SPS 10, 1/SPS 37, 1/SPS 48, 2/SPG 55.
Sonar: SQS 23 — NTDS
M: De Laval GT (6, 7, 8, 14); Allis-Chalmers-Falk on the others; 2 props
Boilers: 4/84 kg/cm² pressure; superheat: 520°C; 85,000 hp
Range: 1,500/30 — 6,000/14   **Electric:** 4,000 kw

REMARKS: Based on the *Mitscher* class. Will put in service the SM 1 ER and then the SM 2 ER. Four 76-mm removed during last overhaul during which the listed electronic equipment was installed. The *King* was trial ship for sea trials of the Vulcan/Phalanx system. Former DLG frigates classified as DDG guided missile destroyers 1-7-75.

GUIDED MISSILE DESTROYERS (*continued*)

Luce (former hull no.)   1971

Dahlgren (former hull no.)   G. Arra 1972

Pratt (former hull no.)   G. Arra 1971

Dewey (former hull no.)   S. Terzibaschitsch 1974

♦ *23 SCB 155 Charles F. Adams class*
  Author. 1956-57 (8), 1957-58 (5), 1959-60 (3), 1960-61 (2).

	Bldr	Laid down	L	In serv.
DDG 2 CHARLES F. ADAMS	Bath Iron Works	5-58	8-9-59	10-9-60
DDG 3 JOHN KING	Bath Iron Works	8-58	30-1-60	4-2-61
DDG 4 LAWRENCE	New York SB (Camden)	10-58	27-2-60	6-1-62
DDG 5 CLAUDE V. RICKETTS (ex-*Biddle*)	New York SB (Camden)	5-59	16-4-60	5-5-62
DDG 6 BARNEY	New York SB (Camden)	8-59	10-12-60	11-8-62
DDG 7 HENRY B. WILSON	Defoe SB (Michigan)	2-58	22-4-59	17-12-60
DDG 8 LYNDE McCORMICK	Defoe SB (Michigan)	4-58	28-7-59	3-6-61
DDG 9 TOWERS	Todd-Pacific (Seattle)	4-58	23-4-59	6-6-61
DDG 10 SAMPSON	Bath Iron Works	3-59	21-5-60	24-6-61
DDG 11 SELLERS	Bath Iron Works	8-59	27-9-60	28-10-61
DDG 12 ROBISON	Defoe SB (Michigan)	4-59	27-4-60	9-12-61
DDG 13 HOEL	Defoe SB (Michigan)	8-59	1-8-60	16-6-62
DDG 14 BUCHANAN	Todd-Pacific (Seattle)	4-59	11-5-60	7-2-62
DDG 15 BERKELEY	New York SB (Camden)	8-60	29-7-61	15-12-62
DDG 16 JOSEPH STRAUSS	New York SB (Camden)	12-60	9-12-61	20-4-63
DDG 17 CONYNGHAM	New York SB (Camden)	5-61	19-5-62	13-7-63

GUIDED MISSILE DESTROYERS (*continued*)

DDG 18 SEMMES	Avondale (New Orleans)	8-60	20-5-61	10-12-62
DDG 19 TATTNALL	Avondale (New Orleans)	11-60	26-8-61	13-4-63
DDG 20 GOLDSBOROUGH	Puget Sound B & DD	1-61	12-12-61	9-11-63
DDG 21 COCHRANE	Puget Sound B & DD	7-61	18-7-62	21-3-64
DDG 22 BENJAMIN STODDERT	Puget Sound B & DD	10-61	8-1-63	12-9-64
DDG 23 RICHARD E. BYRD	Todd-Pacific (Seattle)	4-61	6-2-62	7-3-64
DDG 24 WADDELL	Todd-Pacific (Seattle)	2-61	26-2-63	28-8-64

Sellers (DDG 11)   G. Arra 1972

D: 3,370 tons (4,500 fl)   **Dim:** 133.19 × 14.32 × 6 (fl)
S: 30 kts   **Man:** 20/24 officers, 319/330 men
A: 2 Tartar Mk 11 missile-launchers (II × 1) or 1 Mk 13 missile-launcher (I × 1) beginning with *DDG-16* (40 missiles) — 2/127-mm Mk 42 AA (I × 2) — 6/324-mm ASW Mk 32 TT (III × 2) for Mk 44 or 46 T — 1/Asroc ASW system

Electric Equipt: Radars: 1/SPS 10, 1/SPS 37 or 40, 1/SPS 39 or 52, 2/SPG 51
Sonars: 1/SQS 23 in the hull of the *DDG-2* to the *DDG-15*, then beginning with *DDG-16*, in the bow sonar dome.
M: General Electric GT; 2 props; 70,000 hp
Range: 1,600/30 — 6,000/14
Boilers: 4/84 kg/cm² pressure; superheat: 520°C
Electric: 2,000 kw   **Fuel:** 900 tons

REMARKS: The *DDG 25, 26,* and *27* built at the Defoe Shipbuilding Company, were ordered by Australia; *DLG 28, 29,* and *30* were built in 1965 at the Bath Iron Works for the West Germany Navy.

♦ *4 SCB 222-66 type Decatur class*

		Laid		In	after
	Bldr	down	L	serv.	refit
DDG 31 DECATUR (ex-DD-936)	Bethlehem Steel (Quincy)	9-54	15-12-55	12-56	29-4-67
DDG 32 JOHN PAUL JONES (ex-DD-932)	Charleston NSY	1-54	7-5-55	11-56	23-9-67
DDG 33 PARSONS (ex-DD-949)	Ingalls (Pascagoula)	6-57	19-8-58	10-59	3-11-67
DDG 34 SOMERS (ex-DD-917)	Bath Iron Works	3-57	30-5-58	4-59	2-10-68

Somers (DDG 34)   1968

D: 2,850 tons (4,200 fl)   **Dim:** 127.40 × 13.70 × 6 (fl)
S: 33 kts   **Man:** 22 officers, 313 men
A: 1 Tartar Mk 13 missile launcher (40 missiles) — 1/127-mm Mk 42 AA — 1 Asroc ASW system — 6/324-mm-ASW Mk 32 TT (III × 2) for the Mk 44 or Mk 46 torpedo

GUIDED MISSILE DESTROYERS (continued)

Electron Equipt: Radars: 1/SPS 10, 1/SPS 37 or 40, 1/SPS 52
1/SPG 51 — NTDS
Sonar: 1/SQS 23

M: General Electric GT on *DDG-31, 33, 34,* Westinghouse on *DDG-32;* 2 props

Boilers: 4 Foster-Wheeler (on the *DDG-31* and *33*) Babcock & Wilcox (on the *DDG-32* and *34*)

REMARKS: Alloy superstructure.

♦ *2 modified Mitscher class*

	Bldr	Laid down	L	In serv.
DDG 35 MITSCHER (ex-*DL-2*)	Bath Iron Works	1949	26-1-52	5-53
DDG 36 JOHN S. McCAIN (ex-*DL-3*)	Bath Iron Works	1949	29-2-52	10-53

Mitscher (DDG 35)   J. C. Bellonne 1973

John S. McCain (DDG 36)   1970

D: 3,680 tons (5,155 fl)
Dim: 150.26 (137.16 pp) × 15.24 × 6.40.
S: 35 kts   **Man:** 29 officers, 349 men

A: 2/127-mm AA Mk 42 (I × 2) — 1 single launcher Tartar system Mk 13 (40 missiles) — 1 Asroc ASW system — 6/324-mm AS Mk 32 TT (III × 2) for Mk 44 torpedoes.

Electron Equipt: Radars: 1/SPS 10, 1/SPS 37, 1/SPS 48, 2/SPG 51
Sonar: 1/SQS 23 — NTDS. (?)

M: General Electric GT; 2 props; 75,000 hp

Boilers: 4 86 kg/cm² pressure by Combustion Engineering.

REMARKS: Overhaul begun in 1966. These ships redesignated from DL after their overhaul because of their new armament and the fact that their displacement nearly equals that of the *Charles F. Adams* DDG class. Returned to service after overhaul 29-6-68 (*35*) and 6-9-69 (*36*).

DESTROYERS

♦ *14 Forrest Sherman class*
Author: 1952-53 (3), 1953-54 (3), 1954-55 (5), 1955-56 (7). Projet SCB 240.

A.) *8 ASW refitted (1967-71)*

DD	Bldr	Laid down	L	In serv.
933 BARRY	Mare Island NSY	3-54	1-10-55	31-8-56
937 DAVIS	Bethlehem Steel (Quincy)	2-55	28-3-56	28-2-57
938 JONAS INGRAM	Bethlehem Steel (Quincy)	6-55	8-7-56	19-7-57
940 MANLEY	Bath Iron Works	2-55	12-4-56	1-2-57
941 DUPONT	Bath Iron Works	5-55	8-9-56	1-7-57
943 BLANDY	Bethlehem Steel (Quincy)	12-55	19-12-56	8-11-57
948 MORTON	Ingalls (Pascagoula)	3-57	23-5-58	26-5-59
950 RICHARD S. EDWARDS	Puget Sound B & DD	12-56	21-9-57	5-2-59

Manley (DD 940)   J. C. Bellonne 1973

B.) *6 which will not be modernized nor refitted as the ASW ships*

DD	Bldr	Laid down	L	In serv.
931 FORREST SHERMAN	Boston NSY	10-53	5-2-55	9-11-55

DESTROYERS (*continued*)

942 BIGELOW	Bath Iron Works	7-55	2-2-57	8-11-57
944 MULLINIX	Bethlehem Steel (Quincy)	4-56	18-3-57	7-3-58
945 HULL	Bath Iron Works	9-56	10-8-57	3-7-58
946 EDSON	Bath Iron Works	12-56	1-1-58	7-11-58
951 TURNER JOY	Puget Sound B & DD	9-57	5-5-58	3-8-59

USS Hull (DD 945). Note the Mk 71 203-mm gun on the bow.

Dupont (DD 941)

D: 2,780/2,850 tons (3,518 trials, 4,200 fl)
Dim: 127.40 × 13.70 × 6
S: 33 kts **Man:** 15 officers, 240 men
A: The ASW refits, 2/127-mm (I × 2) Mk 42 — 1 ASW Asroc system — 6/324-mm ASW TT Mk 32 (III × 2) for torpedoes Mk 44 or Mk 46. The others: 3/127-mm AA (I × 3) — 4/324-mm ASW TT (II × 2)
Electron Equipt: On the A:
    Radars: 1/SPS 10, 1/SPS 37 or 40
    Sonar: 1/SQS 23 and 1/SQS 35 towed on certain ships as the *Manley*
On the B:
    Radars: 1/SPS 10, 1/SPS 37
    Sonar: 1/SQS 23
M: General Electric GT except the *DD-931, 933*, which have Westinghouse; 2 props, 70,000 hp
Boilers: 4 Foster-Wheeler (*DD-937, 938, 943, 944, 948*) or Babcock and Wilcox, pressure 84 kg/cm²; superheat: 520°C

REMARKS: Alloy superstructure and gun foundations mounts are designed to shed atomic fallout. From *DD-937* on, the bows are somewhat higher than from *931* to *933*. Four of the same series have been designated as DDGs (see preceding comments). The *Hull* (*DD-945*) was used as trial ship for the 203-mm Mk 71 gun.

OLD DESTROYERS FROM WARTIME BUILDING PROGRAMS (1941–45)

350 destroyers from the *Fletcher* class (2,050 tons), *Allen M. Sumner* class (2,200 tons), and *Gearing* class (2,400 tons) were put in service between 1942 and 1946. Many *Fletcher* class, and since 1970, some *Sumner* and a few *Gearing* have been transferred to foreign navies under the Mutual Assistance Pact: West Germany, Argentina, Brazil, Chile, Columbia, South Korea, Spain, Greece, Italy, Taiwan, Turkey, etc.

Beginning in 1960, some of the *Sumner* class and most of the *Gearing* class were overhauled and modernized in the FRAM 1 or FRAM 2 programs; however, they are all now approaching the end of their service usefulness.

From the viewpoint of naval power for the United States, the remaining ships are of little interest; therefore, only those ships of the *Gearing* class still on active service on 1-10-75 will be listed.

All of these old destroyers are used for reserve training (indicated by *) or are still serving with the fleet.

♦ *41 Gearing (FRAM I) class with one 127-mm twin mount fwd and one aft*

DD	L	DD	L
714 WILLIAM R. RUSH*	8-7-45	**785 HENDERSON***	28-5-45
715 WILLIAM M. WOOD	29-7-45	**788 HOLLISTER***	9-10-45
717 THEODORE R. CHANDLER*	20-10-45	**806 HIGBEE***	12-11-44
718 HAMNER*	24-11-45	**817 CORRY***	28-7-45
743 SOUTHERLAND*	5-10-44	**818 NEW**	18-8-45
763 WILLIAM C. LAWE*	25-2-45	**819 HOLDER***	25-8-45
784 MC KEAN*	31-3-45	**820 RICH***	5-10-45
		821 JOHNSTON*	19-10-45

DESTROYERS (continued)

		L
822	ROBERT H. McCARD*	9-11-45
824	BASILONE	21-12-45
829	MYLES C. FOX*	13-1-45
835	CHARLES P. CECIL*	22-4-45
836	GEO. K. MACKENZIE	13-5-45
837	SARSFIELD	27-5-45
839	POWER*	30-6-45
840	GLENNON	14-7-45
842	FISKE*	8-9-45
846	OZBOURN*	22-12-45
849	RICHARD E. KRAUS	2-3-46
852	LEONARD F. MASON	4-1-46
862	VOGELGESANG*	15-1-45
863	STEINAKER*	13-2-45
864	HAROLD J. ELLISON*	14-3-45
866	CONE*	10-5-45
868	BROWNSON	7-7-45
871	DAMATO*	21-11-45
873	HAWKINS	7-10-44
876	ROGERS*	20-11-4
878	VESOLE	29-12-44
880	DYESS*	26-1-45
881	BORDELON	3-3-45
883	NEWMAN K. PERRY*	17-3-45
885	JOHN R. CRAIG*	14-4-45
886	ORLECK*	12-5-45

Power (DD 839)

J. C. Bellonne 1974

♦ *4 Gearing (FRAM I) class with two 127-mm twin mounts mounted on the fore-castle.* They were the first to be reconstructed.

DD		L
826	AGERHOLM	30-3-46
845	BAUSSELL	19-11-45
867	STRIBLING	8-6-45
890	MEREDITH*	28 6-45

Stribling (DD 867) — 2 mounts forward

♦ *2 Gearing (FRAM I) class with one 127-mm twin mount*

DD		L
825	CARPENTER	30-12-45
827	ROBERT A. OWENS	15-7-46

Robert A. Owens (DD 827)

1970

D: 2,400 tons (3,500/3,600 fl) **Dim:** 119.17 × 12.45 × 3.80 (light)
S: 30 kts **Man:** 14 officers, 260 men
Range: 2,400/25 — 4,800/15
A: 2 to 4/127-mm 38-cal (II × 1 or II × 2) as indicated — 1 Asroc ASW system — 6/324-mm ASW TT (II × 2) Mk 32 for torpedoes Mk 43 or 44
Electron Equipt: Radars: 1/SPS 10, 1/SPS 29, 37, or 40
  Sonars: 1/SQS 23
M: GT **Boilers:** 4 Babcock; 2 props; 60,000 hp **Fuel:** 650 tons

ASW DESTROYERS

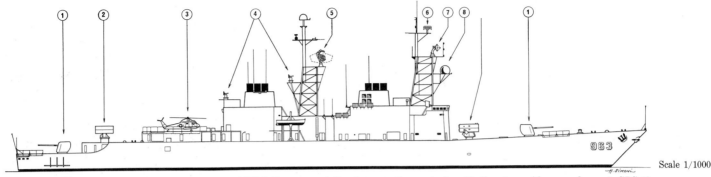

1: 1/127-mm Mk 45 mount — 2: Sea Sparrow — 3: ASW helicopter — 4: Sea Sparrow fire control and helicopter guidance radar — 5: SPS 40 radar — 6: SPS 55 radar — 7: SPG 60 radar — 8: SPQ 9 radar — 9: Asroc system Note: The Sea Sparrow is not yet fitted.

♦ *30 Spruance class*

Bldr: Ingalls SB, Pascagoula (Litton Ind.)

Author.	1968/70	1970/71	1971/72	1972/73	1973/74
Number:	3	6	7	0	7

	Laid down	L	Delivered
DD 963 SPRUANCE	11–72	9–11–73	3–6–76
DD 964 PAUL F. FOSTER	12–3–73	23–2–74	21–1–76
DD 965 KINKAID	6–73	1–6–74	2–76
DD 966 HEWITT	8–73	14–9–74	5–76
DD 967 ELLIOT	12–73	18–1–75	6–76
DD 968 ARTHUR W. RADFORD	31–1–74	27–2–75	1976
DD 969 PETERSEN	24–4–74	21–6–75	1976
DD 970 CARON	1–7–74	24–6–75	1976
DD 971 DAVID R. RAY	23–9–74	23–8–75	1977
DD 972 OLDENDORF	27–12–74	21–10–75	1977
DD 973 JOHN YOUNG	14–2–75	2–12–75	1977
DD 974 COMTE DE GRASSE	4–4–75	10–1–76	. . .
DD 975 O'BRIEN	9–5–75	2–76	. . .
DD 976 MERRILL	16–6–75	3–76	. . .
DD 977 BRISCOE	21–7–75	. . .	. . .
DD 978 STUMP	25–8–75	. . .	. . .
DD 979 CONOLLY	29–9–75	. . .	. . .
DD 980 MOOSBRUGGER	3–11–75	. . .	. . .
DD 981 JOHN HANCOCK	8–12–75	. . .	. . .
DD 982 NICHOLSON	12–1–76	. . .	. . .
DD 983 JOHN RODGERS	. . .	. . .	. . .
DD 984 LEFTWICH	. . .	. . .	. . .
DD 985 CUSHING	. . .	. . .	. . .

D: 7,800 tons (fl) **Dim:** 171.70 (oa) × 161.23 (pp) × 8.5
S: 30 kts **Man:** 18 officers, 240 men
Range: 6,000/20
A: 2/127-mm Mk 45 (I × 2) with a Mk 86 fire control — 1 Asroc system — 2 triple fixed Mk 32 ASW TT — 2 ASW or 1 manned helicopter (SH2 Sea Sprite or 1 SH3 Sea King).

Electron Equipt: Radars: 1/SPS 40 A, 1/SPS 55
Sonars: 1/SQS 53 — NTDS.
M: 4 General Electric gas turbines LM 2500 (based on TF 39 and CF 6 turbojet engines); 2 props; 80,000 hp

REMARKS: The Litton Systems Incorporated design group was assigned this program in June of 1970 and immediately began to construct a special shipyard in Pascagoula, Mississippi, to build these ships.

The construction of the hull is organized in such a fashion that standard prefabricated sections (modules) weighing 1,500 to 2,100 tons completely fitted out (small machinery and its components, piping, wiring, etc.) are joined. Once these elements are brought together, the ship is then 92% complete. The hull is transferred to a pontoon which is submerged for the launching phase. There is no launching in the usual sense of the term. The ship is then finished alongside the pier.

The propulsion machinery has been carefully studied from the viewpoint of silent operation and flexibility. On each of the two shafts two General Electric LM 2,500 gas turbines are coupled to a reduction gear. Each shaft turns a reversible pitch propeller (5.10 m in diameter, 168 rpm at 30 knots). The electric power is furnished by 3 gas turbines each powering one 2,000-kw alternator and mounted in separate compartments. All propulsion machinery is under the control of a single operator from a Central Control Station (CCS).

The hull conformations have been carefully studied to suppress rolling and pitching. Living spaces have been given particular attention with spaces divided by bulkheads for no more than 6 men each and with a recreational area and good sanitary facilities. The comparatively small crew for a ship the size of the *Spruance* class is explained by the advanced automation of all the machinery and systems.

It is expected that the armament of these large destroyers will be augmented by the installation of 2 Vulcan/Phalanx systems, the Harpoon system, and perhaps later 1/203-mm Mk 71 gun. Four slightly different ships of the same class have been ordered by Iran.

Note: the SQS 53 is the most recent version of the SQS 26.

The building of the *Spruance* class ASW destroyers.
View of the assembly plant of the modules at Litton in Pascagoula, Mississippi.
In the two right hand photos one can see the pontoon for launching the ship.

ASW DESTROYERS (*continued*)

Spruance (DD 963)

1975

ASW DESTROYERS (*continued*)

Spruance (DD 963)   1975

    Note that the *DD-974* has been given the name of the French admiral *De Grasse* whose victory over the English fleet under Admiral Thomas Graves in the Chesapeake Bay brought about the surrender at Yorktown and guaranteed the independence of the young republic of the United States.

FRIGATES

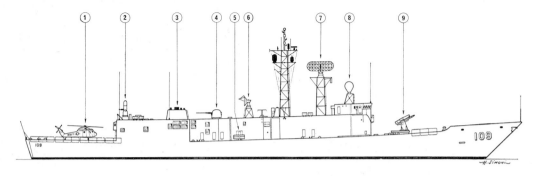

NOTE: The 109 hull number has been replaced by the number 7.

1: ASW helicopter — 2: Vulcan-Phalanx system — 3: Stack — 4: 76-mm OTO Melara — 5: TT Mk 32 — 6: STIR radar — 7: SPS 49 radar — 8: fire control Mk 92 — 9: MK 13 M launcher

♦ *25 FFG, Patrol Frigate class*

D: 3,500 tons (fl)　　**Dim:** 126 (oa) × 13.20 × 7.35 aft

S: 28.5 kts　　**Man:** 185 men

A: 1/Mk 13 launcher permitting as required the launching of Harpoon and SM 1 — 1/76-mm AA OTO Melara compact — later a Vulcan-Phalanx system — 6/324-mm ASW TT Mk 32 (III × 2) — 2 helicopters

Electron Equipt: Radars: 1/SPS 55, 1/SPS 49, 1/STIR, 1 fire control Mk 92
　　　　　　　　　Sonars: 1/SQS 55 — 1

M: 2 LM 2,500 General Electric gas turbines coupled on a single shaft; 1 extended prop, 5.50 m in diameter, with variable and reversible pitch; 40,000 hp

REMARKS: This class will be fitted with two electrically driven screws for maneuvering in restricted waters.

Author	1972-73	1974-75	1975-76
Number	1	3	11

FFG	Bldr	Laid down	L	In serv.
7 OLIVER HAZARD PERRY	Bath Iron Works	1-3-75	. . .	1977
8 N . . .	. . .	. . .	. . .	. . .
9 N . . .	. . .	. . .	. . .	. . .
10 N . . .	. . .	. . .	. . .	. . .
11 N . . .	. . .	. . .	. . .	. . .
12 N . . .	. . .	. . .	. . .	. . .
13 N . . .	. . .	. . .	. . .	. . .
14 N . . .	. . .	. . .	. . .	. . .
15 N . . .	. . .	. . .	. . .	. . .
16 N . . .	. . .	. . .	. . .	. . .
17 N . . .	. . .	. . .	. . .	. . .
18 N . . .	. . .	. . .	. . .	. . .
19 N . . .	. . .	. . .	. . .	. . .
20 N . . .	. . .	. . .	. . .	. . .
21 N . . .	. . .	. . .	. . .	. . .
22 N . . .	. . .	. . .	. . .	. . .
23 N . . .	. . .	. . .	. . .	. . .
24 N . . .	. . .	. . .	. . .	. . .
25 N . . .	. . .	. . .	. . .	. . .

♦ *6 SCR 199B type Brooke class, authorized 61-62 (3).*

FFG	Bldr	Laid down	L	In serv.
1 BROOKE	Lockheed SB (Seattle)	12-62	19-7-63	12-3-66
2 RAMSEY	Lockheed SB (Seattle)	2-63	15-10-63	3-6-67
3 SCHOFIELD	Lockheed SB (Seattle)	4-63	7-12-63	11-5-68
4 TALBOT	Bath Iron Works	5-64	6-1-66	2-4-67
5 RICHARD L. PAGE	Bath Iron Works	11-64	4-6-66	5-8-67
6 JULIUS A. FURER	Bath Iron Works	7-65	22-7-66	11-11-67

D: 2,643 tons/3,425 (fl)　　**S:** 26/25 kts

Dim: 126.33 (121.90 pp) × 13.90 × 7.90 (with sonar)

Man: 16 officers, 225 men

A: 1/127-mm 38-cal AA (fwd — 1 single mm Tartar Mk 22 missile-launcher

FRIGATES (continued)

Julius A. Furer (FFG 6)   J. C. Bellonne 1972

Julius A. Furer (FFG 6)   1975

Talbot (FFG 4) with the same weapons and equipment intended for the Patrol Frigates

(aft) (ready service magazine of 16 missiles) — 1 Asroc ASW system — 6/324-mm ASW Mk 32 TT (III × 2) for Mk 44 or Mk 46 torpedoes — 2/Mk 25 ASW TT (stern) for wire-guided torpedoes. ASW helicopter platform and hangar.

Electron Equipt: Radars: 1/SPS 10, 1/SPS 52, 1/SPG 51
         Sonar: 1/SQS 26

Range: 4,000/20   **M:** GT; 1 prop   **Boilers:** Foster-Wheeler, 35,000 hp

REMARKS: Differ from the *Garcia* (DE-1040) because of the Tartar missile launcher replacing the 127-mm aft. Excellent sea-keeping qualities. Anti-rolling stabilizers. Hangar enlarged for the SH2D Sea Sprite helicopter. The *DEG-4, 5,* and *6* have an Asroc system with rapid reloading. Boilers with pressure combustion. The *Talbot* is used as an experimental ship for the weapons and systems of the Patrol Frigates.

♦ *1 experimental escort ship (1962-62 budget). SCB 198 project.*

	Bldr	Laid down	L	In serv.
AGFF 1 GLOVER	Bath Iron Works	7-63	17-4-65	11-65

D: 2,650 tons (3,500 fl)   **S:** 27 kts
Dim: 126.45 × 13.40 × 7.30 (with sonar)
A: 1/127-mm 38 cal — 1 Asroc ASW system — 6/324-mm Mk 32 ASW TT (III × 2)
Man: 14 officers, 211 men
Electron Equipt: Radars: 1/SPS 40, 1/SPS 10
         Sonars: SQS 26
M: GT; 1 prop
Boilers: 2 Foster-Wheeler 83.4 kg/cm² pressure; 35,000 hp

REMARKS: Pump-jet propeller.

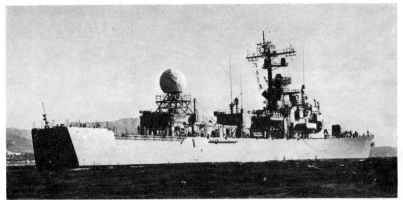

Glover (AGFF 1)   Guiglini 1973

FRIGATES (*continued*)

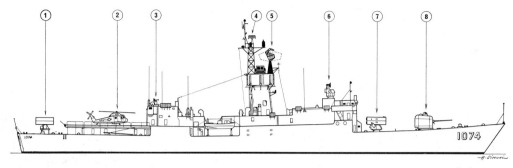

Scale 1/1000

1: BPDMS Sea Sparrow — 2: Sea Sprite ASW Helicopter — 3: Sea Sparrow guidance radar — 4: SPS 10 Radar — 5: SPS 40 Radar — 6: fire control radar — 7: Asroc ASW system — 8: 1/127-mm Mk 42 AA turret

♦ *46/200.65 Knox class*
Author: 1052-1061 (63-64); 1062/1077 (64-65); 1078/87 (65-66); 1088/97 (66-67).

FF	Bldr	Laid down	L	In serv.
1052 KNOX	Todd-Pacific, Seattle	10-65	19-11-66	12-4-69
1053 ROARK	Todd-Pacific, Seattle	2-66	24-4-67	22-11-69
1054 GRAY	Todd-Pacific, Seattle	11-66	3-10-67	4-4-70
1055 HEPBURN	Todd SY, San Pedro	6-66	25-3-67	3-7-69
1056 CONNOLE	Avondale Shipyards	3-67	20-7-68	30-8-69
1057 RATHBURNE	Lockheed, Seattle	1-68	2-5-69	16-5-70
1058 MEYERKORD	Todd SY, San Pedro	9-66	15-7-67	28-12-69
1059 Wm. S. SIMS	Avondale Shipyards	4-67	4-1-69	3-1-70
1060 LANG	Todd SY, San Pedro	3-67	17-2-68	28-3-70
1061 PATTERSON	Avondale Shipyards	10-67	3-5-69	14-3-70
1062 WHIPPLE	Todd-Pacific, Seattle	4-67	12-4-68	22-8-70
1063 REASONER	Lockheed, Seattle	1-69	1-8-70	31-7-71
1064 LOCKWOOD	Todd-Pacific, Seattle	11-67	5-9-68	5-12-70
1065 STEIN	Lockheed, Seattle	6-70	19-12-70	8-1-72
1066 MARVIN SHIELDS	Todd-Pacific, Seattle	4-68	23-10-69	10-4-71
1067 FRANCIS HAMMOND	Todd SY, San Pedro	7-67	11-5-68	25-7-70
1068 VREELAND	Avondale Shipyards	3-68	14-6-69	13-6-70
1069 BAGLEY	Lockheed, Seattle	9-70	29-5-71	6-5-72
1070 DOWNES	Todd-Pacific, Seattle	9-68	12-69	28-8-71
1071 BADGER	Todd SY, San Pedro	2-68	7-12-69	1-12-70
1072 BLAKELY	Avondale Shipyards	6-68	23-8-69	18-7-70
1073 ROBERT E. PEARY (ex-*Conolly*)	Lockheed, Seattle	2-70	25-6-71	23-9-72
1074 HAROLD E. HOLT	Todd SY, San Pedro	5-68	3-5-69	26-3-71
1075 TRIPPE	Avondale Shipyards	7-68	1-11-69	19-9-70
1076 FANNING	Todd SY, San Pedro	12-68	24-1-70	23-7-71
1077 OUELLET	Avondale Shipyards	5-69	7-3-70	12-12-70

Ships with hull numbers *1078* to *1097* are considered the *Joseph Hewes* class, although they are identical to the *Knox* class.

Those ships built by the Avondale shipyards in Westwego, Louisiana, near New Orleans, have been built under the most modern conditions. Very advanced prefabrication, assembly on only three shipbuilding stocks, broadside launch.

FRIGATES (*continued*)

Sims (FF 1059)   G. Arra 1972

Sims (FF 1059)

FF	Bldr	Laid down	L	In serv.
1078 JOSEPH HEWES	Avondale Shipyards	5-69	7-3-70	24-4-71
1079 BOWEN	Avondale Shipyards	7-69	2-5-70	22-5-71
1080 PAUL	Avondale Shipyards	9-69	20-6-70	14-2-71
1081 AYLWIN	Avondale Shipyards	11-69	29-8-70	18-9-71
1082 ELMER MONTGOMERY	Avondale Shipyards	1-70	21-11-70	30-10-71
1083 COOK	Avondale Shipyards	3-70	23-1-71	18-3-72
1084 McCANDLESS	Avondale Shipyards	4-70	27-3-71	22-7-72
1085 DONALD B. BEARY	Avondale Shipyards	7-70	22-5-71	22-7-72
1086 BREWTON	Avondale Shipyards	2-70	24-7-71	8-7-72
1087 KIRK	Avondale Shipyards	12-70	25-9-71	9-9-72

Harold E. Holt (FF 1074)   1972

1088 BARBEY	Avondale Shipyards	2-71	4-12-71	72
1089 JESSE L. BROWN	Avondale Shipyards	4-71	18-3-72	17-2-73
1090 AINSWORTH	Avondale Shipyards	6-71	15-4-72	27-3-73
1091 MILLER	Avondale Shipyards	8-71	3-6-72	30-6-73
1092 THOMAS C. HART	Avondale Shipyards	10-71	2-8-72	28-7-73
1093 CAPODANNO	Avondale Shipyards	12-71	25-2-72	17-11-73
1094 PHARRIS	Avondale Shipyards	3-72	12-72	21-1-74
1095 TRUETT	Avondale Shipyards	4-72	2-73	1-6-74
1096 VALDEZ	Avondale Shipyards	6-72	24-3-73	27-7-74
1097 MOINESTER	Avondale Shipyards	8-72	12-7-73	2-11-74

D: 3,011 tons (4,100 fl) **Dim:** 133.50 × 14.25 × 7.60 (sonar)
S: 27/26 kts **Man:** 15 officers, 205 men
A: 1/127-mm Mk 45 AA — 1 BPDMS Sea Sparrow on some — 1 ASW Asroc system — 4/324-mm Mk 32 TT fixed amidships at a 45° angle, 2 on each side — 1 ASW helicopter
Electron Equipt: Radars: 1/SPS 10, 1/SPS 40, 1 fire control radar
Sonars: 1/SQS 26, SQS 35 on some
M: Westinghouse GT; 1 prop **Boilers:** 2 Babcock & Wilcox or Foster-Wheeler; 35,000 hp **Range:** 4,000/20

REMARKS: These 46 ships make up the most important series of ships built since World War II.

The Asroc system can be loaded quickly and can be used to launch the anti-surface RIM 24B Tartar. Hangar enlarged for the SH2D Sea Sprite helicopter. On the *1078* to *1097* ships a TEAM 5 (SM 5) system is installed for the continual monitoring of ships electronic equipment. Excellent sea-keeping characteristics, but criticized because of the single propeller. Telescoping hangar fitted in this class. Anti-rolling stabilizers.

FRIGATES (continued)

Aylwin (FF 1081) G. Arra 1973
Note the *Sea Sparrow* BPDMS aft.

Sea Sprite helicopter on the **Harold E. Holt (FF 1074)** 1972

Patterson (FF 1061)

♦ *10/199 A Garcia class Author: 1960-71 (2), 61-62 (3), 62-63 (5)*

FF	Bldr	Laid down	L	In serv.
1040 GARCIA	Bethlehem, San Francisco	10-62	31-10-63	21-12-64
1041 BRADLEY	Bethlehem, San Francisco	1-63	26-3-64	15-5-65
1043 EDWARD McDONNELL	Avondale Shipyards	4-63	15-2-64	15-2-65
1044 BRUMBY	Avondale Shipyards	8-63	6-6-64	5-8-65
1045 DAVIDSON	Avondale Shipyards	9-63	3-10-64	7-12-65
1047 VOGE	Defoe SB, Michigan	11-63	8-2-65	25-11-66
1048 SAMPLE	Lockheed, Seattle	7-63	28-4-64	23-3-68
1049 KOELSH	Defoe SB, Michigan	2-64	8-6-65	10-6-67
1050 ALBERT DAVID	Lockheed, Seattle	4-64	19-12-64	19-10-68
1051 O'CALLAHAN	Defoe SB, Michigan	2-64	2-10-65	13-7-68

Garcia (FF 1040) with hangar heightened 1972

D: 2,624 tons (3,490 fl) **Dim:** 126.33 × 13.41 × 7.50 (sonar)
S: 27/26 kts **Man:** 16 officers, 225 men
A: 2/127-mm 38-cal AA (1 fwd, 1 aft) — 1 Asroc ASW system — 6/324-mm Mk 32 ASW TT (III × 2) — Platform and hangar for ASW helicopter
Electron Equipt: Radars: 1/SPS 10, 1/SPS 40
   Sonar: 1/SQS 26
M: General Electric GT; 1 prop
Boilers: 2 Foster-Wheeler, 83.4 kg/cm^2 pressure; superheat 528°; 35,000 hp.
Range: 4,000/20
Electric: ... kw

REMARKS: Same general profile as the *1037-1038* but with heavier armament. Antirolling stabilizers. On the *1047* and *1049* a special ASW NTDS. The boilers are vertical with pressure combustion. Hangar enlarged for SH2D Sea Sprite helicopter.

♦ *2 Bronstein class (author: 1959-60)*

FF	Bldr	Laid down	L	In serv.
1037 BRONSTEIN	Avondale Shipyards	5-61	31-5-62	15-6-63
1038 MC CLOY	Avondale Shipyards	9-61	4-6-62	21-10-63

FRIGATES (continued)

Edward McDonnell (FF 1043) 1970

Garcia (FF 1040) G. Arra 1975

D: 1,640 tons (2,060 fl) **S:** 24 kts
Dim: 103.08 × 12.19 × 4.60 (aft)
A: 2/76-mm AA (II × 1 fwd) — 6/324-mm Mk 32 ASW TT (III × 2) — 1 Asroc ASW system
Electron Equipt: Radars: 1/SPS 10, 1/SPS 40, 1 fire control radar
Sonar: 1/SQS 26
M: 1 geared turbine; 1 propeller **Boilers:** 2 Foster-Wheeler; 20,000 hp

REMARKS: Anti-rolling stabilizers.

McCloy (FF 1038)

PATROL GUNBOATS

♦ *13 gunboats (PG). Project SCB 229/600-65. Author: 62/63 (2), 63/64 (2), 65-66 (3), 66/67 (10)*

	L	In serv.
PG 84 ASHEVILLE	1-5-65	6-8-66
PG 85 GALLUP	15-6-65	22-10-66
PG 86 ANTELOPE	18-6-66	4-11-67
PG 87 READY	12-5-67	6-1-68
PG 88 CROCKETT	6-6-66	24-6-67
PG 89 MARATHON	22-4-67	11-5-68
PG 90 CANON	22-7-67	26-7-68
PG 92 TACOMA	13-4-68	14-7-69
PG 93 WELCH	25-7-68	8-9-69
PG 98 GRAND RAPIDS	4-4-70	5-9-70
PG 99 BEACON	17-5-69	21-11-69
PG 100 DOUGLAS		5-12-69
PG 101 GREEN BAY	14-6-69	5-12-69

Bldr: Tacoma Boat Bldg Co, except *93, 95, 97, 99, 101*, Peterson Bldrs, Inc.

D: 225 tons (240 fl) **Dim:** 50.14 (46.94 pp) × 7.28 × 2.90
S: 40 kts (16 cruising) **Man:** 3 officers, 22 men
A: 1/76-mm fwd with Mk 64 fire control on the gun mount — 1/40-mm AA 4/12.7-mm machine guns (I × 4) — Two mortars on board — Two anti-surface Tartar RIM-24 B missiles (*86, 87, 98, 100*).
M: CODAG propulsion; 1 General Electric Mk 7 LM 1500 GT driven by a J 79 turbojet of 12,500 hp (14,000 max); 2 Cummins Mk 875 V-12 diesels, 725 hp each (875 maximum); 2 props
Range: 325/35 — 1,700/16 **Fuel:** 50 tons

REMARKS: Designed by Gibbs & Cox of New York. Alloy hull. Propellers have variable pitch. An SPG 50 radar. Strong and simple construction. *86* and *87* have a Mk 87 fire control radar which is entirely automatic, requiring only a 3-man crew rather than the six needed for the Mk 63. *PG-95* and *97* transferred to Turkey and *PG-96* to South Korea. *PG-94* decommissioned and disarmed 1975 as research craft. Transfer of *PG-99* and *101* to Greece on 30-6-76.

These patrol gunboats should not be confused with the PGM class which were based on the subchaser boats of World War II which the United States delivered under the Mutual Assistance Pact to many small navies.

PATROL GUNBOATS (*continued*)

Asheville (PG 84)

PG with Standard aft (*PG 96 has been transferred to South Korea*)   1971

♦ *12 motor gunboats (PTF)*

PTF 10, 13 — Bldr: Westermoens Båtbyggeri, Mandal (1962-65).
PTF 17 (17-11-67), **18** (18-1-68), **19** (29-5-68), **20** (7-8-68), **21** (4-11-68), **22** (s/c 8-68) — Bldr: Trumpy (Annapolis, Md.)
PTF 23 (3-11-67), **24** (16-2-68), **25** (23-2-68), **26** (7-3-68) — Bldr: Sewart Seacraft (Berwick, La.)

Grand Rapids (PG 98)   1970

PTF

D:	64 tons (75 fl)	**Dim:**	24.50 × 7.46 × 2.05
S:	40 kts	**Man:**	3 officers, 16 men

A: 2/40-mm AA (I × 2) — 4/20-mm (II × 2)
M: 2 Napier-Deltic diesels with turbo compressors; 6,200 hp
Range: 600/25
PTF 23-26 "OSPREY" class; **D:** 105 tons; **Dim:** 28.80 × 7.10 × 2.13.

REMARKS: Have carried 81-mm mortars and other infantry weapons in support of special raids by SEAL teams, etc.

♦ *4 hydrofoil PHM (Patrol Hydrofoil Missile) class, 1 author. 1972-73, 4 author. 1974-75, 2 author. 1975-76*

	Bldr	Laid down	L	In serv.
PHM 1 PEGASUS	Boeing Co. (Seattle)	1973	9-11-74	5-76
PHM 2 HERCULES	Boeing Co. (Seattle)	1973	. . .	. . .
PHM 3 N . . .	. . .	. . .	. . .	. . .
PHM 4 N . . .	. . .	. . .	. . .	. . .

PATROL GUNBOATS (continued)

Pegasus (PHM 1) Note the Harpoon cannisters on the stern.

The United States, West Germany, and Italy decided, in an agreement signed in November 1972, to make a group study of a hydrofoil (PHM) ship having differing armament but with the same hull and machinery. The following may be built:

4 with Harpoon missiles for the United States;
10 with Exocet missiles for West Germany;
all will be equipped with a 76-mm OTO Melara gun.

The principal characteristics are:

— Displacement .... 218 tons
— Overall length with foil extended ... 40.20 m
— Hull beam .... 8.90 m
— Span of the foil system .... 14.51 m
— Draft with the foils raised .... 2.60 m.
— Draft foilborne .... 2.30 m.

The foils operate fully submerged, have a winged configuration, are supercavitating, and have a "duck" profile. The forward foil is used as a rudder.
Propulsion is as follows:
— foil-borne . . . General Electric LM 2,500 gas turbine with 26,000 hp,
          and 2 centrifugal water-jet pumps with quadruple flow.
— hull-borne . . . 2 MTU 8 V 331 TC 80 diesels, 670 hp each, and two water-jet pumps.

♦ *1 experimental hydrofoil*

	Bldr	Laid down	L	In serv.
PGH 1 FLAGSTAFF	Grumman Aircraft Corp	15-7-66	9-1-68	7-68

D: 57 tons   **Dim:** 24.40 × 12 × 1.35/7.80
S: 50 kts   **Man:** 1 officer, 12 men
A: 1/40-mm fwd — 4/12.7-mm machine guns (II × 2) — 1/81-mm mortar aft

Flagstaff once had a Sheridan tank turret (152-mm gun) installed in place of the fwd 40-mm mount

M: 1 Bristol Siddeley Proteus GT (*2*) or Rolls-Royce (*1*). In cruising, water-jet propulsion; 1 or 2 diesels, each 150 hp.

REMARKS: Alloy hull. At high speed, the forward foils take 70% of the weight of the boat and the after foils 30%. For cruising, the foils are raised perpendicularly. See photo of the *Plainview*. Experimental ship. *PGH-2 Tucumcari* removed from service in 1973.

♦ *1 experimental coastal ASW hydrofoil. Author: 1961-62. SCB-219 project*

	Bldr	Laid down	L	In serv.
AGE (H) 1 PLAINVIEW	Grumman Aircraft Corp.	5-64	28-6-65	1968

D: 320 tons   **Dim:** 64.61 (60.96 pp) × 13.71 × 3.05/7.93
S: 45 kts (14 cruising)   **Man:** 6 officers, 14 men
A: 6/324-mm Mk 32 ASW TT (III × 2)
M: 2 General Electric MS 240 (17,500 hp) gas turbines and 2 cruising diesels, 1,200 hp.

REMARKS: Alloy hull. The foils are 7.50 m in length and each weighs 7 tons. The ship can cruise in 4.50 m waves. The propellers are made of titanium. Trials were frequently delayed by mechanical difficulties.

PATROL GUNBOATS (*continued*)

Plainview (AGE-H 1)

♦ *1 experimental ASW coastal hydrofoil (Author: 1959-60). Project SCB-219.*

	Bldr	Laid down	L	In serv.
PC(H) 1 HIGH POINT	Martinac (Tacoma)	2-61	17-8-62	15-8-63

D: 110 tons

S: 45 kts (12 cruising)

A: 4/ASW TT (II × 2, a mixture of sizes, fixed on each side). Mk 32 torpedoes.

Dim: 35.05 × 9.45 × 2 (foil) 5.10 (cruising)

Man: 1 officer, 13 men

M: 2 Bristol Siddeley Proteus gas turbines, each 3,100 hp, and a diesel of 600 hp for cruising.

REMARKS: Alloy hull.

PATROL CRAFT (SURFACE EFFECT)

The U.S. Navy has a great deal of interest in this type ship. Two small-scale ships are used in experiments employing different techniques.

The SES 100A by the Aerojet Corporation is a vehicle with a rigid skirt riding a captured air bubble and propelled by water jets and the SES 100B of the Bell Company whose propulsion is by "marine" propellers driven by 3 gas turbines.

♦ **SES 100 A**

D: 100 tons   **S:** 80 kts   **Dim:** 24.57 × 12.57

M: 4 Avco Lycoming gas turbines; 12,000 hp; 2 waterjets

♦ **SES 100 B**

D: 100 tons   **S:** 80 kts   **Dim:** 23.80 × 10.70

M: 8 ST 6 J-70 gas turbines from United Aircraft of Canada for lift, 3 FT 12 A-6 Pratt and Whitney gas turbines at supercavitation speeds

The second phase of the trials should be reached in this decade with SES ships of some 2,000 tons. The U.S. Navy is thinking about 3,000 to 4,000-ton ships for 1980 and guided missile ships and aircraft carriers of 10,000 tons during that decade.

Project SWATH (Small Waterplane Twin Hull).

This is a concept of ships made up of 2 submerged hulls on which superstructures are built above-water. A 140-ton ship with this hull structure is now being used for experiments: the SSP (Semi-Submerged Platform).

♦ *Small coastal surveillance and riverine warfare craft*

Beginning in 1965, the operations in Vietnam caused the U.S. Navy to decide to build great numbers of small craft for coastal or riverine warfare.

After 1970 the United States transferred to South Vietnam nearly all patrol craft of the following classes: PCF Swift, PBR Mk 1, PBR Mk 2, ASPB, ATC, CMM, CCB, etc.

MINE WARFARE SHIPS

MINESWEEPERS, OCEAN (*non-magnetic*)

♦ *37 Aggressive/Acme class (author: 1950-51 and 51-52) — 1952-56*

MSO		MSO	
A.	421 AGILE	458	LUCID
	427 CONSTANT	459	NIMBLE
	428 DASH	461	OBSERVER
	429 DETECTOR	462	PINNACLE
	430 DIRECT	464	PLUCK
	431 DOMINANT	471	SKILL
	433 ENGAGE	474	VITAL
	437 ENHANCE	488	CONQUEST
	438 ESTEEM	489	GALLANT
	439 EXCEL	490	LEADER
	440 EXPLOIT	492	PLEDGE

MINESWEEPERS (*continued*)

441 EXULTANT	494 STURDY
442 FEARLESS	495 SWERVE
443 FIDELITY	496 VENTURE
446 FORTIFY	. . .
448 ILLUSIVE	B. 508 ACME
449 IMPERVIOUS	509 ADROIT
455 IMPLICIT	510 ADVANCE
456 INFLICT	511 AFFRAY

Lucid (458)

D:	637 tons (735 fl)	**Dim:**	52.30 × 10.36 × 3.15
S:	13.75 kts	**Man:**	6 officers, 70 men

Range: 2,000/12 — 3,000/10
A: 1 or 2/20-mm AA after modernization
M: 2 diesels and 2 variable pitch props. Either 2 General Motors × 760 hp or 2 Packard × 1,140 hp.
Fuel: 47 tons

REMARKS: Wooden hull; anti-magnetic fittings stressed. With the Packard engine the underway speed is hardly raised, but the sweeping speed is greater. 93 *Agile*-class ships have been built and many of them transferred to other navies. Fitted for mechanical, magnetic, and acoustic sweeping. They also have a sonar mine detector. The B group is fitted as squadron leaders. **D:** 720 tons (780 fl) — **Dim:** 52.73 × 10.69 — **M:** 2,800 hp. They have received new diesels and a sonar mine detector SQS-14. Several have already been taken out of active service, many transferred to other navies, the latest being the *Bold* (MSO-424) and the *Bulwark* (MSO-425) to Taiwan, the *Prime* (MSO-466) and the *Reaper* (MSO-467) to Thailand.

♦ *2 Ability class*

AG 520 ALACRITY (8-6-57)   **AG 521 ASSURANCE** (31-8-57)
Bldr: Peterson Bldrs (Wisconsin) — Author. *1955-56* (1), *1958-59* (1).

D:	818 tons (968 fl)	**Dim:**	57.80 × 10.70 × 3.40
S:	15 kts	**Man:**	7 officers, 75 men

A: 1/40-mm AA
M: General Motors diesels; 2,800 hp; 2 variable pitch props

REMARKS: Wooden hull; anti-magnetic fittings stressed. Commercial diesels which are

heavier and stronger than the Packards of the *Agile* class. UQS-1 sonar for mine detection. Reclassified as AG in 1973 and used to experiment with new systems of ASW detection.

Assurance (521)   A. and J. Pavia

COASTAL MINESWEEPERS (*non-magnetic*)

♦ *7 Bluebird class (MSC ex-AMS) 1952-64*

MSC	MSC	MSC
201 SHRIKE	205 VIREO	207 WHIPPOORWILL
203 THRASHER	206 WARBLER	209 WOODPECKER
204 THRUSH		

D:	320 tons (370 fl)	**Dim:**	42.90 × 8.23 × 2.55
S:	12 kts	**Man:**	39 men
A:	1/20-mm AA	**Range:**	2,500/10.

M: General Motors diesels; 2 props; 880 hp (cruising 1,200 on the *121*, *190/199*
Fuel: 40 tons

REMARKS: 168 of the same class have been transferred under the Mutual Assistance Pact. The United States continues to launch a few of them each year but transfers them immediately to other navies; usually they have four high-speed diesels, each 250 hp, linked to two shafts and with variable pitch propellers. *MSC-121 Bluebird* was transferred in 1974 to Thailand. The remaining seven will be transferred or placed out of service. *MSC-199 Phoebe* scrapped in 7-75. *MSC-204* loaned on 1-7-75 to the Virginia Institute of Marine Sciences. The others removed from active service on the same date but not scrapped.

NOTE: Sixteen shallow water minesweeping boats (MSB) are to be found on the U.S. Navy lists, but they are all in reserve. The Navy does man the *MSI-2 Cape* (240 tons), launched in 1959, for use by the Naval Undersea Research Development Center of San Diego. The *MSI-1 Cove* of the same class has been transferred to the Johns Hopkins Laboratory of Applied Physics, but still belongs to the Navy.

SHIPS FOR AMPHIBIOUS OPERATIONS

COMMAND SHIPS

From the beginning of World War II the United States recognized the necessity of having floating headquarters on board ship where a theater commander of a landing operation would have all the necessary means to carry out his mission.

With this in mind, some cargo ships of the Maritime Commission were purchased while still under construction, the majority (13) of the C 2-S-AJ 1 class, to convert them for such use. These ships were then classified as AGC. The four survivors are discussed later.

Drawing upon the lessons from the war, the U.S. Navy, working with the Marine Corps, studied and brought into service at the beginning of 1971 two ships especially built for this mission.

♦ *2 Blue Ridge class (author: 1964-65, 65-66). Project 400-65.*

LCC (ex-*AGC*)	Bldr	Laid down	L	In serv.
19 BLUE RIDGE	Philadelphia NSY	2-67	4-1-69	14-11-70
20 MOUNT WHITNEY	Newport News SB & DD	1-69	8-1-70	16-1-71

Mount Whitney (LCC 20)   J. C. Bellonne 1973

Mount Whitney (LCC 20)   J. C. Bellonne 1973

Mount Whitney (LCC 20)   1971

D:	19,290 tons (fl)	**S:**	21.5 kts

Dim: 213.60 (183.20 pp) × 25.30 × 8.20
A: 8/76-mm AA (II × 4), 2 BPDMS
Man: 52 officers, 680 men
Electron Equipt: 1/SPS 48, 1/SPS 40, 1/SPS 10 — NTDS — TACAN.
M: General Electric GT; 1 prop
Boilers: 2 Foster-Wheeler; 22,000 hp.

REMARKS: Like all recent amphibious force ships, these have a good cruising speed (20 knots), and excellent communication, transmission, and analysis systems: ACIS (Amphibious Command Information System), NIPS (Naval Intelligence Processing System). Same machinery as the *Iwo Jima* class LPH. Photographic laboratories and document publication facilities. In addition to quarters for ship's company indicated above, quarters are available for a large staff (217 officers, 471 men). LCPL and LCVP small craft are carried in davits. Liaison and transport helicopters (two UH-2, one CH-46 A). Air-conditioned and anti-rolling stabilizers.

♦ *4 Mount McKinley*

LCC (ex-*AGC*)			
7 MOUNT McKINLEY	**12 ESTES**		L: 1943-45.
16 POCONO	**17 TACONIC**		

D: 7,100 tons (12,750 fl)   **S:** 15 kts
Dim: 139.98 (132.58 pp) × 19.20 × 7.25
Man: 36/40 officers, 480/490 men
A: 1/127-mm fwd — 4/40-mm AA (II × 2)
Electron Equipt: Radars: 1/SPS 10, 1/SPS 37, 1/SPS 30
M: 2 GT; 2 props; 6,000 hp   **Boilers:** Two

REMARKS: Modified cargo ships from World War II. Long ago removed from active service.

AMPHIBIOUS ASSAULT SHIPS (LHA and LPH)

♦ *5 Landing Helicopter Assault (LHA)* — Author. 1968-69 (1), 69-70 (2), 70-71 (2).

LHA	Bldr	Laid down	L	In serv.
1 TARAWA	Litton Industries	5-11-71	1-12-73	75
2 SAIPAN	Litton Industries	21-7-72	26-7-74	76
3 BELLEAU WOOD (ex-*Philippine Sea*)	Litton Industries	5-3-72	...	...
4 NASSAU (ex-*Leyte Gulf*)	Litton Industries	23-5-73	...	...
5 DANANG (ex-*Khesanh*)	Litton Industries (Pascagoula)	5-74	...	...

Tarawa (LHA 1) Underway during trials　　　1976

D: 39,300 tons (fl)　　**Dim:** 242.70 × 32.30 × 8.40
S: 20 kts　　**Man:** 163 officers, 1,662 men
Range: 10,000/20
M: GT; 2 props
Electron Equipt: Radars: 1/SPS 10, 1/SPS 40, 1/SPS 52, 1/SPN 35
　　　　　　　　　　ITAWDS (Integrated Tactical Amphibious Warfare
　　　　　　　　　　Data System)
A: 2/BPDMS Sea Sparrow systems — 3/127-mm 54-cal AA (I × 3) —
　　6/20-mm — 30 helicopters

REMARKS: The order for these ships was given to Ingalls Shipbuilding, a division of Litton Industries, Inc. The yard was modified for the construction of the ships. The *LHA 1 Tarawa* commenced underway trials early in 9-75.

The LHA class is a multi-purpose assault transport, a combination of the LPH and the LPD. The ship has the general profile of an aircraft carrier with its superstructure to starboard, flight deck, side elevator to port and starboard, and a well deck for landing craft. It is anticipated that these ships will operate with two *Newport* class LSTs, and this combination of ships will land a Marine Battalion Landing Team with all equipment (1,800 men). Advanced automation; will carry AV-8A Harrier VTOL/STOL aircraft as well as the usual transport helicopters.

♦ *7 Amphibious Assault Ships (LPH)* — Project *P 57* and *401-66.*

LPH	Author	Bldr	Laid down	L	In serv.
2 IWO JIMA	58-59	Puget Sound NSY	4-59	30-9-60	26-8-61
3 OKINAWA	59-60	Philadelphia NSY	4-60	19-8-61	14-4-62
7 GUADALCANAL	60-61	Philadelphia NSY	9-61	16-3-63	20-7-63
9 GUAM	61-62	Philadelphia NSY	11-62	22-8-64	16-1-65
10 TRIPOLI	62-63	Ingalls, Pascagoula	6-64	31-7-65	6-8-66
11 NEW ORLEANS	64-65	Philadelphia NSY	3-66	3-2-68	16-11-68
12 INCHON	65-66	Ingalls, Pascagoula	4-68	5-4-69	20-6-70

Inchon (LPH 12)　　　　　　J. C. Bellonne 1972

Iwo Jima (LPH 2)　　　　　　1973

D: 17,000 tons (18,300 fl)　　**S:** 20 kts
Dim: 182.90 (180.15 pp) × 32 (25.60 wl) × 7.62
Man: 48 officers, 480 men + troops

AMPHIBIOUS ASSAULT SHIPS (*continued*)

La Salle (as AGF 3) 1972

Cleveland (LPD 7)

Shreveport (LPD 12) 1970

Guadalcanal (LPH 7)

AMPHIBIOUS ASSAULT SHIPS *(continued)*

A: 4/76-mm AA (II × 4) — 3 BPDMS Sea Sparrow system — 20/24 CH 46 helicopters 4 CH 53 heavy helicopters, 4 HU-1 observation helicopters, 3 AV-8 A VTOL/STOL aircraft.
Electron Equipt: Radars: 1/SPS 10, 1/SPS 40, 1/SPN 10
M: GT; 1 prop; 23,000 hp
Boilers: 4 Babcock or Combustion Engine

REMARKS: Especially built for the transportation and vertical landing of 2,090 fully-equipped Marines. One side elevator forward to port, one to starboard aft. 70 m. hangar. Up to 7 helicopters can be operated simultaneously on the flight deck. Excellent medical facilities (300 beds). The *Guam* has an ASCAC (Air Surface Classification and Analysis Center).

ASSAULT TRANSPORTS (DOCK AND LANDING SHIP) (LPD AND LSD)

♦ *15 LPD author. 59-60 (1), 60-61 (1), 60-62 (3), 62-63 (4), 63-64 (4), 64-65 (2). SCB 187 A and B/402-66 Projects.*

LPD		Bldr	Laid down	L	In serv.
A.	1 **RALEIGH**	New York NSY	6-60	17-3-62	8-9-62
	2 **VANCOUVER**	New York NSY	11-60	15-9-62	11-5-63
AGF	3 **LA SALLE***	New York NSY	4-62	3-8-63	22-2-64

D: 8,040 tons (13,900 fl) **Dim:** 150.0 (155.43 pp) × 25.60 × 6.40
S: 21 kts **Man:** 28 officers, 430 men
A: 8/76-mm AA (II × 4) — 2 CH-46 helicopters
M: GT; 2 props
Boilers: 2 Babcock; 24,000 hp

REMARKS: *La Salle* modified as a flagship for COMIDEAST Force in the Indian Ocean and reclassified AGF-3.

LPD		Bldr	Laid down	L	In serv.
B.	4 **AUSTIN**	New York NSY	2-63	27-6-64	6-2-65
	5 **OGDEN**	New York NSY	2-63	27-6-64	19-6-65
	6 **DULUTH**	New York NSY	12-63	14-8-65	18-12-65
	7 **CLEVELAND***	Ingalls, Pascagoula	11-64	7-5-65	21-4-67
	8 **DUBUQUE***	Ingalls, Pascagoula	1-65	6-8-66	1-9-67
	9 **DENVER**	Lockheed SB, Seattle	2-64	23-1-65	26-10-68
	10 **JUNEAU**	Lockheed SB, Seattle	1-65	12-2-66	12-7-69
	11 **CORONADO**	Lockheed SB, Seattle	5-65	30-7-66	23-5-70
	12 **SHREVEPORT**	Lockheed SB, Seattle	12-65	22-10-66	14-2-70
	13 **NASHVILLE***	Lockheed SB, Seattle	3-66	7-10-67	12-7-70
	14 **TRENTON**	Lockheed SB, Seattle	8-66	3-8-70	6-3-71
	15 **PONCE**	Lockheed SB, Seattle	10-66	20-5-70	10-7-71

Coronado (LPD 11)   J. C. Bellonne 1972

D: 11,050 tons (17,150 fl) **Dim:** 176.35 (171.30 pp) × 25 × 6.70
S: 20 kts **Man:** 30 officers, 480 men
A: 8/76-mm AA (II × 4) — 2 CH-46 helicopters
Electron Equipt: Radars: 1/SPS 10, 1/SPS 40
M: GT; 2 props
Boilers: 2 Babcock; 24,000 hp

♦ *Raleigh/Austin class*

REMARKS: Combination LSD and assault transport APA; well deck 120 × 15.24. Helicopter platform. Can carry 930 (A) or 840 (B) Marines, 2,000 (A) or 3,900 (B) tons of cargo, 2 CH 46 transport helicopters, small landing craft — either 1 LCU and 3 LCM (6) or 9 LCM (6) or 4 LCM (8) or 28 LVT. Six cranes, one 8.15-ton elevator, two forklifts. The B class has a hangar on the flight deck. The * are fitted for flagship duty.

♦ *5 LSD Anchorage class*
Author. 1965-66 (1), 1966-67 (4). — 404-65 and 66 projects

LSD		L	In serv.
36	**ANCHORAGE**	5-5-68	15-3-69
37	**PORTLAND**	20-12-69	3-10-70
38	**PENSACOLA**	11-7-70	27-3-71
39	**MOUNT VERNON**	20-2-71	13-5-72
40	**FORT FISHER**	24-4-72	12-9-72

Bldr: Ingalls *(36)*, General Dynamics *(37/40)*.

D: 13,650 tons (fl) **Dim:** 169.16 (162.80 pp) × 25.60 × . . .
S: 22/20 kts **Man:** 303 men

ASSAULT TRANSPORTS (continued)

Portland (LSD 37)   G. Arra 1973

A: 8/76-mm AA (II × 4)   **M:** GT; 2 props
Boilers: 2; 24,000 hp

REMARKS: Can carry 337 troops, operate cargo helicopters and carry six. Carry assault landing craft in the well deck (113.28 × 15.24); can accommodate 3 LCU or 29 LCM (6) and many LVT.

♦ *Thomaston class*

ASSAULT DOCK LANDING SHIPS

♦ *8 LSD Thomaston-class*

LSD	L	LSD	L
28 THOMASTON	9-2-54	**32 SPIEGEL GROVE**	10-11-55
29 PLYMOUTH ROCK	7-2-54	**33 ALAMO**	20-1-56
30 FORT SNELLING	6-7-54	**34 HERMITAGE**	12-6-56
31 POINT DEFIANCE	28-9-54	**35 MONTICELLO**	10-8-56

Bldr: Ingalls Shipbuilding, Pascagoula (1953-56)

Plymouth Rock (LSD 29)   G. Arra 1975

D: 6,880 tons (11,270 fl)   **Dim:** 155.45 × 25.60 × 5.80
S: 23 kts   **Man:** 366 men, 109 troops
M: GT; 2 props; 23,000 hp
A: 12/76-mm AA automatic (II × 6)

REMARKS: Helicopter platform; can carry 3 LCU or 21 LCM (6) and 3 to 8 helicopters. Maintenance workshops; 2/50-ton cranes, *34* and *35* air-conditioned; reinforced bow for icebreaking.

♦ *5 LSD Ashland class (18, 19, 20, modernized Fram II)*

LSD	L	LSD	L
14 RUSHMORE	10-5-44	**19 COMSTOCK**	28-4-55
16 CABILDO	28-12-44	**20 DONNER**	6-4-45
17 CATAMOUNT	27-1-45		

D: 4,032 tons (8,700 fl)   **Dim:** 139 × 21.90 × 4.90
S: 16/15 kts   **Man:** 17 officers, 237 men
A: 8 to 12/40-mm AA   **Range:** 8,000/15
M: GT; 2 props; 9,000 hp   **Boilers:** 2 drums, three shells

REMARKS: Helicopter platform; 2/35-ton cranes. Carry 3 LCU or 18 LCM with an LCVP cradled in each. Well deck 103 × 13.30. Several have been transferred, the *Fort Marion* (LSD-22) to Taiwan. Not in active service.

♦ *1 Dock Cargo ship (AKD)*

	Bldr	Laid down	L	In serv.
T-AKD 1 POINT BARROW	Maryland DD Co.	9-56	25-5-57	2-58

D: 9,415 tons (14,094 fl)   **Dim:** 142.05 × 22.55 × 6.10
S: 15 kts   **Man:** 66 + 42 passengers
Range: 10,000/15
Cargo capacity: 4,220 tons
M: GT; 2 props; boilers: 2; 6,000 hp.

REMARKS: Combines the missions of an LSD and an LKA. Bow reinforced against ice. Carries 18 LCM or 3 LCU and 14 LVT; well deck 112 m in length. Two 40-ton cranes. In reserve.

FAST TRANSPORTS (LPR) (ex-APD)

There are only three ships of this class left and they are in reserve. Seven were taken out of service in 1974.

D: 1,400/1,450 tons (2,049 fl)   **Dim:** 93.26 × 11.28 × 4.70
S: 23 kts   **Man:** 212 men
Range: 5,000/15 — 2,000/23
A: 1/127-mm (fwd) — 3/40-mm AA (1 fwd, 2 aft)
M: turbo-electric propulsion; 2 props; 12,000 hp; 2 boilers
Fuel: 350 tons

REMARKS: Modified destroyer escorts. Can carry 162 troops, 4/75-mm howitzers, 6 small trucks, 2 one-ton trucks, 4 jeep-type vehicles. 126 m³ of munitions, 28 m³ of gasoline, 100 m³ of various cargo, 4 LCVP.

TANK LANDING SHIPS

♦ *20 LST Newport class Project 405-66. Author: 1964–65 (1), 1965–66 (8), 1966–67 (11).*

LST	In serv.
1179 NEWPORT	7-6-69
1180 MANITOWOC	24-1-70
1181 SUMTER	20-6-70
1182 FRESNO	22-11-69
1183 PEORIA	21-2-70
1184 FREDERICK	13-6-70
1185 SCHENECTADY	8-8-70
1186 CAYUGA	8-8-70

TANK LANDING SHIPS (continued)

1187 TUSCALOOSA	24-10-70
1188 SAGINAW	23-1-71
1189 SAN BERNARDINO	27-3-71
1190 BOULDER	4-6-71
1191 RACINE	9-7-71
1192 SPARTANBURG COUNTY	1-9-71
1193 FAIRFAX COUNTY	16-10-71
1194 LA MOURE COUNTY	18-12-71
1195 BARBOUR COUNTY	12-2-72
1196 HARLAN COUNTY	8-4-72
1197 BARNSTABLE COUNTY	2-5-72
1198 BRISTOL COUNTY	5-8-92

Bldr: Philadelphia NSY (*1179*), National Steel, San Diego (the others).

Saginaw (LST 1188)   G. Arra 1972

Saginaw (LST 1188)   G. Arra 1972

D: 8,342 tons (fl)   **S:** 20 kts
Dim: 160 × 20.72 × 4.60 (aft with 500 ton load) 1.80 (forward)
Man: 186 men
M: 6 Alco diesels; 2 props; 16,500 hp

Fairfax County (LST 1193)   G. Arra 1973

REMARKS: Can carry 500 tons of cargo and 430 troops. A vertical propeller located aft helps beaching and unbeaching. A mobile aluminum ramp is located forward (34.15 tons) which is linked to the tank deck by a second ramp. These ramps can carry 75 tons. Aft is a helicopter platform, and there is a stern gate for loading and unloading vehicles.

◆ *3 LST. Project SCB-119*

LST	L
1173 SUFFOLK COUNTY	19-9-57
1177 LORAIN COUNTY	22-6-57
1178 WOOD COUNTY	14-12-57

Bldr: Newport News SB (*1176*), American SB, Lorain, Ohio (*1177/8*).

Suffolk County (LST 1173)   G. Arra 1972

TANK LANDING SHIPS (*continued*)

D:	3,860 tons (7,100 fl)	**Dim:**	134.70 × 18.90 × 5.50
S:	15/16 kts	**Man:**	10 officers, 174 men
A:	6/76-mm 50-cal (II × 3)		
M:	6 Nordberg diesels; 2 variable pitch props; 14,000 hp		

REMARKS: Can carry 700 troops. Air-conditioned. Special tanks for aviation fuel. 4 LCVP carried in davits; one LCU and 2 motorized pontoons carried inboard. Helicopter platform. *De Soto County* (LST-1171) and *York County* (LST-1175) transferred to Italy, *Grant County* (LST-1174) to Brazil. None in commission.

♦ *3 LSTs. Project SCB 19.*

LST		L
1157	TERRELL COUNTY	6-12-52
1163	WALDO COUNTY	17-3-53
1169	WHITFIELD COUNTY	22-8-53

Bldr: Bath Iron Works (*1157/63*), Christy Corp., Sturgeon Bay (*1166/69*)

Waldo County (LST 1163)

D:	2,590 tons (5,786 fl)	**Dim:**	117.35 × 16.76 × 3.70
S:	13 kts	**Man:**	116 men
A:	3 or 4/76-mm AA		
M:	4 General Motors diesels; 2 variable pitch props; 6,000 hp		

REMARKS: Draft before beaching: 1.25 m. All already taken out of service or transferred, 3 to Spain and 6 to the Maritime Administration (*1158, 1160, 1161, 1162, 1164, 1165*). In 1973, the *1166* which was used as a station vessel for minesweepers in Haiphong harbor was stricken. The *Westchester County* (LST-1167) was transferred to Turkey in 1974.

♦ *Original LST class* (*numbers prior to 1153*)

1,052 ships of this model (Gibbs and Cox plans) were built from November 1941 until 1947. Since 1955 they have all been named after a county in the United States. Many ships of this class have been placed out of service or transferred to foreign navies. The Vietnam war required the placing in commission of many LSTs previously

removed from the active list, but since the end of hostilities, they have been returned to reserve status. Their characteristics:

D:	1,490 tons (4,080 fl)	**Dim:**	99.98 × 15.24 × 4.36
S:	10.8 kts (8 cruising)	**Man:**	7 or 9 officers, 119 to 220 men
A:	8/40-mm AA (II × 4)	**Range:**	6,000/9
M:	2 diesels; 2 props; 1,800 hp	**Fuel:**	1,060 tons

REMARKS: Trucks and tanks landed through a bow ramp. One LCT and 2 to 6 LCVPs can be carried on deck. Quarters for 145 to 163 passengers. Two different methods of lowering tanks carried on the upper deck: a hoist and 'tween-decks ramp to the landing deck ramp (LST-1 to 513, plus LST-531) or by a single ramp (LST-514 and following except for LST-531).

LANDING CRAFT

The largest type landing craft is now the LCU (Landing Craft Utility). With the exception of an experimental craft of alloy (LCU-1637), they are all of welded steel and have a landing ramp in the bow.

LCU 1472   1965

There are two models:

♦ *1466 class — about 25*

D:	180 tons (360 fl)	**Dim:**	35.97 × 10.69 × 1.83 (fl)
S:	8 kts	**Man:**	14 men
A:	2/20-mm		
M:	3 high speed diesels; 3 props; 675 hp		

REMARKS: The LCU class can usually carry 3 main battle tanks or an equivalent load of trucks and other cargo or 400 troops.

Two delivered in 1965–66 (LCU-1625-26), have a displacement of 210 tons (375 full load), and horizontal engines (experimental ships).

♦ *1610 class — about 40*

D:	195 tons (375 fl)	**Dim:**	41.15 × 8.84 × 1.83 (fl)
S:	11 kts	**Man:**	12/14 men
M:	2 high-speed diesels; 2 props; 2,000 hp		

REMARKS: Several fitted with horizontal engines and Kort nozzles. Exceptionally maneuverable. LCU-1671-1680 were under construction in 1975 at the Marinette Marine Corporation shipyards.

LANDING CRAFT (*continued*)

LCU 1483

LCM 866

♦ *LCVP class* — This class which was given its final design in 1942 is still being produced with very few changes; 1,552 were built between 1950 and 1962 with either wooden or plastic hulls (Mk 5 and 7).

> **D:** about 13 tons (fl)   **S:** 9 kts   **Dim:** 11 × 3.20 × 1.05 (fl)
> **M:** 1 high-speed diesel of 225 hp. Can carry 36 troops or 3.5 tons of cargo.

♦ *LCM 6 class* — 626 built from 1952 to 1967 of welded steel; based on the wartime LCM-3 but longer.

> **D:** 25 tons (55 fl)   **S:** 9 kts   **Dim:** 17.12 × 4.27 × 1.07 (fl)
> **M:** 2 high-speed diesels; 2 props; 650 hp.

♦ *LCM 8 class* — Of the 217 built for the Navy since 1949, 146 are of welded steel, the others of alloy. They can carry tanks of up to 65 tons' weight.

> **D:** 60 tons (113 fl)   **S:** 9 kts   **Dim:** 22.45 × 6.40 × 1.58 (fl)
> **M:** 2 high-speed diesels; 2 props; 650 hp

NOTE: All the LCMs have a landing ramp in the bow.

♦ **LCRS** — used by frogmen and minehunters.

> **Dim:** 12.50 × 8.80 (foils extended), 4.30 (foils retracted)

> **S:** 35 kts max.   **Weight:** 14 tons (3 tons of fuel)
> **M:** 2 Chrysler motors, each 275 hp

AMPHIBIOUS VEHICLES

♦ **DUKW** — Amphibious vehicle with 6 wheels; can carry 25 troops or 2,400 kg of cargo. No longer in use.

> **D:** 9.45 × 2.44   **Man:** 1 man
> **Weight:** (empty) 5.9 tons
> **S:** 80 km (land), 5.5 kts (water borne)
> **Range:** 650 km at 55 km/h (land).

♦ **LCA** *craft* (*1962*)

> **L:** 17 — beam: 6.40 — height 4.20 mounted on treads (14 roadwheels) Can carry 300 men or 24 tons of cargo
> **M:** 2 gas turbines (1,140 hp)
> **S:** 12 kts (35 km/h on land). Experimental.

♦ **LVTP 5**

> **Total weight combat-loaded:** 40 tons
> **S:** 30 mph on land, 6 knots water borne.
> **A:** 1/7.62 mm   **M:** 800-hp gasoline engine
> **Range:** 290 km. Carry 36 troops. Withdrawn from service, 1973.

♦ **LVTP 7**

> **Total weight combat loaded:** 25 tons
> **S:** 50 kmh on land, 9 kts water borne.   **Man:** 3 men
> **Range:** 480 km — 400 hp diesel
> Waterborne propulsion with two water-jet pumps
> **Capacity:** 25 combat equipped troops or 5 tons.
> **A:** 1/12.7-mm
> Former LVTPX-12. Standard equipment for USMC divisions (1 battalion each).

TRANSPORTS (Amphibious Transport and Amphibious Cargo Ships (LPA and LKA)

♦ *2 Paul Revere class*

LPA 248 PAUL REVERE (13-2-54)   **LPA 249 FRANCIS MARION** (11-4-53)

> **D:** 10,709 tons (light) (16,838 fl)
> **Dim:** 170 × 23 × 7.3
> **S:** 22 kts   **Man:** 35 officers, 415 men

Francis Marion (LPA 249)   1969

TRANSPORTS (*continued*)

A: 8/76-mm AA (II × 4)
M: 2 Foster-Wheeler boilers; GT; 22,000 hp.

REMARKS: *LPA-249* (has a helicopter platform); can carry 1,657 troops.

COMMAND SHIPS (none in service)
(*National Military Command System*)

CC	Conversion Author	Bldr	Laid down	L
2 WRIGHT (ex-*AVT-7*)	62-63	New York SB Corp.	2-8-44	1-9-45

1968

D:	14,500 tons (19,600 fl)	**S:**	33 kts
Dim:	208.35 × 23.41 × 8.50		
A:	8/40-mm AA — 5 or 6 helicopters		
Man:	1,720 men (1,156 staff personnel)		
M:	General Electric GT; 4 props; 120,000 hp; 8 boilers		
Fuel:	2,400 tons		

REMARKS: Former light aircraft carrier modified as a communications relay ship. Designed for theater commands requiring excellent radio communications. Had been planned as a ship for the President and his staff in case of nuclear threats.

CC	Bldr	Laid down	L	In serv
1 NORTHAMPTON (ex-*CA-125*)	Bethlehem Steel (Quincy)	31-8-44	27-1-51	3-53

D:	14,700 tons (17,700 fl)	**Dim:**	205.25 × 21.27 × 7.50
S:	32 kts	**Man:**	68 officers, 1,123 men, 450 staff
A:	1/127-mm AA automatic — 2 helicopters		
Armor:	152-mm belt		
M:	General Electric GT; 4 props; 120,000 hp; 4 boilers	**Range:**	8,000/15

REMARKS: Construction as a command ship began in 1948. Excellent transmission and detection equipment. Completely air-conditioned.

1968

◆ *2 major communications relay ships (AGMR). Former aircraft carriers now modified for use by operational forces; the mobility of the ships and the strength of the equipment installed will strengthen weak signals in any part of the world.*

AGMR 2 ARLINGTON* (ex-*Saipan, AVT-6*) N.Y. SB Corp. 28-7-45
Hull and machinery same as the *Wright*.

AGMR 1 ANNAPOLIS* (ex-*Gilbert Islands, CVE-107*) Todd-Pacific 20-7-44
    D: 22,500 tons (fl)   **S:** 18 kts   **Dim:** 169.80 × 31.70 × 11.90
*Stricken in 1975, will be scrapped.

LOGISTIC SUPPORT
SUBMARINE TENDERS (AS)

◆ *4 Spear class for 12 nuclear attack submarines (SSN). Project 702-66.*

AS	Author	Bldr	Laid down	L	In serv.
36 L.Y. SPEAR	65-66	General Dynamics	5-66	7-9-67	28-2-70
37 DIXON	66-67	General Dynamics	9-67	11-69	7-8-71
39 N . . .	. . .	. . .	. . .	. . .	. . .
40 N . . .	. . .	. . .	. . .	. . .	. . .

D:	12,770 tons (22,640 fl) **Dim:** 195.98 × 25.90 × 7.10
S:	20 kts
A:	(a) *AS-36* and *37*: 2/127-mm 38-cal AA (I × 2)
	(b) *AS-39* and *40*: 1 BPDMS Sea Sparrow — 4/20 mm
Electron Equipt:	*AS-39* and *40*: 1/SPS 55, 1/SPS 58 — Sonar: 1/UQN
M:	GT; 1 prop; 20,000 hp

◆ *2 Simon Lake class for 9 SSBN submarines each*

AS	Author	Bldr	Laid down	L	In serv.
33 SIMON LAKE	1962-63	Puget Sound NSY	1-63	8-2-64	7-11-64
34 CANOPUS	1963-64	Ingalls, Pascagoula	3-64	12-2-65	4-11-65

D:	21,000 tons (32,650 fl) **Dim:** 195.98 × 26.51 × 7.01 (light)
S:	18 kts **Man:** 1,420 men

LOGISTIC SUPPORT (continued)

L. Y. Spear (AS 36) 1970

Canopus (AS 34)

A: 4/76-mm AA (II × 2)
M: GT; 1 prop; 20,000 hp
Boilers: 2 Combustion Engine

REMARKS: *AS-34* fitted for Poseidon missiles.

♦ *2 Hunley class for SSBN submarines*

AS	Author	Bldr	Laid down	L	In serv.
31 HUNLEY	1959-60	Newport News SB	11-60	28-9-61	16-6-62
32 HOLLAND	1961-62	Ingalls, Pascagoula	3-62	19-1-63	7-9-63

D: 10,500 tons (18,300 fl)   **Dim:** 182.60 × 25.30 × 7.35
S: 18 kts   **A:** 4/76-mm AA

Holland (AS 32) 1971

Man: 59 officers, 1,023 men, 30 Marines
M: diesel-electric propulsion (10 Fairbanks-Morse diesels); 1 prop; 15,000 hp

REMARKS: The propulsion groups develop 12,000 kw; in addition there are four auxiliary groups (3,000 kw). Rotating travelling crane with 32.5-ton lift. Quarters for 30 officers and 270 men as relief crews for submarines. Air-conditioned. Helicopter platform.

♦ *7 Fulton class*

	Bldr	In serv.
A — AS 19 PROTEUS	Moore SB & DD Co.	31-1-44

   D: 10,250 tons (18,500 fl)   **Dim:** 174.90 × 22.35 × 8.20

Refit in 1959-60 for maintenance of SSBN nuclear submarines. The hull of the ship was cut in order that an additional 13.50-m section could be added to the center for machinery and spare parts, as well as a movable crane which can service both sides of the ship.

	Bldr	L
B — AS 11 FULTON	Mare Island NSY	17-12-40
AS 12 SPERRY	Mare Island NSY	17-12-41
AS 16 HOWARD	Mare Island NSY	16-9-43
W. GILMORE		
(ex-*Neptune*)		
AS 18 ORION	Moore SB & DD	14-10-43

Modernized in 1960-62 under the FRAM program in order to support nuclear submarines (SSN class).

	Bldr	L
C — AS 15 BUSHNELL	Mare Island NSY	14-9-42
AS 17 NEREUS	Puget Sound NSY	12-2-45

   D: 9,750 tons (18,000 fl)   **A:** 2/127-mm
Dim: 161.40 × 22.35 × 8.20 (see Remarks)
S: 15.50 kts   **Man:** 1,300 men (wartime)
M: diesel-electric propulsion, 2 props, 11,500 hp
Fuel: 3,760 diesel

LOGISTIC SUPPORT (*continued*)

Proteus (AS 19)
modified for the maintenance of SSBN submarines

Shbldg. and Sh. Record

AK 260 BETELGEUSE (ex-*Columbia Victory*) — **T-AK 279 NORWALK** (ex-*Norwalk Victory*) — **T-AK 280 FURMAN** (ex-*Furman Victory*) — **T-AK 281 VICTORIA** (ex-*Ethiopia Victory*) — Bldr. U.S.A. 1944-45.

D: 11,150 tons (fl)   **Dim:** 138.70 × 18.98

Amphibious cargo ships modified under the 1962/63, 1963/64 and 1964/65 budgets as logistic support ships (FBM) for maintenance and spare parts (including the Polaris system) necessary for the submarine tenders already discussed. The Ts are manned by a civil service crew and a naval group (MSC).

ARDM-1 OAKRIDGE (ex-*ARD-19*) — **ARDM-2 ALAMOGORDO** (ex-*ARD-26*) — **AFDB-7** (ex-*ARDM-3*) — **LOS ALAMOS** (ex-*ARD-18*) — floating docks *ARD-12* class, originally designed as annexes of the *AS-31/34* class and especially modified for that duty (project 237). The reconstruction included a lengthening and an elevation of the bulkheads for these vessels which can now receive the largest SSBN class submarines.

Dim: 163 × 25

REMARKS: Built as floating support bases for 18/1,500-ton (*Gato*-Guppy) class submarines. Direct current except for the *AS-12* which has alternating, foundries for 250-kg castings. Two separate engine rooms each with 4/2-ton General Motors diesels, 1,600-hp linked with a 1,125-kw generator. Auxiliary machinery: 2 General Motors diesels, each 750 kw in the aft compartment. With two diesels on the line (2,500 hp), 10 knots and 65 days of cruising can be maintained. *AS-15* used as station ship at the Norfolk Naval Base.

Howard W. Gilmore (AS 16)

G. Arra 1975

DESTROYER TENDERS (AD)

♦ *1 AD authorized 1972-73*

♦ *2 Samuel Gompers class. Project SCB-244. Author: 64-66 (1), 65-66 (1), 72-73 (1), 74-75 (1).*

AD	Bldr	Laid down	L	In serv.
37 SAMUEL GOMPERS	Puget Sound NSY	7-64	14-5-66	1-7-67
38 PUGET SOUND	Puget Sound NSY	2-65	16-9-66	27-4-68
40 N . . .	. . .	. . .	. . .	. . .
41 N . . .	. . .	. . .	. . .	. . .

Samuel Gompers (AD 37)

D: 20,500 tons (21,600 fl)   **Dim:** 196.30 × 25.90 × 7.20
S: 18 kts   **Man:** 135 officers, 1,668 men
A: 1/127-mm 38-cal — 1 BPDMS Sea Sparrow system (*AD-40*) — 6/12.7-mm machine guns — 1 helicopter
M: GT; 2 props; 20,000 hp

REMARKS: Maintenance ships for guided missile cruisers and destroyers, six of which can come alongside at one time. Excellent workshops for electronic equipment and surface-to-air missiles.

♦ *5 Dixie class*

AD	Bldr	L	In serv.
AD 14 DIXIE	New York SB Corp.	27-8-39	1940
AD 15 PRAIRIE	New York SB Corp.	5-12-39	1940
AD 17 PIEDMONT	Tampa SB Co.	7-12-42	1944

AD 18 SIERRA	Tampa SB Co.	26-2-43	1944
AD 19 YOSEMITE	Tampa SB Co.	16-5-43	1944

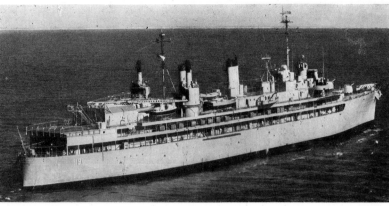

Yosemite (AD 19)   1969

D: 10,400 tons (17,175 fl)   **Dim:** 161.70 × 22.33 × 8.10
S: 18 kts (19.5 during trials)   **Man:** 770 men
A: 2/127-mm 38-cal — 1 helicopter
M: GT; 2 props; 11/12,000 hp
Boilers: 4 Babcock and Wilcox

REMARKS: These support ships go back to pre-1939 programs. Modernized under the FRAM program from 1959 to 1963 to serve as maintenance ships for guided missile ships; they have maintenance workshops and spare parts for missiles and ASW helicopters.

AD 24 EVERGLADES	28-1-44	AD 28 GRAND CANYON	27-4-45
AD 26 SHENANDOAH	1945	AD 29 ISLE ROYALE	18-8-44
		AD 36 BRYCE CANYON	28-1-45

Isle Royale (AD 29)   1970

DESTROYER TENDERS (AD) *(continued)*

D: 9,260 tons (16,635 fl)
Dim: 149.96 (141.75 pp) × 21.25 × 8.50
S: 16.5 kts   **Man:**   826 men
A: 1/127-mm — 4/76-mm — 4/40-mm AA
M: GT; 2 props; 8,500 hp
Boilers: 2 Foster-Wheeler or Babcock.

REMARKS: C3 cargo ships of the U.S. Maritime Commission. Redesigned during construction.

FLEET REPLENISHMENT SHIPS
(AOR, AOE, AFS)

The AOR and the AOE classes represent a combination of AO (tankers) and AE (ammunition ships). The AFS (combat store ship) has as its mission those supply tasks evolved from supply ships, store ships, and seaplane tenders. The AOE and the AOR are designed to accompany and supply operational forces at sea, which accounts for the relatively high speed capability.

♦ *7 AOR Wichita class (Replenishment oilers). Author: 64-67 (1-6).*

AOR	Laid down	L	In serv.
1 WICHITA	6-66	13-3-68	7-6-69
2 MILWAUKEE	11-66	27-1-69	1-11-69
3 KANSAS CITY	4-68	28-6-69	6-6-70
4 SAVANNAH	1-69	25-4-70	5-12-70
5 WABASH	8-69	1-11-70	5-12-71
6 KALAMAZOO	2-70	11-72	11-8-73
7 ROANOKE	21-1-74	17-2-74	. . .

Bldr: General Dynamics — *Author: 65-66 (2), 66-67 (2), 67-68 (2), 72-73 (7).*

Wichita (AOR 1)   1970

D: 38,100 tons (fl)   **Dim:**   200.85 × 29.30 × 10.70
S: 20 kts   **Man:**   16 officers, 350 men
A: 8/76-mm AA (II × 4)
Range: 10,000/17 (2 boilers)
M: 2 GT; 4 combustion engine boilers; 2 props; 32,000 hp

♦ *6 AOE Sacramento class (Fast Combat Support Ships). Author. 60-61 (1), 62-63 (1), 64-65 (1), 65-66 (1). Project SCB 196.*

AOE	Bldr	Laid down	L	In serv.
1 SACRAMENTO	Puget Sound NSY	6-61	14-9-63	14-3-64
2 CAMDEN	New York SB (Camden)	2-64	29-5-65	1-4-67
3 SEATTLE	Puget Sound NSY	10-65	2-3-68	5-4-69
4 DETROIT	Puget Sound NSY	11-66	21-6-69	28-3-70

Detroit (AOE 4)   1972

D: 19,200 tons (53,600 fl)
Dim: 241.40 × 215.80 (pp) × 32.92 × 11.60 (fl)
S: 26 kts   **Man:**   33 officers, 567 men
A: 8/76-mm 50-cal (II × 4)
M: GT; 2 props
Boilers: 4 vertical Combustion Engine, 42.20 kg/cm²; superheat: 480°; 100,000 hp
Range: 10,000/17

REMARKS: The AOE (Fast Combat Support Ship) carries as much petroleum products as the most recent tankers (including 36 million litres of jet fuel), plus 1,600 tons of ammunition (25% of the tonnage carried by a recently constructed AE), 250 tons of refrigerated products, 250 tons of fresh supplies, and other cargo. She also has on board 2 UH 46-A (Sea Knight) cargo helicopters, and has rotating cranes on each side. The ships to be supplied take position on each side at about 60 meters. The AOE has nine supply stations to port and six to starboard with two in particular for missiles. Numbers 1 and 4 each received half of the propulsive machinery of the battleship *Kentucky* whose construction was cancelled in 1946.

♦ *7 AFS Mars class, (Combat Stores Ships). Author 60-61 (1), 61-62 (1), 63-64 (1), 64-65 (2), 65-66 (1), 66-67 (1). Project SCB-208.*
Bldr: National Steel & SB Co., San Diego

AFS	Laid down	L	In serv.
1 MARS	5-62	15-6-63	21-21-63
2 SYLVANIA	8-62	10-8-63	11-7-64
3 NIAGARA FALLS	5-65	25-3-66	29-4-67
4 WHITE PLAINS	10-65	23-7-66	23-11-68
5 CONCORD	3-66	17-12-66	27-11-68
6 SAN DIEGO	3-67	13-4-68	24-5-69
7 SAN JOSE	3-69	13-12-69	23-10-70

D: 16,240 tons (fl)   **Dim:**   177.08 (161.54 pp) × 24.08 × 7.32
S: 20 kts (fl)   **Man:**   25 officers, 370 men
A: 4/76-mm 50-cal
M: GT; 1 prop
Boilers: 3 Babcock and Wilcox; 22,000 hp

FLEET REPLENISHMENT SHIPS (*continued*)

San Jose (AFS 7) 1971

Butte (AE 27) 1970

Butte (AE 27) G. Arra 1972

REMARKS: Two UH-46 A (Sea Knight) cargo helicopters with platform and hangar. She is fitted with cargo masts (M shape) with tension maintenance equipment; transfer from the supply ship to the receiving ship takes 90 seconds. Five holds (1 and 5, spare parts — 3 and 4, provisions — 2, aviation parts) have only two hatches; the different decks are linked by eleven hoists which raise from 40 kg to 5.5 tons; several others feed into the helicopter area. Ten loading areas (five on each side) and the use of palletized cargo help in the control of replenishment. There are four refrigerated compartments, three for the storage of dried provisions. The accounting for spare parts (35,000 different types) which are divided among 40,000 bins and racks is done by five data processing machines including a Univac 1104 computer. Quarters air-conditioned. The tremendous possibilities of development of this class of ship should be recognized. Draws 2.70 m more aft than forward. One boiler always in reserve.

AMMUNITION SHIPS (AE)

♦ *8 Kilauea class [Author: 64-65 (2), 65-66 (2), 66-67 (2), 67-68 (2)].*

	Bldr	Laid down	L	In serv.
AE 26 KILAUEA	Gen. Dynamics	10-3-66	9-8-67	10-8-68
AE 27 BUTTE	Gen Dynamics	21-7-66	9-8-67	29-11-68
AE 28 SANTA BARBARA	Bethlehem, Sparrows Pt	20-12-66	23-1-68	2-70
AE 29 MOUNT HOOD	Bethlehem, Sparrows Pt	8-5-67	17-7-68	7-70
AE 32 FLINT	Ingalls, Pascagoula	4-8-69	9-11-70	20-11-71
AE 33 SHASTA	Ingalls, Pascagoula	10-11-69	3-4-71	4-72
AE 34 MOUNT BAKER	Ingalls, Pascagoula	10-5-70	23-10-71	9-72
AE 35 KISKA	Ingalls, Pascagoula	4-8-71	3-72	12-72

D: 19,937 tons (fl) **S:** 20 kts **Dim:** 169.30 × 24.30 × 8.40
A: 4/76-mm AA (II × 2) **Man:** 38 officers, 373 men
M: GT; 22,000 hp; 1 prop
Boilers: 3 Foster-Wheeler

REMARKS: FAST system for rapid replenishment at sea. Helicopter platform.

♦ *2 Suribachi class*

	Bldr	Laid down	L	In serv.
AE 21 SURIBACHI	Beth. Sparrows Pt	16-5-55	3-5-56	30-3-57
AE 22 MAUNA KEA	Beth. Sparrows Pt	31-1-55	2-11-55	17-11-56

D: 17,500 tons (fl) **S:** 18 kts **Dim:** 153.60 × 21.60 × 8.70
A: 4/76-mm AA (II × 2) **Man:** 16 officers, 376 men
M: GT; 16,000 hp; 1 prop

REMARKS: FAST system

AMMUNITION SHIPS (AE) *(continued)*

Mauna Kea (AE 22)   1970

♦ *3 Nitro class*

	Bldr	Laid down	L	In serv.
AE 23 NITRO	Bethlehem, Sparrows Pt	20-5-57	26-6-58	1-5-59
AE 24 PYRO	Bethlehem, Sparrows Pt	21-10-57	5-11-58	24-7-59
AE 25 HALEAKALA	Bethlehem, Sparrows Pt	10-3-58	17-2-59	3-11-59

Nitro (AE 23)   1968

D: 17,500 tons (fl) **S:** 21 kts **Dim:** 153.60 × 21.60 × 8.70
A: 4/76-mm AA (II × 2) **Man:** 20 officers, 330 men
M: GT; 16,000 hp; 1 prop

REMARKS: FAST system. *AE-23* and *25* now have platforms for cargo helicopters.

♦ *1 former Lassen class AE (1941)* — Not in service.

AE 4 MAUNA LOA (1943)

D: 14,225 tons (fl) **Dim:** 140 × 19.20 × 8.70
A: 4/76-mm AA (II × 2) **S:** 15 kts
M: GT; 1 prop; 6,000 hp

STORE SHIPS (AF)

♦ *2 Rigel class*

	Bldr	L	In serv.
AF 58 RIGEL	Ingalls, Pascagoula	15-3-55	2-9-55
AF 59 VEGA	Ingalls, Pascagoula	26-4-55	10-11-55

Rigel (AF 58)   1968

D: 15,580 tons (fl) **S:** 18 kts **Dim:** 153 × 22.45 × 8.85
A: 4/76-mm AA (II × 2) **M:** GT; 1 Prop; 12,500 hp

REMARKS: Helicopter platform.

♦ *4 old ships in reserve or assigned MSC*
11,500 tons (fl) — 17 kts — 8,500 hp

T-AF 55 ALUDRA (ex-*SS Matchless*) (1944)
12,891 tons (fl) — 15.6 kts — 6,000 hp — 8/76-mm AA (II × 4)

T-AF 49 ZELIMA   AF 52 ARCTURUS   T-AF 54 PICTOR
(ex-*SS Golden Rocket*)   (ex-*USNS Golden Eagle*)   (ex-*SS Great Republic*)
13,900 tons (fl) — 16 kts — 6,000 hp — 2/76-mm AA (I × 2)

AMPHIBIOUS CARGO SHIPS (LKA)

♦ *5 Charleston class*

	Bldr	Laid down	L	In serv.
LKA 113 CHARLESTON	Newport News	5-12-66	2-12-67	14-12-68

AMPHIBIOUS CARGO SHIPS (LKA) (*continued*)

Charleston (LKA 113)   G. Arra 1974

Mobile (LKA 115)   1970

Tulare (LKA 112)

LKA 114 DURHAM	Newport News	10-7-67	29-3-68	24-5-69
LKA 115 MOBILE	Newport News	15-1-68	19-10-68	20-9-69
LKA 116 St. LOUIS	Newport News	3-4-68	4-1-69	22-11-69
LKA 117 EL PASO	Newport News	22-10-68	5-69	12-69

D: 20,800 tons (fl)   **S:** 20 kts   **Dim:** 175 × 24.70 × 7.80
A: 8/76-mm AA (II × 4)   **Man:** 34 officers, 310 men
M: 1 GT; 22,000 hp; 1 prop; 2 boilers

REMARKS: Machinery control is automatic. This series of assault cargo ships is air-conditioned and has a helicopter platform. Its fittings include 2/40-ton lifting booms, 8 of 15 tons, and 50 lifting nets which are hydraulically controlled with 50 winches. This class LKA usually carries 4 LCM (8) and if necessary, 226 passengers.

♦ *1 Tulare class*

	Bldr	Laid down	L	In serv.
LKA 112 TULARE	Bethlehem, San Francisco	16-2-53	22-12-53	12-1-56

D: 18,000 tons (fl)   **Dim:** 169 × 22.90 × 7.40
S: 22 kts   **Man:** 38 officers, 399 men

A: 12/76-mm AA (II × 6)
M: 1 GT; 15,239 hp; 1 prop

REMARKS: Helicopter platform. Loading rigging for 60 tons. Can carry 319 passengers. Will be placed out of service when the *Tarawa* (*LHA-1*) is commissioned. Many cargo ships formerly reserved for amphibious operations are in reserve or have reverted to the Maritime Administration.

♦ *12 old ships (1943-44) in reserve or assigned to the Marine Administration*

LKA 19 THUBAN

13,907 tons (fl) — 16.5 kts — 6,000 hp — 4/76-mm AA (I × 4)

LKA 54 ALGOL, 57 CAPRICORNUS, 61 MULIPHEN, 93 YANCEY, 94 WINSTON, 97 MERRICK, 103 RANKIN, 104 SEMINOLE, 106 UNION, 107 VERMILLION, 108 WASHBURN

13,050 tons (fl) — 15.5 kts — 6,000 hp — 4/40-mm AA (II × 2)

CARGO SHIPS — CONTAINERIZED

♦ *2 AKR class*

T-AKR 9 SEA LIFT (Author: 1962-63) — L: 18-4-65. — In serv: 25-4-67

T-Sea Lift (T-AKR 9)　　　　　　　　　　　　　　　1968

D: 21,700 tons (fl)	**S:** 20 kts	**Dim:**	165 × 25 × 8.8
M: 2 GT — 19,400 hp — 2 props	**Man:**	62 men, 12 passengers	

REMARKS: Roll-on/roll-off equipment. — Stabilizers — Assigned to MSC.

T-AKR 7 COMET — L: 31-7-58

D: 18,150 tons (fl)	**S:** 18 kts	**Dim:**	152 × 23.8 × 8.9
M: 2 GT; 13,200 hp; 2 props	**Man:**	73 men	

REMARKS: Roll-on/roll-off equipment; Denny-Brown stabilizers; assigned to MSC.

REPAIR SHIPS (AR)

5 VULCAN (14-12-40)	**7 HECTOR** (11-11-42)	**9 DELTA** (1941)
6 AJAX (22-8-42)	**8 JASON** (3-4-43)	**12 BRIAREUS** (1941)

	D	Dim	M	Hp	S
AR 5, 7, 8	1941	12,911 tons	161.55 × 22.35 × 7.00	2 GT	10,000	18 kts
AR 9, 12	1941	12,705 tons	149.50 × 21.18 × 8.60	2 GT	8,500	16 kts

REMARKS: Well equipped in every area; powerful booms for lifting. *AR-14 Cadmus* transferred to Taiwan.

REPAIR SHIPS

A. BATTLE DAMAGE REPAIR SHIPS (ARB)

5 MIDAS (ex-*LST-514*)　　　　**7 SARPEDON** (ex-*LST-956*)

Ajax (AR 6)　　　　　　　　　　　　　　　　　1970

B. LANDING CRAFT REPAIR SHIPS (ARL)

8 EGERIA (ex-*LST-136*)　　　　**37 INDRA** (ex-*LST-1147*)
24 SPHINX (ex-*LST-963*)

REMARKS: On these old LST type ships the bow doors are welded shut. The deck structures have been reconstructed as quarters and workshops. Fitted with a 50-ton lifting mast and 2/10-ton booms. Very complete shop facilities. *ARVE-5* fitted for the repair of aviation engines. *ARVE-6* for aviation fuselages. None in service. Several have been transferred.

FLEET OILERS (AO)

♦ *2 AO class 166* (*author. 1975-76*)

		Laid		
	Bldr	down	L	In serv.
AO 166 N . . .	. . .	. . .	. . .	. . .
AO 167 N . . .	. . .	. . .	. . .	. . .
D: **S:** **Dim:**				
A: **M:**				

REMARKS: 220,000 barrels.

AO	AO
36 KENNEBEC	**T 105 MISPILLION**♦
43 TAPPAHANNOCK	**106 NAVASOTA**♦
51 ASHTABULA♦	**T 107 PASSUMPSIC**♦
54 CHIKASKIA	**108 PAWCATUCK**♦
56 AUCILLA	**T 109 WACCAMAW**♦
T 57 MARIAS	**143 NEOSHO**
T 62 TALUGA	**T 144 MISSISSINEWA**
98 CALOOSAHATCHEE♦	**145 HASSAYAMPA**
99 CANISTEO♦	**146 KAWISHIWI**
101 COSHECTON	**147 TRUCKEE**
	148 PONCHATOULA

	Cargo				
D (fl)	capacity	Dim	M	Hp	S
1. AO 51/57, 62/64, 98/99 (1939-46)					
24,830	18,302	168.55 × 22.86 × 9.63	2 GT	13,500	18 kts

FLEET OILERS (AO) *(continued)*

Canisteo (AO 99) 1970

Neosho (AO 143)

2. AO 36 (1942)

21,100	15,850	152.83 × 20.73 × 9.20	2 GT	12,500	16 kts

3. AO 43 (1943)

22,445	16,300	160.32 × 20.73 × 9.40	2 GT	12,000	17 kts

4. AO 101 (1943)

21,880	16,400	150.56 × 20.73 × 9.12	1 GT	6,000	14 kts

5. AO 143/148 (1952-55)

38,000	28,000	199 × 26.20 × 10.70	2 GT	28,000	20 kts

6. AO 105/109 (1964)

34,600	...	199.80 × 22.90 × 9.70	1 GT	13,500	16 kts

REMARKS: — Range: 15/18,000 miles. The majority of the Maritime Commission classes usually have two boilers, four in the number 1 group. The *25* was converted in 1961 into a gasoline and jet fuel carrier (**Man:** 20 officers, 275 men). The *143/148* were built to accompany task forces and carry 130,000 barrels of fuel, 48,700 of aviation gasoline, 8,000 of diesel oil; they are fitted with 8 stations for fast replenishment at sea and have 8-12/76-mm AA (**Man:** 300 men). The ships marked T are assigned to the M.S.C.

The eight ♦ have been modernized and rebuilt (FRAM/Jumbo): 27 m have been added to the hull, the cargo oil capacity increased from 115,000 to 150,000 barrels,

the anti-aircraft defense system renovated, the machinery overhauled, and the auxiliary engines replaced. They were recommissioned in 1964.

MARAD (*Maritime Administration*)

The Maritime Administration of the United States regulates those merchant ships which are government property; it is a civil service administration. Upon occasion the U.S. Navy draws upon the MARAD fleet for ships manned by MARAD personnel or by the M.S.C. It can return as well, while still maintaining ultimate control, ships of this class that it wishes to put in reserve.

M.S.C. (*Military Sealift Command*)

The organization is under the U.S. Navy but operates with civil service personnel. It provides the men and the administration for about 70 transport ships of all types, used by the Department of Defense for overseas cargo lift. Many are interchangeable with similar ships manned by the Navy which one day will be turned over to the M.S.C.; therefore they retain their hull number, but it is preceded by the letter T.

Further in this section will be found a listing of the ships under M.S.C. control, if they are not listed in other areas.

SHIPS ADMINISTERED BY THE MSC

♦ *9 Sealift class*

		Bldr	L
TAO 168	SEALIFT PACIFIC	Todd SY (San Pedro)	13-10-73
TAO 172	SEALIFT ATLANTIC	Bath Iron Works	26-1-74
TAO 169	SEALIFT ARABIAN SEA	Todd SY (San Pedro)	26-1-74
TAO 173	SEALIFT MEDITERRANEAN	Bath Iron Works	9-3-74
TAO 170	SEALIFT CHINA SEA	Todd SY (San Pedro)	20-4-74
TAO 174	SEALIFT CARIBBEAN	Bath Iron Works	. . .
TAO 171	SEALIFT INDIAN OCEAN	Todd SY (San Pedro)	. . .
TAO 175	SEALIFT ARCTIC	Bath Iron Works	. . .
TAO 176	SEALIFT ANTARCTIC	Bath Iron Works	. . .

D: 35,000 tons (fl)　　**Dim:** 176.10 × 25.20 × 9.75
M: 2 diesels; 1 prop; 1,400 hp　　**S:** 16 kts
Cargo capacity: 20,000 tons

OLD OILERS (all 1944-45)

♦ *T 2 class:* **TAO 50 TALLULAH, 67 CACHE, 73 MILLICOMA, 75 SAUGATUCK, 76 SCHUYLKILL, 78 CHEPACHET, 134 MISSION SANTA INEZ**
Cargo capacity: 16,250 tons — **S:** 16 kts — **Dim:** 159.60 × 20.73 × 9.25

♦ *T 5 RM 2 class:* **TAO 165 AMERICAN EXPLORER**
Cargo capacity: 22,900 tons — **S:** 20 kts — **Dim:** 187.45 × 24.40 × 10.60

♦ *T 5 S class:* **TAO 149 MAUMEE**
Cargo capacity: 25,190 tons — **S:** 18 kts — **Dim:** 187.15 × 24.45 × 9.75

♦ *T 1 M BT 2 class:* **TAOG 77 RINCON, 78 NODAWAY, 79 PETALUMA, 80 PISCATAQUA**
Cargo capacity: 4,000 tons — **S:** 10 kts — **Dim:** 99.10 × 14.70 × 5.90

CARGO SHIPS (AK, AF) (all 1944-45)

♦ *VC 2 S class* (*Victory ships*): **TAK 237 GREENVILLE VICTORY, 240 TOWLE, 244 CRAIN, 254 KIMBRO, 274 ROBINSON, 276 PENDLETON.**
D: 11,900 ton (fl) — **S:** 14/16 kts — **Dim:** 137 × 19 × 7.70

CARGO SHIPS (AK, AF) (ALL 1944-45) (*continued*)

♦ *C 3 class:* **TAK 277 SCHUYLER OTIS BLAND**
   Cargo capacity: 10,500 tons — **S:** 17 kts — **Dim:** 145 × 20.12 × 8.70

♦ *C 4 class* **TAK 255 BROSTROM, 267 MARINE FIDDLER**
   Cargo capacity: 13,500 tons — **S:** 15.5 kts — **Dim:** 158.50 × 21.80 × 9.90
   Heavy lift booms.

♦ *C 1 M AY 1 class:* **TAK 180 FENTRESS, 188 HERKIMER, 250 Pvt. FRANK J.
PETRARCA**
   Cargo capacity: 5,900 tons — **S:** 10 kts — **Dim:** 103.22 × 15.34 × 7.16

♦ *Various:* about 30 LST class of the original design and 6 of the *Terrell County* class;
the **1158 TIOGA COUNTY, 1160 TRAVERSE COUNTY, 1162 WAHKIAKUM
COUNTY, 1164 WALWORTH COUNTY, 1165 WASHOE COUNTY** (1952-54)
13 kts and 5,790 tons (fl)

GASOLINE TANKERS (AOG)

AOG 9 KISHWAUKEE

Genesee   1970

   D: 2,020 tons (4,335 fl)   **Dim:** 95 × 14.60 × 4.70
   S: 14 kts   **A:** 4/76-mm   **Man:** 124 men
   M: diesel electric; 2 props; 3,300 hp

All have been transferred or stricken, *AOG-50, 55, 56* in 1975.

CABLE REPAIR SHIPS

ARC 2 NEPTUNE (ex-cable repair ship of the Maritime Admin. *Wm. H. C. Bullard*).
(1948)
T-ARC 6 ALBERT J. MYER (hydrographic ship) (1948)
   D: 7,180 tons   **Dim:** 97 × 14.2 × 10.00
   S: 14 kts   **M:** Uniflow triple expansion; 2 props; 4,800 hp
   Cargo capacity: 4,860 tons

ARC 3 AEOLUS (ex-*AKA-47*)   **ARC 4 THOR** (ex-*Vanadis*, ex-*AKA-49*)
   D: 7,080 tons   **S:** 16 kts   **Dim:** 129.84 × 17.68 × 4.88
   M: turbo-electric propulsion; 6,000 hp; modified in 1954-56. Helicopter platform.
      ARC-2, 3 and *4* in MSC.

Aeolus (ARC 3)   1970

EXPERIMENTAL AND SPECIAL SHIPS

AVM 1 NORTON SOUND — Bldr: Todd SY Corp. (Los Angeles) (28-11-43)
   D: 15,170 tons (fl)   **S:** 18 kts
   Dim: 165.50 (158.50 pp) × 21.11 × 7.05
   M: Allis Chalmers GT; 2 props; 12,000 hp; 4 Babcock and Wilcox boilers

EXPERIMENTAL AND SPECIAL SHIPS (*continued*)

REMARKS: Former seaplane tender converted in 1948 to an experimental ship for missile equipment being tested by the U.S. Navy. Presently fitted with a launcher for the new surface-to-air missiles of the Standard and the BPDMS Sea Sparrow systems in many versions. She is also used for testing the Aegis system (see technical notes at the beginning of this section). Note above the bridge the flat antennae of the SPY 1 radar which are part of this system.

		L
AG 153 COMPASS ISLAND (ex-*Garden State Mariner*)		12-8-53
AG 154 OBSERVATION ISLAND (ex-*Empire State Mariner*)		15-8-53

Mariner-class fast cargo ships modified by the New York Naval Shipyard (1956–58).

Huntsville (T-AGM-7)

Observation Island (AG 154)   1972

D: 9,200 tons (17,600 fl)   **Dim:** 169 × 22.90 × 7.40
S: 20 kts   **M:** GT; 1 prop; 15,000 hp

Anti-rolling stabilizers installed; used for the testing of the inertial navigating system (SINS) and the launch of SSBN missiles.

T-AG 164 KINGSPORT (ex-Victory-class cargo, *AK-239*) (29-5-44)

Satellite relay station — Radome removed in 1970.

D: 15,200 tons   **S:** 17 kts — 8,500 hp   **Man:** 73 men

T-AG 178 FLYER (ex-*American Flyer*) (1945) — Purchased 3-65

D: 8,327 tons   **Dim:** 140 × 19 × 8.50
S: 17 kts   **Man:** 14 officers, 42 men
M: GT; 2 boilers; 1 prop; 6,000 hp

♦ *Missile Range Instrumentation Ships (AGM)*

T-AGM-8 WHEELING
T-AGM-9 GENERAL H. H. ARNOLD
 (ex-*AP-139 Gen. R. E. Callan*)
T-AGM-10 GENERAL HOYT S. VANDENBERG
 (ex- *AP-145 General Harry Taylor*)

Kingsport (T-AG-164)

T-AGM-19 VANGUARD
 (ex-*Mission San Fernando*)
T-AGM-20 REDSTONE (ex-*Mission De Pala*)
T-AGM-22 RANGE SENTINEL
 (ex-*APA-205*) 22-10-69.

These are *Victory*-class ships with the exception of the *AGM-9* and *10* (ex-transports) — **D:** 19,650 tons, and the *AGM-19* and *20* which are T-2 oilers modified with a lengthened mid-section (**Dim:** 181.40 × 22.90).

EXPERIMENTAL AND SPECIAL SHIPS (continued)

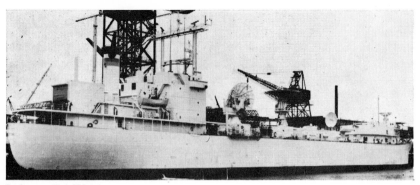

Redstone (T-AGM-20)   Shbldg. and Sh. Record

REMARKS: *T-AGM-3 Longview, 5 Sunnyvale*, and *7 Huntsville* taken out of service in 11 and 12-74.

OCEANOGRAPHIC RESEARCH SHIPS (AGOR)

All of these ships have numerous laboratories (terrestial magnetism, seabed analysis, sound propagation, depth sounding and analysis). Civil service crew, M.S.C. personnel.

(1) *Specially-built ships*

AGOR	Bldr	Laid down	L	In serv.
21 GYRE	Halter Marine Services	9-10-72	7-6-73	14-11-73
22 MOANA WAVE	(New Orleans)	10-10-72	23-6-73	16-1-74

D: 1,190 tons (fl)   **S:** 12.5 kts.   **Dim:** 53.14 × 11.05 × 3.05
Man: 21 men, including researchers
M: 2 super-charged diesels; 1,700 hp; 2 variable pitch props
1/150-hp motor linked to a reversible prop is used for very slow speed.

These ships are manned by personnel from the University of Texas and the University of Hawaii.

♦ AGOR	Author	Bldr	Laid down	L	In serv.
14 MELVILLE	*1965-66*	Northwest Iron Works	7-67	10-7-68	9-69
15 KNORR	*1965-66*	Defoe SB (Michigan)	8-67	21-8-68	7-70

D: 2,075 tons (3,180 fl)   **Dim:** 74.37 (67.05 pp) × 13.80 × 4.70
S: 14 kts   **Range:** 10,000/12
Man: 9 officers, 16 men, 15/25 oceanographers
M: diesel; 2 Voith-Schneider pivoting propulsion nozzles (1 fwd, 1 aft); 2,500 hp

Melville (AGOR 14)   1970

♦ *AGOR Catamaran class/SCB 726-67 project*

T-AGOR	Author	Bldr	Laid down	L	In serv.
16 HAYES	1967-68	Todd-Pacific (Seattle)	11-69	2-7-70	1971

D: 3,080 tons (fl)   **Dim:** 75.10 (67.05 pp) × 24.38 × 5.75
S: 15 kts   **Range:** 6,000/13.5
Man: 11 officers, 33 men, 30 oceanographers
M: high-speed diesels; 2 variable pitch props; 4,800 hp.

REMARKS: Each of the hulls has a 7.31-m beam. Two diesels (165 hp each) for 2 to 4-knot underway speed. Manned by the Hudson Laboratories of Columbia University and fitted for deep soundings.

OCEANOGRAPHIC RESEARCH SHIPS (AGOR)

♦ *T-AGOR SCB 185 project*

	Author	Bldr	Laid down	L	In serv.
3 ROBERT D. CONRAD	1960-61	Gibbs, (Jacksonville)	1-61	26-5-62	8-62
4 JAMES M. GILLISS	1960-61	Christy Corp. (Wisc.)	5-61	19-5-62	9-62
7 LYNCH	1962-63	Marietta Mfg. (W. Va.)	10-62	17-3-64	3-65
9 THOMAS G. THOMPSON	1963-64		9-63	18-7-64	9-65
10 THOMAS WASHINGTON	1963-64	Marinette Marine (Wisconsin)	9-63	1-8-64	10-65
12 DE STEIGUER	1964-65	Northwest Marine	11-65	3-6-66	2-69
13 BARTLETT	1964-65	Iron Works (Portland)	11-65	24-5-66	4-69

D: 1,020 tons (1,370 fl)   **Dim:** 70 (63.70 pp) × 11.28 × 6.30 (fl)
S: 12.5 kts   **Man:** 8 officers, 18 men, 15 oceanographers
Range: 12,000/12
M: Diesel-electric; 2 props (1 in the bow); 1,000 hp

OCEANOGRAPHIC RESEARCH SHIPS (AGOR) (*continued*)

Lynch (AGOR 7)   G. Arra 1975

REMARKS: An auxiliary engine is coupled to a variable pitch propeller to maneuver the ship at extremely slow speeds. A few have an 11.80 beam. *AGOR-5 Charles H. Davis* transferred to New Zealand (8-70).

(2) *Modified ships*

♦ *1 Salvage tug modified from 1958-60*

	L
AGOR 17 CHAIN (ex-*ARS-20*)	3-6-43

D: 2,100 tons (fl)   **S:** 14 kts   **Dim:** 64.50 (62.20 pp) × 11.80 × 4
M: 4 high-speed diesels; 2 props; 3,000 hp; 250-hp engine for slow speeds.
Man: 29 to 40 men; 26/28 oceanographers

♦ *1 former small Arctic type transport refitted in 4-64*

T-AGOR 11 MIZAR (ex-*AK-272*) — Bldr: Avondale — 7-10-57

D: 2,040 tons (5,000 fl)   **Dim:** 78 × 15.30 × 6.50
S: 13 kts   **Man:** 48 men, 38 oceanographers
M: diesel-electric; 2 props; 3,200 hp

AGOR-11 is especially equipped for deep depth research (more than 300 m). Searched for and marked the wreckage of the French submarine *Eurydice*. *AGOR-8 Eltanin* (same class) transferred to the Argentine Navy.

Mizar (T-AGOR 11)   J. C. Bellonne 1971

HYDROGRAPHIC SHIPS (AGS)

(1) *Specially-built ships*

♦ *4 large type ordered in Great Britain* — Bldr: Fairfields, Glasgow

	Author	Laid down	L	In serv.
T-AGS 29 CHAUVENET	1964-65	5-67	13-5-68	12-70
T-AGS 32 HARKNESS	1965-66	6-67	12-6-68	2-71

D: 4,062 tons (fl)   **Dim:** 119.85 (108.81 pp) × 16.45 × 4.70
S: 15 kts   **Man:** 19 officers, 245 men, 8 civilians
Range: 15,000/12
M: 2 Alco diesels; 1 Escher-Wyss prop; 3,600 hp

REMARKS: Especially equipped for the drawing and fast reproduction of charts. Can supply coastal hydrographic ships and helicopters (hangar and platform).

♦ *4 medium type. Project 226.* — *Author. 1964-65*

	Bldr	Laid down	L	In serv.
T-AGS 26 SILAS BENT	American SB (Toledo)	3-64	16-5-64	7-65
T-AGS 27 KANE	Christy Corp. (Wisc.)	12-64	20-11-65	11-66
T-AGS 33 WILKES	Defoe SB, (Mich.)	7-68	31-7-69	6-71
T-AGS 34 WYMAN	Defoe SB, (Mich.)	7-68	30-10-69	1971

D: 1,935 tons (2,560 fl)   **Dim:** 86.90 × 14.63 × 4.60
S: 15 kts   **Range:** 12,000/12
Man: 12 officers, 35 men, 30 hydrographers
M: diesel-electric; 1 prop; 3,000 hp

REMARKS: Has a forward propellor (350 hp) with remote control from the bridge for station keeping purposes. Anti-rolling stabilizers.

Silas Bent (AGS 26)   1966

HYDROGRAPHIC SHIPS (AGS) (*continued*)

	In serv.
◆ **T-AGS 21 BOWDITCH**	9-58
22 DUTTON	10-58
23 MICHELSON	11-58

Ex-*Victory*-class cargo ships.

◆ **T-AGS 36 COASTAL CRUSADER** (ex-*T-AGM-36*) 1945

Former small cargo ship, modified as an oceanographic ship since 1969.

LOGISTIC SUPPORT SHIPS FOR RESEARCH AND SALVAGE SUBMARINES

Deep depth program.

◆ *Project SCB 721-67.* Bldr: Alabama DD and SB Corp., Mobile

ASR	Author	Laid down	L	In serv.
21 PIGEON	1966-67	7-68	13-8-69	4-73
22 ORTOLAN	1967-68	8-68	10-9-69	7-73

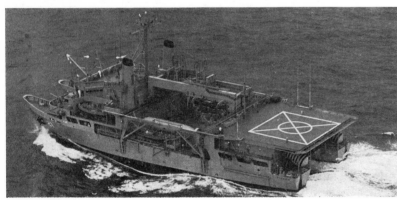

Pigeon (ASR 21)   Alabama DD 1972

D:	4,200 tons (fl)	**Dim:**	76.50 × 26.21 × 5.80
S:	15 kts	**A:**	2/76-mm AA — 4/AA machine guns
Man:	6 officers, 100 men (plus passengers)		
M:	4 high-speed diesels; 2 props; 6,000 hp		

REMARKS: The hulls (7.925-m beam) are separated by a 10.36-m distance (Catamaran). The diving bells and other salvage equipment are lowered between the two hulls by a moving crane. The ship can carry two small DSRV (Deep Submergence Rescue Vessels) submarines. Excellent lowering and handling equipment for up to 60 tons. Trained divers for 250 m depths.

IX 501 KENANOPA (ex-*Elk River*, ex-*LSMR-501*). Modified beginning in 5-67 as the station ship for Sealab III program tests (DSRV small submarines for deep diving, exploration). — **L** (oa) about 68.17; has eight winches, a 60-ton boom, and a decompression chamber.

Kenanopa

SALVAGE SHIPS (ARS)

6 ESCAPE	**34 GEAR**
7 GRAPPLE	**38 BOLSTER**
8 PRESERVER	**39 CONSERVER**
23 DELIVER	**40 HOIST**
24 GRASP	**41 OPPORTUNE**
25 SAFEGUARD	**42 RECLAIMER**
33 CLAMP	**43 RECOVERY**
	1943-44

D:	1,360 tons (1,630 fl)	**Dim:**	64.50 (62.20 pp) × 11.80 × 4

SUBMARINE RESCUE SHIPS (ARS) (continued)

Opportune (ARS 41)   G. Arra 1974

A: 4/40-mm AA   **S:** 14 kts
M: diesel-electric; 2 props; 2,800 hp

REMARKS: Gear (34) manned by a civilian firm working for the navy. *ASR-22 Current* stricken in 6-73.

SUBMARINE RESCUE SHIPS (ASR)

8 COUCAL	13 KITTIWAKE	15 SUNBIRD
9 FLORIKAN	14 PETREL	16 TRINGA

   D: 1,780 tons (2,140 fl)   **S:** 14.5 kts   **Dim:** 75.50 × 12.70 × 4.30
   A: 2/76-mm — 2/40-mm AA   **M:** diesel-electric; 1 prop; 3,000 hp

12 and **20** — Characteristics of the *ATF Apache* class (next page).

   All in service. *ASR-10* sold to Turkey (6-70), *20 Skylark* to Brazil (9-73), *12 Penguin* removed from active list.

Petrel (ASR 14)   1968

SALVAGE AND RESCUE SHIPS (ATS) (Project *719-66*)

ATS	Bldr	Laid down	L	In serv.
1 EDENTON	Brooke Marine, Lowestoft	4-67	15-5-68	1-71
2 BEAUFORT		5-68	20-12-68	1-72
3 BRUNSWICK		6-68	14-10-69	6-72

Edenton (ATS 1)   Brooke 1970

   D: 2,650 tons (3,125 fl)   **Dim:** 88 (80.50 pp) × 15.25 × 4.60
   S: 16 kts   **Man:** 9 officers, 93 men
   M: 4/12-cylinder Paxman diesels, Mk 12 YLCM (900 rpm); 2 Escher-Wyss variable pitch props; 6,000 hp
   Range: 12,000

REMARKS: Can tow a 53,000-ton AOE at 7 knots and lift 250 tons at the bow. Excellent firefighting and salvage equipment. Two cranes (1 fwd, 1 aft). Can carry on salvage operations to a depth of 75 m.

FLEET OCEAN TUGS (ATF)

A. 76 UTE	86 MATACO
84 CREE	91 SENECA
85 LIPAN	92 TAWASA
B. 96 ABNAKI	149 ATAKAPA
100 CHOWANOC	157 NIPMUC
101 COCOPA	158 MOSOPELEA
105 MOCTOBI	159 PAIUTE
106 MOLALA	160 PAPAGO
108 PAKANA	161 SALINAN
110 QUAPAW	162 SHAKORI
113 TAKELMA	
114 TAWAKONI	

   D: 1,280 tons (1,700 fl)   **S:** 16 kts   **Dim:** 61.70 × 11.60 × 4.70
   A: 1/76-mm — 4/40-mm AA — 2/20-mm AA (removed on some ships)
   Man: 85 men   **M:** 4 groups of diesel-electric engines; 2 props; 3,000 hp

FLEET OCEAN TUGS (ATF) *(continued)*

REMARKS: *A* group has one stack, *B* group no stack. Excellent pumping equipment. Several transferred or taken out of service since 1962. *ATF-156 Luiseno* sold to Argentina.

◆ *1 new class tug (author. 1974-75).*

	Bldr	Laid down	L	In serv.
T-ATF 166 N . . .	. . .	. . .	. . .	. . .

    D: 2,000 tons (fl)   **S:** 15 kts   **Dim:** 62.4 × 12.60 × 4.50
    A: 2/20-mm   **Man:** 16 men
    M: 2 diesels; 1 variable pitch prop; 4,500 hp

REMARKS: One 10-ton crane. Manned by civilian personnel of the MSC.

ATA

181 ACCOKEEK, 188 PENOBSCOT, 190 SAMOSET, 195 TATNUCK, 193 STALLION, 213 KEYWADIN.

    D: 534 tons (835 fl)   **Dim:** 43 × 10 × 4
    A: 1/76-mm AA   **S:** 13 kts
    M: diesel-electric; 1 prop; 1,500 hp.

SHIPS FOR MOBILE BASES (floating docks and barracks ships).

The U.S. Navy Large Auxiliary Floating Dry Docks (non-self-propelled) (**AFDB**), Medium Auxiliary Floating Dry Docks (non-self-propelled) (**AFDM**), Small Auxiliary Floating Dry Docks (non-self-propelled) (**AFDL**), and Medium Auxiliary Repair Dry Docks (non-self-propelled) **ARDM** are especially equipped to handle the **SSBN** class submarine and bathyscapes.

HOSPITAL SHIP (AH)

AH 17 SANCTUARY (15-8-44)
    Bldr: Sun SB & DD (Chester, Pa.) (1944)
    D: 11,333 tons (15,226 fl)

Floating dock Oak Ridge (ARD 19) with an SSBN on board

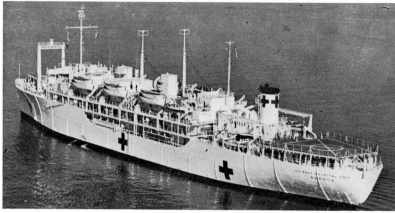

Repose (AH 16)

    Dim: 159.37 (158.49 pp) × 21.85 × 9.15
    S: 17.5 kts   **Man:** 17 officers, 358 men
    M: GT; 2 props; 9,000 hp; 2 Babcock and Wilcox boilers

REMARKS: Excellent air-conditioned living spaces. 24 doctors, 290 medical personnel including 29 nurses. 750 hospital beds.

COAST GUARD

The Coast Guard belongs to the Department of Transportation but its faster ships would be used as ASW escort ships in time of war. The Coast Guard maintains international ice and weather patrol in the Atlantic, and light and buoy service. Personnel are distinct from the U.S. Navy and the service has its own administration. The Coast Guard has its own aviation arm (about 100 helicopters HH-52 A and HH-3F class) and about 60 fixed-wing aircraft including the HU-16E Albatross (range: 800 miles).

PERSONNEL (1973): 40,100 men including 6,037 officers and warrant officers.

Boutwell (WHEC 719)   G. Arra 1972

HIGH ENDURANCE CUTTERS

(1) 12 WHEC (ex-*WPG*) — *High endurance cutters 350-ft class (33 planned)*

	Bldr	Laid down	L	In serv.
715 HAMILTON	All by	1-65	18-12-65	11-67
716 DALLAS	Avondale	2-66	1-10-66	12-67
717 MELLON	Shipyards, Inc.,	7-66	21-1-67	3-68
718 CHASE	Westwego,	10-66	20-5-67	3-68
719 BOUTWELL	Louisiana	12-66	17-6-67	6-68
720 SHERMAN		2-67	28-6-68	8-68
721 GALLATIN		4-67	23-7-68	12-68
722 MORGENTHAU		7-67	10-2-68	1-69
723 RUSH		10-67	16-4-68	7-69
724 MUNRO		2-70	5-12-70	9-71
725 JARVIS		9-70	24-4-71	12-71
726 MIDGETT		4-70	5-4-71	9-71

Rush (WHEC 723) 1970

D: 2,716 tons (3,050 fl) **Dim:** 115.21 (106.70 pp) × 12.80 × 6.10
S: 28 kts (20 cruising) **Man:** 23 officers, 164 men
Range: 9,600/20 — 2,300/28 with GT
A: 1/127-mm 38-cal semi-auto — 4/12.7-mm AA machine guns — 6 ASW TT (III × 2) — 2 illumination RL
M: 2/12-cyl. Fairbanks-Morse diesels, each of 3,500 hp; 2 Pratt and Whitney Mk FT 4 A gas turbines, each 14,000 hp; 2 props; 35,000 hp

REMARKS: CODAG propulsion. Remote control variable pitch propellers, 3.90 m in diameter. Same gas turbine as B 52, F 105 and Boeing 707 aircraft. A single 1.20-m propeller linked to a 350-hp engine is used at an underway speed of 3 knots for certain oceanographic work. Frahm anti-rolling stabilizers. Helicopter platform 26.82 × 12.20 m. An HH-52-A turboshaft helicopter (8 passengers) can be carried; portable hangar. Living spaces air-conditioned. Laboratories for weather and oceanographic research. Welded hull; aluminum superstructure. SQS-36 A sonar, surface, air search and fire control radars. Electric: 1,500 kw. 21 others planned. Four-bladed Escher-Wyss propellers in all ships after *719;* all have a bow propeller with a 350-hp engine.

♦ **5 WHEC** (ex-*WPG*), *Owasco class* (255-ft)

	L		L
41 CHAUTAUQUA	14-5-44	68 ANDROSCOGGIN	16-9-45
65 WINONA	12-4-45	70 PONTCHARTRAIN	29-4-44
67 MINNETONKA	21-11-45	(ex-*Okeechobee*)	
(ex-*Sunapee*)			

Bldrs: Western Pipe & Steel Co., San Pedro, Cal. (*39/44* and *64/68*) Coast Guard SY, Curtis Bay, Md. (*70*)

Klamath (WHEC 66) taken out of service

D: 1,563 tons (1,913 fl) **Dim:** 77.75 (74.67 wl) × 13.10 × 5.50
S: 18 kts **Man:** 143 men
Range: 6,000/18 — 14,800/11
A: 1/127-mm — 2/12.7-mm AA machine guns
M: Westinghouse turbo-electric; 2 props; 4,000 hp **Fuel:** 350 tons

♦ **6 WHEC** (ex-*WPG*), *Campbell class* (327-ft)

	Bldr	Laid down	L	In serv.
31 BIBB	Charleston NSY	8-35	14-1-37	3-37
32 CAMPBELL	Philadelphia NSY	1-5-35	3-6-36	10-36
33 DUANE	Philadelphia NSY	5-35	3-6-36	10-36
35 INGHAM	Philadelphia NSY	1-5-35	3-6-36	11-36
36 SPENCER	New York NSY	9-35	6-1-37	5-37
37 TANEY	Philadelphia NSY	5-35	3-6-36	12-36

D: 2,216 tons (2,785 fl) **Dim:** 99.70 (94.20 wl) × 12.60 × 3.80
S: 19 kts **Man:** 147 men
Range: 4,000/18 — 8,000/12.5 — 12,300/11
A: 1/127-mm 38-cal semi-auto — 4/12.7-mm AA
M: Westinghouse GT; 2 props; 6,200 hp **Fuel:** 572 tons
Boilers: 2 Babcock and Wilcox

HIGH ENDURANCE CUTTERS (*continued*)

Bibb (WHEC 31)

REMARKS: *Taney* has a radar dome above her bridge.

♦ 1 *WTR/WAGW*

		L
379 UNIMAK (ex-*AVP-31*)		27-5-42
Training ship		

Gresham (WHEC 387) now stricken   1971

D:	1,766 tons (2,800 fl)	**Dim:**	94.70 (94.63 wl) × 12.52 × 3.65
S:	17 kts	**Man:**	151 men

Range: 8,000/17
A: 1/127-mm — 2/12.7-mm machine guns
M: diesels; 2 props; 6,000 hp
Fuel: 400 tons

REMARKS: The last of a series of small seaplane tenders (AVP), 18 of which were transferred to the Coast Guard in 1947-48; seven were given to South Vietnam beginning in 1970 and eight taken out of service since 1968. Ready to be scrapped.

MEDIUM ENDURANCE CUTTERS

♦ 16 *WMEC* (ex-*WPC*) — *210-ft class* — (30 planned).

		Bldr	L
615	RELIANCE	1	25-5-63
616	DILIGENCE	1	20-7-63
617	VIGILANT	1	24-12-63
618	ACTIVE	2	31-7-65
619	CONFIDENCE	3	8-5-65
620	RESOLUTE	3	30-4-66
621	VALIANT	4	14-1-67
622	COURAGEOUS	4	18-5-67
623	STEADFAST	4	24-6-67
624	DAUNTLESS	4	21-10-67
625	VENTUROUS	4	11-11-67
626	DEPENDABLE	4	16-3-68
627	VIGOROUS	4	4-5-68
628	DURABLE	3	29-4-57
629	DECISIVE	3	14-12-67
630	ALERT	3	19-10-68

Bldr: 1. Todd shipyards — 2. Christy Corp., Sturgeon Bay, Wis. — 3. Coast Guard SY, Curtis Bay, Md. — 4. American SB, Lorain, Ohio.

Alert (WMEC 630)   1971

D:	759 tons (993 fl)	**Dim:**	64 (61 pp) × 10.36 × 2.20
S:	18 kts	**Range:**	5,000/15 — 2,000/18

Man: 7 officers, 57 men (11 + 85 wartime)
A: 1/76-mm — 1 HH-52-A or HH-3 helicopter. No hangar.
M: 2 supercharged 16-cylinder diesels, each 2,500 hp; 2 variable pitch props; and in the *615-619* 2 gas turbines, each of 2,000 hp, without, however, any increase in speed.
Range: 6,100/13

REMARKS: CODAG propulsion on some; endurance: 15 days. Designed to operate about 500 miles off the coast. High superstructure permitting 360° visibility. No stack,

MEDIUM ENDURANCE CUTTERS (continued)

exhaust at the stern. Towing equipment for a 10,000-ton ship. Air-conditioned except for the machinery compartment.

ICEBREAKERS

	Bldr	L	In serv.
WAGB 10 POLAR STAR	Lockheed SB (Seattle)	15-5-72	12-74
WAGB 11 POLAR SEA	Lockheed SB (Seattle)	6-75	6-76

D: 12,200 tons (fl) **S:** 17 kts **Dim:** 117.85 × 23.78 × 8.54.
M: CODAG propulsion; 3 props; 66,000 hp **Man:** 148 men

The icebreaker *Northwind* (*WAGB-282*).

REMARKS: A total of four may be built to replace the *Westwind* class. The Coast Guard has decided that a nuclear icebreaker would be too expensive.

WAGB 4 GLACIER — Laid down: 8-53 L: 27-8-54 — In serv.: 5-55.
Bldr: Ingalls SB, Pascagoula
D: 5,100 tons (8,500 fl) **Dim:** 94.48 (88.40 pp) × 22.55 × 8.80
S: 17 kts **Man:** 14 officers, 215 men
Range: 29,000/12 — 12,000/17
A: removed in 1969
M: diesel-electric propulsion; 10 Fairbanks-Morse diesels and 2 Westinghouse electric generators; 21,000 hp.

Polar Star (WAGB 10)

Glacier (WAGB 4)

ICEBREAKERS (continued)

REMARKS: Can make way in ice 6-m thick. Welded double hull with insulation cork in the space between the hulls. Carries 2 helicopters (platform on the stern) and one LCVP landing craft. Armament removed.

♦ 4 Northwind/Burton Island class

WAGB 281 WESTWIND	(31-7-43)
WAGB 282 NORTHWIND	(22-5-45)
WAGB 283 BURTON ISLAND	(30-4-46)
WAGB 284 EDISTO	(29-5-46)

Edisto (WAGB 284)

Burton Island (WAGB 283)

D:	3,600 tons (6,500 fl)	**Dim:**	82 (76.20 pp) × 19.50 × 8.80
S:	16 kts	**Man:**	135 men
Range:	38,000/10		

A: Removed in 1969. Helicopter platform.
M: 6 Fairbanks-Morse 10-cylinder diesel engines, each of 2,000 hp, each linked to a Westinghouse generator of 1,375 kw; 3 props, with one forward driven by a 3,000-hp motor and 2 aft driven by 5,000-hp motors (the forward prop has been removed)

REMARKS: Can make way in ice 2.70-m thick. Double hull entirely welded. Portable hangar of alloy metal for the two helicopters carried. WAGB *Eastwind* placed out of service in 1972, *Southwind* in 1974. *Edisto* and *Burton Island* are to be scrapped. *Westwind* and *Northwind* have been fitted with 4 new Enterprise diesel engines.

WAGB 83 MACKINAW (ex-*Manitowoc*) — Bldr: Toledo SB — (6-3-44)

D:	5,000 tons (8,775 fl)	**Dim:**	88.40 × 22.86 × 5.80
S:	16 kts	**Man:**	10 officers, 117 men
Range:	60,000/9		
M:	diesel-electric; 3 props (2 aft, 1 fwd); 10,000 hp		

REMARKS: Built for use on the Great Lakes. Helicopter platform. Fitted with 2/12-ton cranes.

WAGB 38 STORIS (ex-*Eskimo*) — Bldr: Toledo SB (1942)

D:	1,715 tons (1,925 fl)	**Dim:**	70.10 × 13.10 × 4.60
S:	14 kts	**Man:**	10 officers, 96 men
A:	1/76-mm — 2 rocket launchers — 1 helicopter		
M:	diesel-electric propulsion; 1 prop; 1,800 hp		
Range:	22,000/8 — 12,000/14		

REMARKS: Built for use off the Alaskan coast.

PATROL CRAFT

♦ 1. *23 WPB with steel hull, Cape class, 95 feet (1954-59). Series 95-300 and following:*

CAPE CARTER	CAPE JELLISON
CAPE CORAL	CAPE KNOX
CAPE CORWIN	CAPE MORGAN
CAPE CROSS	CAPE NEWAGEN
CAPE CURRENT	CAPE ROMAIN
CAPE FAIRWEATHER	CAPE SHOALWATER
CAPE FOX	CAPE SMALL
CAPE GEORGE	CAPE STARR
CAPE GULL	CAPE STRAIT
CAPE HEDGE	CAPE WASH
CAPE HENLOPEN	CAPE YORK
CAPE HORN	

Bldr: U.S.A. 1953 (*95-300* to *311*), 1955-56 (*95-312* to *320*), 1958-59 (*95-321* to *335*).

See photograph of the Cape class in the Ethiopia section

D:	101.75 tons fl	**Dim:**	28.95 × 5.80 × 1.55
S:	18 kts (cruising fl)	**Man:**	15 men
A:	2/20-mm (I × 2) or 1/40-mm AA and two ASW "mouse traps"		
M:	4 high speed diesels; 2 props; 2,200 hp		
Range:	1,500		

REMARKS: Very complete electronic equipment. Two transferred to Haiti (1956), two to Ethiopia (1958), four to Thailand, one to Saudi Arabia. The *Cape Darby, Falcon,*

PATROL CRAFT (*continued*)

Florida, Kiwanda, Porpoise, Providence, Rosier, Sable, and *Trinity* were transferred to the U.S. Navy in 1969-70 and eventually were given to South Korea. This class patrol boat has served as a prototype for many PGM craft that the United States has given to South American and Asiatic navies under the Mutual Assistance Pact. *Cape Hatteras, Higgon, Upright* to be cannibalized. *Cape Current* in reserve.

Point Class WPB

♦ 2. *53 WPB steel hull WPB Point class, 82 feet (1960-70). 82-301 series following:*

POINT ARENA	POINT HIGHLAND
POINT BAKER	POINT HOBART
POINT BARNES	POINT HOPE
POINT BARROW	POINT HURON
POINT BATAN	POINT JACKSON
POINT BENNET	POINT JUDITH
POINT BONITA	POINT KNOLL
POINT BRIDGE	POINT LEDGE
POINT BROWER	POINT LOBOS
POINT BROWN	POINT LOOKOUT
POINT BUCHON	POINT MARTIN
POINT CAMDEN	POINT MONROE
POINT CARREW	POINT NOWELL
POINT CHARLES	POINT RICHMOND
POINT CHICO	POINT ROBERTS
POINT COUNTESS	POINT SAL
POINT DIVIDE	POINT SPENCER
POINT DORAN	POINT STEEL
POINT ESTERO	POINT STUART
POINT EVANS	POINT SWIFT
POINT FRANCIS	POINT THATCHER
POINT FRANKLIN	POINT VERDE
POINT GLASS	POINT WARDE
POINT HANNON	POINT WELLES
POINT HARRIS	POINT WHITEHORN
POINT HERRON	POINT WINSLOW
POINT HEYER	

Bldr: U.S.A. — 1960-61 (*82-301/331*), 1962-67 (*82-332/370*), 1969-70 (*82-371/82-379*).

D:	64 tons (67 fl)	**Dim:**	25 × 5.25 × 1.95 (fl)
S:	18 kts (see Remarks)	**Man:**	2 officers, 9 men
A:	1/20-mm	**M:**	2 diesels (see Remarks)
Range:	1,400/1,500 at 8/9 kts		

REMARKS: Replaced the 83-foot series which has been removed from the active list. Hull in mild steel. High-speed diesels controlled from the bridge. *82-301/317* have two Cummins diesels, each 600 hp (**S:** 17 kts); the others have 800-hp diesels and 22 knots. *Point Thatcher* (*82-314*) has 2 gas turbines with 1,000-hp (27-knot potential) and variable pitch propellers. Well equipped for salvage and towing. Beginning in 6-65, 26 were sent to Vietnam and 26 replacement units were thereupon ordered.

BUOY TENDERS (*WLB* A, B) and (*WLM* E, D) with a heavy derrick

A. BASSWOOD, BLACKHAW, BLACKTHORN, BUTTONWOOD, CITRUS, CLOVER, CONIFER, COWSLIP, HORNBEAM, MESQUITE, PAPAW, PLANETREE, SASSAFRAS, SEDGE, SPAR, SUNDEW, SWEETBRIAR, SWEETGUM, ACACIA, BALSAM, BITTERSWEET, BRAMBLE, FIREBUSH, GENTIAN, IRIS, LAUREL, MADRONA, MALLOW, MARIPOSA, SAGEBRUSH, SALVIA, SORREL, TUPELO, WOODRUSH, IRONWOOD (1942-1944).

B. JUNIPER.   **C.** FIR, HOLLYHOCK, WALNUT.

	D:	Dim:	Hp	S	M
A	870	54.86 × 11.28 × 3.65	1/1,200	13/14 kts	Diesel-electric
B	794	53.95 × 9.95 × 2.85	900	10.5 kts	Diesel-electric
C	989	53.35 × 9.75 × 3.65	1,350	12 kts	High speed diesels

D. 5 Red class. (*WLM 685/689*).

RED WOOD, RED BEECH, RED BIRCH, RED CEDAR, RED OAK.

Bldr: Coast Guard SY, Curtis Bay (1964-71).

D:	512 tons (fl)	**Dim:**	47.85 × 13.10 × 1.85
S:	12.5 kts	**Man:**	32 men
M:	diesels; 2 props; 1,800 hp		

Reinforced hull for light ice; variable pitch propellers and 1 bow propeller. Ten-ton derrick.

E. 7 White class (*WLM 540/547*).

WHITE BUSH, WHITE HEATH, WHITE HOLLY, WHITE LUPINE, WHITE PINE, WHITE SAGE, WHITE SUMAC (1943).

D:	600 tons (fl)	**S:**	9.5 kts	**Dim:**	40.54 × 9.45 × 2.80
M:	diesel; 1 prop; 600 hp; one 10-ton derrick				

Some smaller craft (WLM and WLI) also have been assigned the names of trees (21) and hand tools (10).

SEA GOING TUGS (*WMEC*)

		D	Hp	S	M
153 CHILULA					
165 CHEROKEE	(1939-43)	1,170	3,000	16 kts	Diesel-electric
166 TAMAROA					
167 ACUSHNET	(1943-44)	1,557	3,000	14 kts	Diesel-electric
168 YOCONA					
194 MODOC (ex-*ATA-194*)	(1943-45)	835	1,500	13 kts	Diesel-electric
202 COMANCHE (ex-*ATA-202*)					

U.S.A. (C.G.) (*continued*)

TRAINING SHIPS AND VARIOUS CLASSES

WIX 327 EAGLE (ex-*Horst Wessel*). Bldr: Blohm and Voss — L: 13-6-36

D: 1,634 tons (1,800 fl)   **Dim:** 90.05 (80.97) × 12 × 4.60
S: 10 kts   **Man:** 260/280 men
M: 2 M.A.N. diesels; 2 props; 500 hp
Fuel: 48 tons

REMARKS: Former sailing school ship of the German Navy. Three-masted, square-rigged vessel with 1,975 m² of sail area.

WAGO 295 EVERGREEN (1943) — oceanographic research ship.

Same characteristics as the *Basswood* (above) — 1,000 hp — **S:** 12 kts

WTR 385 TANAGER (ex-*MSF-385*) (L: 9-12-44) former ocean-going minesweeper, transferred in 1964; fitted for reserve instruction.

♦ *2 Hovercraft type* (*air-cushion vehicles*) **HOVER 1** and **3** (ex-USN *PACV*).

Put in service in Vietnam in 5-66; transferred to the Coast Guard in 10-69. Coastal surveillance of the San Francisco area.

S: 50 kts   **Dim:** 11.92 × 7.01
M: 1 gas turbine   **Man:** 3 men

Hover 01 (ACV)

VENEZUELA

PERSONNEL: 5,700 men including 2,500 marines.

MERCHANT MARINE (1-7-74): 143 ships — 480,230 grt
(tankers: 19 ships — 295,698 grt)

SHIPS IN SERVICE OR UNDER CONSTRUCTION AS OF 1 OCTOBER 1975

		L	D	Main armament
♦ *5 submarines*				
	1 CARITE	1945	1,525	10/533-mm TT
	2 TIBURON	1945	1,517	10/533-mm TT
	2 German type 209	constr.	1,000	
♦ *5 destroyers*				
	3 NUEVA ESPARTA	1952/55	2,600	6/114-mm AA
	2 CARABOBO	1944	2,200	6/127-mm AA, 6 ASW TT
♦ *6 frigates*				
	6 ALMIRANTE CLEMENTE	1955/56	1,300	4/102-mm AA
♦ *12 patrol boats*				
♦ *3 guided missile patrol boats*		1975	150	2 *Otomat*

SUBMARINES

♦ *1 ex-U.S. Balao class purchased in 5-60.*

	Bldr	L	In serv.
S 11 CARITE	Mare Island	25-10-43	12-43
(ex-*Tilefish, SS-307*)	NSY		

D: 1,525/1,825 surfaced/2,300 submerged tons
Dim: 95 (92.72 pp) × 8.25 × 5.20
S: 19/10 kts   **Man:** 9 officers, 66 men
A: 10/533-mm TT (6 fwd, 4 aft)
M: diesel-electric propulsion; 2 props; 6,500/5,400 hp
Fuel: 300 tons

♦ *2 ex-U.S. Guppy II type, transferred in 1972 and 1973*

	Bldr	L
S 12 TIBURON (ex-*Cubera, SS-347*)	Electric Boat Co.	17-6-45
S 13 PICUDA (ex-*Grenadier, SS-525*)	Boston NSY	15-12-44

D: 1,517/1,870 surfaced/2,240 submerged tons
Dim: 93.80 × 8.20 × 5.20
S: 18/13-15 kts   **Man:** 82 men
Range: 10,000/10
A: 10/533-mm TT (6 fwd, 4 aft)
M: diesel-electric propulsion; 3 groups of generators, 2 electric motors; 2 props; 4,800/5,200 hp
Fuel: 300 tons

REMARKS: The *Balao* class was modernized in 1952-54; the fourth generator group was removed to permit the enlargement of the sonar compartment. Two 126-cell batteries.

SUBMARINES (*continued*)

♦ *2 German 209 class, ordered in 1971*

	L		L
S 21 SABALO		**S 22 DELFIN**	

D: 980 surfaced/1,230 submerged tons   **Dim:** 55 × 6.60 × 5.90
S: 21 kts   **Man:** 5 officers, 26 men
A: 8/533-mm TT + 6 reserve torpedoes
M: diesel-electric propulsion; 4 Maybach diesels linked to an AEG generator, 420 kw; 1 Siemens propulsion engine, 5,000 kw.

DESTROYERS

2 ex-U.S. Allen M. Sumner class, transferred 14-7-72 and 31-10-73

	Bldr	L
D 41 CARABOBO	Bethlehem	30-11-44
(ex-*Beatty, DD-756*)	(Staten Island)	
D 51 FALCON	Todd-Pacific	5-12-44
(ex-*Robert K. Huntington, DD-781*)		

D: 2,200 tons (3,320 fl)   **Dim:** 114.75 × 10.45 × 5.80
S: 30 kts   **Man:** 14 officers, 260 men
Range: 1,260/30 — 4,800/15
A: 6/127-mm AA, 38-cal (II × 3) — 2/76-mm AA — 6/324-mm Mk 32 ASW TT (III × 2)
Electron Equipt: Radars: 1/SPS 10, 1/SPS 40
            Sonar: 1/SQS 29
M: GT; 4 Babcock boilers; 2 props; 60,000 hp
Fuel: 650 tons

REMARKS: The *D 51* had been modernized in the FRAM II program.

♦ *3 modified British Battle class*

	Bldr	Laid down	L	In serv.
D 11 NUEVA ESPARTA	Vickers-Armstrongs	24-7-51	19-11-52	11-53
D 21 ZULIA	Vickers-Armstrongs	24-7-51	29-6-53	1955
D 31 ARAGUA	Vickers-Armstrongs	6-53	27-1-55	2-56

D: 2,600 tons (3,670 fl)   **Dim:** 122.52 (117 pp) × 12.80 × 5.80 fl
S: 34.5 kts   **Man:** 20 officers, 236 men

Nueva Esparta (D 11)   1972

A: 6/114-mm AA automatic (II × 3) — 16/40-mm AA (II × 8) — 3/533-mm TT (except for *D 11*) — 2 depth charge projectors — 2 depth charge racks (*11* and *21* two Squids).
Electron Equipt: Radars: 1/AW 52 (*D 11*), 1/SPS 6 the others.
M: Parsons GT; 2 boilers; 2 props; 50,000 hp
Range: 5,000/10

REMARKS: Refit in Great Britain in 1959. Living spaces air-conditioned. *D 11* modernized by Cammell Laird in 1968-69; Seacat missile-launcher installed and has only 4/40-mm AA. *D 21* modernized by the Puerto Cabello navy yard with the technical assistance of Cammell Laird; returned to service in 1973.

FRIGATES

♦ *6 Almirante Clemente class*

D		L
12 ALMIRANTE CLEMENTE		12-54
13 GENERAL FLORES		12-54
22 GENERAL JOSE MORAN		5-2-55
23 ALMIRANTE BRION		4-9-55
32 GENERAL JOSE DE AUSTRIA		15-7-56
33 ALMIRANTE JOSE GARCIA		12-10-56

     Bldr: Ansaldo (Livorno)

General Flores (D 13)

D: 1,300 tons (1,550 fl)   **Dim:** 97.60 × 10.84 × 2.60
S: 32 kts (see remarks)   **Man:** 12 officers, 150 men
Range: 2,500/18 — 4,000/15
A: 4/102-mm AA (II × 2) — 4/40-mm AA (II × 2) — 8/20-mm AA (II × 4) — 2 forward hedgehogs — 4 depth charge projectors — 1 depth charge rack — 3/533-mm TT (III × 1)
M: GT; 2 props; 24,000 hp — 2 Foster-Wheeler boilers
Fuel: 350 tons

REMARKS: Heavily equipped with weapons. In normal service they do not exceed 28/29 knots because of overload. The 102-mm are automatic and radar-directed. The ships are air-conditioned and have Denny-Brown stabilizers, *D 12* and *D 22* have been refitted at Cammell Laird from 1968 to 1975.

♦ *6 based on the Lupo class, ordered in Italy*

N . . .   N . . .   N . . .
N . . .   N . . .   N . . .

REMARKS: See section on Italy.

PATROL BOATS

♦ *6 ordered in Italy in 1975*

D: 500 tons   **S:**   **Dim:**
A:
M:

♦ *5 Ex-U.S. PC (coastal escorts) bought from surplus and overhauled in Venezuela. Assigned to coastal surveillance (1961).*

P 01 MEJILLON (ex-*487*) **P 03 ALCATRAZ** (ex-*565*) **P 06 CARACOL** (ex-*1170*)
P 02 CALAMAR (ex-*566*) **P 04 ALBATROS** (ex-*582*)   Bldr: U.S.A. 1943-44.

D: 280 tons (420 fl)   **Dim:** 53 × 7 × 3.25
S: 18 kts   **Man:** 60/65 men
A: 1/76-mm — 1/40-mm
M: 2 General Motors diesels; 2 props; 2,800 hp

♦ *6 Constitucion class*

	L		L
P 11 CONSTITUCION	1-6-73	**P 14 FEDERACION**	26-2-74
P 12 INDEPENDENCIA	24-7-73	**P 15 LIBERTAD**	5-3-74
P 13 PATRIA	27-9-73	**P 16 VICTORIA**	5-74

Bldr: Vosper-Thornycroft — ordered 5-72; to be delivered after 3-74.

Constitucion   Vosper 1975

D: 150 tons   **S:** 27 kts   **Dim:** 36.88 × 3.7 × . . .
A: 3 with 2/SSM Otomat missiles, 3 with 1/76-mm OTO Melara Compact.
M: MTU diesels; 3,600 hp; 2 props

REMARKS: The first three are fitted as gunboats and have a combination SPQ 2 D Italian radar with a RTN 10 X Orion radar from Selenia and an Elsag computer. The three others have, in addition to the 2 Otomat SSM, 1/40-mm AA. The combination search radar is also an SPQ 2 D.

At variance with what has been stated, the *P 12* will be fitted with two Otomat missiles. At present only the containers are on board, as tests with this missile have not yet made it operational.

♦ *4 ex-U.S. LSM type (placed in service in 1961)*

T 13 LOS MONJES (ex-*LSM-548*)   **T 15 LOS FRAILES** (ex-*LSM-544*)
T 14 LOS ROQUES (ex-*LSM-543*)   **T 16 LOS TESTIGOS** (ex-*LSM-545*)
Bldr: U.S.A. 1943-44

D: 743 tons (1,095 fl)   **Dim:** 61.67 × 10.36 × 2.40 (aft)
S: 12 kts   **Man:** 59 men
A: 1/40-mm AA — 4/20-mm AA
Range: 9,000/11

SURVEILLANCE SMALL CRAFT

♦ *8 delivered in 1954 by Estérel, Cannes*

RIO APURE	RIO CARONI	RIO NEVERI
RIO ARAUCA	**RIO GUARICO**	**RIO TUY**
RIO CABRALES	**RIO NEGRO**	

D: 38.5 tons   **Dim:** 28 (25 pp) × 4.65 × 1.25
S: 28/27 kts   **Man:** 12 men
A: machine gun   **Range:** 750 at 24 kts (cruising speed)
M: 2 Mercedes-Benz 820 MB, 675 hp each

VENEZUELA (*continued*)

SURVEILLANCE SMALL CRAFT (*continued*)

♦ *2 various classes*

RIO SANTO DOMINGUO

D: 40 tons   **S:** 23 kts   **Dim:** 22 × 4.61 × 1.90
M: 2 General Motors diesels; 1,250 hp

GOLFO DE CARIACO

D: 37 tons   **S:** 19 kts   **Dim:** 20 × 5.50 × 2.80

AMPHIBIOUS CRAFT

♦ *1 ex-U.S. LST landing craft, transferred in 6-73*

AMAZONAS (ex-*Vernon County*, LST-1161)

Bldr: Ingalls (Pascagoula) 25-11-52

D: 2,590 tons (5,786 fl)   **Dim:** 117.35 × 16.76 × 3.70
S: 13 kts   **Man:** 116 men
A: 4/76-mm AA
M: 4 G.M. diesels; 2 variable pitch props; 6,000 hp

LOGISTIC SUPPORT

♦ *3 transports*

T 12 LAS AVES (ex-*Dos de Diciembre*) — Bldr: Dubigeon — L: 29-12-54

Las Aves (T 12)

D: 944 tons (fl)   **Cargo:** 215 tons   **Dim:** 71.40 (64.50 pp) × 10.20 × 3
S: 15 kts   **A:** 4/20-mm AA (II × 2)
M: diesels; 2 props; 1,600 hp   **Range:** 2,520/14

REMARKS: Also fitted as the presidential yacht.

T 17 PUNTA CABANA — T 20 N . . . — Bldr: Uraga DD (Japan)

D: 3,000 tons   **S:** 17 kts

♦ *3 net layers*

	L
H 01 PUERTO SANTO (ex-*Marietta*, AN-82)	27-4-45
H 02 PUERTO DE NUTRIAS (ex-*Tunxis*, AN-90)	10-8-44
H 03 PUERTO MIRANDA (ex-*Waxsaw*, AN-91)	15-9-44

Net layers (1942-43), transferred by the U.S.A. (1962-63).

D: 650 tons (785 fl)   **Dim:** 51.35 × 10.25 × 3.35
S: 12 kts   **Man:** 46 men
A: No armament

M: diesel-electric propulsion; 1,500 hp

H 01 assigned to the buoy and lighthouse service as well as being a hydrographic ship.

♦ *1 repair ship, transferred in 6-62*

T 18 GUYANA (ex-*Quirinus*, ex-U.S. *ARL-39*, ex-*LST 1151*), (1946)

D: 1,625 tons (4,100 fl)   **Dim:** 99.98 × 15.24 × 4.36
S: 10 kts (8 cruising)   **Range:** 6,000/8
M: diesels; 2 props; 1,800 hp
A: 8/40-mm AA (IV × 2)

DF 1 (ex-U.S. *YR-48*) floating workshop, transferred in 1965.

♦ *4 tugs*

R 12 FERNANDO GOMEZ (ex-U.S. *YTM-744*)

D: 160 tons   **Dim:** 24.50 × 5.80 × 2.50
S: 10 kts   **Man:** 10 men
M: Clark diesel; 1 prop; 560 hp

R 13 JOSE FELIX RIBAS (1945) (ex-U.S. *YTB-515*)

D: 450 tons

R 14 FABIO GALLIPOLI
R 21 FELIPE LARRAZABAL (ex-U.S. *Utina*, ATF-163)

D: 1,280 tons (1,700 fl)   **Dim:** 61.70 × 11.60 × 4.70
S: 16 kts   **Man:** 85 men
A: 1/76-mm — 4/40-mm AA
M: 4 diesel-electric groups; 2 props; 3,000 hp

REMARKS: Transferred in 9-72.

VIETNAM

North

MERCHANT MARINE (1-7-74): 7 ships — 9,151 grt

North Vietnam has manned the following ships which have been transferred by the U.S.S.R. and the Peoples Republic of China. For characteristics, see those sections.

PATROL BOATS

♦ *2 Soviet S 01 type*
♦ *8/10 Chinese Shanghai type*
♦ *18/20 Chinese Swatow type*

PATROL TORPEDO BOATS

♦ *3 Soviet P 6 type*
♦ *13 Soviet P 4 type*

NOTE: Because of a lack of precise information on the future of the North and South Vietnamese navies after the fall of the Saigon government, it has been decided to retain these sections for the two areas.

The only information available as of 1-6-75 is as follows:

The frigate *HQ 04 Tran Khanh Du* was captured in drydock at the naval shipyard in Saigon by the North Vietnamese.

The *LSM 402 Lam Giang*, the *PGM HQ 604 Keon Ngua* and the small tanker *HQ 474* were all scuttled at sea.

The *LSIL HQ 331 Tam Sat* and *HQ 330 Loi Cong*, the *LSSL Nguyen Duc Dong* and the gunboat *HQ 602 Minh Hoa* all took refuge in Singapore but later returned to Saigon.

The following ships were able to reach the Philippines and have been returned to the U.S. Navy:

10 frigates
HQ 01 TRAN HUNG DAO
HQ 02 TRAN QUANG KHAI
HQ 03 TRAN NHAT DUAT
HQ 05 TRAN QUOC TRAN
HQ 07 DONG DA
HQ 08 CHI LANG II
HQ 11 CHI LINH
HQ 12 NGON HOI
HQ 14 VAN KIEP II
HQ 17 NGO KUYEN

Tran Hung Dao   U.S. Navy 1971

3 LSSL
HQ 228 DOAN NGOC TANG
HQ 229 LUU PHU THO
HQ 231 NGUYEN DUC BONG

1 LSIL
HQ 329 THIEN KICH

1 LST
HQ 502 THI NAI

VIETNAM
South

2 LSM
HQ 401 HAN GIANG
HQ 404 HUONG GIANG

2 PGM
HQ 600 PHU DU
HQ 618 HONG TROC

1 ex-CGS Point class
HQ 702 HUYNH VAN CU

3 repair ships
HQ 800 MY THO
HQ 801 CAN THO
HQ 802 VINH LONG

All other ships appear to have fallen into the hands of the North Vietnamese.

FRIGATES

♦ *2 ex-U.S. DER, transferred in 1971 and 1972*

HQ 01 TRAN HUNG DAO (ex-*Camp, DER-251*)
HQ 04 TRAN KHANH DU (ex-*Forster, DER-334*)   Bldr: U.S.A. (1943)

D:	1,590 tons (2,100 fl)	**Dim:**	93.26 × 11.22 × 4
S:	19 kts	**Man:**	150 men
A:	2/76-mm AA — 6 ASW TT — 1 hedgehog		
Range:	11,500/11	**Fuel:**	300 tons
M:	Fairbanks-Morse diesels; 2 props; 6,000 hp		

♦ *7 ex-U.S. CGS, transferred 1-1-71 (4) and 25-7-72 (3)*

HQ 2 TRAN QUAN KHAI (ex-*Bering Strait, WHEC-382*) — 15-1-44
HQ 3 TRAN NHAT DUAT (ex-*Yakutat, WHEC-380*) — 2-7-42
HQ 5 TRAN QUOC TRAN (ex-*Cook Inlet, WHEC-384*) — 13-5-44
HQ 6 TRAN BINH TRONG (ex-*Castle Rock, WHEC-383*) — 11-3-44
HQ 15 THAM NGU LAO (ex-*Absecon, WHEC-374*) — 3-8-42
HQ 16 LY THOUNG KIET (ex-*Chincoteague, WHEC-375*) — 15-4-42
HQ 17 NGO QUYEN (ex-*McCulloch, WHEC-386*) — 10-7-42

D:	1,766 tons (2,800 fl)	**Dim:**	94.50 × 12.52 × 3.70
S:	17 kts	**Man:**	160 men
A:	1/12.7-mm machine gun	**Range:**	18,000/15
M:	diesels; 2 props; 6,000 hp	**Fuel:**	400 tons

Designed as aircraft supply ships.

FRIGATES (continued)

♦ *7 ex-U.S. PCE/MSF transferred since 1962, the last two in 1970*

HQ 07 DONG DA II (ex-*Crestview, PCE-895*)
HQ 08 CHI LANG II (ex-*Gayety, MSF-239*)
HQ 09 KY HOA (ex-*Sentry, MSF-299*)
HQ 11 CHI LINH (ex-*Shelter, MSO-301*)
HQ 12 NGOG HOI (ex-*Brattleboro, PCER-852*)
HQ 13 HA HOI (ex-*Prowess, MSF-280*)
HQ 14 VAN KIEP II (ex-*Amherst, PCER-853*)
    Bldr: U.S.A. — 1943-44

Ngog Hoi

D:	640/650 tons (900/950 fl)	**Dim:**	56.24 × 10.06 × 2.75
S:	15/14 kts	**Man:**	7 officers, 90 men
A:	1/76-mm AA (on *08/09:* 2/40-mm, 8/20-mm add'l)		
M:	General Motors diesels; 2 props; 1,800/2,400 hp		

REMARKS: *HQ 13* used for reserve training. *HQ 10 Nhut Tao* sunk 19-1-74 during the Paracels engagement.

♦ *1 ex-U.S. PC, transferred in 1960*

HQ 06 VAN DON (ex-*Anacortes, PC-1959*)
    Bldr: U.S.A. 1943-44

D:	280 tons (400 fl)	**Dim:**	52.95 × 7.05 × 3.25
S:	19/18 kts	**Man:**	5 officers, 59 men
A:	1/76-mm — 1/40-mm AA — 4/20-mm AA		
Range:	6,000/10 — 2,300/18	**Fuel:**	62 tons
M:	2 General Motors diesels; 2 props; 2,800 hp		

MINESWEEPERS

♦ **HQ 114 HAM TU** (ex-*MSC-281*)
  HQ 115 CHUONG DONG (ex-*MSC-282*)

U.S. MSC class
Bldr: U.S.A. — 1954-55
Transferred in 1960

Van Don

Bach Dang   1970

D:	370 tons (465 fl)	**Dim:**	43.90 × 7.23 × 2.55
S:	14/13 kts	**Man:**	4 officers, 40/41 men
A:	2/20-mm AA	**Range:**	2,500/12
M:	2 General Motors diesels; 2 props; 1,600 hp		
Fuel:	40 tons		

GUNBOATS AND PATROL BOATS

♦ *20 PGM class, transferred by the U.S.A. since 1963*

HQ 600 PHUDU (ex-*PGM-64*)
HQ 601 TIEN MOI (ex-*PGM-65*)
HQ 602 MINH HOA (ex-*PGM-66*)
HQ 603 KIEN VANG (ex-*PGM-67*)
HQ 604 KEON NGUA (ex-*PGM-68*)
HQ 605 KIM QUI (ex-*PGM-59*)

GUNBOATS AND PATROL BOATS *(continued)*

HQ 606 MAY RUT (ex-*PGM-60*)
HQ 607 NAM DU (ex-*PGM-61*)
HQ 608 HAO LU (ex-*PGM-62*)
HQ 609 TO YEN (ex-*PGM-63*)
HQ 610 DIENH HAI (ex-*PGM-69*)
HQ 611 TRUONG SA (ex-*PGM-70*)
HQ 612 THAI BINH (ex-*PGM-72*)
HQ 613 THI TU (ex-*PGM-73*)
HQ 614 SONG TU (ex-*PGM-74*)
HQ 615 TAT SA (ex-*PGM-80*)
HQ 616 HOANG SA (ex-*PGM-82*)
HQ 617 PHU QUI (ex-*PGM-81*)
HQ 618 HONG TROC (ex-*PGM-83*) (30-9-67)
HQ 619 TO CHAU (ex-*PGM-91*)

Bldr: U.S.A. — 1963-67

D: 100 tons (143 fl)   **S:** 17 kts   **Dim:** 31.00 × 6.40 × 1.83
A: 1/40-mm AA — 2/20-mm AA   **Man:** 2 officers, 25 men
M: Mercedes-Benz or G.M. diesels; 2 props; 1,900 hp

HQ 605 Kim Qui   U.S. Navy

♦ *26 "Point" class patrol boats of the U.S. Coast Guard, transferred since February 1966 (Series 82301)*

Bldr: U.S.A. — 1960-67

HQ 700 LE PHUOC DUI (ex-*Point Garnet*)
HQ 701 LE VAN NGA (ex-*Point League*)
HQ 702 HUYNG VAN CU (ex-*Point Clear*)
HQ 703 NGUYEN DAO (ex-*Point Gammon*)
HQ 704 DAO THUC (ex-*Point Comfort*)
HQ 705 LE NGOC THANH (ex-*Point Ellis*)
HQ 706 NGUYEN NGOG THACH (ex-*Point Slocum*)
HQ 707 DANG VAN HOANH (ex-*Point Hudson*)
HQ 708 LE DINH HUNG (ex-*Point White*)
HQ 709 THUONG TIEN (ex-*Point Dume*)
HQ 710 PHAM NGOC CHAU (ex-*Point Arden*)
HQ 711 DAO VAN DANG (ex-*Point Glover*)
HQ 712 LE DGOC AN (ex-*Point Jefferson*)
HQ 713 HUYNH VAN NGAN (ex-*Point Kennedy*)
HQ 714 TRAN LO (ex-*Point Young*)
HQ 715 BUI VIET THANH (ex-*Point Partridge*)

HQ 716 NGUYEN AN (ex-*Point Caution*)
HQ 717 NGUYEN HAN (ex-*Point Welcome*)
HQ 718 NGO VAN QUYEN (ex-*Point Banks*)
HQ 719 VAN DIEN (ex-*Point Lomas*)
HQ 720 HO DANG LA (ex-*Point Grace*)
HQ 721 DAM THOAI (ex-*Point Mast*)
HQ 722 HUYNH BO (ex-*Point Grey*)
HQ 723 NGUYEN KIM HUNG (ex-*Point Orient*)
HQ 724 HO DUY (ex-*Point Cypress*)
HQ 725 TROUGN BA (ex-*Point Monroe*)

Tran Lo   U.S. Navy

D: 64 tons (67 fl)   **Dim:** 25 × 5.19 × 1.75
S: 17 kts   **Man:** 8/10 men
A: 1 gun carriage with a 12.7-mm machine gun and 1/81-mm mortar
M: Cummins diesels; 2 props; 1,200 hp

♦ *2 ex-U.S. patrol boats*

HQ . . . N . . .   **HQ . . . N . . .**
D: 230 fl   **S:** . . .   **Dim:** 49.50 × 7.20 × 2.85
A: 1/76-mm AA — 1/40-mm AA   **M:** diesels; 2 props

REMARKS: Entered on the 1975 budget as aid for South Vietnam. Probably not delivered.

♦ *107 PCF "Swift" type patrol boats*

Bldr: U.S.A. (Sewart Seacraft) —since 1965.
D: 16 tons (22 fl)   **Dim:** 15.60 × 4.12 × 1.50
S: 25 kts — Hull in light metal
Man: 1 officer, 5 men
A: 3/12.7-mm machine guns (II × 1, I × 1 combined with 1/81-mm mortar).
M: Gray 12 V-721 diesels; 2 props; 960 hp
Endurance: 24 to 36 hours

GUNBOATS AND PATROL BOATS (*continued*)

PCF/Swift boat   U.S. Navy 1970

PCF/Swift boat   U.S. Navy 1969

♦ *84 ASPB* (*Assault support patrol boats*)

Bldr: Gunderson Bros. Portland (1967).

D: 28.7 tons (36 fl)   **Dim:** 15.27 × 4.64 × 1.14
S: 14 kts   **Man:** 6 men
Range: 200/10
A: 2/7.6-mm machine guns (II × 1) midships — 1/20-mm AA (fwd) — 1/81-mm mortar (aft)
M: 2 Detroit Mk 12 V 71 fast diesels; 2 props; 850 hp

Certain modified as MSR class (patrol minesweepers), for river minesweeping with an armament reduced to 2/12.7-mm machine guns, twin mounts in a forward turret.

♦ *293 PBR type river patrol boats, shallow draft*

(1) Ordered in 1965-67 — Bldr: United Boat Builders.

PBR   U.S. 1970

D: 18 tons
Dim: 9.45 × 3.20 × 0.36/.45 (according to spd.)
S: 20/22 kts   **Man:** 1 officer, 4 men
A: 2/12.7-mm machine guns (II × 1 fwd) — 1/12.7-mm machine gun aft — 1 grenade launcher.
M: water-jet propulsion; no rudder; 2 General Electric diesels, 220 hp each.

(2) *PBR Mk 2*, modification of earlier models, ordered at the beginning of 1967. Same armament and propulsion as the Mk 1.

Dim: 9.75 × 3.53

♦ *About 40 STCAN/FOM* (*ex-French river patrol boats*)

STCAN/FOM   U.S. Navy 1970

Length: 10.60   **S:** 10 kts   **Man:** 8 men
A: 12.7-mm and 7.7-mm machine guns behind a protection shield

AMPHIBIOUS SHIPS

♦ *6 ex-U.S. LST class transferred, 3 in 1962-63, 3 in 1969-70*
Bldr: U.S.A. 1942-43

HQ 500 CAM RANH (ex-*LST-975*)
HQ 501 DA KANG (ex-*LST-938*)

AMPHIBIOUS SHIPS (continued)

HQ 502 THI NAI (ex-*LST-529*)
HQ 503 VUNG TAU (ex-*LST-603*)
HQ 504 QUI NHON (ex-*LST-509*)
HQ 505 NHA TRANG (ex-*LST-848*)

- **D:** 2,366 tons (4,080 fl)   **Dim:** 99.98 × 15.25 × 4.30
- **S:** 10 kts   **Man:** 7 officers, 100/105 men
- **A:** Several 40-mm and 20-mm AA
- **Range:** 6,000/9
- **M:** General Motors diesels; 2 props; 1,700 hp
- **Fuel:** 1,060 tons

♦ *7 LSM class 400/403, transferred by France (1955), 404/406 by U.S.A. (1961-63)*

♦ **HQ 400 HAN GIANG** (ex-*LSM-9012*)
HQ 401 HAT GIANG (ex-*LSM-9011*)
HQ 402 LAM GIANG (ex-*LSM-9019*)
HQ 403 NINH GIANG (ex-*LSM-9051*)
HQ 404 HUONG GIANG (ex-*LSM-175*)
HQ 405 TIEN GIANG (ex-*LSM-313*)
HQ 406 HAU GIANG (ex-*LSM-276*)
Bldr: U.S.A.

♦ *H 400 and HQ 401 modified as hospital ships in 1966*

HQ 404 Huong Giang   1970

- **D:** 743 tons (1,100 fl)   **Dim:** 62 × 10.30 × 2.40
- **S:** 13/12 kts   **Man:** 5 officers, 70 men
- **A:** 2/40-mm AA — 4/20-mm AA   **Range:** 3,500/12
- **M:** General Motors diesels; 2 props; 2,800 hp

♦ *9 ex-U.S. LSSL and LSIL class — Bldr: U.S.A. 1942-43*

HQ 228 DOAN NGOG TANG (ex-*LSSL-9*) ⎫
HQ 229 LUU PHU THO (ex-*LSSL-101*) ⎪ transferred between
HQ 230 NGUYEN NGOC LONG (ex-*LSSL-96*) ⎬ 9-65 and 2-66
HQ 231 NGUYEN DUC BONG (ex-*LSSL-129*) ⎭

- **D:** 250 tons (387 fl)   **Dim:** 48.80 × 7.10 × 1.75

HQ 231 Nguyen Duc Bong   U.S. Navy 1970

- **S:** 14 kts   **Man:** 6 officers, 54 men
- **A:** 1/76-mm AA — 4/40-mm AA — 4/20-mm AA — 4 mortars
- **Range:** 5,000/12
- **M:** General Motors diesels; 2 props; 1,600 hp

HQ 327 LONG DAO ⎫
  (ex-*French L-9029*, ex-*U.S. LSIL-698*) ⎪
HQ 328 THAN TIEN ⎪
  (ex-*French L-9035*, ex-*U.S. LSIL-702*) ⎪
HQ 329 THIEN KICH ⎬ transferred
  (ex-*French L-9030*, ex-*U.S. LSIL-887*) ⎪ in 1955-56
HQ 330 LOI CONG ⎪ by France
  (ex-*French L-9034*, ex-*U.S. LSIL-699*) ⎪
HQ 331 TAM SAT ⎭
  (ex-*French L-9033*, ex-*U.S. LSIL-871*)

HQ 331 Tam Sat   U.S. Navy 1970

Same characteristics as the *HQ 228/231*, but — **A:** 1/40-mm — 2/20-mm and 5 mortars (60 to 81-mm) — **Man:** 5 officers, 50 men

AMPHIBIOUS SHIPS (*continued*)

♦ *27 LCU* — **HQ 533 à 599** (ex-*U.S. 1502, 1594, 1476, 1480, 1221, 1466, 1501, 1562, 1475, 1477, 1494, etc.* — Bldr: U.S.A.

Type LCU   U.S. Navy 1970

D:	180 tons/360 (fl)	**Dim:**	35.05 × 10.36 × 1.85
S:	10 kts	**A:**	2/20-mm
M:	3 diesels; 675 hp. Can carry 150 tons or 5 light tanks		

RIVER PATROL BOATS
(Modified LCM and other classes)

♦ *22 armored LCM type* (called "the battleships of the delta")
HQ 1800/1821.

D:	75 tons (fl)	**S:**	8 kts	**Dim:** 18.44 × 5.34 × 1.05
M:	2 diesels			**Man:** 11 men

A: 1/40-mm — 1 81-mm mortar — 1/20-mm — 2/12.7-mm machine guns — 4/7.6-mm machine guns — 2 grenade launchers

♦ *6 LCMM, armored LCM type* modified as river minesweepers (operate in pairs).

LCM (Monitor)   U.S. Navy 1968

S:	8 kts (fl)	**Dim:**	18.44 × 4.34 × 1.05
M:	2 diesels	**Man:**	4 men
A:	2/20-mm (I × 2) — 1/12.7-mm machine gun		

♦ *10 CCB* (*Command Communication Boats*) — **HQ 6100/6108** Command and communication ships.

D:	80 tons (fl)	**Dim:**	18.44 × 5.34 × 1.05
S:	8.5 kts	**Man:**	11 men
M:	2 diesels		
A:	1/40-mm — 1/20-mm — 3/7.6-mm machine guns — 5 grenade launchers — 10 radio transmitters.		

Used in fire support coordination.

RIVER PATROL BOATS (*continued*)

♦ **27 RPC** (*river patrol craft*) — **HQ 7000/7026** — 1966

RPC   U.S. Navy 1970

D:	12 tons	**Dim:**	11 × 3.30 × 1
M:	2 diesels	**S:**	14 kts
A:	4 machine guns		

♦ **28 HQ** — **HQ 3000-3027** *series* — Cutter class small craft.

D:	12 tons	**S:**	25 kts
A:	1/12.7-mm machine gun fwd — 1/20-mm aft		

♦ **100** (*approx.*) **ATC** (*armored troop carriers*) **HQ 1200** *series.*

D:	66 tons (fl)	**Dim:**	17.07 × 5.34 × 1.02
S:	8 kts (fl)	**Man:**	7 men

A: 1/20-mm — 2/12.7-mm machine guns — 4/7.6-mm machine guns — 2 grenade launchers
M: 2 diesels

Can carry a 2.5-ton truck or a 105-mm howitzer, or armored personnel carrier.

♦ There are also some river minesweepers, MSM type, same characteristics as the ATC type and heavily protected.

A: 2/20-mm (I × 2) in a turret, 1/12.7-mm machine gun, 2 grenade launchers
Man: 4/5 men

♦ About 100 old LCM type including about 20 armored, and 250 old LCVPs, some armored.

LCM type — 21/31 tons — **Dim:**   13.60 × 4.27 × 1.20 — **S:** 7.5 kts
LCVP type — 9.13 tons — **Dim:**   10.98 × 3.20 × 0.90 — **S:** 9.0 kts

The armored LCMs have a tank type turret forward (1/40-mm — 1/20-mm); amidships: an 81-mm mortar; on the stern: 3/20-mm.

LCM converted into a river patrol boat   U.S. Navy

These are often LCM 6 (16.15 m), possibly LCM 8; all of them have **A:**   1/20-mm, some 12.7-mm machine guns, and **Man:**   7 men

LCM   U.S. Navy 1970

RIVER PATROL BOATS (*continued*)

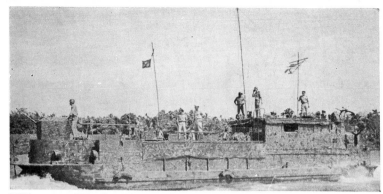

LCM command Monitor (obsolete)   U.S. Navy 1967

LOGISTIC SUPPORT

♦ *2 ex-U.S. former LST type, transferred in 10-70 and 4-71*

HQ 800 MY THO (ex-*Harnett County, AGP-821*)
HQ 801 CAN THO (ex-*Garrett County, AGP-786*)
Bldr: U.S.A. — 1943

Ex-Garrett County (LST 786), *PBR support ship in Vietnam*   1968

   D: 4,100 tons   **S:** 10 kts   **Dim:** 100 × 15.25 × 4.30
   M: General Motors diesels; 2 props; 1,700 hp

Modified as a support ship for river patrol boats with two UH-1 helicopters; excellent radio equipment; **A:** 40-mm AA.

♦ *1 ex-U.S. former LST, transferred in 10-71*

HQ 802 VINH LONG (ex-*Satyr, ARL-23*)
Bldr: U.S.A. (1943)
   D: 3,700 tons (fl)   **S:** 10 kts   **Dim:** 99.85 × 15.25 × 4.36
   M: 2 diesels; 2 props; 1,800 hp

♦ *1 ex-U.S. repair ship transferred in October 1971*

N . . . (ex-*Markab*, AR-23) — Bldr: U.S.A. (1942-44)
   D: 16,500 tons (fl)   **Dim:** 149.66 × 21.20 × 8.50
   S: 16 kts
   M: GT; 2 props; 8,500 hp

♦ *6 ex-U.S. gasoline barges, YOG class*

HQ 470 (ex-*L'Aulne*, ex-*YOG-80*), **HQ 471** (ex-*YOG-33*), **HQ 472** (ex-*YOG-67*), **HQ 473** (ex-*YOG-71*), **HQ 474** (ex-*YOG-131*), **HQ 475** (ex-*YOG-56*)

♦ *2 water barges* — **HQ 9113-HQ 9118.**

♦ *8 ex-U.S. small harbor tugs*

HQ 9500, 9501, 9503, 9504, 9508/9511

VARIOUS

♦ *1 training ship*

HQ 451 HOA GIANG (ex-*Ingénieur en Chef Girod*, ex-*FS-287*)
   Bldr: U.S.A. (1943).

HQ 451 Hoa Giang   U.S. Navy 1970

   D: 720 tons (950 fl)   **Dim:** 53.65 × 9.96 × 3.10
   S: 10 kts   **Man:** 3 officers, 52 men
   A: 2/20-mm AA
   M: 2 General Motors diesels linked to 1 prop; 1,000 hp
   Fuel: 68 tons

REMARKS: Former buoy ship of the French Indochina administration, used by the French navy as a hydrographic ship. Transferred in 12-55 as a supply ship, then used as a training ship since 1966.

YEMEN
Southern

PERSONNEL: 150 men

MERCHANT MARINE (1-7-74): 7 ships — 2,180 grt

PATROL BOATS

♦ *2 Soviet SO 1 type (see U.S.S.R. section) delivered in 4-72*
  3 Osa I have been transferred by the U.S.S.R.

♦ *3 ex-British inshore "-ham" class minesweepers (ex-Bodenham, Blunham, Elsenham) transferred in 1967.*

AL SAQR   AL DAIRAK   AL GHAZALA

D:	120 tons (150 fl)	**Dim:**	32.43 (30.48 pp) × 6.45 × 1.70
S:	13 kts	**Man:**	2 officers, 13 men
A:	1/20-mm AA		
Range:	1,500/12	**Fuel:**	15 tons
M:	Davey-Paxman diesels; 2 props; 1,000 hp		

♦ *4/P 4 and 2/P 6 torpedo boats.*

♦ *2 Soviet Polnocny-class LCT landing craft in 8-73.* They have 4/25-mm AA (II × 2) and 2/140-mm RL (XVIII × 2) for fire support.

♦ *3 Soviet LCM type transferred in 11-70*

YEMENITE ARAB REPUBLIC

PERSONNEL: Approximately 150 men

MERCHANT MARINE (1-7-74): 3 ships — 1,260 grt

♦ *4 Soviet Poluchat-class patrol boats*

♦ *3 Soviet P4 type patrol torpedo boats*

♦ *3 small landing craft*

PERSONNEL: 17,000 men

NAVAL AVIATION: A few Soviet Hound and Hormone helicopters

MERCHANT MARINE (1-7-74): 398 ships — 1,778,423 grt
(tankers: 28 ships — 250,396 grt)

WARSHIPS IN SERVICE OR UNDER CONSTRUCTION AS OF 1 OCTOBER 1975

	L	D	Main armament
♦ *5 submarines*			
3 HEROJ class	1966–67	1,068	6/533-mm TT
2 SUTJESKA class	1958–59	700	6/533-mm TT
♦ *1 destroyer*			
1 SPLIT	1950	2,400	4/127-mm AA, 12/40-mm AA, 5/533-mm TT
♦ *57 guided missile and torpedo patrol boats*			
10 OSA class	1965	160	4/30-mm AA, 4 Styx systems
16 SHERSHEN class	1965	160	4/30-mm AA, 4/533-mm TT
31 HIGGINS class	1951–60	55/60 t	1/40-mm, 2/533-mm TT (21 fitted out as gunboats and have no torpedoes).
♦ *23 patrol boats*			
3 FOUGUEUX class	1954–60	325	2/40-mm, ASW weapons
16 KRALJAVICA class	1953–60	190	1/76-mm, 1/40-mm AA
4 KOTOR class	1967–68	120	4/132-mm
♦ *24 minesweepers*			
4 coastal			
20 shallow water			

SUBMARINES

♦ *3 Heroj class*

	Bldr	Laid down	L	In serv.
821 HEROJ	Uljanik (Pula)	1965	1966	1968
822 JUNAK	Uljanik (Pula)	1966	1967	1969
823 USKOK	Uljanik (Pula)	. . .	. . .	yes

Heroj (821)   1968

D: 1,068 tons (submerged) **Dim:** 64 × 7.20 × 5
S: 15/10 kts **Man:** 55 men
A: 6/533-mm TT **M:** diesels and electric motors; 2,400 hp.

YUGOSLAVIA

♦ *2 Sutjeska class*

	Bldr	Laid down	L	In serv.
811 SUTJESKA	Uljanik (Pula)	1957	28-9-58	9-60
812 NERETVA	Uljanik (Pula)	1957	1959	1962

Neretva (812)   G. Arra

D: 700 tons/820 surfaced/945 submerged **Dim:** 60 × 6.60 × 4.80
S: 14/9 kts **Man:** 38 men **Range:** 4,400/8.6
A: 6/533-mm TT **M:** diesels and electric motors; 1,800 hp

REMARKS: First submarines built in Yugoslavia.

DESTROYERS

♦ *1 French type*

	Bldr	Laid down	L	In serv.
11 SPLIT	"3 Maj" Brodogradiliste (Rijeka)	7-39	3-50	4-7-58

1972

D: 2,400 tons (3,000 fl) **S:** 31 kts **Dim:** 120 (114.70 pp) × 12 × 3.70
A: 4/127-mm (I × 4) — 12/40-mm AA (II × 6) — 4/20-mm AA — 5/533-mm TT (V × 1) — 2 hedgehogs (or Squids) — 6 depth charge projectors — 2 depth charge racks
M: GT; 2 props **Boilers:** 50,000 hp. **Fuel:** 500 tons

REMARKS: Plans from the Loire Shipyards. Equipped to lay 40 mines. U.S. radars and weapons.

CORVETTES

♦ *1 new type* — Bldr: Uljanik (Pula) (laid down: 10-74)

D: 700/800 tons   **S:** ...   **Dim:** ...
A: ...   **M:** ...

REMARKS: Prototype of a new class of corvettes which will be made up of six ships. Swedish armament.

GUIDED MISSILE BOATS AND PATROL TORPEDO BOATS

♦ *10 new class guided missile boats built in Yugoslavia* (?)

D: ...   **S:** ...   **Dim:** ...
A: ...
M: Rolls-Royce gas turbine, 4,500 hp.

♦ *10 Soviet OSA 1 guided missile boats*

TAMBOVSKYI, KOMSOMOL, N . . . , **N** . . . , **N** . . . , **N** . . . , **N** . . . , **N** . . . , **N** . . . , etc.

Bldr: U.S.S.R. — transferred since 1966.

D: 160 tons (190 fl)   **S:** 35 kts   **Dim:** 40.07 (36.95 pp) × 7.00 × 2
A: 4/20-mm AA (II × 2) — 4 Styx SSM   **Man:** 25 men
Electron Equipt: Radars: 1/Square Tie, 1 Drum Tilt.
M: diesels; 3 props; 10,000 hp

♦ *16 Soviet Shershen type patrol torpedo boats* — No. **TC 215** to **TC 230**

Known names: **FRAZ ROSMAN, JOVANOVIC PANAC, DELCEV**

Bldr: U.S.S.R. — transferred since 1966 or built in Yugoslavia (9)

D: 190 tons (fl)   **S:** 35 kts   **Dim:** 34 × 8.00 × 1.50.
A: 4/30-mm AA (II × 2) — 4/533-mm TT (two fixed on each side).
Electron Equipt: Radars: 1/Pot Drum, 1/Drum Tilt
M: 3 diesels; 3 props; 10,000 hp

♦ *31 of the Higgins 108 class.* **TC 102** to **TC 201** — Bldr: Yugoslavia (1951-60)

D: 55/60 tons   **S:** 36 kts   **Dim:** 21 × 6.50 × 2.36
A: 1/40-mm AA — 4/13-mm machine guns (II × 2) — 2 torpedoes
M: Packard motors; 3 props; 5,000 hp   **Man:** 14 men

REMARKS: 21 have no torpedoes and are fitted as gunboats.

PATROL BOATS

♦ *3 French Fougueux class*

PBR 581 UDARNIC (ex-*P-6*) — Bldr: Mediterranean SY (Le Havre) — L: 21-12-54
PBR 551 MORNAR — Bldr: Yugoslavia — In serv.: 9-59
PBR 552 BORAC — Bldr: Yugoslavia — In serv.: 1965

PBR 551 Mornar   1970

D: 325 tons (400 fl)   **Dim:** 51.80 × 6.97 × 2 (light)
S: 18.7 kts   **Man:** 60/62 men
A: *581:* 2/40-mm — 2/20-mm — 1 hedgehog — depth charges
    551: 2/76-mm — 2/40-mm — 2/20-mm — 2 MR 22 RL

PATROL BOATS (*continued*)

PBR 581 Udarnic

M: 4 SEMT-Pielstick diesels; 2 props; 3,240 hp

REMARKS: *PBR 581* identical to the French *Fougueux* class; offshore command. The *Mornar* and the *Borac* based on the *581* and built by Yugoslavia.

◆ *16 Kraljavica class*

PBR 501 to **508** and **509** to **524** — Bldr: Yugoslavia — 1953-60

PBR 512

D: 190 tons (245 fl)   **S:** 20 kts   **Dim:** 41 × 6.30 × 2.10
A: 1/76-mm — 1/40-mm AA — 4/20-mm AA — depth charges
M: diesels; 2 props; 3,300 hp   **Range:** 1,500/12

REMARKS: Some ships of the same class have been transferred to Indonesia and Sudan. The *508* and *509* have slightly different profiles.

◆ *4 Kotor class.*

PC 132 to **PC 135** — Bldr: Yugoslavia — 1967-68
D: 120 tons   **S:** 20 kts   **Dim:** 32 × 5.50 × 2.50
A: 4/13.2-mm (II × 2)   **M:** 2 diesels; 2 props; 900 hp

PC 135   1968

MINELAYERS

M 11 GALEB (ex-Italian *Ramb III*) (1938). Former banana boat armed as an auxiliary cruiser from 1940 to 1945. Reconstruction and rearmed in 1952.

1968

D: 5,182 tons   **Dim:** 117.30 × 15.60 × 5.60
S: 16 kts   **M:** diesels; 2 props

REMARKS: Used as a yacht by the head of state: armament has now been removed. There are two old 66-mm guns on board as saluting battery.

NOTE: Six *DSM 500* minelayers may be in service.

MINESWEEPERS

◆ *4 of the French Sirius class*

M 151 HRABRI (ex-*D-25*) 27-2-56   **M 152 SMELI** (ex-*D-26*) 23-5-56
M 153 SLOBODNI (ex-*D-27*) 26-7-56   **M 161 SNAZNI** (1960).
Bldr: Normand, Le Havre (151/153), transferred at the end of 1957. Characteristics on the following page.

D: 365 tons (424 fl)   **Dim:** 46.40 (42.70 pp) × 8.55 × 2.50
S: 15 kts (11.5 sweeping)   **Man:** 40 men
A: 1/40-mm AA — 1/20-mm AA   **Range:** 3,000/10

MINESWEEPERS (continued)

M: SEMT-Pielstick diesels; 2 props; 2,000 hp   **Fuel:** 48 tons

REMARKS: *Snazni* was built in Yugoslavia with the technical assistance of the Augustin Normand shipyards.

♦ *4 British "-ham" class*

ML 141, ML 142, ML 143, ML 144 (ex-*MSI 98-101*) — Bldr: Yugoslavia — 1964-66

   D: 120 tons   **S:** 14 kts   **Dim:** 32.40 × 6.30 × 1.70
   A: 1/40-mm   **Man:** 22 men
   M: diesels; 2 props; 550 hp   **Range:** 2,000/9   **Fuel:** 15 tons

REMARKS: Built under the M.A.P. and the numbers *98-101* are those assigned by American authorities.

♦ **M 117, M 118, M 119, M 121** — Bldr: Yugoslavia — 1966-68

   D: 131 tons (fl)   **S:** 12 kts   **Dim:** 30 × 5.50 × 1.50
   A: 1/40-mm — 2/12.7-mm machine guns
   M: 2 General Motors diesels; 1,000 hp

Also used for coastal patrol.

♦ **M 103, M 105, M 106, M 109, M 111** to **116, M 120, M 140** — Bldr: Yugoslavia — 1951-53

   D: 90 tons (95 fl)   **Dim:** 25 × 5.80 × 1.90
   S: 12 kts   **A:** 1/20-mm AA
   M: 1 diesel; 1 prop; 135/175 hp

REMARKS: Large craft, no forecastle.

♦ *14 small riverine minesweepers* — **RML 301** to **RML 314**

   D: 38 tons·   **S:** 12 kts   **A:** 1/20-mm AA

AMPHIBIOUS SHIPS

♦ *30 DTM type (200-231)*

   D: approx. 500 tons   **A:** 4/20-mm AA
   Cargo capacity: 3 medium tanks

♦ *1 DTK type (DTK 221)*

   D: approx. 400 tons   **S:** 10 kts   **A:** 1/20-mm — 2 machine guns
   Catamaran hull.

♦ *3 DJT LCM type*

♦ *21 DJG LCP type*

♦ *4 ex-German or Italian LCM type*

D 206 (ex-*MZ 713*), **D 209** (ex-*MZ 717*) (1942) (ex-Italian) — 1942, LCT type.

   D: 239 tons   **S:** 11 kts   **A:** 1/20-mm   **Dim:** 39 × 6.50 × 1.20

D 203, D 204 (ex-German MPF) — 1942-43, LCT type

   D: 220 tons   **S:** 10 kts   **A:** 1/88-mm — 2/20-mm   **Cargo:** 150 tons
   It is rather doubtful that these 4 LCMs are still in service.

HYDROGRAPHIC SHIP

PH 33 ANDREAS MOHOROVIC — Bldr: Gdansk, Poland 1971.

M. N. 1971

   D: 1,475 tons (fl)   **S:** 15 kts   **Dim:** 67 × 10.80 × 4.
   M: 2 diesels

REMARKS: See Soviet Moma class.

LOGISTIC SUPPORT

♦ *2 small transports*

PT 71, PT 72 — Bldr: Yugoslavia (1961-62).

   D: 310 tons (428 fl)   **S:** 7 kts   **Dim:** 43.10 × 6.80 × 4.85.
   M: 300 hp — Appearance of small coastal vessels.

♦ *6 small tankers*

ULJESURA, KIT — **D:** 250 tons

4 PN 13 type — Bldr: Yugoslavia (1951-53) — **D:** 695 tons — **S:** 8.5 kts

♦ *1 salvage vessel*

SPASILAC (1929) — Bldr: Howaldtswerke (Hamburg) — Salvage ship

   D: 740 tons   **Dim:** 52.50 × 7.90 × 3.90.
   S: 17 kts   **M:** triple expansion; 1 prop; 2,000 hp.

REMARKS: Manned by the Italians from 1941 to 1945 under the name of the *Instangabile.*

YUGOSLAVIA (*continued*)
LOGISTIC SUPPORT (*continued*)

♦ *6 tugs*

		Dim	Hp	S
PR 52 (ex-*San Remo*)	1937	173	350	8 kts
PR 58 (ex-*Molara*)	1937	120	250	8 kts
PR 51 (ex-*Porto Conte*)	1936	226	600	11 kts
LR 11 (ex-*Basiluzzo*)	1915	110	180	5 kts
PR 55 (ex-*Snazni*)	1917	100	300	10 kts
PR 54 (ex-*Ustrajni*)	1917	160	250	9 kts

♦ *3 water carriers:* **PV 6, PV 11, PV 13**

VARIOUS

	Bldr	Laid down	L	In serv.
JADRANKA	C.R.D.A. Monfalcone	23-12-38	3-6-39	10-39
(ex-*Biokovo*, ex-*Beli Orao*)				

Jadranka

D: 567 tons (660 fl) **Dim:** 60.45 × 7.93 × 2.70
S: 17 kts (trials: 18.5) **A:** 2/40-mm AA — 2/20-mm AA
M: Sulzer diesels; 2 props; 1,900 hp

REMARKS: Admiralty yacht.

JADRAN — Bldr: Hamburg (1932). Training ship (maneuvers).
Three-masted, yacht profile with raked bow.

D: 720 tons **Dim:** 58 × 8.80 × 4.30
S: 8 kts **Man:** 150 students or midshipmen.
M: Linke-Hofman diesel; 1 prop

ISTRANKA (ex-*Vila*, ex-*Dalmata*) (1896) — former yacht.
D: 260 tons **S:** 12 kts **Dim:** 40.40 × 5.10 × 2.10
M: 1 triple expansion, reciprocating; 235 hp

ZAIRE

MERCHANT MARINE (1-7-74): 9 ships — 38,996 grt
PERSONNEL: 300 men

♦ *6 "Swift" 20-meter small boats delivered in 1972*
♦ *3/12-ton small boats*
♦ *Various other boats and supply barges*

NOTE: In 7-74 a contract was signed with a French group for 12 security and lake patrol boats.

ZANZIBAR

Although part of the federation with Tanzania, Zanzibar has internal autonomy and has its own armed forces.

♦ *4/75-foot Vosper boats*

D: **S:** 24.5 kts **Dim:** 22.0 × 6 × 1.50
A: 2/20-mm **Range:** 800/20
M: 2 diesels; 1,840 hp

INDEX OF SHIPS

1. — Units designated by a letter and number (submarines, mine and amphibious warfare ships, etc.) may be found under the appropriate letter/number combinations.

2. — All ships are indexed by their full names starting with first names.